Good reasons must, of force, give place to better.
JULIUS CAESAR

By the same author

Organic Chemistry: VOLUME 1
The Fundamental Principles
Sixth Edition

Problems and their Solution
in Organic Chemistry

ORGANIC

I. L. Finar, D.Sc., Ph.D.(London), A.R.I.C.
Principal Lecturer in Organic Chemistry
The Polytechnic of North London, Holloway

CHEMISTRY

VOLUME 2

STEREOCHEMISTRY AND THE
CHEMISTRY OF NATURAL PRODUCTS

FIFTH EDITION

Longman

LONGMAN GROUP LIMITED
London
Associated companies, branches and representatives throughout the world

First published 1956
Second Edition 1959
Third Edition 1964
Fourth Edition 1968
Fifth Edition 1975

ISBN 0 582 44312 1

Library of Congress Catalog Card Number: 73–157839

Made and printed in Great Britain by
William Clowes & Sons, Limited,
London, Beccles and Colchester

List of journal abbreviations

Contents

Preface to the fourth edition

In the preface of my earlier book, *Organic Chemistry*, Vol. I, Longmans, Green (1967, 5th edn.), I expressed the opinion that the chemistry of natural products is the application of the principles of Organic Chemistry. The present work is, in this sense, a continuation of Vol. I. It is my belief that a student who has mastered the principles will be well on the road to mastering the applications when he begins to study them. At the same time, a study of the applications will bring home to the student the dictum of Faraday: "Ce n'est pas assez de savoir les principes, il faut savoir *Manipuler*" (quoted by Faraday from the *Dictionnaire de Trevoux*).

In the sections on Stereochemistry, I have assumed no previous knowledge of this subject. This has meant a certain amount of repetition of some of the material in Vol. 1, but I thought that this way of dealing with the subject would be preferable, since the alternative would have led to discontinuity.

The section of this book dealing with natural products has presented many difficulties. I have tried to give a general indication of the problems involved, and in doing so I have chosen, to a large extent, the most typical compounds for fairly detailed discussion. At the same time, I believe that the subject matter covered in this volume, together with that in Vol. I, should serve as a good introduction to the organic chemistry required by students reading for a Special Honours degree in Chemistry. I have given a selected number of reading references at the end of each chapter to enable students to extend their knowledge and also to make up for any omissions I have made. It is impossible to express my indebtedness to those authors of monographs, articles, etc., from which I have gained so much information, and I can only hope that some measure of my gratitude is expressed by the references I have given to their works.

One of the most significant changes in structure determination in the last two decades is the ever-increasing use of physical methods. To help the reader to get some idea of the principles involved, I have rewritten much of Chapter I to give a more comprehensive account of absorption spectroscopy (infrared, ultraviolet, NMR), mass spectrometry, and chromatography. Other sections, *e.g.*, optical rotatory dispersion, have also been expanded.

Many changes have therefore been made in the text. The use of physical methods has now been described for many types of natural products, and Woodward's Rules, the Octant Rule, and the Axial Haloketone Rule have been included. Much more has been written on conformational analysis (including a study of small and medium rings), the determination and specification of configuration, and the stereochemistry of addition and elimination reactions. More syntheses have been added, *e.g.*, oxytocin, morphine, and chlorophyll, and various sections have been rewritten, *e.g.*, the structure of proteins and nucleic acids, the biosynthesis of various types of natural products.

1967   I. L. FINAR

Preface to the fifth edition

This fifth edition has been revised and brought up to date. This has resulted in changes in every chapter of the book. In some cases the text has been rewritten, *e.g.,* resin acids, proteins, enzymes, nucleic acids, etc. In Chapter 1 the sections on spectroscopy and chromatography have been expanded and new topics such as circular dichroism have been added. The section dealing with Stereochemistry now contains a description of the more recent methods of nomenclature used in stereochemistry, an account of molecular symmetry and Brewster's rules, and expansion of neighbouring group participation, asymmetric synthesis, etc.

All chapters dealing with natural products have been expanded and all contain new subject matter. Part of this new material is a description of additional natural products, the aim being to make the contents of each chapter more representative of that group of natural products. Such additions are cedrene, santonin, gibberellins, capsorubin, lapachol, steroidal glycosides and alkaloids, etc. Also, more attention has been given to the configurations, conformations, reactions, synthesis and biosynthesis of natural products.

The other part of the new material deals with natural products whose structures have been elucidated by modern methods, *e.g.,* freelingyne, sesquichamaenol, juvenile hormone, antamanide, quebrachamine, heptaphylline, cephalosporin C, etc. Also, the planning of a synthesis and the use of control elements have been discussed, and these principles have been illustrated with a number of examples, *e.g.,* juvenile hormone, cholesterol, penicillins, morphine, haemin, etc.

I. L. FINAR

1973

1
Physical properties and chemical constitution

§1. Introduction

A tremendous amount of work has been and is being done to elucidate the relationships between physical properties and chemical structure. An ideal state to be achieved is one where the chemist can predict with great accuracy the physical properties of an organic compound whose structure is known, or formulate the correct structure of an organic compound from a detailed knowledge of its physical properties. A great deal of progress has been made in this direction as is readily perceived by examining the methods of elucidating structures of organic compounds over the last few decades. In the early work, the structure of an organic compound was solved by purely chemical means. These are, briefly:

(i) Qualitative analysis.

(ii) Quantitative analysis, which leads to the empirical formula.

(iii) Determination of the molecular weight, which leads to the molecular formula.

(iv) If the molecule is relatively simple, the various possible structures are written down (based on the valency of carbon being four, that of hydrogen one, oxygen two, etc.). Then the reactions of the compound are studied, and the structure which best fits the facts is chosen. In those cases where the molecules are not relatively simple, the compounds are examined by specific tests to ascertain the nature of the various groups present (see, *e.g.*, alkaloids, **14** §4). The compounds are also degraded and the smaller fragments examined. By this means it is possible to suggest a tentative structure.

(v) The final stage for elucidation of structure is synthesis, and in general, the larger the number of syntheses of a compound by *different* routes, the more reliable will be the structure assigned to that compound.

Nowadays, physical methods are considered to be necessary tools for elucidating structures. They are used on the compound itself, and are also used in the examination of the fragments obtained by degradative work. These physical methods, especially X-ray analysis, make synthesis as a means of structure determination less important than previously. Nevertheless, synthesis will still be a very important problem in the production of organic compounds, both natural and synthetic.

There are various criteria for purity. The most common one for solids is m.p. (§4); for liquids, b.p. (§5), density, and refractive index (§8) are used. The examination of the infrared absorption spectrum of a compound (whatever its normal physical state; §12b) is now also used as a test for purity. In all cases, the process of purification is repeated until the physical constant or spectrum

1

remains unchanged. Furthermore, it is best to use at least two methods of purification; a very good combination is recrystallisation and chromatography. Other physical properties that may be used for characterisation are specific rotation (§9), optical rotatory dispersion (§9a), ultraviolet spectroscopy (§12a), X-ray powder photographs (§14a), 'cracking' pattern in a mass spectrometer (§13), etc.

There are various techniques for purifying compounds. The earlier methods were recrystallisation from suitable solvents, distillation and sublimation. The methods used now are much superior: counter-current distribution, electrophoresis, etc., the most important one being chromatography in its various forms (see §15). A more recent method is that of Zone Melting, and this is gaining ground as a means of preparing substances in a state of ultrapurity.

The International System of Units (SI).   This system of units is coming into international use, and has been used in this book, but a few recommended and non-SI units are also used, *e.g.*, wave numbers are given in reciprocal centimetres (cm^{-1}) and not in reciprocal metres (m^{-1}) nor in reciprocal millimetres (mm^{-1}). In general, the SI unit, where used for the first time in the text, is followed (in brackets) by the previously accepted unit.

§2. Van der Waals forces

Ostwald (1910) classified physical properties as **additive** (these properties depend only on the nature and number of atoms in a molecule), **constitutive** (these properties depend on the nature, number and arrangement of the atoms in the molecule), and **colligative** (these properties depend only on the number of molecules present, and are independent of their chemical constitution). It is extremely doubtful whether any one of these three classes of properties is absolutely independent of either or

Table 1.1   Base-units

Physical quantity	Symbol	Name of base-unit	Symbol for unit
length	*l*	metre	m
mass	*m*	kilogramme	kg
time	*t*	second	s
thermodynamic temperature	*T*	kelvin	K
electric current	*I*	ampere	A
amount of substance	*n*	mole	mol

Table 1.2   Prefixes for SI units

Fraction	Prefix	Symbol	Multiple	Prefix	Symbol
10^{-1}	deci	d	10	deka	da
10^{-2}	centi	c	10^{2}	hecto	h
10^{-3}	milli	m	10^{3}	kilo	k
10^{-6}	micro	μ	10^{6}	mega	M
10^{-9}	nano	n	10^{9}	giga	G
10^{-12}	pico	p	10^{12}	tera	T
10^{-15}	femto	f			
10^{-18}	atto	a			

The symbol of the prefix is combined with the unit symbol, but the mass unit is an exception, in this case the prefix being attached to g and not to kg, *e.g.*, mg, *not* μkg (for 10^{-6} kg); Mg, *not* kkg (for 10^{3} kg).

Table 1.3   Derived SI units

Quantity	Symbol	SI unit
activation energy	$E, E\ddagger$	$J\ mol^{-1}$
concentration	c	$mol\ m^{-3}$
density	ρ	$kg\ m^{-3}$
energy	E	J [joule]
enthalpy	H	J
entropy	S	JK^{-1}
force	F	N [newton]
frequency	v, f	Hz [hertz]
gas constant	R	$JK^{-1}\ mol^{-1}$
Gibbs function	G	J
kinetic energy	E_k, T, K	J
molar refraction	R_m	
potential energy	E_p, V, Φ	J
pressure	p, P	$N\ m^{-2}$
quantity of heat	q	J
quantum yield	Φ	
refractive index	n	
specific optical rotatory power	α_m	
thermodynamic energy	U	J
transmittance	T	
wavelength	λ	m
wave number	σ, v	m^{-1}
work	w, W	J

Table 1.4   Non-SI units still in use

Name of unit	Symbol	Definition
angstrom	Å	10^{-8} cm; 10^{-10} m
atmosphere	atm	760 mm Hg
calorie:		
(i) international	cal_{IT}	$4{\cdot}1868J$
(ii) thermochemical	cal	$4{\cdot}184J$*
dyne	dyn	$10^{-5}N$
erg	erg	$10^{-7}J$
gauss	G	$10^{-4}T$ [tesla] $= Vsm^{-2}$ [volt]
litre	l	$10^{-3}\ m^3 = dm^3$
micron	μ	$10^{-6}\ m = \mu m$
millimicron	$m\mu$	$10^{-9}\ m = nm$

*This is the conversion factor used in the text.

both of the others, except for the case of molecular weights, which may be regarded as truly additive and independent of the other two. In constitutive and colligative properties, forces between molecules have a great effect on these properties. Attractive forces between molecules of a substance must be assumed in order to explain cohesion in liquids and solids. Ideal gases obey the equation PV = RT, but real gases do not, partly because of the attractive forces between molecules. Van der Waals (1873) was the first to attempt to modify the ideal gas law for the behaviour of real gases by allowing for these attractive forces (he introduced the term a/v^2 to correct for them). These intermolecular forces are now usually referred to as *van der Waals forces*, but they are also known as *residual* or *secondary valencies*. These forces may be forces of attraction or forces of repulsion; the former explain cohesion, and the latter must be assumed to exist at short distances, otherwise molecules would collapse into one another when intermolecular distances become very small. The distances of closest approach between non-bonded atoms are thus greater than the sum of the covalent radii of the atoms concerned, and are known as *van der Waals radii*. Some values (in Angstroms) are:

H, 1·20;   O, 1·40;   N, 1·50;   S, 1·85;   F, 1·35;   Cl, 1·80;   Br, 1·95;   I, 2·15; CH_3, 2·00
These values are very useful in connection with molecules that exhibit the steric effect, *e.g.*, substituted biphenyl compounds (**5** §2).

Van der Waals forces are electrostatic in nature. They are relatively weak forces (*i.e.*, in comparison with *bond* forces), but they are greater for compounds than for atoms and molecules of elements. In fact, the more asymmetrical the molecule, the greater are the van der Waals forces. These forces originate from three different causes:

(i) Forces due to the interaction between the permanent dipole moments of the molecules (Keesom, 1916, 1921). These forces are known as **Keesom forces** or the **dipole–dipole effect**, and are dependent on temperature.

(ii) Forces which result from the interaction of a *permanent* dipole and *induced* dipoles. Although a molecule may not possess a permanent dipole, nevertheless a dipole may be induced under the influence of neighbouring molecules which do possess a permanent dipole (Debye, 1920, 1921). These forces are known as **Debye forces**, the **dipole-induced dipole effect** or **induction effect**, and are almost independent of temperature.

(iii) London (1930) showed from wave mechanics that a third form of van der Waals forces is also acting. A nucleus and its 'electron cloud' are in a state of vibration, and when two atoms are sufficiently close to each other, the two nuclei and the two electron clouds tend to vibrate together, thereby leading to attraction between different molecules. These forces are known as **London forces**, **dispersion forces**, or **the wave-mechanical effect**, and are independent of temperature.

It should be noted that the induced forces are smaller than the other two, and that the dispersion forces are usually the greatest.

It can now be seen that all those physical properties which depend on intermolecular forces, *e.g.*, melting point, boiling point, viscosity, etc., will thus be largely determined by the van der Waals forces. Physical adsorption of a gas on any surface is believed to be the result of van der Waals forces operating between gas and surface. Chemisorption, however, is believed to occur as a result of the formation of chemical bonds.

§3. **The hydrogen bond**

A particularly important case of electrostatic attraction is that which occurs in *hydrogen bonding* (Vol. I, Ch. 2); it occurs mainly in compounds containing fluorine, oxygen, and nitrogen, and to a less extent, chlorine and sulphur. The energy of a hydrogen bond varies between that of the van der Waals forces ($4·184 \text{ kJ mol}^{-1}$; 1 kcal mol^{-1}) and that of a chemical bond. Some values obtained are: H—F--H, 41·84 kJ; H—O--H, 29·29 kJ; H—N--H, $8·37 \text{ kJ mol}^{-1}$. These are 'weak' hydrogen bonds, and for these the geometry of Z—H and Y is little changed when the hydrogen bond produces the complex Z—H--Y. Hence the bond length of Z—H is almost the same in both Z—H and Z—H--Y. Apart from depending on the nature of the atoms involved, the length of the hydrogen bond also depends on the nature of the other atoms in the groups Z and Y. The bond length H--Y (for F, O, and N) varies from about 2·3 to about 3·0 Å.

There are two types of hydrogen bonding, *intermolecular* and *intramolecular*. Intermolecular bonding gives rise to association, thereby raising the boiling point; it also raises the surface tension and the viscosity, but lowers the dielectric constant. Intermolecular hydrogen bonding may exist in compounds in the liquid or solid state, and its formation is very much affected by the shape of the molecules, *i.e.*, by the *steric* factor; *e.g.*, n-pentanol is completely associated, whereas t-pentanol is only partially associated. Intermolecular hydrogen bonding also affects solubility if the compound can form hydrogen bonds with the solvent.

Intramolecular hydrogen bonding gives rise to *chelation*, *i.e.*, ring formation, and this normally occurs only with the formation of 5-, 6-, or 7-membered rings. When chelation occurs, the ring formed must be planar or almost planar. Should another group be present which prevents the formation of a *planar* chelate structure, then chelation will be diminished or even completely inhibited (Hunter *et al.*, 1938; *cf.* steric inhibition of resonance, Vol. I, Ch. 23). Compound (I) is chelated, but (II) is associated and not chelated. In (I) the *o*-nitro-group can enter into the formation of a *planar* six-membered ring. In (II), owing to the strong repulsion between the negatively charged

(I)   (II)

oxygen atoms of the two nitro-groups, the plane of each nitro-group will tend to be perpendicular to the plane of the benzene ring, and consequently a chelated *planar* six-membered ring cannot be formed.

Although hydrogen bonding is normally involved with F, O, N (and Cl, S), it has been found that the C—H group can participate in hydrogen bonds, but the result is a very weak bond. It is, however, stronger when the H in the C—H is 'activated', *e.g.*, in an active methylene group, acetylenes, etc. On the other hand, Sutor (1963) has shown by X-ray analysis that H in the methyl group in many purines forms fairly strong hydrogen bonds with oxygen atoms present in the molecule.

The presence of hydrogen bonding may be detected by various means, *e.g.*, infrared absorption spectra, X-ray analysis, electron diffraction, examination of boiling points, melting points, solubility, etc. The best method appears to be that of infrared absorption spectra (see § 12b).

§4. Melting point

In a crystalline solid, the ions or molecules are arranged in a particular regular fashion, and this pattern is repeated throughout the crystal. In most solids the ions or molecules are in a state of vibration about their fixed mean positions. These vibrations are due to the thermal energy and their amplitudes are small compared with interatomic distances. As the temperature of the solid is raised, the amplitude of vibration increases and a point is reached when the crystalline structure suddenly becomes unstable; this is the melting point.

In many homologous series the melting points of the n-members rise continuously, tending towards a maximum value. On the other hand, some homologous series show an alternation or oscillation of melting points—'the saw-tooth rule', *e.g.*, in the fatty acid series the melting point of an 'even' acid is higher than that of the 'odd' acid immediately below and above it. It has been shown by X-ray analysis that this alternation of melting points depends on the packing of the crystals. The shape of the molecule is closely related to the melting point; the more symmetrical the molecule, the higher is the melting point. Thus with isomers, branching of the chain (which increases symmetry) usually raises the melting point; also *trans*-isomers usually have a higher melting point than the *cis*-, the former having greater symmetry than the latter (see **4** §5j). In the benzene series, of the three disubstituted derivatives, the *p*-compound usually has the highest melting point.

Apart from the usual van der Waals forces which affect melting points, hydrogen bonding may also play a part, *e.g.*, the melting point of an alcohol is higher than that of its corresponding alkane. This is due to hydrogen bonding, which is possible in the former but not in the latter. Since energy is required to break a hydrogen bond, it is this 'extra' energy that raises the melting point. However, because relatively few hydrogen bonds need be broken to liquefy a crystal, the effect of hydrogen bonding on melting point is comparatively small (see also §5).

Various *empirical* formulae have been developed from which it is possible to calculate melting points; these formulae, however, only relate members of an *homologous* series.

The method of mixed melting points has long been used to identify a compound, and is based on the principle that two different compounds mutually lower the melting point of each component in the mixture. This method, however, is unreliable when the two compounds form a solid solution.

§5. Boiling point

The boiling point of a liquid is that temperature at which the vapour pressure is equal to that of the external pressure. Thus the boiling point varies with the pressure, being raised as the pressure is increased.

In an homologous series, the boiling point usually increases regularly for the n-members, *e.g.*, Kopp (1842) found that with the aliphatic alcohols, acids, esters, etc., the boiling point is raised by 19°C for each increase of CH_2 in the composition. In the case of isomers the greater the branching of the carbon chain, the lower is the boiling point. Calculation has shown that the boiling point of the n-alkanes should be proportional to the number of carbon atoms in the molecule. This relationship, however, is not observed in practice, and the cause of this deviation still remains to be elucidated. One strongly favoured theory attributes the cause to the fact that the carbon chains of n-alkanes in the liquid phase exist largely in a coiled configuration. As the branching increases, the coil becomes denser, and this lowers the boiling point.

In aromatic disubstituted compounds the boiling point of the *ortho*-isomer is higher than that of the *meta*-isomer which, in turn, may have a higher boiling point than the *para*-isomer, but in many cases the boiling points are about the same.

Since the boiling point depends on the van der Waals forces, any structural change which affects these forces will consequently change the boiling point. One such structural change is the branching of the carbon chain (see above). Another type of change is that of substituting hydrogen by a −I group. This introduces a dipole moment (or increases the value of an existing dipole moment), thereby increasing the attractive forces between the molecules and consequently raising the boiling point, *e.g.*, the boiling points of the nitro-alkanes are very much higher than those of the corresponding alkanes. The possibility of intermolecular hydrogen bonding also raises the boiling point, *e.g.*, alcohols boil at higher temperatures than the corresponding alkanes. Because it is necessary to break *all* intermolecular hydrogen bonds in order to obtain the intermolecular hydrogen-bonded liquid as a monomeric vapour (gas), the effect of hydrogen bonding on boiling point is much greater than that on melting point (see §4).

The formation of intramolecular hydrogen bonds decreases the formation of intermolecular bonds, and hence, if only one of a number of isomers can form an intramolecular hydrogen bond, this isomer will have the lowest boiling point (or melting point). Thus, many *ortho*-disubstituted benzenes, *e.g.*, nitrophenols, have lower boiling points (or melting points) than the corresponding *meta*- and *para*-isomers.

§6]

§6. Solubility

When a substance dissolves, its ions or molecules become separated by solvent molecules. Solubility depends on the following intermolecular forces: solvent/solute; solute/solute; solvent/solvent. If the solvent/solute forces are greater than either of the other two, solution will be expected to occur fairly readily. The solubility of a non-electrolyte in water depends, to a very large extent, on whether the compound can form hydrogen bonds with the water, *e.g.*, the alkanes are insoluble, or almost insoluble, in water. Methane, however, is more soluble than any of its homologues. The reason for this is uncertain; hydrogen bonding with water is unlikely, and so other factors must play a part, *e.g.*, molecular size. A useful guide in organic chemistry is that 'like dissolves like', *e.g.*, if a compound contains a hydroxyl group, then the best solvents for that compound also usually contain hydroxyl groups (hydrogen bonding between solvent and solute is possible). This 'rule' is accepted by many who use the word 'like' to mean that the cohesion forces in both solvent and solute arise from the same source, *e.g.*, alkanes and alkyl halides are miscible; the cohesion forces of both of these groups of compounds are largely due to dispersion forces.

In some cases solubility may be due, at least partly, to the formation of a compound between the solute and the solvent, *e.g.*, ether dissolves in concentrated sulphuric acid with the formation of an oxonium salt, $\{(C_2H_5)_2OH\}^+ HSO_4^-$.

The solubility of a substance in a given solvent usually increases with increasing temperature, but the temperature coefficient of the solubility depends on the nature of the particular substance.

§7. Viscosity

Viscosity (the resistance to flow due to the internal friction in a liquid) depends, among other factors, on the van der Waals forces acting between the molecules. Since these forces depend on the shape and size of the molecules, the viscosity will also depend on these properties. At the same time, since the Keeson forces (§2) depend on temperature, viscosity will also depend on temperature; other factors, however, also play a part.

A number of relationships have been found between the viscosity of pure liquids and their chemical structure, *e.g.*,

(i) In an homologous series, viscosity increases with the molecular weight.

(ii) With isomers the viscosity of the n-compound is greater than that of isomers with branched carbon chains.

(iii) Abnormal viscosities are shown by *associated* liquids. Viscosity measurements have thus been used to determine the degree of association in liquids.

(iv) The viscosity of a *trans*-compound is greater than that of the corresponding *cis*-isomer.

Equations have been developed relating viscosity to the shape and size of *large* molecules (*macromolecules*) in solution, and so viscosity measurements have offered a means of determining the shape of, *e.g.*, proteins, and the molecular weight of, *e.g.*, polysaccharides.

One equation for determining molecular weights of macromolecules is $[\eta] = KM^a$ where K and a are empirical constants which depend on the nature of the solvent, the macromolecule and the temperature; M is the molecular weight, and $[\eta]$ is the *intrinsic viscosity*, which is evaluated from the expression

$$\lim_{c \to 0} \left[\frac{1}{c} \cdot \frac{\eta - \eta_0}{\eta_0} \right] = \lim_{c \to 0} \left[\frac{1}{c} \left(\frac{\eta}{\eta_0} - 1 \right) \right]$$

where η and η_0 are the viscosities of the solution and solvent respectively, and c is the concentration of the solution (g/100 ml). The value $\left(\dfrac{\eta}{\eta_0} - 1 \right)$ is known as the *specific viscosity*, and η/η_0 is the *relative viscosity.* The values of K and a are obtained by studying the viscosities of solutions containing macromolecules of known molecular weights.

Attempts have been made to correlate the value of a with the shape of the macromolecule, but the results must be accepted with reserve. Even so, it appears to be a general rule that the value of a of a macromolecule of a given molecular weight is smaller the more elongated the molecule is. Thus, *e.g.*, the value of a for a given macromolecule which is coiled in one solvent is larger than that in a solvent in which the macromolecule becomes uncoiled (through solvation).

§8. Refractive index

Lorentz and Lorenz (1880) simultaneously showed that $R_m = \dfrac{n^2 - 1}{n^2 - 2} \cdot \dfrac{M}{\rho} = \dfrac{n^2 - 1}{n^2 - 2} \cdot V_m$ where R_m is the *molecular refraction*, n the refractive index, M the molecular weight, ρ the density, and V_m the molecular volume. The value of n depends on the wave-length and on temperature; ρ depends on temperature.

Molecular refraction has been shown to have both additive and constitutive properties. The following table of atomic and structural refractions has been calculated for the H_α line.

C	2·413	Cl	5·933
H	1·092	Br	8·803
O(OH)	1·522	I	13·757
O(CO)	2·189	Double bond (C=C)	1·686
O(ethers)	1·639	Triple bond (C≡C)	2·328

Molecular refractions have been used to determine the structure of compounds, *e.g.*, terpenes (see **8** §25). They have also been used to detect the presence of tautomers and to calculate the amount of each form present. Let us consider ethyl acetoacetate as an example; this behaves as the keto form $CH_3COCH_2CO_2C_2H_5$, and as the enol form $CH_3C(OH)=CHCO_2C_2H_5$. The calculated molecular refractions of these forms are:

$CH_3COCH_2CO_2C_2H_5$		**$CH_3C(OH)=CHCO_2C_2H_5$**	
6 C	= 14·478	6 C	= 14·478
10 H	= 10·92	10 H	= 10·92
2 O (CO)	= 4·378	O (OH)	= 1·522
O (ether)	= 1·639	O (CO)	= 2·189
		O (ether)	= 1·639
	31·415	Double bond	= 1·686
			32·434

The observed molecular refraction of ethyl acetoacetate is 31·89; hence both forms are present.

When a compound contains two or more double bonds, the value of the molecular refraction depends not only on their number but also on their relative positions. When the double bonds are *conjugated*, then anomalous results are obtained, the observed molecular refraction being higher than that calculated, *e.g.*, the observed value for hexa-1,3,5-triene is 2·06 units greater than the value calculated. This anomaly is known as *optical exaltation*, and it usually increases with increase in length of conjugation (in unsubstituted chains). Although optical exaltation is characteristic of acyclic compounds, it is also exhibited by cyclic compounds. In single-ring systems, *e.g.*, benzene, pyridine, pyrrole, etc., the optical exaltation is negligible; this has been attributed to resonance. In polycyclic aromatic compounds, however, the exaltation may have a large value. In general, large exaltations are shown by those compounds which exhibit large *electronic* effects.

Another application of the refractive index is its relation to hydrogen bonding. Arshid *et al.* (1955, 1956) have used the square of the refractive index to detect hydrogen-bond complexes.

§9. Molecular rotation

When a substance possesses the property of rotating the plane of polarisation of a beam of plane-polarised light passing through it, that substance is said to be **optically active**. The measurement of the **rotatory power** of a substance is carried out by means of a polarimeter. If the substance rotates the plane of polarisation to the right, *i.e.*, the analyser has to be turned to the right (clockwise) to restore the original field, the substance is said to be *dextrorotatory*; if to the left (anti-clockwise), *laevorotatory*.

It has been found that the amount of the rotation depends, for a given substance, on a number of factors:

(i) *The thickness of the layer traversed.* The amount of the rotation is directly proportional to the length of the active substance traversed (Biot, 1835).

(ii) *The wavelength of the light.* The rotatory power is approximately inversely proportional to the square of the wavelength (Biot, 1835). There are some exceptions, and in certain cases it has been found that the rotation changes sign. This change in rotatory power with change in wavelength is known as *rotatory dispersion*. Hence it is necessary (for comparison of rotatory power) to use monochromatic light; the sodium D line (yellow: 5893Å) is one wavelength that is commonly used (see also §9a).

(iii) *The temperature.* The rotatory power usually increases with rise in temperature, but many cases are known where the rotatory power decreases. Hence, for comparison, it is necessary to state the temperature; in practice, measurements are usually carried out at 20 or 25°C.

(iv) *The solvent.* The nature of the solvent affects the rotation, and so it is necessary to state the solvent used in the measurement of the rotatory power. Not only is the magnitude dependent on the solvent, but so also is the sign of rotation, *e.g.*, atrolactic acid is dextrorotatory in benzene, but is laevorotatory in ether.

(v) *The concentration.* The rotation is approximately directly proportional to the concentration, but deviations from this linear relationship tend to increase with increasing concentration. The causes of this have been attributed to association, dissociation, or solvation (see also vi).

(vi) The amount of rotation exhibited by a given substance when all the preceding factors (i–v) have been fixed may be varied by the presence of other compounds which are not, in themselves, optically active, *e.g.*, inorganic salts. It is important to note in this connection that optically active acids or bases, in the form of their salts, give rotations which are independent of the nature of the non-optically active ion *provided that the solutions are very dilute*. In very dilute solutions, salts are completely dissociated, and it is only the optically active ion which then contributes to the rotation. The molecular rotation of a salt formed from an optically active acid and an optically active base reaches a constant value in dilute solutions, and the rotation is the sum of the rotations of the anion and cation. This property has been used to detect optical activity (see **6** §5a).

When recording the rotations of substances, the value commonly given is the **specific rotation**, $[\alpha]_\lambda^t$. This is generally measured in solution, and is defined by the equation:

$$[\alpha]_\lambda^t = \frac{100\alpha}{lc}$$

where *l* is the thickness of the layer in decimetres, *c* the number of grams of substance per 100 ml of solution, α the *observed* rotation, t the temperature and λ the wavelength of the light used. The solvent should also be stated (see iv).

For *neat* liquids, the specific rotation is given by the equation:

$$[\alpha]_\lambda^t = \frac{100\alpha}{l\rho}$$

where ρ is the density of the liquid in grams per ml.

The **molecular rotation**, $[M]_\lambda^t$, is obtained by multiplying the specific rotation by the molecular weight, M. Since large numbers are usually obtained, a common practice is to divide the result by one hundred; thus:

$$[M]_\lambda^t = \frac{[\alpha]_\lambda^t \times M}{100}$$

Molecular rotations are usually necessary for comparisons involving compounds of different molecular weights. Furthermore, when rotations at the D-line are very small increased rotations may be observed at shorter wavelengths (see also §9a).

The relation between structure and optical activity is discussed later (see **2** §§2; 3). The property of optical activity has been used in the study of the configuration of molecules and mechanisms of various reactions, and also to decide between alternative structures for a given compound. The use of optical rotations in the determination of structure depends largely on the application of two rules.

(i) **Rule of Optical Superposition** (van't Hoff, 1894): When a compound contains two or more chiral (asymmetric) centres, the total rotatory power of the molecules is the algebraic sum of the contributions of each chiral centre. This rule is based on the assumption that the contribution of each chiral centre is independent of the other chiral centres present. This assumption, however, is usually satisfactory only when the chiral centres are far apart. It has also been found that the contribution of a given chiral centre is affected by the presence of chain-branching and unsaturation. Hence the rule, although useful, must be treated with reserve (see also **7** §6; **13** §12a).

A more satisfactory rule is the **Rule of Shift** or the **Displacement Rule** (Freudenberg, 1933): If two chiral molecules A and B are changed in the same way structurally to give A′ and B′, then the differences in molecular rotation (A′ − A) and (B′ − B) are of the same sign. Originally, these structural changes were confined mainly to the modification of a functional group, *e.g.*, the conversion of an acid into its ester or amide. Subsequently, however, these structural changes were extended to include the inversion of a chiral centre already present or the introduction of a new chiral centre (see, *e.g.*, **7** §6a).

(ii) **Distance Rule** (Tschugaev, 1898): The effect of a given structural change on the contribution of a chiral centre decreases the further the centre of change is from the chiral centre (see also **2** §5c).

Only asymmetric molecules have the power, under normal conditions, to rotate the plane of polarisation (of plane-polarised light). Faraday (1845), however, found that any transparent substance can rotate the plane of polarisation when placed in a strong magnetic field. This property of **magnetic optical rotation (Faraday effect)** is mainly an additive one, but is also partly constitutive.

§9a. Optical rotatory dispersion (ORD).   In §9 we have discussed the method of optical rotations using *monochromatic rotations*. There is also, however, the method of *rotatory dispersion*. Optical rotatory dispersion is the change in rotatory power with change in wavelength, and rotatory dispersion measurements are valuable only for chiral compounds. Instruments in which the wavelength can be varied are known as *spectropolarimeters*, and some give automatic recordings of the rotatory dispersion curves. In order to study the essential parts of dispersion curves, it is necessary to measure the optical rotation of a substance right through an absorption band of that substance. This is experimentally possible only if this absorption band is in an accessible part of the spectrum (down to about 200 nm (mμ) on modern instruments). Compounds which have been most extensively studied are those in which the chromophore is the carbonyl group (λ_{max} 280 − 300 nm), but Cotton Effect curves have also been observed for other compounds (which absorb in the near-ultraviolet or visible region), *e.g.*, dithiocarbamate derivatives of α-amino-acids (**13** §4).

There are three types of rotatory dispersion curves: (*a*) Plain curves; (*b*) single Cotton Effect curves; (*c*) multiple Cotton Effect curves. We shall describe (*a*) and (*b*); (*c*) shows two or more peaks and a corresponding number of troughs.

Plain curves. These show no maximum or minimum, *i.e.*, they are *smooth curves*, and may be positive or negative according as the rotation becomes more positive or negative as the wavelength changes from longer to shorter values (Fig. 1.1*a*). Plain curves are also referred to as *normal curves*, the implication of the word *normal* being that the curves contain no peaks, troughs, or inflections, and that the curves do not cross the zero rotation line.

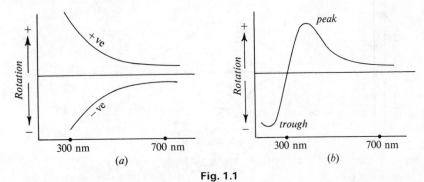

Fig. 1.1

Single Cotton Effect curves. These are *anomalous dispersion curves* which show a maximum and a minimum, both of these occurring in the region of maximum absorption (Fig. 1.1 *b*). The curves are said to be positive or negative according as the peak or trough occurs in the longer wavelength. Thus the curve shown in Fig. 1.1 (*b*) is positive. The terms *peak* and *trough* are preferred to *maximum* and *minimum* (to avoid confusion with the use of the latter terms in absorption spectroscopy). Alternatively, the peaks and troughs are collectively referred to as *extrema*, the first *extremum* being that peak or trough which occurs at the shortest wavelength (see also **2** §11). The vertical distance between the peak and trough is called the *amplitude* and the horizontal distance the *breadth* of the C.E. curve. The *molecular amplitude*, *a*, is defined as follows. If $[\phi]_1$ is the molecular rotation at the extremum (peak or trough) of longer wavelength, and $[\phi]_2$ is the molecular rotation at the extremum of shorter wavelength, then

$$a = \frac{[\phi]_1 - [\phi]_2}{100} = \frac{[\phi]}{100} = 10^{-2}\,[\phi]$$

The wavelength of maximum ultraviolet absorption is referred to as 'the optically active absorption band', and since rotatory dispersion measurements are of value only for chiral compounds, to obtain suitable curves compounds containing a carbonyl group in a chiral environment must be used. Enantiomers have curves which are mirror images of each other; compounds which are enantiomeric in the neighbourhood of the carbonyl group have dispersion curves which are approximately mirror images of each other; and compounds which have the same relative configurations in the neighbourhood of the carbonyl group have dispersion curves of the same sign.

There are many applications of rotatory dispersion: (i) quantitative analytical uses; (ii) identification of the carbonyl group; (iii) location of carbonyl groups; (iv) the determination of relative configurations; (v) the determination of absolute configurations; (vi) the determination of conformation. Some examples of these applications are described in the text (see Index).

§9b. **Circular dichroism (CD).** This is the phenomenon exhibited by compounds for which the molar absorptivities, ε_L and ε_R, of left- and right-circularly polarised light are *unequal* (see **2** §11 for a more detailed discussion). By convention, if $\varepsilon_L > \varepsilon_R$, the CD is said to be positive, and when $\varepsilon_R > \varepsilon_L$, the CD is said to be negative. This difference between ε_L and ε_R, for different wavelengths, can be measured directly by instruments, the result being a **circular dichroism (CD) curve** (Fig. 1.2). The curves so obtained are either positive or negative over the *whole* range of wavelengths, and the sign of the CD curves is the same as that of the ORD curve of the substance. Because of this, CD curves can be used in the same way as ORD curves, but the former have the advantage in that they are easier to interpret.

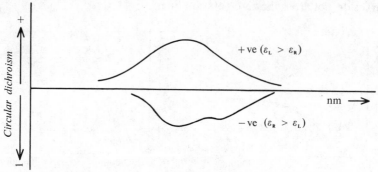

Fig. 1.2

ORD (§9a) and CD are applicable to naturally optically active compounds. However, the Faraday effect (magnetically induced optical activity; §9) is now also used in the form of **magneto-optical rotatory dispersion (MORD)** and **magnetic circular dichroism (MCD)**. The use of these phenomena is different from that of ORD and CD, particularly in that the former give spectroscopic information that is different from that of the latter. This is, of course, partly due to the fact that MORD and MCD can be used with compounds that are *not* naturally optically active.

§10. Dipole moments

When the centres of gravity of the electrons and nuclei in a molecule do not coincide, the molecule will possess a *permanent* electric dipole moment, μ, the value of which is given by $\mu = e \times d$, where e is the electronic charge, and d the distance between the charges (positive and negative centres). Since e is of the order of 10^{-10} e.s.u., and d 10^{-8} cm, μ is therefore of the order 10^{-18} e.s.u. cm^{-1}. This unit is known as the Debye (D), in honour of Debye, who did a great deal of work on dipole moments (SI units: 1 D = 3.335×10^{-30} Asm).

The dipole moment is a vector quantity, and its direction in a molecule is often indicated by an arrow parallel to the line joining the points of charge, and pointing towards the negative end, *e.g.*, H—Cl (Sidgwick, 1930). The greater the value of the dipole moment, the greater is the *polarity* of the bond. It should be noted that the terms *polar* and *non-polar* are used to describe bonds, molecules and groups. Bond dipoles are produced because each atom has a different electronegativity, *i.e.*, attraction for electrons. This unequal electronegativity producing a dipole moment seems to be a satisfactory explanation for many simple molecules, but is unsatisfactory in other cases. Thus a number of factors must operate in determining the value of the dipole moment. It is now believed that *four* factors contribute to the electric bond moment:

(i) The unequal sharing of the bonding electrons arising from the different electronegativities of the two atoms produces a dipole moment.

(ii) In covalent bonds a dipole is produced because of the difference in size of the two atoms. The centres of gravity (of the charges) are at the nucleus of each contributing atom. Thus, if the atoms are different in size, the resultant centre of gravity is not at the mid-point of the bond, and so a bond moment results.

(iii) Hybridisation of orbitals produces asymmetric atomic orbitals; consequently the centres of gravity of the hybridised orbitals are no longer at the parent nuclei. Only if the orbitals are pure *s*, *p* or *d*, are the centres of gravity at the parent nuclei. Thus hybridised orbitals produce a bond moment.

(iv) Lone-pair electrons (*e.g.*, on the oxygen atom in water) are not 'pure' *s* electrons; they are 'impure' because of hybridisation with *p* electrons. If lone-pair electrons were not hybridised, their centre of gravity would be at the nucleus; hybridisation, however, displaces the centre of gravity from the nucleus and so the asymmetric orbital produced gives rise to a bond moment which may be so large as to outweigh the contributions of the other factors to the dipole moment.

The following points are useful in organic chemistry:

(i) In the bond H—Z, where Z is any atom other than hydrogen or carbon, the hydrogen atom is the positive end of the dipole, *i.e.*, $\overset{\rightarrow}{\text{H—Z}}$.

(ii) In the bond $\overset{+}{\text{C}}$—Z, where Z is any atom other than carbon, the carbon atom is the positive end of the dipole, *i.e.*, $\overset{\rightarrow}{\text{C—Z}}$ (Coulson, 1942).

(iii) When a molecule contains two or more polar bonds, the resultant dipole moment of the molecule is obtained by the vectorial addition of the constituent bond dipole moments. A symmetrical molecule will thus be non-polar, although it may contain polar bonds, *e.g.*, CCl_4 has a zero dipole moment although each C—Cl bond is strongly polar.

Since dipole moments are vector quantities, the sum of two equal and opposite group moments will be zero only if the two vectors are collinear or parallel. When the group moment is directed along the axis of the bond formed by the 'key' atom of the group and the carbon atom to which it is joined, then that group is said to have a *linear* moment. Such groups are H, halogen, Me, CN, NO_2, etc. On the other hand, groups which have *non-linear* moments are OH, OR, CO_2H, etc. This problem of linear or non-linear group moments has a very important bearing on the use of dipole data in, *e.g.*, elucidating configurations of geometrical isomers (see **4** §5e), orientation in benzene derivatives, etc.

When any molecule (polar or non-polar) is placed in an electric field, the electrons are displaced from their normal positions (towards the positive pole of the external field). The positive nuclei are also displaced (towards the negative pole of the external field), but their displacement is much less than that of the electrons because of their relatively large masses. These displacements give rise to an *induced* dipole, and this exists only while the external electric field is present. The value of the induced dipole depends on the strength of the external field and is independent of temperature. On the other hand, the value of the permanent dipole moment is dependent on temperature.

Measurement of dipole moments is usually carried out by determining the dielectric constant of the compound in the gaseous or liquid phase, or in *dilute* solution in a *non-polar* solvent such as benzene or carbon tetrachloride. *P*, the *molar polarisation*, is then calculated from the Debye equation:

$$P = \frac{\varepsilon - 1}{\varepsilon + 2} \cdot \frac{M}{\rho} = \frac{4}{3} \pi N \left(\alpha + \frac{\mu^2}{3kT} \right)$$

where ε is the dielectric constant, M the molecular weight, ρ the density, N the Avogadro number, k the Boltzmann constant (*i.e.*, the gas constant per molecule), T the absolute temperature, μ the *permanent electric dipole moment*, and α the *molecular polarisability*, *i.e.*, the dipole moment induced in the molecule when placed in an electric field of unit strength.

The above procedure leads to the value of P, but not to the values of α and μ. One way to evaluate α and μ is to measure ε and ρ at different temperatures. As pointed out above, α is independent of the temperature. Hence, if ε and ρ are measured at different temperatures, the plot of P against $1/T$ should be a straight line whose slope is $4\pi N\mu^2/9k$. Thus μ can be calculated from the slope of the line and α can be calculated from the intercept.

Most dipole moments are in the region of 0 to 8D, and by means of dipole measurements it is possible to obtain information on inductive effects, resonance effects, shapes of molecules (stereochemical and conformational), hydrogen bonding, orientation in benzene derivations, etc.

§11. Magnetic susceptibility

When a substance is placed in a magnetic field, the substance may or may not become magnetised. If I is the *intensity of magnetisation* induced, and H the strength of the magnetic field inducing it, then the strength of the magnetic field in the material, represented by B and known as the *magnetic induction*, is given by

$$B = H + 4\pi I$$

The ratio B/H is called the *magnetic permeability*, μ, of the material.

Since
$$\begin{aligned} B &= H + 4\pi I \\ \therefore \quad B/H &= 1 + 4\pi I/H \\ \therefore \quad \mu &= 1 + 4\pi I/H \\ &= 1 + 4\pi\kappa \end{aligned}$$

where $\kappa \ (= I/H)$ is the *volume magnetic susceptibility* of the material. In chemistry, a more useful quantity than κ is the *molar magnetic susceptibility*, χ_M, obtained from the equation:

$$\chi_M = \kappa \times M/\rho = IM/H\rho$$

where M is the molecular weight of the compound and ρ is its density, *i.e.*, χ_M is obtained by multiplying κ by the molecular volume.

Now, the volume of I can be positive or negative (*i.e.*, the strength of the field, B, in the material may be respectively greater or smaller than the applied magnetic field, H). If I is negative, then χ_M is also negative, and the material is said to be *diamagnetic*. If I is positive, then χ_M is positive, and the material is now said to be *paramagnetic*.

Electrons, because of their spin, possess magnetic dipoles. When electrons are paired (*i.e.*, their spins are anti-parallel), then the magnetic field is cancelled out. Most organic compounds are diamagnetic, since their electrons are paired. 'Odd electron molecules', however, are paramagnetic (see also §12f).

Magnetic susceptibility has been used to obtain information on the nature of bonds and the configuration of co-ordination compounds. Organic compounds which are paramagnetic are generally free radicals (odd electron molecules), and the degree of dissociation of, *e.g.*, hexaphenylethane into triphenylmethyl has been measured by means of its magnetic susceptibility.

In the same way as atomic and structural refractions have been calculated, so have the corresponding diamagnetic susceptibilities been calculated, since molar diamagnetic susceptibility has both additive and constitutive properties. Some values of χ_M are (in 10^{-6} e.m.u.; multiply by $4\pi \times 10^{-6}$ for SI units).

H	$-2\cdot9 \times 10^{-6}$	O (alcohol)	$-4\cdot6 \times 10^{-6}$
C	$-6\cdot0$	O (oxo)	$-1\cdot7$
N (amine)	$-5\cdot6$	Cl	-20
N (ring)	$-4\cdot6$	Br	-31
C=C	$5\cdot5$	benzene	$1\cdot4$

§12. Absorption spectra

When light (this term will be used for electromagnetic waves of any wavelength) is absorbed by a molecule, the molecule undergoes transition from a state of lower to a state of higher energy. If the molecule is monatomic, the energy absorbed can only be used to raise the energy levels of electrons. If, however, the molecule consists of more than one atom, the light absorbed may bring about changes in electronic, rotational or vibrational energy. Electronic transitions give absorption (or emission) in the visible and ultraviolet parts of the spectrum, whereas rotational and vibrational changes give absorption (or emission) respectively in the far and near infrared. Electronic transitions may be accompanied by the other two. A study of these energy changes gives information on the structure of molecules.

Spectrum	Region
Ultraviolet	200–400 nm (mμ)
Visible	400–750 nm (mμ)
Near infrared	12 500–4 000 cm^{-1}
	$(0\cdot8 \times 10^{-3} - 2\cdot5 \times 10^{-3}$ mm; $0\cdot8 - 2\cdot5\ \mu)$
Infrared	4 000–650 cm^{-1}
	$(2\cdot5 \times 10^{-3} - 15\cdot4 \times 10^{-3}$ mm; $2\cdot5 - 15\cdot4\ \mu)$
Microwave	1 mm – 10 cm
	$(3 \times 10^{5} - 3 \times 10^{3}$ MHz)

If I_0 is the intensity of an incident beam of monochromatic light, and I that of the emergent beam which has passed through an absorbing medium of thickness l cm, then

$$I = I_0 10^{-\varepsilon l} \qquad \text{or} \qquad \log_{10} \frac{I_0}{I} = A = \varepsilon l$$

If the absorbing substance is in solution (the solvent being *colourless*), and if c is the concentration (number of moles per litre), then

$$I = I_0 10^{-\varepsilon c l} \qquad \text{or} \qquad \log \frac{I_0}{I} = \varepsilon c l$$

This equation is **Beer's law** (1852), and is obeyed by most solutions provided they are *dilute*. In more concentrated solutions there may be divergencies from Beer's law, and these may be caused by association, changes in solvation, etc.

A is the *absorbance* or *optical density*, and ε is the *molar absorptivity* or *molar extinction coefficient*. If ε [sometimes log ε; or the per cent absorption, *i.e.*, $100(1 - I/I_0)$] is plotted as ordinate against the wavelength (or frequency) as abscissa, the *absorption curve* or *absorption spectrum* is obtained, and this is characteristic of a *pure* compound. On the other hand, the per cent transmission ($100I/I_0$:

the ratio I/I_0 is called the transmittance, T), or the absorbance, A, may be plotted (as ordinate) against wavelength.

Of particular importance are the values of the absorption maxima and their intensity, and these are reported for ultraviolet and visible spectra as, *e.g.*, λ_{max} (EtOH) 2800Å or 280 nm (ε 4 000), which means that the ethanolic solution of the substance has a maximum absorption of 4 000 molar extinction units (1 mol^{-1} cm^{-1}) at a wavelength of 2 800 Å or 280 nm. Infrared spectra are reported as, *e.g.*, ν_{max} (CS$_2$) 1 030 cm^{-1} (s), which means that the compound, in carbon disulphide solution, has a strong absorption maximum at 1 030 cm^{-1}. In recording infrared spectra, it is customary to use the following letters to indicate intensity: m (medium), s (strong), v (variable), v.s. (very strong), and w (weak).

Spectroscopic studies may be divided into two types. Electromagnetic radiation consists of waves composed of an electric vector which is perpendicular to the magnetic vector; and both vectors are perpendicular to the direction of propagation. It is the electric vector which is mainly responsible for absorption of light, and occurs by interaction of this vector with charged electrons and atomic nuclei. Absorption spectra belonging to this type are ultraviolet, visible, infrared, Raman, and microwave spectra. On the other hand, absorption spectra may be obtained by interaction of charged particles with varying magnetic or electric fields. Absorption spectra belonging to this type are nuclear magnetic resonance, electron spin resonance, and mass spectra.

§12a. Ultraviolet and visible spectroscopy (200–750 nm).   The principles of electronic absorption have been described in Vol. 1, Ch. 31. Before discussing their applications, we shall first mention the various terms used. A *chromophore* is any structural feature which produces light absorption in the ultraviolet region or colour in the visible region. An *auxochrome* is any group which, although not a chromophore, brings about a red shift, *i.e.*, a shift of absorption towards the red region of the spectrum, when attached to a chromophore. Thus, the combination of chromophore and auxochrome behaves as a *new* chromophore. A *bathochromic effect* (*red shift*) and a *hypsochromic effect* (*blue shift*) are the shifting of the absorption band to the longer and shorter wavelengths, respectively. A *hyperchromic effect* and *hypochromic effect* are those which respectively increase and decrease the intensity of absorption.

According to M.O. theory, an atom or molecule is excited when *one* electron is transferred from a *bonding* to an *anti-bonding* orbital. Electronic transitions, however, can occur in different ways. A transition in which a bonding σ-electron is excited to an anti-bonding σ-orbital is referred to as a

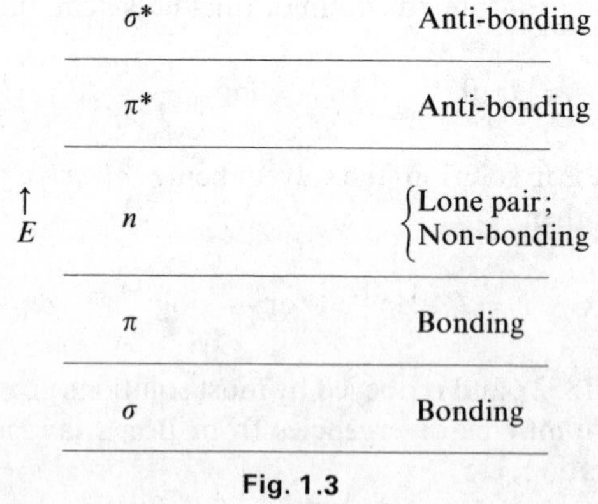

	σ^*	Anti-bonding
	π^*	Anti-bonding
$\uparrow$ E	n	$\begin{cases} \text{Lone pair;} \\ \text{Non-bonding} \end{cases}$
	π	Bonding
	σ	Bonding

Fig. 1.3

$\sigma \rightarrow \sigma^*$ transition. In the same way, $\pi \rightarrow \pi^*$ represents the transition of a bonding π-electron to an anti-bonding π-orbital. An $n \rightarrow \pi^*$ transition represents the transition of *one* electron of a *lone pair*, *i.e.*, a non-bonding pair of electrons, to an anti-bonding π-orbital. This type of transition occurs with compounds containing double bonds involving hetero-atoms, *e.g.*, $\diagup\!\!\!\!\diagdown$C=O, $\diagup\!\!\!\!\diagdown$C=S, $\diagup\!\!\!\!\diagdown$C=N—, etc., and may be represented as follows:

$$\diagup\!\!\!\!\diagdown C \overset{\cdot}{\underset{\cdot}{-}} \ddot{\text{O}} \quad \longleftarrow \quad \diagup\!\!\!\!\diagdown C = \ddot{\text{O}} \quad \longrightarrow \quad \diagup\!\!\!\!\diagdown C \overset{\cdot}{\underset{}{=}} \overset{\cdot}{\underset{}{\text{O}}}$$

$$(\pi \to \pi^*) \qquad\qquad\qquad\qquad\qquad (n \to \pi^*)$$

Figure 1.3 shows diagrammatically the general pattern of the energy levels, and it can be seen that the transitions are brought about by the absorption of different amounts of energy. Of the large number of possibilities, only the following transitions are allowed, and their general order of energy difference is:

$$\sigma \to \sigma^* > n \to \sigma^* > \pi \to \pi^* > n \to \pi^*$$

Isolated double bonds do not give strong bands, but when conjugated systems are present, the bands are usually strong and in the longer wavelength region. Thus, one particularly important application of ultraviolet (and visible) spectroscopy is the detection and elucidation of the nature of conjugated systems (including aromatics). This is often carried out with the use of 'model' molecules, *i.e.*, a 'simple' molecule that differs from the compound under investigation in a way that should have no effect on the chromophore.

Alkanes absorb in the region of 140–150 nm ($\sigma \to \sigma^*$), and when combined with various auxochromes, new absorption bands ($n \to \sigma^*$) are produced at longer wavelengths, *e.g.*, RCl, 170–175; RBr, 200–210; RI, 255–260; ROH and R_2O, 180–185; RNH_2, 190–200 nm. On the other hand, the carbonyl chromophore (in various functional groups) absorbs, in general, above 200 nm, *e.g.*, aldehydes, 180 nm ($\pi \to \pi^*$) and 290–295 ($n \to \pi^*$); ketones 190 ($\pi \to \pi^*$) and 270–280 ($n \to \pi^*$); saturated monocarboxylic acids, 200–210 ($n \to \pi^*$); esters, 200–205 ($n \to \pi^*$); amides, 205–220 ($n \to \pi^*$). It is this absorption at wavelengths longer than 200 nm that permits the identification of many chromophores in compounds.

When ethylenic double bonds are in conjugation or conjugated with a carbonyl group, the absorption moves to longer wavelengths, *e.g.*, for crotonaldehyde, there is one band at 220 nm ($\pi \to \pi^*$) and another at 321 nm ($n \to \pi^*$) [see also Table 1.5].

An interesting point about conjugated systems is that the geometry of conjugated dienes and trienes affects both λ_{max} and ε. In general, the acyclic compound absorbs at a shorter wavelength and has a greater intensity than the corresponding cyclic compound, *e.g.*, butadiene, 217 (ε, 21 000) and cyclohexa-1,3-diene, 257 (ε, 8 000). λ_{max} and ε are also affected by strain in a molecule, the greater the strain, the shorter the wavelength, *e.g.*, cyclobutanone, 281 nm; cyclohexanone, 290 nm. Steric effects, when operating, decrease conjugation, and so the *trans*-isomer will absorb at a longer wavelength than the *cis*-.

Aromatic compounds show a number of bands, *e.g.*, benzene absorbs at 184 (ε, 60 000), 204 (ε, 7 400) and 254 (ε, 200) nm. All are $\pi \to \pi^*$ transitions, and the 254 nm band is called the *benzenoid band* and is characterised by a large degree of fine structure (Fig. 1.4). For benzene derivatives, this benzenoid band generally occurs between 250 and 280 nm, but for polynuclear aromatics it moves to the longer wavelength as the number of rings increases (see Table 1.5).

All substituents in benzene have a bathochromic effect (see Table 1.5). For disubstituted benzenes, the positions of the absorption maxima depend on their orientation, and for *para* disubstitution, whether the substituents electronically assist, *e.g.*, NH_2 and NO_2, or whether they electronically oppose each other, *e.g.*, NH_2 and OMe. In the latter case, the absorption maximum is usually close to that of the 'stronger' chromophore.

The various bands in benzenoid compounds are sometimes referred to by letters, *e.g.*, E (180–220 nm), K (220–250 nm), B (250–290 nm), and R (275–330 nm) bands. The E- and B- bands arise from

Table 1.5

Compound*	λ_{max} nm (mμ) (ε)	Compound	λ_{max} nm (mμ) (ε)
Ethylene	175 (5 000)	Resorcinol	277 (2 200)
Butadiene	217 (21 000)	Quinol	225 (5 000)
Hexàtriene	258 (35 000)		293 (2 700)
Acetaldehyde	180 (10 000)	o-Nitroaniline	222 (16 000)
	290 (15)		275 (5 000)
Acetone	190 (900)	m-Nitroaniline	235 (16 000)
	280 (12)		373 (1 500)
Crotonaldehyde	220 (16 000)	p-Nitroaniline	229 (5 000)
	321 (20)		375 (16 000)
Benzene	204 (7 400)	Naphthalene	220 (100 000)
	254 (200)		275 (5 700)
Toluene	206·5 (7 000)	Anthracene	253 (200 000)
	261 (225)		375 (8 000)
Chlorobenzene	210 (7 400)	Phenanthrene	252 (50 000)
	264 (200)		293 (16 000)
Aniline	230 (8 600)	Furan	205 (6 000)
	280 (1 400)		250 (2)
Nitrobenzene	270 (7 800)	Thiophen	235 (4 500)
Phenol	210 (6 200)	Pyrrole	210 (10 000)
	271 (1 450)		240 (400)
Catechol	214 (6 000)	Pyridine	252 (2 000)
	278 (2 600)	Quinoline	313 (2 500)
		Stilbene (trans)	295 (27 000)
		Stilbene (cis)	280 (10 500)

*In most cases, ethanol is the solvent.

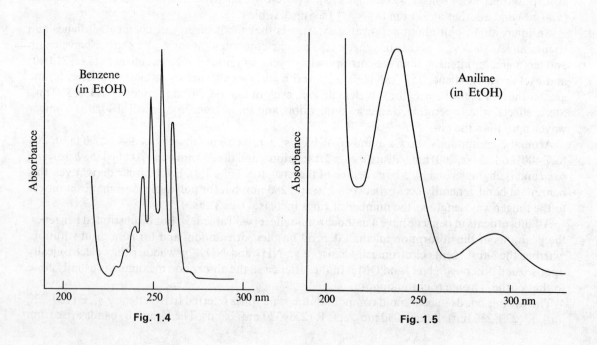

Fig. 1.4   Fig. 1.5

$\pi \to \pi^*$ transitions, the K-band, which is also due to $\pi \to \pi^*$ transitions, is exhibited by aromatic compounds with the benzene ring directly attached to a group containing a multiple bond, *e.g.*, styrene, benzaldehyde, nitrobenzene, benzoic acid, etc. On the other hand, if this group (directly attached to the benzene ring) also contains an atom with a lone pair of electrons, then $n \to \pi^*$ transitions are possible, and these give rise to the R-band. Because the B- and R-bands have an overlapping region and because the B-band has a greater intensity than the R-band, the latter is often 'hidden' by the former.

K- and R-bands also occur with acyclic conjugated systems.

In the earlier literature, letters have been used to designate various types of electronic transitions: $N \to V (\pi \to \pi^*)$; $N \to A (n \to \pi^*)$; $N \to B (n \to \sigma^*)$.

The case of aniline is worth further consideration. In ethanol, λ_{max} is 230 nm (Fig. 1.5), but in dilute aqueous acid, λ_{max} is 203 nm. In the free base, the nitrogen lone pair of electrons can enter into conjugation with the benzene ring. Thus, there is increased delocalisation in aniline and consequently the absorption maximum is shifted to the longer wavelength. In the anilinium cation, the lone pair is no longer available for conjugation with the ring, and so the molecule now behaves like benzene itself (which is the chromophore in both compounds).

Heterocyclic compounds, to a large extent, have u.v. spectra similar to those of the analogous benzenoid compounds (Table 1.5).

Woodward and Fieser have developed empirical rules for calculating $\pi \to \pi^*$ maxima of a given chromophore associated with unsaturation in conjugation and the type and position of substituents in the conjugated system (see **8** §3(viii)).

The final point we shall make here is the effect of solvents. Ethanol is most commonly used since it is a good solvent for many organic compounds and is transparent above 200 nm. However, polar solvents (and those which can form hydrogen bonds) tend to interact electrostatically (and form hydrogen bonds) with various chromophores, *e.g.*, the carbonyl group. This changes the charge distribution in the molecule and results, in effect, in increased delocalisation. For $\pi \to \pi^*$ transitions, both ground and excited states are stabilised, and the absorption moves to longer wavelengths. On the other hand, for $n \to \pi^*$ transitions, the ground state is, *e.g.*, hydrogen-bonded to a lone pair of electrons, whereas in the excited state, hydrogen bonding involves only *one* electron of the lone pair (the other having been promoted to an upper energy state). In these circumstances, the ground state is more stabilised than the excited state, and consequently absorption shifts to the *shorter* wavelengths. This blue shift with increasing polarity of solvent, *e.g.*, cyclohexane $\to$ EtOH $\to$ H_2O, is a useful means of recognising $n \to \pi^*$ transitions.

§12b. Infrared absorption spectra (4 000–650 cm^{-1}). Absorption in the infrared region is due to changes in vibrational energy. The essential requirement for a substance to absorb in this region is that vibrations in the molecule must give rise to an unsymmetrical charge distribution. Thus, it is not necessary for the molecule to possess a *permanent* dipole moment. Just as electronic transitions are quantised, so are rotational and vibrational energy levels also quantised. A non-linear molecule can undergo a number of vibrational motions, the two main types being *stretching* (vibration along the bonds) and *deformation* (*bending*; displacements perpendicular to bonds). Fig. 1.6 illustrates possible modes for a non-linear molecule (asym. = asymmetrical; def. = deformation; str. = stretching; sym. = symmetrical; and the plus and minus signs represent relative movement perpendicular to the page).

When a molecule contains n atoms, there are $3n - 6$ ($3n - 5$ for a linear molecule) fundamental vibrational frequencies. These may not all be different, and may not all appear in the infrared absorption region. The actual number of fundamental frequencies depends largely on the symmetry of the molecule, and the less symmetrical the molecule is, the larger is the number of different vibrational frequencies. Furthermore, there may be present frequencies other than the fundamental ones. These usually correspond to a little less than multiples of the fundamental frequencies, and are known as the *overtones* or *harmonics*. Thus, as *n* increases, the infrared spectrum becomes more and more complicated.

The stretching regions have higher frequencies (shorter wavelengths) than the deformation regions, and the intensities of the former are much greater than those of the latter. Although the masses of the bonded atoms predominantly influence the frequency of the absorption, other effects, *e.g.*, environment (*i.e.*, the nature of neighbouring atoms), steric effects, etc. also play a part. Thus, in general, a particular group will not have a fixed maximum absorption wavelength, but will have a *region* of absorption, the actual maximum in this region depending on the rest of the molecule. The spectrum also depends on the physical state of the compound: gas, liquid (as a thin film), solid (as a thin film or as a mull), or solution (preferably dilute, CCl_4, $CHCl_3$, CS_2).

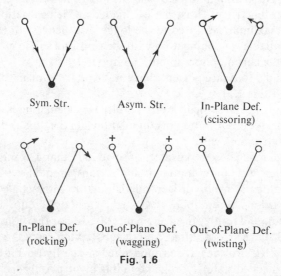

Sym. Str.   Asym. Str.   In-Plane Def.
                                        (scissoring)

In-Plane Def.   Out-of-Plane Def.   Out-of-Plane Def.
(rocking)   (wagging)   (twisting)

Fig. 1.6

In the initial examination of the spectrum, the usual practice is to look for the presence of the various functional groups. In this way it may be possible to assign the compound to some particular structural class (or classes). Knowledge of the molecular formula will often help to reject some of the alternatives, and chemical reactions of the compound will help further in this direction. Identification of a compound is carried out by comparison with published spectra (or with the spectrum of an authentic specimen). The region $1\,400$–650 cm^{-1} is known as the 'finger-print region'; this is the region usually checked for identification, since it is associated with vibrational (and rotational) energy changes of the *molecular skeleton*, and so is characteristic of the compound.

If a band has been found which corresponds to a particular group, the presence of this group should be confirmed by ascertaining the presence of another band which is also characteristic of the group, *e.g.*, saturated aliphatic esters show a strong band in the region $1\,750$–$1\,735$ cm^{-1} (C=O str.) and another strong band in the region $1\,250$–$1\,170$ cm^{-1} (C—O str.). Furthermore, the absence of a band which is characteristic of a particular group is not conclusive evidence that this group is not present in the molecule. One cause for this is that two groups in a molecule may interact, and the result is that both regions are now different from the 'expected' individual regions. It is therefore always desirable to have chemical information about the compound and also spectroscopic data obtained from other methods (u.v. and NMR).

The absorption frequency of a bond formed by two given elements is lowered when either atom is replaced by a heavier isotope. This is made use of in assigning infrared absorption bands, *e.g.*, bands

Table 1.6

Bond	Group	Region (cm^{-1})*
C—H	Methyl (Alkanes)	2 975–2 950
		2 885–2 860
		1 470–1 435 (def.)
		1 385–1 370 (def.)
	Methylene: Alkanes *and*	2 940–2 915
	Cycloalkanes (except	2 870–2 845
	Cyclopropane)	1 480–1 440 (def.)
	Methine	2 990–2 880
=C—H	Alkenes *and* Cycloalkenes	3 040–3 010
	cis-Alkenes	730–665 (def.)
	trans-Alkenes	970–960 (def.)
	Aromatics	3 080–3 030
≡C—H	RC≡C—H	3 310–3 300
C—H	RCHO	2 880–2 650
C=C	Alkene	1 680–1 620
	Conjugated to C=C or C=O	1 660–1 580
	Aromatics	1 625–1 600 (i.p.)
		1 590–1 575 (i.p.)
		1 525–1 475 (i.p.)
C≡C	RC≡CH	2 140–2 100
	R^{1}C≡CR^2	2 260–2 190
C—F	Alkyl fluorides	1 100–1 000
C—Cl	Alkyl chlorides	750–700
C—Br	Alkyl bromides	600–500
C—I	Alkyl iodides	600–500
O—H	Alcohols and Phenols: free	3 670–3 580
	Hydrogen bonded (intermolecular)	3 550–3 230
	Hydrogen bonded (intramolecular)	3 590–3 420
	Acids (free)	3 560–3 500
	Oximes	3 650–3 500
	β-Keto-esters (chelated)	near 2 700
N—H	Aliphatic *and* Aromatic primary *and* secondary amines:	
	free	3 500–3 300 (2 bands for primary; 1 for secondary)
	bonded	3 400–3 100
	Primary amides:	
	free	near 3 500
		near 3 400
	bonded	near 3 350
		near 3 200

*All regions except those specified in brackets are for stretching vibrations.

Table 1.6(*continued*)

Bond	Group	Region (cm^{-1})*
C=O	Acid anhyrides:	
	acyclic	1 840–1 800
		1 780–1 740
	cyclic	1 870–1 830
		1 800–1 760
	Acid chlorides	1 815–1 785
	Acids:	
	aliphatic	1 725–1 700
	aromatic	1 700–1 680
	Aldehydes:	
	aliphatic	1 740–1 720
	aromatic	1 715–1 695
	Amides (primary)	near 1 690
		near 1 650
	α-Diketones	1 730–1 710
	β-Diketones (enol)	1 640–1 540
	γ-Diketones	1 725–1 705
	Esters ($R^1CO_2R^2$)	1 750–1 735
	β-Keto-esters (enol)	1 655–1 635
	Ketones:	
	aliphatic	1 725–1 700
	alkaryl	1 700–1 680
	cyclic	1 780–1 700
	diaryl	1 670–1 660
	Lactones:	
	γ-	1 780–1 760
	δ-	1 750–1 735
	Quinones (2 CO's in one ring)	1 690–1 660
	α, β-Unsaturated acids	1 715–1 690
	α, β-Unsaturated aldehydes	1 705–1 680
	α, β-Unsaturated ketones	1 685–1 665
C—O	Alcohols:	
	primary	near 1 050
	secondary	near 1 100
	tertiary	near 1 150
	Epoxides	1 260–1 240
	Esters	1 250–1 170
	Ethers (—CH_2—O—CH_2—)	1 150–1 060
C—N	Amines:	
	aliphatic	1 220–1 020
	aromatic	
	primary	1 340–1 250
	secondary	1 350–1 280
	tertiary	1 360–1 310
C=N	Oximes (R_2C=NOH)	1 690–1 630
C≡N	Alkyl cyanides	2 260–2 240

*All regions except those specified in brackets are for stretching vibrations.

Bond	Group	Region (cm^{-1})*
NO$_2$	Aliphatic: primary and secondary	1 565–1 545 (NO$_2$ vib.) 1 385–1 360 (NO$_2$ vib.)
	tertiary	1 545–1 530 (NO$_2$ vib.) 1 360–1 340 (NO$_2$ vib.)
	Aromatic	1 550–1 510 (NO$_2$ vib.) 1 365–1 335 (NO$_2$ vib.)
	Benzene substitution: mono-	770–730 710–690
	di; *o-*	770–735
	m-	800–750 720–680
	p-	840–810

*All regions except those specified in brackets are for stretching vibrations.

in CHCl$_3$ which are shifted to lower frequencies in CDCl$_3$ can thus be assigned to the C—H and C—D bonds. The lowering of frequency is also usually observed when one of the atoms is replaced by a heavier atom in the same periodic group (see alkyl halides, Table 1.6).

The absorption regions of functional groups have been obtained empirically. Table 1.6 gives absorption regions for a number of types of bonds.

Six infrared spectra are given in the text: Figs. 1.7–1.12 (Figs. 20–25 are the corresponding NMR spectra; §12e).

Apart from structural elucidation, the study of infrared spectra leads to information on many types of problems, *e.g.*,

(i) Infrared spectroscopy has been used to distinguish between geometrical isomers. It also appears that enantiomers in the *solid* phase often exhibit different absorption spectra. Infrared spectroscopy has also been a very valuable method in conformational studies (see 4 §11).

(ii) The three isomeric disubstituted benzenes have characteristic absorption bands, and this offers a means of determining their orientation (see Vol. I).

(iii) Infrared spectroscopy has given a great deal of information about the problem of free rotation about a single bond; *e.g.*, since the intensity of absorption is proportional to the concentration, it has been possible to ascertain the presence and amounts of different conformations in a mixture (the intensities vary with the temperature when two or more conformations are present).

(iv) Tautomeric mixtures have been examined and the amounts of the tautomers obtained. In many cases the *existence* of tautomerism can be ascertained by infrared spectroscopy (*cf.* iii).

(v) Infrared spectroscopy appears to be the best means of ascertaining the presence of hydrogen bonding (both in association and chelation). In 'ordinary' experiments it is not possible to distinguish between intra- and inter-molecular hydrogen bonding. These two modes of bonding can, however, be differentiated by obtaining a series of spectra at different dilutions. As the dilution increases, the absorption due to intermolecular hydrogen bonding decreases, whereas the intra-molecular hydrogen-bonding absorption is unaffected. Also, measurement of the intensity of the *free* hydroxyl band has been used to ascertain the number of hydroxyl groups present in a molecule (with a known molecular formula).

(vi) It is possible to evaluate dipole moments from infrared spectra.

(vii) When a bond between two atoms is stretched, a restoring force immediately operates. If the

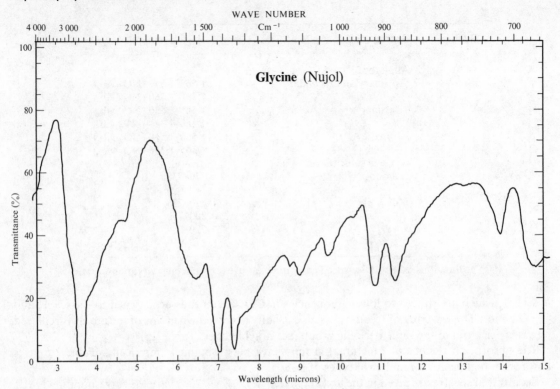

Fig. 1.7

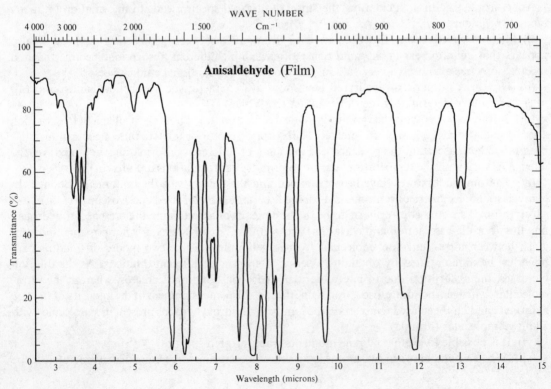

Fig. 1.8

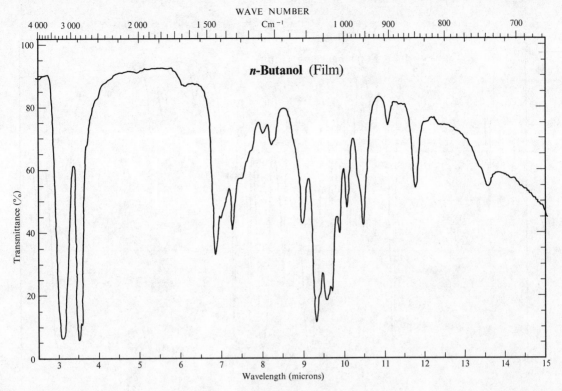

Fig. 1.9

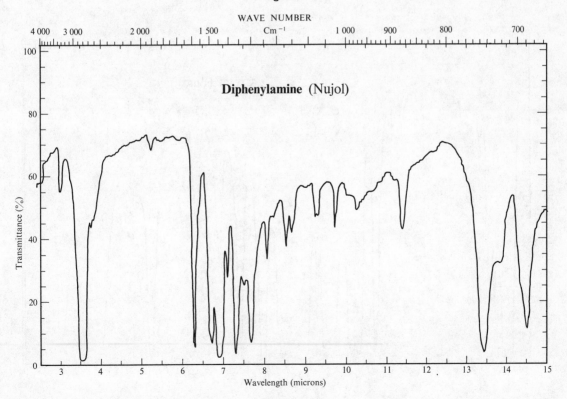

Fig. 1.10

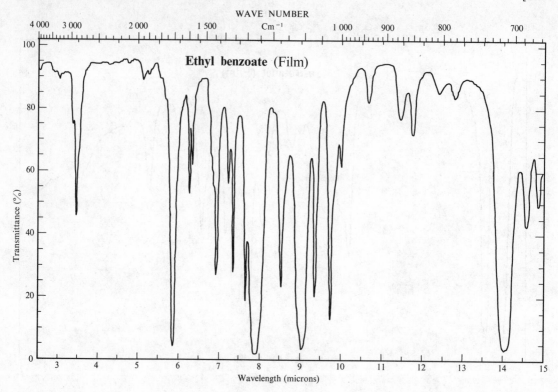

Fig. 1.11

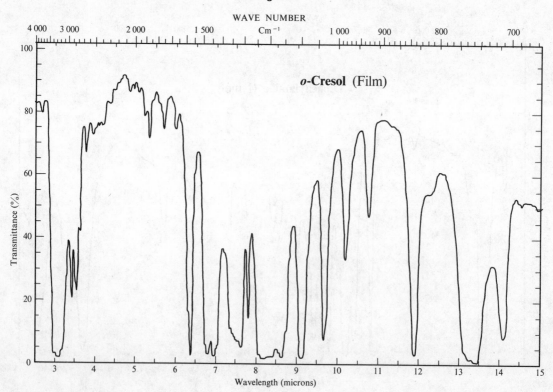

Fig. 1.12

distortion is *small*, the restoring force may be assumed to be directly proportional to the distortion, *i.e.*,

$$f \propto d \quad \text{or} \quad f = kd$$

where k is the *stretching force constant* of the bond. It is possible to calculate the values of these force constants from infrared (vibrational) spectra.

(viii) As an outcome of the large amount of data collected in infrared work, it has become possible to predict group frequencies in various compounds. The results are approximate, and their calculation is based on frequency shifts that have been obtained empirically. The application of these rules to structural problems is used much less than the rules derived for ultraviolet absorption (§12a).

§12c. **Gaseous microwave absorption spectroscopy (1 mm–10 cm).** Microwaves are now studied mainly by means of radio techniques. Microwave spectroscopy consists of two types: *gaseous microwave spectroscopy*, which deals with gases; and *electron spin resonance*, which deals with free radicals (see §12f). Gaseous microwave spectroscopy is concerned with the changes of rotational energy levels of a gas (vapour) when irradiated with microwaves. By means of this method, it is possible to calculate bond lengths, bond angles, dipole moments, energy barriers to hindered rotation, etc. Because of the high resolution obtainable in microwave spectroscopy, chemically similar molecules can be readily distinguished by this means.

Table 1.7 gives the values of some bond energies and Table 1.8 those of bond lengths.

Table 1.7

Bond	Energy		Bond	Energy		Bond	Energy	
	kJ	(kcal)		kJ	(kcal)		kJ	(kcal)
CH_3—H	426·8	(102)	C≡N	866·1	(207)	O=O	497·9	(119)
$MeCH_2$—H	405·8	(97)	C—F	447·7	(107)	O—O	146·4	(35)
Me_2CH—H	393·3	(94)	C—Cl	326·4	(78)	O—H	464·4	(111)
Me_3C—H	374·5	(89·5)	C—Br	284·5	(68)	S—S	225·9	(54)
C—H (av.)	414·2	(99)	C—I	213·4	(51)	S—H	347·3	(83)
C—C	347·3	(83)	C—S	272·0	(65)	S=O	497·9	(119)
C=C	606·7	(145)	H—H	431·0	(103)	F—F	150·6	(36)
C≡C	803·3	(192)	H—N	389·1	(93)	H—F	560·7	(134)
C—O	334·7	(80)	N—N	163·2	(39)	Cl—Cl	242·7	(58)
C=O	694·5	(166)	N=N	418·4	(100)	H—Cl	426·8	(102)
O=C=O	803·3	(192)	N≡N	945·6	(226)	Br—Br	188·3	(45)
C—N	284·5	(68)	N—O	200·8	(48)	H—Br	364·0	(87)
C=N	615·1	(147)	N=O	606·7	(145)	I—I	150·6	(36)
						H—I	297·1	(71)

Table 1.8

Bond	Length (Å)	Bond	Length (Å)	Bond	Length (Å)
C—C	1·54	C—S	1·82	C—F	1·42
C=C	1·40	C—O	1·43	C—Cl	1·77
C≡C	1·21	C=O	1·20	C—Br	1·91
C—H	1·12	O—H	0·97	C—I	2·13
C—N	1·47	N—H	1·03		

§12d. **Raman spectra.**   When a beam of monochromatic light passes through a transparent medium, most of the light is transmitted or scattered without change in wavelength. Some of the light, however, is converted into *longer* wavelengths, *i.e.*, *lower* frequency (a smaller amount of the light may be changed into shorter wavelengths, *i.e.*, higher frequency). The change from *higher to lower* frequency is known as the **Raman effect (Raman shift)**. It is independent of the frequency of the light used, *i.e.*, differences between the Raman and the light frequencies are always the same whatever is the light frequency. This, however, is not the case if the light frequency is close to the electronic or to the vibrational absorption frequency of the molecule. Since Raman spectroscopy is carried out with visible light (usually the blue mercury line, 435·8 nm), the compound to be studied must be colourless. The changes in the internal energy of the molecule result from changes in the vibrational energy of the molecules. Hence, a Raman shift is characteristic of a given bond.

In general, Raman spectroscopy gives the same kind of information as infrared spectroscopy, the main difference between the two being that the former can give more information on symmetrical molecules than can the latter. This is because symmetrical stretching in a symmetrical molecule does not produce an unsymmetrical charge distribution (see §12b). On the other hand, for a compound to be Raman active, the essential requirement is that the vibration must give rise to change in *polarisability* of the molecule.

Raman spectra have been used to obtain information on structure, *e.g.*, the Raman spectrum of formaldehyde in aqueous solution shows the absence of the oxo group, and so it is inferred that formaldehyde is hydrated: $CH_2(OH)_2$. Raman spectra have also been used to ascertain the existence of keto-enol tautomerism and different conformations, to provide evidence for resonance, to differentiate between geometrical isomers, to show the presence of association, and to give information on force constants of bonds.

§12e. **Nuclear magnetic resonance (NMR) spectroscopy.**   In order to explain certain observations in rotational spectra, it was suggested that atomic nuclei spin about their axes. Now, since a rotating charged sphere has associated with it a magnetic moment, then all the charged particles in a nucleus will cause that nucleus to behave (to a first approximation) like a small bar magnet, with its magnetic moment along the axis of rotation. Nuclei are composed of protons and neutrons, the former carrying a unit positive charge, and the latter being electrically neutral. Magnetic properties occur with those nuclei which have (*a*) odd atomic and odd mass numbers, *e.g.*, ^1_1H, $^{15}_7N$, $^{19}_9F$, $^{31}_{15}P$; (*b*) odd atomic number and even mass number, *e.g.*, ^2_1H (D), $^{14}_7N$; (*c*) even atomic number and odd mass number, *e.g.*, $^{13}_6C$. Nuclei which have no magnetic moment are those with even atomic and even mass numbers, *e.g.*, $^{12}_6C$, $^{16}_8O$, $^{18}_8O$, $^{32}_{16}S$. It has been assumed that the particles in such nuclei are paired, *i.e.*, spinning in opposite directions, with the result that there is no resultant spin and consequently no magnetic moment (*cf.* covalent pairs of electrons). In those nuclei where the magnitude of the spin is not zero, the *nuclear spin quantum number*, I, may assume any of the values 1/2, 1, 3/2, 2, etc. Nuclei possessing a resultant spin will thus behave as spinning magnets, and so will tend to orient themselves in an applied magnetic field, and the number of possible energy levels, *i.e.*, orientations with respect to the applied field, is given by $2I + 1$. The simplest example of a spinning nucleus is that of the proton. Here, $I = 1/2$ (*cf.* the electron), and in this case there are only two orientations possible, lined up with or against the direction of the applied field. Since work must be done to turn a magnet against a magnetic field, each orientation corresponds to a different energy state of the nucleus. These levels are quantised (*cf.* ultraviolet and infrared spectroscopy), and so it should be possible to find electromagnetic radiation of a definite frequency which will be absorbed, thereby changing the orientation of the proton from alignment with, to against the field, the change being from a lower to a higher energy level. This electromagnetic radiation is supplied by an oscillator (with its *magnetic field* at right angles to the applied field), and since the position of the absorption peak, *i.e.*, where *resonance* occurs, depends on the frequency of the oscillator or the strength of the applied field (see below), it is possible to change from the lower to the higher energy level by using a variable frequency with a fixed applied magnetic field, or vice versa. In practice, it has been found easier to vary the field rather than the frequency. The result is that the NMR spectrum is usually a graph of signal intensity (ordinate) against magnetic field (abscissa); expressed in milligauss at a fixed frequency. For a given field, the strength of the signal depends on the magnetic moment of the nucleus, and since the proton has one of the largest moments, **proton magnetic resonance (PMR)** is of special importance. Other nuclei used in NMR spectroscopic studies in organic chemistry are ^{13}C, ^{19}F, ^{29}Si, and ^{31}P, but to study these nuclei it is necessary to modify the spectrometer.

The difference between the two energy levels, ΔE, for a proton is given by expression (a), where h is Planck's constant, H the strength of

$$(a) \quad \Delta E = h\gamma H/2\pi \qquad\qquad (b) \quad v = \gamma H/2\pi$$

the field *experienced* by the proton, and γ is the *magnetogyric* (*gyromagnetic*) ratio for the proton. The frequency of the radiation (v) which induces the transition is given by expression (b), since $\Delta E = hv$. Thus, the position of the energy absorption is a function of both the frequency of the oscillator and the strength of the applied field. When radiation is absorbed, the proton changes from the lower to the higher energy state.

For an applied field of 9 400 gauss, the resonance frequency of a proton is about 40 MHz (megahertz = megacycles per second). The energy associated with this frequency is about 0.0167 J mol^{-1} (0.004 cal). Thus, ΔE is very small, and it is because of this that radiofrequency radiation can effect these transitions. Since ΔE is very small, the population in the lower state is only *slightly* greater than that in the higher state. This is the situation when the compound is placed in a magnetic field, and so there is net absorption when the radiofrequency is applied, and it is this absorption which is measured.

In order that a PMR signal be observed, the proton must be in a single state for 10^{-2} to 10^{-1} second. It has also been shown that the spectral line width is inversely proportional the average time the proton occupies the *higher* energy state. Hence, the longer the time spent in this state, the sharper is the line; and conversely, the shorter the time, the broader is the line.

From what has been said above, it might be expected that the resonance frequency for a given field depends only on the nature of the atomic nucleus concerned. This, however, is not the case. The applied field causes electrons round a nucleus to circulate in a plane perpendicular to the field, and these currents produce a field in opposition to the applied field. Thus, the effective magnetic field (H) experienced by the nucleus is smaller than the applied field (H_0), the relationship between the two being given by the expression

$$H = H_0(1 - \sigma)$$

σ (which is non-dimensional) is called the **shielding** or **screening constant**, and has a positive value, but in certain circumstances it may be negative, *i.e.*, the effective field is larger than the applied field. In this case, the proton is said to be deshielded. Since the numerical value of σ depends on the *chemical environment* of a given nucleus, the shielding or deshielding of a nucleus varies with its environment. Shielding causes a shift of the resonance frequency to higher values of the applied field, *i.e.*, the shift is *upfield*. On the other hand, deshielding causes a shift of the resonance frequency to lower values of the applied field, *i.e.*, the shift is *downfield*. The magnitude of this shift is known as the *chemical shift*. Since the value of the field experienced by the sample cannot be determined accurately, chemical shifts are measured *relative* to some standard which contains the nucleus under consideration. Various reference compounds (which are usually added to the sample) for PMR have been used, but tetramethylsilane (TMS), $(CH_3)_4Si$, is particularly useful since it contains twelve *equivalent* protons. The PMR spectrum of this compound shows a single sharp line which occurs at a higher field than any protons in most of the common organic compounds, *i.e.*, most PMR signals occur downfield with respect to TMS (see also below).

The chemical shift may be reported in various ways. Since the resonance frequency is dependent on the strength of the applied field, the shift may be reported as field units (milligauss). However, because the field can be expressed in terms of frequency (see expression (*b*) above), the shift may also be expressed in terms of Hz (c.p.s.). This separation in Hz is also proportional to the frequency of the oscillator, *e.g.*, if the separation between a proton signal and TMS is 60 Hz at 40 MHz, the separation at 60 MHz becomes 90 Hz [60 × 60/40 = 90]. Hence it is desirable to be able to report chemical shifts in units which are independent of the operating conditions of the spectrometer. This has been done by defining the chemical shift, δ, by the expression

$$\delta = \frac{\text{separation in Hz}}{\text{oscillator frequency}} \times 10^6$$

The factor 10^6 is introduced in order to record the chemical shift as a convenient value. This is usually in the range 1–10, and is quoted in parts per million (p.p.m.).

The independence of the chemical shift of the oscillator frequency is shown by the following example. A separation of 60 Hz at an oscillator frequency of 40 MHz becomes 90 Hz at an oscillator frequency of 60 MHz (see above). However, δ remains unchanged: $\delta = (10^6 \times 60)/(40 \times 10^6) = 1\cdot5$ p.p.m.; $(10^6 \times 90)/(60 \times 10^6) = 1\cdot5$ p.p.m.

It is now becoming common practice to express chemical shifts in τ (tau)-values, defined by the expression

$$\tau = 10 - \delta$$

where 10 p.p.m. is the value assigned to the line of TMS. Most protons have positive τ-values (*i.e.*, $\delta < 10$); strongly acidic protons, however, have negative τ-values (*i.e.*, $\delta > 10$). The greater the shielding of the nucleus, the larger is its τ-value (the smaller is δ). Since the degree of shielding depends on the electron density round the proton, any structural feature that decreases this density will cause a decrease in shielding, with consequent lowering of the τ-value (the chemical shift moves downfield). Halogens are electron-attracting (electronegative) groups and when joined to a methyl group, the electron density round each proton is decreased. Consequently, the presence of halogens weakens the induced opposing field, *i.e.*, deshields these protons and so the τ-value will be expected to be lowered (the chemical shift is moved downfield). This prediction is observed in practice. The order of electronegativity of the halogens is I < Br < Cl < F, and the τ-values of the methyl protons are: CH_3I, 7·83; CH_3Br, 7·35; CH_3Cl, 6·98; CH_3F, 5·70 p.p.m.

Similarly, since the order of electronegativity of carbon, nitrogen, and oxygen is C < N < O, the τ-values of the methyl protons in CH_3—C, CH_3—N, CH_3—O are, respectively, 9·12, 7·85, 6·70 p.p.m. Silicon is less electronegative than carbon, and so methyl protons in TMS are more shielded than those in a methyl group attached to carbon, *i.e.*, the protons in TMS absorb upfield with respect to protons in most of the common organic compounds (see Table 1.9).

Figure 1.13 summarises the terminology described in the foregoing account of NMR spectroscopy.

Measurements of NMR spectra are normally carried out on liquids or solutions (5–20 per cent concentration). The best solvents are those which do not contain protons, *e.g.*, deuteriochloroform and other deuterated compounds, carbon tetrachloride, etc. However, because of solubility problems, solvents containing protons may also be used, *e.g.*, chloroform. A difficulty with respect to solutions is that τ-values may change with the nature of the solvent, particularly aromatic solvents. Chemical shifts may also change with concentration in a given solvent. Protons attached to

Table 1.9

Z	CH$_3$Z τ	R'CH$_2$Z τ	R'$_2$CHZ τ	Z	CH$_3$Z τ	R'CH$_2$Z τ	R'$_2$CHZ τ
—R	9·12	8·75	8·50	—I	7·83	6·85	5·78
—CO$_2$R	8·00	7·90	—	—Br	7·35	6·70	5·97
—CN	8·00	7·52	7·3	—Cl	6·98	6·56	5·98
—CONH$_2$	7·98	7·95	—	—OR	6·70	6·64	6·20
—CO$_2$H	7·93	7·65	7·43	—$\overset{+}{N}R_3$	6·67	6·60	6·50
—COR	7·90	7·60	7·5	—OH	6·62	6·42	6·15
—SH, —SR	7·90	7·60	6·90	—OCOR	6·35	5·89	4·95
—NH$_2$, —NR$_2$	7·85	7·50	7·13	—F	5·70	5·66	5·40
—CHO	7·83	7·80	7·60	—NO$_2$	5·67	5·60	5·40

	τ
R—OH	9·5–6·0 (lower for enols; −1 to −6)
Ar—OH	~5·5
R—SH	9–8
Ar—SH	~6·5
RNH$_2$	8·5
ArNH$_2$	6·6–5·0
RCO$_2$H	O to −3

J values (Hz)

$\begin{array}{c} H \\ \diagdown \\ C \\ \diagup \\ H \end{array}$ 10-18   >CH—CH<   0-12 (no rotation)

dihedral angle: 0°, ~8; 90°, ~0; 180°, 9–11

carbon are very little affected, but when attached to atoms such as O, N, S, the chemical shift is very much affected. In the latter case, the changes are due to changes in the degree of hydrogen-bonding, which causes a downfield shift relative to the unbonded state (see also later).

The study of NMR spectra of liquids and solutions is known as **high resolution NMR**. The study of solids, since they give spectra which consist of broad resonance lines, is referred to as **broad line resonance**.

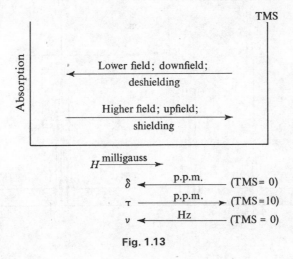

Fig. 1.13

Figure 1.14 is the NMR spectrum of ethanol (liquid; 60 MHz), carried out at low resolution. The position of each peak is characteristic of the environment of a particular proton, and the areas under the curves of the peaks have been shown to be in the ratio $1:2:3$. This ratio corresponds to the number of protons in OH, CH_2 and CH_3, respectively, and so it is therefore possible to 'count' the protons in various environments.

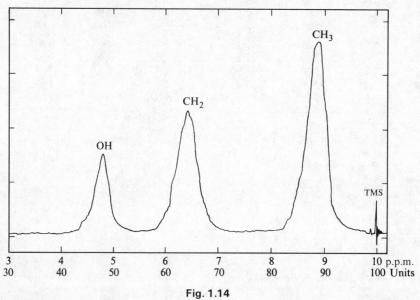

Fig. 1.14

These areas are now evaluated by means of electronic integrators. Integration produces a trace which rises in steps as each proton signal is passed, and the height (between steps) is proportional to the number of protons in that signal (see Fig. 1.15). In this way, the ratios of the numbers of protons in each signal are obtained, and if one number is known, all the others can be estimated. For example,

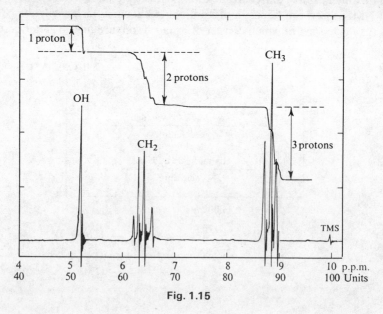

Fig. 1.15

if we know that the compound under examination is a monohydric alcohol then, knowing the position of a hydroxylic atom, we now know that the area of this signal is equivalent to one proton. On the other hand, if we know the molecular formula of the compound, we can also calculate the actual number of different protons. In practice, because of the experimental difficulties, it is unusual to obtain integers from the integration trace. However, the numerical results are usually sufficiently accurate to permit 'counting' of the different types of protons (in Fig. 1.15 the values are 54:37:19).

Spin-spin coupling. Figure 1.15 is the high-resolution NMR spectrum of ethanol (20 per cent in CCl_4; 60 MHz), containing a trace of hydrochloric acid. Instead of the broad bands shown in Fig. 1.14, two have been split into multiplets. The *total* areas under the multiplets are still in the same ratio as before, *i.e.*, 2:3. This fine structure has been explained as being due to shielding of protons by *protons on adjacent carbon atoms*.

First let us consider the influence of the methylene group, CH_2, on the methyl group, CH_3. Each proton in the methylene group may have its magnetic moment lined up with or against the applied field. If we represent the former alignment by an arrow pointing upwards and the latter alignment by an arrow pointing downwards, then there are the following four possible combinations:

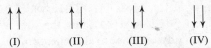

Thus the shielding effect will depend on the type of combination operating. However, combinations (II) and (III) will have the *same* shielding effect on the adjacent methyl group. Hence there are *three different* shielding combinations, and statistically it can be expected that at any given moment, 25 per cent of the methylene protons will be in combination (I), 25 per cent in (IV) and 50 per cent in (III) and (IV). The net result is that the methyl proton signal is split into a triplet, the ratio of the areas being 1:2:1.

If we apply the same argument to the effect of the protons of the methyl group on the methylene protons, then there are eight possible combinations:

As before, each combination in (VI) gives rise to the *same* shielding effect; this is also the case for (VII). The net result is that there are four different shielding combinations, resulting in the splitting of the methylene signal into a quartet, the ratio of the areas being 1:3:3:1.

This fine structure within a particular signal is called *spin-spin splitting*, and the magnitude of the separations between peaks in a multiplet (arising from spin-spin couplings) is called the *spin-spin coupling constant*, and is denoted by the symbol J; its values are given in Hz. The magnitude of J is independent of the oscillator frequency, but the *spacings between signals* is not. Hence, a change in frequency changes the signal separations, but not the spacings in a multiplet. Thus, by measuring the NMR spectra of a given compound at two different oscillator frequencies, if the spacings of a group of lines remain unchanged, the lines are components of a multiplet. If the spacings change, the group of lines arises from non-equivalent protons.

It has been stated above that the origin of multiplets is due to spin-spin coupling between groups of protons. This has been demonstrated by, *e.g.*, the examination of the following deuterated ethanols: (*a*) CD_3CH_2OH. (*b*) CH_3CD_2OH, (*c*) CH_3CH_2OD. Since the coupling constant of deuterium with protons is small ($\sim 1/7$ of J for hydrogen coupling), the result is that single peaks (slightly broadened) are given by protons when adjacent to deuterium. Deuterium signals are far removed from the normal proton signals, and are not observed under the operating conditions (for proton resonance). Thus, all three deuterated ethanols give two signals only: (*a*) gives a doublet and a triplet, (*b*) two singlets, and (*c*) a triplet and a quartet. Because the introduction of deuterium into a molecule leads to a simplified spectrum, this is used as a general method for studying NMR spectra, *i.e.*, for making assignments to various spectral lines.

Since the signal of a methyl group, *e.g.*, in CH_3CD_2OH or TMS, consists of a single line, this means that there is apparently no magnetic coupling between the hydrogen atoms attached to the same carbon atom (*geminal* hydrogens). The three hydrogen atoms are equivalent, all three having the same chemical shift. This leads to the general rule that protons with the same chemical shift do not give rise to observable splitting (see also below). Only when protons are non-equivalent is splitting possible.

There are two types of equivalent protons, *chemically* equivalent and *magnetically* equivalent. *Chemically equivalent protons* are those which occupy chemically equivalent positions, *i.e.*, are in identical chemical environments. Such protons have the *same* chemical shift. A simple test for chemical equivalence of two (or more) protons is to replace each proton one at a time by substituent Z, and if by doing so the *same* compound (or its mirror image) is obtained, then these protons are chemically equivalent. Let us consider ethane, CH_3CH_3, as an example. Replacement of each proton, one at a time, on one carbon atom gives CH_2ZCH_3, which is also obtained when the other carbon atom is treated in the same way (CH_3CH_2Z). Thus, the three hydrogens on *each* carbon atom are chemically equivalent, and *all six* hydrogens are also chemically equivalent. Hence, all have the same chemical shift, and consequently there is no splitting *within* a methyl group and none due to coupling *between* the groups. The observed spectrum of ethane consists of one signal which is a singlet.

A group of two (or more) protons are said to be *magnetically equivalent* when not only do they have the *same* chemical shift, *i.e.*, are chemically equivalent, but also the set of coupling constants to all other protons is identical for each member of the group. This may be illustrated with 1-bromo-2-chloroethane, which is represented by the Newman formula shown, (I) (see also **2** §4). If we assume, for the moment, that this conformation is fixed, it can be seen that H_a and H_b are chemically equivalent, as also are H_c and H_d (for each pair, the chemical environments are identical). The coupling constants, J_{ad} and J_{bd}, however, are not equal, and hence H_a and H_b are *not* magnetically equivalent.

To understand non-magnetic equivalence, we must now consider the problem of the magnitude of the coupling constant. It has been found that the value of *J* decreases very rapidly with increase in the number of bonds connecting the interacting protons. Only two cases are important, the methylene type (two bonds), H—C—H (geminal hydrogens) and the vicinal type (three bonds), H—C—C—H (adjacent carbon atoms). Geminal hydrogens, *e.g.*, H_aH_b or H_cH_d, couple with splitting only if their environments are different (see also **2** §4). If coupling occurs through four or more bonds, the coupling is referred to as *long range coupling*. This is usually negligible for *saturated* compounds, but may be large in *unsaturated* systems (see later).

In addition to depending on the number of intervening bonds, *J* is also *angular dependent*, *i.e.*, its magnitude varies with the angle between the methylene protons (when these are not chemically equivalent), and the *dihedral angle* for vicinal hydrogens. In practice, rotation about a C—C single bond takes place quite readily (see **2** §4). If we take the eclipsed conformation as the starting point, *i.e.*, in (I), the CH_2Br group is kept stationary and the CH_2Cl group is rotated until Cl and Br are in line, and consequently H_aH_c and H_bH_d are also in line (as pairs). In this *eclipsed* conformation, the dihedral angle is $0°$, and then keeping the CH_2Br group stationary, the other group can rotate through $360°$ before the molecule reaches its starting position. It has been found that the value of *J*, for a given pair of vicinal hydrogens, depends on the **dihedral angle (angle of rotation)**, being largest when the angle is 0° or 180°, and very small (or zero) when the angle is 90°. Thus, since the dihedral angle for $H_a H_d$ in (I) is 60° and that for $H_b H_d$ is 180°, J for the latter will be larger than that for the former. Hence, these coupling constants for H_a and H_b with H_d are different, and consequently H_a and H_b are not magnetically equivalent (see also **2** §4 for a further discussion).

The Karplus equation. Karplus (1959), on the basis of valence bond calculations, showed that the coupling constant J for a vicinal pair of hydrogen atoms is a function of the dihedral angle, ϕ, between the two C—H bonds. The Karplus equation has been expressed in a number of ways, e.g., (J in Hz):

(i) $J = C \cos^2 \phi - 0.28$

where C, a constant, has the following values: (a) C = 8·5 Hz for $0° < \phi < 90°$; (b) C = 9·5 Hz for $90° < \phi < 180°$.

(ii) A better relationship was later proposed by Karplus, viz.

$$J = 4.22 - 0.5 \cos \phi + 4.2 \cos^2 \phi$$

Since J is also a function of the electronegativities of any groups in the system, the values of J are approximate, but in the absence of electronegative substituents the values are in fair agreement with the experimental values.

One theory for the transmission of coupling is as follows. A given proton, because of its magnetic moment (due to spin), affects the spins of the electrons forming the covalent C—H bond. This change affects the spins of the C—C electron pair, and this in turn affects the spins of the electron pair in the adjacent C—H bond. Thus, the spin effects of one proton are transmitted through the covalent bonds to the other spinning proton. Since these effects depend only on the structure and geometry of the molecule and are not due to the presence of the applied field, they are independent of the strength of the applied field.

Rules for determining multiplicity. Some simple rules for determining the multiplicity of a signal have been developed, but these usually apply only when $(\Delta v / J) \geqslant 6$ (where Δv in Hz is the separation of the signals of the interacting groups). Spectra of this type are said to be **first-order spectra**.

(i) Equivalent protons, when coupled, do not cause splitting.

(ii) The spacings (i.e., J values) in a multiplet are equal and are also equal to the spacings of a multiplet arising from mutual coupling, e.g., in the NMR spectrum of ethanol, the spacings in the methyl triplet *and* the methylene quartet are all equal.

(iii) The multiplicity of a group of equivalent protons is equal to $(n + 1)$, where n is the number of equivalent protons in the group which are coupled to the first group, e.g., in —O—CH_2—CH_3, the two equivalent methylene protons are coupled to *three* equivalent protons in the methyl group. Hence, $n = 3$, and so there will be *four* lines shown by the two methylene protons. Similarly, the three methyl protons give rise to *three* lines due to coupling with the *two* ($n = 2$) methylene protons. Furthermore, the relative intensities of the individual lines of a multiplet correspond (ideally) to the numerical coefficients of the terms in the binomial expansion $(1 + x)^n$. Thus, the lines of the quartet ($n = 3$) have relative intensities $1:3:3:1$, and those of the triplet ($n = 2$), $1:2:1$. Also, the relative intensities of a multiplet are symmetrical (ideally) about the mid-point of the multiplet.

(iv) When a group of equivalent protons is coupled to groups of equivalent protons, n_a in one group, n_b in another, etc., the multiplicity of that group is equal to $(n_a + 1)(n_b + 1) \ldots$. To illustrate this rule, let us consider the NMR spectrum of *very pure* ethanol (see also below). The methyl group is coupled to the methylene group ($n = 2$), and so the methyl signal will be a triplet. The hydroxyl proton is also coupled to the methylene group, and its signal is therefore a triplet. The methylene group is coupled to *both* the methyl group ($n_a = 3$) and to the hydroxyl proton ($n_b = 1$). Hence, the multiplicity of the methylene signal is given by $(3 + 1)(1 + 1) = 8$, i.e., an octet. This is the spectrum observed in practice (for very pure ethanol; see also below).

When dealing with first-order spectra, it is possible to construct them diagrammatically. Let us consider ethanol (plus a trace of acid) as our example. This spectrum is shown in Fig. 1.15; the diagrammatic spectrum is shown in Fig. 1.16. The signal of the methylene group is a quartet of relative intensities $1:3:3:1$, and so the *total* intensity of this signal $= 1 + 3 + 3 + 1 = 8$ units. Since these 8 units represent two protons, one unit is equivalent to 0·25 proton, and 3 units to 0·75 proton. Hence these four components of the quartet may be drawn as vertical lines, the lengths of which are proportional to the number of protons they represent, *e.g.*, using 5 mm to be equivalent to 0·25 proton (the weakest line of the multiplets in *all* signals), the quartet is then represented by four lines, 5 mm, 15 mm, 15 mm, 5 mm, equally spaced and centred about the τ-value of this signal. In the same way, the intensities of other multiplets in the spectrum may be estimated and represented as vertical lines whose lengths are also based on the arbitrarily chosen unit of 5 mm $= 0·25$ proton. For ethanol, the τ-values of the signals are known, but if the values are not known, it is usually possible to estimate them from tables of τ-values (see, *e.g.*, Table 1.9).

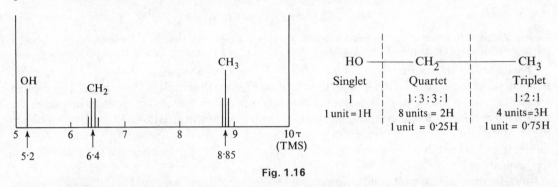

Fig. 1.16

The spectrum given in Fig. 1.16 is idealised. In practice, distortion of intensities may occur, inner lines increasing at the expense of outer lines (*cf.* 1.15). This becomes more pronounced as the ratio $\Delta v/J$ decreases. Since this distortion occurs between *coupled* signals, it may be used to show which groups of protons are coupled.

As we have seen, the simple rules of splitting are applicable only when $(\Delta v/J) \geqslant 6$. When $\Delta v \cong J$, the simple rules no longer hold good. The spectra are now complicated, and it is usually difficult to recognise the pattern of the lines. Mathematical techniques, however, have been developed for analysing complicated spectra. If the chemical shifts and coupling constants of all the magnetic nuclei present in the molecule are known, it is possible to predict the NMR spectrum of the compound. Alternatively, it may be possible to evaluate the chemical shifts and coupling constants from the observed spectrum.

One cause of the appearance of complicated spectra is that the components of a multiplet may overlap. For the purpose of analysing NMR spectra, a notation has been introduced for discussing spin-spin coupling. Protons which have similar chemical shifts are designated by the letters A, B, C, ..., and protons which have similar chemical shifts that are quite different from those of set A, B, C, ..., are designated by the letters ... X, Y, Z. When a proton has a chemical shift that lies between the above two sets and is well separated from both, it is designated by a middle letter of the alphabet, *e.g.*, M. The number of protons of the *same* type is then indicated by a subscript (an integer).

The earliest letters of the alphabet are usually chosen to present those protons which absorb at lower fields, and the choice of letters depends on which protons are different, on how different they are, and whether they are coupled or not. One practice is to designate protons as A and X if $\Delta v/J \geqslant 6$, and if less than this, as A and B. The scheme described so far designates the same letter to protons with the same chemical shift, *i.e.*, to chemically *and* magnetically equivalent protons. One method of indicating that the protons in one group are *not* magnetically equivalent is to repeat the same letter with one of them primed, *e.g.*,

$$CH_3CH_2OH \qquad\qquad CH_3NHCHO \qquad\qquad ClCH_2CH_2Br$$
$$A_3M_2X \qquad\qquad\qquad A_3XY \qquad\qquad\qquad AA'BB'$$

The term *spin system* is used to describe groups of nuclei that are spin-spin coupled among each other, but not with any nuclei outside the spin system. It is not necessary, however, for all the nuclei within the spin system to be coupled to *all* the other nuclei. In many cases, the spin system embraces the complete molecule, *e.g.*, $CH_3CH=CH_2$ is a six-spin system. On the other hand, a molecule may consist of two (or more) parts 'insulated' from each other, and thereby giving rise to two (or more) independent spin systems, *e.g.*, $CH_3CH_2-O-CH_2CH_2CH_3$. This contains two spin systems, the five-spin ethyl group and the seven-spin n-propyl group. The latter is an example of the case where not all nuclei in the spin system are coupled (coupling between OCH_2 and CH_3 is negligible).

Now let us analyse the spectrum of 1-bromo-3-chloropropane. The τ-values (at 40 MHz in $CDCl_3$) are: CH_2Br, 6·30; $-CH_2-$, 7·72; CH_2Cl, 6·45; J value for the first pair is $\sim 6·2$ Hz, $\sim 6·2$ Hz for the second pair, and zero for the first and third groups. Since δ(p.p.m.) = (Hz/r.f.) $\times 10^6$, Hz = $\delta \times$ r.f. $\times 10^{-6}$. Therefore, for the first pair, $\Delta v = 1·42 \times (40 \times 10^6) \times 10^{-6} = 57$. Hence $\Delta v/J = 57/6·2 = \sim 9·2$. This value is greater than 6; and this also is the case for the second pair ($51/6·2 = \sim 8·2$). This spectrum is therefore first-order.

Analysis of this spectrum may now be carried out in a similar manner to that used for ethanol, but here we shall deal with an alternative method, the graphical method. Each component of a multiplet may be represented by a line whose length is proportional to its intensity (*cf.* Fig. 1.16), but here we shall indicate relative intensities by numbers (see Fig. 1.17). The single lines in (i)

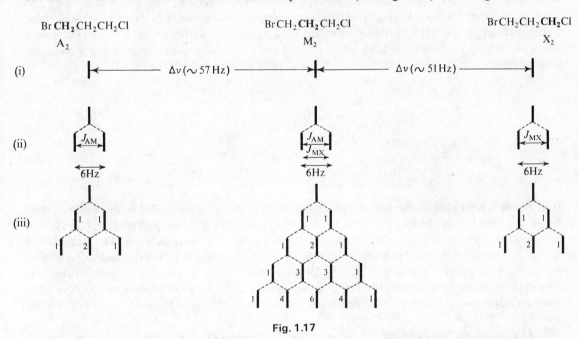

Fig. 1.17

represent each group of equivalent protons, and their spacings are proportional to the differences in chemical shifts. If there were *no* coupling, then each methylene group would have a single line signal, all three signals being of equal intensity. Since, however, A_2 and M_2 are coupled, as are also M_2 and X_2, splitting *does* occur. Let us first consider the signal given by the A_2 group of protons, always bearing in mind the *two* possible orientations of a coupled proton. In the absence of coupling, the signal is the single line shown in Fig. 1.17(i). If we now consider the coupling with *one* proton in the

M_2 group, this produces *two* lines of equal intensity, and they are separated by J_{AM} (Fig. 1.17(ii)). However, since A_2 is also coupled with the *other* proton in M_2, each component of the doublet is split into a *second* doublet, each pair being separated by J_{AM}. Hence, the 'inner' line of one doublet overlaps with that of the other doublet, thereby producing a triplet with equally spaced lines and with relative intensities 1:2:1 (Fig. 1.17(iii)). In the same way, it can be shown that couplings of the protons X_2 with M_2 also produce a triplet. In both cases, using the simple rules of multiplicity, with $n = 2$, the number of lines in the multiplet is 3 ($= n + 1$), and their relative intensities are 1:2:1 (the coefficients of the expansion $(1 + x)^2$).

Now let us consider the signal of M_2. According to the simple rules, their signal would be expected to be a multiplet of *nine* lines $[(2 + 1)(2 + 1) = 9]$. However, by using the scheme outlined for the coupling between A_2 and M_2, the diagram for the signal of M_2 is a multiplet of *five* lines (Fig. 1.17(iii)). It should be emphasised that the pattern of this multiplet is the same whether the M protons are coupled first to the A group, followed by coupling with the X group, or vice versa.

Because all J values are (almost) equal, overlapping of 'inner' components occurs, and consequently the observed number of lines is smaller than that calculated from the simple rules. This situation is generally the case when the J values between different groups of coupled protons are all the same or very nearly the same. Also, in these cases, the total number of lines of the multiplet is given by $N = (n_A + n_X + 1)$. In the example discussed, $n_A = n_X = 2$; hence $N = 5$. Furthermore, the relative intensities of the lines are given by the coefficients of the expansion $(1 + x)^{(n_A + n_X)}$, and the lines are equally spaced.

It can be seen from Fig. 1.15 that the signal from the proton of the hydroxyl group is not split, *i.e.*, there is no evidence of spin-spin coupling between the OH proton and the CH_2 protons, since had there been coupling, the OH proton signal would be expected to be a triplet. This absence of coupling has been explained on the basis that, in the presence of a trace of acids (in this case, hydrochloric acid), there is a rapid exchange of protons between ethanol molecules. This may be represented as shown:

$$C_2H_5\text{—}OH_A + H_B^+ \rightleftharpoons C_2H_5\text{—}\overset{+}{O}\underset{H_B}{\overset{H_A}{\diagup}}$$

$$C_2H_5\text{—}OH_C + C_2H_5\text{—}\overset{+}{O}\underset{H_B}{\overset{H_A}{\diagup}} \rightleftharpoons C_2H_5\text{—}\overset{+}{O}\underset{H_C}{\overset{H_A}{\diagup}} + C_2H_5\text{—}OH_B$$

Since a proton has two spin orientations which have almost the same energy levels, and consequently the populations in these levels are practically equal (see above), the exchanged protons (say H_A and H_B) have about the same chance of having the same or opposite spin orientations. The result is that the CH_2 protons experience both spin couplings to the same extent, the overall effect being a *time-average coupling effect* that is zero. Thus, the CH_2 signal is *not* split by the OH proton. Because this time-average effect is reciprocal, the OH proton signal is also not split by the CH_2 protons, and consequently gives a single sharp line signal. Thus, the CH_2 and OH protons are effectively *decoupled*.

The exchange reaction described is an example of **chemical exchange**, and this is common for protons attached to oxygen, nitrogen, or sulphur. However, for this decoupling to take place, the rate of exchange must be rapid. Calculations have shown that if the rate of exchange per second is much greater than the separation (in Hz) of the two separate signals (had there been no exchange), then decoupling occurs. For pure ethanol the rate of exchange is very much slower than Δv (the separation of the two signals), and so coupling occurs, the CH_2 appearing as an octet and the OH as a doublet (see above). Since the rate of chemical exchange is accelerated by a rise in temperature, *spin decoupling* may sometimes be observed by raising the temperature at which the NMR spectrum is measured. Similarly, *spin decoupling* may be observed by lowering the temperature. It also might be noted here that complications arising from a proton attached to oxygen (or nitrogen) may be removed by deuterium exchange. This is readily carried out by shaking a solution of the compound in deuteriochloroform with a small amount of D_2O. Signals arising from OH (or NH) protons will no longer be observed.

From what has been said, it can be seen that in exchange reactions, the shape of a band depends on the rate of exchange. When the rate is very fast, the signal of the exchanged proton is a single sharp line, and as the rate becomes slower, a point is reached when this begins to broaden, and finally splits into the number of components required for coupling with the vicinal protons. Thus, analysis of the shape of the band affords a means of evaluating the rate of exchange.

As we have seen above, the simple rules for determining multiplicity usually apply only when $(\Delta v/J) \geqslant 6$. We have also seen that Δv (the spacing *between* the signals) is dependent on the oscillator frequency, whereas J is independent of it. Hence, by increasing the oscillator frequency, Δv can be increased, and if increased sufficiently the conditions for obtaining a first-order spectrum $(\Delta v/J) \geqslant 6$, may be fulfilled, thereby resulting in a simplified spectrum. Oscillator frequencies that have been used are 100 MHz, and better still, 220 MHz.

It has been known for some time that the proton resonance peaks can be spread over a wider range of magnetic field strength by the addition of a paramagnetic substance to the solution of the compound under investigation. Two paramagnetic lanthanide chelates have been shown to be particularly useful 'shift reagents': complexes of 1,1,1,2,2,3,3-heptafluoro-7,7-dimethyloctane-4,6-dione with europium (III) and praseodymium (III) [designated as Eu (fod)$_3$ and Pr (fod)$_3$, respectively; Sievers *et al.*, 1971]. These are Lewis acids and form complexes with many Lewis bases, *e.g.*, alcohols, ketones, ethers, esters, etc. The europium chelate produces a downfield shift of the proton signals (in the Lewis base) and the praseodymium chelate produces an upfield shift. In this way, these shift reagents bring about resolution in a 60 MHz spectrometer comparable to the resolution obtained with a 100 MHz (or greater) spectrometer.

Double nuclear resonance. It has been pointed out above that spin-spin coupling may be annihilated by rapid exchange. This annihilation may also be effected as follows. Suppose we have two protons, A and B, in different environments and are coupled. Now suppose the resonance frequency of A is being measured. Then, at the same time as this is being done, a strong radiofrequency field whose frequency is the resonance frequency of B is also applied. This latter field produces both absorption and emission by B many times a second, and consequently coupling of B with A is now prevented, *i.e.*, B is decoupled with respect to A, and the time average of coupling between A and B is zero. Splitting of A by B has been prevented, but it is not possible under the conditions of the experiment to record the resonance of B. By applying double nuclear resonance to each type of proton, each signal can be made to collapse into a singlet line. In this way, the double resonance method produces a much simpler spectrum, and hence makes interpretation easier (*cf.* spectra of deuterated ethanol, above).

NMR spectra of compounds containing multiple bonds. It has been pointed out that the spin-spin coupling constant depends on the number of covalent bonds between the two interacting protons and on their geometry. The former factor is the same for a pair of *cis-trans* 1,2-disubstituted ethylenes.

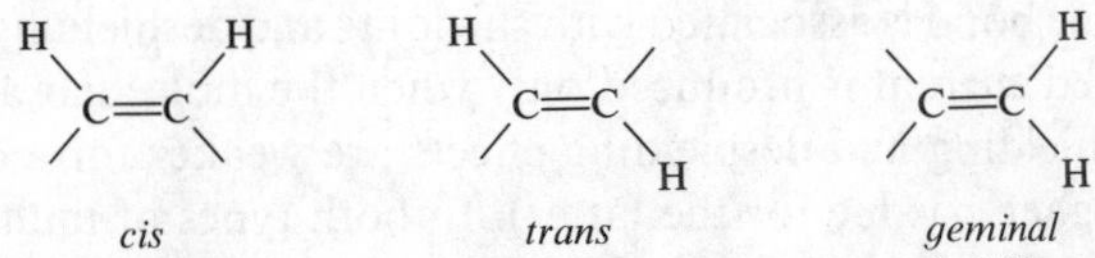

cis	*trans*	*geminal*
J 7–14 Hz	12–19 Hz	0–3 Hz

The latter factor, however, is different, and this produces different J values and so offers a means of distinguishing between *cis* and *trans* isomers.

J values for other groupings involving a double bond are, *e.g.*, (note the long range coupling):

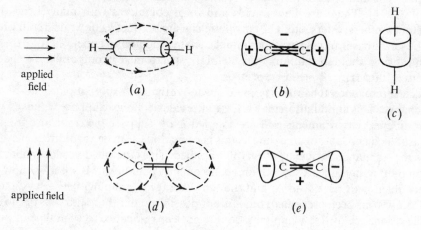

vicinal	allylic	homo-allylic
J 4–10 Hz	(*cis* or *trans*)	0–2 Hz
	0–2 Hz	

Since the electronegativities of the carbon atoms in the following compounds are in the order $C_2H_2 > C_2H_4 > C_2H_6$, it therefore follows that the chemical shifts of the protons should also be in this order. In actual practice, the order is $C_2H_4(\delta \sim 5\,\text{p.p.m.}) > C_2H_2(\delta \sim 2\cdot5) > C_2H_6(\delta \sim 0\cdot9)$. This can be explained on the assumption that a *shielding* effect is operating in acetylene, and is very much smaller in ethylene. The cause of this shielding effect is believed to be as follows. If acetylene is placed in a magnetic field with its molecular axis parallel to the field (Fig. 1.18*a*), the π-electrons circulate in the annular π-molecular orbital, thereby producing an induced field in opposition to the applied field. Thus, protons *in line* with the triple bond are *shielded*, resulting in a decreased chemical shift (increased τ-value). Protons which lie *above* or *below* the bonding line, however, are *deshielded*. The overall result is that there are cones within which shielding is experienced, and outside which deshielding is experienced by protons. This is represented by Fig. 1.18(*b*), *shielding* being indicated by a *positive* sign, and *deshielding* by a *negative* sign.

applied field　　(*a*)　　　　　(*b*)　　　　　(*c*)

applied field　　(*d*)　　　　　(*e*)

Fig. 1.18

If the molecular axis of acetylene is perpendicular to the applied field (Fig. 1.18*c*), no π-electron circulation is produced, and consequently no shielding or deshielding occurs. The effect of these π-electron circulations, averaged out over all possible orientations in the applied field, must therefore produce some shielding (in line with the bond) of acetylenic protons, and this results in a relatively high τ-value ($\sim 7\cdot5$).

In a similar way, a double bond is associated with shielding and deshielding (Figs. 1.18*d* and 1.18*e*), but in this case the induced current is produced only when the molecular axis lies *perpendicular* to the applied field. Also, shielding and deshielding effects are weaker for a double bond than for a triple bond (hence the higher τ-value for the latter). In both types of multiple bonds, double and triple, the magnitude of the induced magnetic field depends on the angle of the molecular axis with respect to the applied magnetic field. Because of this, compounds with multiple bonds are said to be *magnetically anisotropic*.

In addition to this shielding effect in acetylenes, there is also the existence of long range coupling, *e.g.*, in methylacetylene, the methyl group gives a doublet and the acetylenic hydrogen a quartet. This coupling extends over *four* bonds (which includes one triple bond); coupling is absent or negligible over four *single* bonds. This coupling also extends over four bonds when one is a double bond. In both cases, J is small (1–2 Hz).

The NMR spectra of carbonyl compounds are affected by the strong inductive effect ($-I$) of the carbonyl group and also by the magnetic anisotropy of the carbon-oxygen double bond (see ethylene, Figs. 1.18(d) and (e); replace one CH_2 group by oxygen). Both effects deshield an *aldehydic* proton, the result being a very low τ-value 0·1–0·7 p.p.m. On the other hand, protons in *ketones* are deshielded mainly by the $-I$ effect (the protons are at the 'edge' of the shielding cone) and consequently the shift downfield is much less (than for the aldehydic proton), *e.g.*, aliphatic ketones containing the MeCO group have a τ-value 7·8–8·1 for the methyl protons. Thus, infrared spectroscopy will show the presence of a carbonyl group, and the NMR spectrum will distinguish between aldehydes and ketones.

The τ-values of both α- and β-protons in α,β-unsaturated carbonyl compounds occur at lower field than those in alkenes (4·3–5·3), and the value for the β-proton is also dependent on whether it is *cis* or *trans* with respect to the carbonyl group. The usual range for α-protons is $\tau \sim 3\cdot5$–$4\cdot2$ and for β-protons, $\tau \sim 2\cdot4$–$3\cdot5$. This downfield shift for both α- and β-protons may be attributed to the $-I$ effect of the CO group, and the greater shift for the β-proton may be explained by conjugation which results in a small positive charge on the β-carbon atom, thereby increasing deshielding of a β-proton:

$$-CH=CH-C=O \longleftrightarrow -\overset{+}{C}H-CH=C-O^-$$

Since shifts for protons attached to an unsaturated carbon atom further along the chain are fairly close to those of protons in alkenes, this may be used to show whether a double bond is α,β with respect to the carbonyl group.

NMR spectroscopy of aromatic compounds. Let us first consider the case of benzene placed in a magnetic field. The delocalised π-electrons in the ring can move in either direction, but under the influence of a magnetic field applied perpendicular to the molecular plane, circulation takes place in one direction, thereby producing a *ring current* which induces a magnetic field perpendicular to the molecular plane (see Fig. 1.19a). This induced magnetic field assists the applied field *outside* the ring and opposes the applied field *inside* the ring (and volume above and below bounded by the area of the ring; Fig. 1.19b). Thus, there are volumes in which deshielding (negative) and shielding (positive) occur (see also Fig. 1.18). Hence, for the hydrogen atoms of benzene, since they lie in the plane of the ring, their chemical shift occurs at lower field than had the deshielding effect been absent: τ-values of aromatic protons lie between 1·0 and 3·0; those of olefinic protons are 4·3 to 5·3. It is therefore usually assumed that a compound is aromatic if the NMR absorption peaks of the hydrogen atoms attached to the carbon atoms of the ring are at a lower field than that expected for olefinic hydrogen atoms.

For protons lying in the shielding cones (inside and above and below the ring), the chemical shift occurs at a higher field than had the shielding effect been absent, *i.e.*, the τ-value is greater than that of an olefinic proton.

In benzene, no protons lie inside the ring. In simple cyclophanes (Fig. 1.19c), some methylene groups lie directly above the plane of the benzene ring (*i.e.*, in a shielding cone); the τ-values of these methylene protons are higher than those of the others.

The NMR spectrum of benzene is a single line at τ 2·73. In general, the τ-value of a nuclear hydrogen in substituted benzenes is 1·0 to 3·0, and depends on the position of the hydrogen atom and the nature of the substituent group. Let us consider a monosubstituted benzene, C_6H_5Z. If Z is an electron-withdrawing group ($-I$ and/or $-R$), then because of the small positive charges on the o- and p-carbon atoms, o- and p-protons are deshielded, and consequently their resonance absorption occurs at a lower field than that of a proton in benzene. At the same time, the m-proton is also deshielded, but much less so than the o- and p-protons. In general, the effect of deshielding is $o > p > m$. On the other hand, if Z is an electron-donating group ($+I$ and/or $+R$), shielding now occurs, and consequently o-, p-, and m-protons absorb upfield with respect to a proton in benzene,

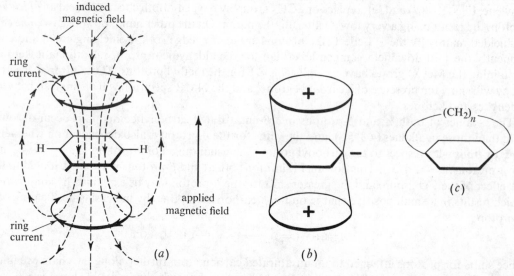

Fig. 1.19

the effect of shielding being also $o > p > m$. If, in both cases, the chemical shifts of the o-, p-, and m-protons are sufficiently different, then coupling between a vicinal (*ortho*) pair of protons can occur, and also long-range coupling between protons *meta* and *para* to each other. In these circumstances, the signal of the five protons in C_6H_5Z is a complicated multiplet. For benzene derivatives, coupling constants are: *ortho*-, 7–10; *meta*, 2–3; *para*, 0–1 Hz. If, however, the spectrum is measured at low resolution, then, unless the differences in chemical shifts (o, m and p) are relatively large, the aromatic ring signal is essentially a singlet, *e.g.*, this is usually the case for Z = Cl, Br, R, CH_2Y (Y = R, Cl, OH, NH_2).

Figures 1.20–1.25 are, respectively, the NMR spectra (at 60 MHz) of glycine, p-anisaldehyde, n-butanol, diphenylamine, ethyl benzoate, and o-cresol (see also the corresponding infrared spectra, Figs. 1.7–1.12).

§12f. Electron spin resonance (ESR).   Since electrons possess spin, they behave as spinning magnets and so will tend to orient themselves in an applied magnetic field. The spin of one electron of a covalent pair and its interaction with a magnetic field is cancelled by the equal and opposite spin of its partner. An unpaired electron, however, will have an interaction that is not cancelled out. If a molecule contains only one unpaired electron, then the spin number can be either $+\frac{1}{2}$ or $-\frac{1}{2}$. Thus there are only two orientations possible, lined up with or against the direction of the field. This state of affairs is the same as that for PMR (§12e). Hence, by choosing a suitable strength for the magnetic field, the unpaired electron can be made to absorb in the microwave region (thereby changing from its alignment with, to against the field; the change is from a lower to a higher energy level). The energy

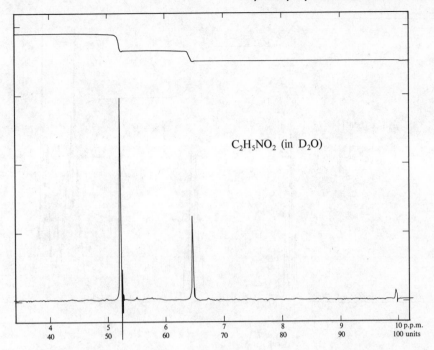

Fig. 1.20

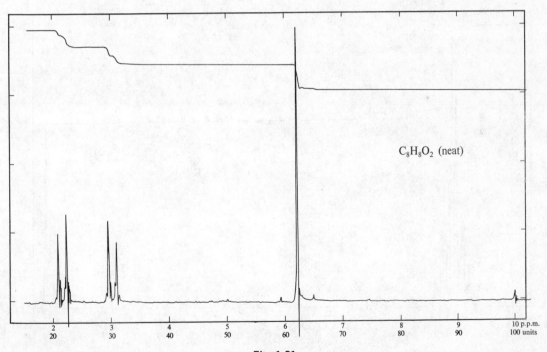

Fig. 1.21

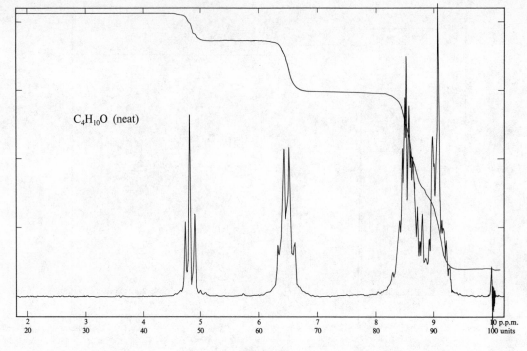

Fig. 1.22

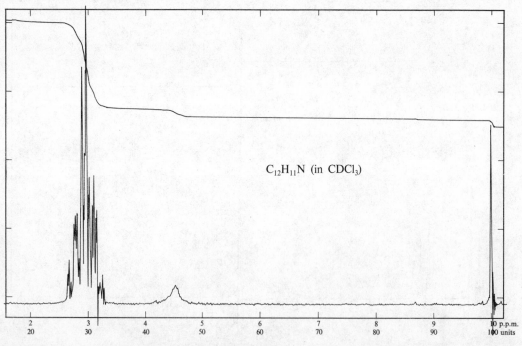

Fig. 1.23

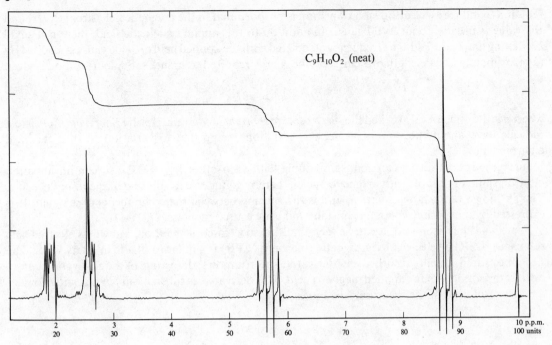

Fig. 1.24

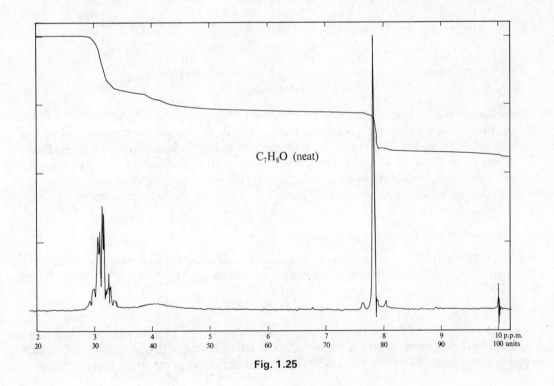

Fig. 1.25

required to induce an electron spin transition is proportional to the magnetic field strength H_0, and the value is usually about 3 400 gauss. In addition to this applied magnetic field, there is a small oscillating magnetic field. The frequency associated with the applied field of 3 400 gauss is 9 500 MHz (approximately a wavelength of 3 cm), and the energy required to induce the spin transition is given by

$$\Delta E = h\nu = g\beta H_0$$

where g is the g-factor (also called the *spectroscopic splitting factor*) and β is the *Bohr magneton*. Most radicals have about the same g value, the variations being due to variations in the chemical environment.

Just as magnetic nuclei can spin-spin couple with each other (*cf.* NMR), so can an unpaired electron spin-spin couple with magnetic nuclei, thereby giving rise to splitting of the resonance line. This is known as *hyperfine splitting*, and is the spacing between the components of a signal. It is expressed by a hyperfine coupling constant and is measured in gauss (*cf.* NMR).

From what has been said, it can be seen that this spectroscopic method, known as **electron spin resonance (ESR)** or **electron paramagnetic resonance (EPR)** is similar to NMR in many ways. The ESR spectrum is usually recorded as a derivative spectrum (first derivative of the absorption curve) against the strength of the applied magnetic field. This derivative is substantially dy/dx, and provides a better resolution of the spectrum (see Fig. 1.26).

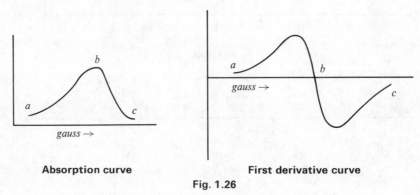

Absorption curve   **First derivative curve**

Fig. 1.26

The intensity of ESR lines depends on a number of factors, *e.g.*, it is proportional to the applied field (H_0) and to the concentration of the free radical. Hence, it is possible to measure the concentration of free radicals and to study stable and transient free-radical intermediates in organic reactions.

ESR spectroscopy offers a means of elucidating structural problems, particularly those of free radicals, *e.g.*, the hyperfine structure shown by the protons in the triphenylmethyl free radical, $Ph_3C\cdot$, indicates that the unpaired electron is not located on the methyl carbon atom.

§13. Mass spectrometry

When a compound, in a high vacuum, is bombarded with electrons in a mass spectrometer, it is converted into positive ions by loss of an electron (positive ions may also be produced by other methods).

$$M + e \rightarrow M^+ + 2e$$

The positive ion, M^+ (or P^+), is known as the **molecular ion** (or the **parent ion**), and is formed when the energy of the electrons is equal to that of the ionisation potential (usually 10–15 electronvolts). In practice, the energy of the electrons is 50–70 eV, and under these conditions the molecular ion is formed with an excess of energy, large enough for it to break down into a mixture of neutral and positively charged fragments, and the latter, if they have an excess of energy, also undergo further fragmentation, etc.

Most ions carry a unit positive charge, but some may carry a double (or greater) positive charge (and some ions may be negatively charged by electron *capture*). All *positive* ions are accelerated in an electric field and separated by their passing through an electric field and then a magnetic field. In this way, ions which have the same mass/charge (m/e) ratio are collected into beams, and fall on a collector plate. Thus, the ions are sorted out according to their mass/charge ratios, and so the masses of the ions can be determined. Since most ions have a unit positive charge, m/e is equivalent to m. To be of value, however, the instrument must be capable of at least separating, *i.e.*, *resolving*, adjacent beams of m/e and $(m + 1)/e$. Mass spectrometers are now available which are capable of very high resolution, being able to differentiate between ions whose masses differ in the third decimal place.

If a positive ion is doubly-charged, it will behave, as far as collection in a beam is concerned, in the same way as a singly-charged ion of half the mass. There is also the problem of isotopes, *e.g.*, at low resolution, $^{12}C_2H_2$ and $^{12}C^{13}CH$ both have m/e of 26; but if these differ in the third decimal place, it is possible to differentiate between them by high resolution. Since *individual* ions are collected in the mass spectrometer, then the molecular ion will also give rise to a number of peaks, *e.g.*, bromine exists as ^{79}Br and ^{81}Br. Thus, the molecular ion of methyl bromide will appear (low resolution) at peaks of m/e 94 ($^{12}CH_3{}^{79}Br$), 95 ($^{13}CH_3{}^{79}Br$), 96 ($^{12}CH_3{}^{81}Br$), and 97 ($^{13}CH_3{}^{81}Br$). The relative intensities of these $M^+, (M + 1)^+, \ldots$, peaks depend on the abundance ratios of the isotopes in the molecule (see Table 1.10). It can therefore be seen that mass spectrometry affords a means of determining accurate isotopic abundance ratios, molecular weights and consequently molecular formulae (these are obtained from tables).

Table 1.10

Element	Mass	%	Element	Mass	%
H	1	99·985	F	19	100
D	2	0·015	S	32	95·0
C	12	98·89	S	33	0·74
C	13	1·11	S	34	4·24
N	14	99·63	Cl	35	75·4
N	15	0·37	Cl	37	24·6
O	16	99·76	Br	79	50·6
O	17	0·04	Br	81	49·4
O	18	0·20	I	127	100

The mass spectrum is a plot of ion beam intensities (ordinate) against mass/charge (m/e), and for any pure compound is characteristic of that compound, *i.e.*, a pure compound is characterised by its **cracking pattern** (and its molecular ion, if it has one). It should be noted that by cracking pattern is meant not only the fragmentation pattern, but also that the relative abundance of the peaks are fixed ratios. Since mass spectra are dependent on the conditions of the experiment, these spectra are reproducible only if the conditions are identical. Hence it is best to use the same instrument and the same conditions for the purpose of comparisons.

The largest peak in a mass spectrum corresponds to the most abundant ion, and is known as the **base peak**. The base peak is used to report mass spectra in a standardised form; its intensity is arbitrarily given the value of 100, and all other peaks are reported as percentages of the base peak. This series of calculated values is the cracking pattern, and it may be described in the form of a line diagram (bar graph; see Fig. 1.27), or may be reported in tabular form in which mass numbers and relative abundances are listed.

The interpretation of a mass spectrum is difficult, complications arising from various sources. The main source of difficulty is that the molecular ion may undergo rearrangement to give fragmentation patterns not anticipated from the structure of the compound, *e.g.*,

$$ABC + e \rightarrow [ABC]^+ + 2e$$

$$[ABC]^+ \rightarrow [AB]^+ + C\cdot \quad \text{or} \quad AB\cdot + C^+ \quad \text{or} \quad [BC]^+ + A\cdot \quad \text{or} \quad [AC]^+ + B\cdot, \text{etc.}$$

Metastable ions. If an ion (molecular or fragment), m_1^+, is accelerated *before* it breaks down, then, when it decomposes into m_2^+ and m_3, part of the kinetic energy of m_1^+ is lost to the neutral fragment m_3, and m_2^+ continues to be accelerated and is then collected.

$$m_1^+ \rightarrow m_2^+ + m_3$$

Ion m_2^+, *produced in this way*, is *not* recorded as mass m_2, but as mass m^*, where $m^* = m_2^2/m_1$. This ion, known as a *metastable ion*, is usually recorded as a weak broad peak, and is not (usually) an integral value. It is evaluated from the *recorded* masses m_1 and m_2, which arise from m_1^+ ions undergoing decomposition and acceleration in the normal way. The presence of metastable peaks is very useful for deducing fragmentation mechanisms, since they indicate the conversion of m_1^+ into m_2^+ in *one* step; *e.g.*, three ions, m/e 32, 31, and 30 were recorded. This suggests loss of a hydrogen atom one at a time. A broad peak (metastable peak), however, was also recorded at 28·1, and since 28·1 = $30^2/32$, this means that ion m/e 32 was converted into ion m/e 30 in *one* step. It should be emphasised, however, that the absence of a metastable peak does not indicate that ion m/e 32 → ion m/e 30 does not occur, and it is also possible that ion m/e 31 → ion m/e 30 occurs.

Mass spectrometry may be used with gases, liquids, and solids, and only very small amounts of material are necessary (a few μg). It has proved extremely valuable for the determination of accurate molecular weights, obtaining molecular formulae, elucidation of structure, quantitative analysis of mixtures, ionisation potentials, and bond strengths.

Cracking patterns are largely dependent of the relative labilities of bonds, relative stabilities of possible fragment ions and neutral molecules, etc. Many examples are discussed later, but some general principles are mentioned here. When alternative fragmentations are possible, splitting usually occurs in all the alternative ways, but the direction leading to the most stable carbonium ion and/or free radical is the one that predominates. Most molecules show a peak for the molecular ion, the stability of which is usually in the order: aromatics > conjugated acyclic polyenes > alicyclics > n-hydrocarbons > ketones > ethers > branched-chain hydrocarbons > alcohols. The ease of formation of a molecular ion depends on the type of electron removed; the order is usually n (lone-pair electron) > π (pi-electron) > σ (sigma-electron). However, since the bombardment electron energy is 50–70 eV, *all* types of electrons may be removed, the one most easily removed being that from the atom with the lowest ionisation potential. Rearrangements occur most readily when a hydrogen atom is involved in a six-membered cyclic transition state or when 1,2-shifts are involved.

As an example of some of the principles discussed, we shall describe the mass spectrum of ethanol. Fig. 1.27 is the line diagram (bar graph), and shows the most intense lines. Since there are many decomposition paths, only some of these will be considered. Single headed arrows are used to denote the transfer of one electron (*homolytic fission*), and when the position of the positive charge is known, a plus sign is placed above that atom. When, however, the position of the positive charge is uncertain, the ion is enclosed in square brackets with the symbol $+$ as a superscript. Since the oxygen atom (with two lone pairs) in ethanol is the one with the lowest ionisation potential, one form of the molecular ion (M^+; m/e 46) will have the positive charge on the oxygen atom. However, in order to

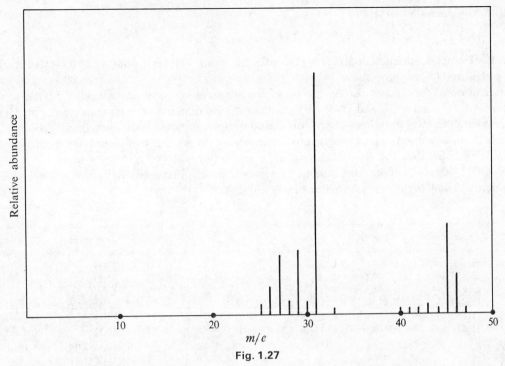

Fig. 1.27

propose various paths for the decompositions, it will be necessary to consider other forms of the molecular ion in which the position of the positive charge is uncertain (as we saw above, all types of electrons, n, π, and σ may be removed). It should be also noted that in some cases a path may be postulated which involves the transfer of *two* electrons (*heterolytic fission*), but this appears to be uncommon.

$$CH_3\!-\!CH_2\!-\!\overset{..}{O}H + e \longrightarrow CH_3\!-\!CH_2\!-\!\overset{..+}{O}H + 2e \quad m/e\ 46\ (M^+)$$

$$CH_3\!-\!CH_2\!-\!\overset{..+}{O}H \longrightarrow CH_3\!\cdot + CH_2\!\!=\!\!\overset{+}{O}H \quad m/e\ 31\ (M\text{-}15)$$

$$CH_3\!-\!\underset{\underset{H}{|}}{CH}\!-\!\overset{..+}{O}H \longrightarrow H\!\cdot + CH_3\!-\!CH\!\!=\!\!\overset{+}{O}H \quad m/e\ 45\ (M\text{-}1)$$

$$CH_3\!-\!CH_2\!-\!OH + e \longrightarrow [CH_3\!-\!CH_2\!-\!OH]^{\ddagger} + 2e \quad (M^+)$$

$$[CH_3\!-\!CH_2\!-\!OH]^{\ddagger} \longrightarrow HO\!\cdot + CH_3\!-\!CH_2^{+} \quad m/e\ 29\ (M\text{-}17)$$

Although it may often be possible to predict the mass spectrum of a known compound, it is usually much more difficult, if not impossible in many cases, to elucidate the structure of a compound from its observed mass spectrum. Hence, in general, other information is required, and this is usually spectroscopic data: ir, uv, and NMR. High resolution mass spectrometry permits elucidation of molecular formulae, and this knowledge then enables the double bond equivalents (D.B.E.), *i.e.*, the number of double bonds and/or rings, in the compound to be ascertained. If the general formula of the compound is $C_aH_bN_cO_d$, then

$$D.B.E. = a + 1 - (b - c)/2$$

e.g., (i) Benzene is C_6H_6.

D.B.E. $= 6 + 1 - 6/2 = 4$ (3 double bonds; 1 ring).

(ii) Allylamine is C_3H_7N.

$$D.B.E. = 3 + 1 - (7 - 1)/2 = 1 \text{ (1 double bond).}$$

Univalent elements, such as halogens, may be replaced by one hydrogen atom, and bivalent elements may be ignored (*cf.* oxygen, above).

The major peaks and peaks near the molecular ion are examined, and m/e values are listed in terms of $M–m/e$. By checking m/e and $M–m/e$ values against a list of common fragments (see Table 1.11), and knowing the fragmentation patterns of compounds containing various functional groups, it is possible to make a great deal of progress towards solving the structure of an unknown compound. It should be noted that it is not necessary to identify every peak.

Table 1.11 lists some of the more common fragments which appear as ions and/or lost as radicals or molecules (only the lowest isotopic values are given).

Table 1.11

m/e	Fragment	m/e	Fragment	m/e	Fragment
1	H	41	C_3H_5	71	C_5H_{11}
2	H_2	42	C_3H_6	72	$C_4H_8NH_2$
14	CH_2	43	C_3H_7, CH_3CO	73	$CO_2C_2H_5$
16	O, NH_2	44	CO_2, $CH_2{=}CHOH$,	74	$CH_2{=}C(OH)OCH_3$
17	OH		$C_2H_4NH_2$	77	C_6H_5
18	H_2O, NH_4	45	C_2H_5O, CH_3CHOH,	78	C_6H_6
19	F		CO_2H	79	C_6H_7, Br
20	HF	46	NO_2	80	HBr
26	C_2H_2, CN	51	C_4H_3	83	C_6H_{11}
27	C_2H_3, HCN	53	C_4H_5	85	C_6H_{13}
28	C_2H_4, CO, N_2	55	C_4H_7	88	$CH_2{=}CH(OH)OC_2H_5$
29	C_2H_5, CHO	56	C_4H_8	91	C_7H_7
30	CH_2NH_2, NO	57	C_4H_9, C_2H_5CO	93	C_6H_5O
31	CH_2OH, CH_3O	58	$C_3H_6NH_2$, $CH_2{=}C(OH)CH_3$	94	C_6H_6O
32	CH_3OH	59	CO_2CH_3, C_2H_5CHOH,	97	C_7H_{13}
33	SH		$CH_2{=}C(OH)NH_2$	99	C_7H_{15}
34	H_2S	60	$CH_2{=}CO_2H_2$	105	C_6H_5CO
35	Cl	65	C_5H_5	127	I
36	HCl	66	C_5H_6	128	HI
39	C_3H_3	69	C_5H_9		
40	CH_2CN	70	C_5H_{10}		

Since fragmentation patterns depend on the nature of the bond undergoing fission, the stability of the ion, radical, and/or neutral molecule produced, small changes in structure (change in the nature of the chain, introduction or removal of a particular group, etc.) can have a large effect on the fragmentation patterns (see, however, the mass spectrometric shift technique, **14** §29). On the other hand, the use of isotopes does not change the pattern and hence may be used for the determination of structure and to establish fragmentation pathways. These problems are dealt with in the following sections, in which the mass spectra of compounds are discussed mainly according to the nature of the functional group present. Applications of mass spectrometry are dealt with throughout the text.

§13a. Hydrocarbons.   Alkanes. Since the stability of carbonium ions is in the order t > s > prim., fission of bonds in alkanes occurs preferentially at branched carbon atoms. When alternative fissions can occur, it is the heaviest side-chain that is eliminated preferentially. Since alkyl carbonium ions are formed, all of them (with ^1H and ^{12}C) will give peaks of odd masses. In particular, n-alkanes give a series of peaks separated by 14 mass units (CH_2). The relative abundance of these peaks is usually greatest for $C_3H_7^+$ (43), $C_4H_9^+$ (57), and $C_5H_{11}^+$ (71), and decreases fairly regularly for the larger masses. Furthermore, each peak is generally accompanied by peaks of mass 1 and 2 units lower, corresponding to the loss of 1 and 2 hydrogen atoms, respectively.

The molecular ion is always present for n-alkanes, its intensity decreasing with increasing molecular weight. On the other hand, the greater the branching in the alkane, the less is the likelihood of the appearance of the molecular ion and, if this does appear, its intensity is usually low.

Cycloalkanes. Since ring structures are more stable than the corresponding acyclic structures, the parent ions of the former are usually more intense than those of the latter. Also, α-cleavage (bond between ring and side-chain) is highly favoured. When the ring itself fragments, it usually does so by loss of two carbon atoms as C_2H_4 (28) and C_2H_5 (29), *e.g.*,

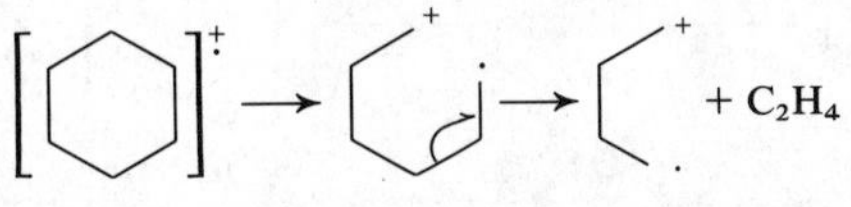

$$\left[\bigcirc\right]^{+} \longrightarrow \quad \longrightarrow \quad + \; C_2H_4$$

Alkenes. The molecular ion of mono-alkenes is usually present and tends to undergo allylic cleavage (*i.e.*, at the β-bond with respect to the double bond), with the positive charge usually remaining with the fragment containing the double bond, since the allyl ion is stabilised by resonance.

$$\left[CH_2\!\!=\!\!CH\!\!-\!\!\underset{\alpha}{CH_2}\!\!-\!\!\underset{\beta}{R}\right]^{+} \longrightarrow R\cdot + CH_2\!\!=\!\!CH\!\!-\!\!CH_2{}^{+} \longleftrightarrow \overset{+}{C}H_2\!\!-\!\!CH\!\!=\!\!CH_2$$

If the formation of a six-membered cyclic T.S. involving a γ-hydrogen is possible, a **McLafferty rearrangement** usually occurs to give two alkenes, and the positive charge may reside with either alkene, *e.g.*,

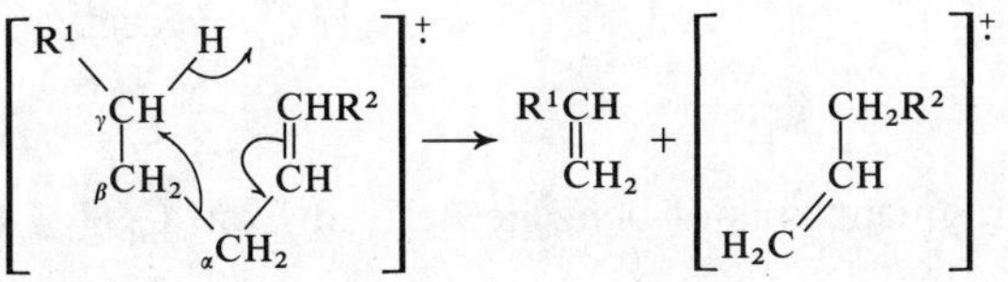

$$\left[\begin{array}{c} R^1 \quad\quad H \\ {}_\gamma CH \quad\quad CHR^2 \\ {}_\beta CH_2 \quad CH \\ {}_\alpha CH_2 \end{array}\right]^{+} \longrightarrow \begin{array}{c} R^1CH \\ \| \\ CH_2 \end{array} + \left[\begin{array}{c} CH_2R^2 \\ CH \\ H_2C \end{array}\right]^{+}$$

Thus, the mass spectra of mono-alkenes are characterised by the presence of peaks $C_nH_{2n} - 1$ (27, 41, 55, 69, etc.) and peaks C_nH_{2n} (28, 42, 56, etc.).

A difficulty encountered with alkenes is that, because of the ready migration of the double bond, fragmentation of isomeric alkenes are often similar.

Cycloalkenes. The presence of one double bond in the ring introduces a possible pathway involving the *retro Diels–Alder reaction*, *i.e.*, the *reversal* of the Diels–Alder reaction. This may be illustrated with cyclohexene, for which two alternative fragment ions are possible:

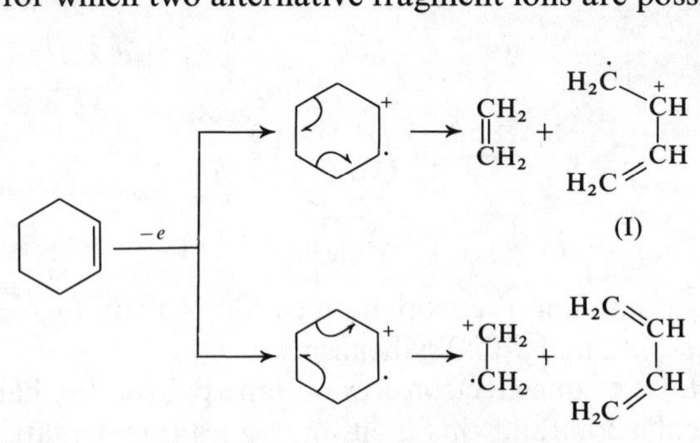

Which path predominates depends on the relative stabilities of the ions produced. (I) is far more resonance-stabilised than (II), and hence the former predominates.

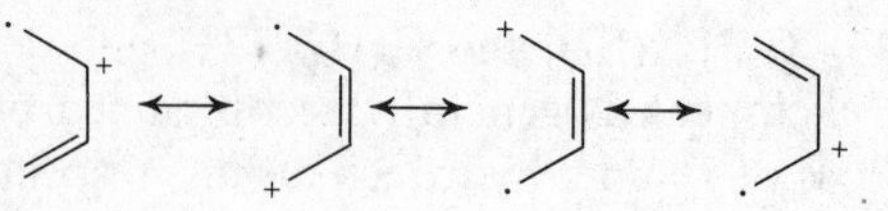

Arenes. Molecular ions of alkylbenzenes (and benzene) are strong, and are usually accompanied by $(M + 1)$ and $(M + 2)$ peaks (due to ^{13}C and/or D). **Benzene** shows a large number of peaks, *e.g.*, $C_6H_6^{+\cdot}$ (78). $C_6H_5^{+}$ (77), $C_4H_5^{+}$ (53), $C_4H_3^{+}$ (51), $C_4H_3^{+}$ (50), and $C_3H_3^{+}$ (39). All of these usually occur in the mass spectra of *all* benzene derivatives, but here we shall discuss the derivation of the most important peaks.

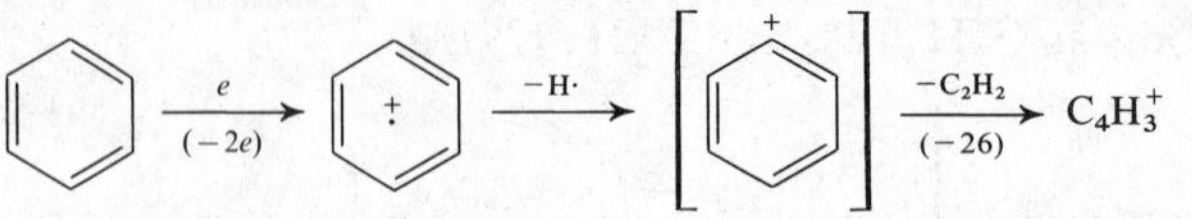

M^+; 78 *m/e* 77 *m/e* 51

The base peak for benzene is the molecular ion, M^+ (78), and also present are $(M + 1)$, 79 ($C_5^{13}CH_6$), (C_6H_5D), and $(M + 2)$, 80 ($C_4^{13}C_2H_6$), ($C_5^{13}CH_5D$), ($C_6H_4D_2$). The peak at *m/e* 51 ($C_4H_3^+$) is usually confirmed by the presence of a metastable peak at 33·8 ($51^2/77$).

Toluene has a strong molecular ion peak, but the base peak has *m/e* 91, and corresponds to the *tropylium cation* (believed to be derived from the less stable *benzylium cation*).

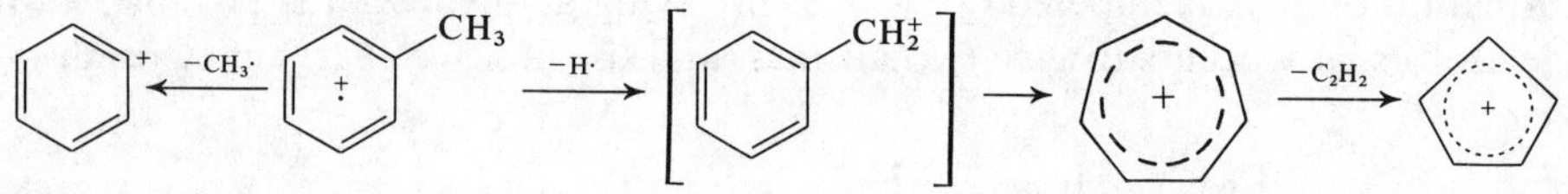

m/e 77 M^+ 92 *m/e* 91 *m/e* 65

In addition, there are the fragment ions of benzene derived from $C_6H_5^+$ (formed by loss of the methyl group).

In general, alkylbenzenes predominantly undergo β-cleavage in the side-chain to give the tropylium cation, but if the side-chain contains three (or more) carbon atoms, a McLafferty rearrangement also occurs:

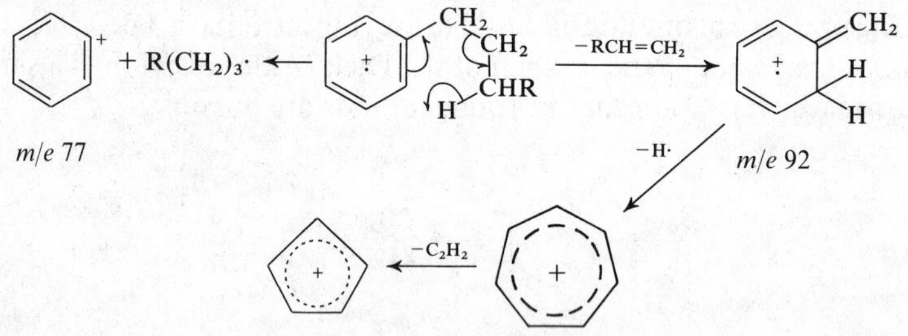

m/e 65 *m/e* 91

Xylenes eliminate one methyl group and the tropylium cation is again formed. In general, it is difficult to distinguish between *o*-, *m*-, and *p*-dialkylbenzenes.

§13b. Halides. Alkyl halides. Loss of one electron from a lone pair on the halogen atom occurs most readily to form the molecular ion, and this then undergoes fragmentation in a way which depends on the nature of the halogen atom and on the nature of the alkyl group. Since Cl and Br exist as isotopes, the molecular ions appear as doublets of mass M and $M + 2$. However, because the abundance ratios are quite different (see Table 1.10), alkyl chlorides and bromides may be readily distinguished. Some of the fragmentation patterns are:

$$RCH_2CH_2^+ + X\cdot \xleftarrow{\text{Br, I}} [RCH_2CH_2\text{---}X]^{\ddagger} \xrightarrow{\text{F, Cl}} [RCH\text{=\!=}CH_2]^{\ddagger} + HX$$

$$\downarrow$$

$$RCH_2\cdot + CH_2\text{=\!=}X^+$$

These are the predominant paths and the intensity of M^+ is in the order I > Br > Cl > F, and decreases with increase in the size of the alkyl group. The $RCH_2CH_2^+$ and $[RCH\text{=\!=}CH_2]^{\ddagger}$ fragments undergo further fragmentation typical of alkanes and alkenes, respectively. Alkyl halides (predominantly for Cl and Br) containing six or more carbon atoms in a straight chain also fragment to give the ion $C_4H_8X^+$:

$$\begin{array}{c} R\diagdown\diagup X^{\cdot+}\\ CH_2\quad CH_2\\ |\qquad |\\ CH_2\text{---}CH_2 \end{array} \longrightarrow R\cdot + \begin{array}{c} X^+\\ \diagup\diagdown\\ CH_2\quad CH_2\\ |\qquad |\\ CH_2\text{---}CH_2 \end{array}$$

Aryl halides. For *nuclear* aromatic halides, the intensity of the molecular ion is usually strong. This is also the situation if methyl groups are present in the ring, but if an ethyl (or larger group) is present, then β-cleavage competes with the loss of the halogen atom (see also arenes, above).

$$\left[\right]^{\ddagger} \xrightarrow{-X\cdot} \left[\right]^{+}_{m/e\ 77} \xrightarrow{-C_2H_2} C_4H_3^+ \quad m/e\ 51$$

Benzyl halides behave as follows:

$$\left[\text{---}CH_2Cl\right]^{\ddagger} \xrightarrow{-Cl\cdot} \left[\text{---}CH_2^+\right] \longrightarrow \left(+\right) \longrightarrow \cdots$$

Chlorides and bromides give M (strong) and $M + 2$ (fairly strong) molecular ions due to the two isotopes; fluorides and iodides are monoisotopic and only M is strong (other very weak molecular ions are due to ^{13}C and/or D).

§13c. **Hydroxy-compounds.** **Alkanols.** The mass spectrum of ethanol is shown in Fig. 1.27, but here we shall describe the mass spectra of alcohols from a general point of view. Usually, strong peaks are shown by fragmentation involving β-cleavage (*i.e.*, the C—COH bond), and the fragment containing the hydroxyl group is stabilised by resonance:

$$\left[\begin{array}{c} R^2\\ |\\ R^1\text{---}C\text{---}\overset{\cdot\cdot+}{O}H\\ |\\ R^3 \end{array}\right] \longrightarrow R^1\cdot + \left[\begin{array}{c} R^2\\ \diagdown\\ \overset{\cdot}{C}\text{---}\overset{\cdot\cdot+}{O}H\\ \diagup\\ R^3 \end{array} \longleftrightarrow \begin{array}{c} R^2\\ \diagdown\\ C\text{=\!=}\overset{+}{O}H\\ \diagup\\ R^3 \end{array}\right]$$

The alkyl group with the heaviest mass is eliminated preferentially, but ions also appear for alternative eliminations. Further fragmentation may also occur as follows ($R^2 = H$, $R^3 = C_2H_5$):

$$\left[CH_3\text{---}CH_2\text{---}CH\text{=\!=}\overset{+}{O}H \longleftrightarrow \begin{array}{c} CH_2\text{---}H\\ CH_2\diagdown\quad\diagup\\ \overset{+}{CH}\text{---}OH \end{array}\right] \longrightarrow C_2H_4 + [CH_2\text{---}OH]^+ \quad m/e\ 31$$

Hence, both s- and t-alcohols can also show peaks at m/e 31 (the most characteristic ion of alcohols).

Primary and secondary alcohols usually give weak molecular ions, and for tertiary alcohols the molecular ion is very weak or absent. Long-chain alcohols show peaks at M-18 due to the loss of a molecule of water and formation of a cyclic ion (*cf.* alkyl halides):

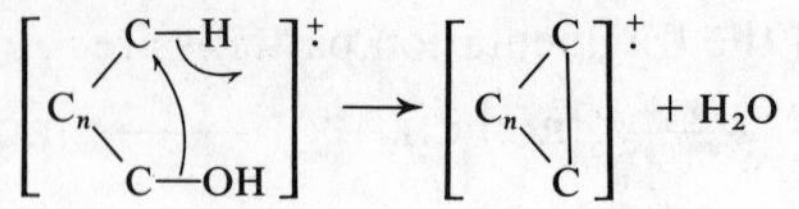

$$\left[\begin{matrix} C\!-\!H \\ C_n \\ C\!-\!OH \end{matrix} \right]^{\ddagger} \longrightarrow \left[\begin{matrix} C \\ C_n \\ C \end{matrix} \right]^{\ddagger} + H_2O$$

On the other hand, a McLafferty rearrangement can also occur with loss of water:

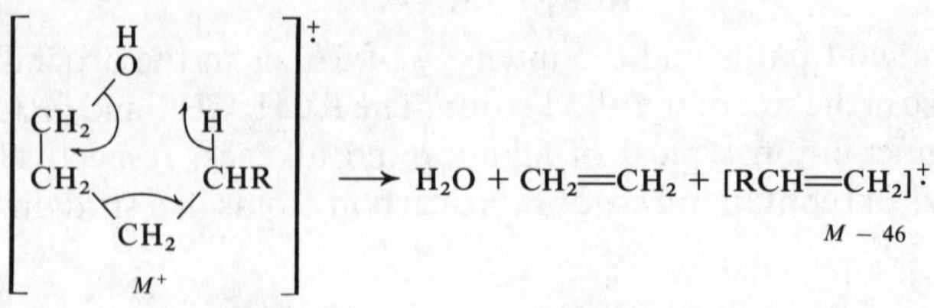

$$\left[\begin{matrix} H \\ O \\ CH_2 \\ CH_2 \quad CHR \\ CH_2 \end{matrix} \right]^{\ddagger} \longrightarrow H_2O + CH_2\!=\!CH_2 + [RCH\!=\!CH_2]^{\ddagger}$$

$$M - 46$$

In general, long-chain alcohols also show the fragmentation patterns of alkanes and alkenes.

Cycloalkanols. Fragmentation paths taken by cycloalkanols give rise to many identical fragment ions, but their relative intensities depend largely on the size of the ring, e.g.,

(I)

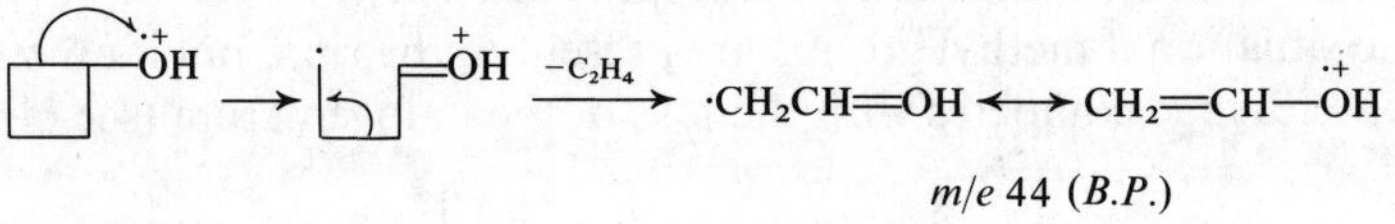

$$\cdots CH_2CH\!=\!OH \longleftrightarrow CH_2\!=\!CH\!-\!\overset{\cdot+}{OH}$$

$$m/e\ 44\ (B.P.)$$

(II)

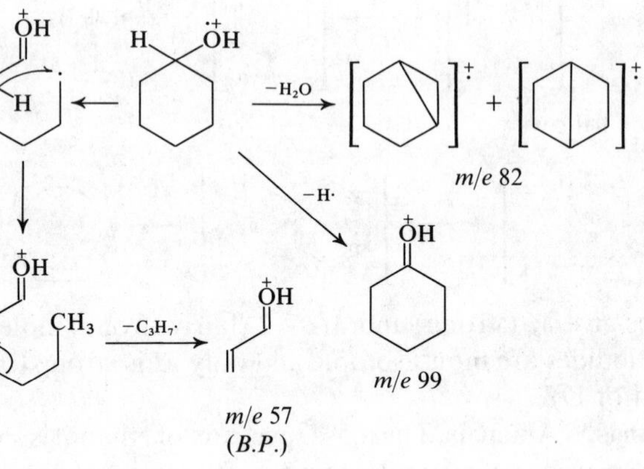

$$-H_2O \longrightarrow \quad m/e\ 82$$

$$-H\cdot$$

$$\overset{+}{OH} \quad m/e\ 99$$

$$-C_3H_7\cdot$$

$$m/e\ 57 \\ (B.P.)$$

Aryl alcohols. Benzyl alcohol shows an intense peak for the molecular ion, which undergoes the following fragmentations:

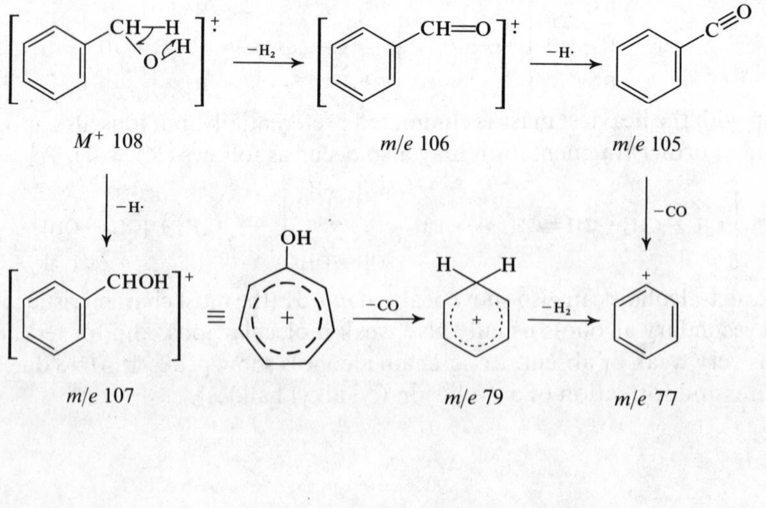

$$M^+\ 108 \qquad \overset{-H_2}{\longrightarrow} \qquad m/e\ 106 \qquad \overset{-H\cdot}{\longrightarrow} \qquad m/e\ 105$$

$$-H\cdot \qquad\qquad\qquad\qquad\qquad\qquad -CO$$

$$m/e\ 107 \qquad\qquad \overset{-CO}{\longrightarrow}\quad m/e\ 79 \quad \overset{-H_2}{\longrightarrow}\quad m/e\ 77$$

o-Substituted benzyl alcohols may behave differently from the *m*- and *p*-isomers in that they can also undergo elimination of a molecule of water by rearrangement (A = CH_2, O):

$$M^+ \qquad\qquad M - 18$$

Phenols. The molecular ion of phenols is usually very intense and fragments in various ways according to whether other substituent groups are present, *e.g.*, phenol itself:

$$M^+ \; 94 \qquad\qquad m/e \; 94 \qquad\qquad m/e \; 66$$
$$m/e \; 93 \qquad\qquad m/e \; 65$$

Cresols form the hydroxytropylium ion, *e.g.*,

$$M^+ \; 108 \qquad\qquad m/e \; 107 \qquad m/e \; 79 \qquad m/e \; 77$$

§13d. Thiols. As might have been anticipated, the fragmentation paths of thiols are similar to those of the corresponding oxygen analogues. However, because of the relatively large abundance of the ^{34}S isotope to the ^{32}S isotope (see Table 1.10), the M and $(M + 2)$ peaks are characteristic of sulphur-containing compounds. Straight-chain thiols undergo β-cleavage (bond β to the sulphur atom) to give a base peak of 47 (CH_2SH), and also readily eliminate hydrogen sulphide to give an intense $(M - 34)$ peak. Just as s- and t-alcohols can show the peak at m/e 31 (CH_2OH), so can s- and t-thiols show the peak at m/e 47 (CH_2SH).

§13e. Ethers, acetals and ketals.   Aliphatic ethers. The molecular ion of ethers is weak, and the principal modes of fission occur through α- and β-cleavage:

$$R_3^1C^+ + R^2O\cdot \;\overset{\alpha}{\longleftarrow}\; [R^1\overset{\beta}{-\!\!-}CR_2^1\overset{\alpha}{-\!\!-}OR^2]^+ \;\overset{\beta}{\longrightarrow}\; R^1\cdot + CR_2^1 = \overset{+}{O}R^2$$

Ethers containing α-substituted alkyl groups also undergo *double* cleavage and rearrangement, and the resulting oxygen-containing fragment ions have high intensity and may even be the base peaks:

This is the mechanism for the formation of ions m/e 45, 59, etc.

Phenolic ethers give a strong molecular ion peak and undergo several fragmentation patterns. One follows that of phenol, *e.g.*,

$$
\left[\underset{M^+\ 108}{\text{(phenyl)}-OCH_3}\right]^{\ddagger} \xrightarrow{-CH_3\cdot} \left[\underset{m/e\ 93}{\text{(phenyl)}-O}\right]^{+} \xrightarrow{-CO} \underset{m/e\ 65}{\text{(cyclopentadienyl cation)}}
$$

An alternative path involves a rearrangement:

$$
\left[\text{(aryl–O–CH}_2\text{, H)}\right]^{\ddagger} \xrightarrow{-CH_2O} \left[\underset{m/e\ 78}{\text{(benzene)}}\right]^{\ddagger} \xrightarrow{-H\cdot} \underset{m/e\ 77}{\text{(phenyl cation)}} \xrightarrow{\text{etc.}}
$$

If the alkyl group contains two or more carbon atoms, then rearrangement can occur with elimination of an alkene (*cf.* alkyl ethers):

$$
\left[\text{(aryl–O–CH}_2\text{, CHR, H)}\right]^{\ddagger} \longrightarrow \left[\underset{m/e\ 94}{\text{(cyclohexadienone, H, H)}}\right]^{\ddagger} + RCH{=}CH_2
$$

Acetals. Acetals are 1,1-diethers, and because of this their mass spectra are characterised by molecular ions of extremely low intensity and peaks of high intensity due to the following paths of fragmentation (at the highly branched central carbon atom).

$$
\left[\begin{array}{c} H \\ R^1{-}\overset{|}{\underset{|}{C}}{-}OR^2 \\ OR^2 \end{array}\right]^{\ddagger} \longrightarrow R^1{-}\overset{+}{\underset{\underset{OR^2}{|}}{\overset{\overset{H}{|}}{C}}}{-}OR^2 + {}^+\overset{\overset{H}{|}}{\underset{\underset{OR^2}{|}}{C}}{-}OR^2 + R^1{-}\overset{\overset{H}{|}}{\underset{\underset{OR^2}{|}}{C}}{}^+
$$

Ketals behave in a similar fashion to acetals.

$$
\left[\begin{array}{c} R^2 \\ R^1{-}\overset{|}{\underset{|}{C}}{-}OR^3 \\ OR^3 \end{array}\right]^{\ddagger} \longrightarrow R^1{-}\overset{+}{\underset{\underset{OR^3}{|}}{\overset{\overset{R^2}{|}}{C}}}{-}OR^3 + {}^+\overset{\overset{R^2}{|}}{\underset{\underset{OR^3}{|}}{C}}{-}OR^3 + R^1{-}\overset{\overset{R^2}{|}}{\underset{\underset{OR^3}{|}}{C}}{}^+
$$

Of special importance is the ethylene ketal (dioxolan), since this is a very useful group for protecting ketones. At the same time, because of its stability, the ethylene ketal is very useful for structure determination by means of mass spectrometry (see **11 §4**).

§13f. Thioethers.   Dialkyl sulphides undergo fragmentation patterns similar to those of the dialkyl ethers (§13e), *e.g.*,

$$
\underset{M^+\ 118}{CH_3CH_2\overset{\overset{CH_3}{|}}{CH}{-}\overset{\cdot+}{S}{-}CH_2CH_3} \xrightarrow{-CH_3\cdot} \underset{m/e\ 103}{CH_3CH_2\overset{\overset{CH_3}{|}}{CH}{-}\overset{+}{S}{=}CH_2}
$$

$$
\Big\downarrow {-C_2H_5\cdot} \qquad \searrow {-CH_3\cdot}
$$

$$
\underset{m/e\ 89}{CH_3CH{=}\overset{+}{S}{-}CH_2,\ H{-}CH_2} \qquad\qquad \underset{m/e\ 103}{CH_3CH_2CH{=}\overset{+}{S}{-}CH_2,\ H{-}CH_2}
$$

$$
\Big\downarrow {-C_2H_4} \qquad\qquad\qquad\qquad \Big\downarrow {-C_2H_4}
$$

$$
\underset{m/e\ 61}{CH_3CH{=}\overset{+}{S}H} \qquad\qquad\qquad \underset{m/e\ 75}{CH_3CH_2CH{=}\overset{+}{S}H}
$$

Dialkyl sulphides show characteristic M and $(M + 2)$ peaks, and are readily distinguished from their isomeric thiols in that they do not show a peak at $M - 34$ (they do *not* eliminate a molecule of hydrogen sulphide; see §13d).

Ethylene thioketals show the same fragmentation patterns as those of the corresponding ketals (§13e).

§13g. Aldehydes and ketones. **Aliphatic aldehydes** give molecular ions of low intensity and readily undergo α-cleavage to produce acylium ions:

$$H\cdot + RC{\equiv}O^+ \longleftarrow RCH{=}\overset{\cdot+}{\ddot{O}} \longrightarrow R\cdot + HC{\equiv}O^+ \quad (m/e\ 29)$$

The presence of ions $M - 1$ and m/e 29 are usually characteristic of aldehydes (R^+ is also formed). It should be noted that the ion m/e 29 could also be $C_2H_5{}^+$, which is given by the higher aldehydes (the two ions may be distinguished by high resolution).

Aldehydes also undergo β-cleavage (the ion m/e 43 could also be $C_3H_7{}^+$):

$$[R{-}CH_2{-}CH{=}O]^{\cdot+} \longrightarrow R\cdot(M - 43) + [CH_2{=}CH{-}O]^+ \quad (m/e\ 43)$$

When a γ-hydrogen atom is present, the McLafferty rearrangement also occurs:

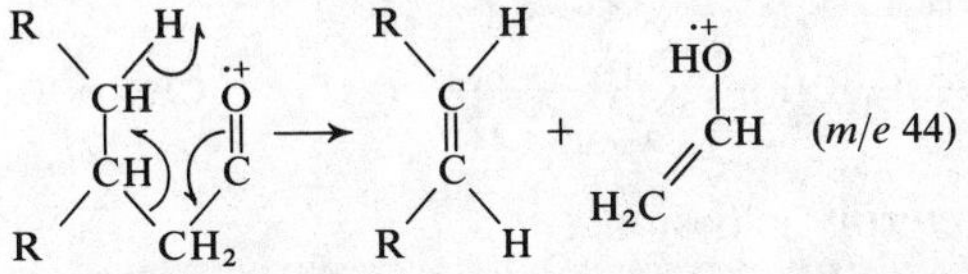

Aliphatic ketones undergo fragmentation patterns similar to those of aldehydes, but the intensity of the molecular ion is very strong, and loss of the group with the heavier mass occurs predominantly. Hence, for methyl ketones, the acylium ion, $CH_3C{\equiv}O^+$ (m/e 43; also equivalent to $C_3H_7{}^+$) is often the base peak. Alkyl ions are also produced, as well as alkenes and $CH_2{=}CR{-}OH$ by the McLafferty rearrangement.

Aromatic aldehydes and ketones. The fragmentation patterns of aromatic aldehydes (R = H), ketones (R = R), acids (R = OH), methyl esters (R = OMe), and amides (R = NH$_2$) are similar in that all undergo β-cleavage with loss of R· and formation of the benzoyl cation. All give strong peaks for the molecular ion.

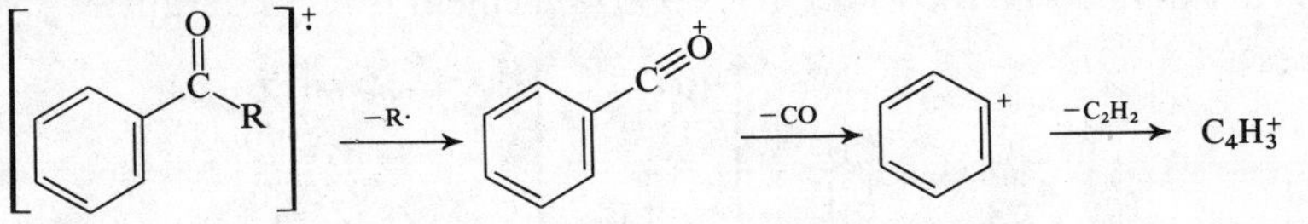

Esters in which the alkyl group is ethyl or higher also eliminate alkenes (*cf.* ethers, §13e).

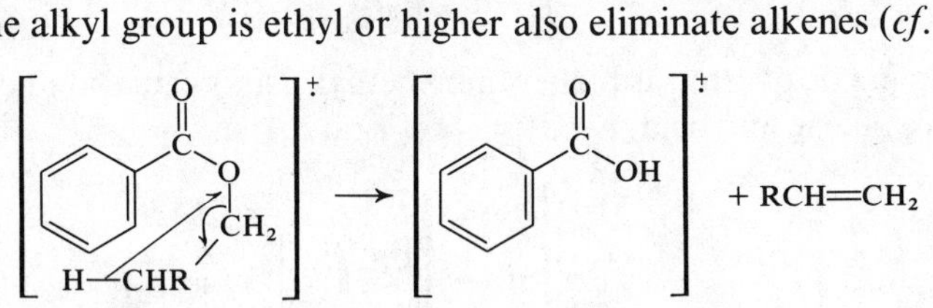

o-Substituted acids and esters (A = CH$_2$, O, NH), in addition to undergoing fragmentations described above, fragment by the McLafferty rearrangement:

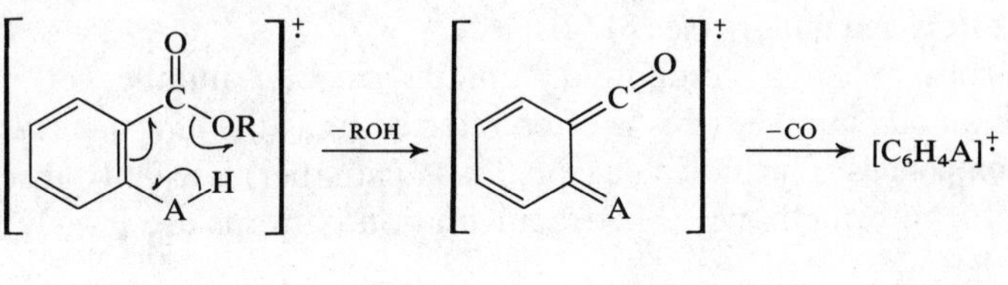

Cycloalkanones. One common path followed is fission at the 1,2-bond in the ring (*cf.* alkanones, above, and cycloalkanols, §13c), *e.g.*,

(I)

$$\cdots \xrightarrow{\text{CH}_3,\ -\text{C}_2\text{H}_5\cdot} \quad m/e\ 55$$

(II)

$$\longrightarrow \text{C}_2\text{H}_4 + \text{CO} + [\text{C}_2\text{H}_4]^{+}$$
$$m/e\ 28$$

(III)

$$\longrightarrow \quad \begin{array}{c}\text{CH}_2{=}\text{CHO}\cdot \\ + \\ \text{CH}_2{=}\text{CH}{-}\overset{+}{\text{C}}\text{H}_2\end{array}$$
$$m/e\ 41$$

Note the unusual cases of heterolytic fission.

§**13h. Acids, esters and amides.**   Aliphatic acids, esters, and amides undergo similar fragmentation patterns, *e.g.*, α-cleavage for lower members (Z=OH, OR, NH$_2$):

$$\text{R}\cdot + \overset{+}{\text{O}}{\equiv}\text{C}{-}\overset{\cdot\cdot}{\text{Z}} \longleftrightarrow \text{O}{=}\text{C}{=}\overset{+}{\text{Z}} \longleftarrow \left[\text{R}{-}\overset{\overset{\text{O}}{\|}}{\text{C}}{-}\text{Z}\right]^{\ddagger} \longrightarrow [\text{R}{-}\text{CO}]^{+} + \text{Z}\cdot$$
$$m/e = 28 + \text{Z} \qquad\qquad\qquad\qquad\qquad\qquad\qquad M - \text{Z}$$

Also, R and Z may carry the positive charge. Hence, peaks are obtained at $M - 17$ and m/e 45 (Z = OH), $M - 31$, $M - 45$, and m/e 59, 73 (Z = OMe and OEt, respectively), and $M - 16$ and m/e 44 (Z = NH$_2$). Since they are more volatile than their corresponding acids, esters are used preferentially. All can undergo the McLafferty rearrangement if they contain a γ-hydrogen atom:

$$\longrightarrow \begin{array}{c}\text{CH}_2 \\ \| \\ \text{CH}_2\end{array} + \left[\begin{array}{c}\text{HO} \\ \backslash \\ \text{C}{-}\text{Z} \\ \| \\ \text{CH}_2\end{array}\right]^{\ddagger} \qquad \begin{array}{l} m/e\ 60\ (\text{Z} = \text{OH}); \\ 74\ (\text{Z} = \text{OMe}); \\ 88\ (\text{Z} = \text{OEt}); \\ 59\ (\text{Z} = \text{NH}_2) \end{array}$$

When the alkyl group in OR of esters is higher than methyl, esters can also undergo the McLafferty rearrangement to give alkene and acid, *e.g.*,

$$\left[\begin{array}{c}\text{CH}_3\text{C} \quad \text{O} \\ \diagdown \diagup \\ \text{CH}_2 \quad \text{CR} \\ \text{O} \end{array}\right]^{\ddagger} \longrightarrow \left[\begin{array}{c}\text{CH}_3\text{CH} \\ \| \\ \text{CH}_2\end{array}\right]^{\ddagger} + \text{RCO}_2\text{H}$$

Aromatic acids, esters and amides (see §13g).

§**13i. Nitro-compounds.** When a compound contains an *odd* number of nitrogen atoms, its molecular weight is an *odd* number (this is often referred to as the *nitrogen rule*).

Aliphatic nitro-compounds. The molecular ion (an *odd* number) is usually absent, but if present, is very weak (except for nitromethane). The fragmentation patterns are largely those of the parent alkane (§13a), but in addition there are two peaks of fair intensity, one at m/e 30 (NO^+) and the other at m/e 46 (NO_2^+).

Aromatic nitro-compounds. The molecular ion peak of aromatic mononitro-compounds is strong and has an odd mass number. For nitrobenzene, the fragmentation pattern is:

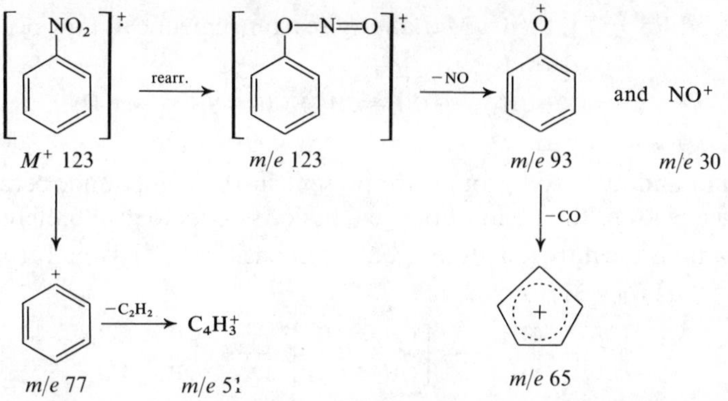

When an *o*-substituent is present and is capable of interacting with the nitro-group, additional paths of fragmentation are now possible, *e.g.*, *m*- and *p*-nitrotoluenes follow fragmentation paths similar to that of nitrobenzene, but the *o*-isomer also fragments as follows:

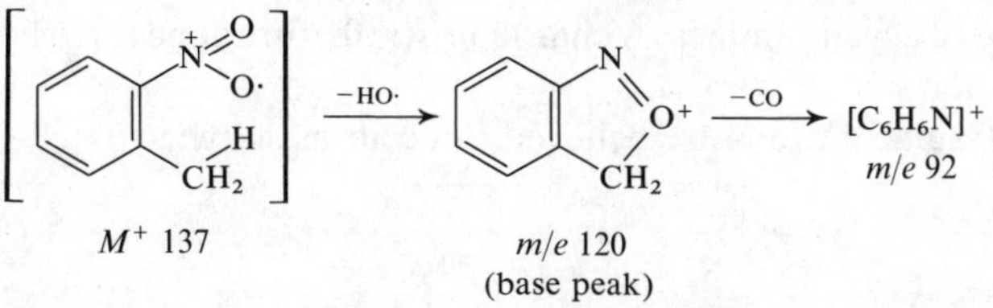

§13j. Cyanides. The molecular ion for alkyl cyanides (an *odd* mass number) is either very weak or absent, but an ($M + 1$) peak can be observed if increased pressures are used. In general the fragmentation pattern of the parent alkane is observed (§13a), but if the *straight* hydrocarbon chain contains four or more carbon atoms, the base peak is usually m/e 41. This results from a McLafferty rearrangement.

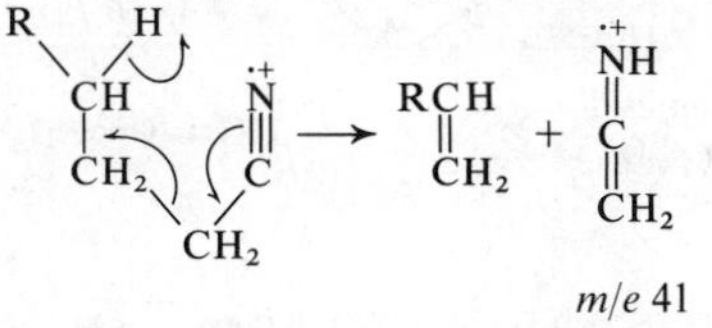

$$m/e\ 41$$

Another ion often found is $(M - 1)^+$; it is not very intense and arises from loss of hydrogen from the molecular ion.

§13k. Amines.   Aliphatic amines. When the amine contains an *odd* number of nitrogen atoms, its molecular weight is an *odd* number. The molecular ion of amines is very weak or absent, and its most characteristic fragmentation pattern is *via* β-cleavage, *e.g.*,

Thus, the base peak of primary amines is m/e 30 provided no branching occurs at the α-carbon atom. The presence of this peak, however, does not necessarily mean that the amine is primary, since s- and t-amines can also give rise to this peak via McLafferty rearrangements. The behaviour of these amines is similar to that of the ethers (§13e); β-cleavage occurs preferentially to eliminate the largest alkyl group, *e.g.*, ($R^1 > R^2$ and R^3):

$$R^1-CH_2-\overset{..+}{N}R^2R^3 \longrightarrow R^{1\cdot} + CH_2{=}\overset{+}{N}R^2R^3$$

If, *e.g.*, R^2 = Me and R^3 = Et, then a McLafferty rearrangement can now occur:

$$CH_2{=}\overset{+}{\underset{CH_3}{N}}\overset{H-CH_2}{\overset{|}{{-}CH_2}} \longrightarrow CH_2{=}CH_2 + CH_2{=}\overset{+}{\underset{CH_3}{N}}H \quad (m/e\ 44)$$

When both amino and hydroxyl groups are present in the compound, because the ionisation potential of nitrogen is lower than that of oxygen, fission occurs to give preferentially the positive fragment which contains the nitrogen atom, *e.g.*, the intensity of $CH_2{=}\overset{+}{N}H_2$ (m/e 30) is about ten times that of $CH_2{=}\overset{+}{O}H$ (m/e 31).

$$\overset{\cdot CH_2}{\underset{OH}{|}} + \overset{CH_2}{\underset{{}^+NH_2}{||}} \longleftarrow \left[\overset{CH_2{-}CH_2}{\underset{OH\quad NH_2}{|\qquad|}}\right]^{\ddagger} \longrightarrow \overset{CH_2}{\underset{{}^+OH}{||}} + \overset{CH_2}{\underset{NH_2}{|}}$$

The order of stability of fragments of the above type is:

$$CH_2{=}\overset{+}{N}H_2 > CH_2{=}\overset{+}{S}H > CH_2{=}\overset{+}{O}H.$$

Cyclic imines. The intensity of the molecular ion (odd mass number for one nitrogen atom) is much greater than that of acyclic amines. A characteristic feature appears to be loss of an α-hydrogen to give the $(M - 1)^+$ ion.

Pyrrolidine. Some fragmentations are believed to occur as shown.

1-Methylpyrrolidine

The important point to note is that there appears to be little loss of $CH_3 \cdot$.

Piperidine. Many of the fragmentation paths are less certain than those for the pyrrolidines.

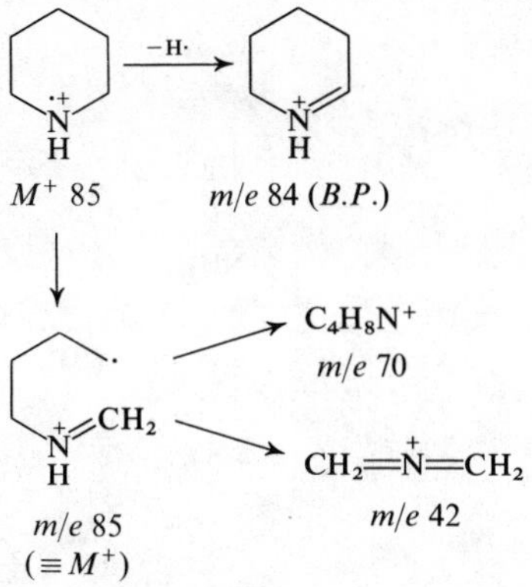

M^+ 85 m/e 84 (B.P.)

$C_4H_8N^+$
m/e 70

$CH_2{=}\overset{+}{N}{=}CH_2$
m/e 42

m/e 85
($\equiv M^+$)

Aromatic amines. The peak for the molecular ion is strong and has an odd mass number. Primary amines lose a molecule of HCN, *e.g.*,

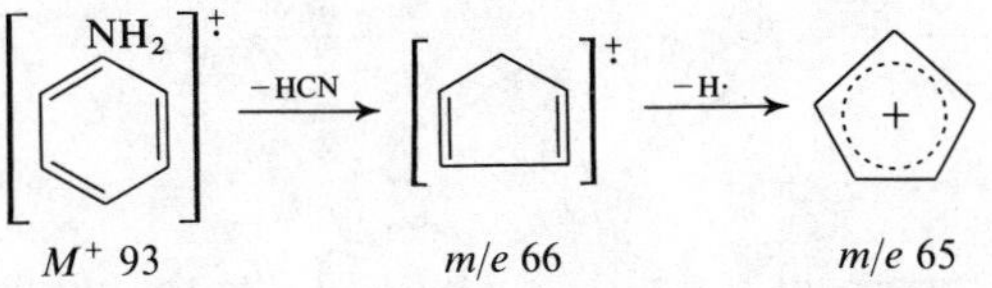

M^+ 93 m/e 66 m/e 65

Alkyl groups attached to the nucleus or to the nitrogen atom readily undergo β-cleavage, *e.g.*,

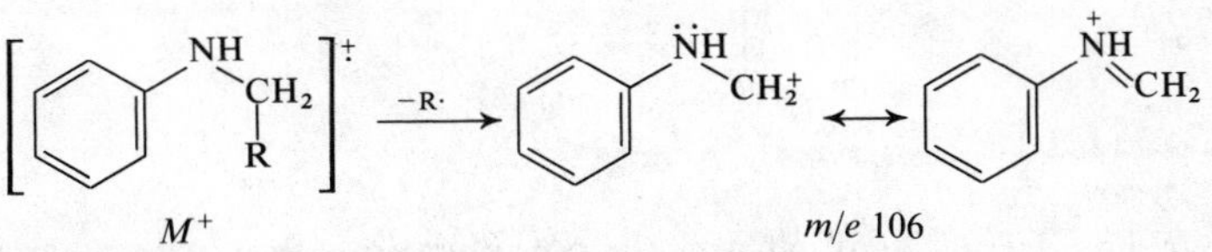

M^+ m/e 106

§13l. Heterocyclic compounds. Heterocyclic compounds undergo fragmentation in some ways that resemble the benzenes. We shall here deal with only a limited number of examples, and in all cases the molecular ion is produced by loss of one electron of the lone pair on the hetero-atom (*cf.* the corresponding acyclic compounds).

Furan. The strongest three peaks are at m/e 29, 39 and 68.

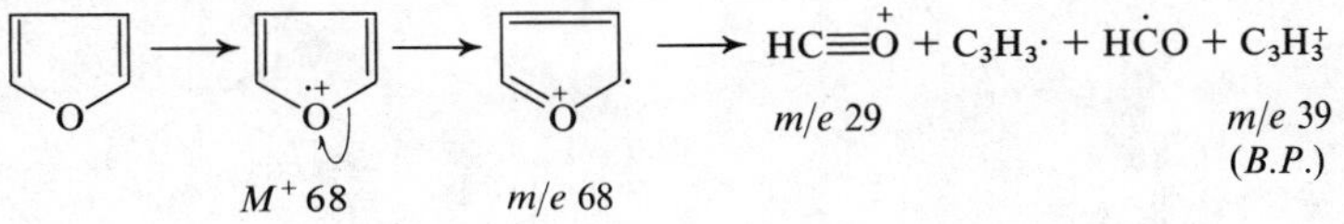

$HC{\equiv}\overset{+}{O} + C_3H_3 \cdot + H\dot{C}O + C_3H_3^+$

M^+ 68 m/e 68 m/e 29 m/e 39 (B.P.)

When alkyl groups are present, there are some entirely different paths, *e.g.*,

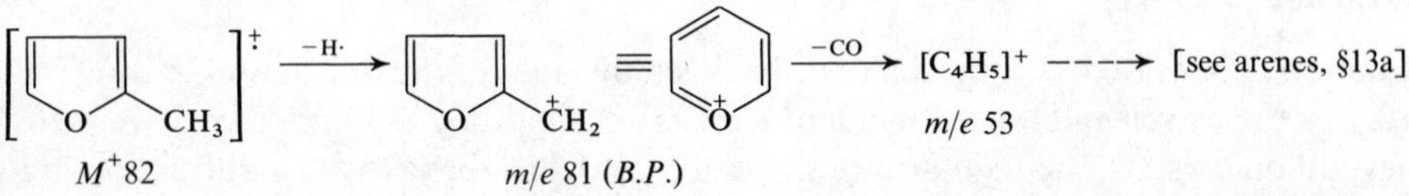

$[C_4H_5]^+$ - - - -> [see arenes, §13a]

M^+ 82 m/e 81 (B.P.) m/e 53

Pyrrole. The strongest four peaks are at m/e 28, 39, 41, and 67. The molecular ion has an odd mass number.

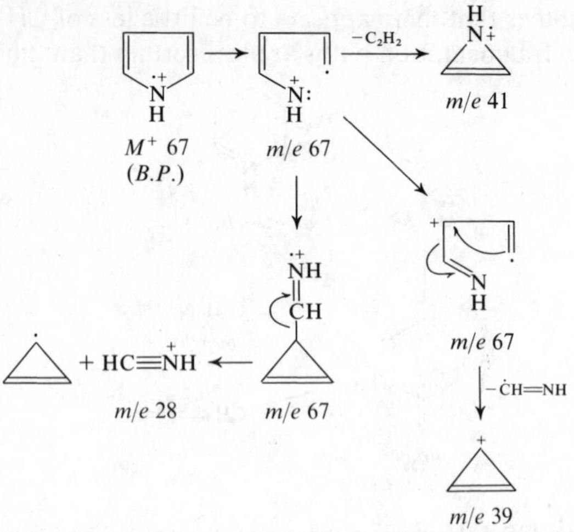

$-C_2H_2$ $m/e\ 41$

$M^+\ 67$ $m/e\ 67$
$(B.P.)$

$m/e\ 67$

$+ \ HC{\equiv}\overset{+}{N}H \ \longleftarrow$ $-\dot{C}H{=}NH$

$m/e\ 28$ $m/e\ 67$

$m/e\ 39$

In C-alkylpyrroles, there are some similarities to the furan analogues, e.g.,

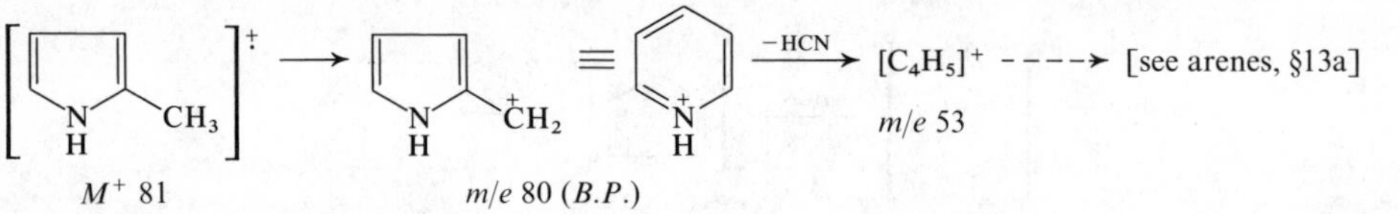

$-HCN$ $[C_4H_5]^+ \ -\ -\ -\ {\longrightarrow}$ [see arenes, §13a]

$M^+\ 81$ $m/e\ 80\ (B.P.)$ $m/e\ 53$

Pyridine. The strongest two peaks are at m/e 52 and 79; the molecular ion has an odd mass number.

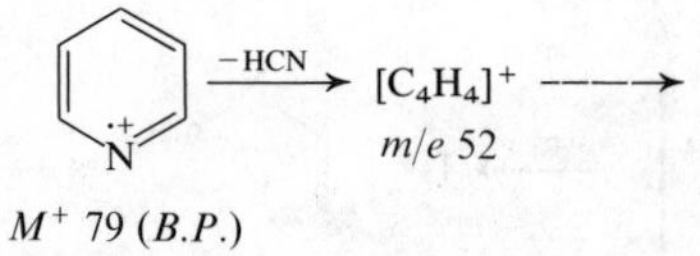

$-HCN$ $[C_4H_4]^+ \ -\ -\ -\ -\ {\longrightarrow}$

$M^+\ 79\ (B.P.)$ $m/e\ 52$

The following pyridine derivative illustrates the complications that arise when alkyl substituents are present.

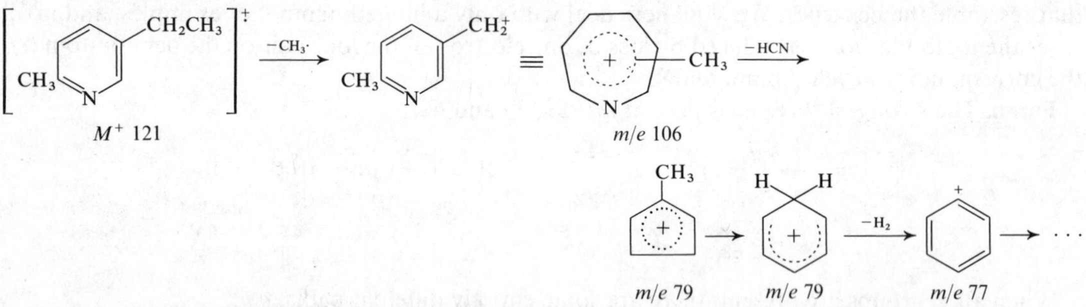

$M^+\ 121$ $m/e\ 106$

$-CH_3{\cdot}$ $-HCN$

$m/e\ 79$ $m/e\ 79$ $m/e\ 77$

$-H_2$

§14. Diffraction methods

For diffraction of light to occur, the distance between the lines of the diffraction grating must be the same order as the wavelength of the incident light. This condition is fulfilled by X-rays (0·7–1·5 Å) when they fall on crystals, the regular atomic pattern of which behaves as a diffraction grating (the interatomic distances are usually 1–2 Å). In the same way, since electron or neutron beams moving at suitable speeds behave as light waves of the appropriate wavelength for diffraction to occur, *electron diffraction* ($\lambda = 0{\cdot}06$ Å) and *neutron diffraction* ($\lambda = 1$ Å) methods are also used.

§14a. X-ray diffraction. X-ray analysis is usually applied to solids, but may also be used with liquids and gases. X-ray analysis requires a crystal large enough to produce a diffraction pattern (about 0·1 mm). If a single crystal of this size cannot be obtained, it is possible to use a mass of minute crystals—this is the *powder method*.

The X-ray diffraction pattern is usually recorded on a photographic plate, and the estimation of the relative intensities is done visually. More accurate results, however, are obtained by the use of Geiger or scintillation counters to measure the intensities. Because crystals are three-dimensional, it is necessary to take a series of photographs, *e.g.*, 1 000–5 000 for a crystal of a simple organic compound. Hence, the crystal is usually turned on a spindle. Since X-rays are diffracted mainly by the orbital electrons of the atoms, the diffraction will be a function of the atomic number. Because of this, it is difficult to differentiate between atoms whose atomic numbers are very close together, *e.g.*, carbon and nitrogen. Furthermore, since the scattering power of hydrogen atoms (for X-rays) is very low, it is normally impossible to locate these atoms except in very favourable conditions, and then only with fairly simple compounds.

Two problems are involved in the interpretation of X-ray diffraction patterns, *viz.*, the dimensions of the unit cell and the positions of the individual atoms in the molecule. The positions of the diffracted beams depend on the dimensions of the *unit cell*, which is defined as the simplest repeatable unit of the crystal lattice. A knowledge of these dimensions leads to the following applications:

(i) Identification of substances; this is done by looking up tables of unit cells.

(ii) Determination of molecular weights. If V is the volume of the unit cell, ρ the density of the compound, and n the number of molecules in a unit cell, then the molecular weight, M, is given by

$$M = \frac{V\rho}{n}$$

(iii) Determination of the shapes of molecules. Many long-chain polymers exist as fibres, *e.g.*, cellulose, keratin. These fibres are composed of bundles of tiny crystals with one axis parallel, or nearly parallel, to the fibre axis. When X-rays fall on the fibre in a direction perpendicular to its length, then the pattern obtained is similar to that from a single crystal rotated about a principal axis. It is thus possible to obtain the unit cell dimensions of such fibres (see, *e.g.*, rubber, **8** §35).

The intensities of the diffracted beams depend on the positions of the atoms in the unit cell. A knowledge of these relative intensities leads to the arrangement of the atoms within the molecule. Thus, by X-ray analysis, it is possible to determine the complete structure—molecular and spatial—of any crystalline compound. With the introduction of computers, calculations from X-ray data can now be quickly performed, and so the use of this method for structural determination will become common. This method will therefore, in principle, make chemical methods superfluous. A particularly interesting example is the alkaloid thelepogine, $C_{20}H_{31}NO$. Its structure has been determined entirely by X-ray analysis; no chemical work was carried out (Fridrichsons *et al.*, 1960).

X-ray analysis has also been used to determine the conformation of various molecules and the absolute configurations of enantiomers (**2** §5). It should also be noted that when the structure of a compound is known, X-ray analysis is particularly valuable for determining bond lengths, valency angles, and hydrogen bonding.

§14b. Electron diffraction. Electron diffraction is another direct method for determining the spatial arrangement of atoms in a molecule, and is usually confined to gases or compounds in the vapour state, but can be used with very thin crystals. Electrons are diffracted by the electrostatic fields arising from electrons and nuclei in the atoms. Higher accuracy may be obtained than with X-rays, and also other information may be obtained, *e.g.*, hydrogen atoms are easier to locate with electron diffraction than with X-ray diffraction.

By means of electron diffraction it is possible to obtain values of bond lengths and the size and shape of molecules, particularly macromolecules. Electron diffraction studies have been particularly useful in the investigation of conformations (see **4** §11).

§14c. Neutron diffraction. A beam of *slow* neutrons is diffracted by crystalline substances, diffraction being due to interaction of the neutrons with the atomic nuclei. Neutron diffraction is particularly useful for determining the positions of *light* atoms, a problem which is very difficult, and often impossible, with X-ray analysis. Thus neutron diffraction is extremely useful for locating hydrogen atoms. Because of this, this method is very useful in the study of hydrogen bonding.

In addition to studying solids, neutron diffraction has also been applied to gases, pure liquids and solutions.

§15. Chromatography.

Chromatography is the means of separating of two or more substances by distribution between two phases, one fixed (the *stationary* phase) and the other moving (the *mobile* phase). Various types of chromatography are possible, and in its various forms, chromatography is used for the separation, isolation, purification and identification of components of a mixture. The technique may be used over a range of quantities of material—micro to preparative scale.

The various forms of chromatography are generally named by the nature of the two phases used, the mobile phase being given first, *e.g.*, liquid–solid, gas–liquid, etc.

§15a. Adsorption chromatography. When the fixed phase is a solid and the moving phase is a liquid, the process is usually called **column** chromatography. The common type of apparatus used is shown in Fig. 1.28. The mixture is dissolved in a suitable solvent, and the solution is allowed to pass down

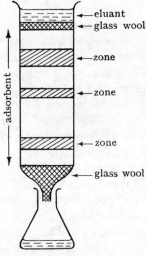

Fig. 1.28

the column, either under gravity or by gentle suction. In this way, the solutes are adsorbed on different parts of the column, but the zones are usually so close together that the components cannot be separated. The procedure now is to allow another suitable solvent to pass down the column; the result is the development of a *chromatogram*. In the chromatogram, the components of the mixture are separated into definite zones (see Fig. 1.28), and the solvent used for this purpose is called the *eluant*. The column is sucked dry and the adsorbent pushed out, each separate zone being extracted with some solvent. This procedure is satisfactory only if the zones are coloured. On the other hand, if the substances are colourless, then they may be converted into coloured derivatives, *e.g.*, dinitro-phenylhydrazones of carbonyl compounds give coloured zones. Alternatively, the column may be *eluted* by continued passage of the eluant, whereby each zone is washed off the column and each eluate collected separately. If the components are colourless, their zones may sometimes be clearly shown up under ultraviolet light, and so elution can be followed readily. In other cases, the sample can be made radioactive and can be detected by a Geiger counter.

In addition to elution with one solvent, several solvents may be used in succession, each eluting agent being more effective than the preceding one.

The nature of the solvent is very important in adsorption chromatography. The solvent used for preparing the solution of the mixture is the least polar solvent possible. Elution is then usually carried out with a more polar solvent or several solvents, the polar character being increased as each zone is washed out. The order of increasing eluting power is (for silica gel): light petrol < cyclohexane < carbon tetrachloride < benzene < methylene dichloride < chloroform < ether < ethyl acetate < acetone < propanol < ethanol < methanol < water < acetic acid. It should be noted that in this *eluotropic series*, the eluting power runs roughly parallel with the polarity of the eluant. However, the order of an eluotropic series depends on the nature of the adsorbent, *e.g.*, the above order is roughly reversed for activated carbon. It also depends on the nature of the components in the mixture.

The activity (adsorptive power) of an adsorbent depends on its nature and on its method of preparation. The following is the order of increasing activity of some common adsorbents: cellulose < starch < sucrose < calcium carbonate < magnesia < silica gel < alumina < activated charcoal. Of these, alumina is the most widely used and is used in three forms—acidic, basic and neutral.

Now let us consider the components of the mixture. These, in general, are more strongly adsorbed on a given adsorbent the more polar is the functional group in the component. However, the chemical nature of the component may be a deciding factor in the choice of the adsorbent, *e.g.*, an aldehyde or ketone may undergo self-condensation on the surface of alumina.

§15b. Partition chromatography. In this method, the fixed phase consists of a liquid substance strongly adsorbed on a solid column (as support), *e.g.*, silica gel. The mixture of substances is dissolved in a solvent (the moving phase) which is immiscible with the adsorbed solvent (the fixed phase). This solution is allowed to pass slowly down the column, and is then followed by pure solvent. The solutes become distributed between the fixed and mobile phases, and because of their different partition coefficients the solutes are separated by elution. In practice, the fixed phase is usually water, and the moving phase is a water-immiscible solvent (or mixture of solvents).

§15c. Paper chromatography. This is a special case of partition chromatography; a strip or sheet of filter paper now replaces the adsorbent column. A drop of the aqueous solution containing the mixture is placed on the paper strip, either near one corner or in the middle of one edge, and the strip is then dried. The moving phase either ascends or descends the paper strip (according to the way the experiment is performed). The dried paper strip is placed in a suitable glass vessel containing the organic solvent that has been previously saturated with water. One edge of the paper strip is placed just below the level of the solvent, and when the solvent front has progressed a suitable distance the distance moved by the solvent is marked and the paper strip is then allowed to dry in air. If the solutes are colourless (as is usually the case), the paper is sprayed with a solution of a suitable compound which reacts with the various components to form coloured spots (see 13 §3). Where these coloured spots appear indicates the position of each component on the paper strip. The ratio of the distance travelled by a component to the distance travelled by the solvent front is characteristic of each component, and is known as the R_F value (this value depends on the experimental conditions).

The above method is the ascending method. In the descending method, the solvent is in a container at the top, and the paper strip is bent over so as to dip into the solvent.

Two-dimensional chromatography offers a better means of separation than the one-dimensional method. A drop of the solution is placed near one corner of a large square paper strip, allowed to dry, and then immersed in the solvent as described above. The components occupy different positions which are near this edge and parallel to it. The paper is now dried, turned through 90°, the edge placed in the solvent, etc. After being dried, the paper is sprayed and re-dried. The final result is a two-dimensional chromatogram (each component now has two R_F values).

Pfeiffer *et al.* (1965) have introduced the technique of 'stereo-chromatography', *i.e.*, three-dimensional chromatography. This is carried out by using compressed paper-pulp blocks.

§15d. Thin-layer chromatography (TLC).   This is a special case of adsorption chromatography (§15a) and uses a *chromoplate* as the column, *i.e.*, a glass strip coated with a thin uniform layer of the adsorbent (alumina, silica gel, etc.). The plate is spotted with a small amount of the solution containing the mixture, and then placed vertically in a suitable solvent in a closed tank, but the spot is not covered by the solvent. Development of the chromatogram occurs by capillary movement of the solvent up the adsorbent layer. If the components of the mixture are coloured, the spots are readily located. If the components are colourless, the dried plate is sprayed with iodine vapour or with a solution of a suitable compound. In this way, the positions of the components are revealed. Alternatively, the spots can be located by irradiation of the plate with ultraviolet light (*cf.* §15a). Identification is made from the R_F values (§15c).

TLC is better than paper chromatography in several ways, one being that it can be used to separate much smaller amounts of substances. Also, since only short travel distances are required, separation is rapid.

§15e. Zone electrophoresis.   The basis of this method is that ions in a dispersion medium move with different speeds under the influence of an applied potential difference, anions moving to the cathode and cations to the anode. The mobility of an ion depends on the experimental conditions, and so paper electrophoresis is carried out simultaneously on the mixture and the individual reference compounds. Let us consider the separation of the mixture of amino-acids obtained from the hydrolysis of a protein. In acid buffer solution, each amino-acid carries a positive charge for every amino group present, $RCHNH_3{}^+CO_2H$ (see also **13** §3). A strip of filter paper is marked with a line near one end and parallel to the short edge. This line is spotted with a drop of the solution containing the mixture of amino-acids. In the same way, a number of other strips are prepared, each one being spotted with a solution containing only *one* of the reference amino-acids. The strips are dried and then saturated with a buffer solution, and laid side by side on a glass plate, placed horizontally, and the two ends of each strip are bent and immersed in tanks containing the buffer solution. In each tank there is a platinum electrode, and the P.D. is applied across them. Since, in the case we are discussing, the ions are positively charged, the origin lines are placed nearer the anode, and so the ions travel along the paper towards the cathode. After a few hours, the strips are dried, sprayed with ninhydrin solution (**13** §4) and dried again. Comparison of the distances travelled by the components in the mixture with those of the reference compounds leads to identification of the former.

A more recent modification of this method is to use cellulose acetate, starch gel, etc., instead of a strip of paper. When paper is used, the method is often referred to as **paper electrophoresis**. This method is of particular value with large molecules, *e.g.*, proteins, nucleic acids, polysaccharides, etc.

§15f. Ion-exchange chromatography.   In this method the solid phase consists of a synthetic resin. Two types of exchange resins are used, cation and anion exchangers. In this way, mixtures of bases or acids may be separated. As an illustration let us consider the separation of amino-acids obtained by the hydrolysis of a protein with dilute hydrochloric acid. The amino-acids will therefore be present as their hydrochlorides,

$$RCHNH_3 + CO_2H\}Cl^-$$

If this solution is passed down a column containing a cation-exchange resin, then exchange occurs whereby the amino-acid remains attached to the resin. A suitable resin for this purpose is one that contains benzenesulphonic acid residues incorporated into the macromolecules of the resin. Thus the resin may be represented as $Res-SO_3H$. When the amino-acid solution passes down the column, the following exchange occurs:

$$Res-SO_3^-\}H^+ + RCHNH_3^+CO_2H\{Cl^- \rightleftharpoons Res-SO_3^-\}RCHNH_3^+CO_2H + HCl$$

Thus the amino-acids are held on the column. Elution of the column with buffer solutions of different pH values causes removal of the amino-acids. The more weakly basic the amino-acid is, the more readily it will be removed, and by increasing the pH of the eluant, the more basic amino-acids will then be removed. Hence a separation is effected by stepwise elution.

Since amino-acids contain carboxyl groups, they may be separated by passing a solution of their sodium salts down a column containing an anion-exchange resin. In practice, cation-exchange chromatography is the better method.

Apart from their use in separation of mixtures, ion-exchange resins are being increasingly used as catalysts in various reactions, *e.g.*, hydrolysis, esterification, etc.

§15g. **Gas chromatography.**   When the moving phase is a mixture of gases, the usual method is to use a stationary solid phase—gas-solid chromatography, GSC—or a solid coated with a non-volatile liquid—gas-liquid chromatography, GLC. In GSC and GLC, a 'carrier' gas such as nitrogen or hydrogen replaces the solvent in column chromatography. In GLC, the solid may be finely powdered kieselguhr, Celite, etc., and the non-volatile liquid depends on the nature of the compounds to be separated; liquids used are paraffin (high-boiling fractions), dinonyl phthalate, polyethylene glycol, etc. This technique is suitable for substances which are volatile without decomposition up to about 300°C.

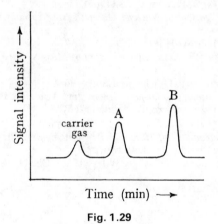

Fig. 1.29

As the mixture of gases passes through the column, partition occurs between gas mixture and stationary phase just as in partition chromatography (§15b). Since the partition coefficients are different, the individual components are carried along the column at different rates and emerge at the far end of the apparatus in distinct '*zones*' separated by carrier gas. Detection is carried out in several ways, all being instrumental methods which give automatic recording. The most common detector makes use of thermal conductivity. This property changes with the concentration of the eluted gas, and these changes are recorded by a resistance thermometer. The result is a plot of signal intensity against time. Fig. 1.29 shows the 'chromatogram' of the mixture of two gases A and B. The first peak corresponds to the carrier gas, and the other two to the pure components A and B. Identification of each fraction may be made by actual isolation or by the *retention time, i.e.,* the time required for the component to pass through the apparatus compared with the retention times of *known* samples *under the same conditions.* Alternatively, gas chromatography may be used in conjunction with an infrared or a mass spectrometer. The gases issuing from the gas chromatograph are directed into the instrument which records the infrared or mass spectrum of each gas. This is the most reliable way of identifying the components.

Although GSC is not so widely used as GLC, the former with dimethyldioctadecyl ammonium bentonite as the stationary phase is particularly suitable for the chromatographic separation of aromatic isomers, *e.g.,* xylenes, toluidines, cresols (White *et al.,* 1959), and dichlorobenzenes (Covan *et al.,* 1961).

REFERENCES

WEISSBERGER (ed.), *Technique of Organic Chemistry*, Interscience Publishers (1960, 3rd edn.).
BRAUDE and NACHOD (eds.), *Determination of Organic Structures by Physical Methods*, Academic Press. Vol. 1 (1955); Nachod and Phillips, Vol. 2 (1962); Nachod and Zuckerman, Vol. 3 (1971); Vol. 4 (1971).
SCHWARZ (ed.), *Physical Methods in Organic Chemistry*, Oliver and Boyd (1964).
PIMENTAL and MCCLELLAN, *The Hydrogen Bond*, Freeman and Co. (1960).
DJERASSI, *Optical Rotatory Dispersion*, McGraw-Hill (1960).
CRABBÉ, *Optical Rotatory Dispersion and Circular Dichroism in Organic Chemistry*, Holden-Day (1965).
BRIAT and DJERASSI, 'Applications of Magnetic Circular Dichroism and Optical Rotatory Dispersion Measurements', *Nature*, 1968, **217**, 918.
SCHATZ and MCCAFFERY, 'The Faraday Effect', *Q. Rev.* 1969, **23**, 552.
WILLIAMS and FLEMING, *Spectroscopic Methods in Organic Chemistry*, McGraw-Hill (1966).
DYKE, FLOYD, SAINSBURY and THEOBALD, *Organic Spectroscopy: An Introduction*, Penguin Books (1971).
CROSS and JONES, *Introduction to Practical Infrared Spectroscopy*, Butterworths (1969, 3rd edn.).
BIBLE, *Interpretation of NMR Spectra*, Plenum Press (1965).
JACKMAN and STERNHELL, *Applications of Nuclear Magnetic Spectroscopy in Organic Chemistry*, Pergamon Press (1969, 2nd edn.).
BIEMANN, *Mass Spectrometry*, McGraw-Hill (1962).
BUDZIKIEWICZ, DJERASSI, and WILLIAMS, *Interpretation of Mass Spectra of Organic Compounds*, Holden-Day (1964).
HILL, *Introduction to Mass Spectrometry*, Heyden and Son (1966).
REED, *Applications of Mass Spectrometry to Organic Chemistry*, Academic Press (1966).
MCLAFFERTY, *Interpretation of Mass Spectra*, Benjamin (1966).
BEYNON, SAUNDERS, and WILLIAMS, *The Mass Spectra of Organic Molecules*, Elsevier (1968).
PORTER and BALDAS, *Mass Spectrometry of Heterocyclic Compounds*, Wiley-Interscience (1971).
HEFTMANN, *Chromatography*, Reinhold (1967, 2nd edn.).
NEWMAN (ed.), *Steric Effects in Organic Chemistry*, Wiley (1956). Ch. 11. 'Steric Effects on Certain Physical Properties'.

2 Optical isomerism

§1. Stereoisomerism

Stereochemistry is the 'chemistry of space', *i.e.*, stereochemistry deals with the *spatial* arrangements of atoms and groups in a molecule. **Stereoisomerism** is exhibited by isomers having the *same* structure but differing in their spatial arrangement, *i.e.*, having different *configurations*. Different configurations are possible because carbon forms mainly covalent bonds and these have direction in space. The covalent bond is formed by the overlapping of atomic orbitals, the bond energy being greater the greater the overlap of the component orbitals. To get the maximum overlap of orbitals, the orbitals should be in the same plane. Thus *non-spherical* orbitals tend to form bonds in the direction of the greatest concentration of the orbital, and this consequently produces a *directional* bond (see also Vol. I, Ch. 2).

There are two types of stereoisomerism, **optical isomerism** and **geometrical isomerism** (*cis-trans* **isomerism**). It is not easy to define them, but their meanings will become clear as the study of stereochemistry progresses. Even so, it is highly desirable to have some idea about their meanings at this stage, and so the following summaries are given.

Optical isomerism is characterised by compounds having the same structure but different configurations, and because of their *molecular asymmetry* these compounds rotate the plane of polarisation of plane-polarised light. Optical isomers have similar physical and chemical properties; the most marked difference between them is their action on plane-polarised light (see **1** §9). Optical isomers may rotate the plane of polarisation by *equal* and *opposite* amounts; these optical isomers are **enantiomers** (see §2). On the other hand some optical isomers may rotate the plane of polarisation by different amounts; these are **diastereoisomers** (see §7b). Finally, some optical isomers may possess no rotation at all; these are diastereoisomers of the *meso*-type (see §7d).

Geometrical isomerism is characterised by compounds having the same structure but different configurations, and because of their *molecular symmetry* these compounds do *not* rotate the plane of polarisation of plane-polarised light. Geometrical isomers differ in all their physical and in many of their chemical properties. They can also exhibit optical isomerism if the structure of the molecule, apart from giving rise to geometrical isomerism, is also asymmetric. In general, geometrical isomerism involves molecules which can assume different stable configurations, the ability to do so being due, *e.g.*, to the presence of a double bond, a ring structure, or the steric effect (see Ch. 4 and 5).

§2. Optical isomerism

It has been found that only those structures, crystalline or molecular, which are *not* superimposable on their mirror images, are optically active. Such structures may be *dissymmetric*, or *asymmetric*. Asymmetric structures have no elements of symmetry at all, but dissymmetric structures, although possessing some elements of symmetry, are nevertheless still capable of existing in two forms (one the mirror image of the other) which are not superimposable. To avoid unnecessary complications, we shall use the term asymmetric to cover both cases (of asymmetry and dissymmetry; see also §3a and §6).

A given molecule which has at least one element of symmetry (§6) when its 'classical' configuration (*i.e.*, the Fischer projection formula; §5) is inspected may, however, have a conformation (§4a) which is devoid of any element of symmetry. At first sight, such a molecule might be supposed to be optically active. In practice, however, it is not; individual molecules are optically active, but statistically, the whole collection of molecules is not. It therefore follows that when a molecule can exist in one or more conformations, then provided that at least one of the conformations (whether preferred or not) is superimposable on its mirror image, the compound will not be optically active (see §11 for a discussion of this problem).

Optical activity due to crystalline structure. There are many substances which are optically active in the solid state only, *e.g.*, quartz, sodium chlorate, benzil, etc. Let us consider quartz, the first substance shown to be optically active (Arago, 1811). Quartz exists in two crystalline forms, one of which is dextrorotatory and the other laevorotatory. These two forms are mirror images and are not superimposable. Such pairs of crystals are said to be *enantiomorphous* (quartz crystals are actually hemihedral and are mirror images). X-ray analysis has shown that the quartz crystal lattice is built up of silicon and oxygen atoms arranged in left- and right-handed spirals. One is the mirror image of the other, and the two are not superimposable. When quartz crystals are fused, the optical activity is lost. Therefore the optical activity is entirely due to the *asymmetry of the crystalline structure*, since fusion brings about only a physical change. Thus we have a group of substances which are optically active only so long as they remain solid; fusion, vaporisation or solution in a solvent causes loss of optical activity.

Optical activity due to molecular structure. There are many compounds which are optically active in the solid, fused, gaseous or dissolved state, *e.g.*, glucose, tartaric acid, etc. In this case the optical activity is entirely due to the *asymmetry of the molecular structure* (see, however, §11). The original molecule and its non-superimposable mirror image are known as *enantiomorphs* (this name is taken from crystallography), *enantiomers*, or *optical antipodes*.

Properties of enantiomers. It appears that enantiomers are identical physically except in two respects:

(i) their manner of rotating polarised light; the rotations are equal but opposite.

(ii) the absorption coefficients for dextro- and laevocircularly polarised light are different; this difference is known as *circular dichroism* (see also 3 §8 and §11).

The crystal forms of enantiomers may be mirror images of each other, *i.e.*, the crystals themselves may be enantiomorphous, but this is unusual [see also §10(i)]. Enantiomers are similar chemically, but their rates of reaction with other optically active compounds are usually different [see §10(vii)]. They may also be different physiologically, *e.g.*, (+)-histidine is sweet, (−)-tasteless; (−)-nicotine is more poisonous than (+)-. The mass spectra of enantiomers (and their corresponding racemates) are identical, and so are their NMR spectra (see also §7a).

§3. The tetrahedral carbon atom

In 1874, van't Hoff and Le Bel, independently, gave the solution to the problem of optical isomerism in organic compounds. van't Hoff proposed the theory that if the four valencies of the carbon atom are arranged tetrahedrally (not necessarily regular) with the carbon atom at the centre, then all the cases of isomerism known are accounted for. Le Bel's theory was substantially the same as van't Hoff's, but differed in that whereas van't Hoff believed that the valency distribution was definitely tetrahedral and fixed as such, Le Bel believed that the valency directions were not rigidly fixed, and did not specify the tetrahedral arrangement, but thought that *whatever* the spatial arrangement, the molecule *Cabde* would be *asymmetric*. Later work has shown that van't Hoff's theory is more in keeping with the facts (see below). Both van't Hoff's and Le Bel's theories were based on the assumption that the four hydrogen atoms in methane are equivalent; this assumption has been shown to be correct by means of chemical and physico-chemical methods. Before the tetrahedral arrangement was proposed, it was believed that the four carbon valencies were planar, with the carbon atom at the centre of a square (Kekulé, 1858).

Pasteur (1848) stated that all substances fell into two groups, those which were superimposable on their mirror images, and those which were not. In substances such as quartz, optical activity is due to the dissymmetry of the *crystal* structure, but in compounds like sucrose the optical activity is due to *molecular* dissymmetry. Since it is impossible to have molecular dissymmetry if the molecule is flat, Pasteur's work is based on the idea that molecules are three-dimensional and arranged dissymmetrically. A further interesting point in this connection is that Pasteur quoted an irregular tetrahedron as one example of a dissymmetric structure. Also, Paterno (1869) had proposed *tetrahedral models* for the structure of the isomeric compounds $C_2H_4Cl_2$ (at that time it was thought that there were three isomers with this formula; one ethylidene dichloride and two ethylene dichlorides).

§3a. Evidence for the tetrahedral carbon atom.   The molecule CX_4 constitutes a five-point system, and since the four valencies of carbon are equivalent, their disposition in space may be assumed to be symmetrical. Thus there are three symmetrical arrangements possible for the molecule CX_4, one planar and two solid—pyramidal and tetrahedral. By comparing the number of isomers that have been prepared for a given compound with the number predicted by the above three spatial arrangements, it is possible to decide which one is correct.

Compounds of the types Ca_2b_2 and Ca_2bd. Both of these are similar, and so we shall only discuss molecule Ca_2b_2.

(i) If the molecule is planar, then *two* forms are possible (Fig. 2.1). This planar configuration can be either square or rectangular; in each case there are two forms only.

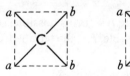

Fig. 2.1

(ii) If the molecule is pyramidal, then *two* forms are possible (Fig. 2.2). There are only two forms, whether the base is square or rectangular.

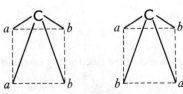

Fig. 2.2

(iii) If the molecule is tetrahedral, then only *one* form is possible (Fig. 2.3; the carbon atom is at the centre of the tetrahedron).

In practice, only one form is known for each of the compounds of the types Ca_2b_2 and Ca_2bd; this agrees with the tetrahedral configuration.

Fig. 2.3

Compounds of the type $Cabde$. (i) If the molecule is planar, then *three* forms are possible (Fig. 2.4).

Fig. 2.4

(ii) If the molecule is pyramidal, then *six* forms are possible; there are three pairs of enantiomers. Each of the forms in Fig. 2.4, drawn as a pyramid, is not superimposable on its mirror image, *e.g.*, Fig. 2.5 shows one pair of enantiomers.

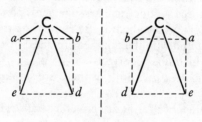

Fig. 2.5

(iii) If the molecule is tetrahedral, there are *two* forms possible, one related to the other as object and mirror image, which are not superimposable, *i.e.*, the tetrahedral configuration gives rise to one pair of enantiomers (Fig. 2.6).

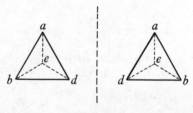

Fig. 2.6

In practice, compounds of the type $Cabde$ give rise to only one pair of enantiomers; this agrees with the tetrahedral configuration.

When a compound contains four different groups attached to a carbon atom, that carbon atom is said to be asymmetric (actually, of course, it is the *group* which is asymmetric; a *carbon atom* cannot be asymmetric). The majority of optically active compounds (organic) contain one or more asymmetric carbon atoms. It should be remembered, however, that the *essential* requirement for optical activity is the *asymmetry of the molecule*. A molecule may contain two or more asymmetric carbon atoms and still not be optically active (see, *e.g.*, §7d).

A most interesting case of an optically active compound containing one asymmetric carbon atom is the resolution of *s*-butylmercuric bromide, EtMeCHHgBr (Hughes, Ingold *et al.*, 1958). This appears to be the first example of the resolution of a simple organometallic compound where the asymmetry depends only on the carbon atom attached to the metal.

Chirality. As we have seen, the structures of enantiomers differ only in 'handedness', one being left-handed and the other being right-handed. Any molecule which is not superimposable on its mirror image is said to possess *chirality* (from the Greek *kheir*, hand). Thus, the term *chirality* means 'having handedness'. This term was first introduced by Kelvin (1884), and has been used by Cahn *et al.* in their system for the specification of absolute configuration (see §5d). Chirality expresses the necessary and sufficient condition for the existence of enantiomers (*i.e.*, chirality is now equivalent to asymmetry or dissymmetry, as described in §2). The adjective *chiral* is equivalent to being left- or right-handed, and so a *chiral centre* is one which can be left- or right-handed. On the other hand, when a molecule is superimposable on its mirror image, that molecule does not possess 'handedness' (*i.e.*, it is not asymmetric) and is said to be *achiral*. The commonest cause of optical activity is the presence of one or more chiral centres which, in organic chemistry, are usually asymmetric carbon atoms.

From what has been said above, it can be seen that chiral molecules are those which can exist as enantiomers, and that enantiomers have opposite chirality. Furthermore, since chirality expresses the necessary and *sufficient* condition for the existence of enantiomers, chirality is therefore, strictly speaking, equivalent to dissymmetry (chiral molecules may possess axes of symmetry; see §6). Achiral molecules are *symmetric* or *non-dissymmetric* (the latter term is preferred by many authors).

Isotopic asymmetry. In the optically active compound *Cabde*, the groups *a*, *b*, *d* and *e* (which may or may not contain carbon) are all different, but two or more may be *structural* isomers, *e.g.*, propylisopropylmethanol is optically active. The substitution of hydrogen by deuterium has also been investigated in recent years to ascertain whether these two atoms are sufficiently different to give rise to optical isomerism. The earlier work gave conflicting results, but later work, however, is definitely conclusive in favour of optical activity, *e.g.*, Eliel (1949) prepared optically active phenylmethyldeuteromethane, $CH_3CHDC_6H_5$, by reducing optically active phenylmethylmethyl chloride (α-phenylethyl chloride), $CH_3CHClC_6H_5$, with lithium aluminium deuteride; Ross *et al.* (1956) have prepared (−)-2-deuterobutane by reduction of (−)-2-chlorobutane with lithium aluminium deuteride; and Alexander *et al.* (1949) reduced *trans*-2-*p*-menthene with deuterium (Raney nickel catalyst) and obtained a 2,3-dideutero-*trans*-*p*-menthane (I) that was slightly laevorotatory. Alexander (1950) also reduced (−)-menthyl toluene-*p*-sulphonate and obtained an optically active 3-deutero-*trans*-*p*-menthane (II).

(I)   (II)

Some other optically active compounds with deuterium asymmetry are, *e.g.*, (III; Streitwieser, 1955) and (IV; Levy *et al.*, 1957):

$$CH_3CH_2CH_2CHDOH \qquad CH_3CHDOH$$
$$\text{(III)} \qquad\qquad\qquad \text{(IV)}$$

A point of interest here is that almost all optically active deuterium compounds have been prepared from optically active precursors. Exceptions are (V) and (VI), which have been resolved by Pocker (1961) [see also **6** §5c].

$$C_6H_5CHOHC_6D_5 \qquad C_6H_5CDOHC_6D_5$$
$$\text{(V)} \qquad\qquad\qquad \text{(VI)}$$

It might be noted that chirality produced by replacement of hydrogen by deuterium is of two types: (i) deuterium is directly attached to the chiral centre (asymmetric carbon atom), *e.g.*, (III) and (IV); (ii) deuterium is *not* directly attached to the chiral centre, *e.g.*, (V).

Further evidence for the tetrahedral carbon atom

(i) Conversion of the *two* forms (enantiomers) of the molecule *Cabde* into *Ca₂bd* results in the formation of *one* compound only (and disappearance of optical activity), *e.g.*, both dextro- and laevo-rotatory lactic acid may be reduced to the *same* propionic acid, which is not optically active. These results are possible only with a tetrahedral arrangement (Fig. 2.7; see §5 for the convention for drawing tetrahedra).

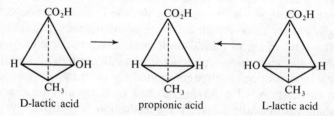

D-lactic acid   propionic acid   L-lactic acid

Fig. 2.7

(ii) If the configuration is tetrahedral, then interchanging any two groups in the molecule *Cabde* will produce the enantiomer, *e.g.*, *b* and *e* (see Fig. 2.8). Fischer and Brauns (1914), starting with (+)-isopropylmalonamic acid, carried out a series of reactions whereby the carboxyl and the carbonamide groups were interchanged; the product was (−)-isopropylmalonamic acid. It is most important to note that in this series of reactions no bond connected to the asymmetric carbon atom was ever broken (for an explanation, see Walden Inversion, Ch. 3).

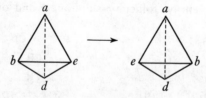

Fig. 2.8

This change from one enantiomer into the other is in agreement with the tetrahedral theory. At the same time, this series of reactions shows that optical isomers have identical structures, and so the difference must be due to the spatial arrangement.

$$
\begin{array}{ccc}
\underset{\text{(+)-acid}}{\overset{\displaystyle CONH_2}{\underset{\displaystyle CO_2H}{H-C-CH(CH_3)_2}}}
& \xrightarrow{CH_2N_2} &
\underset{\text{(+)}}{\overset{\displaystyle CONH_2}{\underset{\displaystyle CO_2CH_3}{H-C-CH(CH_3)_2}}}
& \xrightarrow{HNO_2} &
\underset{\text{(−)}}{\overset{\displaystyle CO_2H}{\underset{\displaystyle CO_2CH_3}{H-C-CH(CH_3)_2}}}
\end{array}
$$

$$
\xrightarrow{N_2H_4}
\underset{\text{(−)}}{\overset{\displaystyle CO_2H}{\underset{\displaystyle CONHNH_2}{H-C-CH(CH_3)_2}}}
\xrightarrow{HNO_2}
\underset{\text{(−)}}{\overset{\displaystyle CO_2H}{\underset{\displaystyle CON_3}{H-C-CH(CH_3)_2}}}
\xrightarrow{NH_3}
\underset{\text{(−)-acid}}{\overset{\displaystyle CO_2H}{\underset{\displaystyle CONH_2}{H-C-CH(CH_3)_2}}}
$$

(iii) X-ray crystallography, dipole moment measurements, absorption spectra and electron diffraction studies show that the four valencies of carbon are arranged tetrahedrally with the carbon atom inside the tetrahedron.

It should be noted in passing that the tetrahedra are not regular unless four identical groups are attached to the central carbon atom; only in this case are the four bond lengths equal. In all other cases the bond lengths will be different, the actual values depending on the nature of the atoms joined to the carbon atom (see **1** §12b).

§4. Two postulates underlie the tetrahedral theory

(i) **The principle of constancy of the valency angle.** Mathematical calculation of the angle subtended by each side of a regular tetrahedron at the central carbon atom (Fig. 2.9) gives a value of 109° 28′. Originally, it was postulated (van't Hoff) that the valency angle was fixed at this value. It is now known, however, that the valency angle may deviate from this value. The four valencies of

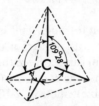

Fig. 2.9

carbon are formed by hybridisation of the $2s^2$ and $2p^2$ orbitals, *i.e.*, there are four sp^3 bonds (see Vol. I, Ch. 2). Quantum mechanical calculations show that the four carbon valencies in the molecule Ca_4 are equivalent and directed towards the four corners of a regular tetrahedron. Furthermore, quantum-mechanical calculations require the carbon bond angles to be close to the tetrahedral value, since change from this value is associated with loss in bond strength and consequently decrease in stability. According to Coulson *et al.* (1949), calculation has shown that the *smallest* valency angle that one can reasonably expect to find is 104°. It is this value which is found in the cyclopropane and cyclobutane rings, these molecules being relatively unstable because of the 'bent' bonds (Coulson; see Baeyer Strain Theory, Vol. I, Ch. 19).

(ii) **The principle of free rotation about a single bond.** Originally, it was believed that internal rotation about a single bond was completely free. Let us consider the ethane molecule, $CH_3{-}CH_3$, and let us imagine that one methyl group is rotated about the C—C bond as axis with the other group at rest. Suppose we use, as the starting point, the position in which two C—H bonds are parallel, *i.e.*, these four atoms lie in a plane (Fig. 2.10c). In this position, the *dihedral angle* (*angle of rotation* or *angle of torsion*) is zero, and if the rotation is free, then as the dihedral angle changes, the energy content of the molecule will remain constant (the plot of energy content against the dihedral angle will be a horizontal line). In this situation, the two 'halves' can assume, with complete freedom, an infinite number of positions relative to each other. Thus, the entropy of the molecule will be a maximum. Pitzer *et al.* (1936) calculated the entropy of ethane based on the assumption that the *internal rotation* was free, and found that calculated value was greater than the observed value. This means that there is less freedom to assume all possible dihedral angles than was expected on the principle of free rotation. Pitzer therefore assumed that the internal rotation is hindered by a potential energy barrier, and calculated the change in entropy with increasing barrier height. When he assumed a barrier of 12·55 kJ mol^{-1} (3 kcal), the calculated and observed entropies were brought into good agreement. The potential energy curve obtained for ethane is shown in Fig. 2.10a and, by convention, the potential energy is measured relative to the energy of the most stable form. Because of the existence of potential energy barriers, the result is *mutual oscillation* (*libration*) about the conformations with minimum potential energy, thereby producing 'more order' (more restriction) than had there been no barriers.

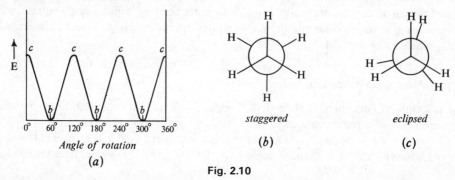

$$\text{(a)} \qquad \qquad staggered \qquad \qquad eclipsed$$

(a)   (b)   (c)

Fig. 2.10

Figure 2.10b is the Newman projection formula. This is obtained by viewing the molecule along the bonding line of the two carbon atoms, with the carbon atom nearer to the eye being designated by equally spaced radii, and the carbon atom further from the eye by a circle with three equally spaced radial extensions. Figure 2.10b represents the *staggered* (or *transoid*) conformation (in which the hydrogen atoms are as far apart as possible), and Fig. 2.10c the *eclipsed* (or *cisoid*) conformation in which the hydrogen atoms are as close together as possible). It can be seen from Fig. 2.10a that the energy of the eclipsed conformation is greater than that of the staggered conformation. The potential energy barrier (11·92 kJ mol^{-1}) is much too small for either confirmation to remain stable, *i.e.*, the eclipsed and staggered forms are readily interconvertible and hence neither can be isolated as such. However, the staggered conformation is the preferred form, *i.e.*, its population is greater than that of the eclipsed form (see below).

Now let us consider the case of ethylene dichloride. According to Bernstein (1949), the potential energy of ethylene dichloride undergoes the changes shown in Fig. 2.11 when one CH_2Cl group is rotated about the C—C bond with the other CH_2Cl at rest. There are two positions of minimum energy, one corresponding to the staggered (transoid or anti) form and the other to the gauche (skew) form, the latter possessing approximately 4·6 kJ more than the former. The fully eclipsed (cisoid) form possesses about 18·83 kJ more energy than the staggered form and thus the latter is the preferred form, *i.e.*, the molecule is largely in this form. Dipole moment studies show that this is so in practice, and also show (as do Raman spectra studies) that the ratio of the two forms varies with the temperature. Furthermore, infrared, Raman spectra and electron diffraction studies have shown that the gauche form is also present. According to Mizushima *et al.* (1938), only the staggered form is present at low temperatures.

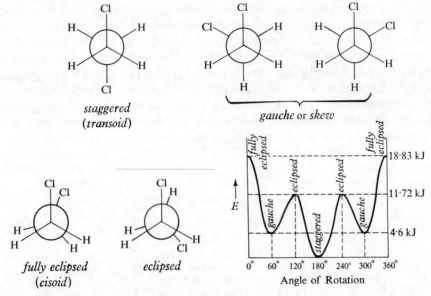

Fig. 2.11

The problem of internal rotation about the central C—C bond in n-butane is interesting, since the values of the potential energies of the various forms have been used in the study of cyclic compounds (see cyclohexane, **4** §11). The various forms are shown in Fig. 2.12, and if the energy content of the staggered form is taken as zero, then the other forms have the energy contents shown (Pitzer, 1951).

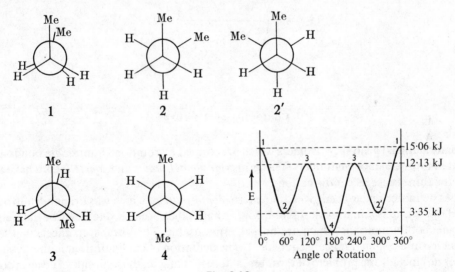

Fig. 2.12

From the foregoing account it can be seen that, in theory, there is no free rotation about a single bond. In practice, however, it may occur if the potential barriers of the various forms do not differ by more than about 40 kJ mol^{-1}. Free rotation about a single bond is generally accepted in *simple* molecules. Restricted rotation, however, may occur when the molecule contains groups large

enough to impede free rotation, *e.g.*, in *ortho*-substituted biphenyls (see Ch. 5). In some cases resonance can give rise to restricted rotation about a 'single' bond.

In addition to the nomenclature of conformers described above—staggered (*anti*), skew (gauche),
etc., conformers are also described in terms of the dihedral angle between specified groups. Thus, the
dihedral angle for the skew form of n-butane (2 and 2', Fig. 2.12) is 60°; for the staggered (*anti*) form
(4, Fig. 2.12) the dihedral angle is 180°. In many cases, however, the exact dihedral angle is not
known, and to describe these cases, the following nomenclature in terms of approximate dihedral
angles has been proposed (Klyne and Prelog, 1960). The terms *syn* and *anti* are used to indicate
respectively a dihedral angle smaller or greater than 90°. The terms 'periplanar' and 'clinal'
respectively describe approximately planar (0° ± 30° and 180° ± 30°) and inclined positions (all
other angles).

Dihedral angle	Designation	Symbol
− 30° to + 30°	± *syn*-periplanar	± sp
+ 30° to + 90°	+ *syn*-clinal	+ sc
+ 90° to + 150°	+ *anti*-clinal	+ ac
+ 150° to − 150°	± *anti*-periplanar	± ap
− 30° to − 90°	− *syn*-clinal	− sc
− 90° to − 150°	− *anti*-clinal	− ac

This method of nomenclature is summarised in the diagram.

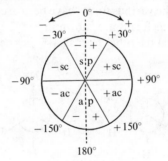

Conformational prefixes

§4a. Conformational analysis.   Isomers which are formed by rotation about single bonds are called
different **conformations** or **conformers**. The terms *rotational isomers* and *constellations* have also been
used in the same sense as conformations.

Various definitions have been given to the term *conformation* (which was originally introduced by
W. N. Haworth, 1929). In its widest sense, conformation has been used to describe different spatial
arrangements of a molecule which are not superimposable. This means, in effect, that the terms
conformation and *configuration* are equivalent. The definition of configuration, in the classical sense
(§1), does not include the problem of the internal forces acting on the molecule. The term conformation, however, is the spatial arrangement of the molecule when all the internal forces acting on the
molecule are taken into account. In this more restricted sense, the term conformation is used to
designate different spatial arrangements arising by twisting or rotation of bonds of a *given* configuration (used in the classical sense).

The existence of potential energy barriers between the various conformations shows that there are
internal forces acting on the molecule. The nature of these interactions that prevent free rotation

about single bonds, however, is not completely clear. According to one theory, the hindering of internal rotation is due to dipole-dipole forces. Calculation of the dipole moment of ethylene dichloride on the assumption of free rotation gave a value not in agreement with the experimental value. Thus free rotation cannot be assumed, but on the assumption that there is interaction between the two groups through dipole–dipole attractive or repulsive forces, there will be preferred conformations, *i.e.*, the internal rotation is not completely free. This restricted rotation is shown by the fact that the dipole moment of ethylene dichloride increases with temperature; in the staggered form the dipole moment is zero, but as energy is absorbed by the molecule, rotation occurs to produce finally the eclipsed form in which the dipole moment is a maximum. Further work, however, has shown that factors other than dipole–dipole interactions must also be operating in opposing the rotation. One of these factors is **steric repulsion**, *i.e.*, repulsion between the non-bonded atoms (of the rotating groups) when they are brought into close proximity (*cf.* the van der Waals forces, 1 §2). The existence of steric repulsion may be illustrated by the fact that although the bond moment of C—Cl is greater than that of C—Br, the energy difference between the eclipsed and staggered conformations of ethylene dichloride is less than that of ethylene dibromide. Furthermore, if steric repulsion does affect internal rotation, then in the ethylene dihalides, steric repulsion between the hydrogen and halogen atoms, if sufficiently large, will give rise to two other potential energy minima (these correspond to the two skew forms, and these have been shown to be present; see Fig. 2.11, §4).

Other factors also affect stability of the various conformations. Staggered and skew forms always exist in molecules of the type CH_2Y—CH_2Z (where Y and Z are Cl, Br, I, CH_3, etc.), and usually the staggered form is more stable than the skew. In a molecule such as ethylene chlorohydrin or ethylene glycol, however, intramolecular hydrogen bonding is possible in the skew form but not the staggered. This would stabilise the molecule by about 20–29 kJ mol^{-1}, and this is great enough to make the skew form more stable than the staggered. Infrared spectroscopy has shown that the skew form predominates.

ethylene chlorohydrin   ethylene glycol

In addition to the factors already mentioned, there appear to be other factors that cause the absence of complete free rotation about a single bond, *e.g.*, the energy barrier in ethane is too great to be accounted for by steric repulsion only. Several explanations have been offered; *e.g.*, Pauling (1958) has proposed that the energy barrier in ethane (and in similar molecules) results from repulsions between adjacent bonding pairs of electrons, *i.e.*, the bonding pairs of the C—H bonds on one carbon atom repel those on the other carbon atom. Thus the preferred conformation will be the staggered one (*cf.* 6 §1). It is still possible, however, that steric repulsion is also present, and this raises the barrier height.

When the stability of a molecule is decreased by internal forces produced by interaction between constituent parts, that molecule is said to be under **strain**. In view of the foregoing discussion, it can be seen that there are four contributing sources to strain: (i) steric strain, (ii) dipole-dipole interactions, (iii) bond angle strain, and (iv) bond opposition strain. Which of these plays the predominant part depends on the nature of the molecule in question. This study of the existence of preferred conformations in molecules, and the relating of physical and chemical properties of a molecule to its preferred conformation, is known as **conformational analysis**. The energy differences between the various conformations determine which one is the most stable, and the ease of transformation depends on the potential energy barriers that exist between these conformations. It should be noted that the molecule, in its *unexcited* state, will exist largely in the conformation of lowest energy content. If, however, the energy differences between the various conformations are small, then when *excited*, the molecule can take up a less favoured conformation, *e.g.*, during the course of reaction with other molecules (see **4** §12).

So far, we have considered the conformations of saturated compounds. Conformational studies of unsaturated compounds and compounds containing the oxo group have led to some unexpected results, *e.g.*, microwave spectroscopy has shown that the preferred conformations of propene

propene   acetaldehyde   propionaldehyde

(Herschbach *et al.*, 1958) and acetaldehyde (Kilb *et al.*, 1957) are the eclipsed forms, and NMR spectroscopy has shown that the predominant conformation of propionaldehyde is the one in which the methyl group and oxygen atom are eclipsed (Pople *et al.*, 1960). The reason for these observations is uncertain.

Many methods are now used to investigate the conformations of molecules: thermodynamic calculations, dipole moments, X-ray and electron diffraction, infrared and ultraviolet spectroscopy, chemical methods, etc.

A particularly useful method for studying the conformations of molecules is NMR spectroscopy. However, before dealing with this, let us first consider the chemical shifts of the protons of CH_3, CH_2, and the CH group in acyclic compounds and the chemical shift of a proton attached to O, N, etc. As we have seen (**1** §12e), the more electronegative Z is in the groups —CH—Z and —Z—H, the more is the proton deshielded and consequently the lower is the τ-value (see Table 1.9).

Let us now consider ethyl chloride, and since the most stable conformation is the staggered one, the molecule may be represented as (I), (II), and (III). In (I), the environments of H_a and H_c are identical, but differ from that of H_b. This can be seen to be the case by replacing each proton, one at a time, by Z. This procedure for H_a and H_c produces mirror images, and so the two protons are chemically equivalent, but for H_b the substituted product is different, and therefore H_b is not

(I)   (II)   (III)

chemically equivalent to H_a and H_c. The coupling constants of H_a with H_d and H_e are different because of the different dihedral angles, and similarly for H_c. Thus, H_a and H_c are chemically but not magnetically equivalent. By using similar arguments, it can be shown that H_d and H_e are also chemically but not magnetically equivalent. Hence, if the population of ethyl chloride conformation were *completely* represented by (I), protons H_a and H_c would give one signal and H_b another signal, provided that the chemical shifts were sufficiently different (0·1–0·2 p.p.m.), *i.e.*, the methyl group would give *two* signals. In practice, the methyl group gives only *one* signal (a triplet), and therefore protons H_a, H_b, and H_c must be equivalent. This is explained on the basis that there is free rotation about the carbon-carbon single bond. When the methyl group rotates (with respect to the CH_2Cl group), it can take up the other two stable staggered conformations, (II) and (III), the result being that each proton has an average environment. Since these average environments are identical, rotation results in the equivalence of H_a, H_b, and H_c.

This equivalence may be demonstrated as follows. Let P_I, P_{II}, P_{III} be the populations in conformations (I), (II), and (III), respectively, where $P_I + P_{II} + P_{III} = 1$. Also, let δ (the chemical shift) of any proton *trans* (*anti*) to another proton be x, and y if *trans* to Cl. Now, the observed δ of a given proton is the sum of the δ-contributions in each conformation, and so it follows that:

$$\delta(H_a) = P_I x + P_{II} y + P_{III} x$$
$$\delta(H_b) = P_I y + P_{II} x + P_{III} x$$
$$\delta(H_c) = P_I x + P_{II} x + P_{III} y$$

Since all three populations are equal (all three are indistinguishable because all protons, as such, are identical), *i.e.*, $P_I = P_{II} = P_{III} = 1/3$, therefore

$$\delta(H_a) = \delta(H_b) = \delta(H_c) = 2/3x + 1/3y$$

Hence, all three protons have the same (average) chemical shift (in the freely rotating state) and so there is no observable splitting for the methyl group.

Application of this method to protons H_d and H_e gives:

$$\delta(H_d) = P_I x + P_{II} x + P_{III} x = x$$
$$\delta(H_e) = P_I x + P_{II} x + P_{III} x = x$$

From the above discussion, it can be seen that if ethyl chloride were undergoing slow rotation, it would be an ABB′CC′ spin system, but when undergoing fast rotation, it is an A_3B_2 spin system (see also below).

$$(IV) \qquad\qquad (V) \qquad\qquad (VI)$$

Now let us consider the case of 1-bromo-2-chloroethane, and if we use the same arguments as before, then in (IV), H_a and H_b are chemically but not magnetically equivalent, and this is also true for H_c and H_d. Also, if δ for a proton *trans* to a proton is x, *trans* to Cl is y, and *trans* to Br is z, then:

$$\delta(H_a) = P_{IV} x + P_V y + P_{VI} x$$

$$\delta(H_b) = P_{IV} x + P_V x + P_{VI} y$$

In this molecule, although $P_V = P_{VI} \neq P_{IV}$, it still follows that $\delta(H_a) = \delta(H_b)$. In the same way, it can be shown that $\delta(H_c) = \delta(H_d)$.

We can extend the argument by also considering the possible coupling constants. If J_t and J_s represent, respectively, the vicinal *trans* and skew coupling, then:

$$J_{ad} = P_{IV} J_t + P_V J_s + P_{VI} J_s$$
$$J_{bd} = P_{IV} J_s + P_V J_t + P_{VI} J_s$$

Since $P_V = P_{VI} \neq P_{IV}$, therefore $J_{ad} \neq J_{bd}$. Hence, H_a and H_b (and also H_c and H_d) are chemically but not magnetically equivalent. Application of this method will show that the three protons in the methyl group in ethyl chloride are magnetically equivalent, as are also the two protons in the CH_2Cl group, for the freely rotating molecule.

Finally, let us consider a molecule of the type $R^1R^2CHCHR^3R^4$. Each carbon atom is asymmetric, and the environments of H_a are different in all three conformations, and this is also true for H_b.

(VII)   (VIII)   (IX)

Furthermore, because of the different steric effects, the three populations will be different (*i.e.*, $P_{VII} \neq P_{VIII} \neq P_{IX}$). Hence, the chemical shifts of H_a (and those of H_b) are different in each conformation. If rotation were slow, the NMR spectrum would be a composite of all three spectra (three AB spin systems for each pair of enantiomers). If the temperature is raised, the rate of rotation is increased, and the result is an average of chemical shifts and coupling constants to give one AB spin system (for each pair of enantiomers). These averages, however, will be weighted in favour of the most stable conformation, *i.e.*, the one with the highest population.

Now let us consider the case of amides. Infrared spectroscopic evidence has indicated that amides are resonance hybrids, and this is supported by NMR studies, *e.g.*, the two methyl groups in dimethylformamide give two separate signals at room temperature. This can be explained on the basis that, because of the partial double bond character of the C—N bond, the two methyl groups

have *different* environments, one methyl group being *cis* and the other *trans* to the hydrogen atom. At room temperature the rate of rotation about the C—N bond is slow enough for the two methyl groups to be non-equivalent. As the temperature is raised, the signals broaden and finally collapse to a single line. At these higher temperatures, the molecule has absorbed sufficient energy to overcome the energy barrier to rotation to make the average environment of the two methyl groups the same, *i.e.*, the two methyl groups are *now* equivalent.

§4b. **Differences in stability and reactivity of diastereoisomers.** The stabilities of diastereoisomers of compounds containing two asymmetric carbon atoms (§7b) are generally different, but these differences are usually small. The *meso*-form (§7d) is generally more stable than either of the active forms, and the *erythro* compounds are generally more stable than the *threo* compounds (see §7b for the meanings of these prefixes). This may be demonstrated by consideration of the molecule

meso   active

CSML—CSML, where S, M, and L represent the smallest, medium, and largest groups, respectively. First let us consider the *meso*-form and one active form, each being drawn in its most stable conformation (S = S, M = M, L = L; *e.g.*, $HO_2CCHOHCHOHCO_2H$). The basis of the argument is the general principle that crossed steric interactions between groups of different size are less than the sum of the steric interactions between groups of equal size. The sum of the skew interactions in the *meso*-form is: $2(L:M) + 2(M:S) + 2(L:S)$, whereas in the active form the sum is: $2(L:M) + (M:M) + 2(L:S) + (S:S)$. Therefore, since $(M:M + S:S) > 2(M:S)$, the *meso*-form is under less steric strain than the active form, and consequently is the more stable diastereoisomer.

If any two of the groups are not the same, *e.g.*, $HO_2CCHOHCHOHCHO$, the compound will be the *erythro*- or *threo*-isomer, and using the same arguments as before it will be found that the former is more stable than the latter. This has been established experimentally for many pairs of *meso*- and racemic and of *erythro*- and *threo*-isomers (see also Cram's rule, 3 §7).

When we consider the differences in reactivity between diastereoisomers, the main controlling factor is the height of the energy barrier leading to the transition state. This may be assessed in terms of two factors: the *steric factor* which is concerned with the conformational requirements of groups not involved in the reaction, and the *stereoelectronic factor* which is concerned with the spatial relationships that exist between electrons involved in bond formation and/or bond breaking in the transition state. Acyclic systems can usually adjust themselves to the stereoelectronic requirements of the transition state, about 4·2–8·4 kJ/mol being required in the process. With cyclic systems, because of their relative rigidity, adjustment in a similar fashion may be far more difficult (see Ch. 4).

The foregoing account of the problem of conformations of molecules has been mainly qualitative. It is also of interest to consider the problem from a semi-quantitative point of view. The most convenient parameters for defining the spatial arrangement of the atoms in a molecule are bond lengths, bond angles, and torsional (dihedral) angles, and the changes in energy content in the molecule will depend on the changes in these parameters. These changes—bond stretching (and compression), bond angle bending, and bond torsion—are collectively called *molecular deformations*.

Bond stretching and compression. If the potential energy of two particles in their equilibrium position, *i.e.*, when they are separated by the bond length, (r), is taken as zero, then the P.E., V_r, of the two particles when the bond length is changed by Δr is given by the expression

$$V_r = \tfrac{1}{2}k_r(\Delta r)^2$$

where k_r is the *bond stretching force constant* (see 1 §12b). For both C—C and C—H bonds, k_r is about 5×10^5 dynes/cm (5 N/cm) and the above expression (for these two bonds) reduces to

$$V_r = 350(\Delta r)^2 \text{ kcal/mol/Å}^2 = 1464(\Delta r)^2 \text{ kJ/mol/Å}^2$$

With the C—C bond length equal to 1·54 Å, then a change of 2 per cent, *i.e.*, 0·031 Å, is equal to a change in P.E. of $\sim$1·42 kJ/mol.

Bond angle bending. If the C—C—C valency angle in saturated *n*-hydrocarbons is taken as the standard value ($\sim$112°), then any deviation from this value produces *angle strain* (also known as *Baeyer strain* or *classical strain*). If the angle deformation is $\Delta\theta$, then the angle strain, V_θ, is given by the expression

$$V_\theta = \tfrac{1}{2}k_\theta(\Delta\theta)^2$$

where k_θ is the *bond bending force constant*. Since k_θ has similar values for most C—C—C bond angles, the above expression may be reduced to

$$V_\theta = 0·01(\Delta\theta)^2 \text{ kcal/mol/deg}^2 = 0·042(\Delta\theta)^2 \text{ kJ/mol/deg}^2$$

Thus, if $\Delta\theta = 6°$, then $V_\theta = 1·5$ kJ/mol. This is roughly the same value as V_r for a 2 per cent change in r (see above). If we consider acyclic compounds only, then the maximum value for $\Delta\theta$ is about 10–12°. Thus, an angle deformation of 6° is about 50 per cent of the maximum value. Hence angle deformation is more easily brought about than linear deformation.

Bond torsion. As we have seen, the P.E. of the system varies with the torsional angle, $\Delta\phi$. If V_0 is the *torsional energy barrier*, i.e., the barrier height between a maximum and a minimum, then the variation in P.E., V_ϕ (the *torsional strain* or *Pitzer strain*) is given by the expression

$$V_\phi = \tfrac{1}{2}V_0(1 + n \cos \Delta\phi) \text{ kcal/mol} = 2\cdot1 V_0(1 + n \cos \Delta\phi) \text{ kJ/mol}$$

where n is the number of P.E. minima that occur in the rotation through 360°. This equation may be applied to molecules such as ethane (Fig. 2.10; $n = 3$).

Steric repulsion. This interaction between non-bonded atoms is also a function of the three parameters r, θ, and ϕ. These three may be replaced by a fourth parameter, ρ, the distance between non-bonded atoms, i.e., V_ρ, the *steric strain*, is estimated in terms of ρ.

It can therefore be seen that *molecular strain energy* is the sum of the four contributing factors, V_r, V_θ, V_ϕ, and V_ρ. Furthermore, since a molecule will normally be in the state corresponding to its lowest P.E., strain energy is thus the increase in energy which is produced by deviations of the parameters *from their most favourable values*. Unfortunately, it is not easy to estimate the various contributions, but even so, it may be possible to obtain approximate values which may be used in judging the stabilities of various conformations. It also appears that, in general, molecules are subject to very little linear deformations. This, however, is not the case when the transition state is entered by the molecule during reaction.

§5. Conventions used in stereochemistry

The original method of indicating enantiomers was to prefix each one by d or l according as it was dextrorotatory or laevorotatory. van't Hoff (1874) introduced a $+$ and $-$ notation for designating the configuration of an asymmetric carbon atom. He used mechanical models (built of tetrahedra), and the $+$ and $-$ signs were given by observing the tetrahedra of the mechanical model from the centre of the model. Thus a molecule of the type $CabdCabd$ may be designated $+ +$, $- -$, and $+ -$. E. Fischer (1891) pointed out that this $+$ and $-$ notation can lead to wrong interpretations when applied to molecules containing more than two asymmetric carbon atoms (the signs given to each asymmetric carbon atom depend on the point of observation in the molecule). Fischer therefore proposed the use of plane projection diagrams of the mechanical models instead of the $+$ and $-$ system. It is important to note here that the Fischer projection formulae are always those of the eclipsed conformations.

Fischer, working on the configurations of the sugars (see **7** §1), obtained the plane formulae (I) and (II) for the enantiomers of saccharic acid, and **arbitrarily** chose (I) for dextrorotatory saccharic acid, and called it d-saccharic acid. He then, from this, deduced formula (III) for d-glucose. Furthermore, Fischer thought it was more important to indicate stereochemical relationships than merely to indicate the actual direction of rotation. He therefore proposed that the **prefixes d and l should**

(I)   (II)   (III)

refer to stereochemical relationships and not to the direction of rotation of the compound. For this scheme to be self-consistent (among the sugars) it is necessary to choose *one* sugar as standard and then refer all the others to it. Fischer apparently intended to use the scheme whereby the compounds derived from *a given aldehyde sugar* should be designated according to the *direction of rotation of the parent aldose*.

Natural mannose is dextrorotatory. Hence natural mannose will be *d*-mannose, and all derivatives of *d*-mannose, *e.g.*, mannonic acid, mannitol, mannose phenylhydrazone, etc., will thus belong to the *d*-series. Natural glucose is dextrorotatory. Hence natural glucose will be *d*-glucose, and all its derivatives will belong to the *d*-series. Furthermore, Fischer (1890) converted natural mannose into natural glucose as follows:

$$d\text{-mannose} \rightarrow d\text{-mannonic acid} \rightarrow d\text{-mannolactone} \rightarrow d\text{-glucose}$$

Since natural glucose is *d*-glucose (according to Fischer's scheme), the prefix *d* for natural glucose *happens* to agree with its dextrorotation (with *d*-mannose as standard). Natural fructose can also be prepared from natural mannose (or natural glucose), and so will be *d*-fructose. Natural fructose, however, is laevorotatory, and so is written as *d*(−)-fructose, the symbol *d* indicating its *stereochemical* relationship to the parent aldose glucose, and the symbol − placed in parentheses before the name indicating the *actual direction of rotation*.

More recently the symbols *d* and *l* have been replaced by D and L for configurational relationships, *e.g.*, L(+)-lactic acid. Also, when dealing with compounds that cannot be referred to an arbitrarily chosen standard, (+)- and (−)- are used to indicate the sign of the rotation. The prefixes *dextro* and *laevo* (with hyphens) are also used.

Fischer's proposal to use *each aldose* as the arbitrary standard for its derivatives leads to some difficulties, *e.g.*, natural arabinose is dextrorotatory, and so is to be designated D-arabinose. Now natural arabinose (D-arabinose) can be converted into mannonic acid which, if D-arabinose is taken as the parent aldose, will therefore be D-mannonic acid. This same acid, however, can also be obtained from L-mannose, and so should be designated as L-mannonic acid. Thus in cases such as this the use of the symbol D or L will depend on the *historical order* in which the stereochemical relationships were established. This, obviously, is an unsatisfactory position, which was realised by Rosanoff (1906), who showed that if the enantiomers of glyceraldehyde (a molecule which contains only *one* asymmetric carbon atom) are chosen as the (arbitrary) standard, then a satisfactory system for correlating stereochemical relationships can be developed. He also proposed that the formula of dextrorotatory glyceraldehyde should be written as in Fig. 2.13(*c*), in order that the arrangement of its asymmetric carbon atom should agree with the arrangement of C_5 in Fischer's projection formula for natural glucose (see formula (III) above).

It is of great interest to note in this connection that in 1906 the active forms of glyceraldehyde had not been isolated, but in 1914 Wohl and Momber separated DL-glyceraldehyde into its enantiomers, and in 1917 they showed that dextrorotatory glyceraldehyde was stereochemically related to natural glucose, *i.e.*, with D(+)-glyceraldehyde as arbitrary standard, natural glucose is D(+)-glucose (see **7** §1).

The accepted convention for drawing D(+)-glyceraldehyde—the agreed (*arbitrary*) standard—is shown in Fig. 2.13(*a*). The tetrahedron is drawn so that three corners are imagined to be *above* the plane of the paper, and the fourth *below* the plane of the paper. Furthermore, the spatial arrangement of the four groups joined to the central carbon atom *must be placed as shown in Fig. 2.13(a)*, *i.e.*, **the accepted convention for drawing D(+)-glyceraldehyde places the hydrogen atom at the left and the hydroxyl group at the right, with the aldehyde group at the top corner.** Now imagine the tetrahedron to rotate about the horizontal line joining H and OH until it takes up the position shown in Fig. 2.12(*b*). This is the *conventional* position for a tetrahedron, groups joined to *full horizontal* lines being *above* the plane of the paper, and those joined to *broken vertical* lines being *below* the plane of the paper. The *conventional plane-diagram* is obtained by drawing the full horizontal and broken vertical lines of Fig. 2.13(*b*) as full lines, placing the groups as they appear in Fig. 2.13(*b*), and taking the asymmetric carbon atom to be at the point where the lines cross. Although Fig. 2.13(*c*) is a plane-diagram, it is most important to remember that horizontal lines represent groups above the plane, and vertical

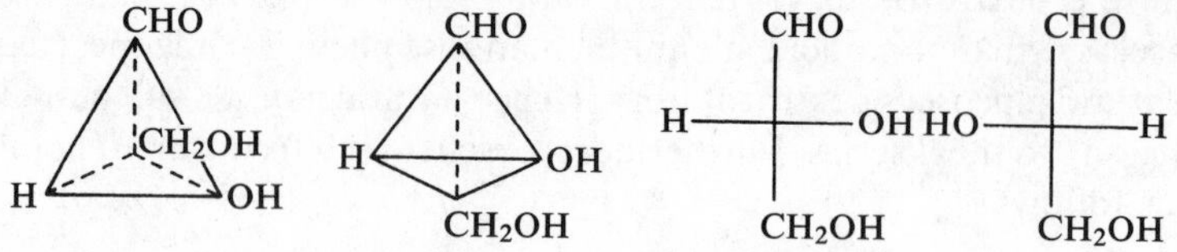

(*a*)   (*b*)   (*c*)   (*d*)

Fig. 2.13

lines groups below the plane of the paper. Many authors prefer to draw Fig. 2.13(*c*) [and Fig. 2.13(*d*)] with a *broken* vertical line. Fig. 2.13(*d*) represents the plane-diagram formula of L(−)-glyceraldehyde; here *the hydrogen atom is to the right and the hydroxyl group to the left*. Thus any compound that can be prepared from, or converted into, D(+)-glyceraldehyde will belong to the D-series. Similarly, any compound that can be prepared from, or converted into, L(−)-glyceraldehyde will belong to the L-series. When representing relative configurational relationships of molecules containing more than one asymmetric carbon atom, *the asymmetric carbon atom of glyceraldehyde is always drawn at the bottom*, the rest of the molecule being built up from this unit (but see below).

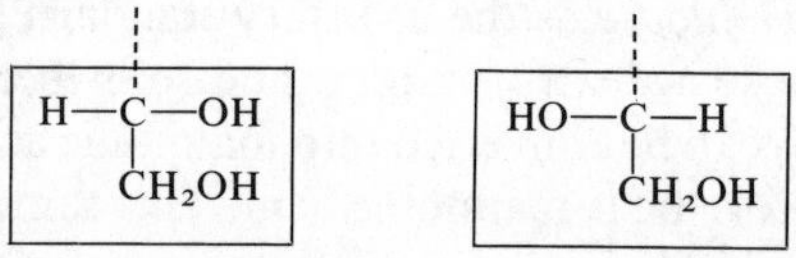

D-series   L-series

Thus we have a scheme of classification of *relative* configurations based on D(+)-glyceraldehyde as *arbitrary* standard. Even on this basis confusion is still possible in relating configurations to the standard (see later).

Until recently there was no way of determining, with certainty, the *absolute* configuration of molecules. *Arbitrary choice* makes the configuration of D(+)-glyceraldehyde have the hydrogen to the left and the hydroxyl to the right. Bijvoet *et al.* (1951), however, have shown by X-ray analysis of sodium rubidium tartrate that it is possible to differentiate between the two optically active forms, *i.e.*, it is possible to determine the *absolute* configuration of these two enantiomers. These authors showed that natural dextrorotatory tartaric acid has the configuration assigned to it by Fischer (who correlated its configuration with that of the saccharic acids). The configurations of the tartaric acids, however, are a troublesome problem. Fischer wrote the configuration of natural dextrorotatory tartaric acid as (IV). If we use the convention of writing the glyceraldehyde unit at the bottom, then

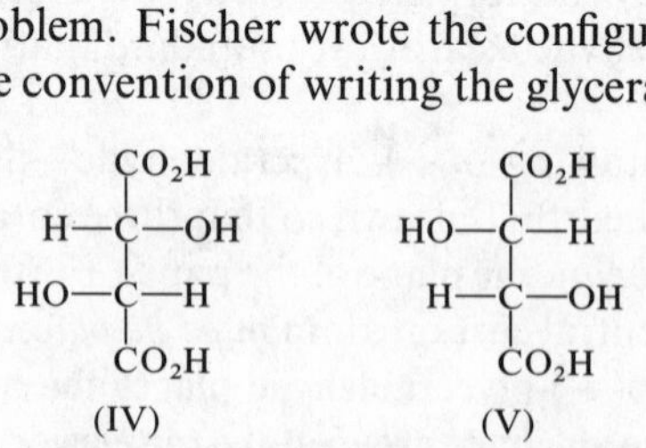

(IV)   (V)

(IV) is L(+)-tartaric acid and (V) is D(−)-tartaric acid. This relationship (to glyceraldehyde) is confirmed by the conversion of D(+)-glyceraldehyde into laevorotatory tartaric acid *via* the

Kiliani reaction (see Vol. I). Thus $(-)$-tartaric acid is $D(-)$-tartaric acid (V). On the other hand, $(+)$-tartaric acid can be converted into $D(-)$-glyceric acid, and so $(+)$-tartaric acid is $D(+)$-tartaric acid (IV). In this reduction of $(+)$-tartaric acid to $(+)$-malic acid (by hydriodic acid), it has been

$$
\begin{array}{ccc}
\underset{\text{D(+)-glyceraldehyde}}{\begin{array}{c} CHO \\ H-\underset{|}{\overset{|}{C_1}}-OH \\ CH_2OH \end{array}}
\xrightarrow{\text{HCN}}
\underset{\begin{array}{c} \\ \end{array}}{\begin{array}{c} CN \\ H-\underset{|}{\overset{|}{C_2}}-OH \\ H-\underset{|}{\overset{|}{C_1}}-OH \\ CH_2OH \end{array}}
+
\begin{array}{c} CN \\ HO-\underset{|}{\overset{|}{C_2}}-H \\ H-\underset{|}{\overset{|}{C_1}}-OH \\ CH_2OH \end{array}
\xrightarrow[\text{(ii) oxidation}]{\text{(i) hydrolysis}}
\underset{\begin{array}{c} meso\text{-tartaric} \\ \text{acid} \end{array}}{\begin{array}{c} CO_2H \\ H-\underset{|}{\overset{|}{C_2}}-OH \\ H-\underset{|}{\overset{|}{C_1}}-OH \\ CO_2H \end{array}}
+
\underset{\begin{array}{c} (-)\text{-tartaric} \\ \text{acid} \end{array}}{\begin{array}{c} CO_2H \\ HO-\underset{|}{\overset{|}{C_2}}-H \\ H-\underset{|}{\overset{|}{C_1}}-OH \\ CO_2H \end{array}}
\end{array}
$$

assumed that it is C_1 which has been reduced, *i.e.*, in *this* case the configuration of C_2 has been correlated with glyceraldehyde and not that of C_1 as in the previous set of reactions. Had, however, C_2 been reduced, then the final result would have been $(+)$-tartaric acid *still through the intermediate*,

$$
\underset{\text{(IV)}}{\begin{array}{c} CO_2H \\ H-\underset{|}{\overset{|}{C_2}}-OH \\ HO-\underset{|}{\overset{|}{C_1}}-H \\ CO_2H \end{array}}
\rightarrow
\underset{\begin{array}{c} (+)\text{-malic} \\ \text{acid} \end{array}}{\begin{array}{c} CO_2H \\ H-\underset{|}{\overset{|}{C_2}}-OH \\ CH_2 \\ CO_2H \end{array}}
\rightarrow
\underset{\begin{array}{c} (+)\text{-}\beta\text{-malamic} \\ \text{acid} \end{array}}{\begin{array}{c} CO_2H \\ H-\underset{|}{\overset{|}{C_2}}-OH \\ CH_2 \\ CONH_2 \end{array}}
\rightarrow
\underset{\begin{array}{c} (+)\text{-isoserine} \end{array}}{\begin{array}{c} CO_2H \\ H-\underset{|}{\overset{|}{C_2}}-OH \\ CH_2NH_2 \end{array}}
\rightarrow
\underset{\begin{array}{c} D(-)\text{-glyceric} \\ \text{acid} \end{array}}{\begin{array}{c} CO_2H \\ H-\underset{|}{\overset{|}{C_2}}-OH \\ CH_2OH \end{array}}
\leftarrow
\underset{\begin{array}{c} D(+)\text{-glyceraldehyde} \end{array}}{\begin{array}{c} CHO \\ H-\underset{|}{\overset{|}{C}}-OH \\ CH_2OH \end{array}}
$$

$(+)$-*malic acid* (two exchanges of groups give the same malic acid as before). Since $(+)$-malic acid has been correlated with $(+)$-glyceraldehyde (see §9a), $(+)$-tartaric acid should be designated $D(+)$-tartaric acid. The designation $L(+)$-tartaric acid is used by those chemists who regard this acid as a carbohydrate derivative (see also §5d).

$$
\underset{\text{(IV)}}{\begin{array}{c} CO_2H \\ H-\underset{|}{\overset{|}{C_2}}-OH \\ HO-\underset{|}{\overset{|}{C_1}}-H \\ CO_2H \end{array}}
\rightarrow
\underset{\begin{array}{c} (+)\text{-malic} \\ \text{acid} \end{array}}{\begin{array}{c} CO_2H \\ CH_2 \\ HO-\underset{|}{\overset{|}{C_1}}-H \\ CO_2H \end{array}}
\dashrightarrow
\underset{\begin{array}{c} D(-)\text{-glyceric} \\ \text{acid} \end{array}}{\begin{array}{c} CH_2OH \\ HO-\underset{|}{\overset{|}{C_1}}-H \\ CO_2H \end{array}}
$$

§5a. Correlation of configurations.

As we have seen (§5), since the relative configurations of $(+)$-tartaric acid and $(+)$-glyceraldehyde have been established, it is now possible to assign *absolute* configurations to many compounds whose relative configurations to $(+)$-glyceraldehyde are known, since the configurations assigned to them are actually the absolute configurations. The methods used for correlating configurations are:

(i) Chemical reactions without displacement at the chiral centre concerned (see §5b).

(ii) Chemical reactions with displacement at the chiral centre concerned (see the Walden inversion, **3** §§3, 4).

(iii) X-ray analysis (see §5).

(iv) Asymmetric inductive correlation (see asymmetric synthesis **7** §7).

(v) Optical rotations: (*a*) Monochromatic rotations (see §5c, and carbohydrates, **7** §6; steroids, **11** §5). (*b*) Rotatory dispersion (see steroids, **11** §5).

(vi) The study of quasi-racemic compounds (see §9a).

(vii) Enzyme studies.

The above methods normally apply to compounds containing *one* chiral centre. When several chiral centres are present, the usual procedure is to establish the stereochemistry of the centres relative to each other and then to correlate one of the centres with glyceraldehyde. It can also be seen that it is better still if it is possible to correlate more than one centre with glyceraldehyde.

Knowledge of absolute configurations is very valuable in the study of optical activity and the mechanisms of organic reactions. Also, it is considered necessary to know absolute configurations in order to obtain a complete understanding of biochemical processes.

§5b. **Correlation of configurations without displacement at the chiral centre concerned.**   Since no bond joined to the chiral centre is ever broken, this method is an extremely valuable method of correlation. Before discussing examples, the following point is worth noting. For amino-acids, natural ($-$)-serine, $HOCH_2CH(NH_2)CO_2H$, was chosen as the arbitrary standard. Thus correlation with glyceraldehyde was indicated by D_g or L_g, and with serine by D_s or L_s. These two standards have now been correlated, and it has been shown that $L_g = L_s$, *i.e.*, natural ($-$)-serine belongs to the L-series (with glyceraldehyde as absolute standard; see also **13** §4).

The following examples illustrate this method of correlation.

(i)

$$
\begin{array}{ccccccccc}
\text{CHO} & & \text{CO}_2\text{H} & & \text{CO}_2\text{H} & & \text{CO}_2\text{H} & & \text{CO}_2\text{H} \\
\text{HO}{-}\text{H} & \xrightarrow{\text{HgO}} & \text{HO}{-}\text{H} & \xleftarrow{\text{HNO}_2} & \text{HO}{-}\text{H} & \xrightarrow{\text{NOBr}} & \text{HO}{-}\text{H} & \xrightarrow{\text{Na/Hg}} & \text{HO}{-}\text{H} \\
\text{CH}_2\text{OH} & & \text{CH}_2\text{OH} & & \text{CH}_2\text{NH}_2 & & \text{CH}_2\text{Br} & & \text{CH}_3 \\
\text{L}(-)\text{-glyceraldehyde} & & \text{L}(+)\text{-glyceric} & & \text{L}(-)\text{-isoserine} & & \text{L-} & & \text{L}(+)\text{-lactic} \\
& & \text{acid} & & & & & & \text{acid}
\end{array}
$$

It can be seen from this example that change in the sign of rotation does not necessarily indicate a change in configuration.

(ii)

$$
\begin{array}{ccccccc}
\text{Me} & & \text{Me} & & \text{Me} & & \text{Me} \\
\text{HO}{-}\text{H} & \xrightarrow[\text{(ii) Na/EtOH}]{\text{(i) EtOH/HCl}} & \text{HO}{-}\text{H} & \xrightarrow{\text{HBr}} & \text{HO}{-}\text{H} & \xrightarrow[\text{(ii) hydrolysis}]{\text{(i) KCN}} & \text{HO}{-}\text{H} \\
\text{CO}_2\text{H} & & \text{CH}_2\text{OH} & & \text{CH}_2\text{Br} & & \text{CH}_2\text{CO}_2\text{H} \\
\text{D}(-)\text{-lactic} & & \text{D-} & & \text{D-} & & \text{D}(-)\text{-}\beta\text{-hydroxy-} \\
\text{acid} & & & & & & \text{butyric acid}
\end{array}
$$

(iii)

$$
\begin{array}{ccccccc}
\text{Me} & & \text{Me} & & \text{Me} & & \text{Me} \\
\text{H}{-}\text{OH} & \xrightarrow[\text{(ii) Na/EtOH}]{\text{(i) EtOH/HCl}} & \text{H}{-}\text{OH} & \xrightarrow{\text{HI}} & \text{H}{-}\text{OH} & \xrightarrow{\text{H}_2/\text{Pd}} & \text{H}{-}\text{OH} \\
\text{CH}_2\text{CO}_2\text{H} & & \text{CH}_2\text{CH}_2\text{OH} & & \text{CH}_2\text{CH}_2\text{I} & & \text{CH}_2\text{CH}_3 \\
\text{L}(+)\text{-}\beta\text{-hydroxy-} & & \text{L-} & & \text{L-} & & \text{L}(+)\text{-butan-2-ol} \\
\text{butyric acid} & & & & & &
\end{array}
$$

(iv) Another example is that in the terpene series (see **8** §23e).

(v) All the previous examples are acyclic or alicyclic compounds. When, however, the compound contains a phenyl group attached to the asymmetric carbon atom, correlation with glyceraldehyde is carried out either by breaking down the phenyl group, leaving only C_1 (usually as CO_2H) attached to the asymmetric carbon atom, or by building up a cyclohexane ring from C_1 (usually present as CO_2H), and preparing this compound by reduction of the original phenyl compound.

$$
\begin{array}{ccc}
\text{C}_1\text{O}_2\text{H} & \xleftarrow{\text{oxidation}} & \bigcirc\!\!-\!\text{(phenyl)} \\
\text{H}{-}\text{Y} & & \text{H}{-}\text{Y} \xrightarrow[\text{cat.}]{\text{H}_2} \text{H}{-}\text{Y} \\
\text{Z} & & \text{Z} \qquad\qquad \text{Z} \\
& \xrightarrow{\text{synthesis}} &
\end{array}
$$

An example of this method is the correlation of ($+$)-lactic acid with ($-$)-mandelic acid. Since the

former is L(+), the latter is therefore L(−). At the same time, (−)-phenylmethylmethanol is also
L(−).

$$\text{(+)-lactic acid} \qquad \text{(−)-}$$

§5c. **Correlations by use of monochromatic optical rotations.** A consequence of the Distance Rule
(**1** §9) is that molecular rotations of higher members of homologous series containing one chiral
centre tend to reach a limiting value or zero value, *e.g.*, long-chain fatty acids containing an α-methyl
group have molecular rotations which approach the value of ~28°. As the methyl group shifts
nearer to the centre of the chain, the molecular rotations get smaller and smaller.

   The application of the method of monochromatic optical rotations is based on the above generalisation. This may be restated as follows: If two compounds have the *same absolute configuration*,
then if their structures differ only at some distance from their chiral centres, the molecular rotations
have the same sign and have approximately the same magnitude, *e.g.*, acyclic secondary alcohols
with the formula shown in (I; $m > n$) are all dextrorotatory (for the sodium D-line).

A very interesting point about this generalisation is that deviations are most likely to occur when the structural difference involves the introduction of a group that absorbs in the near ultraviolet. Thus, the hydroxy-acids represented by (II), in which R = H, Me, Et, Pr, etc., are all laevorotatory, whereas when R = Ph, the acid is dextrorotatory.

§5d. Specification of absolute configurations.   Since the configuration of (+)-tartaric acid has been related to that of (+)-glyceraldehyde (§5), and since the absolute configuration of (+)-tartaric acid has been determined (§5), it is now possible to assign *absolute* configurations to many compounds whose relative configurations to (+)-glyceraldehyde are known. This raised the problem of using *one* system of specifying absolute configurations. Cahn *et al.* (1956, 1964) have proposed such a system and this is now widely used. Let us first consider the procedure for a molecule containing one asymmetric carbon atom (one chiral centre).

(i) The four groups are first ordered according to the **sequence rule**. According to this rule, the groups are arranged in *decreasing atomic number* of the atoms by which they are bound to the asymmetric carbon atom. If two or more of these atoms have the same atomic number, then the relative priority of the groups is determined by a similar comparison of the atomic numbers of the *next* atoms in the groups (*i.e.*, the atoms joined to the atom joined to the asymmetric carbon atom). If this fails, then the next atoms of the group are considered. Thus one works *outwards* from the asymmetric carbon atom until a selection can be made for the sequence of the groups.

When multiple bonds or rings are present, the procedure for determining priority is as follows. Both atoms attached to the multiple bond are considered to be duplicated (for a double bond) or triplicated (for a triple bond), *e.g.*,

$$-CH{=}CH- \;\equiv\; -\underset{\underset{C}{|}}{C}H-\underset{\underset{C}{|}}{C}H- \qquad\qquad -C{=}O \;\equiv\; -\overset{\overset{C}{|}}{\underset{\underset{O}{|}}{C}}{-}C$$

$$-\overset{\overset{H}{|}}{C}{=}O \;\equiv\; -\overset{\overset{H}{|}}{\underset{\underset{O}{|}}{C}}{-}C \qquad\qquad -C{\equiv}N \;\equiv\; -\overset{\overset{N\;\;C}{|}}{\underset{\underset{N\;\;C}{|}}{C}}{-}N$$

The priority sequence is then determined by consideration of the duplicated or triplicated 'structure' in which there are *phantom atoms*, *e.g.*, —CHO is —CH(O)—O(C) and —CH(OH)$_2$ is —CHOH—OH (the phantom atoms in the former are those in parentheses). Both groups contain a carbon atom joined to two oxygen atoms, but since C precedes H, —CHO precedes —CH(OH)$_2$ in priority.

Ring systems are treated as branched chains, and if unsaturated, then duplication is used for a double bond (or triplication for a triple bond). By using these rules, it can be shown that the order of priority sequence (for some of the common substituents) is: I, Br, Cl, SO$_3$H, SH, F, OCOR, OR, OH, NO$_2$, NR$_2$, NHR, NH$_2$, CO$_2$R, CO$_2$H, COR, CHO, CH$_2$OH, CN, Ph, CR$_3$, CHR$_2$, CH$_2$R, CH$_3$, D, H.

(ii) Next is determined whether the sequence describes a right- or left-handed pattern on the molecular model as viewed according to the **conversion rule**. When the four groups in the molecule C*abcd* have been ordered in the priority *a*, *b*, *c*, *d*, the conversion rule states that their spatial pattern shall be described as right- or left-handed according as the sequence *a* → *b* → c is clockwise or anticlockwise when viewed from an external point on the side *remote* from *d* (the group with the lowest priority), *e.g.*, (I) in Fig. 2.14 shows a right-handed (*i.e.*, clockwise) arrangement.

(iii) Absolute configuration labels are then assigned. The asymmetry leading under the sequence and conversion rules to a right- and left-handed pattern is indicated by R and S respectively (R; *rectus*, right; S; *sinister*, left).

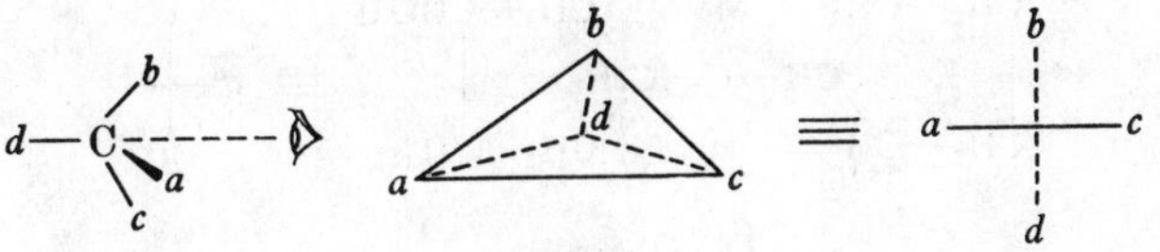

Fig. 2.14

Let us first consider bromochloroacetic acid (II). The priority of the groups according to the sequence rule is Br (a), Cl (b), CO_2H (c) and H (d). Hence by the conversion rule, (II) is the (R)-form ($a \to b \to c$ is clockwise).

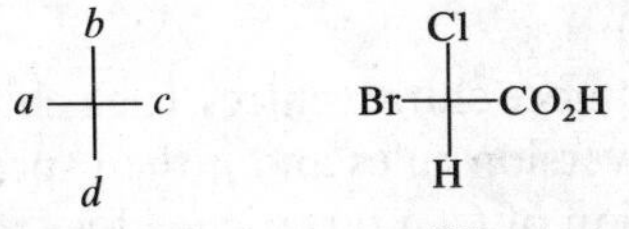

(II)

Now let us consider D(+)-glyceraldehyde. By *convention* it is drawn as (III) (this is also the *absolute* configuration). Reference to the sequence list gives the priority sequence: OH (a), CHO (b), CH_2OH (c), and H (d). Since the interchanging of two groups inverts the configuration, the sequence (III) $\to$ (IV) $\to$ (V) gives the *original* configuration. Since (V) corresponds to (VI), it thus follows that D(+)-glyceraldehyde is (R)-glyceraldehyde.

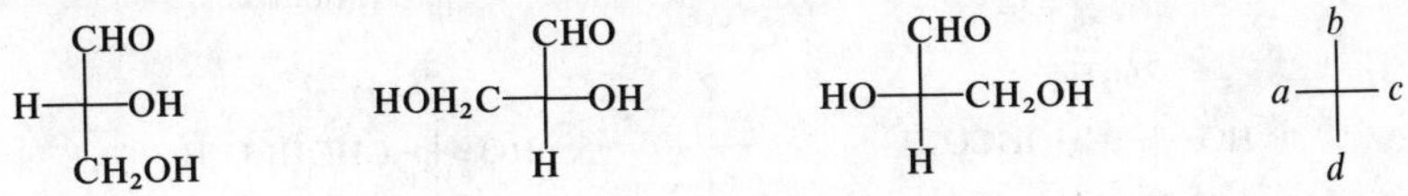

D(+)- L(−)- D(+)-
(III) (IV) (V) (VI)

This scheme can be applied to the deutero compound (VII), which is therefore the (R)-form.

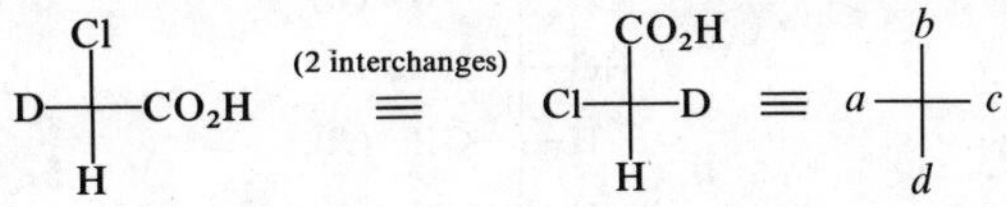

(VII)

On the other hand, (VIII) is the (S)-form, since $a \to b \to c$ is anticlockwise.

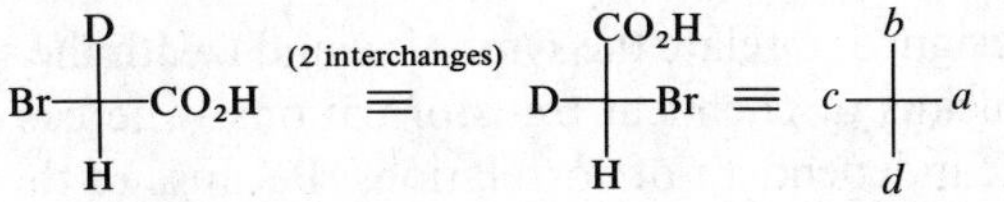

(VIII)

By reference to the sequence list above, it can be seen that (IX) is the (S)-form.

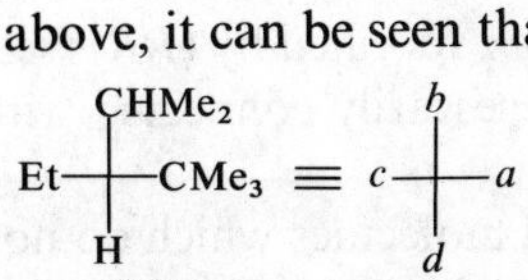

(IX)

Now let us consider some ring systems. As pointed out above, these systems are treated as branched chains, etc. Hence (X) is the (*S*)-form, since the CHOH group in the left-hand ring is reached before that in the right-hand ring.

$$CH_2—CH_2 \quad Me \quad CH_2—CHOH$$

$$CH—C—CH$$

$$CH_2—CH \quad H \quad CH_2—CH_2 \qquad \equiv \quad a—\!\!\!\!\begin{array}{c} c \\ | \\ | \\ d \end{array}\!\!\!\!—b$$

$$OH$$

(X)

The same procedure is used when the asymmetric carbon atom is in the ring, *e.g.*, (XI) is the (*S*)-form (see also **8** §23e).

$$\begin{array}{c} CH_2 \\ H_2C \qquad CF_2 \quad H \\ H_2C \qquad C \\ CH_2 \qquad Me \end{array} \qquad \begin{array}{c} a \\ | \\ C \cdots d \\ b \qquad c \end{array} \qquad \equiv \qquad b—\!\!\!\!\begin{array}{c} a \\ | \\ | \\ d \end{array}\!\!\!\!—c$$

(XI)

When a molecule contains two or more chiral centres, each chiral centre is assigned a configuration according to the sequence and conversion rules and is then specified with *R* or *S*, *e.g.*, (+)-tartaric acid. Thus the absolute configuration of (+)-tartaric acid is (*RR*)-tartaric acid:

$$\begin{array}{c} CO_2H \\ H—\!\!\!\!\begin{array}{c} | \\ 2 \\ | \end{array}\!\!\!\!—OH \\ CHOHCO_2H \end{array} \quad \equiv \quad \begin{array}{c} CO_2H \\ H—\!\!\!\!\begin{array}{c} | \\ 2 \\ | \end{array}\!\!\!\!—OH \\ HO—\!\!\!\!\begin{array}{c} | \\ 1 \\ | \end{array}\!\!\!\!—H \\ CO_2H \end{array} \quad \equiv \quad \begin{array}{c} CHOHCO_2H \\ HO—\!\!\!\!\begin{array}{c} | \\ 1 \\ | \end{array}\!\!\!\!—H \\ CO_2H \end{array}$$

||| (2 interchanges) ||| (2 interchanges)

$$\begin{array}{c} CO_2H \\ HO—\!\!\!\!\begin{array}{c} | \\ 2 \\ | \end{array}\!\!\!\!—CHOHCO_2H \\ H \end{array} \qquad \begin{array}{c} b \\ | \\ a—\!\!\!\!\begin{array}{c} \\ | \\ \end{array}\!\!\!\!—c \\ d \end{array} \qquad \begin{array}{c} CO_2H \\ HO—\!\!\!\!\begin{array}{c} | \\ 1 \\ | \end{array}\!\!\!\!—CHOHCO_2H \\ H \end{array}$$

In a similar way it can be demonstrated that D(+)-glucose has the absolute configuration shown.

$$\begin{array}{c} CHO \\ H—\!\!\!\!—OH \quad (R) \\ HO—\!\!\!\!—H \quad (S) \\ H—\!\!\!\!—OH \quad (R) \\ H—\!\!\!\!—OH \quad (R) \\ CH_2OH \end{array}$$

D(+)-glucose

The sequence rule was designed to relate the symbols D and L with the symbols *R* and *S*. However, D and L are obtained by means of chemical transformations, whereas *R* and *S* are derived from geometrical models and are independent of correlations. Because of this, *R* and *S* must be applied only to compounds whose absolute stereochemistry has been determined; they do not necessarily correlate chemical families, *e.g.*, (+)-tartaric acid, whether it be D or L (according to the method of correlation) has an *absolute configuration* specified by (*RR*) (see also **13** §4). It should be noted that in the same way as D and L are not necessarily connected with the direction of rotation, nor are *R* and *S*.

The absolute configurations of chiral molecules which do not contain asymmetric carbon atoms may also be specified by an extension of the system described above (see **5** §2a and **5** §6a).

§6. Elements of symmetry

The test of superimposing a formula (tetrahedral) on its mirror image definitely indicates whether the molecule is symmetric or not; it is asymmetric if the two forms are not superimposable. The most satisfactory way in which superimposability may be ascertained is to build up models of the molecule and its mirror image. Usually this is not convenient, and so, in practice, one determines whether the molecule possesses (i) a plane of symmetry, (ii) a centre of symmetry or (iii) an alternating axis of symmetry. If the molecule contains at least one of these elements of symmetry, the molecule is symmetric; if none of these elements of symmetry is present, the molecule is asymmetric.

It should be remembered that it is the Fischer projection formula that is normally used for inspection. As pointed out in §2, it is necessary, when dealing with conformations, to ascertain whether at least one of them has one or more elements of symmetry. If such a conformation can be drawn, then the compound is *not* optically active.

(i) **A plane of symmetry** divides a molecule in such a way that points (atoms or groups of atoms) on the one side of the plane form mirror images of those on the other side. This test may be applied to both solid (tetrahedral) and plane-diagram formulae, *e.g.*, the plane-formula of the *meso*-form of *CabdCabd* possesses a plane of symmetry; the other two, (+) and (−), do not (see also below).

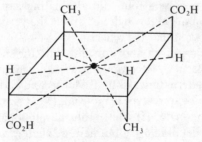

(ii) **A centre of symmetry** is a point from which lines, when drawn on one side and produced an equal distance on the other side, will meet identical points in the molecule. This test can be satisfactorily applied only to three-dimensional formulae, particularly those of ring systems, *e.g.*, 2,4-dimethylcyclobutane-1,3-dicarboxylic acid (Fig. 2.15). The form shown possesses a centre of symmetry which is the centre of the ring. This form is therefore optically inactive.

Fig. 2.15

Another example we shall consider here is dimethyldiketopiperazine; this molecule can exist in two geometrical isomeric forms, *cis* and *trans* (see also **4** §11c). The *cis*-isomer has no elements of symmetry and can therefore exist in two enantiomeric forms; both are known. The *trans*-isomer has a centre of symmetry and is therefore optically inactive.

It is important to note that only *even-membered* rings can possibly possess a centre of symmetry.

(iii) **Alternating axis of symmetry.** A molecule possesses an *n*-fold alternating axis of symmetry if, when rotated through an angle of 360°/*n* about this axis and then followed by reflection in a plane perpendicular to the axis, the molecule is indistinguishable from the original molecule. Let us consider the molecule shown in Fig. 2.16(*a*) [1,2,3,4-tetramethylcyclobutane]. This contains a four-fold

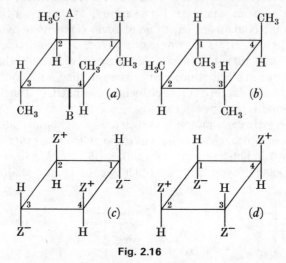

Fig. 2.16

alternating axis of symmetry. Rotation of (*a*) through 90° about axis **AB** which passes through the centre of the ring perpendicular to its plane gives (*b*), and reflection of (*b*) in the plane of the ring gives (*a*). It also happens that this molecule possesses two vertical planes of symmetry (through each diagonal of the ring), but if the methyl groups are replaced alternately by the chiral groups $(+)$—$CH(CH_3)C_2H_5$ and $(-)$—$CH(CH_3)C_2H_5$, represented by Z^+ and Z^- respectively, the resulting molecule (Fig. 2.16*c*) now has no planes of symmetry. Nevertheless, this molecule is *not* optically active since it does possess a four-fold alternating axis of symmetry [reflection of (*d*) (which is produced by rotation of (*c*) through 90° about the vertical axis) in the plane of the ring gives (*c*); it should be remembered that the reflection of a $(+)$-form is the $(-)$-form].

The cyclobutane derivative (*c*) given above to illustrate the meaning of an alternating axis of symmetry is an imaginary molecule. No compound was known in which the optical inactivity was due to the existence of *only* an alternating axis until McCasland and Proskow (1956) prepared such a molecule for the first time. This is a spiro-type of molecule (**5** §7), *viz*., 3,4,3′,4′-tetramethylspiro-(1,1′)-dipyrrolidinium *p*-toluenesulphonate, (I) (the *p*-toluenesulphonate ion has been omitted). This molecule is discussed in some detail in **6** §2a but here we shall examine it for its alternating axis of symmetry. Molecule (I) is superimposable on its mirror image and hence is not optically active. It does not contain a plane or centre of symmetry, but it does contain a four-fold alternating axis of symmetry. To show the presence of this axis, if (I) rotated through 90° about the co-axis of both rings, (II) is obtained. Reflection of (II) through the central plane (*i.e.*, through the N atom) perpendicular to this axis gives a molecule identical and coincident with (I).

McCasland *et al.* (1959) have now prepared a second compound, a pentaerythritol ester, whose optical inactivity can be attributed *only* to the presence of a four-fold alternating axis of symmetry (R = menthyl group; see **8** §16):

$$(-)-ROCH_2COOCH_2 \qquad CH_2OCOCH_2OR(-)$$
$$C$$
$$(+)-ROCH_2COOCH_2 \qquad CH_2OCOCH_2OR(+)$$

In practice one decides whether a molecule is symmetric or not by looking only for a plane or centre of symmetry, since no *natural* compound has yet been found to have an alternating axis of symmetry. The presence of two or more asymmetric carbon atoms will definitely give rise to optical isomerism, but nevertheless *some* isomers may not be optically active because these *molecules as a whole* are not asymmetric (see §7d).

Molecular symmetry.   In the above account, the test of determining whether a molecule is optically active has been to show the absence of the three elements of symmetry, (i), (ii), and (iii). We shall now consider this problem in some more detail. Symmetry problems are solved by mathematical methods known as **Group Theory**. A complete set of symmetry elements in any given molecule is known as a **point group**, i.e., a point group describes the type of symmetry to which the molecule belongs. A point group is one example of groups which form the basis of group theory.

The symmetry of a molecule can be completely described in terms of **symmetry elements**, and the operations carried out to ascertain the presence of symmetry elements are known as **symmetry operations**. The basic operations are *rotations* and *reflections*. A symmetry operation may be defined as an operation which results in the conversion of the molecule into an equivalent configuration, *i.e.*, the molecule obtained after the operation is indistinguishable from the original molecule. As far as molecules are concerned, a symmetry element is a point, line or plane with respect to which one or more symmetry operations are performed. There are four basic kinds of symmetry elements, and each of these is designated by a symbol which is also used to represent the corresponding symmetry operation.

Axis of symmetry (C_n). A C_n axis of symmetry is an axis about which the molecule can be rotated by $360°/n$ ($2\pi/n$ rad) and thereby produce a molecule indistinguishable from the original molecule (rotation is usually taken as clockwise). The subscript n indicates the *order* of the axis, *i.e.*, the largest value of n for which the rotation through $360°/n$ produces an equivalent configuration. Some values of n (for the vertical axis) are as shown.

$$C_2 \qquad C_3 \qquad C_\infty \qquad C_6 \qquad C_2$$

All *linear* molecules have a C_∞ axis; an equivalent configuration is always obtained whatever is the angle of rotation. Benzene possesses a C_6 axis perpendicular to the plane of the ring; it also has six C_2 axes in the plane of the ring. Ethylene has three C_2 axes, one collinear with the C—C double bond, the second perpendicular to the plane of the molecule and passing through the centre of the double, and the third perpendicular to the first two and passing through the centre of the double bond.

When the value of n is one, the axis is a C_1 axis. The C_1 symmetry operation is carried out by rotating the molecule through 360°. The result is a molecule identical with the original molecule. The C_1 axis is said to be a *trivial axis*; all molecules possess a trivial axis. Also, every molecule possesses an *identity of symmetry* (E), which is observed by an *identity operation* (E). The operation can be carried out in various ways, *e.g.*, by rotation through $360°$, *i.e.*, one identity element of symmetry is C_1, a trivial axis. Since, *e.g.*, C_3 represents the operation of rotation by $120°$ $(2\pi/3 \text{ rad})$ about the C_3 axis, repetition of this operation effects the overall rotation of $240°$ $(2 \times 2\pi/3 \text{ rad})$, and another repetition effects the overall rotation of $360°$ $(2\pi \text{ rad})$. Each result may be indicated by the symbol C_3, C_3^2, and C_3^3, respectively. At the end of the last operation, the molecule is identical with the original molecule. Hence $C_3^3 = E$.

The C_n axis is known as a *proper axis*; only one or more *rotations* about the axis are involved. When the molecule contains two or more axes of the same order, they are usually differentiated by superscript dashes, *e.g.*, C_2, C_2', and C_2'', etc. If two or more are equivalent, this is indicated by use of the same superscript dash, *e.g.*, C_2, two C_2', and two C_2''.

It is important to note that symmetry operations involving rotations are applied to the *whole* molecule. Since rotations of one part of the molecule with respect to another bring about changes in conformation (§4a), strictly speaking the application of symmetry operations is to molecular conformations and not to 'molecules'. This may be illustrated with ethylene dichloride (see Fig. 2.11). The staggered form has a centre of symmetry, but not the fully eclipsed form. Hence, the study of molecular symmetry is the study of the molecule in a *particular* conformation (see also §11).

Plane of symmetry (σ). This has been defined above [see (i)]. If we suppose that the plane of symmetry is in the xy plane (of the Cartesian co-ordinates x, y, z) then, after changing the sign of the z co-ordinate for each atom from z to $-z$, the configuration of the molecule is equivalent to that of the original molecule. It also follows that repetition of the operation σ results in the original molecule. Hence $\sigma^2 = E$. It might also be noted that the reflection plane contains a C_2 axis $(C_2^2 = E)$.

When the C_n axis with the largest order (n is the greatest) is regarded as being vertical (coincident with the z-axis), planes of symmetry which are also vertical are indicated by the subscript v, *i.e.*, σ_v. If the reflection plane is in the plane of the paper, this plane of symmetry is indicated by σ_v, and if it is perpendicular to the plane of the paper, then by σ_v'. When the reflection plane is horizontal (*i.e.*, in the xy plane; C_n axis coincident with the z-axis), the plane is represented as σ_h. When a reflection plane is diagonal, *i.e.*, bisects the angles between two equivalent axes, this is indicated by σ_d.

Centre of symmetry *(i)*. This has been defined above [see (ii)]. If we use the Cartesian co-ordinate system, it can be seen that if the molecule has a centre of symmetry, then changing the co-ordinates (x, y, z) of every atom, *with this centre as origin*, to $(-x, -y, -z)$ produces an equivalent configuration of the molecule. This operation, also denoted by i, is known as **inversion** and hence a *centre of symmetry* is also called a **centre of inversion**.

Alternating axis of symmetry (S_n). This has been defined above [see (iii)]. Since the operation S_n involves rotation followed by reflection, an *alternating axis of symmetry* is also called a **rotation-reflection axis of symmetry**. This type of axis is called an *improper axis*; two steps are involved: rotation first (about an axis) followed by reflection (the order of operations may be reversed without affecting the result).

From what has been said above, it can be shown that $S_1 \equiv \sigma$ and $S_2 \equiv i$. The cyclobutane and spiro-N-compounds described have an S_4 axis. In this case, there is neither a plane nor a centre of symmetry present.

As we have seen, if a molecule is not superimposable on its mirror image, that molecule can exhibit optical activity. Such molecules are (*a*) asymmetric; these are completely devoid of any symmetry elements (except a trivial axis); or (*b*) dissymmetric; these have proper axes but no improper axis. It therefore follows that if a molecule has an S_n axis, that molecule is not optically active, whereas if it has no S_n axis, that molecule is optically active. Alternatively, if a C_n axis is the only symmetry element present in a molecule, that molecule is optically active.

Of all the possible point groups (see above), those of C_n and D_n contain only proper axes of rotation as their symmetry element. Hence, only molecules belonging to these groups are capable of exhibiting optical activity. For our purpose, we may define a C_n point group as one which contains the symmetry element C_n. A D_n point group is one which contains the symmetry elements C_n and n C_2 axes. The C_2 axes are all perpendicular to the C_n axis and make equal angles with each other. The D_n point group is also known as *dihedral symmetry* (n is the principal axis). All other point groups contain at least one of the symmetry elements S_n, σ, or i, *e.g.*, an S_n point group contains the symmetry element S_n, a C_{nv} point group contains a C_n axis of symmetry and *nσ* planes of symmetry, all of which contain C_n.

§7. The number of isomers in optically active compounds

The number of optical isomers that can theoretically be derived from a molecule containing one or more chiral centres is of fundamental importance in stereochemistry.

§7a. Compounds containing one chiral centre. With the molecule $Cabde$ only two optical isomers are possible, and these are related as object and mirror image, *i.e.*, there is one pair of enantiomers, *e.g.*, D- and L-lactic acid. If we examine an *equimolecular* mixture of dextrorotatory and laevorotatory lactic acids, we shall find that the mixture is optically inactive. This is to be expected, since enantiomers have equal but opposite rotatory power. Such a mixture (of equimolecular amounts) is said to be **optically inactive by external compensation**, and is known as a **racemic modification** (see also §9); it is designated as r-, ($\pm$)- or DL-, *e.g.*, r-tartaric acid, ($\pm$)-limonene, DL-lactic acid.

Thus a compound containing *one* chiral centre can exist in *three* forms: ($+$), ($-$) and ($\pm$).

Conversion of molecule Ca_2bd into $Cabde$. Let us consider as an example the bromination of propionic acid to give α-bromopropionic acid.

$$CH_3CH_2CO_2H \xrightarrow{Br_2/P} CH_3CHBrCO_2H$$

(II) and (III) (Fig. 2.17) are enantiomorphs, and since molecule (I) is symmetrical about its vertical axis, it can be anticipated from the theory of probability that either hydrogen atom should be replaced equally well to give ($\pm$)-α-bromopropionic acid. This actually does occur in practice.

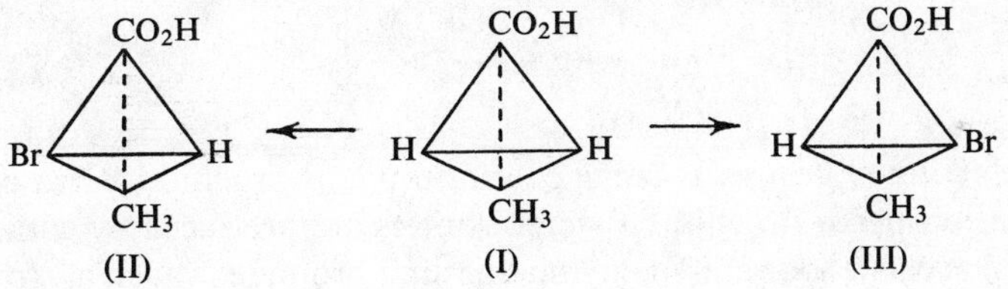

Fig. 2.17

From what has been said above, it would appear that the two hydrogen atoms in (I) are alike. This is certainly true for their behaviour towards bromine, but the point to note is that a pair of enantiomers was produced, *i.e.*, replacement of one or the other hydrogen does not produce the *same* molecule. These two hydrogen atoms are therefore said to be **enantiotopic**. This term may be defined as follows: Two atoms or groups in a molecule are enantiotopic if replacement of each in turn by some other group leads to a pair of enantiomers. The case of propionic acid is an example of enantiotopic groups by *internal comparison*, *i.e.*, the two groups are in the *same* molecule. There are also enantiotopic groups by *external comparison*. Enantiotopic groups of this type are corresponding atoms or groups in a pair of enantiomers, *e.g.*, the two methyl groups or bromine atoms in (II) and (III) are enantiotopic. If separate replacement produces the *same* molecule, the atoms or groups are said to be **homotopic**.

Prochirality. If a centre in a molecule bears enantiotopic groups, that centre is said to be **prochiral**. Alternatively, a molecule that contains enantiotopic groups is prochiral, and *vice versa*. Thus, the carbon atom in (I) is prochiral since replacement of one hydrogen atom by bromine produces a chiral centre (§3a). Also, the prefix *pro* is used to designate a hydrogen (or any ligand) attached to a prochiral centre and the two enantiotopic hydrogens (or ligands) are distinguished by use of the symbols R and S. The symbol to be used is determined by the specification of the chiral molecule produced by replacing a hydrogen atom by deuterium, *e.g.*,

$$
\begin{array}{ccc}
\underset{\text{(I)}}{\overset{\displaystyle CO_2H}{\underset{\displaystyle CH_3}{H-\!\!\!\!\!\mid\!\!\!\!\!-H}}}
\longrightarrow
\underset{\text{(Ia)}}{\overset{\displaystyle CO_2H}{\underset{\displaystyle CH_3}{D-\!\!\!\!\!\mid\!\!\!\!\!-H}}}
\equiv
\overset{\displaystyle a}{\underset{\displaystyle b}{c-\!\!\!\!\!\mid\!\!\!\!\!-d}}
\equiv
\underset{\text{(S)}}{\overset{\displaystyle b}{\underset{\displaystyle d}{c-\!\!\!\!\!\mid\!\!\!\!\!-a}}}
\qquad
\underset{\text{(Ib)}}{\overset{\displaystyle CO_2H}{\underset{\displaystyle CH_3}{H_S-\!\!\!\!\!\mid\!\!\!\!\!-H_R}}}
\end{array}
$$

The hydrogen replaced in (I) to give (Ia) is therefore *pro-S*-hydrogen, and consequently the other prochiral hydrogen is *pro-R*-hydrogen. This may be indicated by writing the formula of (I) as (Ib).

Nuclei which experience equal magnetic shielding have identical chemical shifts; such nuclei are said to be *isochronous*. Thus, chemically equivalent protons are isochronous, but so are enantiotopic (prochiral) protons, since these also experience equal magnetic shielding, *i.e.*, the signals have the same chemical shifts. However, if dissolved in chiral solvents, then the chemical shifts of enantiotopic (prochiral) protons in a compound may be different.

As we have seen, when (I) reacts with bromine, the pair of enantiomers (II) and (III) are formed in equal amounts. This is due to the fact that when enantiotopic (prochiral) groups react with an achiral reagent, the transition states involved have *equal* energy contents. On the other hand, if the reagent is chiral, the transition states are diastereoisomeric (see also §7b). Since these have *different* energy contents, the two rates of reaction are different, thereby resulting in the formation of a pair of enantiomers in *unequal* amounts. This may be illustrated by the oxidation of ethanol with the enzyme *alcohol dehydrogenase*; only *one* of the two enantiotopic (prochiral) hydrogen atoms is removed to form acetaldehyde. This may be formulated as shown, and it should be noted that the product in this case is not optically active.

$$
\overset{\displaystyle Me}{\underset{\displaystyle OH}{H-\!\!\!\!\!\mid\!\!\!\!\!-H}}
\;\xrightarrow{\text{enzyme}}\;
\overset{\displaystyle Me}{\underset{\displaystyle O}{H-\overset{\textstyle |}{\underset{\textstyle \parallel}{C}}}}
$$

In addition to referring to groups as being enantiotopic or prochiral, *faces* of double bonds are also said to be enantiotopic or prochiral if stereoisomers are produced by addition reactions, *e.g.*, the reaction between acetaldehyde and phenylmagnesium bromide (attack at 'front' and at 'back'):

$$
\underset{O}{\overset{H\quad Me}{\diagdown C \diagup}}
\;\xrightarrow{PhMgBr}\;
\underset{OH}{\overset{Ph}{Me-\!\!\!\!\!\mid\!\!\!\!\!-H}}
+
\underset{Ph}{\overset{OH}{Me-\!\!\!\!\!\mid\!\!\!\!\!-H}}
$$

$$
\text{'front'} \qquad\qquad \text{'back'}
$$

For the purpose of naming the enantiotopic or prochiral faces, the sequence rule (§5d) is used in two dimensions.

$$
\underset{a}{\overset{b\quad c}{\diagdown C \diagup}}
\qquad\qquad
\underset{a}{\overset{c\quad b}{\diagdown C \diagup}}
$$

$$
\textit{re}\text{-face} \qquad\qquad \textit{si}\text{-face}
$$

If the order of precedence is $a > b > c$, then, if the groups are in a clockwise arrangement, that face is called *re* (*rectus*), and if in an anticlockwise arrangement, *si* (*sinister*).

This nomenclature may be extended to the ethylenic double bond, *each end of the double bond being treated separately*, *e.g.*,

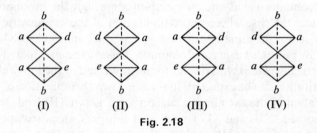

§7b. **Compounds containing two different chiral centres.** When we examine the molecule $CabdCabe$, *e.g.*, α,β-dibromobutyric acid, $CH_3CHBrCHBrCO_2H$, we find that there are *four* possible spatial arrangements for this type of molecule (Fig. 2.18). (I) and (II) are enantiomers (the configurations of *both* asymmetric carbons are reversed), and an equimolecular mixture of them forms a racemic modification; similarly for (III) and (IV). Thus there are six forms in all for a compound of the type $CabdCabe$: two pairs of enantiomers and two racemic modifications.

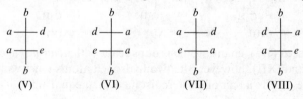

Fig. 2.18

(I) and (III) are not identical in configuration and are not mirror images (the configuration of *one* of the two asymmetric carbon atoms is reversed); they are known as **diastereoisomers**, *i.e.*, they are optical isomers but not enantiomers (mirror images; but see also 4 §4). Diastereoisomers differ in physical properties such as melting point, density, solubility, dielectric constant and specific rotation. Chemically they are similar, but their rates of reaction with other optically active compounds are different (see below). The mass spectra of diastereoisomers may exhibit differences (*cf.* enantiomers, §2). These differences are usually too small to be significant for acyclic diastereoisomers; this is believed to be due mainly to the fact that these molecules are capable of free rotation about the single bonds joined to the chiral centres. On the other hand, the mass spectra of alicyclic diastereoisomers may differ to such an extent that it may be possible to deduce the stereochemistry of each diastereoisomer from its mass spectrum.

The NMR spectra of diastereoisomers are also different (see below).

The plane-diagrams of molecules (I–IV) (Fig. 2.18) will be (V–VIII), respectively, as shown. It

b	b	b	b
a——d	d——a	a——d	d——a
a——e	e——a	e——a	a——e
b	b	b	b
(V)	(VI)	(VII)	(VIII)

should be remembered that groups joined to horizontal lines lie above the plane of the paper, and those joined to vertical lines lie below the plane of the paper (§5).

Instead of writing down all the possible configurations, the number of optical isomers for a compound of the type $CabdCabe$ may be obtained by indicating the *configuration* of each asymmetric carbon atom by the symbol $+$ or $-$, or by D or L; thus;

$$+ \quad - \quad + \quad - \qquad\qquad D_1 \quad L_1 \qquad D_1 \quad L_1$$
$$\text{or}$$
$$+ \quad - \qquad - \quad + \qquad\qquad D_2 \quad L_2 \qquad L_2 \quad D_2$$
$$\underbrace{}_{(\pm)} \qquad \underbrace{}_{(\pm)} \qquad\qquad \underbrace{}_{DL} \qquad \underbrace{}_{DL}$$

Pairs of enantiomers of the type $CabdCabe$ are distinguished by the prefixes *erythro* and *threo*. The former is the one in which the identical groups can eclipse each other (*a,a* and *b,b*) in one conformation, whereas the latter is the one in which this cannot be done. These names are derived from erythrose and threose, the tetrose sugars (see 7 §1). For the relative stabilities of the diastereoisomers, see §4a.

Conversion of molecule Ca_2bCabe into $CabdCabe$. Let us consider the bromination of β-methyl-valeric acid to give α-bromo-β-methylvaleric acid.

$$CH_3CH_2CH(CH_3)CH_2CO_2H \xrightarrow{\ Br_2/P\ } CH_3CH_2CH(CH_3)CHBrCO_2H$$

β-Methylvaleric acid contains *one* asymmetric carbon atom, but the bromine derivative contains *two*. Let us first consider the case where the configuration of the asymmetric carbon atom in the starting material is D_1 (IX). Bromination of this will produce molecules (X) and (XI); these are diastereoisomers and are produced in *unequal* amounts. This is to be anticipated; the two α-hydrogen atoms are not symmetrically placed with respect to the lower half of the molecule, and consequently different rates of substitution can be expected. In the same way, bromination of the starting material in which the configuration of the asymmetric carbon atom is L_1 (XII) leads to the formation of a mixture of diastereoisomers (XIII and XIV) in unequal amounts. One can expect, however, that the amount of (XIII) produced from (XII) would be the same as that of (X) from (IX) since, in both

cases, the positions of the bromine atoms with respect to the methyl group are the same. Similarly, the amount of (XIV) from (XII) will be the same as that of (XI) from (IX). Thus bromination of $(\pm)$-β-methylvaleric acid will result in a mixture of four bromo derivatives which will consist of two racemic modifications in unequal amounts, and the mixture will be optically inactive.

As we have already seen (§7a), enantiotopic groups react with *achiral* reagents at the *same* rates. In the molecules (IX) and (XII), however, the two hydrogen atoms react with bromine, an achiral reagent, at *different* rates to give a pair of diastereoisomers in unequal amounts. These two hydrogen atoms are therefore said to be **diastereotopic**. This term may be defined as follows: Two atoms or groups in a molecule are diastereotopic if replacement of each in turn by some other group leads to a pair of diastereoisomers. The molecule we have discussed is an example of diastereotopic groups by *internal comparison*, *i.e.*, the two groups are in the *same* molecule. On the other hand, corresponding groups in a pair of diastereoisomers are said to be diastereotopic by *external comparison* (see also §10a).

The term *diastereotopic faces* may be used with respect to the faces of a double bond when one of the groups attached to the unsaturated carbon atom contains a chiral centre.

A centre in a molecule which bears diastereotopic groups is also said to be prochiral (*cf.* §7a), and the term 'heterotopic' has been used to describe atoms or groups which are not homotopic (§7a) without differentiation being made whether the atoms or groups are enantiotopic or diastereotopic.

For enantiotopic groups, the transition states for reactions with achiral reagents have the same energy contents, but for reactions with chiral reagents, the transition states are diastereoisomeric and the energy contents are different (§7a). For diastereotopic groups, the transition states with *both* achiral and chiral reagents are diastereoisomeric and consequently the diastereoisomeric products are formed in unequal amounts.

Protons in diastereotopic groups show different chemical shifts (since their environments are different). Such protons are said to be *anisochronous*, *i.e.*, the signals do not have the same chemical shifts. These different chemical shifts are exhibited whether the solvent is chiral or achiral (*cf.* enantiotopic groups, §7a).

§7c. Compounds containing three chiral centres.   A molecule of this type is $CabdCabCabe$, *e.g.*, the pentoses, and the number of optical isomers possible is *eight* (four pairs of enantiomers):

$$
\begin{array}{cc@{\qquad}cc@{\qquad}cc@{\qquad}cc}
D_1 & L_1 & D_1 & L_1 & D_1 & L_1 & L_1 & D_1 \\
D_2 & L_2 & D_2 & L_2 & L_2 & D_2 & D_2 & L_2 \\
D_3 & L_3 & L_3 & D_3 & D_3 & L_3 & D_3 & L_3 \\
\underbrace{\qquad}_{DL} & & \underbrace{\qquad}_{DL} & & \underbrace{\qquad}_{DL} & & \underbrace{\qquad}_{DL} &
\end{array}
$$

All the cases discussed so far are examples of a series of compounds which contain n *structurally distinct* carbon atoms, *i.e.*, they belong to the series $Cabd(Cab)_{n-2}Cabe$. In general, if there are n asymmetric carbon atoms in the molecule (of this series), then there will be 2^n optically active forms and 2^{n-1} resolvable forms (*i.e.*, 2^{n-1} pairs of enantiomers). These formulae also apply to *monocyclic* compounds containing n different asymmetric carbon atoms; they may or may not apply to *fused ring systems* since spatial factors may play a part in the possible existence of various configurations (see, *e.g.*, camphor, **8** §23a).

§7d. Compounds of the type $Cabd(Cab)_xCabd$.   In compounds of this type the two *terminal* asymmetric carbon atoms are *similar*, and the number of optically active forms possible depends on where x is *odd* or *even*.

(i) Even series. (a) $CabdCabd$, *e.g.*, tartaric acid. In a compound of this type the rotatory power of each asymmetric carbon atom is the same. Now let us consider the number of optical isomers possible.

$$
\begin{array}{cccc}
D & L & D & L \\
D & L & L & D \\
(I) & (II) & (III) & (IV)
\end{array}
$$

In molecules (I) and (II), the upper and lower halves reinforce each other; hence (I), as a whole, has the dextro- and (II) the laevo-configuration, *i.e.*, (I) and (II) are optically active, and enantiomeric.

On the other hand, in (III) the two halves are in opposition, and so the molecule, *as a whole*, will not show optical activity. It is also obvious that (III) and (IV) are identical, *i.e.*, there is only *one* optically inactive form of *CabdCabd*. Molecule (III) is said to be **optically inactive by internal compensation**, and is known as the **meso-form**, and is a diastereoisomer of the pair of enantiomers (I) and (II). The *meso*-form is also known as the *inactive* form and has been represented as the *i*-form; **the meso form cannot be resolved** (see also §10). Thus there are four forms possible for the molecule *CabdCabd*: one pair of enantiomers, one racemic modification and one *meso*- (*i*-) form. These forms for tartaric acid are:

$$
\begin{array}{ccc}
\text{CO}_2\text{H} & \text{CO}_2\text{H} & \text{CO}_2\text{H} \\
\text{HO}\!-\!\!-\!\text{H} & \text{H}\!-\!\!-\!\text{OH} & \text{H}\!-\!\!-\!\text{OH} \\
\text{H}\!-\!\!-\!\text{OH} & \text{HO}\!-\!\!-\!\text{H} & \text{H}\!-\!\!-\!\text{OH} \\
\text{CO}_2\text{H} & \text{CO}_2\text{H} & \text{CO}_2\text{H} \\
\text{L-} & \text{D-} & meso\text{-}(i\text{-})
\end{array}
$$

- - - - - - - plane of symmetry

$\underbrace{\hspace{4cm}}_{\text{DL-}}$

Inspection of these formulae shows that the D- and L- forms do not possess any elements of symmetry; the *meso*-form, however, possesses a plane of symmetry.

(b) *CabdCabCabCabd*, *e.g.*, saccharic acid,

$$\text{HO}_2\text{CCHOHCHOHCHOHCHOHCO}_2\text{H}$$

The rotatory powers of the two terminal asymmetric carbon atoms are the same, and so are those of the middle two (the rotatory powers of the latter are almost certainly different from those of the former; equality would be fortuitous). The possible optical isomers are as follows (V–XIV):

D_1	L_1	D_1	L_1	D_1	L_1	D_1	L_1	D_1	D_1
D_2	L_2	L_2	D_2	D_2	L_2	D_2	L_2	D_2	L_2
D_2	L_2	L_2	D_2	D_2	L_2	L_2	D_2	L_2	D_2
D_1	L_1	D_1	L_1	L_1	D_1	D_1	L_1	L_1	L_1
(V)	(VI)	(VII)	(VIII)	(IX)	(X)	(XI)	(XII)	(XIII)	(XIV)

$\underbrace{\hspace{2cm}}_{\text{DL}}$ $\underbrace{\hspace{2cm}}_{\text{DL}}$ $\underbrace{\hspace{2cm}}_{\text{DL}}$ $\underbrace{\hspace{2cm}}_{\text{DL}}$ *meso*-forms

Molecules (V) and (VI) are optically active (enantiomeric) and are not 'internally compensated'; (VII) and (VIII) are optically active (enantiomeric) and are not 'internally compensated'; (IX) and (X) are optically active (enantiomeric) but are 'internally compensated at the ends'; (XI) and (XII) are optically active (enantiomeric) but are 'internally compensated in the middle'; (XIII) and (XIV) are *meso*-forms and are optically inactive by (complete) internal compensation. Thus there are eight optically active forms (four pairs of enantiomers), and two *meso*-forms.

In general, in the series of the type $Cabd(Cab)_{n-2}Cabd$, if n is the number of asymmetric carbon atoms and n is *even*, then there will be 2^{n-1} optically active forms, and $2^{(n-2)/2}$ *meso*-forms.

(ii) Odd series. (*a*) *CabdCabCabd*, *e.g.*, trihydroxyglutaric acid. If the two terminal asymmetric carbon atoms have the same configuration, then the central carbon atom has two identical groups joined to it and hence cannot be asymmetric. If the two terminal configurations are opposite, then the central carbon atom has apparently four different groups attached to it (the two ends are mirror images and not superimposable). Thus the central carbon atom becomes asymmetric, but at the same time the two terminal atoms 'compensate internally' to make the *molecule as a whole* symmetric (there is now a plane of symmetry), and consequently the compound is not optically active. In this molecule the central carbon atom is said to be *pseudo-asymmetric*, and is designated 'D' and 'L' (or ⊕ and ⊖ if the + and − convention is used; §7b). There will, however, be *two meso*-forms since the pseudo-asymmetric carbon atom can have two different configurations (see XV–XVIII). Thus there are five forms in all: two optically active forms (enantiomers), one racemic modification, and

$$
\begin{array}{c}
Cabd \\
| \\
Cab \\
| \\
Cabd
\end{array}
\quad
\begin{array}{cccc}
\text{D} & \text{L} & \text{D} & \text{D} \\
 & & \text{---'D'----'L'---} & \\
\text{D} & \text{L} & \text{L} & \text{L} \\
\end{array}
\quad
\begin{array}{l}
\textit{plane of} \\
\textit{symmetry}
\end{array}
$$

$$
\underbrace{\text{(XV) (XVI)}}_{\text{DL}} \quad \underset{\textit{meso} \ \ \textit{meso}}{\text{(XVII) (XVIII)}}
$$

two *meso*-forms. The following are the corresponding trihydroxyglutaric acids, all of which are known.

$$
\begin{array}{cccc}
\underset{\text{D}}{
\begin{array}{c}
\text{CO}_2\text{H} \\
\text{HO——H} \\
\text{H——OH} \\
\text{H——OH} \\
\text{CO}_2\text{H}
\end{array}}
&
\underset{\text{L}}{
\begin{array}{c}
\text{CO}_2\text{H} \\
\text{H——OH} \\
\text{HO——H} \\
\text{HO——H} \\
\text{CO}_2\text{H}
\end{array}}
&
\underset{\textit{meso}}{
\begin{array}{c}
\text{CO}_2\text{H} \\
\text{H——OH} \\
\text{H——OH} \\
\text{H——OH} \\
\text{CO}_2\text{H}
\end{array}}
&
\underset{\textit{meso}}{
\begin{array}{c}
\text{CO}_2\text{H} \\
\text{H——OH} \\
\text{HO——H} \\
\text{H——OH} \\
\text{CO}_2\text{H}
\end{array}}
\end{array}
$$

Inspection of the structure of the trihydroxyglutaric acid shows that the four groups attached to the pseudo-asymmetric carbon atoms are of two types in pairs: one pair consists of two different groups which are achiral (H and OH), and the other pair consists of two groups which are enantiomeric ($-\text{CHOHCO}_2\text{H}$). These are the characteristics of a pseudo-asymmetric carbon atom, *i.e.*, the molecule is of the type $Cabd\underset{\text{D L}}{d}$ (see also below).

(*b*) *CabdCabCabCabCabd*. In this molecule the central carbon atom is pseudo-asymmetric when the left-hand side of the molecule has the opposite configuration to that of the right-hand side; the central carbon atom is symmetrical when both sides have the same configuration. In all other cases the central carbon atom is asymmetric, the molecule now containing five asymmetric carbon atoms. The following table shows that there are *sixteen* optical isomers possible, of which twelve are optically active (six pairs of enantiomers), and four are *meso*-forms.

Ends with opposite configurations

$$
\begin{array}{cccc}
\text{D}_1 & \text{D}_1 & \text{D}_1 & \text{D}_1 \\
\text{D}_2 & \text{D}_2 & \text{L}_2 & \text{L}_2 \\
\text{'D'} & \text{'L'} & \text{'D'} & \text{'L'} \\
\text{L}_2 & \text{L}_2 & \text{D}_2 & \text{D}_2 \\
\text{L}_1 & \text{L}_1 & \text{L}_1 & \text{L}_1 \\
\textit{meso} & \textit{meso} & \textit{meso} & \textit{meso}
\end{array}
$$

Note the characteristics of the pseudo-asymmetric carbon atom (the central one): two different achiral groups (*a* and *b*) and two enantiomeric groups in pairs (D_1D_2, L_1L_2; D_1L_2, L_1D_2) [see above in (*a*)].

Ends with the same configurations

$$
\begin{array}{cccc}
\text{D}_1 & \text{L}_1 & \text{D}_1 & \text{L}_1 \\
\text{D}_2 & \text{L}_2 & \text{L}_2 & \text{D}_2 \\
 & & & \\
\text{D}_2 & \text{L}_2 & \text{L}_2 & \text{D}_2 \\
\text{D}_1 & \text{L}_1 & \text{D}_1 & \text{L}_1 \\
\underbrace{}_{\text{DL}} & & \underbrace{}_{\text{DL}} &
\end{array}
$$

Molecule with five asymmetric carbon atoms

D_1	L_1		D_1	L_1		D_1	L_1		D_1	L_1
D_2	L_2		D_2	L_2		D_2	L_2		D_2	L_2
D	L		L	D		D	L		L	D
D_2	L_2		D_2	L_2		L_2	D_2		L_2	D_2
L_1	D_1		L_1	D_1		D_1	L_1		D_1	L_1
⎵ DL			⎵ DL			⎵ DL			⎵ DL	

In general, in the series of the type $Cabd(Cab)_{n-2}Cabd$, if n is the number of 'asymmetric' carbon atoms and n is *odd*, then there will be 2^{n-1} optical isomers, of which $2^{(n-1)/2}$ are *meso*-forms and the remainder optically active forms.

§8. The racemic modification

The racemic modification is an equimolecular mixture of a pair of enantiomers, and it may be pre-pared in several ways.

(i) Mixing of equimolecular proportions of enantiomers produces the racemic modification.

(ii) Synthesis of chiral compounds from achiral compounds always results in the formation of the racemic modification. This statement is true only if the reaction is carried out in the absence of other optically active compounds or circularly polarised light (see asymmetric synthesis, 3 §7).

(iii) **Racemisation.** The process of converting an optically active compound into the racemic modification is known as **racemisation**. The $(+)$- and $(-)$-forms of most compounds are capable of racemisation under the influence of heat, light or chemical reagents. Which agent is used depends on the nature of the compound, and at the same time the ease of racemisation also depends on the nature of the compound, *e.g.*,

(*a*) Some compounds racemise so easily that they cannot be isolated in the optically active forms.

(*b*) A number of compounds racemise spontaneously when isolated in optically active forms.

(*c*) The majority of compounds racemise with various degrees of ease under the influence of different reagents.

(*d*) A relatively small number of compounds cannot be racemised at all.

When a molecule contains two or more asymmetric carbon atoms and the configuration of only *one* of these is inverted by some reaction, the process is then called *epimerisation*.

Many theories have been proposed to explain racemisation, but owing to the diverse nature of the structures of the various optically active compounds, one cannot expect to find *one* theory which would explain the racemisation of *all* types of optically active compounds. Thus we find that a number of mechanisms have been suggested, each one explaining the racemisation of a particular type of compound.

A number of compounds which are easily racemisable are those in which the asymmetric carbon atom is joined to a hydrogen atom and can undergo tautomeric change. Let us consider the case of keto-enol tautomerism: In the keto-form (I) the carbon joined to the hydrogen atom and the oxo group is asymmetric; in the enol-form, (II), this carbon atom has lost its asymmetry. When the enol-form reverts to the keto-form, it can do so to produce the original keto molecule (I), but owing to its symmetry, the enol-form can produce equally well the keto-form (III) in which the configuration

$$-\underset{|}{\overset{H}{\underset{|}{C}}}-C=O \rightleftharpoons -C=C-OH \rightleftharpoons -\underset{|}{\overset{|}{\underset{H}{C}}}-C=O$$

(I)   (II)   (III)

of the asymmetric carbon atom is opposite to that in (I). Thus racemisation, according to this scheme, occurs *via* the enol-form, *e.g.*, ($-$)-lactic acid is racemised in aqueous sodium hydroxide, and this change may be formulated:

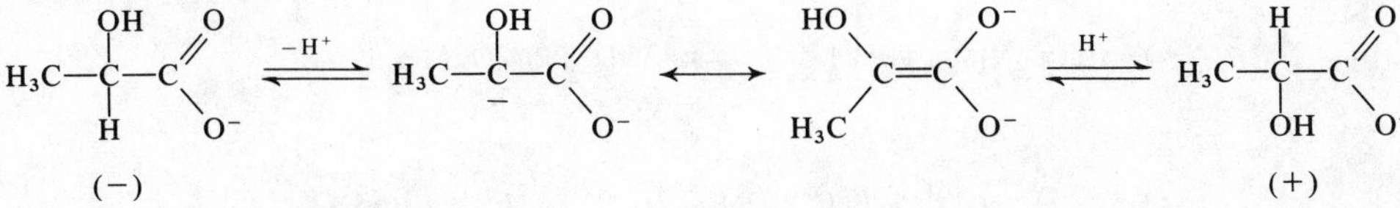

There is a great deal of evidence to support this tautomeric mechanism. When the hydrogen atom joined to the asymmetric carbon atom is replaced by some group that prevents tautomerism (enolisation) then racemisation is also prevented (at least under the same conditions as the original compound), *e.g.*, mandelic acid, $C_6H_5CHOHCO_2H$, is readily racemised by warming with aqueous sodium hydroxide. On the other hand, atrolactic acid, $C_6H_5C(CH_3)(OH)CO_2H$, is not racemised under the same conditions; in this case keto-enol tautomerism is no longer possible (*i.e.*, formation of the intermediate carbanion is not possible).

Racemisation of compounds capable of exhibiting keto-enol tautomerism is catalysed by acids and bases. Since keto-enol tautomerism is also catalysed by acids and bases, then if racemisation proceeds *via* enolisation, the rates of racemisation and enolisation should be the same. This relationship has been established by means of kinetic studies, *e.g.*, Bartlett *et al.* (1935) found that the rate of acid-catalysed iodination of 2-butyl phenyl ketone was the same as that of racemisation in acid solution. This is in keeping with both reactions involving the rate-controlling formation of the enol (see Vol. I, Ch. 10):

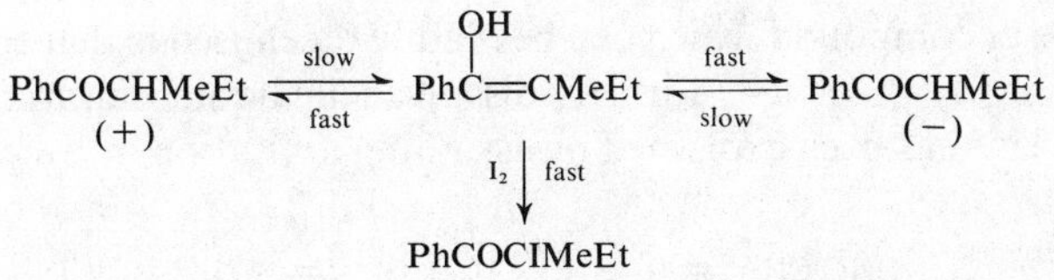

On the other hand, on the basis that the rate-determining step in base-catalysed enolisation and racemisation is the formation of the enolate ion, then the two processes will also occur at the same rate.

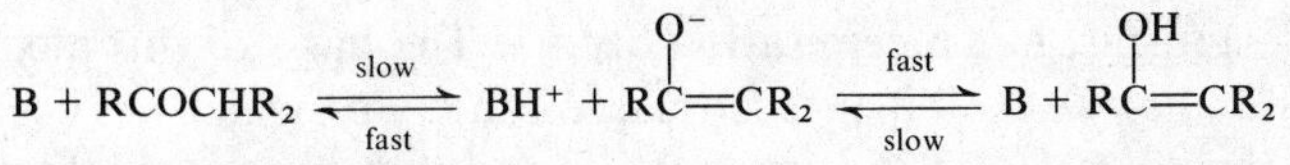

Hsü *et al.* (1936) found that the rates of bromination and racemisation (in the presence of acetate ions) of 2-*o*-carboxybenzyl-1-indanone were identical.

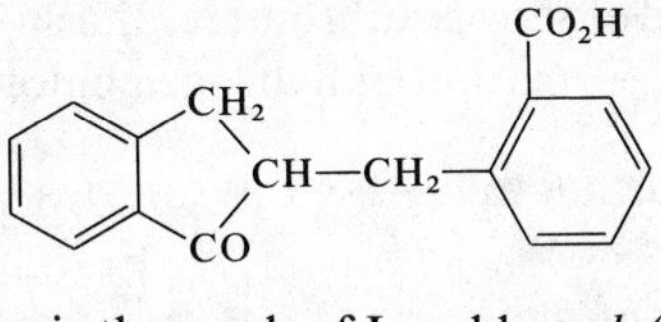

Further support for this mechanism is the work of Ingold *et al.* (1938) who showed that the rate of racemisation of ($+$)-2-butyl phenyl ketone in dioxan-deuterium oxide solution in the presence of NaOD is the same as the rate of deuterium exchange. This is in keeping with the formation of the enolate ion (or carbanion), which is common to both reactions.

There are many compounds containing an asymmetric carbon atom which can be racemised under suitable conditions although there is no possibility of tautomerism. A number of different types of compounds fall into this group, and the mechanism proposed for racemisation depends on

$$O^-$$
$$PhC{=}CMeEt$$

$$(+){-}PhCOCHMeEt + OD^- \underset{fast}{\overset{slow}{\rightleftharpoons}} HOD + PhCOCMeEt$$

D$_2$O; fast / slow   slow \ fast

$$PhCOCDMeEt \qquad\qquad (-){-}PhCOCHMeEt$$
$$+$$
$$OD^-$$

the type of compound under consideration. In the case of compounds of the type of $(-)$-limonene (**8** §13), which is racemised by strong heating, the mechanisms proposed are highly speculative, *e.g.*, according to Kincaid *et al.* (1940), molecules of the type C*abde* can only be racemised by the breaking of bonds. A number of optically active secondary alcohols can be racemised by heating with a sodium alkoxide. This has been explained by a reversible dehydrogenation (Hückel, 1931) and there is some evidence to support this mechanism (Doering *et al.*, 1947, 1949). It has also been found that the presence of a trace of carbonyl compound (generally formed by atmospheric oxidation) is necessary for this reaction.

$$R^1{-}\underset{H}{\overset{R^2}{C}}{-}OH \overset{-2H}{\rightleftharpoons} R^1{-}\overset{R^2}{C}{=}O \overset{+2H}{\rightleftharpoons} R^1{-}\underset{R^2}{\overset{H}{C}}{-}OH$$
$$(+){-} \qquad\qquad\qquad\qquad\qquad\qquad\qquad (-){-}$$

Another different type of compound which can be readily racemised is that represented by α-chloro-ethylbenzene. When the $(+)$- or $(-)$-form is dissolved in liquid sulphur dioxide, spontaneous racemisation occurs. This has been explained by assuming ionisation into a carbonium ion (Polanyi *et al.*, 1933).

$$C_6H_5CHClCH_3 \rightleftharpoons C_6H_5\overset{+}{C}HCH_3 + Cl^- \rightleftharpoons C_6H_5CHClCH_3$$
$$(+){-} \qquad\qquad\qquad\qquad\qquad\qquad\qquad (-){-}$$

The carbonium ion is planar (the positively charged carbon atom is in a state of trigonal hybridisation) and consequently symmetric; recombination with the chlorine ion can occur equally well to form the $(+)$- and $(-)$-forms, *i.e.*, racemisation occurs. The basis of this mechanism is that alkyl halides in liquid sulphur dioxide exhibit an electrical conductivity, which has been taken as indicating ionisation. Hughes, Ingold *et al.* (1936), however, found that pure α-chloroethylbenzene in pure liquid sulphur dioxide does not conduct, but when there is conduction, then styrene and hydrogen chloride are present. These authors showed that under the conditions of purity, the addition of bromine leads to a quantitative yield of styrene dibromide, and so suggested that the rate of racemisa-tion is accounted for by the rate of formation of hydrogen chloride; thus:

$$C_6H_5CHClCH_3 \overset{slow}{\longrightarrow} C_6H_5\overset{+}{C}HCH_3 + Cl^-$$

$$C_6H_5\overset{+}{C}HCH_3 \overset{fast}{\longrightarrow} C_6H_5CH = CH_2 + H^+$$

It is the recombination of the styrene with the hydrogen chloride that produces the racemised product; this may be written as follows

$$C_6H_5CHClCH_3 \rightleftharpoons C_6H_5CH = CH_2 + HCl \rightleftharpoons C_6H_5CHClCH_3$$
$$(+){-} \qquad\qquad\qquad\qquad\qquad\qquad\qquad (-){-}$$

α-Chloroethylbenzene can also be readily racemised by means of Lewis acids, *e.g.*, SbCl$_5$,

$HgCl_2$, etc. In this case, the mechanism is believed to be similar to that proposed by Polanyi (see above). Thus:

$$C_6H_5CHClCH_3 + SbCl_5 \rightleftharpoons C_6H_5\overset{+}{C}HCH_3 + SbCl_6^- \rightleftharpoons C_6H_5CHClCH_3 + SbCl_5$$
$$(+)-$$

The racemisation of optically active hydrocarbons containing a tertiary hydrogen atom is very interesting. It has been shown that such hydrocarbons undergo hydrogen exchange when dissolved in concentrated sulphuric acid (Ingold *et al.*, 1936), and the mechanism is believed to occur *via* a carbonium ion (Burwell *et al.*, 1948).

$$R_3CH + 2H_2SO_4 \longrightarrow R_3C^+ + HSO_4^- + SO_2 + 2H_2O$$
$$R_3C^+ + R_3CH \longrightarrow R_3CH + R_3C^+, \text{ etc.}$$

This reaction is very useful for racemising optically active hydrocarbons, *e.g.*, Burwell *et al.* (1948) racemised optically active 3-methylheptane in concentrated sulphuric acid (the carbonium ion is flat):

$$
\begin{array}{cccc}
\quad CH_3 & \quad CH_3 & \quad CH_3 & \quad CH_3 \\
\quad | & \quad | & \quad | & \quad | \\
C_2H_5-CH-C_4H_9 + C_2H_5-C^+-C_4H_9 & \longrightarrow & C_2H_5-C^+-C_4H_9 + C_2H_5-CH-C_4H_9 \\
(+)- & & & (\pm)-
\end{array}
$$

Optically active hydrocarbons can also be racemised by means of aluminium chloride, the mechanism again probably being *via* the formation of a carbonium ion, *e.g.*, 2-phenylbutane:

(I) $\qquad\qquad C_6H_5CH(CH_3)C_2H_5 + AlCl_3 \longrightarrow C_6H_5\overset{+}{C}(CH_3)C_2H_5 + HAlCl_3^-$
$\qquad\qquad\quad (+)-$

(II) $\qquad C_6H_5CH(CH_3)C_2H_5 + C_6H_5\overset{+}{C}(CH_3)C_2H_5 \longrightarrow C_6H_5C(CH_3)C_2H_5 + C_6H_5CH(CH_3)C_2H_5$
$\qquad\qquad (+)- \qquad\qquad\qquad\qquad\qquad\qquad\qquad\qquad\qquad (\pm)-$

The racemisation of other types of optically active compounds is described later (see biphenyl compounds, **5** §4; nitrogen compounds, **6** §2a; phosphorus compounds, **6** §3b; arsenic compounds, **6** §4a).

§9. Properties of the racemic modification

The racemic modification may exist in three different forms in the solid state.

(i) **Racemic mixture.** This is also known as a ($\pm$)-**conglomerate**, and is a mechanical mixture of two types of crystals, the ($+$)- and ($-$)-forms; there are two phases present. The physical properties of the racemic mixture are mainly the same as those of its constituent enantiomers. The most important difference is the m.p. (see §9a).

(ii) **Racemic compound.** This consists of a pair of enantiomers in combination as a molecular compound; only one solid phase is present. The physical properties of a racemic compound are different from those of the constituent enantiomers, but in solution racemic compounds dissociate into the ($+$)- and ($-$)-forms.

(iii) **Racemic solid solution.** This is also known as a *pseudo*-**racemic compound**, and is a solid solution (one phase system) formed by a pair of enantiomers crystallising together due to their being isomorphous. The properties of the racemic solid solution are mainly the same as those of its constituent enantiomers; the m.p.s may differ (see §9a).

§9a. **Methods for determining the nature of a racemic modification.** One simple method of examination is to estimate the amounts of water of crystallisation in the enantiomers (only one need be examined) and in the racemic modification; if these are different, then the racemic modification is a racemic compound. Another simple method is to measure the densities of the enantiomers and the racemic modification; again, if these are different, the racemic modification is a racemic compound; *e.g.*, tartaric acids.

	D-Tartaric acid	L-Tartaric acid	Racemic tartaric acid
Melting point	170°C	170°C	206°C
Water of crystallisation	None	None	1H$_2$O
Density	1·7598	1·7598	1·697
Solubility in H$_2$O (at 20°C)	139 g/100 ml	139 g/100 ml	20·6 g/100 ml

There are, however, two main methods for determining the nature of a racemic modification: a study of the freezing-point curves and a study of the solubility curves (Roozeboom, 1899; Andriani, 1900).

Freezing-point curves. These are obtained by measuring the melting points of mixtures containing different amounts of the racemic modification and its corresponding enantiomers. Various types of curves are possible according to the nature of the racemic modification. In Fig. 2.19(*a*) the melting points of all mixtures are higher than that of the racemic modification alone. In this case the racemic modification is a racemic mixture (a eutectic mixture is formed at the point of 50 per cent composition of each enantiomer), and so addition of either enantiomer to a racemic mixture *raises* the melting point of the latter; (±)-pinene is an example of this type. In Fig. 2.19(*b*) and (*c*) the melting points of the mixtures are lower than the melting point of the racemic modification which, therefore, is a racemic compound. The melting point of the racemic compound may be above that

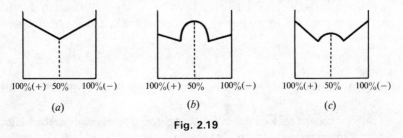

	100%(+) 50% 100%(−)	100%(+) 50% 100%(−)	100%(+) 50% 100%(−)
	(*a*)	(*b*)	(*c*)

Fig. 2.19

of each enantiomer (Fig. 2.19*b*) or below (Fig. 2.19*c*); in either case the melting point is *lowered* when the racemic compound is mixed with an enantiomer; an example of Fig. 2.19(*b*) is methyl tartrate, and one of Fig. 2.19(*c*) is mandelic acid.

When the racemic modification is a racemic solid solution, three types of curves are possible (Fig. 2.20). In Fig. 2.20(*a*) the freezing-point curve is a horizontal straight line, all possible compositions having the same melting point, *e.g.*, (+)- and (−)-camphor. In Fig. 2.20(*b*) the freezing-point curve shows a maximum, *e.g.*, (+)- and(−)-carvoxime; and in Fig. 2.20(*c*) the freezing-point curve shows a minimum, *e.g.*, (+)- and (−)-isopentyl (isoamyl) carbamate.

In a number of cases there is a transition temperature at which one form of the racemic modification changes into another form, *e.g.*, (±)-camphoroxime crystallises as the racemic solid solution above 103°C, whereas below this temperature it is the racemic compound that is obtained [see also §10(i)].

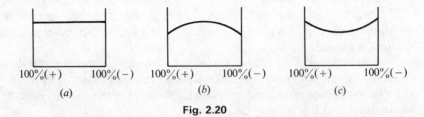

	100%(+) 100%(−)	100%(+) 100%(−)	100%(+) 100%(−)
	(*a*)	(*b*)	(*c*)

Fig. 2.20

Correlation of configurations by means of quasi-racemic compounds. Fredga (1944) has introduced the study of quasi-racemic compounds as a means of correlating configurations (§5), their formation being detected by studying the melting-point curves of the two components. The curves obtained are similar to those of the racemic modification shown in Fig. 2.19a and b, and 2.20a, but with the quasi-racemic compounds these curves are unsymmetrical (since the m.p.s of the components will be different). An unsymmetrical curve 2.19a indicates a eutectic mixture, an unsymmetrical 2.20a a solid solution, and an unsymmetrical 2.19b a quasi-racemic compound. Curves for quasi-racemic compounds are given only by compounds (containing one asymmetric carbon atom) which have closely similar structures but opposite configurations, e.g., (I) and (II). On the other hand, curves

$$
b-\underset{\underset{d}{|}}{\overset{\overset{a}{|}}{C}}-e \qquad e-\underset{\underset{d}{|}}{\overset{\overset{a}{|}}{C}}-f
$$

(I)   (II)

of the other two types are given by compounds of *like* configuration (but some cases are known where the configurations have been opposite). Various examples of this method of correlating configurations have now been described; e.g., Fredga (1941) showed (partly by chemical methods and partly by using the quasi-racemate method) that (+)-malic acid (III) and (−)-mercaptosuccinic acid (IV) had opposite configurations. He then showed (1942) that (−)-mercaptosuccinic acid formed a

$$
\begin{array}{ccc}
CO_2H & CO_2H & CO_2H \\
H-\!\!\!-OH & HS-\!\!\!-H & H-\!\!\!-Me \\
CH_2CO_2H & CH_2CO_2H & CH_2CO_2H \\
\text{(III)} & \text{(IV)} & \text{(V)}
\end{array}
$$

quasi-racemic compound with (+)-methylsuccinic acid (V). Therefore (IV) and (V) have *opposite* configurations and consequently (+)-malic acid and (+)-methylsuccinic acid have the *same* configuration (see also **8** §§10(vi) and 23e). It is of interest to note that McPhail et al. (1966) have confirmed, by X-ray analysis, the absolute configuration of methylsuccinic acid established by Fredga.

Mislow et al. (1956) have applied the m.p. curves in a somewhat different manner. They worked with 3-mercapto-octanedioic acid (VI) and 3-methyl-octanedioic acid (VII). These authors found that compounds (−)-VI and (+)-(VII) gave solid solutions for all mixtures (unsymmetrical 2.20a), whereas (+)-(VI) and (+)-(VII) give a diagram with a single eutectic (unsymmetrical 2.19a). These

$$
\begin{array}{cc}
CH_2CO_2H & CH_2CO_2H \\
H-\underset{|}{C}-SH & H-\underset{|}{C}-Me \\
(CH_2)_4CO_2H & (CH_2)_4CO_2H \\
\text{(−)-form} & \text{(+)-form} \\
\text{(VI)} & \text{(VII)}
\end{array}
$$

results indicate that (−)-(VI) and (+)-(VIII) have the same absolute configuration, whereas (+)-(VI) and (+)-(VII) have opposite configurations.

Solubility curves. The interpretation of solubility curves is difficult, but in practice the following simple scheme based on solubility may be used. A small amount of one of the enantiomers is added to a *saturated* solution of the racemic modification, and the resulting solution is then examined in a polarimeter. If the solution exhibits a rotation, then the racemic modification is a compound, but if the solution has a zero rotation, then the racemic modification is a mixture or a solid solution. The reasons for this behaviour are as follows. If the racemic modification is a mixture or a solid solution, then the solution (in some solvent) is saturated with respect to each enantiomer and consequently cannot dissolve any of the added enantiomer. If, however, the racemic modification is a compound, then the solution (in a solvent) is saturated with respect to the compound form but not with respect to either enantiomer; hence the latter will dissolve when added and thereby produce a rotation. It should be noted that this simple method does not permit a differentiation to be made between a racemic mixture and a racemic solid solution.

Infrared spectroscopy is also being used to distinguish a racemic compound from a racemic mixture or a racemic solid solution. In the latter the spectra are identical, but are different in the former. These observations are also true for X-ray powder diagrams, and so X-ray analysis in the solid state may also be used.

§10. Resolution of racemic modifications

Resolution is the process whereby a racemic modification is separated into its two enantiomers. In practice the separation may be far from quantitative, and in some cases only one form may be obtained. Furthermore, the form isolated need not be optically pure, *i.e.*, it may consist of the (+)- and (−)-forms in unequal amounts, but in this case the process is usually referred to as *partial resolution*. A large variety of methods for resolution have now been developed, and the method used in a particular case depends largely on the chemical nature of the compound under consideration.

(i) **Mechanical separation.** This method is also known as **spontaneous resolution by crystallisation**, and was introduced by Pasteur (1848). It depends on the crystallisation of the two forms separately, which are then separated by hand. The method is applicable only for racemic *mixtures* where the *crystal* forms of the enantiomers are themselves enantiomorphous (§2). Pasteur separated sodium ammonium racemate in this way. The transition temperature of sodium ammonium racemate is 28°C; above this temperature the racemic compound crystallises out, and below this temperature the racemic mixture. Now Pasteur crystallised his sodium ammonium racemate from a concentrated solution at room temperature, which must have been below 28°C, since, had the temperature been above this, he would have obtained the racemic compound, which cannot be separated mechanically. Actually, Staedel (1878) failed to repeat Pasteur's separation since he worked at a temperature above 28°C.

(ii) **Preferential crystallisation by inoculation.** A supersaturated solution of the racemic modification is treated with a crystal of one enantiomer (or an isomorphous substance), whereupon this form is precipitated. The resolution of glutamic acid by inoculation has been perfected for industrial use (Ogawa *et al.*, 1957; Oeda, 1961). Harada *et al.* (1962) have also resolved the copper complex of DL-aspartic acid by inoculation.

Except for the two amino-acids mentioned above, this method of resolution has been found impractical or resulted in partial resolution only. Harada (1965), however, has now obtained total optical resolution of *free* α-amino-acids by the inoculation method. Resolution was effected by seeding the supersaturated aqueous solutions with pure crystals of L- or D-isomer of the amino-acid.

(iii) **Biochemical separation** (Pasteur, 1858). Certain bacteria and moulds, when they grow in a dilute solution of a racemic modification, destroy one enantiomer more rapidly than the other, *e.g.*, *Penicillium glaucum* (a mould), when grown in a solution of racemic ammonium tartrate, attacks the (+)-form and leaves the (−).

This biochemical method of separation has some disadvantages:

(*a*) Dilute solutions must be used, and so the amounts obtained will be small.

(*b*) One form is always destroyed and the other form is not always obtained in 50 per cent yield since some of this may also be destroyed.

(*c*) It is necessary to find a micro-organism which will attack only one of the enantiomers.

(iv) **Conversion into diastereoisomers** (Pasteur, 1858). This method, which is the best of all the methods of resolution, consists in converting the enantiomers of a racemic modification into diastereoisomers (§7b); the racemic modification is treated with an optically active substance and the diastereoisomers thereby produced are separated by fractional crystallisation. Thus racemic acids may be separated by optically active bases, and *vice versa*, *e.g.*,

$$(D_{acid} + L_{acid}) + 2D_{base} \rightarrow (D_{acid}D_{base}) + (L_{acid}D_{base})$$

These two diastereoisomers may then be separated by fractional crystallisation and the acids (enantiomers) regenerated by hydrolysis with inorganic acids or with alkalis. In practice it is usually easy to obtain the less-soluble isomer in a pure state, but it may be very difficult to obtain the more-soluble isomer. In a number of cases this second (more-soluble) isomer may be obtained by preparing it in the form of *another* diastereoisomer which is less soluble than that of its enantiomer. On the other hand, separation and purification of the diastereoisomers may be successfully achieved by chromatography (see also (vi), below).

Resolution by means of diastereoisomer formation may be used for a variety of compounds, *e.g.*,

(*a*) *Acids.* The optically active bases used are mainly alkaloids: brucine, quinine, strychnine, cinchonine, cinchonidine and morphine. Synthetic optically active bases are also used, *e.g.*, benzimidazoles, menthylamine, α-phenylethylamine.

(*b*) *Bases.* Many optically active acids have been used, *e.g.*, tartaric acid, camphor-β-sulphonic acid and particularly α-bromocamphor-π-sulphonic acid (see **8** §23a).

(*c*) *Alcohols.* These are converted into the acid ester derivative using either succinic or phthalic anhydride (Pickard and Kenyon, 1912). The acid ester, consisting of equimolecular amounts of the

(+)- and (−)-forms, may now be resolved as for acids. Racemic alcohols may also be resolved by diastereoisomer formation with optically active acyl chlorides (to form esters) or with optically active isocyanates (to form urethans):

$$R^1OCH_2COCl + R^2OH \longrightarrow R^1OCH_2CO_2R^2 + HCl$$
$$R^1NCO + R^2OH \longrightarrow R^2NHCO_2R^2$$

In these equations R^1 is the (−)-menthyl group (**8** §16); recently *N*-(−)-menthyl-*p*-sulphamyl-benzoyl chloride, (I), has been used (Mills *et al.*, 1950).

(I)

3β-Acetoxy-Δ^5-etienic acid (*cf.* **11** §3) has been found very useful for resolving (±)-alcohols (*inter alia*, Djerassi *et al.*, 1961).

(*d*) *Aldehydes and Ketones.* These have been resolved by means of optically active hydrazines, *e.g.*, (−)-menthylhydrazine. Sugars have been resolved with (+)-isopentanethiol (*cf.* **7** §1). Nerdel *et al.* (1952) have resolved oxo compounds with D-tartramide acid hydrazide,

$$NH_2COCHOHCHOHCONHNH_2;$$

this forms diastereoisomeric tartramazones. On the other hand, Shillington *et al.* (1958) have converted oxo compounds into their 4-carboxyphenylsemicarbazones by means of a 4-carboxyphenyl-semicarbazide,

Since these derivatives contain a carboxyl group, they can be resolved like acids, *e.g.*, with brucine, and finally hydrolysed to liberate the optically active oxo compounds.

Another method of resolution is reduction of the oxo compound to the corresponding alcohol, which is then resolved and the separated enantiomers re-oxidised.

Adams *et al.* (1966) have resolved ketones *via* enamine formation. The enamine, produced by condensation of the ketone with pyrrolidine in the presence of a trace of *p*-toluenesulphonic acid (see also Vol. I), is converted into iminium salts containing optically active anions, *e.g.*, (+)-camphor-10-sulphonate anion (represented as Z⁻ in the equation):

$$R^1CH_2COR^2 + HN\rangle \xrightarrow{\text{TsOH}} R^1CH{=}CR^2{-}N\rangle \xrightarrow{\text{HZ}} \left\{R^1CH{=}CR^2{-}\overset{+}{\underset{H}{N}}\rangle\right\} Z^-$$

iminium salt

Recrystallisation from suitable solvents gives the (+)- and (−)-forms.

(*e*) *Amino-compounds.* These may be resolved by conversion into diastereoisomeric anils by means of optically active aldehydes. Amines have also been resolved *via* their salts using, *e.g.*, (+)-tartaric acid (see also vi). α-Amino-acids have been resolved by preparing the acyl derivative with an optically active acyl chloride, *e.g.*, (−)-menthoxyacetyl chloride (*cf. alcohols*). Another method of resolving DL-amino-acids is asymmetric enzymic synthesis (**3** §7). The racemic amino-acid is converted into the acyl derivative which is then allowed to react with aniline in the presence of the enzyme papain at the proper pH (Albertson, 1951). Under these conditions only the L-amino-acid derivative reacts to form an insoluble anilide; the D-acid does not react but remains in the solution.

$$\underset{\text{DL-acid}}{\overset{\text{NHCOR}^2}{R^1CHCO_2H}} + C_6H_5NH_2 \xrightarrow{\text{papain}} \underset{\text{L-acid}}{\overset{\text{NHCOR}^2}{R^1CHCONHC_6H_5}} + \underset{\text{D-acid}}{\overset{\text{NHCOR}^2}{R^1CHCO_2H}}$$

Amino-acids have also been resolved by other means (see (ii), (vi) and **13** §4).

Although amino-acids contain both an amino-group and a carboxyl group, they usually cannot be resolved in the straightforward way as amines or acids. This is due to the fact that amino-acids behave as dipolar ions (see **13** §4).

Asymmetric transformation. Resolution of racemic modifications by means of salt formation (the diastereoisomers are salts; *cf. acids* and *bases*) may be complicated by the phenomenon of *asymmetric transformation.* This is exhibited by compounds that are optically unstable, *i.e.*, the enantiomers are readily interconvertible

$$(+)\text{-C} \rightleftharpoons (-)\text{-C}$$

Suppose we have an optically stable (+)-base (one equivalent) dissolved in some solvent, and this is then treated with one equivalent of an optically unstable (±)-acid. At the moment of mixing, the solution will contain equal amounts of [(+)-Base·(+)-Acid] and [(+)-Base·(−)-Acid]; but since the acid is optically unstable, the two diastereoisomers will be present in unequal amounts when equilibrium is attained.

$$[(+)\text{-Base·}(+)\text{-Acid}] \rightleftharpoons [(+)\text{-Base·}(-)\text{-Acid}]$$

According to Jamison and Turner, first-order asymmetric transformation is the establishment of equilibrium *in solution* between the two diastereoisomers which must have a *real* existence. In second-order asymmetric transformation it is necessary that one salt should crystallise from solution; the two diastereoisomers need not have a real existence in solution. In second-order asymmetric transformation it is possible to get a complete conversion of the acid into the form that crystallises; the form may be the (+)- or (−)-, and which one it is depends on the nature of the base and the solvent.

Many examples of first- and second-order asymmetric transformation are known, and a large number of these compounds are those which owe their chirality to restricted rotation about a single bond (see Ch. 5), *e.g.*, Mills and Elliott (1928) tried to resolve *N*-benzenesulphonyl-8-nitro-1-naphthylglycine, (II), by means of the brucine salt. These authors found that either diastereoisomer

$$C_6H_5SO_2 \quad CH_2CO_2H$$

(structure II with NO$_2$)

(II)

could be obtained in approximately 100 per cent yield by crystallisation from methanol and acetone, respectively. Another example of second-order asymmetric transformation is hydrocarbostyril-3-carboxylic acid. This compound contains an asymmetric carbon atom, and Leuchs (1921), attempting to resolve it with quinidine, isolated approximately 90 per cent of the (+)-form. Optical instability in this case is due to keto-enol tautomerism (*cf.* §8).

(keto-enol tautomerism structures)

A very interesting example of second-order asymmetric transformation is 2-acetomethylamido-4′,5-dimethylphenylsulphone, (III). When this compound was crystallised from a supersaturated

(structure III)

(III)

solution in ethyl (+)-tartrate, the crystals obtained had a rotation of +0·2°; evaporation of the mother liquor gave crystals with a rotation of −0·15° (Buchanan *et al.*, 1950).

(v) Another method of resolution that has been tried is the conversion of the enantiomers into *volatile* diastereoisomers, which are then separated by fractional distillation. So far, the method does not appear to be very successful, only a partial resolution being the result; *e.g.*, Bailey and Hass (1941) converted (±)-pentan-2-ol into its diastereoisomers with L(+)-lactic acid, and then partially separated them by fractional distillation.

(vi) **Chromatography.** Optically active substances may be selectively adsorbed by some optically active adsorbent, *e.g.*, Henderson and Rule (1939) partially resolved *p*-phenylenebisiminocamphor on lactose as adsorbent; Bradley and Easty (1951) have found that wool and casein selectively adsorb (+)-mandelic acid from an aqueous solution of (±)-mandelic acid. A particularly important case of resolution by chromatography is that of Tröger's base (see **6** §2c).

Jamison and Turner (1942) have carried out a chromatographic separation without using an optically active adsorbent; they partially resolved the diastereoisomers of (−)-menthyl (±)-mandelate by preferential adsorption on alumina. It is also interesting to note that the resolution of a racemic acid by salt formation with an optically active base is made more effective by the application of chromatography (see also §10(iv)). More recently, enzymic and chromatographic methods have been developed for the *direct* separation of enantiomers (*inter alia*, Rogozhin, 1971; Gil-Av, 1972).

GSC and GLC have been used with great success for resolving racemic modifications, *e.g.*, s-butanol and s-butyl bromide have been separated into two overlapping fractions using a column of starch or ethyl tartrate as the stationary phase (Karagounis *et al.*, 1959). On the other hand, Casanova *et al.* (1961) have resolved the diastereoisomeric ketals from ($\pm$)-camphor by GLC, and Halpern *et al.* (1965) have resolved in the same way DL-amino-acids *via* their ($-$)-menthyl ester derivatives (see also **13** §4) and *via* their acyl derivatives. Amines may also be resolved *via* acylation with optically active acid chlorides. Halpern *et al.* (1966) have used *N*-trifluoroacetyl-L-prolyl chloride, and separated the diastereoisomers by GLC, *e.g.*, 2-aminobutane and 2-aminopentane have been obtained optically pure.

Beckett *et al.* (1957) have introduced a novel method for correlating and determining configurations (*cf.* §9). These authors have prepared 'stereoselective adsorbents'. These are adsorbents prepared in the presence of a suitable reference compound of known configuration, *e.g.*, silica gel in the presence of quinine. Such an adsorbent exhibits higher adsorptive power for isomers related to the reference compound than for their stereoisomers, provided that their structures are not too dissimilar from that of the reference compound. Thus, silica gel prepared in the presence of quinine adsorbs quinine more readily than its stereoisomer quinidine; cinchonidine (configurationally related to quinine) is adsorbed more readily than its stereoisomer cinchonine (configurationally related to quinidine).

(vii) **Kinetic method of resolution.** Marckwald and McKenzie (1899) found that ($-$)-menthol reacts more slowly with ($-$)-mandelic acid than with the ($+$)-acid. Hence, if insufficient ($-$)-menthol is used to completely esterify ($\pm$)-mandelic acid, the resulting mixture of diastereoisomers will contain more ($-$)-menthyl ($+$)-mandelate than ($-$)-menthyl ($-$)-mandelate. Consequently there will be more ($-$)-mandelic acid than ($+$)-mandelic acid in the *unchanged* acid, *i.e.*, a partial resolution of ($\pm$)-mandelic acid has been effected (see also **6** §5b).

(viii) Ferreira (1953) has partially resolved ($\pm$)-narcotine and ($\pm$)-laudanosine (1–2·5 per cent resolution) *without* the use of optically active reagents. He dissolved the racemic alkaloid in hydrochloric acid and then *slowly* added pyridine; the alkaloid was precipitated, and it was found to be optically active. The explanation offered for this partial resolution is as follows (Ferreira). When a crystalline racemic substance is precipitated from solution, a crystallisation nucleus is first developed. Since this nucleus contains a relatively small number of molecules, there is more than an even chance that it will contain an excess of one enantiomer or other. If it be assumed that the forces acting on the growth of crystals are the same kind as those responsible for adsorption [*cf.* (vi)], the nucleus will grow preferentially, collecting one enantiomer rather than the other. Crystallisation, when carried out in the usual manner, results in the formation of crystals containing more or less equivalent numbers of both enantiomers.

(ix) **Channel complex formation** has also been used to resolve racemic modifications (see Vol. I). This also offers a means of carrying out a resolution without chiral reagents, *e.g.*, Schlenk (1952) added ($\pm$)-2-chloro-octane to a solution of urea and obtained, on fractional crystallisation, the two urea inclusion complexes urea/($+$)-2-chloro-octane and urea/($-$)-2-chloro-octane.

Baker *et al.* (1952) have prepared tri-*o*-thymotide, and found that it formed clathrates with ethanol, n-hexane, etc. Powell *et al.* (1952) have shown that tri-*o*-thymotide crystallises as a racemate, but that resolution takes place when it forms clathrates with n-hexane, benzene or chloroform. By

tri-*o*-thymotide

means of seeding and slow growth of a single crystal, it is possible to obtain the (+)- or (−)-form depending on the nature of the seed. Furthermore, crystallisation of tri-o-thymotide (dl) from a solvent which is itself a racemic modification (d'l') and which forms a clathrate, produces crystals of the types dd' and ll'. Thus such (solvent) racemic modifications can be resolved, e.g., s-butyl bromide has been resolved in this way.

§10a. Optical purity. An optically pure compound is one which has been prepared in 100 per cent purity, i.e., optical purity is expressed as a percentage, e.g., if the (maximum) specific rotation of compound A is +50° and an impure sample has a rotation of +30°, this sample is 60 per cent optically pure. For a racemic modification, the optical purity is zero.

The difficult problem with respect to optical purity is to be able to ascertain whether a specimen of an enantiomer is 100 per cent optically pure. Several criteria may be used. The simplest criterion is that which considers a crystalline compound to be optically pure if, after repeated crystallisation, the melting point and rotation remain unchanged. This, however, may not be a correct conclusion, e.g., the resolution of a racemic solid solution may lead to the isolation of a partially resolved enantiomer which, after repeated crystallisation, does not change its rotation (see Fig. 2.20a). The conclusion, however, that the compound is optically pure is strengthened if both of its enantiomers can be prepared and their rotations are equal and opposite.

There are several methods which may be used for ascertaining optical purity and are reliable within certain experimental limits. One method uses isotopic dilution. A known weight of the enantiomer being examined is mixed, in solution, with a known weight of its racemic modification which has been labelled with an isotope. After recrystallisation, the isotope content of the racemic modification is then determined. Suppose the enantiomer under consideration is the (+)-form. In this case, the recovered racemic modification will contain unlabelled (+)-form as well as labelled (+)-form, and it is therefore possible to calculate the dilution factor (since known weights of both were used). If, however, the (+)-enantiomer is not optically pure, some unlabelled (−)-form will also be present in the recovered racemic modification. In this case, the isotope dilution factor will be less than the predicted one.

Other methods make use of enzymes or conversion into other compounds of known optical purity. NMR spectroscopy may also be used to determine optical purity. It has already been pointed out that the NMR spectra of a pair of enantiomers are identical (§7a). Now suppose that a racemic modification is completely converted into a pair of diastereoisomers, e.g.,

$$
\begin{array}{cc}
\text{R}^1\!\!-\!\!\overset{\displaystyle \text{R}^2}{\underset{\displaystyle \text{R}^3}{\text{C}}}\!\!-\!\!\text{NH}_2 + \text{R}^1\!\!-\!\!\overset{\displaystyle \text{R}^3}{\underset{\displaystyle \text{R}^2}{\text{C}}}\!\!-\!\!\text{NH}_2 & \xrightarrow{(+)\text{-}CHabCOCl} \quad \text{R}^1\!\!-\!\!\overset{\displaystyle \text{R}^2}{\underset{\displaystyle \text{R}^3}{\text{C}}}\!\!-\!\!\text{NH}\!\!-\!\!\overset{\displaystyle\text{O}}{\text{C}}\!\!-\!\!\overset{\displaystyle\text{H}}{\underset{\displaystyle b}{\text{C}}}\!\!-\!a + \text{R}^1\!\!-\!\!\overset{\displaystyle \text{R}^3}{\underset{\displaystyle \text{R}^2}{\text{C}}}\!\!-\!\!\text{NH}\!\!-\!\!\overset{\displaystyle\text{O}}{\text{C}}\!\!-\!\!\overset{\displaystyle\text{H}}{\underset{\displaystyle b}{\text{C}}}\!\!-\!a \\
(+)\text{-}(\text{I}) \qquad (−)\text{-}(\text{I}) & (\text{II}a) \qquad\qquad\qquad (\text{II}b)
\end{array}
$$

In the enantiomers (+)-(I) and (−)-(I), corresponding pairs of groups are enantiotopic and their chemical shifts are identical. This is no longer the case for corresponding groups in (IIa) and (IIb). Corresponding pairs are now in diastereoisomeric environments. Thus, the protons of the group CH are diastereotopic (§7b), and if the acid chloride is optically pure, the two different proton signals will have the same intensities in their NMR spectra. If reaction between the optically pure acid chloride (in excess) is carried out with a resolved specimen of (I), then only one signal for the CH proton will be observed if (I) is optically pure. If (I) is not optically pure, then (IIa) and (IIb) will be formed in unequal amounts and two signals will be observed for the CH proton. It is then possible to calculate the optical purity of (I) from the ratio of the intensities of the two signals.

§11. The cause of optical activity

Two important points that arise from the property of optical activity are: What types of structure give rise to optical activity, and why? Fresnel (1822) suggested the following explanation for optical activity in crystalline substances such as quartz, basing it on the principle that any simple harmonic motion along a straight line may be considered as the resultant of two opposite circular motions. Fresnel assumed that plane-polarised light, on entering a substance in a direction parallel to its optic axis, is resolved into two beams of circularly polarised light, one right-handed (dextro-) and the other left-handed (laevo-) and both having the same frequency. If these two component beams travel through the medium with the same velocity, then the issuing resultant beam suffers no rotation of its plane of polarisation (Fig. 2.21a). If the velocity of the left-circularly polarised component is,

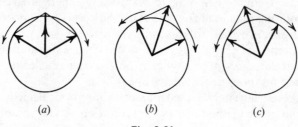

(a)   (b)   (c)

Fig. 2.21

for some reason, retarded, then the resultant beam is rotated through some angle to the right (in the direction of the faster circular component; Fig. 2.21b). Similarly, the resultant beam is rotated to the left if the right-circularly polarised component is retarded (Fig. 2.21c). Fresnel tested this theory by passing a beam of plane-polarised light through a series of prisms composed alternately of dextro- and laevorotatory quartz (Fig. 2.22). Two separate beams emerged, each circularly polarised in

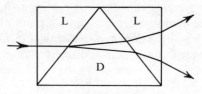

Fig. 2.22

opposite senses; this is an agreement with Fresnel's explanation. Fresnel suggested that when plane-polarised light passed through an optically active crystalline substance, the plane of polarisation was rotated because of the retardation of one of the circular components. Stated in another way, Fresnel's theory requires that the refractive indices for right- and left-circularly polarised light should be different for optically active substances. It has been shown mathematically that only a very small difference between these refractive indices gives rise to fairly large rotations, and that if the refractive index for the left-circularly polarised light is greater than that for the right component the substance, will be dextrorotatory. The difficulty of Fresnel's theory is that it does not explain *why* the two circular components should travel with different velocities. It is interesting to note, however, that Fresnel (1824) suggested that the optical activity of quartz is due to the structure being built up in right- and left-handed spirals (*cf.* §2).

If n_L and n_R respectively represent the refractive indices for left- and right-circularly polarised light then, if these are different, the substance is said to exhibit *circular birefringence*. If $n_L > n_R$, the emergent linearly-polarised resultant is rotated to the right. Since refraction and absorption of light are interconnected, the implication is that if $n_L > n_R$ in the *long* wavelength region where the optically active substance is *transparent*, then $\varepsilon_L > \varepsilon_R$ (where ε is the molar absorptivity) for the *shorter* wavelength region where light is *absorbed*. This effect, *i.e.*, when ε_L and ε_R are unequal, is known as **circular dichroism** (see §9b.1). The combined phenomenon of circular dichroism and unequal velocity of travel of left- and right-circularly polarised light is known as the **Cotton effect** (§9a.1). Now, ORD and CD curves are studied in the region of maximum absorption of the optically active compound, *i.e.*, in the region of an *optically active chromophore*. Such a chromophore is either inherently asymmetric, *e.g.*, twisted biphenyls (§2.5), or inherently symmetric, *e.g.*, a carbonyl group. In the latter, when this is in an asymmetric environment, it then behaves as an asymmetric chromophore, *i.e.*, optical activity is induced in the chromophore by the environment. Because of this, the carbonyl chromophore is referred to as an inherently symmetric, but asymmetrically perturbed, chromophore. The amplitudes of the ORD curves of compounds containing inherently asymmetric chromophores are usually much greater than those containing asymmetrically perturbed symmetric chromophores.

Drude (1900) showed that if a molecule possessed a structure such that when light is absorbed an electron is displaced along a right-handed helical path, then the result is a positive circular dichroism ($\varepsilon_L > \varepsilon_R$), and the molecule is dextrorotatory at longer wavelengths where $n_L > n_R$. In the enantiomer, the electron is displaced along a left-handed helical path when light is absorbed, the result being a negative circular dichroism ($\varepsilon_R > \varepsilon_L$) and an optical laevorotation ($n_R > n_L$) at longer wavelengths. This theory of optical rotatory power has been modified by quantum mechanics treatment. A helical motion is the resultant of two components, a linear and a circular displacement. A linear and a circular charge-displacement produce an electric and magnetic dipole moment, respectively. If a transient electric dipole and a magnetic dipole are produced by absorption of light, the molecule is circularly dichroic. If the two moments are parallel, the circular dichroism is positive; if the two moments are antiparallel, the circular dichroism is negative. If the two moments are mutually perpendicular, then no circular dichroism results.

Now let us consider the problem of optical activity of substances *in solution*. In this case the optical activity is due to the *molecules* themselves, and not to crystalline structure (see also §2). Any *crystal* which has a plane of symmetry *but not a centre of symmetry* (§6) rotates the plane of polarisation, the rotation varying with the direction in which the light travels through the crystal. No rotation occurs if the direction of the light is perpendicular or parallel to the plane of symmetry. If we assume that

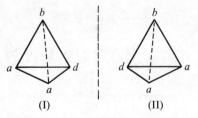

Fig. 2.23

molecules in a solution (or in a pure liquid) behave as individual crystals, then any molecule having a plane but not a centre of symmetry will also rotate the plane of polarisation, provided that the light travels through the molecule in any direction other than perpendicular (or parallel) to the plane of symmetry. Let us consider the molecule Ca_2bd (Fig. 2.23). This has a plane of symmetry, and so molecule (I) and its mirror image (II) are superimposable. Now let us suppose that the direction of plane-polarised light passing through molecule (I) makes an angle $\theta°$ with the plane of symmetry, and that the resultant rotation is $+\alpha°$. Then if the direction of the light through molecule (II) also makes an angle $\theta°$ with the plane of symmetry, the resultant rotation will be $-\alpha°$. Thus the *total* rotation produced by molecules (I) and (II) is *zero*. In a solution of compound Ca_2bd there will be an *infinite number of molecules in random orientation*. Statistically one can expect to find that whatever the angle θ is for molecule (I), there will always be molecule (II) also being traversed by light entering at angle θ. **Thus, although each individual molecule rotates the plane of polarisation by an amount depending on the value of θ, the statistical sum of the contributions of the individual molecules will be zero.**

When a molecule is not superimposable on its mirror image, then if only one enantiomer is present in the solution, the rotation produced by each individual molecule will (presumably) depend on the angle of incidence (with respect to any face), but there will be no compensating molecules (*i.e.*, mirror image molecules) present. Hence, in this case, there will be a net rotation that is *not* zero, the actual value being the statistical sum of the individual contributions (which are all in the *same* direction). Thus, if we consider the behaviour of a compound in a solution (or as a pure liquid) *as a whole*, then the observed experimental results are always in accord with the statement that **if the molecular structure of the compound is chiral, that compound will be optically active** (§2). Any compound composed of molecules possessing a plane but not a centre of symmetry is, considered *as a whole*, optically inactive, the net zero rotation being the result of 'external compensation' (*cf.* §7a). This point is of great interest in connection with molecules that can exist in different conformations (§4). Let us consider *meso*-tartaric acid, a compound that is optically inactive by internal compensation (§7b). X-ray studies (Stern *et al.*, 1950) have shown that the staggered form of the molecule is the favoured one (Fig. 2.24a). This has a centre of symmetry, and so molecules in this configuration are *individually* optically inactive. On the other hand, *meso*-tartaric acid is usually represented by the plane-diagram formula in Fig. 2.24(b). This corresponds to the eclipsed form, and has a plane of symmetry. In this conformation the *individual* molecules are optically active except when the direction of the light is perpendicular (or parallel) to the plane of symmetry; the net rotation is zero by 'external compensation'. It is possible, however, for the molecule to assume, at least theoretically, many conformations which have no elements of symmetry, *e.g.*, Fig. 2.24(c). All molecules in this

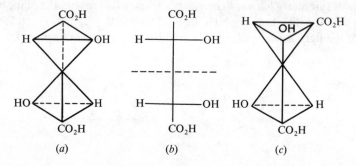

(a)   (b)   (c)

Fig. 2.24

conformation will contribute *in the same direction* to the net rotation. If the *total number* of molecules present were in this conformation, then *meso*-tartaric acid would have some definite rotation. On the theory of probability, however, for every molecule taking up the conformation in Fig. 2.24(c), there will also be present its mirror image molecule, thereby giving a net *zero* rotation due to 'external compensation'. As we have seen, *meso*-tartaric acid is optically inactive (as shown experimentally), and by common usage the inactivity is said to be due to *internal compensation* (§7b).

§12. Correlations of sign and magnitude of rotation with absolute configuration

Brewster (1959, 1961) has devised an empirical correlation (for rotation with the sodium D line) and has used a number of general rules for this purpose. These general rules are based on the following hypothesis: A centre of optical activity can usefully be described as an asymmetric screw pattern of polarisability. This screw pattern, however, may arise in one of two ways or as a combination of both of them:

(i) *Atomic asymmetry*. If the tetrahedral system XABCD has the absolute configuration shown in (I), it is dextrorotatory when the order of polarisability of the groups is A > B > C > D.

Provided the groups A, B, C, and D are atoms or simple groups (which do not introduce conformational problems), the rules for the prediction of the sign (and magnitude) of rotation are readily applied.

(ii) *Conformational asymmetry*. In this case, the polarisability is caused by the conformation of the groups in the molecule. When this is present, its contribution to the molecular rotation is usually larger than that due to atomic asymmetry. Application of the rules for the prediction of the sign (and magnitude) of rotation is far more difficult for conformational asymmetry than for atomic asymmetry.

Atoms and groups can be arranged in order of decreasing polarisability, the individual polarisabilities being derived from the atomic refractions of the atoms attached to the asymmetric carbon atom. In this way, the following order of polarisabilities has been obtained: I > Br > SH > Cl > Ph = CO_2H > Me > NH_2 > OH > H > D > F.

Let us now use α-phenylethyl chloride (II) to illustrate the application of the rules for atomic asymmetry. The absolute configuration of (R)-α-phenylethyl chloride has been shown to be (II). Reference to the order of the

polarisabilities of the groups gives the configuration (I). Therefore this enantiomer is predicted to be dextrorotatory. This is the case in practice (the (R)-form is the dextrorotatory enantiomer). If we referred to a table of values of polarisabilities, we would also find that the magnitudes of the predicted and observed rotations are in fair agreement (see the appropriate reading references for further information).

REFERENCES

GILMAN, *Advanced Organic Chemistry*, Wiley (1943, 2nd edn.). Vol. I. Ch. 4. 'Stereoisomerism'.
WHELAND, *Advanced Organic Chemistry*, Wiley (1960, 3rd edn.).
PARTINGTON, *An Advanced Treatise on Physical Chemistry*, Longmans, Green. Vol. IV (1953), p. 290 *et seq.* 'Optical Activity'.
ELIEL, *Stereochemistry of Carbon Compounds*, McGraw-Hill (1962).
ELIEL, ALLINGER, ANGYAL and MORRISON, *Conformational Analysis*, Interscience (1965).
MISLOW, *Introduction to Stereochemistry*, Benjamin (1965).
ELIEL and ALLINGER (eds.), *Topics in Stereochemistry*, Interscience. Vols. 1–6 (1967–1971).
CAHN, 'An Introduction to the Sequence Rule: A System for the Specification of Absolute Configuration', *J. chem. Educ.*, 1964, **41**, 116.
ELIEL, 'Recent Advances in Stereochemical Nomenclature', *J. chem. Educ.*, 1971, **48**, 163.
Progress in Stereochemistry, Butterworths. Vol. 1. 1954; ————.
Cotton, *Chemical Applications of Group Theory*, Wiley-Interscience (2nd edn., 1971).
MASON, 'Optical Rotatory Power', *Quart. Rev.*, 1963, **17**, 20.
BARTON and COOKSON, 'The Principles of Conformational Analysis', *Quart. Rev.*, 1956, **10**, 44.
NEWMAN (ed.), *Steric Effects in Organic Chemistry*, Wiley (1956). Ch. I. 'Conformational Analysis'.
PETHRICK and WYN-JONES, 'The Determination of Energies Associated with Internal Rotation', *Quart. Rev.*, 1969, **23**, 301.
WILSON, 'Conformational Studies on Small Molecules', *Chem. Soc. Rev.*, 1972, **1**, 293.
BREWSTER, 'A Useful Model of Optical Activity', *J. Am. chem. Soc.*, 1959, **81**, 5475, 5483, 5493.
BREWSTER, 'Some applications of the Conformational Dissymmetry Rule', *Tetrahedron*, 1961, **13**, 106.

3 Nucleophilic substitution at a saturated carbon atom, asymmetric synthesis

The most extensively studied type of heterolytic substitution in saturated compounds is the nucleophilic type, *i.e.*, the S_N1 and S_N2 mechanisms.

One-stage process. When two molecules simultaneously undergo covalency change in the rate-determining step, the mechanism is called *bimolecular* and is labelled S_N2 (substitution, nucleophilic, bimolecular).

Two-stage process. In this case the first step is the *slow* heterolysis of the compound to form a carbonium ion, and this is then followed by the second step of *rapid* combination of the carbonium ion with the nucleophilic reagent. The rate-determining step is the first, and since in this step only *one* molecule is undergoing covalency change, the mechanism is called *unimolecular* and is labelled S_N1 (substitution, nucleophilic, unimolecular).

The symbols S_N1 and S_N2 were introduced by Ingold (1928), the number in the symbol referring to the *molecularity* of the reaction and *not* to the kinetic order. Any complex reaction may be designated by the molecularity of its rate-determining stage, the molecularity of the rate-determining stage being defined as the *number of molecules* necessarily undergoing covalency change (Ingold, 1933). It is also important to note that the definitions of S_N1 and S_N2 mechanisms do not take into account the solvation of the initial molecules and the transition states. Solvation energies play a very important part in determining the activation energies of reactions in solution (see §2e).

A number of differences exist between S_N2 and S_N1 reactions, *e.g.*, (i) When both reactants are present in small and controllable concentrations, S_N2 reactions are second-order and S_N1 reactions are first-order. In a bimolecular reaction, if one of the reactants is in constant excess, *e.g.*, one reactant is the solvent, then the mechanism is still bimolecular but the reaction is now of the first order. On the other hand, although the unimolecular mechanism often leads to first-order kinetics, it may, under certain circumstances, follow a complicated kinetic expression.

(ii) The S_N2 mechanism *always* leads to inversion of the configuration of the products, whereas with the S_N1 mechanism there may be inversion and/or retention, the amount of each depending on various factors (see later).

(iii) No rearrangement is possible with the S_N2 mechanism, but is possible (and often occurs) with the S_N1 mechanism.

(iv) The rate constant of an S_N2 reaction with a given substrate depends on the nature of the nucleophile, and for a given nucleophile, on the nature of the leaving group in the substrate.

The nucleophilic reagent may be negatively charged or neutral; the primary requirement is that it must possess an unshared pair of electrons which it can donate to a nucleus capable of sharing this pair. One widely studied example of nucleophilic aliphatic substitution is that of the hydrolysis of alkyl halides (T.S. = transition state; see also §2e).

$$S_N2 \quad Y^- + R{-}X \xrightarrow{\text{slow}} \overset{\delta^-}{Y}{\cdots}R{\cdots}\overset{\delta^-}{X} \xrightarrow{\text{fast}} Y{-}R + X^-$$
$$\text{T.S.}$$

$$S_N1 \quad R{-}X \xrightarrow{\text{slow}} \overset{\delta^+}{R}{\cdots}\overset{\delta^-}{X} \xrightarrow{\text{fast}} R^+ + X^-$$
$$\text{T.S.}$$

$$R^+ + Y^- \xrightarrow{\text{fast}} RY$$

Of particular interest is the evidence for the S_N1 mechanism. A fundamental part of this mechanism is the postulate of carbonium ions as transient intermediates. Triarylmethyl carbonium ions have been isolated as their salts, e.g., triphenylmethyl perchlorate, $Ph_3C^+ClO_4^-$, and borofluoride, $Ph_3C^+BF_4^-$ (Dauben et al., 1960). The stability of ions such as these is attributed to resonance. On the other hand, since the order of stability of alkyl carbonium ions is tertiary > secondary > primary, success is more likely to be achieved in the isolation of tertiary alkyl carbonium ions. Thus, Olah et al. (1964) have prepared, e.g., $Me_3C^+SbF_6^-$, and their infrared studies have substantiated the planar sp^2 hybridised structure of the simple alkyl carbonium ions.

A point of interest in connection with the S_N1 mechanism is that it is S_N1 because the rate-determining step is ionisation of RX. If, however, combination with Y^- is the rate-determining step, then the mechanism is referred to as the $S_N2(C^+)$ mechanism (substitution, nucleophilic, bimolecular, with a rapidly formed carbonium ion; Hughes, Ingold et al., 1954). An example of this type is the Friedel–Crafts reaction involving diarylmethanols and arenes in the presence of a strong acid (Bethell et al., 1958, 1959).

$$Ar_2^1CHOH + H^+ \underset{}{\overset{\text{fast}}{\rightleftharpoons}} Ar_2^1CHOH_2^+ \underset{}{\overset{\text{fast}}{\rightleftharpoons}} H_2O + Ar_2^1CH^+ \xrightarrow[\text{slow}]{Ar^2H} Ar_2^1CH{-}Ar^2 + H^+$$

One other point that will be mentioned here is the problem of nomenclature. The term 'carbonium ion' has been commonly used, but other terms have been proposed. Olah (1972) has suggested that the general name 'carbocation' be used for positive ions of carbon compounds (cf. 'carbanions' for negative ions). Carbocations are of two types: (i) *Carbenium ions*. These are trivalent ('classical') ions containing an sp^2-hybridised electron deficient carbon atom, and tend to be planar.

(ii) *Penta-* or *tetraco-ordinated* ('non-classical') *ions* containing a carbon atom involved in three, two-electron covalent bonds and a fourth two-electron three-centre bond. These are *carbonium ions* (this is in line with 'onium ions).

trivalent carbenium ion   pentaco-ordinated   tetraco-ordinated

carbonium ions

e.g.,

Carbenium ions have been differentiated from carbonium ions by means of spectroscopic studies, e.g., i.r., NMR (Olah et al., 1970, 1972).

§2

Any factor that affects the energy of activation (E) of a given type of reaction will affect the rate and/or the mechanism. The following discussion is largely qualitative, and because of this, one cannot be sure which are the predominant factors in deciding the energy of activation. We shall discuss, for the hydrolysis of alkyl halides, the influence of the following factors: The nature of R (polar and steric effects); the nature of X and Y; and the nature of the solvent.

§2a. **The nature of R.**   (a) *Polar effects.* Let us consider the series EtX, i-PrX, and t-BuX. Since the methyl group has a $+ I$ effect, the larger the number of methyl groups on the carbon atom of the C—X group, the greater will be the electron density on this carbon atom. This may be represented qualitatively as follows:

$$\text{Me}\longrightarrow\overset{\delta-}{\text{CH}_2}\longrightarrow\text{X} \qquad \begin{matrix}\text{Me}\\ \quad\\ \text{Me}\end{matrix}\!\!\!\overset{2\delta-}{\text{CH}}\!\!\longrightarrow\!\text{X} \qquad \begin{matrix}\text{Me}\\ \text{Me}\longrightarrow\\ \text{Me}\end{matrix}\!\!\!\overset{3\delta-}{\text{C}}\!\!\longrightarrow\!\text{X}$$

This increasing negative charge on the central carbon atom increasingly opposes attacks at this carbon by a negatively charged nucleophilic reagent; it also opposes, to a lesser extent, attack by a neutral nucleophilic reagent since this still donates an electron pair. Thus the formation of the transition state for the S_N2 mechanism is opposed more and more as the charge on the central carbon atom increases. (There is also an increasing steric effect operating; this is dealt with in §2b.) The anticipated result, therefore, is that as the number of methyl groups increases on the central carbon atom, the S_N2 mechanism is made more difficult in passing from EtX to t-BuX. On the other hand, since the S_N1 mechanism involves ionisation of RX (in the rate-determining step), any factor that makes easier the ionisation of the molecule will therefore facilitate the S_N1 mechanism. The anticipated result, therefore, is that the greater the negative charge on the central carbon atom, the easier will be the ionisation of RX since X is displaced with its covalent electron pair; thus the tendency for the S_N1 mechanism should increase from EtX to t-BuX.

An alternative explanation for the effect of the nature of R is as follows. When the S_N1 mechanism is favoured, it therefore follows the activation energy for this path is less than that for the S_N2; and *vice versa.* Since the S_N1 reaction proceeds through a carbonium ion, the more stable this ion the lower is the activation energy, and the more favoured will be this mechanism. Now, the order of stabilities of carbonium ions is prim. $< s < t$, and hence the tendency for the S_N1 mechanism to operate will be t-BuX $>$ i-PrX $>$ EtX, and the reverse tendency for the S_N2 mechanism.

These predicted results have been verified experimentally. Hughes, Ingold *et al.* (1935–1940) examined the rates of hydrolysis of alkyl bromides in alkaline aqueous ethanol at 55°C:

	MeBr	EtBr	i-PrBr	t-BuBr
2nd-order rate const. $\times 10^5$	2 140	170	4·7	
1st-order rate const. $\times 10^5$			0·24	1 010

It can be seen from these results that MeBr and EtBr undergo hydrolysis by the S_N2 mechanism, i-PrBr by *both* S_N2 and S_N1, and t-BuBr by S_N1 only. Thus, as the polar effects in the alkyl group produce an increasing electron density on the central carbon atom, the rate of the S_N2 mechanism decreases and a point is reached where the mechanism changes over to S_N1. With i-PrBr both S_N2 and S_N1 mechanisms operate, and the rate of the S_N2 mechanism is much less than that of the S_N2 mechanism for EtBr. With t-BuBr the electron density on the central carbon atom is so great that the S_N2 mechanism is completely inhibited; a very rapid hydrolysis occurs by the S_N1 mechanism only. Since the mechanism is S_N1, it therefore means that the hydroxide ion does not enter into the rate-determining step of the hydrolysis (§1). This has been proved as follows. The hydrolysis of t-BuBr was carried out in an alkaline solution containing less than the equivalent amount of hydroxide ion (compared with the alkyl bromide). Thus, although the solution was originally alkaline, as the hydrolysis proceeds, the solution becomes neutral and finally acid; nevertheless, the rate of the hydrolysis was dependent only on the alkyl bromide concentration.

As pointed out above, there are reactions which occur under intermediate conditions, *i.e.*, at the border-line between the extreme S_N1 and S_N2 mechanisms. Some authors believe that in this border-line region there is only *one* mechanism operating, *e.g.*, Prevost (1958) has postulated, on theoretical grounds, the existence of a more universal 'mesomechanism'. There is, however, much experimental work in favour of concurrent S_N1 and S_N2 mechanisms operating. Gold (1956) has described evidence for this view, and more recently Swart *et al.* (1961) have shown that the exchange reaction between diphenylmethyl chloride and radiochlorine (as LiCl*) in dimethylformamide occurs by a simultaneous S_N1–S_N2 mechanism. On the other hand, Fava *et al.* (1963) studied the following isotopic exchange with methyl cyanide as solvent ($\overset{*}{S}$ = ^{35}S):

$$Ar_2CHSCN + \overset{*}{S}CN^- \longrightarrow Ar_2CH\overset{*}{S}CN + SCN^-$$

The authors used various *p*- and *p,p'*-substituted diphenylmethyl (benzhydryl) thiocyanates, and showed that the 4-nitro compound obeyed a second-order rate law and the 4,4'-dimethyl derivative obeyed a first-order rate law. These results were interpreted as indicating S_N2 and S_N1 mechanisms respectively. The unsubstituted and the 4-chloro compound obeyed mixed first- and second-order rate laws, and the authors interpret this as a region of simultaneous S_N1 and S_N2 mechanisms.

The actual position where the mechanism changes over from S_N2 to S_N1 in a graded series, *e.g.*, in the alkyl halides, is not fixed but depends on other factors such as the concentration and nature of the nucleophilic reagent, and on the nature of the solvent (see below).

Experimental work has shown that higher n-alkyl groups behave similarly to ethyl. For a given set of conditions, the kinetic order is the same, but the rates tend to decrease as the number of carbon atoms increases, *e.g.*, Hughes, Ingold *et al.* (1946, 1948) showed that the reactions between primary alkyl bromides and ethoxide ion in dry ethanol are all S_N2, and their relative rates (at 55°C) are Me, 17·6; Et, 1·00; n-Pr, 0·31; n-Bu, 0·23; n-pentyl, 0·21. Similar results were obtained for secondary alkyl groups. In these cases the mechanisms were both S_N2 and S_N1, but the rates for one or other order were reasonably close, *e.g.*, for the second-order reactions of secondary bromides with ethoxide ion in dry ethanol at 25°C, Hughes, Ingold *et al.* (1936–   ) found that the relative rates were: i-Pr, 1·00; 2-n-Bu, 1·29; 2-n-pentyl, 1·16; 3-n-pentyl, 0·93. These authors also showed that higher tertiary alkyl groups behaved similarly to t-Bu, all showing a strong tendency to react by the S_N1 mechanism.

When hydrogen atoms in methyl chloride are replaced by phenyl groups, the mechanism of the hydrolysis may be changed (from S_N2). The presence of a phenyl group produces a carbonium ion which can be stabilised by resonance; this acts as the driving force to produce ionisation; *e.g.*,

Thus one can anticipate that as the number of phenyl groups increases, the stability of the carbonium ion produced will increase, *i.e.*, the carbonium ion will be formed more readily and consequently the S_N1 mechanism will be increasingly favoured. Thus in the series MeCl, PhCH$_2$Cl, Ph$_2$CHCl, Ph$_3$CCl, it has been found that in alkaline solution the hydrolysis of methyl chloride proceeds by the S_N2 mechanism, that of phenylmethyl chloride by both S_N2 and S_N1, and that of diphenylmethyl chloride by S_N1; the hydrolysis of triphenylmethyl chloride is too fast to be measured, but this high rate is very strong evidence for an S_N1 mechanism.

Various groups in the *para*-position of the phenyl nucleus either assist or oppose ionisation. It has been found that alkyl groups enhance ionisation in the order Me > Et > i-Pr > t-Bu. Since this order is the reverse of that expected from the general inductive effects of these groups, it has been explained by the hyperconjugative effects of these groups (which are in this order; see Vol. I). On the other hand, a nitro-group retards the ionisation; and this attributed to the electron-with-drawing effect of this group.

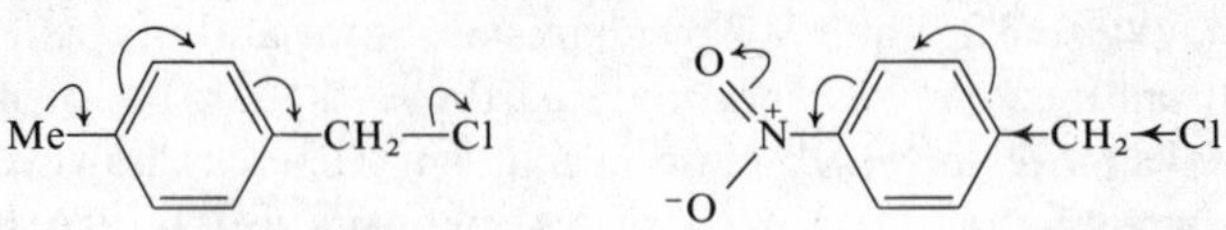

Another 'group' that has a polar effect is deuterium, which appears to be electron-releasing with respect to hydrogen. Thus, deuteration at the α-carbon atom increases the rate of solvolysis in certain types of S_N1 reactions, *e.g.*, the rate of solvolysis of Ph_2CDCl is about 17 per cent faster than that of Ph_2CHCl. This effect of deuterium is an example of the *secondary isotope effect*. On the other hand, it appears that substitution of H by D on an α-carbon atom has very little effect on the rates of S_N2 reactions. In some cases, however, the rate is decreased, and it has been suggested that deutera-tion increases the energy of activation (see also the ponderal effect, §2b).

Another group of interest is the carbonyl group; this is electron-attracting (through resonance):

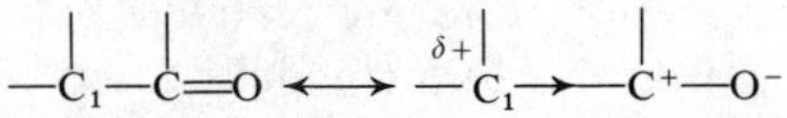

$$-\overset{|}{\underset{|}{C_1}}-\overset{|}{\underset{}{C}}=O \longleftrightarrow -\overset{\delta+|}{\underset{|}{C_1}} \rightarrow -\overset{|}{\underset{}{C}}{}^{+}-O^{-}$$

Hence, the covalent electron-pair of a halogen atom attached to C_1 is drawn closer to C_1 and consequently it is more difficult for this halogen atom to ionise. Thus the S_N1 mechanism is opposed, and at the same time, the small positive charge on C_1 encourages the S_N2 mechanism. It can therefore be anticipated that any electron-attracting (or withdrawing) group will tend to inhibit the S_N1 mechanism for a compound with an α-halogen atom. Such groups are CO_2R, NO_2, CN, etc.; *e.g.*, both ethyl α-bromopropionate and diethyl bromomalonate undergo hydrolysis by the S_N2 mechanism.

On the other hand, the carboxylate ion has a $+I$ effect due to its negative charge and hence its presence should enhance the ionisation of an α-halogen atom. At the same time, the α-carbon atom tends to acquire a small negative charge, and this will tend to oppose the approach of a hydroxide ion. Thus there are two influences acting, one increasing the tendency for the S_N1 mechanism and the other decreasing the tendency for the S_N2; both therefore oppose the S_N2 mechanism. Some experimental results that illustrate these arguments are the alkaline hydrolyses of the following compounds:

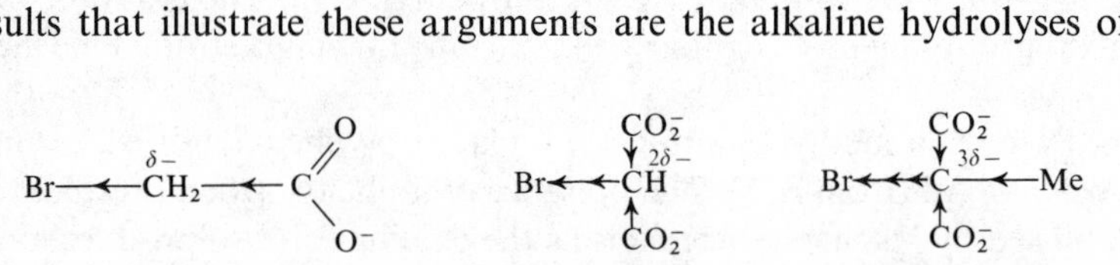

A point of interest in connection with the S_N1 mechanism is that it is catalysed by heavy metal salts, particularly silver salts. This is believed to be due to the formation of complexes, thereby facilitating ionisation, which is the rate-determining step. Complex-formation occurs by donation of a lone pair of electrons on the halogen atom to an empty orbital of the metal ion.

$$R-\overset{..}{X} + Ag^+ \underset{fast}{\overset{fast}{\rightleftharpoons}} [R-X-Ag]^+ \xrightarrow{slow} AgX + R^+ \xrightarrow[fast]{OH^-} ROH$$

§2b. The nature of R.   (*b*) *Steric effects.* In the transition state for the S_N2 mechanism, there are five atoms or groups bonded or partly bonded to the reaction carbon atom (see §4). Thus the larger the bulk of these groups, the greater will be the compression energy (*i.e.*, greater steric strain) in the transition state and consequently the reaction will be *sterically hindered*. The problem is different for the S_N1 mechanism. Here, the transition state does not contain more than four groups attached to the reaction carbon atom and hence one would expect that steric hindrance should be less important. On the other hand, if the molecule undergoing the S_N1 mechanism contains particularly large groups, then the first step of ionisation may relieve the steric strain (**2** §4a) and so assist the formation of the carbonium ion, *i.e.*, the reaction may be *sterically accelerated* (see below).

Let us now examine some examples involving steric effects.

(i) The following series of alkyl halides, MeX, EtX, isoPrX and t-BuX, may be made to undergo the S_N2 mechanism under suitable conditions (*cf.* §2a); the transition state contains three σ-bonds (sp^2 hybridisation) in one plane and two partial bonds which are collinear and perpendicular to this plane. Thus we have:

$$
\begin{array}{cccc}
\overset{\displaystyle H}{\underset{\displaystyle H}{\overset{|}{\underset{/}{Y^{-\frac{1}{2}}\!-\!\!-\!\!-\!C\!-\!\!-\!\!-\!X^{-\frac{1}{2}}}}}}\;H
&
\overset{\displaystyle Me}{\underset{\displaystyle H}{\overset{|}{\underset{/}{Y^{-\frac{1}{2}}\!-\!\!-\!\!-\!C\!-\!\!-\!\!-\!X^{-\frac{1}{2}}}}}}\;H
&
\overset{\displaystyle Me}{\underset{\displaystyle Me}{\overset{|}{\underset{/}{Y^{-\frac{1}{2}}\!-\!\!-\!\!-\!C\!-\!\!-\!\!-\!X^{-\frac{1}{2}}}}}}\;H
&
\overset{\displaystyle Me}{\underset{\displaystyle Me}{\overset{|}{\underset{/}{Y^{-\frac{1}{2}}\!-\!\!-\!\!-\!C\!-\!\!-\!\!-\!X^{-\frac{1}{2}}}}}}\;Me
\end{array}
$$

Inspection of these transition states shows that steric hindrance increases as the hydrogen atoms are progressively replaced by methyl groups. This increasing steric effect has been demonstrated by Hughes *et al.* (1946), who showed that the relative reactivities of the alkyl bromides towards iodide ions in acetone (by the S_N2 mechanism) are: Me, 10 000; Et, 65; isoPr, 0·50; t-Bu, 0·039. However, as we saw above (§2a), the polar effect opposes the S_N2 mechanism in the order t-Bu > isoPr > Et > Me. Hence this factor will also affect rates in the same direction as steric effects. On the other hand, if we now consider the S_N2 mechanism for n-propyl; isobutyl and neopentyl halides, then, since there are no methyl groups on the α-carbon atom, polar effects are almost completely absent (inductive effects fall off very rapidly from the source). Hence any differences in reaction rates among these three compounds may be attributed solely to steric effects (but see later).

$$
\begin{array}{ccc}
\overset{\displaystyle H\;\;Me\;\;H}{\overset{\diagdown\;|\;\diagup}{\underset{\displaystyle H\;H}{\underset{\diagup\;}{\overset{\displaystyle C}{|}\\ Y^{-\frac{1}{2}}\!-\!\!-\!\!-\!C\!-\!\!-\!\!-\!X^{-\frac{1}{2}}}}}}
&
\overset{\displaystyle Me\;Me\;H}{\overset{\diagdown\;|\;\diagup}{\underset{\displaystyle H\;H}{\underset{\diagup\;}{\overset{\displaystyle C}{|}\\ Y^{-\frac{1}{2}}\!-\!\!-\!\!-\!C\!-\!\!-\!\!-\!X^{-\frac{1}{2}}}}}}
&
\overset{\displaystyle Me\;Me\;Me}{\overset{\diagdown\;|\;\diagup}{\underset{\displaystyle H\;H}{\underset{\diagup\;}{\overset{\displaystyle C}{|}\\ Y^{-\frac{1}{2}}\!-\!\!-\!\!-\!C\!-\!\!-\!\!-\!X^{-\frac{1}{2}}}}}}
\end{array}
$$

At first sight one would not expect n-PrX to show an added steric effect when compared with EtX since the added methyl group can occupy a position close to the plane of the transition state (*i.e.*, the plane containing the three σ-bonds), and so would not offer any appreciable steric hindrance. In practice, however, n-propyl halides are less reactive than the corresponding ethyl halides (*cf.* §2a). Magat *et al.* (1950) have offered the following explanation. The smaller the number of conformations available in the activated as compared with the initial state produces a decrease in the frequency factor (A in the Arrhenius equation $k = Ae^{-E/RT}$). In n-propyl halides (2 H and 1 Me) there is only one conformation for the transition state whereas for ethyl halides (3 H) there are three equivalent conformations. Thus the frequency factor for n-propyl halides is 1/3 that for the ethyl halides, and so the rate constant (k) of the former will be 1/3 that of the latter (on the assumption that E of both reactions is the same).

In isobutyl halides the methyl groups will produce a large steric effect since at least one methyl group will be fairly close to X or Y. It has been shown experimentally that isobutyl halides are less reactive than n-propyl halides. Finally, in neopentyl halides, the presence of three methyl groups produces a very large steric effect. In the 'normal' transition state, the entering and displaced groups are collinear. This is readily possible with all the halides except possibly isobutyl halides; but it is not possible with neopentyl halides because of the presence of the three methyl groups (in the t-butyl group). Thus in the transition state involving the neopentyl group, the Y---C---X bonds are not collinear but 'bent away' from the t-butyl group. Such a 'bent' transition state has a large compression energy and so is far more difficult to form than a 'normal' transition state. Experimental data are in agreement with these ideas, *e.g.*, Hughes *et al.* (1946) showed the following relative (S_N2) reaction rates towards the ethoxide ion at 95°C:

$$Et : isoBu : Me_3CCH_2 :: 1 : 0.04 : 10^{-5}$$

These very slow S_N2 reactions of neopentyl halides occur with the neopentyl group remaining intact. By changing the solvent conditions so that the mechanism becomes S_N1, the products are no longer neopentyl derivatives but rearranged products formed by a 1,2-shift (see **8** §23d).

The foregoing discussion (of both polar and steric effects) has been purely qualitative, but Ingold (1957) has considered steric effects on a quantitative basis. One reaction discussed is the following iodine exchange by the S_N2 mechanism:

$$I^- + RI \longrightarrow IR + I^-$$

The iodine positions in the transition states were calculated in terms of the amount of stretching (Δl) of the C—I half-bond and the deviation (Δa) of the I---C---I bond angle from 180° (*i.e.*, the amount of bending):

R	Δl (Å)	Δa (degrees)
Me	0·36	0·0
Et	0·37	3·8
isoPr	0·38	5·0
t-Bu	0·40	0·0
n-Pr	0·37	3·8
isoBu	0·39	5·0
neoPe	0·43	17·6

It can be seen that there is no bending in the methyl and t-butyl transition states (these are symmetrical), but all the other transition states have bent bonds and all show stretching, some more than others. The neo-compound has both the largest stretching and the largest bending, and so will be the least reactive of all, and can be expected to be much less reactive than any of the others because of the very large increase in bending. Thus stretching and bending are both important factors in transitions states.

Ingold has also calculated steric increments of activation energies, with the energy of the methyl transition state being taken as zero. The values obtained for the reaction follow the order neoPe > isoBu > t-Bu > isoPr > n-Pr = Et > Me. For the exchange reactions $Cl^- + RCl$ and $Br^- + RBr$ *both* followed the order neoPe > t-Bu > isoBu > isoPr > n-Pr = Et > Me. The *observed* increments of activation energies (with MeX as zero) are all higher than the steric increments. If this difference is attributed to the contribution by the polar effect, then it is found that the differences may be correlated with contributions of methyl groups only on the α-carbon atom; β-methyl groups do not produce any appreciable differences. Thus the order of polar effect is t-Bu > isoPr > neoPe = isoBu = n-Pr = Et > Me. However, when Ingold calculated the frequency factors of reaction rate, he found a factor, which was neither polar nor steric, was also operating. This he called the *ponderal effect* because it depends on mass and is independent of bulk and distribution of any charge which the group may carry. The addition of neutrons (which have mass but no bulk and no charge) to an alkyl group by means of isotopic substitution would produce a pure ponderal effect (*cf.* the replacement of H by D in the secondary isotope effect). Thus there are three factors which can affect rates of reaction: polar, steric, and ponderal.

(ii) So far, we have discussed steric effects in alkyl halides only. However, these effects may also operate in S_N reactions involving other types of compounds. A very interesting example is 1-chloro-apocamphane (I). Bartlett *et al.* (1938) found that this compound does not react with reagents that normally react with alkyl halides, *e.g.*, it is unaffected when refluxed with aqueous ethanolic potassium hydroxide or with ethanolic silver nitrate. As we have seen, the hydrolysis of t-butyl chloride takes place by the S_N1 mechanism. 1-Chloroapocamphane is a tertiary chloride, but since it does not ionise, the S_N1 mechanism is not possible. This failure to ionise is believed to be due to the fact that the carbonium ion is flat (sp^2 hybridisation). Removal of the chloride ion from (I) would produce a positive carbon atom which *cannot* become planar because of the steric requirements of the bridged-ring structure. Furthermore, since the rear of the carbon atom of the C—Cl group is 'protected' by the bridge, the S_n2 mechanism is not possible (since the nucleophilic reagent must

Cl   Br   Br   Br

H

(I)   (II)   (III)   (IV)

attack from the rear; see §4). The failure to replace bromine in 1-bromotriptycene (II) is explained similarly (Bartlett *et al.*, 1939). On the other hand, Doering *et al.* (1953) showed that (III) gave the corresponding alcohol when heated with aqueous silver nitrate at 150°C for two days, and (IV) gave the corresponding alcohol after four hours at room temperature. The reason for this behaviour (as compared with the other bridged compounds) is not certain, but it has been suggested that the extra bonds in the larger bridge in (IV) help to relieve the strain in the formation of the carbonium ion which tries to assume a planar configuration.

(iii) Steric effects also operate in the solvolysis of tertiary halides. (*Solvolysis* is the nucleophilic reaction in which the *solvent* is the nucleophilic reagent.)

$$R_3C-X \xrightarrow{H_2O} R_3C^+ + X^-$$

tetrahedral   planar; trigonal
(large strain)   (small strain)

Brown *et al.* (1949) showed that these compounds are subject to steric acceleration. It was shown that as R increases in size, the rate of solvolysis increases. However, the larger R is, the more slowly will the carbonium ion be expected to react with the solvent molecules, and so a factor is introduced which opposes steric acceleration. Carbonium ions can undergo elimination reactions to form alkenes (see Vol. I), and Brown *et al.* (1950) have shown that this elimination reaction increases as the R groups become larger (see also 4 §5m).

§2c. **The nature of the halogen atom.** Experimental work has shown that the nature of the halogen atom has very little effect, if any, on *mechanism*, but it does affect the *rate* of reaction. Thus it has been found that in both S_N1 and S_N2 reactions, the rate follows the order RI > RBr > RCl. It has been suggested that a contributing factor to this order is steric strain, since the volume order of these halogen atoms is I > Br > Cl. Another contributing factor which has been suggested is that the polarisability of the C—X bond decreases in the order C—I > C—Br > C—Cl.

Experimental work has shown that many S_N2 reactions of alkyl chlorides and bromides are catalysed by the presence of iodide ions. This may be explained on the basis that the activation energies of both steps in reaction (i) are lower than the activation energy of the one-step reaction (ii):

(i) $I^- + R-Cl \longrightarrow I-R + Cl^- \xrightarrow{OH^-} ROH + I^- + Cl^-$

(ii) $HO^- + R-Cl \longrightarrow HO-R + Cl^-$

As an outcome of much experimental work, it has been found that the order of ease of displacement of groups is not fixed. In general, the stronger the displaced group is as a base, the less facile is it as a 'leaving group' in displacement reactions. However, the order of ease of displacement depends on a number of factors, e.g., the nature of the alkyl group, solvent, etc. It appears that the order is generally:

$$OTs > I > Br > Cl > OH_2^+ > F > OAc > NR_3^+ > OR > NR_2$$

§2d. The nature of the nucleophilic reagent.   The more pronounced the nucleophilic reactivity of the reagent, the more the S_N2 mechanism will be favoured as compared with the S_N1 mechanism, since in the latter the nucleophilic reagent does not enter into the rate-determining step.

It can be anticipated that as nucleophilic reactivity decreases, the rate of an S_N2 reaction will decrease for a given series of substitutions (under similar conditions), and when the nucleophilic activity is sufficiently low, the mechanism may change from S_N2 to S_N1.

Just as the order of ease of displacement of groups depends on a number of factors, so does the order of *nucleophilicity* (nucleophilic reactivity). In general, the order of nucleophilicity is:

$$PhS^- > CN^- > I^- > EtO^- > OH^- > Br^- > PhO^- > Cl^- > Me_3N$$

It should be noted that *nucleophilicity* is the ability to form bonds to *carbon atoms*, whereas *basicity* is the *affinity for protons*. It should also be noted that nucleophilicity is a kinetic property, *i.e.*, is a measure of rate of reaction, whereas basicity is a thermodynamic property, *i.e.*, is a measure of the value of the equilibrium constant. Even so, it might have been expected that there would be some sort of parallelism between the two. Although this is often the case, deviations also occur, particularly with elements in the same periodic group, *e.g.*, RS^- is much more reactive as a nucleophile but is much less basic than RO^-. One possible explanation is that the former has greater polarisability than the latter (*cf.* §2c). On the other hand, the degree of solvation of the two ions will be different, and this may be an important factor.

§2e. The effect of the solvent on mechanisms and reaction rates.   Experimentally, it has been found that the ionising power of a solvent depends on at least two factors, dielectric constant and solvation.
Dielectric constant. A very rough generalisation is that ionisation of the solute increases both in amount and speed the higher the dielectric constant of the solvent.
Solvation. This factor appears to be more important than the dielectric constant. Solvation is the interaction between solvent molecules and solute molecules, and is partly accounted for by the attraction of a charge for a dipole. If the solute has polarity, then solvent molecules will be attracted to the solute molecules. The greater the polarity of the solvent, the greater the attraction and consequently the more closely the solvent molecules will be drawn to the solute molecules. Thus more electrostatic work is done and so more energy is lost by the system, which therefore becomes more stable. Hence, increasing the dielectric constant of the solvent increases the ionising potentiality of the solute molecules, and the higher the polarity of the solvent the more stable becomes the system due to increased solvation. Solvation, however, may also be partly due to certain chemical properties, *e.g.*, sulphur dioxide has an electrophilic centre (the sulphur atom carries a positive charge); hydroxylic solvents can form hydrogen bonds.

Some common solvents and their dielectric constants and dipole moments (in Debye units) are: water (81·1; 2–3); formic acid (48·0; 1·5); nitrobenzene (35·7; 4·0); ethanol (25·8; 1·7); acetone (21·3; 3·0); acetic acid (7·1; 1–1·5); chloroform (4·6; 1·1); ether (4·3; 1·25); benzene (2·3; 0); carbon tetrachloride (2·2; 0).

There is also another problem that may arise. This is that although the solute molecules have ionised, the oppositely charged ions behave as a single unit, the pair being held together by electrostatic attraction. Such a complex is known as an *ion-pair*, and their recombination is known as *internal return*. It has now been shown that the majority of reactions involving carbonium-ion intermediates proceed *via* ion-pairs rather than dissociated ions. According to some authors there are two types of ion-pairs:

(i) *Intimate* or *internal* ion-pairs. These are enclosed in a solvent cage and the ions of the pair are *not* separated by solvent molecules.

(ii) *Loose* or *external* ion-pairs. The ions of these pairs are separated by solvent molecules but still behave as a pair. External ion-pairs may also give rise to ion-pair return (*external return*), but they are more susceptible to attack by other reagents than are intimate ion-pairs.

Thus, when ionisation takes place, the following steps are possible:

$$\xrightarrow{\text{Ionisation}} \qquad\qquad \xrightarrow{\text{Dissociation}}$$

$$RX \underset{-1}{\overset{1}{\rightleftharpoons}} R^+X^- \underset{-2}{\overset{2}{\rightleftharpoons}} R^+ \| X^- \overset{3}{\rightleftharpoons} R^+ + X^-$$

$$\qquad\quad \text{intimate} \qquad\;\; \text{external} \qquad\quad \text{dissociated}$$
$$\qquad\quad \text{ion-pair} \qquad\;\; \text{ion-pair} \qquad\qquad \text{ions}$$

N.B. (i) -1 is internal return; (ii) -2 is external return; (iii) only equilibrium 3 is sensitive to a common ion effect; this is because an ion-pair behaves as a single particle, as has been shown by the effect on the depression of the freezing point ($i = 1$); (iv) the formation of ion-pairs is favoured in solvents of low polarity. This is due to the fact that highly polar solvents, although they assist ionisation, *i.e.*, encourage the S_N1 mechanism, also cause dissociation by solvation of the ions.

There is a great deal of evidence to support the formation of ion-pairs as intermediates, *e.g.*, *the special salt effect*. In the acetolysis of some alkyl tosylates, the rate of acetolysis is increased sharply on the addition of *small* amounts of lithium bromide or lithium perchlorate. On further addition of the salt, the rate drops to the normal essentially linear acceleration (which is caused by the *normal salt effect*). The explanation offered for the special salt effect is as follows.

$$ROTs \rightleftharpoons R^+OTs^- \rightleftharpoons R^+ \| OTs^- \rightleftharpoons R^+ + OTs^-$$
$$(I) \qquad\quad (II) \qquad\qquad (III) \qquad\qquad\quad (IV)$$

$$\qquad\qquad\qquad\qquad\quad \downarrow \text{LiBr} \qquad\qquad\; \downarrow \text{LiBr}$$

$$\qquad\qquad\qquad\qquad R^+ \| Br^- \qquad\qquad RBr$$
$$\qquad\qquad\qquad\qquad\quad (V)$$

The solvent-separated ion-pair (III) may collapse to regenerate (II) and (I) or dissociate to give (IV). In the presence of, *e.g.*, lithium bromide, (III) but not (II) is 'trapped' to form (V) and so is prevented from reforming (II); (IV) reacts in the normal way to give the products. Because of the removal of (III) to form (IV) and thence the products, the return of (III) to (II) and (I) is prevented, thereby rapidly increasing the rate of formation of the product.

A point to note about intimate ion-pairs is that their geometry is very similar to that of the transition states from which they are derived. Thus, in an intimate ion-pair, the negative ion is very close to the carbonium-ion face from which it departed.

In general, S_N1 reactions will be written as direct dissociation into the two ions unless ion-pairs must be used to explain, in detail, the course of the reaction.

A number of equations have been proposed correlating rates and the nature of the solvent, but none is completely general (see below). Hughes and Ingold (1935, 1948) proposed the following qualitative theory of solvent effects: (i) Ions and polar molecules, when dissolved in polar solvents, tend to become solvated. (ii) For a given solvent, solvation tends to increase with increasing magnitude of charge on the solute molecules or ions. (iii) For a given solute, solvation tends to increase with the increasing dipole moment of the solvent. (iv) For a given magnitude of charge, solvation decreases as the charge is spread over a larger volume. (v) The decrease in solvation due to the dispersal of charge will be less than that due to its destruction.

Since the rate-determining step in the S_N1 mechanism is ionisation, any factor assisting this ionisation will therefore facilitate S_N1 reactions. Solvents with high dipole moments are usually good ionising media and, in general, it has been found that the more polar the solvent the greater is the rate of S_N1 reactions. We have, however, also to consider the problem of solvation.

$$R\text{---}X \xrightarrow{\text{slow}} \overset{\delta+}{R} \text{---} \overset{\delta-}{X} \xrightarrow{\text{fast}} R^+ + X^- \xrightarrow[\text{slow}]{OH^-} ROH$$

Increasing the polarity of the solvent will greatly increase the reaction rate, and since the transition state has a larger charge than the initial reactant molecule, the former is more solvated than the latter (rule ii). Thus the transition state is more stabilised than the reactant molecule, and solvation therefore lowers the energy of activation and so the reaction is assisted.

The rates of S_N2 reactions are also affected by the polarity of the solvent.

$$HO^- \; R\text{---}X \xrightarrow{\text{slow}} \overset{\delta-}{HO}\text{---}R\text{---}\overset{\delta-}{X} \xrightarrow{\text{fast}} HO\text{---}R + X^-$$

A solvent with high dipole moment will solvate both the reactant ion and the transition state, but more so the former than the latter, since in the latter the charge, although unchanged in magnitude ($\delta- = -1/2$), is more dispersed than in the former (rule iv). Thus solvation tends to stabilise the reactants more than the transition state, $i.e.$, the activation energy is increased and so the reaction is retarded.

Now let us consider the Menschutkin reaction (1890):

$$R_3N \; R\text{---}X \longrightarrow R_3\overset{\delta+}{N}\text{---}R\text{---}\overset{\delta-}{X} \longrightarrow R_4N^+X^-$$

The charge on the transition state is greater than that on the reactant molecules; hence the former is more solvated than the latter. Thus the energy of activation is lowered and the rate of reaction thereby increased. Also, the greater the polarity of the solvent, the greater should be the solvation. The foregoing predictions have been observed experimentally.

In the following S_N2 reaction, charges decrease in the transition state,

$$HO^- \; R\overset{+}{N}R_3 \longrightarrow \overset{\delta-}{HO}\text{---}R\text{---}\overset{\delta+}{N}R_3 \longrightarrow HOR + R_3N$$

and hence increasing the polarity of the solvent will retard the reaction; and retardation will be greater than that in the S_N2 hydrolysis of alkyl halides (see above; only the hydroxide ion is charged in this case).

The polarity of the solvent not only affects rates of reactions, but may also change the mechanism of a reaction, $e.g.$, Olivier (1934) showed that the alkaline hydrolysis of benzyl chloride in 50 per cent aqueous acetone proceeds by both the S_N2 and S_N1 mechanisms. In water as solvent, the mechanism was changed to mainly S_N1. The dipole moment of water is greater than that of aqueous acetone, and consequently the ionisation of benzyl chloride is facilitated.

Another example we shall consider is the hydrolysis of the alkyl bromides, MeBr, EtBr, isoPrBr and t-BuBr. As we have seen (§2a), Hughes, Ingold $et\ al.$ showed that in aqueous alkaline ethanol the mechanism changed from S_N2 for MeBr and EtBr to both S_N2 and S_N1 for isoPrBr, and to S_N1 for t-BuBr. These results were explained by the $+I$ effects of the R groups, but it also follows that the greater the ionising power of the solvent, the less will be the $+I$ effect of an R group necessary to change the mechanism from S_N2 to S_N1. Formic acid has been found to be an extremely powerful ionising solvent for alkyl halides, and the relative rates of hydrolysis, at $100°C$, for the above series of bromides with the very weak nucleophilic reagent water, dissolved in formic acid, was found to be (Hughes $et\ al.$, 1937, 1940): MeBr, 1·00; EtBr, 1·71; isoPrBr, 44·7; t-BuBr, $ca.$ 10^8. This continuous increase in reaction rate shows that the mechanism is mainly S_N1 (the rate increasing with the increasing $+I$ effect of the R group). Thus both MeBr and EtBr are also hydrolysed by the S_N1 mechanism under these favourable conditions of high solvent-ionising power.

Solvents may also affect the proportions of the products in competitive reactions, *i.e.*, the attack on the same substrate by two substituting reagents in the same solution:

$$RY \xleftarrow{\quad Y \quad} RX \xrightarrow{\quad Z \quad} RZ$$

In the S_N2 mechanism there is only one reaction step, and so the overall rate and product ratio will be determined by that stage. In the S_N1 mechanism, however, the rate is determined by the rate of ionisation of RX, and the product ratio is thus determined by the competition of the fast second steps (see also **4** §5m). It therefore follows that for solvent changes, in the S_N2 mechanism the rate and product ratio will proceed in a parallel fashion, whereas in the S_N1 mechanism the rate and product ratio will be independent of each other. A simple example that illustrates this problem is the solvolysis of benzhydryl chloride (diphenylmethyl chloride). Hammett *et al.* (1937, 1938) showed that the solvolysis of benzhydryl chloride in initially neutral aqueous ethanol gave benzhydryl ethyl ether and benzhydrol. Hughes, Ingold *et al.* (1938) showed that if ethanol is first used as solvent and then water is progressively added, the overall rate increases, but there is very little increase in benzhydrol formation; the main effect is an increased rate of formation of benzhydryl ethyl ether. Hence the rate of the reaction and the ratio of the products are determined independently; this is consistent with the S_N1 mechanism but not with the S_N2.

It can be seen from this example that kinetic solvent effects may be used to differentiate between S_N2 and S_N1 mechanisms.

The above discussion of solvent effects has been purely qualitative, but it is also of interest to consider the problem in a quantitative way. This involves the use of the following thermochemical cycle.

RX (solvated) $\xrightarrow[\text{(ionisation)}]{1}$ R$^+$ solvated + X$^-$ (solvated)

2 | (desolvation) 6 ↑ (solvation) 7 ↑ (solvation)

                          R$^+$ (vapour)   X$^-$ (vapour)

                          4 ↑ ($-e$) 5 ↑ ($+e$)

RX (vapour) $\xrightarrow[\text{(dissociation)}]{3}$ R·(vapour) + X·(vapour)

Then, if the enthalpy change for each step is represented by the number (of the step) as a subscript, it follows from Hess's law that

$$\Delta H_1 = \Delta H_2 + \Delta H_3 + \Delta H_4 + \Delta H_5 + \Delta H_6 + \Delta H_7$$

(where ΔH_4 is the ionisation energy of R· and ΔH_5 is the electron affinity of X·).

All of these values except ΔH_2 have been calculated from suitable experimental data, and the value of ΔH_2 has been estimated. The values given in the following discussion are those used by Frazer and Singer (see Reading References).

In the gas phase, if the reaction is homolytic, ΔH for step 3 in the above cycle is ΔH_3. If we use methyl chloride as our example, then ΔH_3 is +80 kcal. If, however, the reaction is heterolytic,

$$\Delta H = \Delta H_3 + \Delta H_4 + \Delta H_5 = +334 \cdot 7 + 970 \cdot 7 - 364 \cdot 0 = 941 \cdot 4 \text{ kJ}$$

It can be seen that heterolytic reaction in the gas phase is very unfavourable energetically. If the reaction is carried out in water (as solvent), then

$$\Delta H_1 = +33 \cdot 7 + 334 \cdot 7 + 970 \cdot 7 - 364 \cdot 0 - 343 \cdot 1 - 288 \cdot 7$$
$$= +343 \cdot 1 \text{ kJ}$$

This much more favourable value is due to the large contribution of the heats of solvation (ΔH_6 and ΔH_7).

As we have already seen, in the S_N1 mechanism (with all ions and molecules solvated):

$$RX_{(aq.)} \underset{slow}{\rightleftharpoons} R^+_{(aq.)} + X^-_{(aq.)} \xrightarrow[fast]{H_2O} ROH_{(aq.)} + H^+_{(aq.)}$$

the rate order is t-Bu > isoPr > Et > Me. The following table (Frazer and Singer, 1964) gives the values of ΔH_1 (heat of ionisation in kJ mol^{-1}) for various alkyl halides.

Group	Cl	Br	I
Me	343·1	343·1	364·0
Et	238·5	213·4	238·5
isoPr	104·6	96·23	115·1
t-Bu	71·13	62·76	75·31

Inspection of this table shows that in going in a downward direction for a given halogen atom, ΔH_1 decreases rapidly. Moreover, calculations have shown that ΔH_1 and E (activation energy) are almost identical. Hence the rate of the S_N1 reaction will increase in the downward direction, *i.e.*, t-Bu > isoPr > Et > Me.

It has been mentioned (§2c) that the rates of both S_N1 and S_N2 reactions for a given alkyl group is RI > RBr > RCl. The above table indicates the order (for S_N1) RBr > RCl > RI. This illustrates the point that even though a quantitative approach to a problem is always desirable, unless all the necessary values are known (reasonably) accurately, estimates may lead to some wrong conclusions. This is more the case with reactions in solution than with gas-phase reactions.

It has been mentioned above that a number of equations have been proposed correlating rates of solvolysis and the nature of the solvent. We shall now discuss this problem in a little more detail. One of the outstanding difficulties in this connection is that the structure of liquids is still uncertain. One quantitative correlation was proposed by Grunwald and Winstein (1948, 1951). This is the linear free energy equation (see, *e.g.*, the Hammett equation, Vol. 1):

$$\log (k/k_0) = mY$$

The *standard reaction* chosen for this equation is the solvolysis of t-butyl chloride, and the *standard solvent* is 80 per cent aqueous ethanol (80 volumes of ethanol and 20 volumes of water). This substrate was chosen for the standard reaction because it has been well established that it undergoes solvolysis by the S_N1 mechanism. Hence, k_0 is the rate constant for the solvolysis of t-butyl chloride by the S_N1 mechanism in the standard solvent. k is the rate constant for the solvolysis of any particular compound in any given solvent; Y is a parameter that is a measure of the *ionising power* of the given solvent; m is a parameter that is a measure of the *sensitivity* of the rate of solvolysis of the particular compound to changes in the ionising power of the solvent. By definition, $m = 1·00$ for t-butyl chloride, and $Y = 0·00$ for the standard solvent.

Experimental results showed that the values of m were close to unity for compounds undergoing solvolysis by the S_N1 mechanism, but were much smaller (between 0·25 and 0·35) for compounds undergoing solvolysis by the S_N2 mechanism. This is in keeping with expectation that S_N1 reactions would be sensitive to the ionising power of the solvent, whereas S_N2 reactions would not. Thus, the determination of m could be used as a means of ascertaining whether a particular compound is undergoing solvolysis by the S_N1 or S_N2 mechanism in a given solvent.

If m and Y were truly characteristic of the nature of the compound and the solvent, respectively, the plot of $\log k$ for a particular compound against the values of Y of different solvents would be a straight line with slope *m*. In practice, many deviations from the equation have been observed. Winstein *et al.* (1956) modified the original equation, and other workers have also proposed various correlations. The difficulty of obtaining a good correlation between rates of solvolysis and some property of solvents is due to the fact that, apart from the problem of the structure of liquids (see above), factors other than those considered in deriving the equations must be determined and consequently included in the equation.

§3. The Walden inversion (Optical inversion)

By a series of replacement reactions, Walden (1893, 1895) transformed an optically active compound into its enantiomer. In some cases the product is 100 per cent optically pure, *i.e.*, the inversion is quantitative; in other cases the product is a mixture of the (+)- and (−)-forms in unequal amounts, *i.e.*, inversion and retention (racemisation) have taken place.

The phenomenon was first discovered by Walden with the following reactions:

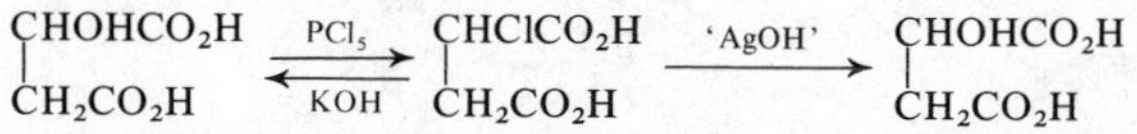

$$\begin{array}{ccc}
\text{CHOHCO}_2\text{H} & \xrightarrow[\text{KOH}]{\text{PCl}_5} & \text{CHClCO}_2\text{H} & \xrightarrow{\text{`AgOH`}} & \text{CHOHCO}_2\text{H} \\
| & & | & & | \\
\text{CH}_2\text{CO}_2\text{H} & & \text{CH}_2\text{CO}_2\text{H} & & \text{CH}_2\text{CO}_2\text{H}
\end{array}$$

(−)-malic acid (I)   (+)-chlorosuccinic acid (II)   (+)-malic acid (III)

In one, and only one, of the two reactions must there be an interchange of position between the two groups, *e.g.*, if the configuration of (I) corresponds with that of (II), the inversion of configuration must have taken place between (II) and (III). The term *Walden inversion* is applied to any step in a reaction in which inversion of configuration occurs.

As the above experiment stands, there is no way of telling which step is accompanied by inversion. As we have seen (**2** §5b), change in sign of rotation does not necessarily mean that inversion of configuration has occurred. Various methods of correlating configuration have already been described (**2** §5a), but here we shall describe the method where bonds attached to the chiral centre are broken during the course of the reactions. This method was established by Kenyon *et al.* (1925), who carried out a series of reactions on optically active hydroxy compounds. Now it has been established that in the esterification of a monocarboxylic acid by an alcohol under ordinary conditions, the reaction proceeds by the acyl-oxygen fission mechanism (see also Vol. I); thus;

$$\text{R}^1\text{CO—OH} \quad \text{H—OR}^2 \longrightarrow \text{R}^1\text{COOR}^2 + \text{H}_2\text{O}$$

Kenyon assumed that in all reactions of this type the R^2—O bond remained intact and consequently no inversion of the alcohol is possible. The following chart shows a series of reactions carried out on ethyl (+)-lactate; Ts = tosyl group = *p*-toluenesulphonyl group, $p\text{-MeC}_6\text{H}_4\text{SO}_2\text{-}$; the symbol ↝ is used to represent inversion of configuration in that step. (IV) and (VI) have the same relative configurations even though the sign of rotation has changed. Similarly, (IV) and (V) have the same relative configurations. Reaction of (V) with potassium acetate, however, produces (VII), the enantiomer of (VI). Therefore inversion must have occurred in the formation of (VII); (V) and (VI) are produced without inversion since in these cases the C—O bond in (IV) is never broken. It should be noted here that if inversion is going to take place at all, the *complete group* attached to the chiral centre must be removed (in a displacement reaction) (*cf.* Fischer's work on (+)-isopropylmalonamic acid, **2** §3a). The converse, however, is not true, *i.e.*, removal of a complete group does not invariably result in inversion (see later, particularly §4).

The above series of reactions has been used as a standard, and all closely analogous reactions are assumed to behave in a similar way, *e.g.*, the action of lithium chloride on the tosylate (V) is assumed

$$
\begin{array}{ccc}
\overset{Me}{\underset{H}{\diagdown}}\overset{CO_2Et}{\underset{OH}{C}}\diagup & \xrightarrow{\;TsCl\;} & \overset{Me}{\underset{H}{\diagdown}}\overset{CO_2Et}{\underset{OTs}{C}}\diagup \\
(+)\text{-; (IV)} & & (+)\text{-; (V)}
\end{array}
$$

$$
\begin{array}{ccc}
\Big\downarrow Ac_2O & & \Big\downarrow AcO^-K^+ \\
\overset{Me}{\underset{H}{\diagdown}}\overset{CO_2Et}{\underset{OAc}{C}}\diagup & & \overset{Me}{\underset{H}{\diagdown}}\overset{OAc}{\underset{CO_2Et}{C}}\diagup \\
(-)\text{-; (VI)} & & (+)\text{-; (VII)}
\end{array}
$$

to be analogous to that of potassium acetate, and the chloride produced thus has an inverted configuration:

$$
\overset{Me}{\underset{H}{\diagdown}}\overset{CO_2Et}{\underset{OTs}{C}}\diagup \xrightarrow[\;o\;]{\;LiCl\;} \overset{Me}{\underset{H}{\diagdown}}\overset{Cl}{\underset{CO_2Et}{C}}\diagup
$$
$$
\text{(V)}
$$

By similar procedures, Kenyon *et al.* (1929, 1930) showed that (+)-octan-2-ol and (+)-2-chloro-, 2-bromo- and 2-iodo-octane have the same relative configurations; and also that (+)-α-hydroxy-ethylbenzene (PhCHOHMe), (+)-α-chloro- and (+)-α-bromoethylbenzene have the same relative configurations (see also the S_N2 mechanism, §4).

§4. Mechanism of the Walden inversion

As the result of a large amount of work on the Walden inversion, it has been found that at least three factors play a part in deciding whether inversion or retention (racemisation) will occur: (i) the nature of the reagent; (ii) the nature of the substrate; (iii) the nature of the solvent. Hence it is necessary to explain these factors when dealing with the mechanism of the Walden inversion.

Many theories have been proposed, but we shall discuss only the Hughes–Ingold theory, since this is the one now accepted. According to this theory, aliphatic nucleophilic substitution reactions may take place by either the S_N2 or S_N1 mechanism (see also §5).

$$
S_N2 \qquad\qquad HO^- \; R\overset{\frown}{-}X \longrightarrow \overset{\delta-}{HO}\text{---}R\text{---}\overset{\delta-}{X} \longrightarrow HO\text{---}R + X^-
$$

Hughes *et al.* (1935) studied (*a*) the interchange reaction of (+)-2-iodo-octane with radioactive iodine (as NaI*) in acetone solution, and (*b*) the racemisation of (+)-2-iodo-octane by ordinary sodium iodide under the same conditions. These reactions were shown to take place by the S_N2 mechanism, and the rate of racemisation was shown to be twice the rate of radioactive exchange, *i.e.*, every iodide–iodide* displacement is always accompanied by inversion. (Suppose there are *n* molecules of optically active iodo-octane. When $n/2$ molecules have exchange with I* and in doing so have been inverted, racemisation is now complete although the exchange has taken place with only *half* of the total number of molecules.) Thus this experiment leads to the *assumption* that inversion always occurs in the S_N2 mechanism. This is fully supported by other experimental work, *e.g.*, Hughes *et al.* (1936, 1938) studied the reaction of optically active α-bromoethylbenzene and α-bromopropionic acid with radioactive bromide ions, and again found that the rate of racemisation was twice the rate of exchange.

Since S_N2 reactions always occur with inversion (this is known as the *stereokinetic rule* for S_N2

reactions), then provided the molecularity of the S_N reaction can be determined kinetically, it is possible to correlate the configuration of the reactant with that of the product.

There are *four* S_N2 charge-types of reaction:

					Reagent	Substrate
1.	Y^-	$+ RX$	$\rightarrow YR$	$+ X^-$	negative	neutral
2.	Y^-	$+ RX^+$	$\rightarrow YR$	$+ X$	negative	positive
3.	Y	$+ RX$	$\rightarrow YR^+$	$+ X^-$	neutral	neutral
4.	Y	$+ RX^+$	$\rightarrow YR^+$	$+ X$	neutral	positive

The stereokinetic rule for S_N2 reactions is well established for only reactions of type 1. Hughes, Ingold *et al.* (1960) have also shown that the rule applies to type 2, *e.g.*, the reaction between a sulphonium iodide and sodium azide:

$$N_3^- + \begin{array}{c} Ph \\ \diagdown \\ C - \overset{+}{S}Me_2 \\ \diagup \quad | \\ H \quad \\ Me \end{array} \longrightarrow N_3 - \begin{array}{c} Ph \\ \diagup \\ C \\ | \quad \diagdown \\ \quad H \\ Me \end{array} + Me_2S$$

Another example is the reaction between the acetoxy ion and the $(+)$-trimethyl-α-phenylethyl-ammonium ion to give the inverted product (Snyder *et al.*, 1949):

$$AcO^- + \begin{array}{c} Ph \\ \diagdown \\ C - \overset{+}{N}Me_3 \\ \diagup \quad | \\ H \quad \\ Me \end{array} \longrightarrow AcO - \begin{array}{c} Ph \\ \diagup \\ C \\ | \quad \diagdown \\ \quad H \\ Me \end{array} + Me_3N$$

Hughes *et al.* (1964) have also shown that the reaction between thiourea and the dimethyl-1-phenylsulphonium ion (as iodide) in methyl cyanide solution gives the thiouronium salt with substantially complete inversion; this is an example of type 4.

$$SC(NH_2)_2 + CHMePhSMe_2^+ \longrightarrow CHMePhSC(NH_2)_2^+ + Me_2S$$

Examples of type 3 are also known, *e.g.*, the Menschutkin reaction (§2e):

$$R_3^1N + R^2{-}Br \longrightarrow R_3^1\overset{+}{N}{-}R^2\}Br^-$$

Now let us consider the S_N1 mechanism.

$$R\overset{\frown}{{-}}X \longrightarrow \overset{\delta+}{R}{-}\overset{\delta-}{X} \longrightarrow R^+ + X^- \xrightarrow{OH^-} ROH + X^-$$

When the reaction proceeds by this mechanism, then inversion and retention (racemisation) will occur, the amount of each depending on various factors. The carbonium ion is flat (trigonal hybridisation), and hence attack by the nucleophilic reagent can take place equally well on either side, *i.e.*, equal amounts of the $(+)$- and $(-)$-forms will be produced; this is racemisation. Furthermore, on the basis that an ion-pair is formed first, the leaving group will protect its side from attack by the nucleophile, *i.e.*, inversion will occur exclusively or will predominate. Only if there is complete dissociation of the ion-pair into the individual ions can complete racemisation be expected; the shielding effect of the retiring ion is now lost. Also, racemisation will be encouraged by low concentration of the nucleophile. An example of inversion is that due to Bunton *et al.* (1955), who studied the reaction of ^{18}O-enriched water with optically active s-butanol in aqueous perchloric acid, and found that the overall rate of racemisation is twice that of the oxygen exchange. Thus every oxygen exchange causes complete inversion of configuration (*cf.* the iodide–iodide* exchange described above). Bunton proposed the following mechanism to explain these results:

$$\text{EtMeCHOH} + \text{H}^+ \underset{\text{fast}}{\overset{\text{HClO}_4}{\rightleftharpoons}} \text{EtMeCHOH}_2^+ \tag{2}$$

$$\text{EtMeCHOH}_2^+ \underset{}{\overset{\text{slow}}{\rightleftharpoons}} \overset{\delta+}{\text{EtMeCH}}\text{---}\overset{\delta+}{\text{OH}_2} \tag{3}$$

$$\text{H}_2\text{O}^* + \overset{\delta+}{\text{EtMeCH}}\text{---}\overset{\delta+}{\text{OH}_2} \underset{}{\overset{\text{fast}}{\rightleftharpoons}} \overset{\delta+}{\text{H}_2\text{O}^*}\text{---}\text{EtMeCH}\text{---}\overset{\delta+}{\text{OH}_2} \underset{}{\overset{\text{fast}}{\rightleftharpoons}} \overset{+}{\text{H}_2\text{O}^*}\text{—CHMeEt} + \text{H}_2\text{O} \tag{4}$$

$$\overset{+}{\text{H}_2\text{O}^*}\text{—CHMeEt} \overset{\text{fast}}{\rightleftharpoons} \text{HO}^*\text{—CHMeEt} + \text{H}^+ \tag{5}$$

(4) occurs before the $\text{OH}_2{}^+$ has completely separated in (3), and so this side is shielded and the H_2O^* is forced to attack on the other side as shown; the result is thus inversion. The above reaction proceeds by the S_N1 mechanism since (3) is the rate-determining step (only *one* molecule is undergoing covalency change in this step). Had the reaction been S_N2, complete inversion would have been obtained. It was shown, however, that the reaction rate was independent of the concentration of H_2O^*. The mechanism is therefore S_N1, since had it been S_N2, the kinetic expression would require the concentration of the H_2O^*:

$$\text{H}_2\text{O}^* + \text{EtMeCHOH}_2^+ \overset{\text{slow}}{\rightleftharpoons} \overset{\delta+}{\text{H}_2\text{O}^*}\text{---}\text{EtMeCH}\text{---}\overset{\delta+}{\text{OH}_2} \overset{\text{fast}}{\longrightarrow} \overset{+}{\text{H}_2\text{O}^*}\text{—CHMeEt} + \text{H}_2\text{O}$$

In general, net inversion is usually observed for short-life carbonium ions. Ions of this type are produced from s- and t-alkyl derivatives. On the other hand, diarylmethyl carbonium ions have a long life (due to spreading of charge). Thus $\text{Ar}^1\text{Ar}^2\text{CHX}$ undergoes solvolysis by the S_N1 mechanism to give a completely racemised product. These observations offer a means of estimating the relative stabilities of carbonium ions.

The stereochemical course of S_N1 reactions may also be affected by neighbouring group participation (see, *e.g.*, §6a).

§5. The S_Ni mechanism

Another important S_N reaction is the S_Ni type (substitution, nucleophilic, internal). The reaction between thionyl chloride and alcohols has been studied extensively. A well-examined example is the alcohol α-phenylethanol, PhCHOHMe; this is an *arylmethanol*, and according to Hughes, Ingold *et al.* (1937) the first step is the formation of a chlorosulphite. No inversion occurs at this stage (which is a four-centre reaction); in the following equation, R = PhMeCH-:

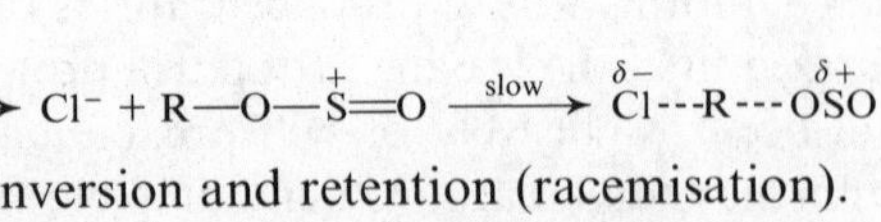

$$\text{R—O} \quad \text{S}=\text{O} \longrightarrow \text{R—O—S}=\text{O} + \text{HCl}$$

This chlorosulphite could then form α-chloroethylbenzene by one or more of the following mechanisms:

(i) S_N2. This occurs with inversion.

$$\text{R—O—S}=\text{O} \overset{\text{fast}}{\longrightarrow} \text{Cl}^- + \text{R—O—}\overset{+}{\text{S}}=\text{O} \overset{\text{slow}}{\longrightarrow} \overset{\delta-}{\text{Cl}}\text{---R---}\overset{\delta+}{\text{OSO}} \overset{\text{fast}}{\longrightarrow} \text{Cl—R} + \text{SO}_2$$

(ii) S_N1. This occurs with inversion and retention (racemisation).

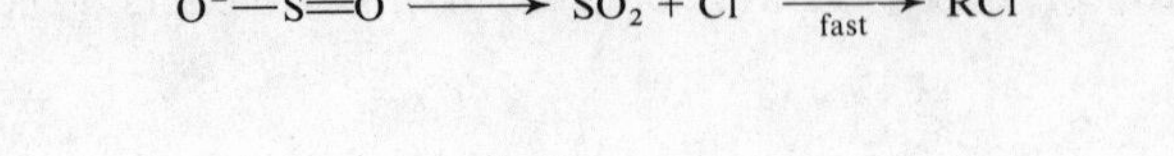

$$\text{R—O—S}=\text{O} \overset{\text{slow}}{\longrightarrow} \text{R}^+ + \text{O}^-\text{—S}=\text{O} \overset{\text{fast}}{\longrightarrow} \text{RCl} + \text{SO}_2$$

The second stage may possibly be:

$$\text{O}^-\text{—S}=\text{O} \overset{\text{fast}}{\longrightarrow} \text{SO}_2 + \text{Cl}^- \overset{\text{R}^+}{\underset{\text{fast}}{\longrightarrow}} \text{RCl}$$

(iii) S_Ni. This occurs with retention (the reaction is effectively a four-centre type).

$$R-O \quad \longrightarrow \quad \left[R--O \atop Cl \right] \longrightarrow RCl + SO_2$$

In practice, the α-chloroethylbenzene obtained has almost complete retention of configuration, and consequently the mechanism must be S_Ni.

There appears to be some doubt that the S_Ni mechanism is a one-step process. It has been suggested that the S_Ni mechanism, like the S_N1 mechanism (§2e), can proceed *via* ion-pairs, the amount of ionisation depending largely on the nature of the solvent, *e.g.*, the rate of decomposition of chlorosulphites increases with increasing polarity of the solvent. Thus, S_N1 and S_Ni mechanisms may be regarded as extremes, the latter operating when the product has retention of configuration. On this basis, the S_Ni may be formulated as follows:

$$R-O \atop Cl \; S=O \; \rightleftharpoons \; R^+ \; O \atop Cl \; S=O \; \longrightarrow RCl + SO_2$$

ion-pair

Because of the geometry of the ion-pair, the chlorine atom is forced to attack the carbonium ion from the *same* side as the original R—O bond, with consequent retention of configuration (see §2e).

The formation of the carbonium ion (ion-pair or otherwise) in the S_N1 mechanism is supported by much experimental work, *e.g.*, the chlorosulphite of 3-methylbutan-2-ol, on heating, gives t-amyl chloride (Lee *et al.*, 1961). This is readily explained by the formation of initially a secondary carbonium ion which then rapidly rearranges to the more stable tertiary carbonium ion.

$$Me_2CH-CHMe-OSOCl \longrightarrow [Me-CH-\overset{+}{C}H-Me]\,\bar{O}SOCl \longrightarrow$$
$$\underset{Me}{|}$$

$$[Me-\overset{+}{C}-CH_2Me]\,\bar{O}SOCl \longrightarrow Me_2CClCH_2Me + SO_2$$
$$\underset{Me}{|}$$

When α-phenylethanol and thionyl chloride react in the presence of pyridine, the α-chloroethyl-benzene obtained has the inverted configuration (Hughes, Ingold *et al.*, 1937). The explanation offered is that the S_N2 mechanism is operating, the substrate now being a pyridine complex:

$$ROSOCl + C_5H_5N \longrightarrow Cl^- + ROSO\overset{+}{N}C_5H_5 \longrightarrow \overset{\delta-}{Cl}---R---\overset{\delta-}{O}SO\overset{+}{N}C_5H_5 \longrightarrow Cl-R + SO_2 + C_5H_5N$$

Another example of the S_Ni mechanism (*i.e.*, with retention of configuration) is the decomposition of alkyl chloroformates (Kenyon *et al.*, 1933).

$$R-O \atop Cl \; C=O \; \longrightarrow \; R^+ \; O \atop Cl \; C=O \; \longrightarrow RCl + CO_2$$

ion-pair

§6. Participation of neighbouring groups in nucleophilic substitutions

So far, we have discussed polar effects (inductive and resonance) and steric effects on the rates and mechanisms of reactions. In recent years it has been found that another factor may also operate in various reactions. This factor is known as *neighbouring group participation*. Here we have a group attached to the carbon atom *adjacent* to the carbon atom where nucleophilic substitution occurs and, during the course of the reaction, becomes bonded or partially bonded to the reaction centre to form a *non-classical* or *bridged* ion. Thus the rate and/or the stereochemistry of a reaction may be affected. When a reaction is accelerated by neighbouring group participation, that reaction is said to be *anchimerically assisted* (Winstein *et al.*, 1953). For anchimeric assistance to occur, the neighbouring group, which behaves as a nucleophilic reagent, must be suitably placed stereochemically with respect to the group that is ejected; this is the *trans*-configuration. Neighbouring group participation is also of great importance in the 1,2-shifts. As we shall see below, neighbouring group participation may also involve a group further removed than the carbon atom adjacent to the reactive centre.

In order to measure anchimeric assistance (kinetic acceleration), it is necessary to be able to estimate reaction rates that would be obtained had there been no neighbouring group participation. This can frequently be done with cyclic structures, since the geometry of the molecule often restricts the possibility of neighbouring group participation to the *trans*-isomer, the unassisted rate therefore corresponding to that for the *cis*-isomer. Acyclic structures are much more difficult to study because it is not easy to separate anchimeric assistance from polar and steric effects.

Because of the difficulties in estimating reaction rates in the absence of neighbouring group participation, it is necessary to have a reasonably large increase in rate to justify the conclusion that the rate increase is due to anchimeric assistance only. It appears that a five-fold increase has been accepted as a minimum, but obviously the case is stronger if much larger values are obtained (see also §6e).

In addition to anchimeric assistance as evidence for the formation of non-classical carbonium ions, other criteria have been used, *e.g.*, stereochemistry of the reaction and structure of the products. In the latter case, the product differs from that which would be expected in the absence of neighbouring group participation.

If we accept the existence of bridged ions, the question to be answered is why should such ions be formed in preference to classical carbonium ions in any particular reaction. One reasonable answer is that when several intermediates are possible, the most stable one is the one likely to be formed. Since charge is more diffuse in the bridged ion than the classical ion, the former would be expected to be more stable than the latter (see also **8** §23d).

Whether a group Z can enter into neighbouring group participation depends on the nature of Z, and for a given Z it usually depends on the size of the ring that can be formed (by n.g.p.). The following sections illustrate some examples of neighbouring group participation.

§6a. Neighbouring carboxylate anion.   Hughes, Ingold *et al.* (1937) studied the following reaction of methyl D-α-bromopropionate:

$$MeCHBrCO_2Me \longrightarrow MeCH(OMe)CO_2Me$$

With concentrated methanolic sodium methoxide, the reaction was shown to be S_N2, and the product was L-methoxy ester (100 per cent inversion). Under these conditions, the nucleophilic reagent is the methoxide ion, and the reaction is first order with respect to both methoxide ion and ester. When the ester was subjected to methanolysis, *i.e.*, methanol was the solvent (no methoxide ion now present), the product was again L-methoxy ester (100 per cent inversion). The reaction was now first order (*i.e.*, pseudo first order), but still S_N2, the nucleophilic reagent being the solvent molecules of methanol. When the sodium salt of D-α-bromopropionic acid was hydrolysed in dilute sodium hydroxide solution, the mechanism was shown to be S_N1, and the product was now D-α-hydroxypropionate anion (100 per cent retention). In concentrated sodium hydroxide solution, however, the mechanism was S_N2 (due to the high concentration of the hydroxide ion), and the product was L-α-hydroxypropionate anion (100 per cent inversion).

The explanation for retention is uncertain, but a favoured theory is that an α-lactone is formed first

(Kenyon *et al.*, 1936), with expulsion of the bromide ion. Thus, the side opposite to that of the expelled bromide ion is protected from attack by the hydroxide ion, which is consequently forced to attack from the same side as that of the expelled bromide ion, thereby leading to retention of configuration.

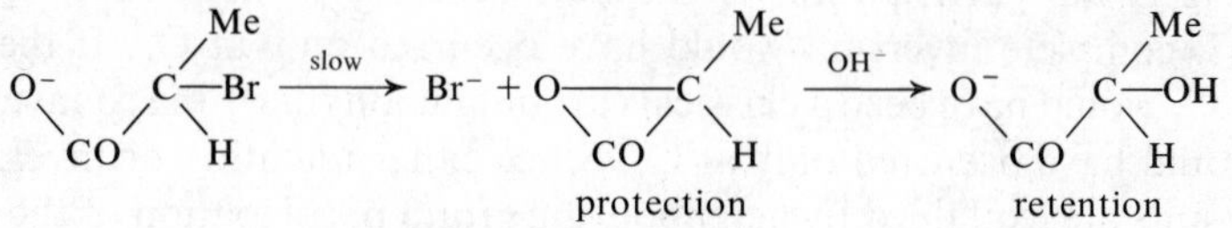

Hughes, Ingold *et al.* (1950) showed that the deamination of optically active alanine by nitrous acid gave an optically active lactic acid with retention of configuration. This is also explained by neighbouring group participation of the α-carboxylate anion:

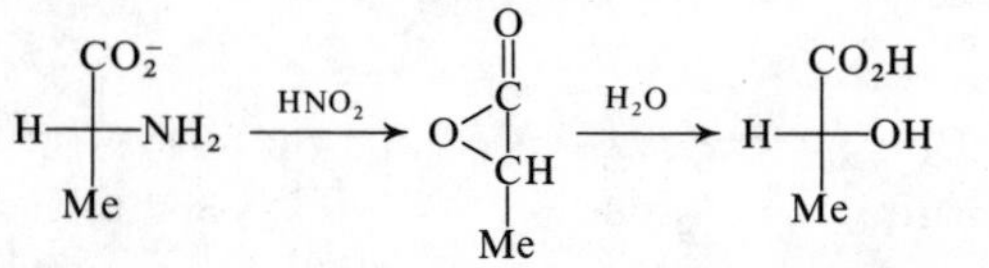

D(−)-alanine   D(−)-lactic acid

A good example of the effect of ring-size in neighbouring group participation involving the carboxylate ion is shown by the anions of the bromocarboxylic acids:

(I)

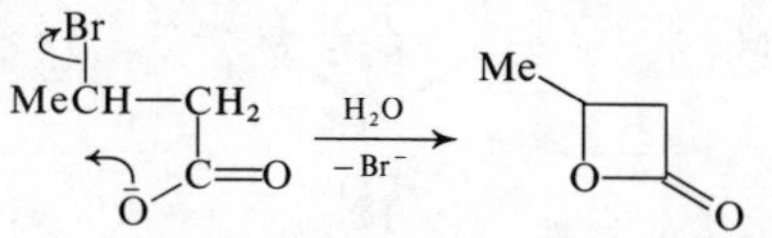

(II)

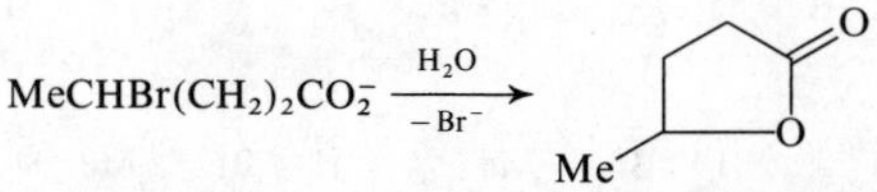

(III) $Br(CH_2)_6CO_2^- \xrightarrow[-Br^-]{H_2O} HO(CH_2)_6CO_2^-$

Lactones containing a four- to seven-membered ring can be formed under these experimental conditions, but not eight-membered rings (and larger ones). Whether a three-membered α-lactone ring is actually formed for α-bromopropionic acid is still uncertain, but such a lactone has been isolated for 2-butyl-2-bromohexanoic acid. In this case, presumably steric effects of the large butyl groups prevent attack of the hydroxide ion. At the same time, these large groups will tend to stabilise the small ring (through 'squeezing' the angle O—CHBu$_2$—CO).

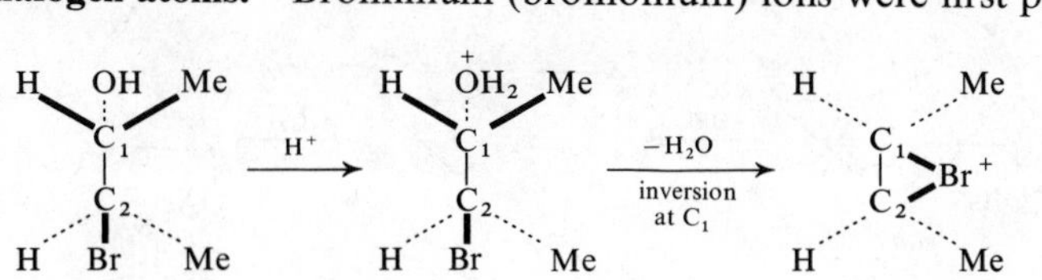

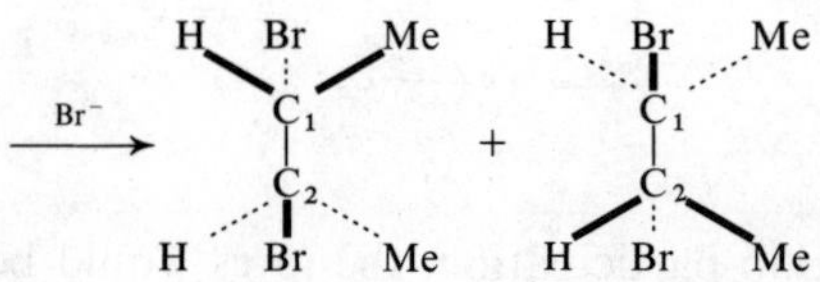

§6b. **Neighbouring halogen atoms.** Brominium (bromonium) ions were first proposed by Roberts and Kimball (1937) as intermediates in the addition of bromine to alkenes (see **4** §51). The existence of this cyclic brominium ion has been demonstrated by Winstein and Lucas (1939), who found that the action of fuming hydrobromic acid on (−)-*threo*-3-bromobutan-2-ol gave (±)-2,3-dibromobutane. If no neighbouring group participation of bromine occurred in the above reactions, then if the reaction were S_N2; complete inversion would have occurred only at C_1. If the reaction were the ordinary S_N1, the C_1 would have been a classical carbonium ion (flat), and so inversion and retention (racemisation) would have occurred only at C_1. Since either retention or inversion occurs at *both* C_1 and C_2, the results are explained by neighbouring group participation of the bromine atom.

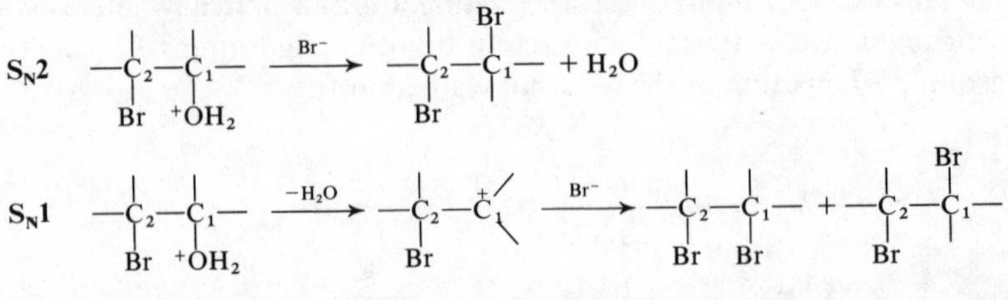

The above mechanism also explains the formation of *meso*-2,3-dibromobutane by the action of fuming hydrobromic acid on optically active *erythro*-3-bromobutan-2-ol (I); (II) and (III) are identical and correspond to the *meso*-form.

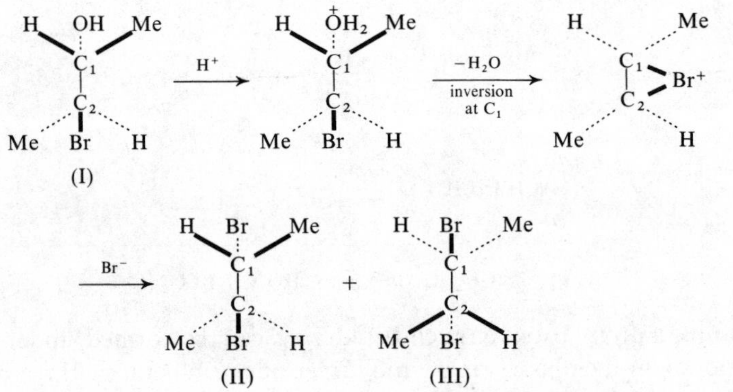

There is evidence that all the halogen atoms can form cyclic ions and offer anchimeric assistance, *e.g.*, Winstein *et al.* (1948, 1951) studied the acetolysis of *cis*- and *trans*-2-halogeno-cyclohexyl brosylates (*i.e.*, *p*-bromobenzenesulphonates; this group is often written as OBs):

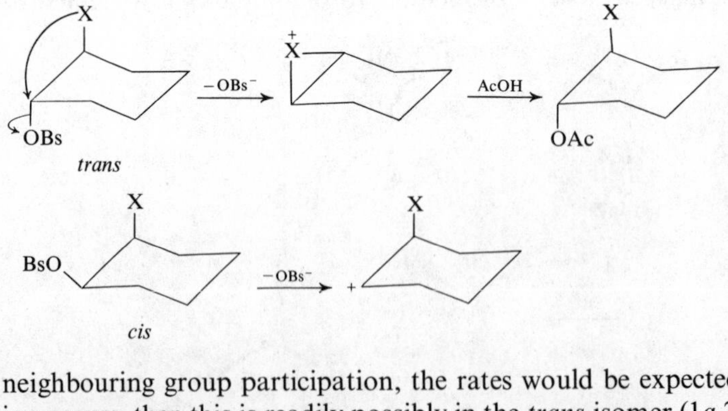

In the absence of neighbouring group participation, the rates would be expected to be about the same. If participation occurs, then this is readily possibly in the *trans*-isomer (1*a*,2*a*) by attack of X at the *rear* of the ejected OBs$^-$ ion, but this is not so for the *cis*-isomer (1e,2a; see **4** §11a). The rate ratios observed were:

$$trans/cis: \text{X} = \text{I}, 2{\cdot}7 \times 10^6/1; \quad \text{X} = \text{Br}, 800/1; \quad \text{X} = \text{Cl}, 3{\cdot}8/1.$$

Thus iodine affords the greatest anchimeric assistance and chlorine the least (see also §6c).

§6c. Neighbouring hydroxyl or alkoxyl group.   Hydroxyl groups may enter into neighbouring group participation, one way being *via* the alkoxide ion. Thus, Bartlett (1935) showed that alkali converts *trans*-2-chlorocyclohexanol into cyclohexene oxide, and proposed a mechanism in which an alkoxide ion is formed first and this then ring-closes with ejection of the chloride ion:

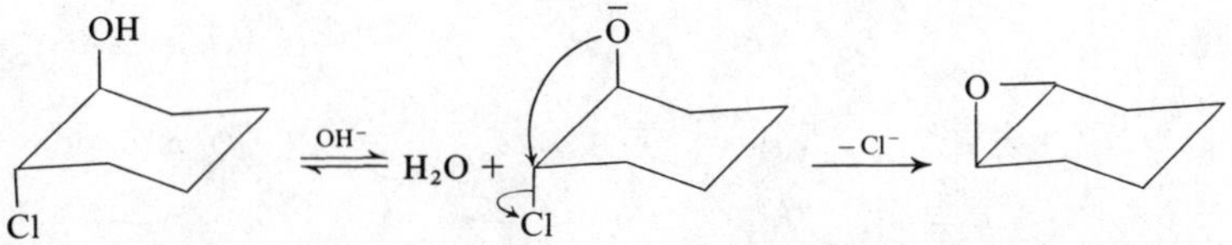

Bergvist (1948) showed that this reaction proceeds more than 100 times as fast as that when the *cis*-compound is used. Here again, the *trans*-form permits ready attack at the rear of the chloride ion whereas the *cis*-isomer does not (*cf.* §6b). The fact that the *cis*-form does react may be explained by assuming that the reaction proceeds *via cis*-elimination of the chlorine atom (see **4** §5m). This would require a distorted (*i.e.*, highly strained) transition state, and consequently the activation energy for this path would be greater than that for *trans*-elimination.

Another example is the conversion of sugars into epoxy-sugars (see **7** §9).

The hydroxyl group itself may also participate as a neighbouring group, the most important example being the case with chlorohydrins of the type $Cl(CH_2)_nOH$. In these compounds, anchimeric assistance is greatest when $n = 4$ (to give a five-membered ring), far less for $n = 5$ (to give a six-membered ring), and is absent for other values of n. Thus, tetramethylene chlorohydrin in water is converted into tetrahydrofuran about 10^3 times as fast as ethylene chlorohydrin is converted into ethylene epoxide. This is readily explained on the basis that five-membered rings are very stable.

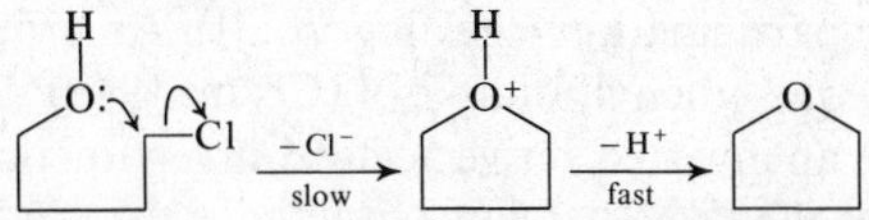

Alkoxyl groups behave similarly to hydroxyl groups in neighbouring group participation, *i.e.*, show anchimeric assistance in the formation of five-membered rings, and to a far less extent in the formation of six-membered rings. Thus, the acetolysis of 4-methoxybutyl brosylate is about 650 times as fast as that of *n*-butyl brosylate. It should be noted, however, that there appears to be some doubt about this explanation.

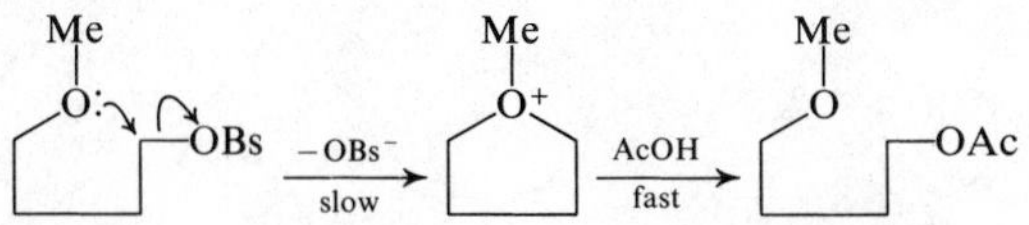

§6d. Neighbouring acetoxyl group.   Winstein *et al.* (1942, 1943) showed that a neighbouring acetoxyl group leads to the formation of an acetoxonium ion. *trans*-2-Acetoxycyclohexyl brosylate (I) forms *trans*-1,2-diacetoxycyclohexane (II) when treated with silver acetate, and the same product (II) is obtained when the starting material is *trans*-2-acetoxycyclohexyl bromide (III). The authors believe that the course of the reaction, based on the stereochemical evidence, proceeds through the *same* acetoxonium ion (IV). This mechanism is supported by the fact that in each case, when the reaction was carried out in the presence of a small amount of water, the product was now the mono-acetate of *cis*-cyclohexane-1,2-diol (V); some diacetate of this *cis*-diol was also obtained.

Further support for the formation of (IV) is afforded by the fact that the *cis*-isomers of (I) and (III) undergo the same reactions but at much slower rates. The formation of the intermediate (V*a*) is

supported by the fact that when the solvolysis of (I) is carried out in ethanol, (VI) is obtained (Winstein *et al.*, 1943).

§6e. Neighbouring phenyl group.   One type of molecular rearrangement is the 1,2-*shift*, and this may involve neighbouring group participation (see also Vol. I). An example is the acetolysis of the tosylates (*p*-toluenesulphonates) of 3-phenylbutan-2-ol (Cram, 1949). If the mechanism were S_N2, then each tosylate would produce an inverted active acetate, inversion occurring only at the C—OTs carbon atom, the result being that the *threo*-tosylate would give the *erythro*-acetate and the *erythro*-tosylate the *threo*-acetate. If the mechanism were S_N1, ionisation of the tosyloxy group would produce the classical carbonium ion and the expected result would be racemisation (and retention) at the C—OAc carbon atom, the net result being that both *threo*- and *erythro*-tosylate yield the same product. Cram found that the L-*threo*-tosylate gave the racemic *threo*-acetate, whereas the L-*erythro*-

tosylate produced the almost optically pure L-*erythro*-acetate. Hence the mechanism cannot be S_N2 or S_N1. These results, however, can readily be explained on the basis of the formation of an intermediate bridged carbonium ion, the *phenonium cation* (*cf.* §6b).

This phenonium cation is symmetrical, and since attack by an acetic acid molecule can be expected to occur with equal probability at carbons 1 and 2, products (1) and (2) will be formed in equal amounts. As these are mirror images, the result is therefore the racemic modification. The phenonium cation from the L-*erythro*-tosylate is also attacked at carbons 1 and 2 with equal probability, and gives the *same* optically active product [(1) = (2)] which has the same configuration as the starting material.

L-*erythro*-tosylate

The above explanation is completely satisfactory for the results given, but is no longer so when other experimental work is also considered. In acetic acid, the L-*threo*-tosylate racemises at a rate which is considerably faster than the rate of formation of *p*-toluenesulphonic acid, and it was estimated that 80 per cent of the tosylate is racemised *before* its conversion into the acetate (Winstein *et al.*, 1952). It was therefore suggested that an ion-pair is formed, and this can undergo racemisation through internal return prior to the formation of the postulated phenonium ion which leads to the products (see §2e). Not only are acetates formed in this reaction, but so are alkenes (25–35 per cent), and when the structures of these alkenes are considered, the results are not explained on the basis of a phenonium ion intermediate. Cram (1952) therefore proposed that a classical cation is formed as well as the bridged ion. The mechanism was then further elaborated to explain the formation of 4 per cent of *erythro*-acetate from *threo*-tosylate. (This formation of *erythro*- from the *threo*-compound has been termed 'leakage' from the *threo* to the *erythro* system.)

Brown *et al.* (1965) have examined this reaction and have provided evidence to show that the results can be explained in terms of a rapidly equilibrating pair of classical ions (see also **8** §23d):

T.S.

In this case, the phenonium ion may be regarded as the *transition state* formed from either classical carbonium ion and not as the *intermediate* proposed above.

Another example involving the phenyl group is the ethanolysis of the conjugate base of 2-(*p*-hydroxyphenyl)ethyl bromide (I), which is about 10^6 times as fast as that of the corresponding *p*-methoxy-compound (II) (Winstein *et al.*, 1963).

The oxygen atom in (I) is much more electron-releasing than that in (II), and so the intermediate

(I*a*, which has been isolated) is much more stable than (II*a*). Hence, reaction involving the formation of (I*a*) requires a lower energy of activation than that involving the formation of (II*a*), and so the former proceeds faster than the latter. This, of course, is based on the argument that the formation of (I*a*) or (II*a*) is the rate-determining step.

§6f. **Some other examples of neighbouring group participation.** Many nucleophilic groups can enter into neighbouring group participation but, as we have seen, the extent depends on the structure of the molecule. The sulphur compound (I) undergoes hydrolysis in aqueous dioxan about 10^4 times

as fast as that of the oxygen analogue. As we have seen (§6c), *alkoxyl groups* exhibit neighbouring group participation only when the formation of a five- (and six-) membered ring is involved.

Similarly, the alkaline hydrolysis of (III) proceeds much faster than that of n-butyl bromide (to n-butanol); the five-membered ring is stable.

On the other hand, the alkaline hydrolysis of (IV) produces the rearranged product (V). The course of this reaction is readily explained on the basis that a cyclic intermediate is formed and that this

undergoes attack at the CH_2 group rather than at the CHEt group because of less steric effects at the former carbon atom.

Double bonds can also enter into neighbouring group participation, *e.g.*, the acetolysis of 4-methylpent-3-enyl tosylate proceeds about 1 200 times as fast as that of ethyl tolylate. The products are 2-cyclopropylpropene and 4-methylpent-3-enyl acetate:

$$\underset{Me}{\overset{Me}{>}}C{=}CH{\diagdown}CH_2{-}OTs \xrightarrow[slow]{OTs^-} \underset{Me}{\overset{Me}{>}}C{\overset{\delta+}{=\!\!=}}CH\text{------}\overset{\delta+}{CH_2} \xrightarrow{AcOH}$$

(VI)

$$\underset{Me}{\overset{Me}{>}}C{=}CH{\diagdown}CH_2{-}OAc \;+\; \underset{Me}{\overset{H_2C}{>}}C{-}CH{\diagup}CH_2\triangle CH_2$$

The intermediate ion (VI) is the homoallylic cation (see also **11** §4d).

ASYMMETRIC SYNTHESIS (Asymmetric Induction)

§7. Partial asymmetric synthesis

Partial asymmetric synthesis may be defined as a method for preparing optically active compounds from symmetric compounds by the intermediate use of optically active compounds, but without the necessity of resolution (Marckwald, 1904). In ordinary laboratory syntheses, a symmetric compound always produces the racemic modification (**2** §7a).

This definition included the term 'partial' in order to distinguish this type of asymmetric synthesis from another type in which a 'physical reagent' was used instead of optically active compounds. This physical reagent was circularly polarised light, and in this case the process was labelled an 'absolute asymmetric synthesis' (see §8). It is now common practice to regard asymmetric synthesis as a special case of stereoselectivity (**4** §5k) in which a prochiral unit (centre or face) is converted into a chiral centre and results in unequal amounts of stereoisomers (with concomitant optical activity of the product). In this 'definition', no distinction is drawn between 'chemical' and 'physical' methods. Even so, the term 'absolute' is still often used to specify the use of a physical 'reagent'.

The first asymmetric synthesis was carried out by Marckwald (1904), who prepared an active (−)-valeric acid (laevorotatory to the extent of about 10 per cent of the pure compound) by heating the half-brucine salt of ethylmethylmalonic acid at 170°C.

(I) and (II) are diastereoisomers; so are (III) and (IV). (V) and (VI) are enantiomers, and since the mixture is optically active, they must be present in unequal amounts. Marckwald believed this was due to the different rates of decomposition of diastereoisomers (I) and (II), but according to Eisenlohr and Meier (1938), the half-brucine salts (I) and (II) are not present in equal amounts in the solid form (as thought by Marckwald). These authors suggested that as the less soluble diastereoisomer

$$\underset{C_2H_5}{\overset{H_3C}{>}}C\underset{CO_2H}{\overset{CO_2H}{<}} \xrightarrow{(-)\text{-brucine}} \underset{H_5C_2}{\overset{H_3C}{>}}C\underset{CO_2H}{\overset{CO_2H[(-)\text{-brucine}]}{<}} \;+\; \underset{H_5C_2}{\overset{H_3C}{>}}C\underset{CO_2H[(-)\text{-brucine}]}{\overset{CO_2H}{<}} \xrightarrow{170°C}$$

(I)   (II)

$$\underset{H_5C_2}{\overset{H_3C}{>}}C\underset{H}{\overset{CO_2H[(-)\text{-brucine}]}{<}} \;+\; \underset{H_5C_2}{\overset{H_3C}{>}}C\underset{CO_2H[(-)\text{-brucine}]}{\overset{H}{<}} \xrightarrow{HCl} \underset{H_5C_2}{\overset{H_3C}{>}}C\underset{H}{\overset{CO_2H}{<}} \;+\; \underset{H_5C_2}{\overset{H_3C}{>}}C\underset{CO_2H}{\overset{H}{<}}$$

(III)   (IV)   (V)   (VI)

crystallised out (during evaporation of the solution), some of the more soluble diastereoisomer spontaneously changed into the less soluble diastereoisomer to restore the equilibrium between the two; thus the final result was a mixture of the half-brucine salt containing a larger proportion of the less soluble diastereoisomer. If this be the explanation, then we are dealing with an example of asymmetric transformation and not of asymmetric synthesis (see **2** §10). Further work, however, has shown that Marckwald had indeed carried out an asymmetric synthesis. Kenyon and Ross (1951) decarboxylated optically active ethyl hydrogen ethylmethylmalonate (VII) and obtained an optically inactive product, ethyl $(\pm)$-α-methylbutyrate (VIII).

$$
\underset{\substack{\text{(VII)}\\ \text{active}}}{\overset{\text{H}_3\text{C}\quad\text{CO}_2\text{H}}{\underset{\text{H}_5\text{C}_2\quad\text{CO}_2\text{C}_2\text{H}_5}{\text{C}}}}
\longrightarrow
\text{CO}_2 +
\underset{\substack{\text{(VIII)}\\ \text{inactive}}}{\overset{\text{H}_3\text{C}\quad\text{H}}{\underset{\text{H}_5\text{C}_2\quad\text{CO}_2\text{C}_2\text{H}_5}{\text{C}}}}
$$

These authors (1952) then decarboxylated the cinchonidine salt of (VII) and still obtained the optically inactive product (VIII).

$$
\underset{\substack{}}{\overset{\text{H}_3\text{C}\quad\text{CO}_2\text{H(cinchonidine)}}{\underset{\text{H}_5\text{C}_2\quad\text{CO}_2\text{C}_2\text{H}_5}{\text{C}}}}
\longrightarrow
\underset{\substack{\text{(VIII)}\\ \text{inactive}}}{\overset{\text{H}_3\text{C}\quad\text{H}}{\underset{\text{H}_5\text{C}_2\quad\text{CO}_2\text{C}_2\text{H}_5}{\text{C}}}}
+ \text{CO}_2 + \text{cinchonidine}
$$

Kenyon and Ross suggested the following explanation to account for their own experiments and for those of Marckwald. Decarboxylation of diastereoisomers (I) and (II) takes place *via* the formation of the same carbanion (I*a*), and decarboxylation of (VII) and its cinchonidine salt *via* (VII*a*).

$$
\underset{\text{(I)}}{\overset{\text{H}_3\text{C}\quad\text{CO}_2\text{H[}(-)\text{-brucine]}}{\underset{\text{H}_5\text{C}_2\quad\text{CO}_2\text{H}}{\text{C}}}}
$$

$$
\underset{\text{(II)}}{\overset{\text{H}_3\text{C}\quad\text{CO}_2\text{H}}{\underset{\text{H}_5\text{C}_2\quad\text{CO}_2\text{H[}(-)\text{-brucine]}}{\text{C}}}}
$$

$$
\Bigg\rangle \longrightarrow
\underset{\text{(I}a)}{\overset{\text{H}_3\text{C}}{\underset{\text{H}_5\text{C}_2}{\overset{|}{\text{C}}}}\!-\!\text{CO}_2\text{H[}(-)\text{-brucine]}}
$$

$$
\underset{\text{(VII)}}{\overset{\text{H}_3\text{C}\quad\text{CO}_2\text{H}}{\underset{\text{H}_5\text{C}_2\quad\text{CO}_2\text{C}_2\text{H}_5}{\text{C}}}}
$$

$$
\underset{}{\overset{\text{H}_3\text{C}\quad\text{CO}_2\text{H(cinchonidine)}}{\underset{\text{H}_5\text{C}_2\quad\text{CO}_2\text{C}_2\text{H}_5}{\text{C}}}}
$$

$$
\Bigg\rangle \longrightarrow
\underset{\text{(VII}a)}{\overset{\text{H}_3\text{C}}{\underset{\text{H}_5\text{C}_2}{\overset{|}{\text{C}}}}\!-\!\text{CO}_2\text{C}_2\text{H}_5}
$$

Combination of carbanion (I*a*) with a proton will produce diastereoisomers (III) and (IV) in different amounts, since, in general, diastereoisomers are formed at different rates. Since the carbanion may be represented as a resonance hybrid of (I*a*) and (I*b*), this carbanion is essentially flat. Also,

$$
\underset{\text{(I}a)}{\overset{\text{H}_3\text{C}}{\underset{\text{H}_5\text{C}_2}{\overset{|}{\text{C}}}}\!-\!\overset{\text{O}}{\underset{\text{OH}}{\text{C}}}}
\; [(-)\text{-brucine}]
\longleftrightarrow
\underset{\text{(I}b)}{\overset{\text{H}_3\text{C}}{\underset{\text{H}_5\text{C}_2}{\text{C}}}\!=\!\overset{\bar{\text{O}}}{\underset{\text{OH}}{\text{C}}}}
\; [(-)\text{-brucine}]
$$

because of the presence of the chiral centre in $(-)$-brucine, the two faces of the carbanion are diastereotopic (**2** §7b). Since (VIIa) may also be represented as a resonance hybrid of (VIIa) and (VIIb), the molecule is essentially flat and has enantiotopic faces (**2** §7a).

$$\underset{(\text{VII}a)}{\overset{H_3C}{\underset{H_5C_2}{>}}\overset{\bar{\ddot{C}}-C\overset{O}{<}}{}_{OC_2H_5}} \quad \longleftrightarrow \quad \underset{(\text{VII}b)}{\overset{H_3C}{\underset{H_5C_2}{>}}C=C\overset{\bar{O}}{<}_{OC_2H_5}}$$

Hence, carbanion (VIIa) will give equimolecular amounts of the enantiomers of (VIII). If the formation of optically active α-methylbutyric acid (V and VI) were due to different rates of decarboxylation of (III) and (IV) (Marckwald's explanation) or to partial asymmetric transformation during crystallisation (Eisenlohr and Meier's explanation), then these effects are nullified if Kenyon's explanation is correct, since the intermediate carbanion is the *same* for both diastereoisomers. Thus, if the asymmetric transformation theory were correct, then decarboxylation of the *dibrucine* salt of ethylmethylmalonic acid to α-methylbutyric acid should give an optically inactive product, since only one type of crystal is now possible (asymmetric transformation is now impossible).

$$\underset{H_5C_2}{\overset{H_3C}{>}}C\overset{CO_2H[(-)\text{-brucine}]}{\underset{CO_2H[(-)\text{-brucine}]}{<}} \quad \longrightarrow \quad \underset{H_5C_2}{\overset{H_3C}{>}}\bar{C}-CO_2H[(-)\text{-brucine}]$$

$$\text{(I}a\text{)}$$

On the other hand, if the carbanion (Ia) is an intermediate in this decomposition, it is still possible to obtain an optically active product. Kenyon and Ross did, in fact, obtain a laevorotatory product.

McKenzie (1904) carried out a number of asymmetric syntheses by reduction of the keto group in various keto-esters in which the ester group contained a chiral group, *e.g.*, benzoylformic acid was esterified with $(-)$-menthol, the ester reduced with aluminium amalgam, and the resulting product hydrolysed; the mandelic acid so obtained was slightly laevorotatory.

$$C_6H_5COCO_2H + (-)\text{-}C_{10}H_{19}OH \longrightarrow C_6H_5COCO_2C_{10}H_{19} + H_2O \xrightarrow{\text{Al/Hg}}$$
$$C_6H_5CHOHCO_2C_{10}H_{19} \xrightarrow{H_2O} C_6H_5CHOHCO_2H + (-)\text{-}C_{10}H_{19}OH$$
$$(-)\text{-rotation}$$

Similarly, the pyruvates of $(-)$-menthol, $(-)$-pentyl alcohol and $(-)$-borneol gave an optically active lactic acid (slightly laevorotatory) on reduction.

$$CH_3COCO_2R(-) \xrightarrow{[H]} CH_3CHOHCO_2R(-) \xrightarrow{H_2O} CH_3CHOHCO_2H + (-)\text{-ROH}$$
$$(-)\text{-rotation}$$

McKenzie (1904) also obtained similar results with Grignard reagents, *e.g.*, the $(-)$-menthyl ester of benzoylformic acid and methylmagnesium iodide gave a slightly laevorotatory atrolactic acid.

$$C_6H_5COCO_2C_{10}H_{19} + CH_3MgI \longrightarrow C_6H_5C\overset{OMgI}{\underset{CH_3}{<}}CO_2C_{10}H_{19} \xrightarrow{H_2O} C_6H_5C\overset{OH}{\underset{CH_3}{<}}CO_2H + (-)\text{-}C_{10}H_{19}OH$$
$$(-)\text{-rotation}$$

Another example of asymmetric synthesis involving the use of a Grignard reagent is the *reduction* of 3,3-dimethylbutan-2-one into a dextrorotatory 3,3-dimethylbutan-2-ol by means of $(+)$-2-methylbutylmagnesium chloride (Mosher *et al.*, 1950). The authors explained the result by

$$(CH_3)_3CCOCH_3 \xrightarrow{(+)\text{-}CH_3CH_2CH(CH_3)CH_2MgCl} (CH_3)_3CCHOHCH_3$$
$$(+)\text{-rotation}$$

postulating the formation of a cyclic transition state in which the preferred configuration has the methyl group of the optically active Grignard reagent on the same side of the ring as the larger of the two groups in the ketone. This configuration of the T.S. is preferred because steric effects are less than in

$$\begin{array}{c} \text{Cl} \\ | \\ \text{Mg} \\ \text{H}_2\text{C} \quad \text{O} \\ \text{Et} \quad | \quad || \quad \text{Me} \\ \underset{\text{Me}}{\text{C}} \quad \underset{\text{H}}{\cdots} \quad \underset{\text{CMe}_3}{\text{C}} \end{array} \longrightarrow \begin{array}{c} \text{CH}_2 \\ || \\ \text{C} \\ \text{Et} \quad \text{Me} \end{array} + \begin{array}{c} \text{OH} \\ | \\ \text{Me}_3\text{C} — \text{Me} \\ | \\ \text{H} \\ (+) \end{array}$$

the alternative T.S., and so the energy content of the former is lower than that of the latter. Mosher used a variety of ketones and obtained a predominance of one enantiomer, but the optical purity was always low (most values were between ~4 and 10 per cent). This suggests that the energy differences between the two transition states may be small. Mosher *et al.* (1961, 1966), however, have concluded that the size of the groups is not the only factor that determines the stereoselectivity of these asymmetric reductions. In fact, although the actual size of a group is fixed, it appears that its effective size depends on the environment and on the mechanism of the reaction. This may lead to difficulties in predicting the steric course of a particular reaction.

In the above examples, the reduction involves a hydrogen atom transfer from the chiral β-carbon atom of the Grignard reagent. Morrison (1967) has shown that isopropyl phenyl ketone is reduced by, *e.g.*, $PhMeCHCH_2CH_2MgCl$, in which the β-carbon atom is not chiral, to give predominantly one enantiomer of $PhCHOHPr^i$. The two hydrogen atoms in the Grignard reagent are diastereotopic (by internal comparison) and so produce diastereoisomeric transition states with the ketone, thereby resulting in the formation of excess of one enantiomer over the other (see **2** §7b).

Doering *et al.* (1950) have carried out the reduction of ketones by means of the Meerwein–Ponndorf–Verley method. The reduction of methyl isohexyl ketone with (+)-butan-2-ol in the presence of aluminium 2-butoxide gave (+)-methylisohexylmethanol. Here again the results are explained by the formation of a cyclic transition state with the isohexyl group predominantly on the same side .as the methyl group of the butoxide. In both reactions, transfer of a hydride ion takes place.

$$\begin{array}{c} \text{Al} \\ \text{O} \quad \text{O} \\ \text{Et} \quad || \quad | \quad \text{Me} \\ \underset{\text{Me}}{\text{C}} \quad \underset{\text{H}}{\cdots} \quad \underset{\text{C}_6\text{H}_{13}}{\text{C}} \end{array} \longrightarrow \begin{array}{c} \text{O} \\ || \\ \text{C} \\ \text{Et} \quad \text{Me} \end{array} + \begin{array}{c} \text{Al} \\ \text{O} \\ | \quad \text{Me} \\ \text{HC} \\ \text{C}_6\text{H}_{13} \end{array}$$

On the other hand, Bothner-By (1951) reduced butanone with lithium aluminium hydride in the presence of (+)-camphor, and thereby obtained (+)-isoborneol (from the camphor) and a small amount of a dextrorotatory butan-2-ol. The reducing agent in this case is a complex aluminohydride ion formed from lithium aluminium hydride and camphor, *e.g.*, $Al(OR)H_3^-$.

$$CH_3COC_2H_5 \xrightarrow[(+)\text{-camphor}]{LiAlH_4} CH_3CHOHC_2H_5$$
$$(+)\text{-rotation}$$

Turner *et al.* (1949) carried out a Reformatsky reaction (see Vol. I) using acetophenone, (−)-menthyl bromoacetate and zinc, and obtained a dextrorotatory β-hydroxy-β-phenylbutyric acid.

$$\begin{array}{c} \text{H}_5\text{C}_6 \\ \quad \text{C}=\text{O} + \text{Zn} + \text{CH}_2\text{BrCO}_2\text{C}_{10}\text{H}_{19} \\ \text{H}_3\text{C} \end{array} \longrightarrow \begin{array}{c} \text{H}_5\text{C}_6 \quad \text{OZnBr} \\ \quad \text{C} \\ \text{H}_3\text{C} \quad \text{CH}_2\text{CO}_2\text{C}_{10}\text{H}_{19} \end{array} \longrightarrow \begin{array}{c} \text{H}_5\text{C}_6 \quad \text{OH} \\ \quad \text{C} \\ \text{H}_3\text{C} \quad \text{CH}_2\text{CO}_2\text{H} \\ (+)\text{-rotation} \end{array}$$

Reid *et al.* (1962) have also used aldehydes in the Reformatsky reaction, *e.g.*, benzaldehyde gave a laevorotatory β-hydroxy-β-phenylpropionic acid.

Alkenes have been oxidised with optically active peroxy-acids to give optically active epoxides, *e.g.*, Montanari *et al.* (1969) used (+)-peroxycamphoric acid:

$$
\begin{array}{ccc}
\mathrm{Ph} & \mathrm{Me} & \\
\quad \mathrm{C}\!\!=\!\!\mathrm{C} \quad & \xrightarrow{\ \ (+)\text{-}RCO_3H\ \ } & \quad \mathrm{C}\text{---}\mathrm{C} \quad \\
\mathrm{H} & \mathrm{H} & \mathrm{H}\quad \mathrm{O}\quad \mathrm{H} \\
& & (+)\text{-}
\end{array}
$$

Asymmetric hydrogenation has also been effected with the use of a rhodium complex containing, *e.g.*, (+)- or (−)-PhCHMeNHCHO as ligands (McQuillin *et al.*, 1969).

$$
\mathrm{PhCMe}\!\!=\!\!\mathrm{CHCO_2Me} \xrightarrow[\mathrm{H_2}]{(+)\text{-cat.}} (+)\text{-PhCHMeCH_2CO_2Me}
$$

Hydroboronation of the olefinic double bond is discussed in **4** §5l.

Prelog *et al.* have studied, by means of conformational analysis, the steric course of the addition of Grignard reagents to benzoylformic (phenylglyoxylic) esters of chiral alcohols. If the letters S, M and L refer respectively to small, medium and large groups attached to the carbinol carbon atom of the chiral alcohol, then the general reaction may be written:

$$
\mathrm{C_6H_5COCO_2CSML} \xrightarrow{\ \ RMgX\ \ } \mathrm{C_6H_5CR(OH)CO_2CSML} \xrightarrow{\ \ hydrol.\ \ } \mathrm{C_6H_5CR(OH)CO_2H}
$$

Prelog *et al.* found that the configuration of the asymmetric carbon atom in the stereoisomer that predominated in this reaction could be correlated with that of the carbinol carbon of the alcohol. The authors considered that the most stable conformation of the ester was the one in which the two oxo groups are planar and *trans* to each other. It was also believed that the atoms O—C also lie in this plane, *i.e.*, the fragment shown is essentially planar. The problem now was the rotation of the

$$
\begin{array}{c}
\mathrm{O} \\
\parallel \\
\mathrm{Ph}\diagdown\ \mathrm{C}\ \diagup\ \mathrm{C} \\
\mathrm{C}\quad\quad\mathrm{O} \\
\parallel \\
\mathrm{O}
\end{array}
$$

group CSML about the single O—C bond. There are three energetically favourable conformations, and they are those in which, *in turn*, S, M, and L will (i) lie in the plane; (ii) in front of the plane; (iii) behind the plane, of the rest of the molecule (*i.e.*, the fragment shown). Prelog originally proposed (1953) that the most populated conformation was that in which group S lay in this plane and the groups M and L skew (IX*a* and X*b*; see Chart, in which the thick lines represent groups in front, broken lines groups behind, and ordinary lines groups in the plane). Prelog, however, later (1956) proposed that the most populated conformation was that in which group L lay in the plane and the groups S and M skew (IX*b* and X*c*; see Chart). The third energetically favourable conformation in which the M group lies in the plane is also shown in the Chart (IX*c* and X*a*). The enantiomeric alcohols (IX) and (X) each give rise to the three energetically favourable conformations for the corresponding ester (see Chart).

Another assumption made by Prelog (1953) was that the Grignard reagent attacks the oxo group (of PhCO) from the less hindered side. With methylmagnesium iodide as the Grignard reagent, the resulting α-hydroxy-acid is atrolactic acid (IX*d* or X*d*). The direction of attack is indicated in the

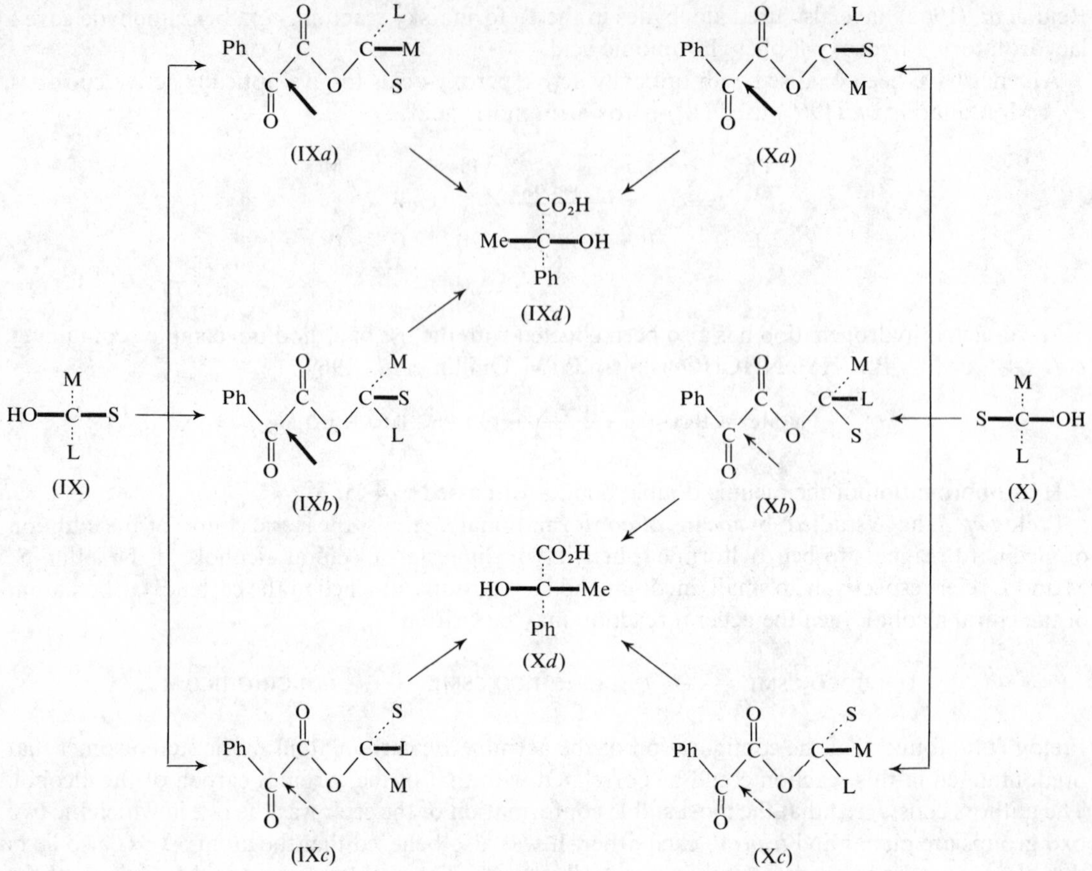

(IXa)

(Xa)

CO_2H
Me—C—OH
Ph
(IXd)

M
HO—C—S
L
(IX)

(IXb)

(Xb)

M
S—C—OH
L
(X)

CO_2H
HO—C—Me
Ph
(Xd)

(IXc)

(Xc)

Prelog's generalisation

Chart by a thick arrow when attack is from the front face and a broken arrow when attack is from the back. This may be illustrated as shown, with (IX*b*) as the example.

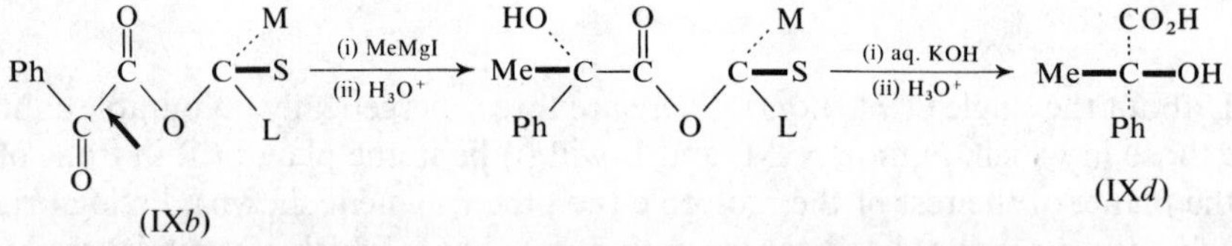

(IX*b*) $\xrightarrow[\text{(ii) } H_3O^+]{\text{(i) MeMgI}}$ $\xrightarrow[\text{(ii) } H_3O^+]{\text{(i) aq. KOH}}$ CO_2H
Me—C—OH
Ph
(IX*d*)

Examination of the Chart shows that the predominant enantiomer of atrolactic acid produced is related to the configuration of the chiral alcohol. (IX), *via* the most populated conformation (IX*b*), produces (IX*d*), and (X), *via* the most populated conformation (X*c*), produces (X*d*), the enantiomer of (IX*d*). It might be noted that even if each set of conformations were present in *equal* populations, the *same* results are achieved since *two* of each set of three produce the *same* atrolactic acid. Hence, all chiral alcohols of the type CSML(OH) which are stereochemically related, *i.e.*, the groups S, M, and L have the same spatial relationship, will produce the same enantiomer of atrolactic acid in excess. Also, if the sign of rotation of the atrolactic acid produced in excess is measured, the stereochemical relationships of the chiral alcohols can be determined. Now, (−)-menthol, (−)-borneol, and (−)-octan-2-ol are all configurationally related to L(−)-glyceraldehyde and all give (−)-atrolactic acid as the predominant enantiomer. The absolute configurations of these alcohols have been established; they are as shown (see also **8** §23e).

(−)-menthol   (−)-borneol   (−)-octan-2-ol

All have the same configuration for groups S, M, and L, and all are alcohols of the type (IX), *e.g.*,

(−)-octan-2-ol   (IX)

It therefore follows that (−)-atrolactic acid is (IX*d*). Hence, if the configuration of the chiral alcohol is known, it is possible to deduce that of the enantiomer of atrolactic produced in excess, and *vice versa*. This method of correlating configurations has been called the 'atrolactic acid method'. Furthermore, since the absolute configuration of (−)-atrolactic acid is that of (IX) [determined as described above, and confirmed by other methods], (−)-atrolactic acid is the (*R*)(−)- and (+)-atrolactic acid is the (*S*)(+)-acid. Hence, the absolute configurations of chiral alcohols can be correlated with the sign of rotation of the atrolactic acid produced in excess.

It also follows from the above discussion that if the keto-acid is pyruvic acid and the Grignard reagent is phenylmagnesium bromide then, for a given chiral alcohol, the atrolactic acid is predicted to have the opposite sign of that produced by benzoylformic acid and methylmagnesium iodide. The Ph and Me groups are now interchanged; this is illustrated as shown.

(XI) corresponds to (IX*b*), but now atrolactic acid (X*d*) is obtained in excess. These predictions have been verified by Prelog *et al.*

An alternative method for the determination of the absolute configuration of a chiral alcohol is that due to Horeau (1961–1964). The alcohol is acetylated in pyridine with an excess of (±)-phenylethylacetic anhydride, (PhCHEtCO)$_2$O, then the excess of the anhydride is hydrolysed and the optical activity of the phenylethylacetic acid is measured. Since one enantiomer of the anhydride reacts with the alcohol faster than the other, the other enantiomer will be in excess in the recovered acid (*cf.* the kinetic method of resolution, **2** §10(vii)). From the rotation of this acid, the configuration of the alcohol may be deduced from the following *empirical* rule: The alcohol with the absolute configuration (X) gives, by application of Prelog's method, excess of (+)-atrolactic acid (X*d*) and, by Horeau's method, excess of (−)-phenylethylacetic acid (X*e*).

(X)   (X*d*)   (X*e*)

Horeau's method is more convenient to carry out than Prelog's method, and has the added advantage in being highly stereoselective.

Cram *et al.* (1952) have also dealt with asymmetric syntheses in which the molecule contains a chiral centre that belongs to the molecule, *i.e.*, remains in the molecule, *e.g.*, the Kiliani reaction in

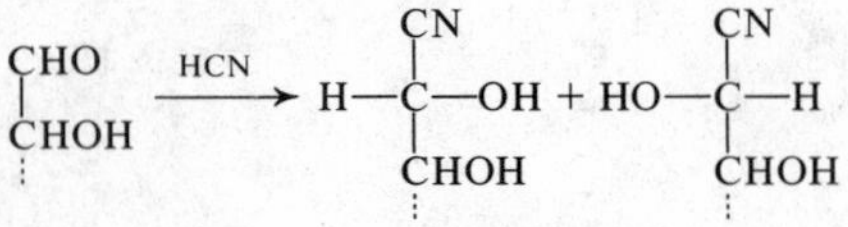

$$\underset{\substack{| \\ \text{CHOH}}}{\overset{\text{CHO}}{|}} \xrightarrow{\text{HCN}} \quad H-\underset{\substack{| \\ \text{CHOH}}}{\overset{\overset{\text{CN}}{|}}{\underset{}{C}}}-OH + HO-\underset{\substack{| \\ \text{CHOH}}}{\overset{\overset{\text{CN}}{|}}{\underset{}{C}}}-H$$

which the two diastereoisomers are formed in unequal amounts. These workers studied in great detail the conversion of acyclic compounds which contained one chiral centre adjacent to an oxo group to the corresponding alcohols, and as a result of their work have formulated the rule of 'steric control of asymmetric induction'. This is: 'In non-catalytic reactions of the type shown, that diastereoisomer will predominate which would be formed by the approach of the entering group from the *least hindered side* of the double bond when the rotational conformation of the C—C bond is such that the double bond is flanked by the two least bulky groups attached to the adjacent asymmetric centre.' Thus, using the Newman projection formulae ($Z = MgX$):

(a)

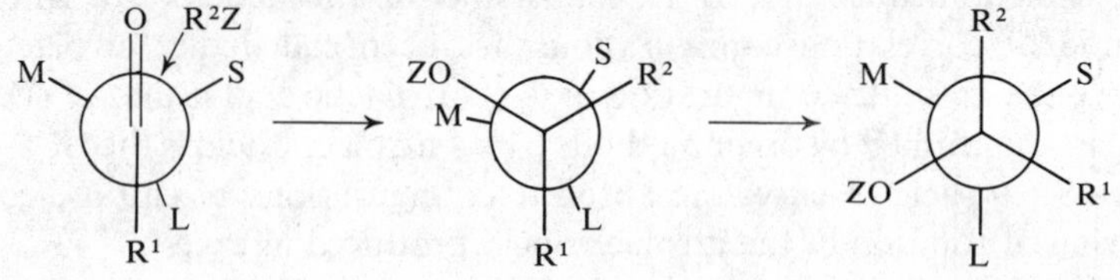

(eclipsed)   (staggered)

(b)

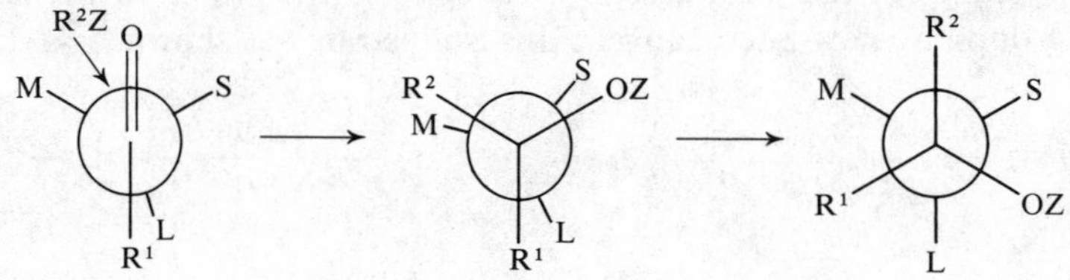

According to Cram's rule, the product from reaction (*a*) should predominate. An example that demonstrates this is the reaction between α-phenylpropionaldehyde (S = H, M = Me, L = Ph) and methylmagnesium bromide ($R^1 = Me$); two products can be formed, *viz.*, (XII) (the *erythro*-compound) and (XIII) (the *threo*-compound):

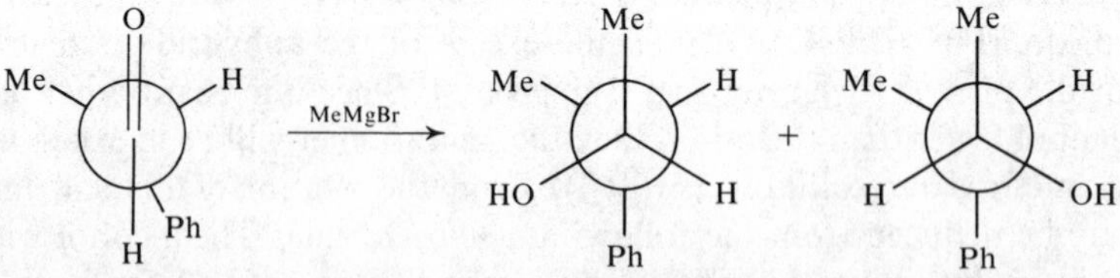

(XII)   (XIII)

The *erythro*-compound (XII) is the major product (*cf.* **2** §4a).

Some exceptions to the predictions have been observed, particularly when group L is very large. Other models have been proposed.

Karabatsos (1967), using certain assumptions, has been able to predict semiquantitatively from the Cram model (non-catalytic type) the stereospecificity of the product.

As pointed out above, the rule will not apply to catalytic reduction, and it also does not apply to compounds in which the asymmetric carbon atom is joined to a group capable of complexing with the reagent, *e.g.*, OH, NH_2. In this case, a different model is to be used (Cram *et al.*, 1959). Such a model is a rigid cyclic one and the predominant product is as shown:

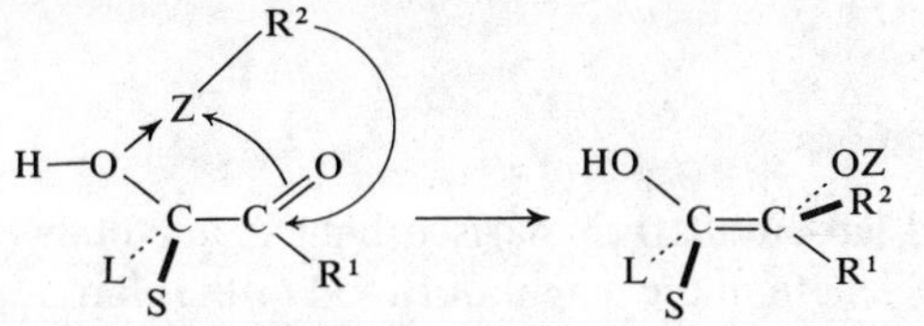

The influence of enzymes on the steric course of reactions has also been investigated, *e.g.*, Rosenthaler (1908) found that emulsin converted benzaldehyde and hydrogen cyanide into dextrorotatory mandelonitrile which was almost optically pure. It has been found that in most enzymic reactions the product is almost 100 per cent of one or other enantiomer. Enzymes are proteins and are optically active (see also **13** §12), but since they are so 'one-sided' in their action, it appears likely that the mechanism of the reactions in which they are involved differs from that of asymmetric syntheses where enzymes are not used. It has been suggested that enzymes are the cause of the formation of optically active compounds in plants. Although this is largely true, the real problem is: How were the optically active enzymes themselves produced? Ferreira's work [**2** §10(viii)], however, shows that optically active compounds may possibly be produced in living matter by activation of a racemic modification. This theory appears to be superior to that of the formation of optically active compounds by the action of naturally polarised light (see §8).

Asymmetric syntheses involving elimination reactions have also been carried out to prepare optically active alkenes, *e.g.*, Goldberg *et al.* (1966) subjected (−)-*cis*-4-methylcyclohexyl hydratropate to pyrolysis and obtained (−)-4-methylcyclohexene (in very low optical purity).

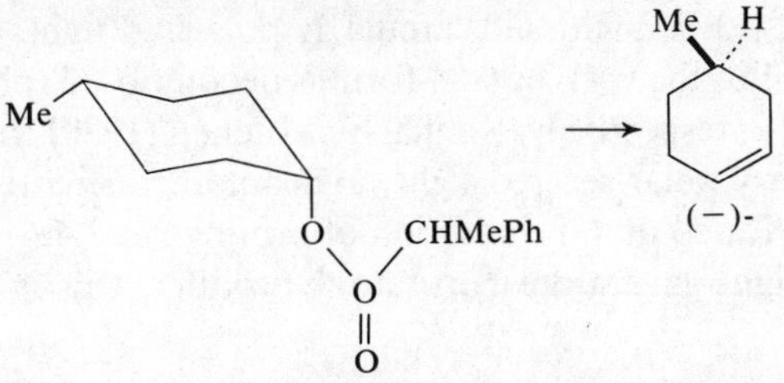

(−)-*cis*

Now let us consider reactions in which the products are *not* chiral but have been formed by two identical groups in the substrate reacting at different rates. These are highly stereoselective, and since they involve enzymes, may be regarded as a special class of asymmetric synthesis. A classical example of this type is the oxidation of citric acid (XIV) to α-ketoglutaric acid (XV) by means of an enzyme:

$$HO_2CCH_2{-}\overset{H}{\underset{CO_2H}{C}}{-}CH_2CO_2H \xrightarrow{\text{enzyme}} HO_2CCH_2CH_2COCO_2H$$

(XIV) (XV)

According to this equation, only the right-hand side methylene group is oxidised; the two groups are enantiotopic and react at different rates with a chiral reagent (see **2** §7a). This was demonstrated by the use of deuterium-labelled citric acid (XIV*a*) to give (XV*a*).

$$HO_2CCD_2-\overset{\overset{\displaystyle H}{|}}{\underset{\underset{\displaystyle CO_2H}{|}}{C}}-CH_2CO_2H \xrightarrow{\text{enzyme}} HO_2CCD_2CH_2COCO_2H$$

(XIV*a*)   (XV*a*)

§8. Absolute asymmetric synthesis

As we have seen, right- and left-circularly polarised light is unequally absorbed by enantiomers, provided the light has a wavelength in the neighbourhood of the characteristic absorption bands of the compound (*cf.* **2** §11).

It has been suggested that circularly polarised light produced the first natural active compounds, and to support this theory, racemic modifications have been irradiated with circularly polarised light and attempts made to isolate one enantiomer. There was very little success in this direction until W. Kuhn and Braun (1929) claimed to have obtained a small rotation in the case of ethyl α-bromopropionate. The racemic modification of this compound was irradiated with right- and left-circularly polarised light (of wavelength 2 800 Å), and the product was found to have a rotation of + or −0·05°, respectively. Thus we have the possibility of preparing optically active products from inactive substances *without* the intermediate use of optically active reagents (*cf.* Ferreira's work). This type of synthesis is known as an **absolute asymmetric synthesis**; it is also known as an **absolute asymmetric decomposition** (or **destruction**), since one enantiomer is decomposed (or destroyed) preferentially. On the other hand, there is another type of absolute asymmetric synthesis in which a chiral physical 'reagent' converts an achiral substrate into a chiral product (see below).

From 1930 onward, more conclusive evidence for absolute asymmetric decompositions has been obtained, *e.g.*, W. Kuhn and Knopf (1930) irradiated (±)-α-azidopropionic dimethylamide, $CH_3CHN_3CON(CH_3)_2$, with right-circularly polarised light and obtained an undecomposed product with a rotation of +0·78°; with left-circularly polarised light, the undecomposed product had a rotation of −1·04°. Thus the (−)- or (+)-form is decomposed (photochemically) by right- or left-circularly polarised light, respectively. Similarly, Mitchell (1930) irradiated humulene nitrosite with right- and left-circularly polarised red light, and obtained slightly optically active products.

Davis and Heggie (1935) found that the addition of bromine to 2,4,6-trinitrostilbene in a beam of right-circularly polarised light gave a dextrorotatory product; this is an example of an absolute asymmetric synthesis.

Small (+)-rotations were also observed when a mixture of ethyl fumarate and anhydrous hydrogen peroxide in ethereal solution was irradiated with right-circularly polarised light (Davis *et al.*, 1945).

As mentioned above, there has been much speculation about how optically active compounds are produced in nature. A difficulty of the 'circularly polarised light' theory is that, up to the present, no satisfactory answer has been offered to explain the source of such light in nature. On the other hand, Lee *et al.* (1956) showed that electrons emitted in β-decay are polarised, and if they slow down they lose some of their energy by emission of γ-radiation which is circularly polarised. Garay (1968) has irradiated D- and L-tyrosine with β-particles derived from strontium-90 Y and showed that the D-enantiomer was decomposed more quickly. He failed to 'activate' racemic DL-tyrosine, but suggested that β-particle bombardment may be the source of optically active compounds in nature.

REFERENCES

INGOLD, *Structure and Mechanism in Organic Chemistry*, Bell and Sons (1969, 2nd edn.).

HINE, *Physical Organic Chemistry*, McGraw-Hill (1962, 2nd edn.).

GOULD, *Mechanism and Structure in Organic Chemistry*, Holt and Co. (1959).

BUNTON, *Nucleophilic Substitution at a Saturated Carbon Atom*, Elsevier (1963).

STREITWIESER, 'Solvolytic Displacement Reactions at Saturated Carbon Atoms', *Chem. Rev.*, 1956, **56**, 571.

BETHELL and GOULD, 'The Structure of Carbonium Ions', *Quart. Rev.*, 1958, **12**, 173.

FRAZER and SINGER, 'Thermochemical Cycles', *Educ. in Chemistry*, 1964, **1**, 39.

CAPON, 'Neighbouring Group Participation', *Quart. Rev.*, 1964, **18**, 45.

BROWN, MORGAN and CHLOUPEK, 'Structural Effects in Solvolytic Reactions', *J. Am. chem. Soc.*, 1965, **87**, 2137.

LEFFLER and GRUNWALD, *Rates and Equilibria of Organic Reactions*, Wiley (1963).

KOSOWER, *An Introduction to Physical Organic Chemistry*, Wiley (1968).

CRAM and KOPECKY, 'Models for Steric Control of Asymmetric Induction', *J. Am. chem. Soc.*, 1959, **81**, 2748.

ELIEL, *Stereochemistry of Carbon Compounds*, McGraw-Hill (1962).

MISLOW, *Introduction to Stereochemistry*, Benjamin (1965).

BOYD and MCKERVEY, 'Asymmetric Synthesis', *Quart. Rev.*, 1968, **22**, 95.

MORRISON and MOSHER, *Asymmetric Organic Reactions*, Prentice-Hall (1971).

4 Geometrical isomerism, stereochemistry of alicyclic compounds

§1. Nature of geometrical isomerism

Maleic and fumaric acids both have the same molecular formula $C_4H_4O_4$, but differ in most of their physical and in many of their chemical properties, and neither is optically active. It was originally thought that these two acids were structural isomers; this is the reason for different names being assigned to each form (and to many other geometrical isomers). It was subsequently shown, however, that maleic and fumaric acids were not structural isomers, *e.g.*, both (i) are catalytically reduced to succinic acid; (ii) add one molecule of hydrogen bromide to form bromosuccinic acid; (iii) add one molecule of water to form malic acid; (iv) are oxidised by alkaline potassium permanganate to tartaric acid (the *stereochemical* relationships in reactions (ii), (iii) and (iv) have been ignored; they are discussed later in §5). Thus both acids have the same structure, *viz.*, $HO_2CCH{=}CHCO_2H$. van't Hoff (1874) suggested that if we assume there is *no free rotation about a double bond*, two spatial arrangements are possible for the formula $HO_2CCH{=}CHCO_2H$, and these would account for the isomerism exhibited by maleic and fumaric acids. Using tetrahedral diagrams, van't Hoff represented a double bond by placing the tetrahedra edge to edge (Fig. 4.1). From a *mechanical* point of view, such an arrangement would be rigid, *i.e.*, free rotation about the double bond is not to be expected.

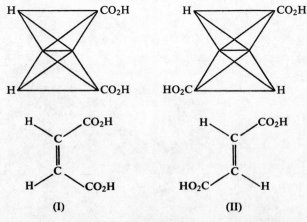

Fig. 4.1

Furthermore, according to the above arrangement, the two hydrogen atoms and the two carboxyl groups are all in one plane, *i.e.*, the molecule is flat. Since a flat molecule is superimposable on its mirror image, maleic and fumaric acids are therefore not optically active (**2** §2). As we shall see later, modern theory also postulates a planar structure for these two acids. These representations (Fig. 4.1) of a double bond are essentially equivalent to the 'banana-shaped' orbital representation (see Fig. 4.4).

The type of isomerism exhibited by maleic and fumaric acids is known as **geometrical isomerism** or ***cis-trans*** **isomerism**. One isomer is known as the *cis*-compound, and the other as the *trans*, the *cis*-compound being the one which (usually) has identical or similar atoms or groups, on the *same* side (see also §4). Thus molecule (I) is *cis*-butenedioic acid, and (II) is *trans*-butenedioic acid. As will be shown later (§5a), (I) is maleic acid and (II) fumaric acid.

Geometrical isomerism is exhibited by a wide variety of compounds, and they may be classified into three groups:

(i) Compounds containing a double bond: C=C, C=N, N=N.

(ii) Compounds containing a cyclic structure—homocyclic, heterocyclic and fused ring systems.

(iii) Compounds which may exhibit geometrical isomerism due to restricted rotation about a single bond (see **5** §3 for examples of this type).

§2. Stabilities of alkenes

One way of measuring the stability of an alkene is the determination of its heat of hydrogenation, *e.g.*, (ΔH in kJ mol^{-1}):

$$CH_2=CH_2 \qquad MeCH=CH_2 \qquad MeCH_2CH=CH_2$$
$$-137.2 \qquad\qquad -125.9 \qquad\qquad -126.8$$
$$MeCH=CHMe \qquad\qquad Me_2C=CH_2$$
$$cis, -119.7; trans, -115.5 \qquad\qquad -118.8$$

Since the reaction is exothermic, the smaller ΔH is (numerically), the more stable is the alkene *relative* to its parent alkane. Thus, it is only possible to compare the stabilities of different alkenes which produce the *same* alkane on hydrogenation. This arises from the fact that the enthalpy of formation of alkanes is not a purely additive property; it also depends on, *e.g.*, steric effects, and these tend to vary from molecule to molecule. Since the three n-butenes all give n-butane on reduction, it follows that the order of their stabilities is: *trans* 2-ene > *cis* 2-ene > 1-ene.

This order may be explained in terms of steric effects and hyperconjugation. In but-1-ene, steric repulsion is virtually absent. In the but-2-enes, the two methyl groups in the *cis* isomer, being closer together than in the *trans* isomer, experience greater steric repulsion and consequently the *cis* form is under greater strain than the *trans*. Thus steric repulsion destabilises a molecule. On the other hand, hyperconjugation stabilises a molecule and is small in but-1-ene but much larger in the but-2-enes. Since *trans*-but-2-ene is the most stable isomer, it follows that hyperconjugation has a greater stabilising effect than steric repulsion a destabilising effect (in these three butenes).

Stabilities of alkenes may also be compared by the determination of their heats of combustion (exothermic reaction), *e.g.*, (ΔH in kJ mol^{-1}):

$$MeCH_2CH=CH_2 \qquad\qquad MeCH=CHMe \qquad\qquad Me_2C=CH_2$$
$$-2\,719 \qquad\qquad cis, -2\,712; trans, -2\,707 \qquad\qquad -2\,703$$

In this case all four butenes may be compared, since all give the *same* products on combustion, *viz.*, $4CO_2 + 4H_2O$. The order of stabilities is thus: iso > *trans* 2-ene > *cis* 2-ene > 1-ene.

In general, the order of stability of alkenes is:

$$R_2C=CR_2 > R_2C=CHR > R_2C=CH_2 \sim RCH=CHR \ (trans > cis) > RCH=CH_2 > CH_2=CH_2$$

Rotation about a double bond. We have already seen that, theoretically, there is always some opposition to rotation about a *single* bond and that, in many cases, the opposition may be great enough to cause the molecule to assume some preferred conformation (2 §4). When we consider the problem of rotation about a *double* bond, we find that there is always considerable opposition to the rotation. Let us first consider the simple case of ethylene; Fig. 4.2(*a*) shows the energy changes in the molecule when one methylene group is rotated about the carbon–carbon double bond with the other methylene group at rest. Thus there are two *identical* favoured positions (one at 0° and the other at 180°), and the potential energy barrier is 167·4 kJ mol^{-1}. The examination of many olefinic compounds has shown that the potential energy barrier for the C=C bond varies with the nature of the groups attached to each carbon, *e.g.*,

$$CH_2=CH_2, \ 167\cdot4 \ kJmol^{-1}$$
$$C_6H_5CH=CHC_6H_5, \ 179\cdot1 \ kJmol^{-1}$$
$$CH_3CH=CHCH_3, \ 75\cdot3 \ kJmol^{-1}$$
$$HO_2CCH=CHCO_2H \ 66\cdot1 \ k \ mol^{-1}$$

Let us consider the case of maleic and fumaric acids in more detail. It can be seen from the diagram (Fig. 4.2*b*) that there are *two* favoured positions, with the *trans*-form more stable than the *cis*, the energy difference between the two being 25–29 kJ mol^{-1}. The conversion of the *trans* to the *cis* requires 66·1 kJ energy, but the reverse change requires about 42 kJ (see also §6 for a further discussion of *cis-trans* isomerisation).

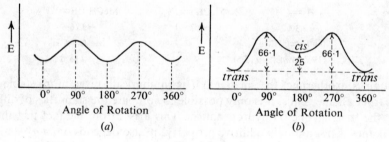

Fig. 4.2

§3. Modern theory of the nature of double bonds

In the foregoing account of geometrical isomerism, the distribution of the carbon valencies was assumed to be tetrahedral (as postulated by van't Hoff). According to one modern theory, the four valency bonds of a carbon atom are distributed tetrahedrally only in *saturated* compounds. In such compounds the carbon is in a state of *tetrahedral hybridisation*, the four sp^3 bonds being referred to as σ-bonds (see Vol. I, Ch. 2). In olefinic compounds, however, the two carbon atoms exhibit the *trigonal* mode of hybridisation. In this condition there are three coplanar valencies (three σ-bonds produced from sp^2 hybridisation), and the fourth bond (π-bond) at right angles to the trigonal hybrids (Fig. 4.3). π-Bonds, which are weaker than σ-bonds, tend to overlap as much as possible in order to make the bond as strong as possible. Maximum overlap is achieved when the molecule is planar, since in this configuration the two p_z orbitals are parallel. Distortion of the molecule from the planar configuration decreases the overlap of the π-electrons, thereby weakening the π-bond; and this distortion can only be effected by supplying energy to the molecule. It is therefore this tendency to produce **maximum overlap of the π-electrons in the π-bond** that gives rise to resistance of rotation about a 'double' bond. For simplicity we shall still represent a 'double' bond by the conventional method, *e.g.*, C=C, but it should always be borne in mind that *one* of these bonds is a σ-bond (sp^2 bond), and the *other* is a π-bond perpendicular to the σ-bond. It is these π-electrons (*mobile electrons*) which undergo the electromeric and resonance effects. They are held less firmly than the σ-electrons and are more exposed to external influences; it is these π-electrons which are responsible for the high reactivity of unsaturated compounds.

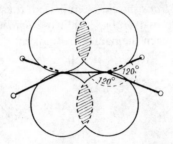

Fig. 4.3

In compounds containing a triple bond, *e.g.*, acetylene, the two carbon atoms are in a state of *digonal* hybridisation; there are two σ-bonds (*sp* bonds) and two π-bonds (one p_y and one p_z orbital), both perpendicular to the σ-bonds which are collinear (see Vol. I, Ch. 2).

The above treatment of the double (and triple) bond is in terms of sp^2 (and *sp*) hybridisation and π-bonds. It is still possible, however, to use sp^3 hybridisation to describe carbon–carbon multiple bonds; this treatment gives rise to 'banana-shaped' orbitals, *i.e.*, 'bent' bonds (Fig. 4.4; see also Vol. I):

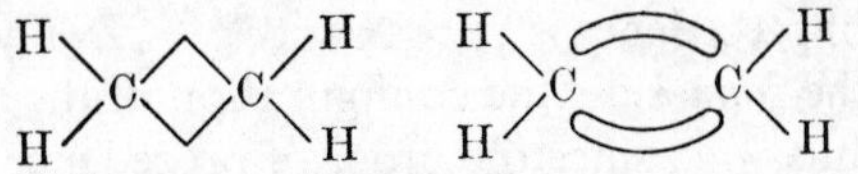

Fig. 4.4

This method of approach still produces a 'rigid' molecule, and so again there is no free rotation about the double bond.

Quantum mechanical arguments show that both methods of representing these bonds are equal to each other, each method having certain advantages. The σ—π bond method is more convenient for describing transitions from one state into another (*e.g.*, in electronic spectra; **1** §12a), whereas the bent bond method is more convenient for describing electron distribution in a molecule.

§4. Nomenclature of geometrical isomers

When geometrical isomerism is due to the presence of *one* double bond in a molecule, it is easy to name the geometrical isomers if two groups are identical, *e.g.*, in molecules (I) and (II), (I) is the *cis*-isomer and (II) the *trans*; similarly (III) is *cis* and (IV) is *trans*. When, however, all four groups are different, nomenclature is more difficult. In this case it has been suggested that the prefixes *cis* and *trans* should indicate the disposition of the *first two* groups named, *e.g.*, the two stereoisomers of 1-bromo-1-chloro-2-iodoethylene, (V) and (VI); (V) is *cis*-1-bromo-2-iodo-1-chloroethylene or *trans*-1-chloro-2-iodo-1-bromoethylene; (VI) is *cis*-1-chloro-2-iodo-1-bromoethylene or *trans*-1-bromo-2-iodo-1-chloroethylene. On the other hand, since this method of nomenclature usually

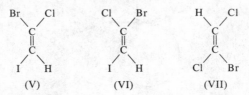

(I)   (II)   (III)   (IV)
cis   trans   cis   trans

deviates from the rule of naming groups in alphabetical order, it has been suggested that the groups corresponding to the prefix *cis* or *trans* should be italicised, thus (V) may be named *cis*-1-*bromo*-1-chloro-2-*iodo*ethylene and (VI) *trans*-1-*bromo*-1-chloro-2-*iodo*ethylene. This method, it must be admitted, would offer difficulties when the names are spoken.

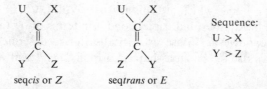

(V)   (VI)   (VII)

These difficulties have now been overcome by the introduction of a new system of nomenclature. Let us consider the molecule UXC=CYZ. The groups U and Z, and the groups Y and Z are now arranged in order of precedence in accordance with the Sequence Rule in the *R—S* system (see **2** §5d).

seqcis or Z   seqtrans or E

Sequence:
U > X
Y > Z

Let us suppose that the order of precedence is U > X and Y > Z. Then, if the groups U and Y (both of *higher* precedence) are on the *same* side, the configuration of the alkene is seq*cis*, and if they are on *opposite* sides, seq*trans*. Thus, *e.g.*, since the order of precedence of Br, Cl, I, and H is Br > Cl and I > H, (V) is seq*cis* and (VI) is seq*trans*.

An alternative scheme—the *E—Z* system—uses the symbols Z (German: *zusammen* = together) and E (German: *entgegen* = opposite). Thus, (V) is (Z)-1-bromo-1-chloro-2-iodoethylene, and (VI) is the corresponding (E)-isomer. These symbols correspond to seq*cis* (Z) and seq*trans* (E), but do not necessarily correspond to *cis* and *trans* (in the earlier nomenclature), *e.g.*, (VII) is *trans*-1,2-dichloro-2-bromoethylene, but by the *E—Z* system is the (Z)-isomer (H < Cl, Cl < Br; hence seq*cis* or Z).

The naming of *faces* of compounds containing double bonds has been discussed in **2** §7a.

Some pairs of geometrical isomers have trivial names, *e.g.*, maleic and fumaric acids, angelic and tiglic acids, etc. (*cf.* §1). Sometimes the prefix iso has been used to designate the *less* stable isomer, *e.g.*, crotonic acid (*trans*-isomer) and isocrotonic acid (*cis*-isomer; the *cis*-isomer is usually the less stable of the two; see §2). The use of iso in this connection is undesirable since it already has a specific meaning in the nomenclature of alkanes. The prefix allo has also been used to designate the less stable isomer (*cis*), *e.g.*, allocinnamic acid.

When geometrical isomers contain two or more double bonds, nomenclature may be difficult, *e.g.*, (VIII). In this case the compound is considered as a derivative of the longest chain which contains the maximum number of double bonds, the prefixes *cis* and *trans* being placed before the numbers indicating the positions of the double bonds to describe the relative positions of the carbon atoms in the main chain, thus (VIII) is 3-isopropylhexa-*cis*-2,*cis*-4-diene.

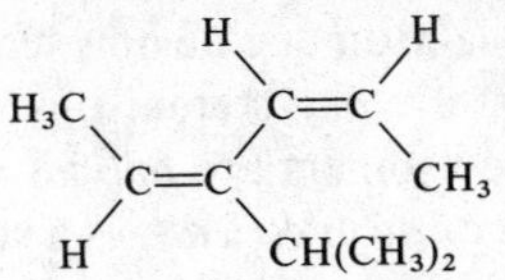

(VIII)

If a compound has two double bonds, *e.g.*, $CHa{=}CH{-}CH{=}CHb$, four geometrical isomers are possible:

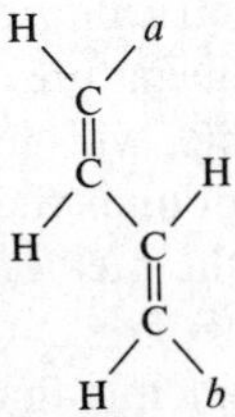

cis-trans 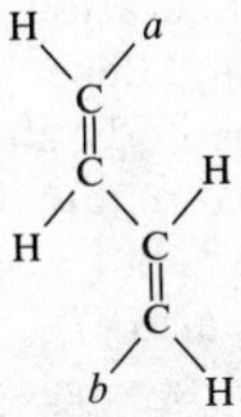   cis-cis 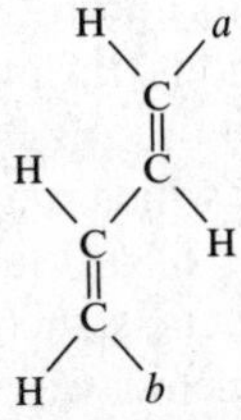   trans-cis 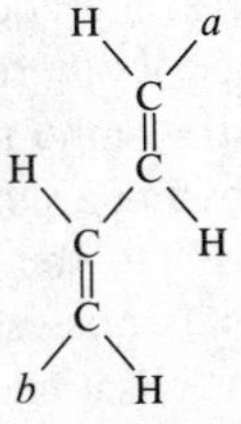   trans-trans

The number of geometrical isomers is 2^n, where n is the number of double bonds; this formula applies only to molecules in which the ends are different. If the ends are identical, *e.g.*, $CHa{=}CH{-}CH{=}CHa$, then the number of stereoisomers is $2^{n-1} + 2^{p-1}$, where $p = n/2$ when n is even, and $p = (n+1)/2$ when n is odd (Kuhn *et al.*, 1928).

Geometrical isomerism is also exhibited by cumulenes provided that the number of adjacent double bonds is odd, *e.g.*, 1,4-di-3-nitrophenyl-1,4-diphenylbutatriene exists in two forms (Kuhn *et al.*, 1959). On the other hand, cumulenes containing an even number of double bonds exhibit optical isomerism (see **5** §6).

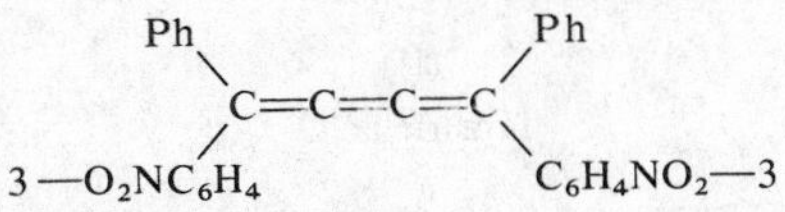

cis 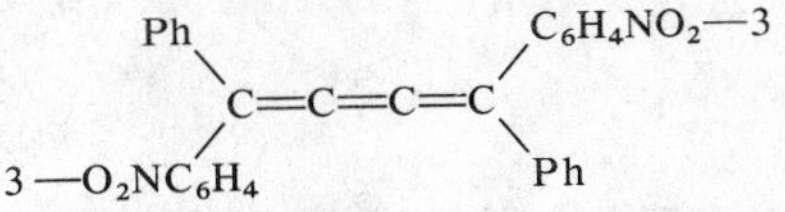   trans

It has previously been pointed out that geometrical isomers, as such, are not optically active, but if they contain chiral centres, then they will also exhibit optical isomerism (**2** §1). In such circumstances, the presence of the double bond leads to a larger number of optical isomers. This type of isomerism is known as *geometrical enantiomerism*. If Z^+ and Z^- represent mirror-image forms of an asymmetric group, then a molecule of the type CZ—CZ will exist as one pair of enantiomers and one *meso*-form (CZ$^+$—CZ$^+$, CZ$^-$—CZ$^-$, and CZ$^+$—CZ$^-$ (see **2** §7d)). If we now consider a molecule containing these two Z groups attached to an olefinic carbon atom as shown, then *four* optically active forms are now possible (*cf.* **2** §6).

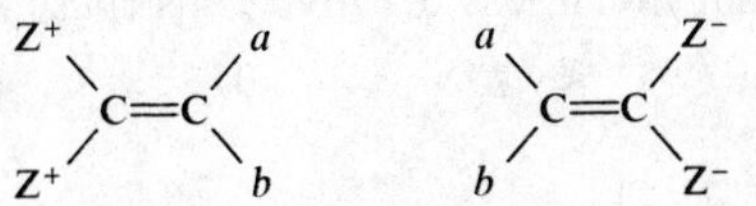

pair of enantiomers

pair of enantiomers

It might also be noted that geometrical isomers are now classified as diastereoisomers. According to the new definition, *diastereoisomers* are *any* stereoisomers which are not enantiomers of each other, *i.e.*, the restriction that diastereoisomers are *optical isomers* has been dropped (see **2** §7b). Thus this type of isomerism—*cis-trans* or *geometrical*—is a sub-class of the general phenomenon of diastereoisomerism.

§5. Determination of the configuration of geometrical isomers

There is no general method for determining the configuration of geometrical isomers. In practice one uses a number of different methods, the method used depending on the nature of the compound in question. At the same time, the use of several methods, if applicable, will give more reliable results. The following are methods which may be used mainly for compounds that owe their geometrical isomerism to the presence of a double bond, but several of the methods are special to geometrical isomers possessing a cyclic structure (see also §7).

§5a. Method of cyclisation. Wislicenus was the first to suggest the principle that *intramolecular* reactions are more likely to occur the closer together the reacting groups are in the molecule. This principle appears always to be true for reactions in which *rings* are formed, but does not hold for elimination reactions in which a double (or triple) bond is produced (see *e.g.*, §5m).

(*a*) Of the two acids maleic and fumaric, only the former readily forms a cyclic anhydride when heated; the latter does not form an anhydride of its own, but when strongly heated, gives maleic anhydride. Thus (I) is maleic acid, and (II) is fumaric acid.

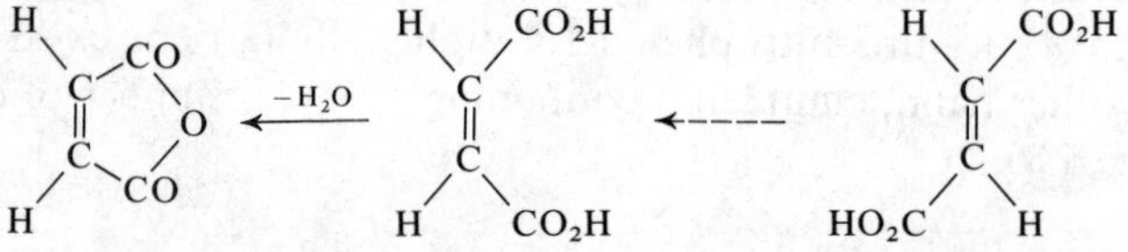

(I)
maleic acid

(II)
fumaric acid

Cyclisation reactions must be performed carefully, since one isomer may be converted into the other during the cyclising process, and so lead to unreliable results. In the above reaction, somewhat vigorous conditions have been used; hence there is the possibility that interconversion of the stereoisomers has occurred. Since maleic acid cyclises readily, and fumaric acid only after prolonged heating, the former is most probably the *cis*-isomer, and the latter the *trans* which forms maleic anhydride *via* the formation of maleic acid (see also §6). The correctness of the conclusion for the configurations of the two acids may be tested by hydrolysing maleic anhydride in the cold; only maleic acid is obtained. Under these mild conditions it is most unlikely that interconversion occurs, and so we may accept (I) as the configuration of maleic acid.

(*b*) Citraconic acid forms a cyclic anhydride readily, whereas the geometrical isomer, mesaconic acid, gives the same anhydride but much less readily. Thus these two acids are:

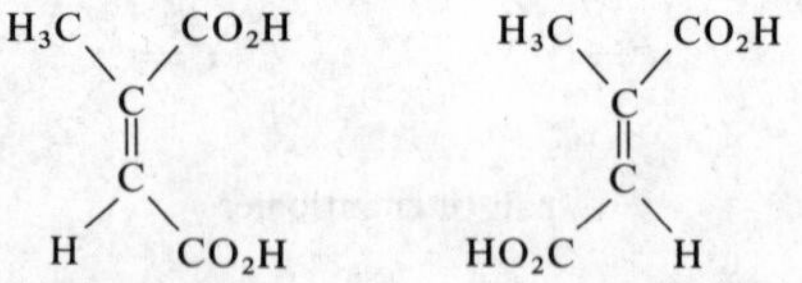

citraconic acid

mesaconic acid

(*c*) There are two *o*-hydroxycinnamic acids, one of which spontaneously forms the lactone, coumarin, whereas the other does not. Thus the former is the *cis*-isomer, coumarinic acid, and the latter the *trans*-isomer, coumaric acid.

coumarin   coumaric acid   coumarinic acid

(*d*) Two forms of hexahydroterephthalic acid are known, one of which forms a cyclic anhydride, and the other does not. Thus the former is the *cis*-isomer, and the latter the *trans* (see also §§9; 11c).

cis-acid   *trans*-acid

§5b. **Method of conversion into compounds of known configuration.** In a number of cases it is possible to determine the configurations of pairs of geometrical isomers by converting them into compounds, the configurations of which are already known. As an example of this type let us consider the two forms of crotonic acid, one of which is known as crotonic acid (m.p. 72°C), and the other as *iso-crotonic* acid (m.p. 15·5°C). Now there are two trichlorocrotonic acids, (III) and (IV), one of which can be hydrolysed to fumaric acid. Therefore this trichlorocrotonic acid must be the *trans*-isomer, (III); consequently the other is the *cis*-isomer (IV). Both these trichlorocrotonic acids may be reduced by sodium amalgam and water, or by zinc and acetic acid, to the crotonic acids, (III) giving crotonic acid (V) and (IV) giving isocrotonic acid (VI). Thus crotonic acid is the *trans*-isomer, and isocrotonic the *cis* (von Auwers *et al.*, 1923).

fumaric acid   (III)   (IV)

(V)   (VI)
crotonic acid   isocrotonic acid

Another example is the reduction of crotonaldehyde (known to be the *trans*- (seq*trans* or *E*-) form) into *trans*- (seq*trans* or *E*-) crotyl alcohol.

§5c. Method of conversion into less symmetrical compounds. Certain pairs of geometrical isomers may be converted into less symmetrical compounds in which the number of geometrical isomers is increased, and by considering the number of products obtained from each original stereoisomer, it is possible to deduce the configurations of the latter. *E.g.*, there are two 2,5-dimethylcyclopentane-1,1-dicarboxylic acids, and these, on heating, are decarboxylated to 2,5-dimethylcyclopentane-1-carboxylic acid. Consideration of the following chart shows that the *cis*-form of the original dicarboxylic acid can give rise to *two* stereoisomeric monocarboxylic acids, whereas the *trans*-form can produce only *one* product. Thus the configurations of the dicarboxylic acids are determined (see also §10).

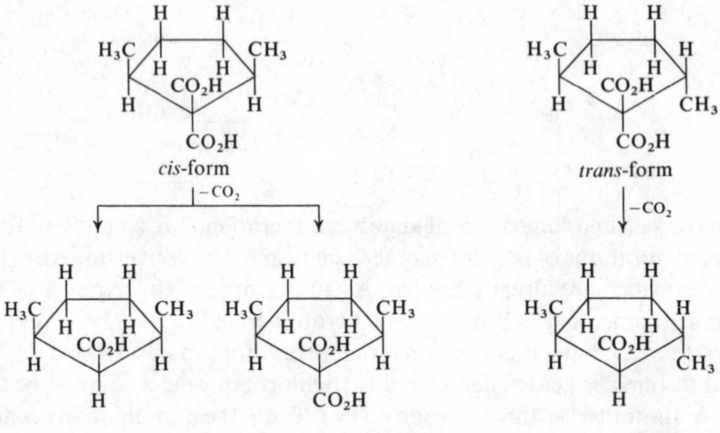

cis-form   trans-form

$-CO_2$ $-CO_2$

§5d. Method of optical activity. In many pairs of geometrical isomers one form may possess the requirements for optical activity (**2** §2), whereas the other form may not. In such cases a successful resolution of one form will determine the configuration, *e.g.*, there are two hexahydrophthalic acids; the *cis*-form possesses a plane of symmetry and consequently is optically inactive. The *trans*-form, however, possesses no elements of symmetry, and so should be resolvable; this has actually been resolved (see also §11c).

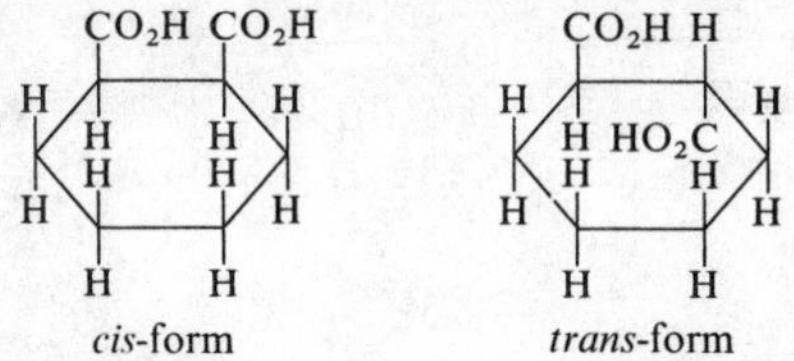

cis-form   trans-form
optically inactive   resolvable

§5e. Method of dipole moments. The use of dipole moments to assign configurations to geometrical isomers must be used with caution. The method is satisfactory so long as the groups attached to the olefinic carbon atoms have linear moments (see **1** §10), *e.g.*, *cis*-1,2-dichloroethylene has a dipole moment of 1·85 D; the value of the dipole moment of the *trans* isomer is zero. When, however, the groups have non-linear moments, then the vector sum in the *trans*-isomer will no longer be zero and the difference between the dipole moments of the *cis*- and *trans*-isomers may be too small to assign configuration with any confidence, *e.g.*, the dipole moment of diethyl maleate is 2·54 D and that of diethyl fumarate is 2·38 D.

§5f. X-ray analysis method. This method of determining the configuration of geometrical isomers is probably the best where it is readily applicable (see also **1** §14).

§5g. Spectroscopic methods. (*a*) *Ultraviolet and visible absorption spectra.* It has previously been pointed out (**1** §12a) that absorption in compounds containing conjugation is due to $\pi \to \pi^*$ transitions, and that the longer the conjugated system, the longer is the wavelength of the absorption and the larger is the molar extinction coefficient. If, then, the structure of the molecule is such as to prevent planarity, the overlap of the π-electrons is diminished, resulting in shorter wavelength and lower extinction coefficient. One factor that can decrease overlap is the steric factor, and since this would be larger in the *cis*-isomer than in the *trans*-, the latter would be expected to have the higher λ_{max} and ε. An example that illustrates this is stilbene.

cis (or *Z*)   *trans* (or *E*)

A number of resonating structures are possible for both forms, and in all cases the C—C bond will have partial double-bond character, and consequently the molecule will tend to be planar. However, in the case of the *cis*-form, owing to the proximity of the two (large) benzene rings, there will be steric hindrance, resulting in decreased resonance, *i.e.*, decreased overlap of the π-electrons due to steric inhibition of resonance. This argument is supported by the fact that λ_{max} and ε for *cis*-stilbene are 278 nm (9 350), and for *trans*-stilbene are 294 nm (24 000).

(*b*) *Infrared absorption spectra* (see also **1** §12). Absorption brought about by $=$C—H bending is much more intense than that brought about by C$=$C stretching, and *cis*- and *trans*-isomers of the type shown may be distinguished by the different ν_{max} observed for the $=$C—H bending.

ν_{max} 730–665 cm^{-1} 970–960 cm^{-1}

(*c*) *NMR spectra*. The use of NMR spectroscopy for distinguishing between *cis*- and *trans*-isomers of the type CH*a* $=$ CH*a* is based on the fact that the two hydrogen atoms have different coupling constants in each compound (see Table 1.9). This method may also be used to distinguish geometrical isomers of the type:

methyl citraconate   and   methyl mesaconate

The chemical shift of the olefinic proton in each isomer is different (and so is the methyl proton shift).

(*d*) *Mass spectrometry*. In general, *trans*-isomers give molecular ions of higher intensity than those of the corresponding *cis*-isomers. Also, the greater the steric effects in the molecule, the greater is this difference in the intensities. Similarly, the intensities of the fragment ions are greater for the *trans*-isomer than for the *cis*-, and this difference is increased by using electrons of lower energy (*i.e.*, below 50–70 *e*V; see **1** §13).

§5h. **Method of surface films.** Long-chain geometrical isomers which contain a terminal group capable of dissolving in a solvent will form surface films, but only the *trans*-form can form a close-packed film, *e.g.*, the long-chain unsaturated fatty acids.

cis- (or *Z*-) form   *trans-* or (*E*-)

§5i. Method of formation of solid solutions. In compounds which owe their property of geometrical isomerism to the presence of an olefinic bond, the shape of the *trans*-form is similar to that of the corresponding saturated compound, whereas that of the *cis*-form is different, *e.g.*, the shapes of fumaric and succinic acids are similar, but the shape of maleic acid is different from that of succinic acid. Now, molecules which are approximately of the same size and shape tend to form solid

fumaric acid   succinic acid   maleic acid

solutions. Thus fumaric acid forms a solid solution with succinic acid, whereas maleic acid does not; hence the configurations of maleic and fumaric acids may be determined.

§5j. Methods based on generalisations of physical properties. Comparison of the physical properties of geometrical isomers of known configurations has led to the following generalisations:

(*a*) The melting point and intensity of absorption of the *cis*-isomer are *lower* than those of the *trans*.

(*b*) The boiling point, solubility, heat of combustion, heat of hydrogenation, density, refractive index, dipole moment and dissociation constant (if the compound is an acid) of the *cis*-isomer are *greater* than those of the *trans*.

Based on certain of these generalisations is the **Auwers–Skita rule** (1915, 1920), *viz.*, in a pair of *cis-trans* isomers the *cis* has the higher boiling point, density and refractive index. This rule has been used to elucidate configurations, particularly in terpenoid chemistry, *e.g.*, the menthones (see **8** §16), but it has now been shown that the use of this rule may give misleading results (see §11a).

It can be seen from the above physical properties that the *trans*-form is usually the stabler of the two isomers, *i.e.*, the *trans*-isomer is the form with the lower internal energy (*cf.* §2).

Thus, in general, the above physical properties may be used to determine the configurations of unknown geometrical isomers, but the results should always be accepted with reserve, since exceptions are known. Even so, determination of as many as possible of the above physical properties will lead to reliable results, since deviations from the generalisations appear to be manifested in only one or two properties. It should also be noted that where the method of dipole moments can be applied, the results are reliable (*cf.* §5e).

Another method based on generalisations of physical properties is that suggested by Werner. Werner (1904) pointed out that ethylenic *cis-trans* isomers may be compared with the *ortho-* and *para*-isomers in the benzene series, the assumption being made that the melting points of the *cis-* and *ortho*-isomers are lower than those of the corresponding *trans-* and *para*-isomers, *e.g.*,

cis- (or *Z*-) crotonic acid   *o*-toluic acid
m.p. 15·5°C   m.p. 105°C

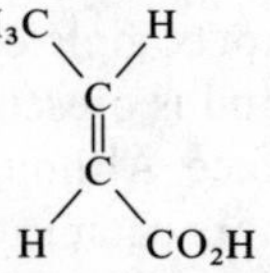

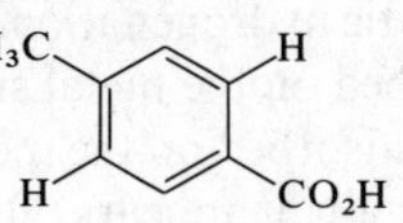

trans- (or E-) crotonic acid   p-toluic acid
m.p. 72°C   m.p. 180°C

Thus comparison of melting points offers a means of assigning configurations to geometrical isomers. Examination of the above structures shows that, as far as the shape of the molecule is concerned, the benzene ring may be regarded as usurping the function of C=C in the olefinic compound. By making use of this idea, it has been possible to assign configurations to difficult cases of geometrical isomerism, e.g., there are two ethyl α-chlorocrotonates, and by comparing their physical properties with ethyl 5-chloro-o- and 3-chloro-p-toluates, configurations may be assigned to the chlorocrotonates.

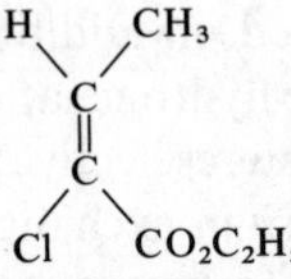

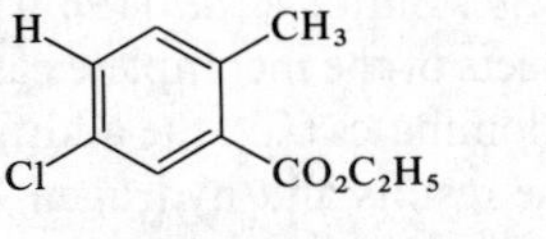

b.p. 56°C/10 mm   b.p. 122°C

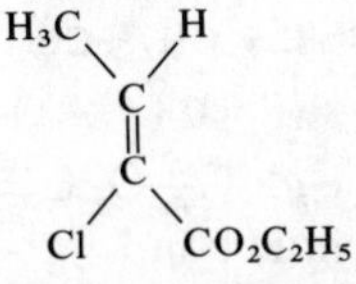

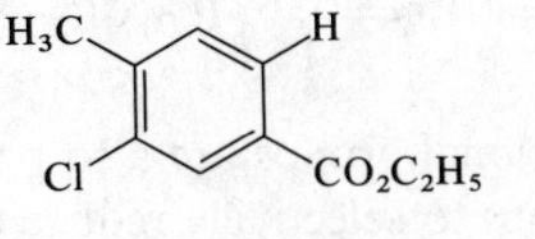

b.p. 61°C/10 mm   b.p. 130°C

§5k. **Method of stereoselective addition and elimination reactions.**   The term *stereoselective reaction* is used in those cases where a given substrate produces diastereoisomeric products in different amounts. If one diastereoisomer predominates very much over the other, the reaction is said to be highly stereoselective. If the two products are formed in almost equal amounts, the reaction is then said to be weakly stereoselective. The term *stereospecific reaction* has been used in the same sense as stereoselective reaction, but now the tendency is to restrict the use of stereospecific to a reaction in which different stereoisomers produce different products or act at different rates, e.g., the biochemical method of resolution is a stereospecific reaction (**2** §10(iii)).

§5l. **Addition reactions.**   (a) *Reduction.* Catalytic hydrogenation of alkenes and alkynes normally gives the *cis*-addition product. Thus, the catalytic hydrogenation (Pd) of *cis*-2,3-diphenylbutene in acetic acid gives almost completely (98 per cent) *meso*-2,3-diphenylbutane, and the *trans*-isomer gives the (±)-product (Cardew *et al.*, 1957).

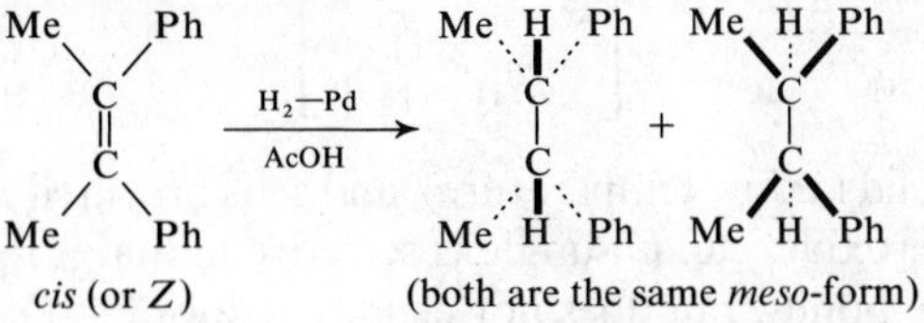

cis (or Z)   (both are the same *meso*-form)

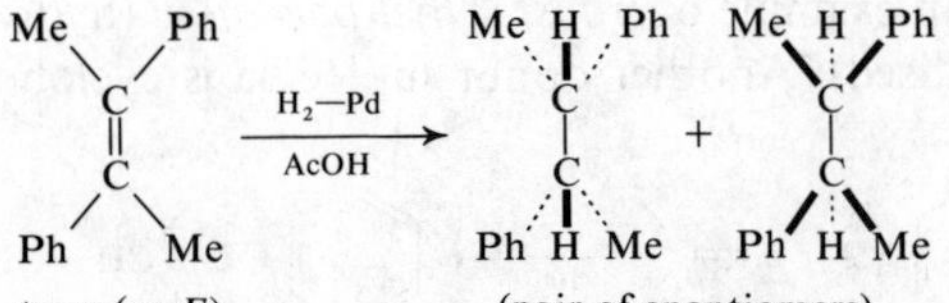

trans (or E)   (pair of enantiomers)

The mechanism of catalytic hydrogenation is still not completely understood. It is widely accepted that the hydrogen is adsorbed on the metal surface and is present as hydrogen atoms ($H_2 \rightarrow 2H\cdot$), and that the alkene is also adsorbed on the metal surface. Although the nature of the bonding to the metal in both cases is uncertain, it appears that it is more chemical than physical, and so is described as a *chemisorptive bond*. Linstead *et al.* (1942), from their studies on catalytic hydrogenation, proposed that the less hindered side of an unsaturated molecule is adsorbed on the metal surface, and that this is then followed by the *simultaneous* addition of two hydrogen atoms. In this way, the addition to form the *cis*-product was explained (attack must be from one side only). Furthermore, since chemisorption has converted hydrogen into hydrogen atoms and has broken one of the multiple bonds, the activation energy of catalytic hydrogenation is considerably lower than that in the uncatalysed reaction.

Later work has shown that this mechanism is unsatisfactory. Isomerisation of alkenes may occur during hydrogenation, *e.g.*, Smith *et al.* (1962) isolated, in addition to n-butane, *cis*- and *trans*-but-2-ene from the products of the incomplete catalytic hydrogenation of but-1-ene. Also, although *cis*-addition usually predominates (*i.e.*, the addition is stereoselective), *trans*-addition may occur and even predominate. These results and hydrogen–deuterium exchange experiments lead to the conclusion that addition of the adsorbed hydrogen atoms occurs one at a time and that the reaction is reversible (*cf.* catalytic dehydrogenation), *e.g.*, (asterisks indicate metallic sites):

$$H_2 + CH_2{=}CH_2 \rightleftharpoons \underset{*}{H} \quad \underset{*}{H} + \underset{*}{CH_2}{-}\underset{*}{CH_2} \rightleftharpoons \underset{*}{H} + \underset{*}{CH_2}{-}CH_3 \rightleftharpoons CH_3{-}CH_3$$

When reducible functional groups are also present, *e.g.*, $C{=}O$, $C{\equiv}N$, CO_2R, etc., it is usually possible to find conditions to selectively reduce the olefinic bond.

The stereochemical course of the catalytic reduction of cyclic systems—cycloalkenes and aromatics—depends on the nature of the catalyst, *e.g.*, the reduction of 1,2-dimethylcyclohexene in the presence of platinum in acetic acid gives predominantly *cis*-addition, whereas with palladium *trans*-addition predominates (see also the decalins, §11d).

By using suitable conditions, *e.g.*, $Pd{-}BaSO_4{-}S$ as catalyst, it is possible to isolate alkenes when alkynes are reduced (see also 3 §7; asymmetric hydrogenation).

Now let us consider chemical reduction. The olefinic bond is not reduced by metal and acid, sodium and ethanol, lithium aluminium hydride, etc. unless it is α, β with respect to certain groups, *e.g.*, $C{=}O$.

Some chemical reagents, however, do reduce olefinic bonds, *e.g.*, alkenes are reduced to *cis* products by di-imide, and this stereospecificity can be explained by the formation of a cyclic T.S.

Di-imide is an unstable solid (at low temperature), and so is prepared *in situ*, *e.g.*, by the oxidation hydrazine with hydrogen peroxide, etc. Di-imide is selective in that it reduces carbon—carbon and nitrogen—nitrogen multiple bonds, but does not usually reduce $C{=}O$, NO_2, $C{\equiv}N$, etc.

Reduction by di-imide is an example of *transfer hydrogenation* (hydrogen is supplied by a donor molecule which is itself oxidised). Another donor molecule is cyclohexene (which is oxidised to benzene):

This system reduces many types of functional groups, *e.g.*, olefinic and acetylenic bonds, NO_2, —N=N—, etc.

A *terminal* double bond may be reduced by sodium in liquid ammonia *in the presence of an alcohol* (MeOH or EtOH; alcohols are stronger acids than ammonia). This method is known as the **Birch reduction**, and is believed to proceed stepwise *via* an anionic free radical:

$$RCH=CH_2 \xrightarrow{\frac{Na}{e}} R\dot{C}H\bar{C}H_2 \xrightarrow{EtOH} R\dot{C}HCH_3 \xrightarrow{\frac{Na}{e}} R\bar{C}HCH_3 \xrightarrow{EtOH} RCH_2CH_3$$

The double bond is also reduced in excellent yield by $NaBH_4$—$PtCl_2$ (Brown *et al.*, 1962).

Alkynes are converted by the Birch reduction into the *trans*-alkenes.

Hydroboronation (hydroboration). Alkynes are reduced by diborane to trialkenylboranes which, on treatment with propionic acid, give the *cis*-addition products. Di-isobutylaluminium hydride also gives *cis*-addition (see also Vol. I). The stereospecific *cis*-addition has been explained by the reaction proceeding stepwise through an intermediate cyclic transition state.

Stereospecific *cis*-addition also occurs with alkenes to give alkanes and, as with alkynes, occurs *via* a cyclic transition state. This may be formulated as shown:

$$RCH=CH_2 \xrightarrow{BH_3} RCH_2CH_2BH_2 \xrightarrow{RCH=CH_2} (RCH_2CH_2-)_2BH \xrightarrow{RCH=CH_2} (RCH_2CH_2-)_3B$$

Trialkylboranes are readily oxidised by alkaline hydrogen peroxide to alcohols, the *overall hydration* being *cis*. A possible mechanism is one which involves a 1,2-shift (see also Vol. I).

$$R_3B + \bar{O}OH \longrightarrow R_2\overset{R}{B}\!\!-\!\!O\!\!-\!\!\overset{}{O}H \longrightarrow R_2B\!\!-\!\!OR + OH^- \longrightarrow R_2B\!\!-\!\!OH + RO \xrightarrow{H_2O} R_2BOH + ROH + OH^-$$

Hydroboronation can be carried out with the chiral reagent 'di-3-pinanylborane' (di-isopino-campheylborane), (II), which is prepared from either (+)- or (−)-α-pinene (I; see **8** §22a). Also, since oxidation of the (+)-derivative with alkaline hydrogen peroxide gives (−)-isopinocampheol (III) without inversion (see above), the configuration of the borane is established.

(I)   (II)   (III)

In this way, *cis*-alkenes which are relatively sterically unhindered, may be converted into chiral alcohols, the predominant enantiomer of which can be predicted, *e.g.*, with *cis*-but-2-ene, the predominant enantiomer is the (*R*)-form when the chiral reagent is (−).

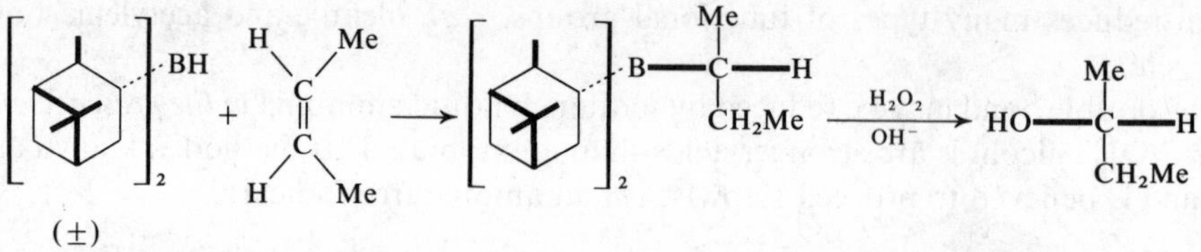

(±)

Asymmetric syntheses with this borane derivative have been used mainly for the preparation of chiral alcohols, but other types of compounds have also been prepared, *e.g.*, chiral ketones (by oxidation of the alcohol).

(*b*) *Hydroxylation*. The configuration of the product formed by hydroxylation of a double bond depends on the nature of the hydroxylating agent used and on the conditions under which the reaction is carried out. Permanganate and osmium tetroxide apparently always give *cis*-addition, whereas permonosulphuric acid (Caro's acid) and perbenzoic acid give *trans*-addition. On the other

Reagent	Type of addition	Maleic acid	Fumaric acid
$KMnO_4$	*cis*	*meso*tartaric acid	DL-tartaric acid
OsO_4	*cis*	*meso*tartaric acid	DL-tartaric acid
H_2SO_5	*trans*	DL-tartaric acid	*meso*tartaric acid
$C_6H_5COO_2H$	*trans*	DL-tartaric acid	*meso*tartaric acid
H_2O_2—OsO_4	*cis*	*meso*tartaric acid	DL-tartaric acid
H_2O_2—SeO_2	*trans*	DL-tartaric acid	*meso*tartaric acid

hand, hydroxylation with hydrogen peroxide catalysed by osmium tetroxide in t-butanol gives *cis*-addition; if the reaction is catalysed by selenium dioxide in t-butanol or in acetone, then the addition is *trans* (see also below). The table above shows the products formed by hydroxylation of maleic and fumaric acids.

With potassium permanganate and osmium tetroxide the *cis*-addition is readily explained by assuming the formation of a cyclic organo-metallic intermediate, *e.g.*, with permanganate:

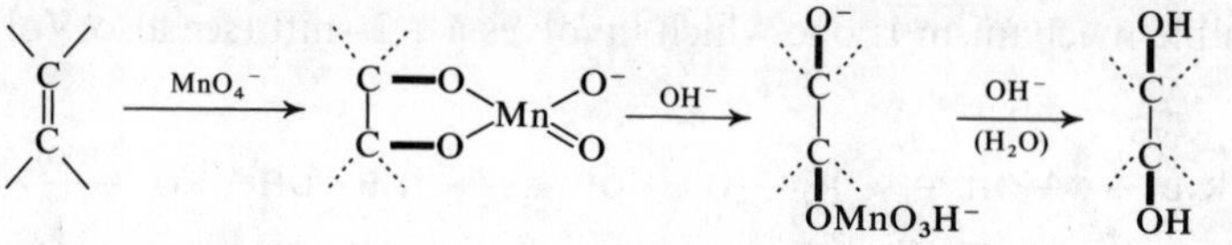

This cyclic intermediate is definitely known in the case of osmium tetroxide (see Vol. I); for potassium permanganate it may be assumed that the permanganate ion, MnO_4^-, behaves in a similar manner. This is supported by the work of Wiberg *et al.* (1957), who used potassium permanganate labelled with ^{18}O and showed that *both* glycol oxygen atoms come from the permanganate ion. This also indicates that fission of the cyclic compound occurs between the O and Mn atoms.

With per-acids the hydroxylation results in *trans*-addition. The first product of oxidation is an epoxide (Prileschaiev reaction; see Vol. I). Evidence from kinetic studies on solutions of epoxides under high pressure strongly suggests that acid-catalysed hydrolysis is a bimolecular substitution of the conjugate acid (Whalley *et al.*, 1959). This will result in *trans*-hydroxylation. Thus:

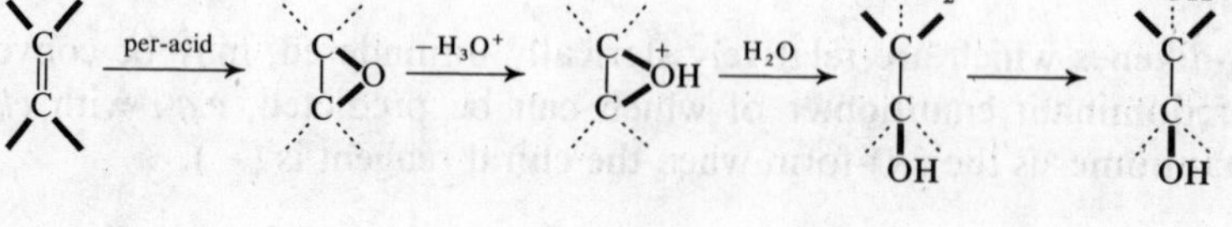

The addition of hydrogen peroxide may result in *cis* or *trans* compounds. Which occurs depends on the conditions of the experiment, *e.g.*, the catalyst (see above). Where *trans*-addition occurs, the mechanism may possibly be through the epoxide, but a free hydroxyl radical mechanism could also result in the *trans*-glycol. *Cis*-addition in the presence of certain oxides probably occurs *via* a cyclic intermediate.

(*c*) (i) *Diels–Alder reaction.* The addition of a dienophile to a diene in the Diels–Alder reaction is stereospecific; each geometrical isomer forms the *cis*-additon product. Since it is usually possible to determine the configuration of the cyclic adduct, this offers a means of ascertaining the configuration of the dienophile. *E.g.*, butadiene forms adducts with *cis*- and *trans*-cinnamic acids, and hence determination of the configurations of the stereoisomeric adducts will determine the configurations of the cinnamic acids (see §11c); thus:

cis (or *Z*)   *cis*

trans (or *E*)   *trans*

The mechanism and stereochemical course of the Diels–Alder reaction are discussed in Vol. I, Chs. 19 and 31.

(ii) *Addition of methylene.* This also is a stereospecific reaction, each geometrical isomer forming the *cis*-addition product. Thus, *e.g.*, Skell *et al.* (1956, 1959) showed that methylene (carbene), from the photolysis of diazomethane, added to *cis*- and *trans*-but-2-ene in a *cis*-fashion:

cis (or *Z*)   *cis*

trans (or *E*)   *trans*

This stereospecificity, however, is lost when the reaction is carried out in the presence of an inert gas (nitrogen), *i.e.*, each substrate now gives a mixture of the *cis*- and *trans*-products (Anet *et al.*, 1960). Duncan *et al.* (1962) also showed that methylene formed by the photolysis of keten added to the above substrates in a non-stereospecific manner.

According to Skell *et al.* (1956) the stereospecificity of the reaction is due to the addition of singlet methylene, which forms both bonds simultaneously:

The non-stereospecific reaction is attributed to the addition of methylene in the triplet state:

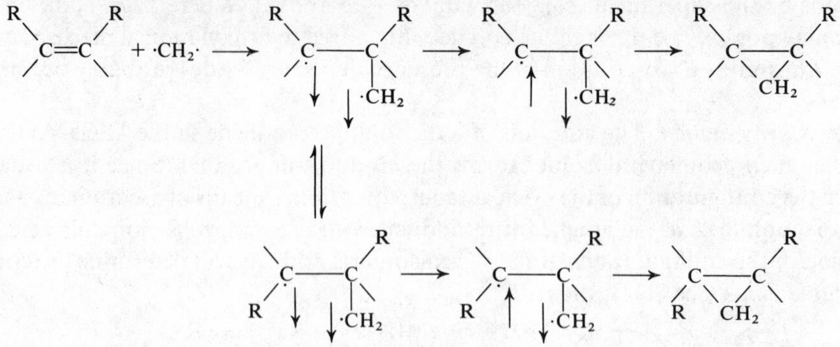

In the triplet state, the two electrons have parallel spins, and methylene behaves as a diradical. Also, to account for the non-stereospecificity, it is assumed that rotation about the single bond is more rapid than spin inversion (see also Vol. I, Ch. 4).

(*d*) *Polar addition of halogens and halogen acids.* All the evidence for the *polar* addition of halogens and halogen acids indicates a two-stage electrophilic mechanism (see Vol. I, Ch. 4), *e.g.*,

$$CH_2 =\!\!=CH_2 \quad Br\!-\!Br \longrightarrow \overset{+}{C}H_2CH_2Br + Br^- \longrightarrow CH_2BrCH_2Br$$

$$CH_2 =\!\!=CH_2 \quad H\!-\!Cl \longrightarrow \overset{+}{C}H_2CH_3 + Cl^- \longrightarrow CH_2ClCH_3$$

In order to account for *trans*-addition, Roberts and Kimball (1937) suggested that the first step is the formation of a bridged halogenium ion, *e.g.*, with bromine the brominium (bromonium) ion is formed first. If a classical carbonium ion were formed first, then one could expect free rotation about the newly-formed single bond and in this case the stereochemical addition would not be the one observed in practice. Thus for maleic acid the reaction may be formulated as follows:

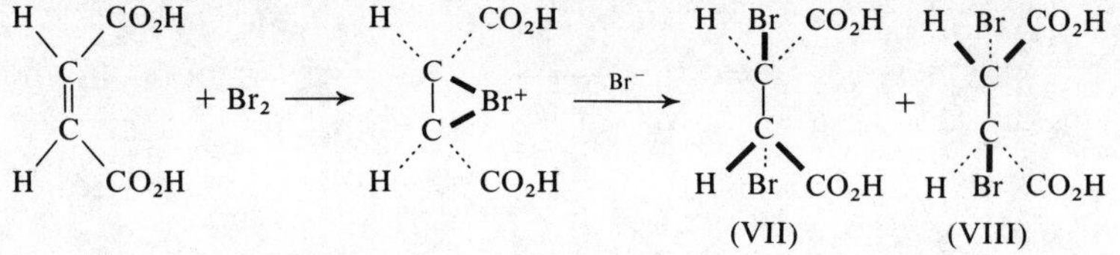

Since the bromide ion can attack 'conveniently' only along the $C\!-\!Br^+$ bonding line and on the side remote from the bromine, a Walden inversion occurs at the carbon atom attacked. Since the brominium ion is symmetrical, it can be anticipated that either carbon atom will be attacked equally well, thereby resulting in the formation of (VII) and (VIII) in equal amounts, *i.e.*, maleic acid will produce ($\pm$)-dibromosuccinic acid. Winstein and Lucas (1939) have demonstrated the existence of this bridged ion (see **3** §6b).

The above mechanism explains *trans*-addition, but, as we have seen, although this predominates, it is not exclusive. The reason for this is not certain, but it is possible that the bridged ion is not firmly held, *i.e.*, the ring opens to give the classical carbonium ion, and this is followed by rotation about the single $C\!-\!C$ bond due to steric repulsion between the carboxyl groups. This would explain the experiments of Michael (1892) that both the maleate ion and fumarate ion add chlorine or bromine to give mainly *meso*-dihalogenosuccinic acid. The configurations of the products indicate that *trans*-addition has occurred with the fumarate ion but *cis*- addition with the maleate ion. Roberts and Kimball, however, have explained these results by assuming that the intermediate maleate brominium ion (*cis*) changes to the fumarate brominium ion (*trans*) due to the powerful repulsions of the negatively charged carboxylate ion groups.

In all of the foregoing examples, addition of halogen and halogen acid has been shown to be predominantly *trans*, and where the results were not in accord with this, explanations have been offered in terms of steric effects. This, however, cannot be used to satisfy all cases where '*cis*-addition' has occurred, *e.g.*, Dewar *et al.* (1963) found that both *cis*- and *trans*-1-phenylpropene add deuterium bromide (or chloride), under conditions giving rise to the polar mechanism, to give predominantly (88 per cent) the *cis*-addition product. As an explanation, the authors propose a mechanism involving the rate-determining formation of a classical carbonium ion as an ion-pair (IX) where the halide

$$
\begin{array}{cc}
\underset{\text{(IX)}}{\overset{\text{H}\quad \text{X}^-}{-\overset{|}{\underset{|}{\text{C}}}-\overset{+}{\underset{|}{\text{C}}}-}} & \underset{\text{(X)}}{\overset{\text{H}}{-\overset{|}{\underset{|}{\text{C}}}-\overset{|}{\underset{\text{X}^-}{\overset{+}{\text{C}}}}-}}
\end{array}
$$

ion is held on the *same* side of the original double bond as the entering proton. Collapse of this ion-pair thus gives the *cis*-adduct but, at the same time, *rearrangement* of (IX) to the isomeric ion-pair, (X), gives the *trans*-adduct. Dewar suggests that *cis*-addition should be the rule in electrophilic additions proceeding through a classical carbonium ion, and that the predominance of *trans*-addition, as commonly observed, is due to steric effects. Other examples of *cis*-addition are also known, *e.g.*,

cis-addition (75%)   trans-addition (25%)

On the other hand, *trans*-butene adds chlorine in the absence of solvent to give exclusively the *trans*-addition product. It would therefore appear that the stereochemical course of addition of

electrophilic reagents depends on the nature of the alkene, the addendum, and on the conditions.

Alkynes undergo *nucleophilic* addition with strong bases to give predominantly *trans*-addition, *e.g.*,

(*e*) *Free radical additions.* The addition of hydrogen bromide to acyclic alkenes in the presence of light or peroxides is a free-radical reaction (see the Peroxide Effect, Vol. I). The reaction is stereospecifically *trans* at low temperatures, but at room temperature the two isomers give the same mixture of diastereoisomers, *e.g.*, the addition of hydrogen bromide to *cis*- and *trans*-2-bromobut-2-ene at −78°C gives *meso*- and (±)-2,3-dibromobutane, respectively. At room temperature, however, both bromobutenes give the same mixture of products (Goering *et al.*, 1959). The results may be explained as follows. Since attack by the bromine atom can occur equally well at the upper carbon atom from the front (as shown in the equations; note the $(E-Z)$ nomenclature) and the back (*i.e.*, the upper carbon atom has enantiotopic faces; **2** §7a), the *cis*-isomer gives only the *meso*-product because the abstraction of hydrogen from the hydrogen bromide is faster than the internal rotation (of the free radical produced from *cis*-butene). For similar reasons, the *trans*-isomer gives

only the $(\pm)$-product. At room temperature, however, the less stable radical (from *cis*-butene) equilibrates with the more stable radical (from *trans*-butene) by internal rotation which is now faster than the hydrogen abstraction. The result is that both butenes give the *same* mixture of diastereo-isomers. In both cases, the addition of hydrogen is *trans* with respect to the bromine atom.

Free radical addition to cyclic alkenes is *trans*; no rotation is now possible, *e.g.*, Goering *et al.* (1952) showed that 1-bromocyclohexene added hydrogen bromide in the presence of benzoyl peroxide to give *cis*-1,2-dibromocyclohexane (note that the two bromine atoms are equatorial and axial, respectively).

§5m. **Elimination reactions.** In alkene-forming eliminations, two mechanisms are possible, E1 and E2, *i.e.*, unimolecular and bimolecular eliminations.

E1 $\quad H-CR_2-CR_2-Z \xrightleftharpoons{\text{slow}} Z^- + H-CR_2-\overset{+}{C}R_2 \xrightarrow{\text{fast}}$

$\quad\quad H^+ + CR_2{=}CR_2$

E2 $\quad Y + H-CR_2-CR_2-Z \longrightarrow YH + CR_2{=}CR_2 + Z^-$

Two other mechanisms are also believed to operate in certain circumstances (see below). All of these mechanisms of elimination belong to the ionic type (see also later).

Evidence for the E1 mechanism has been obtained in several ways, *e.g.*, the rate law for many eliminations is first-order (alkyl halide only), *i.e.*, rate = $k[RX]$. This is consistent with the mechanism given.

Evidence for the E2 mechanism comes from the fact that the rate law for many eliminations is second-order, *i.e.*, *rate* = $k[RX][B]$. There is, however, a difficulty here. The second-order rate law is consistent with the one-step mechanism given above, but it is also consistent with the following two-step mechanism:

$$\text{Et}\bar{\text{O}} + \text{PhCH}_2\text{CH}_2\text{Br} \underset{}{\overset{\text{fast}}{\rightleftharpoons}} \text{EtOH} + \text{Ph}\bar{\text{C}}\text{HCH}_2\text{Br}$$

$$\text{PhCH}^{\frown}\!\!-\!\text{CH}_2\!-\!^{\frown}\text{Br} \xrightarrow{\text{slow}} \text{PhCH}\!=\!\text{CH}_2 + \text{Br}^-$$

A simplified derivation of the rate law for this reaction is as follows. Since the reaction is carried out in ethanol, the concentration of the *ethanol produced* in the first step may be neglected. Hence:

$$K = [\text{Ph}\bar{\text{C}}\text{HCH}_2\text{Br}]/([\text{PhCH}_2\text{CH}_2\text{Br}][\text{OEt}^-])$$
$$\therefore \quad \text{rate} = k[\text{Ph}\bar{\text{C}}\text{HCH}_2\text{Br}] = kK[\text{PhCH}_2\text{CH}_2\text{Br}][\text{OEt}^-]$$

Since k and K are both constants, their product may be replaced by a constant k', and the rate law is:

$$\text{rate} = k'[\text{PhCH}_2\text{CH}_2\text{Br}][\text{OEt}^-]$$

i.e., the rate law is second-order. Thus, kinetics cannot distinguish between these two possible elimination mechanisms.

In the second mechanism, a slow unimolecular elimination occurs in the conjugate case (cB) of the reactant, and hence this mechanism is called the **E1cB** or **carbanion mechanism**. Since the first step must be reversible (acid-conjugate base equilibrium), if ethanol containing EtOD is used as solvent, it would be expected that the original bromide would incorporate deuterium. Skell *et al.* (1945) examined this reaction and found that after the reaction was half-completed, the recovered bromide did not contain deuterium. Hence, *this* mechanism is not E1cB, but is E2.

More O'Ferall (1970) has presented a great deal of evidence to show that in aqueous solution 9-fluorenylmethanol undergoes base-catalysed β-elimination to form dibenzofulvene by an E1cB mechanism ($\text{RCH}_2 = $ fluorene):

$$\text{RCH}_2\text{CH}_2\text{OH} + \text{OH}^- \rightleftharpoons \text{R}\bar{\bar{\text{C}}}\text{H}^{\frown}\!\!-\!\text{CH}_2\!-\!^{\frown}\text{OH} \rightleftharpoons \text{RCH}\!=\!\text{CH}_2 + \text{OH}^-$$

Schlosser *et al.* (1967) have obtained evidence for the existence of the **E2cB mechanism** in the reaction between *cis*-styryl chloride and an organolithium base.

Many examples in the literature show that *trans* elimination occurs more readily than *cis*, *e.g.* (also see later):

(*a*) Michael (1895) showed that reaction 1 was about 50 times as fast as 2.

(*b*) Chavanne (1912) showed that reaction 1 was about 20 times as fast as 2.

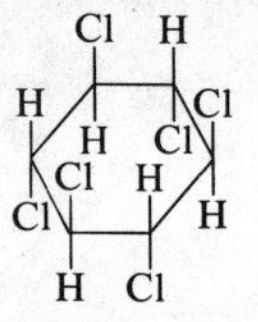

(c) Cristol (1947) showed that the β-isomer of hexachlorocyclohexane underwent base-catalysed elimination with great difficulty, whereas under the same conditions all the other known isomers (four at that time; see also §11c) readily underwent second-order elimination to form trichlorobenzenes; the β-isomer is the only one in which *all* the 1,2-HCl pairs are *cis*. Thus in the E2 reaction, the *trans* requirement is necessary (see also below).

According to Hughes and Ingold, bimolecular elimination reactions (E2) take place when the two groups (to be eliminated) are *trans* and the groups and the two carbon atoms (to which the groups are attached) *all lie in one plane*. In this way the planar transition state will be readily formed. As the proton is being removed from the β-carbon atom by the base, the 'liberated' covalent pair of electrons attacks the α-carbon atom from the rear, thereby forming the double bond with displacement of the halogen atom. This type of sequence is not possible when the β-hydrogen atom is *cis* to the halogen atom, *i.e.*, the stereoelectronic requirement is that the groups which are to be eliminated must be in the *trans* position (see also **2** §4a).

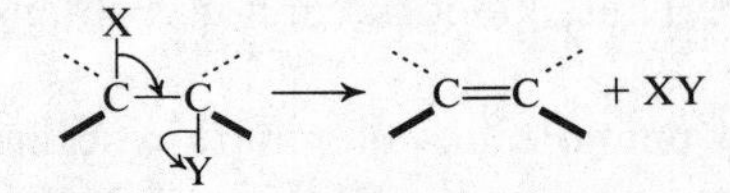

The foregoing evidence for *trans*-elimination has come from a study of 'rigid' molecules. However, there is also abundant evidence obtained from the study of the products and rates of reaction involving acyclic compounds. A classical example is the debromination of 2,3-dibromobutane by means of potassium iodide in acetone solution. Winstein *et al.* (1939) showed that this reaction is bimolecular (first order in dibromide and first order in iodide ion). Thus, in the transition state, the two carbons (of the CBr groups) and the two bromine atoms will be in the staggered position. Now, 2,3-dibromobutane exists in (+)-, (−)- and *meso*-forms, and it has been shown that the (±)-form gives *cis*-butene, whereas the *meso*-form gives *trans*-butene. If we accept the debromination mechanism proposed by Mulders *et al.* (1963), we may then write these eliminations as follows:

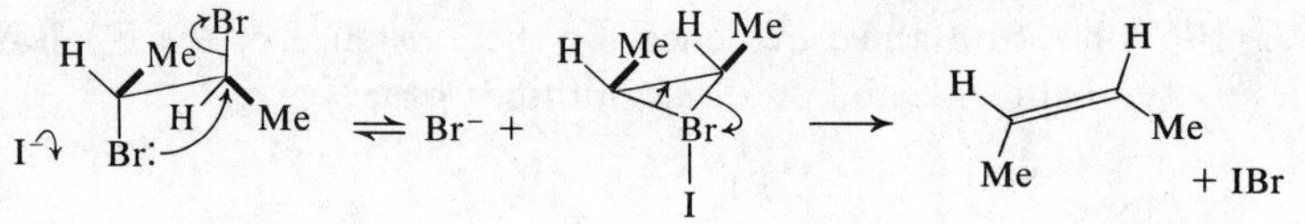

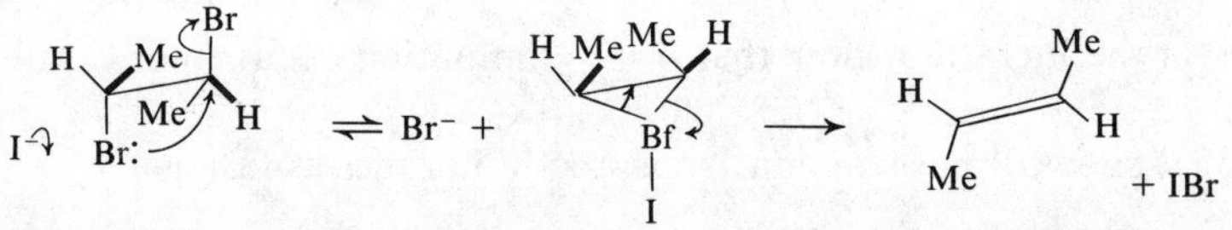

In the bridged-ion intermediate from the (±)-form, the two methyl groups become eclipsed; in the *meso*-form a methyl group becomes eclipsed with a hydrogen. Thus the energy of activation of the transition state of the (±)-form will be greater than that of the *meso*-form and consequently the latter should be formed more readily, *i.e.*, the *meso*-form should undergo debromination more readily than the (±)-form. Winstein *et al.* (1939) have shown that this is so in practice, the rate of debromination being about twice as fast.

Other examples of E2 reactions which show that *trans*-elimination occurs readily are the following. Cram *et al.* (1952) have shown that the base-catalysed dehydrobromination of the diastereoisomeric 1-bromo-1,2-diphenylpropanes (I and II) gives alkenes that can only arise by *trans* elimination (I is the *erythro* compound and II is the *threo*).

(I)   *cis* (or *Z*)

(II)   *trans* (or *E*)

Cram *et al.* (1956) also examined the elimination reaction of the following 'onium ion with base (Hofmann exhaustive methylation):

$$\text{PhCHMeCHPhNMe}_3^+\}\,I^- \xrightarrow{\ \text{OEt}^-\ } \text{PhMeC}{=}\text{CHPh}$$

This 'onium ion exists in two forms, *threo* and *erythro*, and the results were that the *threo*-compound gave the *trans*-alkene and the *erythro*-compound the *cis*-alkene; this is in keeping with *trans*

threo   *trans* (or *E*)

erythro   *cis* (or *Z*)

elimination. The rates of elimination, however, were very different, the *threo*-form reacting over 50 times as fast as the *erythro*. In the *cis*-product, the two phenyl groups become eclipsed and hence the energy of activation for this product is greater than that for the *trans*-product, and consequently the latter is formed more readily (see also below).

A more complicated example of elimination is the case of 2-bromobutane. This, on dehydro-bromination, forms *trans*- and *cis*-but-2-ene in a ratio of about 6:1 (Lucas *et al.*, 1925). This result may be explained by *trans*-elimination occurring simultaneously from two *different* conformations, and one might expect at first sight that, since the staggered conformation is more stable than the skew, the population of the former is greater than that of the latter and consequently the *trans*-product would predominate. According to the **Curtin–Hammett principle**, however, this explanation is incorrect. This principle may be stated as follows: Provided that the activation energy of the reaction is large compared with the barrier to rotation, *i.e.*, the rates of formation of the products are *slower* than the rate of interconversion of the conformers, the relative amounts of the products do not depend on the relative populations of the conformations, but only on the energies of the transition states leading to the products. However, although the *product ratio* is independent of the

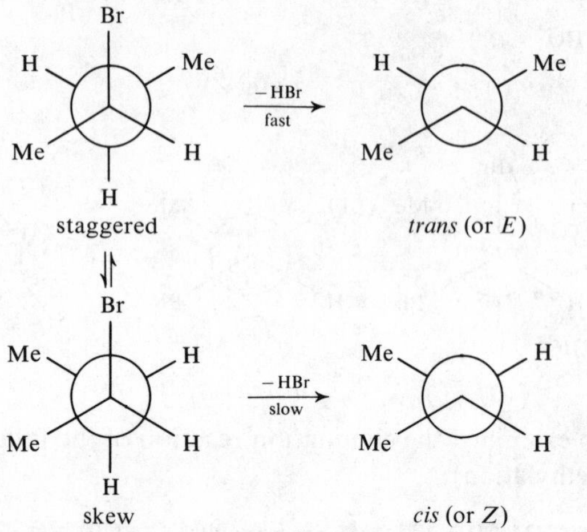

population ratio of the conformers, the *rate of formation* of the products does depend on the population ratio. As we have seen above, in the *cis*-transition state, the two large groups become eclipsed, and consequently the activation energy for this reaction is higher than that which gives the *trans*-product. Hence the *trans*-product is formed faster than the *cis*-. Furthermore, it should also be noted that since both reactions proceed by *trans*-elimination, both conformations satisfy the stereo-electronic requirements equally well.

The Curtin–Hammett principle should always be considered when attempting to analyse the observed preferred configuration of a product in reactions involving a conformationally mobile system (see, *e.g.*, §12).

An interesting point that now arises is: What is the mechanism when the two eliminated groups *cannot* assume the *trans*-position? This was first answered by postulating somewhat complicated mechanisms, but now there is a great deal of evidence to show that bimolecular eliminations may, in certain circumstances, proceed by a *cis*-elimination (*cf.* addition reactions, above). Cristol *et al.* (1960) examined the following elimination reaction, where $Y = SMe_2^+$ or NMe_3^+ (the latter is the Hofmann exhaustive methylation). The reaction was shown to occur by the E2 mechanism, and so it follows that 1-phenylcyclohexene is formed by a *cis*-elimination and 3-phenylcyclohexene by the normal *trans*-elimination. Ingold (1963) has explained the *cis*-elimination by proposing that the

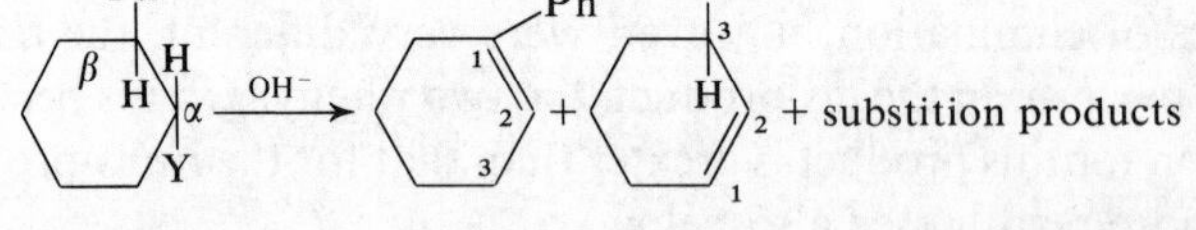

$Y = SMe_2^+$	22%	2%	61%
$Y = NMe_3^+$	64%	2%	8%

bond changes no longer occur simultaneously (as in *trans*-elimination). The more difficult it is to detach the C_α group (*i.e.*, Y), the further ahead will the proton transfer proceed on C_β (as compared with the breaking of the C_α bond), thereby building up a negative charge on C_β. As this negative charge builds up, the electron-pair is becoming increasingly available for forming the double bond when C_α is 'free'. This uncoupling of the C_α and C_β bond charges, because of the sequence described, permits phenyl conjugation to control the orientation of the elimination, *i.e.*, *cis*-elimination is now favoured. Since it has been shown (from other experiments) that it is more difficult to detach the NMe_3^+ group than the SMe_2^+ group, the presence of the former will therefore lead to more *cis*-elimination than the latter.

The *cis*-eliminations described above occur by the E2 mechanism. Now let us consider the E1 mechanism. It has long been believed that the product composition (substitution and elimination products) in S_N1 reactions was independent of the leaving group (in halides, *p*-toluenesulphonates, etc.). The experiments which led to this conclusion were carried out in fairly highly basic solvents, *e.g.*, aqueous ethanol. However, Winstein *et al.* (1963) found that the product composition of the solvolysis of a series of t-butyl compounds in water was independent of the leaving group, but this was no longer true when the solvolysis was carried out in more weakly basic solvents such as ethanol or acetic acid. The explanation offered is that in the latter solvents ionisation to an ion-pair occurs, and the counter-ion then assists in the removal of a proton from the carbonium ion, different counter-ions reacting at different rates. Cram *et al.* (1963) have also shown that the product composition of a series of 2-phenylbut-2-yl compounds in acetic acid depends on the nature of the leaving group. On the other hand, Skell *et al.* (1963), by using *erythro*- and *threo*-3-deuterobut-2-yl *p*-toluenesulphonates in different solvents, were able to estimate the amount of *cis*- and *trans*-elimination by determining the deuterium content of the but-2-enes produced.

Thus, four products are possible from the *erythro*-isomer, two types of elimination occurring with each conformation (*cf.* the Curtin–Hammett principle above). It was shown that *cis*-elimination varied from 0 per cent with sodium ethoxide in ethanol to 100 per cent when nitrobenzene was the solvent. The explanation offered for the latter result is that, in nitrobenzene, the departing *p*-toluenesulphonate anion assists in the removal of the β-proton (or deuteron) to yield *cis*-elimination products.

Molecular eliminations. Most eliminations occur by a polar mechanism (see above), whereas cyclic eliminations are unimolecular non-polar reactions which take place in *one* step. Most occur when the compound is subjected to pyrolysis, and proceed via a cyclic T.S. This mechanism is supported by the fact that these reactions show a *negative* entropy of activation (a cyclic structure has less freedom than an open-chain structure). In general, *trans*-elimination occurs in the polar mechanism (see above), whereas in pyrolytic eliminations, the elimination is *cis*. This is a consequence of the formation of a cyclic T.S.; both the eliminated proton and 'leaving group' are in the *cis*-position.

An advantage of cyclic eliminations is that no carbon skeleton rearrangement occurs (*cf.* dehydration of alcohols). Also, in the pyrolysis of esters and xanthates of s- and t-alcohols, mixtures of alkenes are produced, but the terminal alkene is favoured over the non-terminal alkene (*cf.* Sayteff's rule; see Vol. I).

(*a*) **Pyrolysis of esters.** The esters are usually acetates:

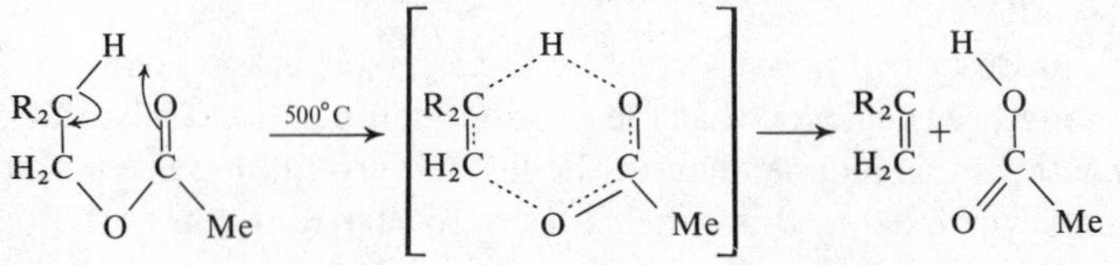

In many cases, pyrolysis of the alcohol with acetic anhydride is simpler than starting with the preformed ester (Aubrey *et al.*, 1965).

(*b*) **Pyrolysis of xanthates.** This is known as the *Tschugaev* (*Chugaev*) *reaction* (1899).

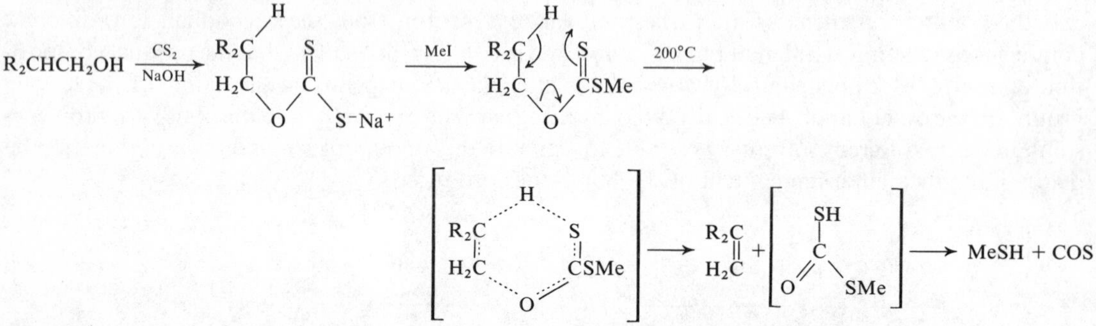

The yield of alkene is increased by heating the xanthate with, *e.g.*, chloroacetic acid ($-CS^-Na^+ \rightarrow$ $-CSCH_2CO_2H$), and then refluxing this in feebly acid solution. Alternatively, heating the xanthate derivative in the presence of a Lewis acid catalyst, *e.g.*, BF_3, shortens the reaction time and the yield is increased.

(*c*) **Cope reaction** (1949). This is the reaction in which alkenes are formed when amine oxides are heated:

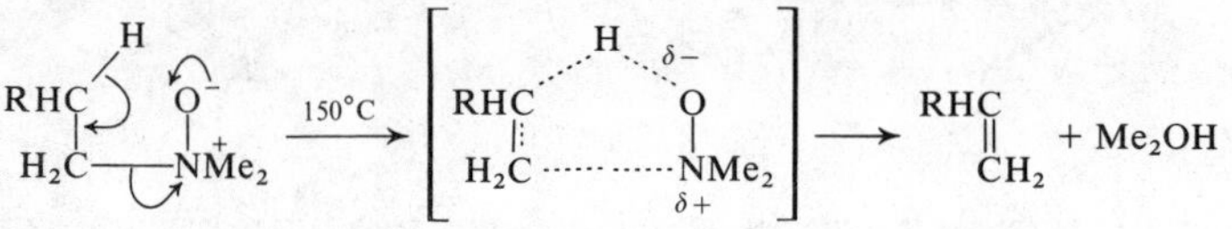

The reaction may also be carried out in dimethyl sulphoxide or tetrahydrofuran at room temperature (Cram *et al.*, 1962).

§6. Interconversion (stereomutation) of geometrical isomers

The *cis*-isomer, being usually the more labile form, is readily converted into the *trans*-form under suitable physical or chemical conditions. The usual chemical reagents used for stereomutation are halogens and nitrous acid, *e.g.*,

$$\text{maleic acid} \xrightarrow{\text{Br}_2;\text{I}_2} \text{fumaric acid}$$

$$\text{oleic acid} \xrightarrow{\text{HNO}_2} \text{elaidic acid}$$

Other methods such as distillation or prolonged heating above the melting point also usually convert the *cis*-isomer into the *trans*, but, in general, the result is a mixture of the two forms.

The conversion of the *trans*-isomer into the *cis* may be effected by means of sunlight, but the best method is to use ultraviolet light in the presence of a trace of bromine.

Photochemical *cis-trans* isomerisations. *cis-trans*-Isomerisation can be carried out (usually in solution) by irradiation alone or in the presence of a sensitiser or a catalyst (see also Vol. I, Ch. 31). In general, an equilibrium mixture is reached, the *cis-trans* ratio remaining constant no matter how much longer the irradiation is continued. This condition, called a **photostationary state**, is independent of which isomer is the starting material and always contains predominantly the *cis*-isomer. The actual ratio of the *cis-trans* forms, however, depends on a number of factors, *e.g.*, solvent, temperature, nature of the sensitiser, etc.

The *cis-trans* isomerisation of the stilbenes has been examined in great detail, and so we shall use this as our example. The evidence is strongly in favour that the reaction proceeds via a triplet state (Ph—ĊH—ĊH—Ph), but since the *cis-trans* ratio depends on the temperature, several theories have been proposed to explain the isomerisation. According to one theory, the *cis-* and *trans-*forms give *different* excited states, and the temperature

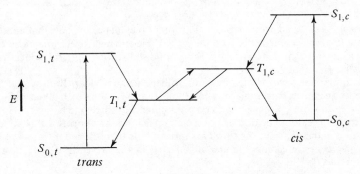

Fig. 4.5

effect is due to the existence of an energy barrier between these excited states (Fig. 4.5). Because of steric effects, the *cis*-isomer has a higher energy content than the *trans* in the ground state, and this is also (usually) the case for the corresponding excited states. Also, because of this larger steric effect, the molar absorptivity of the *cis*-isomer is (usually) lower than that of the *trans*-isomer. Hence, the population of the *trans* excited state is greater than that of the *cis*. These excited states can return to their respective ground states (Fig. 4.5) or, by rotation, the *cis** (T_1) and *trans** (T_1) become interconvertible. However, in this interconversion, only the *cis** → *trans** is energetically favourable (Fig. 4.5), but nevertheless, the overall process favours the *trans* → *cis* interconversion. The reason for this is that the *trans* population is greater than that of the *cis*, and the *cis* → *cis** is more difficult than the *trans* → *trans** (see above).

In *photosensitised cis-trans* isomerisation, the sensitiser excitation energy (of the T state) must be higher than that of the *cis-* and *trans*-isomers for energy transfer to occur. Hence, in practice, as long as the sensitiser has a triplet energy state above a certain minimum, the *cis-trans* ratio is very little affected by the nature of the sensitiser. Thus, if benzophenone is the sensitiser (donor), the mechanisms for the isomerisation of stilbene (acceptor) may be written:

(I) $Ph_2CO(S_0) \xrightarrow{hv} [Ph_2CO]^*(S_1) \rightarrow [Ph_2CO]^*(T_1)$

(II) $[Ph_2CO]^*(T_1) + cis\text{-}Ph_2C_2H_2 \rightarrow Ph_2CO(S_0) +$ $\left[\begin{array}{c} \overset{H}{\underset{Ph}{\diagdown}} \overset{}{\underset{}{\text{Ċ—Ċ}}} \overset{H}{\underset{Ph}{\diagup}} \end{array}\right]^* (T_1)$

(III) $[Ph_2CO]^*(T_1) + trans\text{-}Ph_2C_2H_2 \rightarrow Ph_2CO(S_0) +$ $\left[\begin{array}{c} \overset{Ph}{\underset{H}{\diagdown}} \overset{}{\underset{}{\text{Ċ—Ċ}}} \overset{H}{\underset{Ph}{\diagup}} \end{array}\right]^* (T_1)$

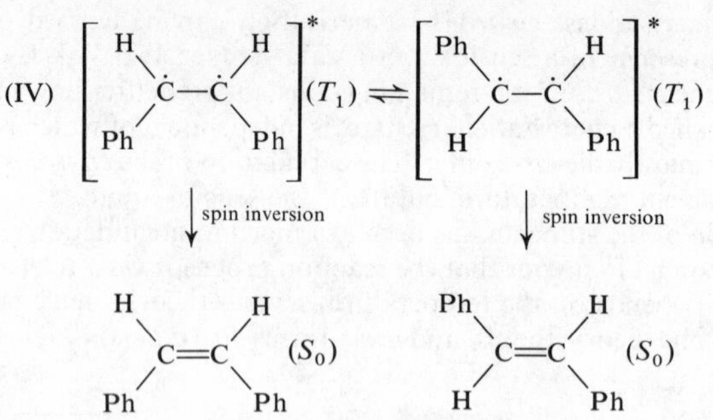

(IV) $\left[\begin{array}{c} H \quad\quad H \\ \dot{C}-\dot{C} \\ Ph \quad\quad Ph \end{array}\right]^{*} (T_1) \rightleftharpoons \left[\begin{array}{c} Ph \quad\quad H \\ \dot{C}-\dot{C} \\ H \quad\quad Ph \end{array}\right]^{*} (T_1)$

$\downarrow$ spin inversion $\downarrow$ spin inversion

$\begin{array}{c} H \quad\quad H \\ C=C \\ Ph \quad\quad Ph \end{array} (S_0)$ $\begin{array}{c} Ph \quad\quad H \\ C=C \\ H \quad\quad Ph \end{array} (S_0)$

Actually, the mechanism given is an over-simplification; there is evidence to show that another triplet state of stilbene (intermediate in energy content between the *cis* and *trans* triplet states) may also be produced. This triplet state, because it can be reached *directly* from the ground state (normally a forbidden transition) has been called a **phantom triplet** (Hammond, 1960).

The structures of the *cis* and *trans* triplet states of stilbene are not clear. Both would be expected to be resonance hybrids (of the canonical forms given in equations II and III, above), but because rotation can occur, the CH—CH bond in both would be expected to be predominantly single in character. However, because of the different steric effects operating, the double bond character in the two forms will be different, presumably greater in the *trans* than in the *cis*, since the former is more stable than the latter (Fig. 4.5).

Photochemical *cis-trans* isomerisation can also be effected in the presence of, *e.g.*, bromine or iodine. A probable mechanism is:

$$Br_2 \xrightarrow{h\nu} 2Br\cdot$$

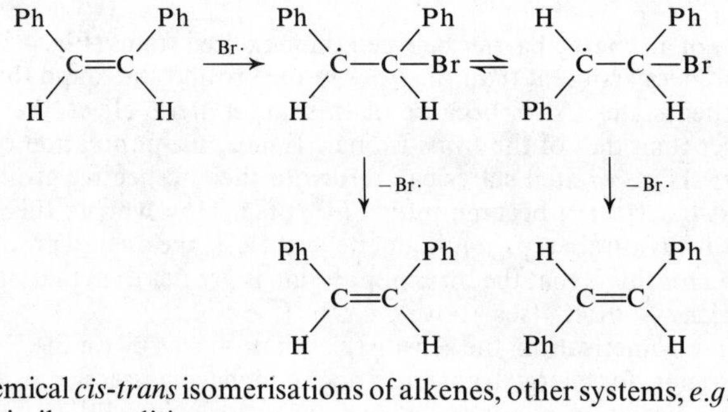

$\begin{array}{c} Ph \quad\quad Ph \\ C=C \\ H \quad\quad H \end{array} \xrightarrow{Br\cdot} \begin{array}{c} Ph \quad\quad Ph \\ \dot{C}-\dot{C}-Br \\ H \quad\quad H \end{array} \rightleftharpoons \begin{array}{c} H \quad\quad Ph \\ \dot{C}-\dot{C}-Br \\ Ph \quad\quad H \end{array}$

$\downarrow -Br\cdot$ $\downarrow -Br\cdot$

$\begin{array}{c} Ph \quad\quad Ph \\ C=C \\ H \quad\quad H \end{array}$ $\begin{array}{c} H \quad\quad Ph \\ C=C \\ Ph \quad\quad H \end{array}$

In addition to photochemical *cis-trans* isomerisations of alkenes, other systems, *e.g.*, oximes, azo-compounds, can be isomerised under similar conditions.

Thermal *cis-trans* isomerisation is believed to occur by paths similar to those of photochemical isomerisation.

Boron trifluoride also catalyses the conversion of *cis*- into *trans*-stilbene. In this case the mechanism is less certain, but a reasonable one is:

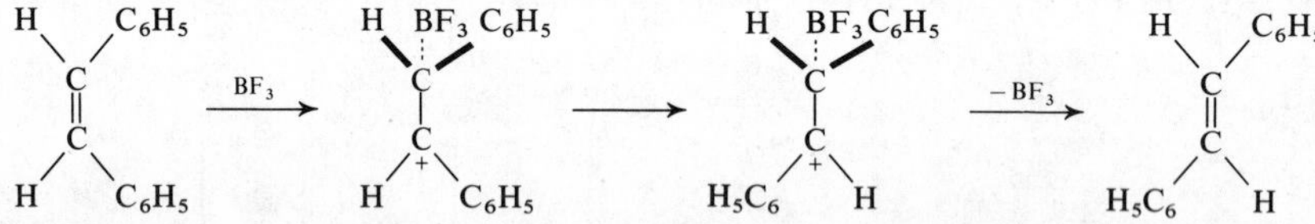

$\begin{array}{c} H \quad\quad C_6H_5 \\ C \\ \| \\ C \\ H \quad\quad C_6H_5 \end{array} \xrightarrow{BF_3} \begin{array}{c} H \quad BF_3 \quad C_6H_5 \\ C \\ | \\ \overset{+}{C} \\ H \quad\quad C_6H_5 \end{array} \longrightarrow \begin{array}{c} H \quad BF_3 \quad C_6H_5 \\ C \\ | \\ \overset{+}{C} \\ H_5C_6 \quad\quad H \end{array} \xrightarrow{-BF_3} \begin{array}{c} H \quad\quad C_6H_5 \\ C \\ \| \\ C \\ H_5C_6 \quad\quad H \end{array}$

In many compounds containing the group C=C—C=O, the *cis*-form is readily transformed into the *trans* in acid solution. The mechanism of this change is uncertain, but at least one case has been studied in great detail. Noyce *et al.* (1963), using *cis*-cinnamic acid as substrate, showed that the rate-determining step is the addition of a proton, and the mechanism proposed is:

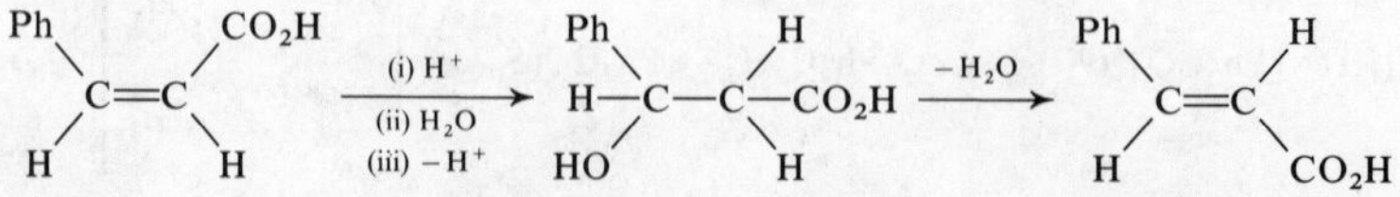

$\begin{array}{c} Ph \quad\quad CO_2H \\ C=C \\ H \quad\quad H \end{array} \xrightarrow[\substack{(ii)\ H_2O \\ (iii)\ -H^+}]{(i)\ H^+} \begin{array}{c} Ph \quad\quad H \\ H-C-C-CO_2H \\ HO \quad\quad H \end{array} \xrightarrow{-H_2O} \begin{array}{c} Ph \quad\quad H \\ C=C \\ H \quad\quad CO_2H \end{array}$

In a number of cases, conversion of the *trans-* into the *cis-*isomer may be effected by a series of reactions based on stereoselective *trans-*addition and *trans-*elimination, *e.g.*, the conversion of *trans-*hex-3-ene into *cis-*hex-3-ene (Hoff *et al.*, 1951).

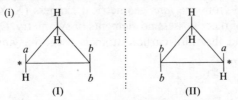

§7. Stereochemistry of cyclic compounds

Geometrical and optical isomerism may exist in any sized ring. In the following account, the saturated rings are treated as rigid flat structures, and the groups attached to the ring-carbon atoms are regarded as being above or below the plane of the ring. Furthermore, the examples described deal only with those cases in which the chiral centres are part of the saturated ring system. In general, the pattern of optical isomerism followed by cyclic compounds is similar to that of the acyclic compounds. The main difference between the two is that, since there is no free rotation about ring-carbon atoms, geometrical isomerism may therefore be manifested as well as optical isomerism. On the other hand, geometrical isomerism may exist without optical isomerism. Since no ambiguity arises with the *cis-trans* nomenclature of geometrical isomerism of *cyclic structures*, this nomenclature has been retained only for cyclic systems.

When we come to describe cyclohexane (§11), we shall also introduce the principles of conformational analysis of ring systems, and then apply these principles to the various ring systems (§14).

Classification of monocyclic systems. Monocyclic systems have been classified according to the number of carbon atoms in the ring: *small rings*, 3–4; *common rings*, 5–7; *medium rings*, 8–11; *large rings*, 12–. As we shall see, many chemical properties depend on the class of the cycloalkane, and these differences in behaviour have been explained largely in terms of steric strain.

§8. Cyclopropane types

Molecule (I) contains one chiral centre (*), and is not superimposable on its mirror image molecule (II). Thus (I) and (II) are enantiomers, *i.e.*, a cyclopropane derivative containing one chiral centre

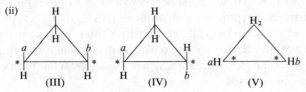

can exist in two optically active forms (and one racemic modification; *cf.* **2** §7a). Molecule (III) contains two different chiral centres, and since it has no elements of symmetry (**2** §6), it is not superimposable on its mirror image molecule. Thus (III) can exist in two optically active forms (and one racemic modification). Structure (III), however, is capable of exhibiting geometrical isomerism, the two geometrical isomers being (III) and (IV). Now (IV) also contains two different chiral centres, and these are not disposed towards each other as in (III). Since (IV) possesses no elements of symmetry, it can also exist in two optically active forms which are different from those of (III). Thus (V), which may be regarded as the non-committal way of writing the configurations (III) and (IV), is similar, as far as *optical isomerism* is concerned, to the acyclic molecule *CabdCabe*, *i.e.*, there are four optically active forms in all (two pairs of enantiomers). In general, any monocyclic system can exist in 2^n optically active forms, where *n* is the number of different chiral centres (*cf.* **2** §7c). Molecule (VI) contains two similar chiral centres and can exist as

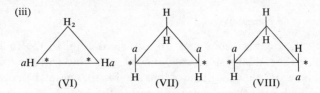

geometrical isomers (VII) and (VIII). (VII) has a (vertical) plane of symmetry and therefore represents a *meso*-form. (VIII), however, possesses no elements of symmetry and can therefore exist in two optically active forms (and one racemic modification). (IX) contains three different chiral

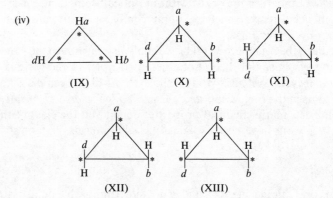

centres and can therefore exist in $2^3 = 8$ optically active forms (four pairs of enantiomers). Each pair of enantiomers is derived from the *four* geometrical isomers (X–XIII). Inspection of these configurations shows that all of them possess no elements of symmetry. (XIV) contains two similar asymmetric carbon atoms, and the third carbon atom is pseudo-asymmetric (*cf.* **2** §7d). Three

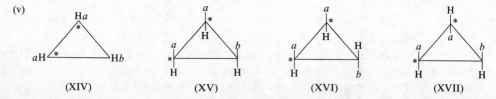

geometrical isomers, (XV)–(XVII), are possible; (XV) and (XVI) each possess a (vertical) plane of symmetry, and therefore each represents a *meso*-form. (XVII), however, possesses no elements of symmetry and so can exist in two optically active forms (and one racemic modification). (XVIII) contains three similar asymmetric carbon atoms which are all pseudo-asymmetric. Two geometrical isomers are possible, (XIX) and (XX), both of which possess at least one (vertical) plane of symmetry, and therefore represent *meso*-forms.

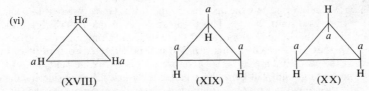

(vi)   (XVIII)   (XIX)   (XX)

In the above account, the stereochemistry of the cyclopropane ring has been dealt with from the theoretical point of view, and thus most of the ideas connected with the stereochemistry of monocyclic systems have been described. In the following sections more emphasis is laid on specific examples, and any further points that arise are dealt with in the appropriate section.

§9. Cyclobutane types (see also §14)

Two examples of the cycobutane type are truxillic and truxinic acids; truxillic acid is 2,4-diphenyl-cyclobutane-1,3-dicarboxylic acid, and truxinic acid is 3,4-diphenylcyclobutane-1,2-dicarboxylic acid. *cis*-Cinnamic acid (allocinnamic acid), on irradiation with light, forms mainly β-truxinic acid and *trans*-cinnamic acid, together with some of the dimer of the latter, α-truxillic acid (de Jong, 1929). Bernstein *et al.* (1943) found that irradiation of commercial *trans*-cinnamic acid gave only β-truxinic acid. When *trans*-cinnamic acid was slowly recrystallised from aqueous ethanol, dried, and then irradiated, only α-truxillic acid was obtained. Schmidt *et al.* (1964), however, have re-investigated the photo-dimerisation of *trans*-cinnamic acid. This acid exists in two crystal modifications, the stable α-form and the metastable β-form. It was shown that the α-form gives pure α-truxillic acid only. The β-form gives pure β-truxinic acid at temperatures where the β → α phase transformation of the monomer is sufficiently slow, but at higher temperatures α-truxillic acid is also formed (this arises from the β → α phase change).

It might be noted here that the course of the above solid-state reactions is determined by the geometry of the crystal structures of the substrates. This phenomenon has been referred to by the authors as *topochemistry* (*cf.* §16).

Truxillic acid. This acid can exist theoretically in five stereoisomeric forms, all of which are known (the acid is of the type I). All five are *meso*-forms, (II–V) having planes of symmetry, and (VI) a centre of symmetry.

(I)

(II)
peri-

(III)
ε-

(IV)
γ-

(V)
epi-

(VI)
α-

The configurations of these stereoisomers have been assigned as follows. When *one* of the carboxyl groups is converted into the anilido-group, $CONHC_6H_5$, *two* of the five forms give optically active compounds, each giving a pair of enantiomers. Now only the stereoisomers with the two phenyl groups in the *trans*-position can produce chiral molecules under these conditions; the remaining forms will each have a (vertical) plane of symmetry. Thus only (IV) and (VI) satisfy the necessary conditions. One of these is known as the α-acid (m.p. 274°C) and the other the γ-acid (m.p. 288°C). This then raises the problem: Which is which? This is readily answered by the fact that of the anilido-derivatives of these two acids, only one can be dehydrated to a cyclic N-phenyl imide, —CO—N(C₆H₅)—CO—. This reaction can be expected to take place only when the two carboxyl groups are in the *cis*-position (see §5a). Therefore (IV) is γ-truxillic acid, and (VI) is α-truxillic acid (since the acid with the melting point 288°C has been called the γ-acid). By considering the ease of formation of the cyclic anhydride, the configurations of the remaining three stereoisomers may be determined. Two form anhydrides readily, and therefore one of these acids must be (II) and the other (III). The third acid does not form its own anhydride, but gives a mixture of the anhydrides produced by (II) and (III). Thus the third acid, *epi*-truxillic acid, is (V). The final problem is to decide which of the two, (II) and (III), is *peri*-truxillic acid, and which is ε-truxillic acid. *peri*-Truxillic acid, under the influence of aluminium chloride, undergoes an internal Friedel–Crafts reaction to form a truxonic acid (VII) and a truxone (VIII). This is only possible when the phenyl and carboxyl groups are in the *cis*-position. Thus (II) is *peri*-truxillic acid, and therefore (III) is ε-truxillic acid.

truxonic acid
(VII)

truxone
(VIII)

Truxinic acid.   This acid can exist theoretically in six geometrical isomeric forms, four of which are resolvable; thus ten forms in all are possible theoretically. Truxinic acid is of the type (IX) and the six geometrical isomers possible are (X–XV). (X) and (XI) are *meso*-forms (each has a plane of symmetry); (XII–XV) are resolvable

(IX)

(X)
ω-

(XI)
β-

(XII)
neo-

(XIII)
ζ-

(XIV)
μ-

(XV)
δ-

(theoretically), since all possess no elements of symmetry. The configurations of these stereoisomers have been determined by methods similar to those used for the truxillic acids; it appears, however, that only four of these six forms are known with certainty, *viz.*, β, δ, ζ and *neo*.

§10. Cyclopentane types (see also §14)

A number of examples involving the stereochemistry of the five-membered ring occur in natural products, *e.g.*, camphoric acid (**8** §23a), furanose sugars (**7** §7b). In this section we shall discuss the case of 2,5-dimethylcyclopentane-1,1-dicarboxylic acid. This acid can exist in two geometrical isomeric forms, which may be differentiated by decarboxylation, the *cis*-isomer giving two mono-carboxylic acids, (I) and (II), and the *trans*-isomer one monocarboxylic acid, (III) (see §5c). All three acids contain two similar asymmetric carbon atoms and one pseudo-asymmetric carbon atom. Both

(I) and (II) possess a (vertical) plane of symmetry, and are therefore *meso*-forms; (III) possesses no elements of symmetry, and can therefore exist in two optically active forms (and one racemic modification). All the possible forms are known, and (I) and (II) have been differentiated as follows. The

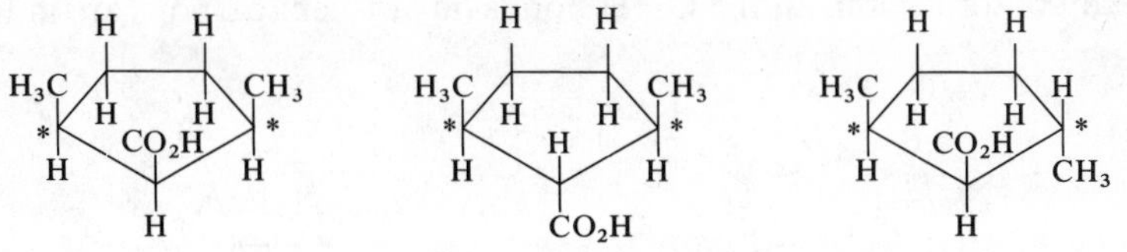

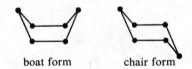

(I)   (II)   (III)

diethyl ester of the *cis*-dicarboxylic acid (IV) can be partially hydrolysed to the monoethyl ester, which most probably has the configuration (V). This is based on the assumption that the carbethoxyl group on the same side as the two methyl groups is far more resistant to attack than the other carbethoxyl group because of the steric effect (see §12). Decarboxylation of (V) gives (VI), and this, on hydrolysis, gives (I). Thus the configuration of (I) (and therefore also of (II)) is determined. These assignments are supported by the fact that (II) is esterified more rapidly than (I). Also, (I) can be isomerised to (II) on heating in acetic acid containing hydrogen chloride. This indicates that the latter is the more stable isomer, *i.e.*, is the *trans*-isomer (since this is more stable than the *cis*; see §5j).

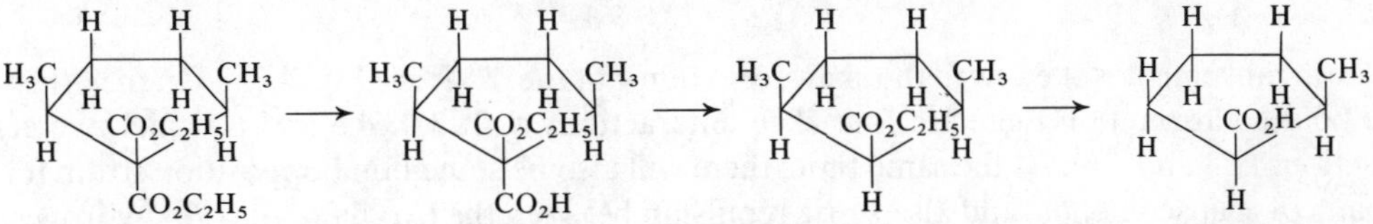

(IV)   →   (V)   →   (VI)   →   (I)

§11. Cyclohexane types.

The stereochemistry of cyclohexane and its derivatives presents a detailed example of the principles of conformational analysis (**2** §4a). The principles are the same as those for acyclic compounds, but because of the 'rigidity' of cyclic systems, additional problems are involved. On the basis of the tetrahedral theory, two forms are possible for cyclohexane, neither of which is planar. These two forms, known as **boat** and **chair conformations** (Fig. 4.6), were first proposed by Sachse (1890; see Vol. I, Ch. 19), who also pointed out that both are strainless.

boat form   chair form

Fig. 4.6

The chair form is 'rigid' (in the sense that it resists distortion), and when it is transformed into the boat form some angular deformation is necessary. The energy barrier in this process has been determined from NMR spectral data; it is about 37·7–46·0 kJ mol^{-1} (Sheppard *et al.*, 1961; Jensen *et al.*, 1962; see Fig. 4.8). This value is large enough for each conformation to retain its identity, but is not large enough to prevent their rapid interconversion at room temperature. Thus it is not possible to isolate each conformation.

The chair and boat forms are both free from angle strain, but because of differences in steric strain and bond opposition strain, the two forms differ in energy content. According to Hassel *et al.* (1963), there *is* a small amount of angle strain, the ring angles being $\sim 111\cdot5°$ (*not* the normal angle of $109\cdot5°$). Figures 4.7(*a*) and 4.7(*b*) represent the chair and boat conformations and the directions of the C—H bonds. In the chair conformation, all the C—H bonds on adjacent carbons are in the skew position

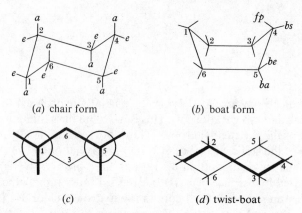

(*a*) chair form   (*b*) boat form

(*c*)   (*d*) twist-boat

Fig. 4.7

(*i.e.*, the arrangement is skew as in the skew form of n-butane, **2** §4; see Fig. 4.7*c*). On the other hand, in the boat conformation there are four skew interactions (1,2; 3,4; 4,5 and 6,1) and two eclipsed interactions (2,3 and 5,6). At the same time, there will also be some bond opposition strain for these two pairs of eclipsed bonds, and also steric repulsion between the two flag-pole (*fp*) hydrogens (at 1 and 4), which are $1\cdot83$ Å apart (see Table below). Hence the total strain in the boat conformation is larger than that in the chair conformation, and consequently the former is less stable than the latter. The boat form, however, is flexible and can readily be distorted into many shapes, and in these the hydrogen eclipsings and the flag-pole interactions are reduced (Fig. 4.7*d*). According to Hendrickson (1961), the twist-boat contains $6\cdot7$ kJ mol^{-1} less energy than the classical boat form. Several workers have calculated the energy difference between the flexible and chair forms of cyclohexane, *e.g.*, Johnson *et al.* (1960), from measurements of heat of combustion and other measured quantities, have found that the energy difference is $22\cdot2 \pm 1\cdot26$ kJ mol^{-1} (at 25°C; vapour phase). This value has been confirmed by the work of Allinger *et al.* (1960); their value is $24\cdot7 \pm 2\cdot5$ kJ mol^{-1}. These data are shown in Fig. 4.8. Thermodynamic calculations have shown that the population of the flexible boat form of cyclohexane is about one to two in a thousand at 25°C. Hassel *et al.*

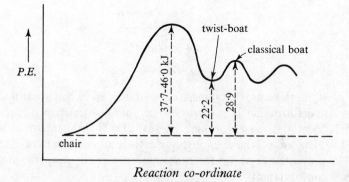

Reaction co-ordinate

Fig. 4.8

(1943) were the first to show, by means of electron diffraction studies, that at room temperature the cyclohexane molecules are mainly in the chair conformation. Also, the examination of cyclohexane derivatives by X-ray and electron diffraction has shown the presence of the chair conformation (see also below). However, the boat conformation has been found in certain molecules, but their number is relatively small.

The nature of the intermediate in the transformation of one chair form into the other is not certain. Jensen *et al.* (1962) believe that the transition state (of the intermediate) is the structure approximately halfway between the chair and the twist-boat form.

Inspection of Fig. 4.7(*a*) shows that the twelve hydrogen atoms in the chair conformation are not equivalent; there are two sets of six. In one of these sets the six C—H bonds are parallel to the threefold axis of symmetry of the molecule; these are the **axial** (*a*) **bonds** (they have also been named ε- or *polar* bonds). In the other set the six C—H bonds make an angle of 109° 28′ with the axis of the ring (or ±19° 28′ with the horizontal plane of the ring); these are the **equatorial** (*e*) **bonds** (they have also been named κ-bonds). On the other hand, in Fig. 4.7(*b*) it can be seen that the 'end' of the boat is different stereochemically from the chair conformation; the various C—H bonds have been named: **flag-pole** (*fp*), **bowsprit** (*bs*), **boat-equatorial** (*be*), and **boat-axial** (*ba*).

Angyal and Mills (1952) have calculated the distances between the various hydrogen atoms (and carbon atoms) in both the chair and boat conformations.

Conformation	Position	H—H (Å)
Chair	1*e*,2*e*	2·49
(Fig. 4.7*a*)	1*e*,2*a*	2·49
	1*a*,2*a*	3·06
	1*a*,3*a*	2·51
Boat	2*a*,3*a*	2·27
(Fig. 4.7*b*)	2*e*,3*e*	2·27
	1*fp*,4*fp*	1·83

Since the boat conformation occurs in relatively few cases, in the following account we shall study mainly the problem of the chair conformation. Inspection of the above table shows that for hydrogen atoms, the interactions 1*e*,2*e*, 1*e*,2*a*, and 1*a*,3*a* are about the same. Furthermore, a study of accurate scale models has shown that with any axial substituent (which is necessarily larger than hydrogen), the 1*a*,3*a* interactions are larger than 1*e*,2*e* or 1*e*,2*a* interactions. Using these principles, we can now proceed to study the conformations of cyclohexane derivatives.

Because of the mobility of the chair conformation, one chair form is readily converted into the other chair form, and in doing so all *a*- and *e*-bonds in the first now become *e*- and *a*-bonds, respectively, in the second.

Both forms are identical and so cannot be distinguished. If, however, one hydrogen is replaced by some other atom or group, the two forms are no longer identical, *e.g.*, methylcyclohexane. In the *a*-methyl conformation there are 1,3-interactions acting, whereas in the *e*-methyl conformation these

a-methyl   *e*-methyl

interactions are absent; instead, the *weaker* 1,2-interactions are acting. Thus the energy content of axial conformation is greater than that of the equatorial, and consequently the latter will be the preferred form. Hassel (1947) has shown experimentally from electron-diffraction studies that the *e*-methyl conformation predominates in methylcyclohexane. Hassel *et al.* (1950) have also shown that in chlorocyclohexane the *e*-form also predominates and that very little of the *a*-form is present.

NMR spectroscopy has also been used as a method for determining conformation. The NMR spectra of unsubstituted cycloalkanes (except cyclopropane) show a τ-value around 8·5 p.p.m. due to the methylene protons (*cf.* acyclic methylene value, 8·7). As we have seen, cyclohexane exists in two stable chair conformations (I) and (II) which are undergoing rapid interconversion at room temperature. Let us suppose that cyclohexane is a rigid molecule, *i.e.*, no interconversion occurs.

Then, because the environments of axial and equatorial hydrogens are different, the chemical shifts will be different. The general rule is that axial protons absorb upfield with respect to equatorial hydrogens. At the same time, coupling occurs between axial and equatorial hydrogens attached to the *same* carbon atom, and coupling also occurs between *vicinal* hydrogens. Since the coupling constant depends on the dihedral angle, *J* for vicinal axial—equatorial hydrogens (skew; dihedral angle of 60°) will be smaller (2–4 Hz) than that (5–12 Hz) for vicinal axial—axial hydrogens (*trans*; dihedral angle of 180°). The overall result would be an NMR spectrum in which multiplets would have different *J* values. At room temperature, cyclohexane is *not* a rigid molecule, and since the interconversion rate is rapid, both axial and equatorial hydrogens have the same average environment, thereby giving rise to a single sharp line. When the spectrum of cyclohexane is measured at about $-100°$C, two signals are observed, one due to axial and the other to equatorial hydrogens. Under these conditions, the interconversion rate is sufficiently slowed down for each type of proton to show its own chemical shift.

Now let us consider a monosubstituted cylohexane, *e.g.*, chlorocyclohexane (III and IV). Since the equatorial chlorine conformation (III) is favoured, the populations of (III) and (IV) are different, and consequently the time spent by a *given* hydrogen atom (axial or equatorial) will be longer in conformation (III) than in (IV). Even so, because of rapid interconversion at room temperature, only *one broad* proton signal is observed. When the temperature is cooled below $-55°$C, two broad peaks are observed (see also §12).

A detailed investigation of the infrared specta of cyclohexanes and particularly of rigid systems (such as steroids) has shown that the absorption maximum of a given substituent group depends on whether its orientation is axial or equatorial, *e.g.*,

$$a\text{-Cl}, \sim 690; e\text{-Cl}, \sim 740 \text{ cm}^{-1}.$$
$$a\text{-OH}, 1000\text{--}1010; e\text{-OH}, 1030\text{--}1040 \text{ cm}^{-1}.$$

In general, the stretching frequency (C–Z) for an equatorial orientation is higher than that for an axial one by about 10–50 cm^{-1}. This applies to the C—O stretching frequency in cyclohexanols (see above), but not to the O—H bond. An α-axial bromine atom has very little effect on the C=O stretching frequency, but an α-equatorial bromine atom increases the C=O stretching frequency by about 20 cm^{-1}. These generalisations have been used to assign orientations to substituents (see also §12).

Measurements of ORD and CD curves (**1** §§9a; 9b) are very valuable for assigning conformations to cyclohexanones (see **11** §6).

Mass spectrometry may also be used to distinguish between *cis* and *trans* isomers of cyclohexane derivatives (see §5g).

§11a.   Now let us discuss the conformations of disubstituted cyclohexanes. Here we have a number of factors to consider: position isomerism, stereoisomerism (geometrical and optical), the relative sizes of the two substituents, and the nature of the substituents.

(i) **1,2-Compounds.** It should be noted that in these *cis*-compounds one substituent must be axial and the other equatorial. If the substituents differ in size, the 1,3-interactions will be most powerful when the larger group is axial. Thus the conformation with the lower energy will be the one in which

Classical formula   *Conformations*

cis-1,2   1e,2a   1a,2e

the larger group is equatorial, *i.e.*, this is the preferred form. An example of this type is *cis*-2-methyl-cyclohexanol; the methyl group is larger than the hydroxyl, and so the preferred form can be expected to be 1*a*-hydroxyl,2*e*-methyl. This has been shown to be so in practice. In general, the greater the difference in size between the two substituents, the greater will be the predominance of the form with the larger group in the equatorial conformation.

The classical formula of the *cis*-compound when the two substituents are identical has a plane of symmetry and is therefore not resolvable. If the conformational diagram is inspected, then for the *cis*-compound with $Y_1 = Y_2$, there are no elements of symmetry and hence it is not superimposable on its mirror image. When this conformation flips, the resulting conformation is the mirror image of the original one (this is clearly seen from the equivalent conformation). Since the strain is identical in the original and flipped conformations, their populations are equal and consequently this 1,2-disubstituted cyclohexane ($Y_1 = Y_2$) is optically inactive by *external* compensation. However, this type of compound has never yet been resolved, and this is due to the fact that the two enantiomers are readily interconvertible. In effect, each enantiomer undergoes very rapid autoracemisation.

Classical formula   *Conformations*

trans-1,2   1e,2e   1a,2a

Whether Y_1 and Y_2 are identical or not, the two conformations are different, and because of the 1,3-interactions the *e,e*-form will be the preferred form. Furthermore, this form will be more stable than the *cis*-isomer (*a,e*-form). An example that illustrates this is 2-methylcyclohexanol. The *trans*-form has been shown to be more stable than the *cis*; the latter is readily converted into the former when heated with sodium, and also the reduction of 2-methylcyclohexanone (with sodium and ethanol) produces the *trans*-alcohol.

Both the classical formula and the *e,e*- (and *a,a*) conformation of the *trans*-1,2-compound (whether Y_1 and Y_2 are identical or not) are not superimposable on their mirror images. Also, neither conformation can be converted into its mirror image by flipping. Hence, a *trans*-1,2-disubstituted cyclohexane exists as a pair of enantiomers (whether $Y_1 = Y_2$ or not).

(ii) **1,3-Compounds.** The two *trans*-conformations are identical when the two Y groups are identical. The *cis-e,e*-form will be more stable than the *cis-a,a*, and will also be more stable than the *trans-e,a*-conformation, *e.g.*, the most stable conformation of 1,3-dimethylcyclohexane has been shown to be the *cis*-1,3-*e,e*-form. It should be noted that this situation is the reverse of that of the 1,2-dimethylcyclohexanes.

The Auwers–Skita rule (§5j) has been shown to break down when applied to 1,3-disubstituted cyclohexanes: the reverse holds good. Allinger (1954) modified the rule for cyclohexanes as follows: The isomer which has the higher boiling point, refractive index and density is the one with the less

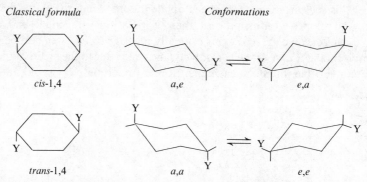

stable configuration. Thus, according to this rule, the *trans*-1,3-disubstituted cyclohexanes have the higher physical constants (the *trans*-form has more axial substituents than the more stable *cis*-form); *e.g.*, Macbeth *et al.* (1954) have shown that the physical constants of (±)-*trans*-3-methylcyclohexyl-amine are higher than those of its *cis*-isomer.

(iii) **1,4-Compounds.**

The two *cis*-conformations are identical when the Y groups are identical. Also, the *trans-e,e*-form will be more stable than the *cis-a,e*-form.

§11b. The arguments used for the disubstituted cyclohexanes can also be applied to the higher substituted cyclohexanes. As the result of a large amount of work, the following generalisations may be made:

(i) In cyclohexane systems, mono-, di-, tri- and poly-substituted derivatives always tend to take up the chair conformation whenever possible.

(ii) The chair conformation with the maximum number of equatorial substituents will be the preferred conformation. This generalisation, however, is only satisfactory when the internal forces due to dipole interactions or hydrogen bonding are absent. When these are present, it is necessary to determine which forces predominate before a conformation can be assigned to the molecule.

(iii) The energy barriers between the various conformations are too small to prevent interconversion (but see §12).

Now let us apply these generalisations to various compounds. Cyclohexane-1,3-diol has been shown to have the diaxial rather than the diequatorial orientation. This can be explained on the basis that intramolecular hydrogen bonding (which has been shown to be present from infrared spectra) can stabilise the diaxial but not the diequatorial form. The conformation of the ring is the chair form,

boat   twist boat

but when intramolecular hydrogen bonding is possible between groups in the 1 and 4 positions, the molecule may then assume a boat conformation rather than the chair in which this hydrogen bonding is not possible. However, what have been considered to be boat conformations may be twist-boat forms in some cases, e.g., Stolow (1961) showed, from infrared spectral data, that 2,5-di-t-butyl-cyclohexane-1,4-diol exists in several conformations, with one having the twist-boat form.

Another class of compounds which are of great interest are the derivatives of cyclohexanone. If we assume that the C atom of the CO group is trigonally hybridised, then this has little effect on the shape of the ring. On the other hand, if we assume tetrahedral hybridisation with banana bonds, then very little effect on the shape of the ring would be expected. Also, since the oxygen atom in acetaldehyde is eclipsed with a hydrogen atom in the preferred conformation (2 §4a), it follows that cyclohexanone has no appreciable strain. Because the axial hydrogen is absent at the carbonyl group, an axial group at C-3 has only *one* 1,3-interaction (at C-5), and similarly an axial group at C-5 has only *one* 1,3-interaction (at C-3). Hence, an axial group at C-3 or C-5 in cyclohexanone will be more stable than in cyclohexane. This has been referred to as the '3-alkyl ketone effect'.

cyclohexanone

First, we shall consider 2-bromocyclohexanone; the two possible chair forms are:

e-Br   a-Br

On the basis that a substituent preferably takes up an equatorial conformation, it would therefore be expected that the conformation 2e-bromocyclohexanone would be favoured. Infrared studies, however, have shown that the a-bromo conformation predominates. This has been explained as follows. The C—Br and C=O bonds are both strongly polar, and when the bromine is equatorial the dipolar repulsion is a maximum, and a minimum when the bromine is axial. Since the axial form predominates, this equatorial dipolar repulsion must therefore be larger than the 1,3-interactions. When, however, other substituents are present, the 1,3-interactions may become so large as to outweigh the dipolar effect and the bromine would now be equatorial. Such is the case with 2-bromo-4,4-dimethylcyclohexanone.

Now let us consider cyclohexane-1,4-dione. Le Fèvre *et al.* (1935) showed that this compound has a dipole moment (μ) of $1\cdot2$ D. Since the chair form has $\mu = 0$, the conformation must be some other one. Mossel *et al.* (1963) have examined this dione by dipole measurement and X-ray analysis and conclude from their results that the molecule has a twist-boat conformation.

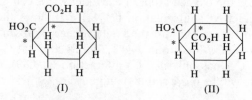

$\mu = 0$ $\mu > 0$ $\mu > 0$

§11c.   The foregoing discussion has been confined to determining preferred conformations. If we now examine the stereochemistry of cyclohexane derivatives, we find that, up to the present time, the number of geometrical (and optical) isomers obtained from a given cyclohexane derivative is in agreement with the number that can be expected from a planar ring with the substituents lying above and below the plane of the ring. We shall now, therefore, discuss the stereochemistry of some cyclohexane derivatives from the classical point of view.

(i) *Hexahydrophthalic acids* (cyclohexane-1,2-dicarboxylic acids). Two geometrical isomers are theoretically possible, the *cis*, (I), and the *trans*, (II). Molecule (I) has a plane of symmetry, and

therefore represents the *meso*-form; (II) has no elements of symmetry, and can therefore exist in two optically active forms (and one racemic modification). All of these possible forms are known, and it has been found that the *cis*-compound, (I), forms a cyclic anhydride readily, whereas the *trans*-compound, (II), forms a cyclic anhydride with difficulty (*cf.* §5a).

(ii) *Hexahydroisophthalic acids* (cyclohexane-1,3-dicarboxylic acids). Two geometrical isomers are possible; the *cis*-form (III) has a plane of symmetry, and therefore represents the *meso*-form; (IV) has no elements of symmetry, and can therefore exist in two optically active forms (and one racemic

modification). All of these forms are known; the *cis*-isomer forms a cyclic anhydride, whereas the *trans*-isomer does not.

(iii) *Hexahydroterephthalic acids* (cyclohexane-1,4-dicarboxylic acids). Two geometrical isomers are possible; the *cis*-form (V) has a plane of symmetry, and the *trans*-form (VI) a centre of symmetry.

Hence neither is optically active. They may be distinguished by the fact that the *cis*-isomer forms a cyclic anhydride, whereas the *trans*-isomer does not. The cyclic anhydride will have a boat conformation.

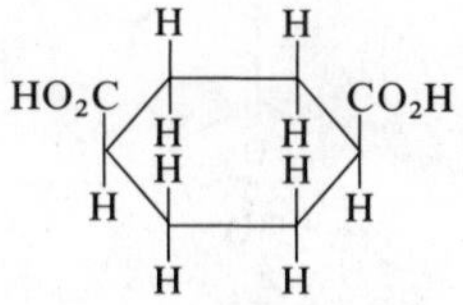

(V) 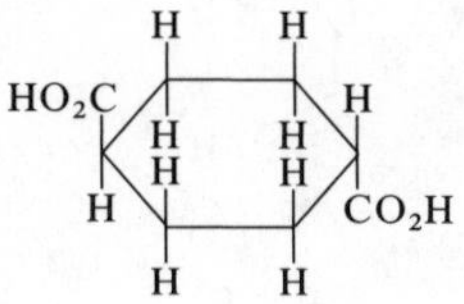   (VI)

(iv) *Inositol* (hexahydroxycyclohexane). There are eight geometrical isomers possible theoretically, and only *one* of these is not superimposable on its mirror image molecule; thus there are nine forms in all (and also one racemic modification). If we imagine that we looking down at the molecule, and insert the groups which appear *above* the plane of the ring, then the eight geometrical isomers may be represented as follows:

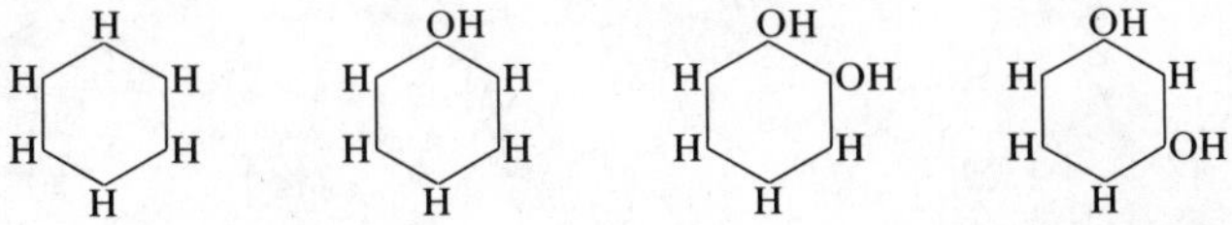

myo-inositol

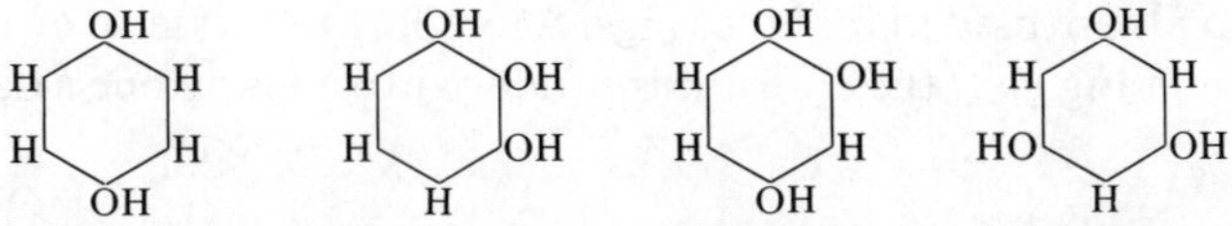

resolvable   scyllitol

Examination of these configurations shows that all except one—the one labelled resolvable—have at least one plane of symmetry, and so are all *meso*-forms. All the *meso*-forms and both of the optically active forms are known; of these *myo*-inositol, scyllitol and (+)- and (−)-inositol occur naturally.

(v) *Benzene hexachloride* (hexachlorocyclohexane). Here again eight geometrical isomers are possible theoretically; seven are known, α, β, γ, δ, ε, η, θ; the γ-isomer is a powerful insecticide (see Vol. 1). All have been shown to exist in the chair form, and the conformations that have been assigned are:

α-, *aaeeee*; β-, *eeeeee*; γ-, *aaaeee*; δ-, *aeeeee*; ε-, *aeeaee*.

Of these forms, it is the β- which loses hydrogen chloride with the greatest difficulty (see §5m). All of the other stereoisomers possess at least one pair of chlorine atoms *cis* to each other (thus having H and Cl *trans*). Cristol (1949) has also identified the α-isomer as the (±)-form.

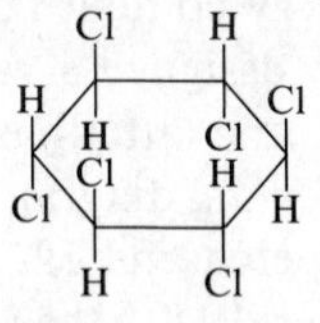

β- α-

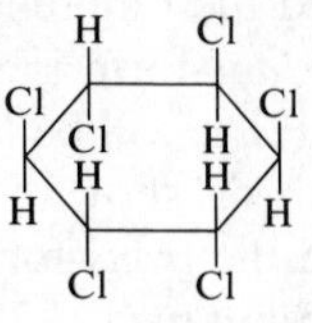

§11d. **Fused systems.** (*a*) *Decalins and decalols.* As we have seen, the boat and chair forms of cyclohexane are readily interconvertible, and the result is that cyclohexane behaves as if it were planar. Mohr (1918), however, elaborated Sachse's theory, and predicted that the fusion of two cyclohexane rings, *e.g.*, as in decalin, should produce the *cis*- and *trans*-forms which would be sufficiently stable to retain their identities. This prediction has now been confirmed experimentally.

Several conventions have been introduced to represent these isomers. One convention uses *full* lines to represent groups *above* the plane of the molecule, and *broken* lines to represent those *below* the plane (*cf.* §5l); thus *cis*-decalin will be (I) and *trans*-decalin (II). This convention appears to be

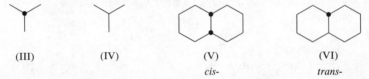

(I)   (II)

cis-   *trans-*

the one most widely used (see, *e.g.*, Steroids, Ch. 11), but there is another, introduced by Linstead (1937), which is favoured by many. According to this convention, a hydrogen atom is represented as being above the plane of the ring when drawn as in (III), and *below* the plane when drawn as in (IV); thus *cis*-decalin will be (V), and *trans*-decalin (VI).

(III)   (IV)   (V)   (VI)

                                 cis-   *trans-*

The configurations of the decalins are complicated, the complication arising from the fact that a number of strainless modifications are possible, which differ in the type of 'locking', *i.e.*, whether axial or equatorial bonds are used to fuse the rings. According to Hassel *et al.* (1946), *cis*- and *trans*-decalins are as shown in Fig. 4.9; the *cis*-form is produced by joining one axial and one equatorial

cis-decalin   *trans*-decalin

doubly-crossed
cis-decalin

Fig. 4.9

bond of each ring, whereas the *trans*-form is produced by joining the two rings by equatorial bonds only; in both cases the cyclohexane rings are all chair forms (see also below). However, Geneste *et al.* (1964) have proposed a 'doubly-crossed' conformation for *cis*-decalin (see Fig. 4.9). This has about the same energy content as the *cis*-chair/chair conformation.

Johnson (1953) has calculated the difference in energy content between these two forms in the following simple manner. The *trans*-form is arbitrarily assigned a value of zero energy, and when this form is compared with the *cis*, it will be found that the latter has three extra skew interactions involving the two axial bonds (this is shown in the following diagram; the *cis*-form has 3 staggered and 15 skew arrangements, and the *trans*-form 6 staggered and 12 skew). On the basis that skew interaction of the hydrogens in n-butane is 3·35 kJ (Pitzer, 1940), the total energy difference between the *cis*- and *trans*-forms is 3 × 3·35 = 10·05 kJ. This value agrees well with that of Rossini *et al.*

(1960) from measurements of heat of combustion. It might be noted, in passing, that if these two decalins are regarded as 1,2-disubstituted cyclohexanes, then the *trans*-form (*e,e*) would be expected to be more stable than the *cis*- (*e,a*).

We shall now deal with the determination of configuration in the decalin series. The configurations may be ascertained by using the Auwers–Skita rule (see §5j). Hückel (1923, 1925), however, isolated two forms of 2-decalol and determined their configurations by the following chemical methods. 2-Naphthol, on hydrogenation in the presence of nickel as catalyst, gave two 2-decalols, (VII) and (VIII), each of which, on oxidation with chromic acid, gave a decal-2-one (IX and X). These two decalones each gave, on oxidation with permanganate, a cyclohexane-1,2-diacetic acid. These diacetic acids were geometrical isomers; one was resolvable and therefore must be the *trans*-isomer (XII); and the other, which was not resolvable, must therefore be the *cis*-isomer (XI) (this is the *meso*-form). Thus the configurations of the two decalols and the two decalones are established:

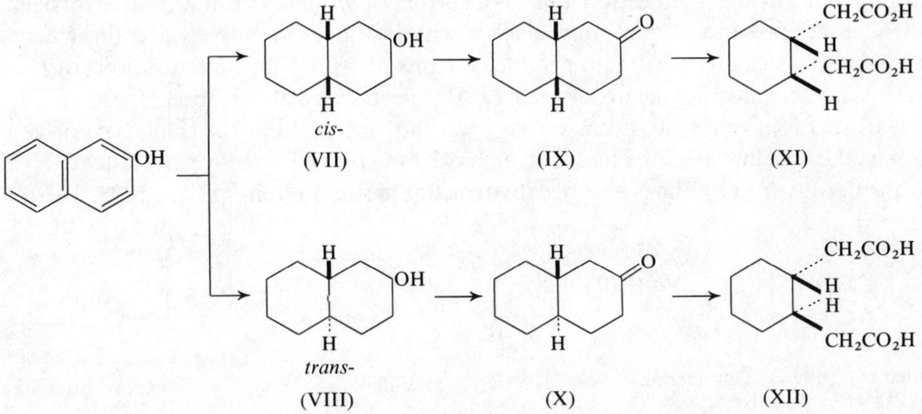

In addition to the two cyclohexane-1,2-diacetic acids (which are formed by scission of the 2,3-bond of the decalone), two other geometrical isomers were also obtained, *viz. cis-* and *trans*-cyclohexane-1-carboxyl-2-propionic acids (XIII) and (XIV) (these are formed by scission of the 1,2-bond of the decalone).

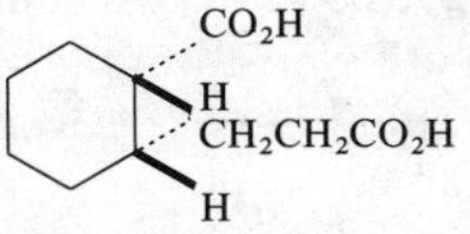

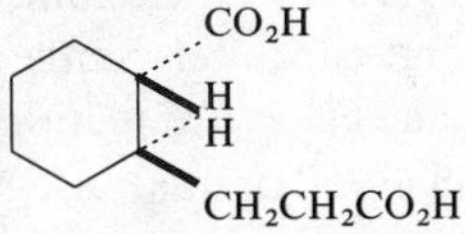

The conversion of 2-naphthol into two decalols does not prove that the two decalols are the *cis-* and *trans*-isomers described above. It is possible that both compounds could have been the *cis-* and *trans*-forms of a *given* decalol; since the carbon atom of the CHOH group in the 2-decalol is asymmetric, it can exist in *two* configurations, *i.e.*, each decalol, (VII) and (VIII), can exist in two forms;

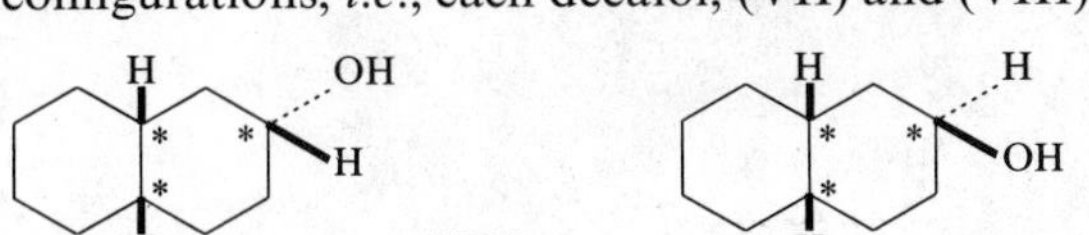

(VIIa) and (VIIIa). Had the two decalols been the two forms of either (VII) or (VIII), then on their oxidation, only *one* decalone would have been produced. Since, however, *two* decalones were obtained, the two decalols must be of the types (VII) and (VIII)—one of each, or even a mixture of the pairs; further proof of the existence of the types (VII) and (VIII) lies in the fact that the two decalones gave geometrical isomers of cyclohexane-1,2-diacetic acid.

Consideration of formulae (VIIa) and (VIIIa) shows the presence of three chiral centres in each of the four possible forms, and since all four possess no elements of symmetry, four pairs of enantiomers should be possible theoretically. Actually all eight forms have been isolated, but their configurations have not yet been established with certainty.

There are only *two* geometrical isomers possible for the decalins, and their configurations have been established by the reduction of the two decalones, (IX) and (X), by means of the Wolff–Kishner method (Eisenlohr *et al.*, 1924; see also Vol. I); each decalone gives the corresponding decalin. It is interesting to note in this connection that Willstätter *et al.* (1924) found that hydrogenation of naphthalene in the presence of platinum black as catalyst gives mainly *cis*-decalin, whereas in the presence of nickel as catalyst the main product is *trans*-decalin. The configurations of the decalins have also been determined by means of their NMR spectra (see also below).

Various other fused ring systems have also been shown to exhibit the same type of geometrical isomerism as the decalins, *e.g.*, the hydrindanols exist in *cis*- and *trans*-forms (Hückel *et al.*, 1926), and also the decahydroquinolines and decahydroisoquinolines (Helfer *et al.*, 1923, 1926).

| *cis*-hydrindanol. | *trans*-hydrindanol. | Decahydroquinolines | Decahydroisoquinolines |
| Two forms; both *meso*- | Resolvable | | |

It has already been pointed out that in monosubstituted cyclohexanes, the preferred conformation is the one with the substituent equatorial, but owing to the low energy barrier between this and the axial form, the two are readily interconvertible. In the case of the monosubstituted decalins, the problem is more complicated. In *cis*-decalin, since ring fusion involves equatorial and axial bonds, the molecule is mobile and can interchange with the other *cis*-form, *i.e.*, there are two *cis*-forms possible (XV and XVI), and these are identical and in equilibrium (*cf.* cyclohexane). This has been shown to be so by Hassel (1950); thus:

(XV)   (XVI)

Musher *et al.* (1958) distinguished between *cis*- and *trans*-decalin by means of their NMR spectra. *cis*-Decalin shows one proton peak, whereas *trans*-decalin shows two. The former isomer is capable of rapid interconversion, but the latter is not since it is a rigid system, and so equatorial and axial protons are held in different environments, the result being two different chemical shifts (*cf.* cyclohexane, §11).

Now let us consider *cis*-2-decalol. Here there are four possible conformations which, in pairs, are in equilibrium. Two arise from (XV) (XV*a* and XV*b*), and two from (XVI) (XVI*a* and XVI*b*).

In (XV*a*) and (XVI*b*) the hydroxyl group is equatorial, and so these two conformations contain about the same energy. In (XVI*a*) and (XV*b*) the hydroxyl group is axial, and on the basis that an equatorial conformation is more stable than an axial, then (XV*a*) and (XVI*b*) will contribute more to the actual state of the molecule than will (XVI*a*) and (XV*b*), *i.e.*, the hydroxyl group in *cis*-2-decalol should possess more equatorial character than axial. It is also interesting to note that the two axial forms do not contain the same energy. In (XV*b*) the *a*-hydroxyl group is involved in the normal 1,3-hydrogen interactions (at 4 and 9), but in (XVI*a*) the interaction is the normal 1,3- with the hydrogen at 4 and the larger 1,3-interaction with the CH_2 group at 8. Thus (XVI*a*) should be less stable than (XV*b*).

(XV*a*)   (XVI*a*)

(XV*b*)   (XVI*b*)

In *trans*-decalin there is only one stable conformation, since the ring fusions use equatorial bonds. If the molecular conformations were 'inverted', the two ring fusions would now have to be axial, and this type of fusion is impossible. The axial bonds on adjacent carbon atoms are pointing in *opposite directions* and the carbon atoms are too far apart to form a bond in a *six-membered* ring. It is possible, however, for larger rings to have this conformation. Thus, in *trans*-2-decalol, there are only two conformations possible, (XVII) and (XVIII). Furthermore, the latter, with the equatorial-

(XVII)   (XVIII)

hydroxyl conformation, would be expected to be more stable than the former (with the axial hydroxyl).

(*b*) *Polycyclic systems.* Many natural products contain polycyclic systems consisting of fused six-membered rings, but sometimes they also contain a five-membered ring, *e.g.*, steroids. One type of compound which has been studied in great detail is perhydrophenanthrene. Ten stereoisomeric forms are possible: four pairs of enantiomers and two *meso*-compounds. These are as shown, the method of naming being as follows. The prefixes *cis* and *trans* denote the stereochemistry of the ring fusions, *e.g.*, *cis*-hydrogens at 4b (13) and 8a (14) give *cis* A/B, *trans*-hydrogens at 4b (13) and 8a (14) give *trans* A/B, and *cis*-hydrogens at 4a (12) and 10a (11) give *cis* B/C. On the other hand, the prefixes *syn* and *anti* denote the terminal orientation of the rings with respect to each other, *e.g.*, if the bond joining rings A and C, *i.e.*, bond 4a—4b (12–13) has *cis*-hydrogens at these carbon atoms, then rings A and C are *syn* with respect to each other, and if the hydrogens are *trans*, rings A and C are *anti*.

The axial or equatorial orientation of the ring-fusion bonds with respect to the central ring, B, are as shown. In 4 and 5, the rings A/B and B/C are both *cis* as in *cis*-decalin, and so these molecules are mobile systems, *i.e.*, they exist in two interconvertible forms. Molecules 1, 2 and 3, however, have at least one *trans* A/B or B/C, and hence are not mobile systems, *e.g.*, for 2 to change into its other form, *trans* B/C would have to become *cis* B/C, but this is not possible since in the latter case the ring

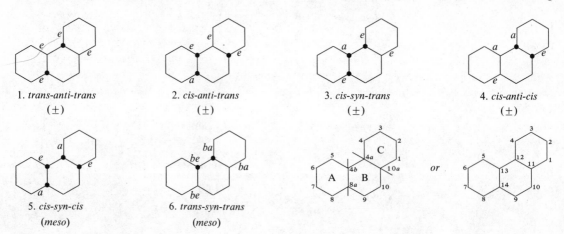

1. *trans-anti-trans*
   (±)

2. *cis-anti-trans*
   (±)

3. *cis-syn-trans*
   (±)

4. *cis-anti-cis*
   (±)

5. *cis-syn-cis*
   (*meso*)

6. *trans-syn-trans*
   (*meso*)

or

fusion would have to be *a,a* (*cf. trans*-decalin). Also, in isomers 1–5 all three rings are in chair forms, but in 6 the central ring, B, is in the classical boat conformation. This isomer will therefore be the highest energy form of all and so is the least stable. Furthermore, since in 1 all the rings are fused by equatorial bonds, this isomer will be the most stable form; it may be regarded as the equivalent of two *trans*-decalins. Isomers 2 and 3 are therefore each the equivalent of a *cis*- and a *trans*-decalin, and so would be expected to be of equal energy content, but greater than that of 1. Isomers 4 and 5 are each the equivalent of two *cis*-decalins. It has been found, however, that the interactions in a polycyclic system containing 1,3-axial fusion bonds are greater than those in a similar system containing 1,2-axial bonds. Thus 4 is more stable than 5.

The foregoing account has been qualitative, but its basis is the work of Johnson (1953) who estimated the differences in energy between the various isomers. Furthermore, Linstead *et al.* (1950) have elucidated the configurations of a number of perhydrophenanthrene derivatives, and the work on the stabilities of their compounds is in good agreement with the estimated stabilities.

There are five stereoisomeric perhydroanthracenes, and these have the configurations shown.

trans-syn-trans
(*meso*)

cis-anti-trans
(±)

cis-anti-cis
(*meso*)

cis-syn-cis
(*meso*)

trans-anti-trans
(±)

§12. Effect of conformation on the course and rate of reactions

Since the environments of axial and equatorial groups are different, it may be expected that the reactivity of a given group will depend on whether it is axial or equatorial. Now S_N2 reactions always occur with inversion (**3** §4). Hence if the geometry of the molecule is such as to hinder the approach of the attacking group (Z) along the bonding line remote from the group to be expelled (Y), then the S_N2 reaction will be slowed down. Examination of formulae (I) and (II) shows that the transition state for an S_N2 reaction is more readily formed when Y is axial (I) than when it is equatorial (II).

(I)   (II)

In (I), the approach of Z is unhindered, but in (II) the approach of Z is hindered by the rest of the ring. Thus S_N2 reactions take place more readily with an axial substituent than with an equatorial.

The study of S_N1 reactions in cyclohexane derivatives is made difficult because of the ease with which elimination reactions usually occur at the same time. It can be expected, however, that an S_N1 reaction will be sterically accelerated for an axial substituent, since the formation of a carbonium ion will relieve the steric strain due to 1,3-interactions. On the other hand, Since these 1,3-interactions are absent for an equatorial substituent, no steric acceleration will operate in this conformation.

A particularly interesting example of concurrent S_N1 and S_N2 mechanisms and the involvement of neighbouring group participation is the acetolysis of *trans*-4-methoxycyclohexyl tosylate. Noyce *et al.* (1960) have shown that the products of the acetolysis of the tosylate labelled with tritium in position 1 (*i.e.*, *trans*-4-methoxy[1-^{3}H]cyclohexyl tosylate) are as shown in the Chart. This mechanism was proposed to account for the fact that the *trans*-isomer (non-tritiated) underwent acetolysis about 5·6 times as fast as the *cis*-isomer (hence n.g.p. in the former), the scrambling of the tritium (hence the intermediate bicyclic oxonium cation), and the fact that the *trans*-4-methoxy[1-^{3}H]-cyclohexyl acetate was produced in larger amount than the corresponding *trans*-[4-^{3}H]-compound (hence all of the *trans*-acetate cannot have been formed from the oxonium cation, in which case the tritium should have been scrambled equally between the 1- and 4-positions).

So far, we have examined reactions in which the bond linking an atom to the ring is broken. Now let us consider reactions in which this does not occur, *e.g.*, esterification and ester hydrolysis by the $A_{AC}2$ mechanism (see Vol. I). For the present purpose, we may write the equation as shown:

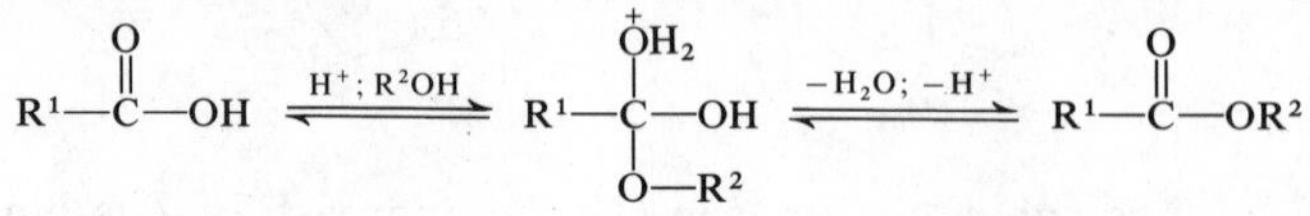

$$R^1-\underset{\underset{}{\overset{\overset{O}{\parallel}}{C}}}{}-OH \xrightleftharpoons[]{H^+;\ R^2OH} R^1-\underset{\underset{O-R^2}{\overset{\overset{\overset{+}{O}H_2}{|}}{C}}}{}-OH \xrightleftharpoons[]{-H_2O;\ -H^+} R^1-\underset{}{\overset{\overset{O}{\parallel}}{C}}-OR^2$$

$$(A)$$

In the esterification of cyclohexanol ($R^2 = C_6H_{11}$; $R^1 = R$), the reaction proceeds through the intermediate (A). Replacement of the hydroxylic hydrogen in R^2OH by the large group (shown in A) very much increases the non-bonded interactions (in R^2O), far more so for an axial than for an equatorial OH. Hence the former would be expected to be esterified more slowly than the latter. Since hydrolysis by the $A_{AC}2$ mechanism is the reverse of esterification, hydrolysis also proceeds through the intermediate (A). In this case, the ester already has the large group R^1CO attached to the oxygen atom of R^2O, but in the formation of (A) hybridisation of the carbonyl carbon atom has changed from sp^2 (flat) tp sp^3 (tetrahedral). Thus, the volume of the group has increased in (A) and consequently non-bonded interactions are increased. Hence the axial ester would be expected to undergo hydrolysis more slowly than the equatorial ester.

If we now consider esterification of cyclohexanecarboxylic acid ($R^1 = C_6H_{11}$; $R^2 = R$) and the hydrolysis of its esters, then, since both proceed through the intermediate (A), and using the same arguments as before, the axial conformer would be expected to undergo esterification and hydrolysis more slowly than the equatorial conformer.

Similar arguments applied to hydrolysis by the $B_{AC}2$ mechanism (see Vol. I) will also show that the axial ester would be expected to undergo hydrolysis more slowly than the equatorial ester.

These predictions are borne out in practice.

The relative rates of oxidation of secondary *a*- and *e*-alcohols to ketones by chromic acid (or hypobromous acid) is the reverse of the relative rates of hydrolysis of their carboxylic esters, *i.e.*, an *a*-hydroxyl is more readily oxidised than an *e*-. The reason for this is that the rate-determining step in this oxidation is a direct attack on the hydrogen atom of the C—H bond. If the hydroxyl is axial, the hydrogen is equatorial, and *vice versa* (see also **11** §4d); thus:

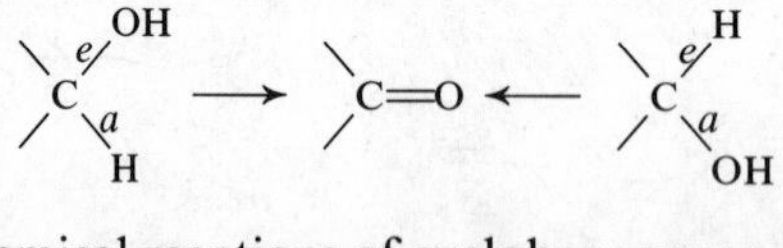

Let us now consider some chemical reactions of cyclohexanones. Enolisation would, at first sight, appear to occur equally well with either an axial or equatorial hydrogen atom on the α-carbon atom. Corey *et al.* (1956), however, showed that it is the axial hydrogen atom which is mainly involved, and this has been attributed to the stereoelectronic factor (**2** §4a). Reduction of the carbonyl group may occur in two ways: approach from the axial side will produce an equatorial alcohol (since the C—H bond produced is axial); and approach from the equatorial side will produce an axial alcohol (since the C—H bond formed is equatorial). Catalytic hydrogenation results predominantly in the formation of the axial alcohol. This may be explained by assuming that the ketone is adsorbed on the catalyst preferentially from the less-hindered equatorial side, and since the adsorbed hydrogen must also come from this side the product is the axial alcohol [cf. §5la]. On the other hand, reduction with metal and acid gives predominantly the equatorial alcohol. In this case, the proton (abstracted from H_3O^+) is small and so can approach an unhindered carbonyl group equally well from either side, but since the equatorial conformation is more stable than the axial, e-alcohol is the main product. Because the predominant product depends on its relative stability, this has been referred to as an example of **product development control**. When the reducing reagent is aluminium isopropoxide (MPV reduction), the predominant product is now the a-alcohol. Because of the large spatial require-ments in the cyclic transition state, the aluminium complex will preferentially be formed from the less hindered equatorial side (see **2** §7). Since the predominant product depends on steric factors, this is an example of **steric approach control** (Dauben et al., 1956).

Reduction of cyclohexanone derivatives with lithium aluminium hydride or with sodium boro-hydride generally produces the equatorial alcohol as the predominant product. In these reductions, the spatial requirements of the aluminium hydride and borohydride ions are much less than those of aluminium isoproxide. The product is therefore an example of product development control. If, however, the ketone is sterically hindered, e.g., if the ketone is 3,3-dimethylcyclohexanone, the axial alconol is the predominant product. Here we have an example of steric approach control.

All of these reductions which result in a predominant stereoisomeric product are examples of asymmetric synthesis (see **3** §7).

When cyclohexanones are halogenated, the 2-a-derivative is formed more readily than the 2-e-isomer (dipolar effect). Even so, the final product may be predominantly the 2-e-isomer due to 1,3-interactions (see §11b).

Elimination reactions are also of great importance in cyclic compounds. As we have seen (§5m), in ionic E2 reactions the two groups eliminated are normally in the trans position. In cyclohexane systems this geometrical requirement is only found in trans-1,2-diaxial compounds, and these compounds thus undergo ready elimination reactions. In rigid systems, e.g., the trans-decalin type, elimination in trans-1,2-diequatorial compounds is slower than in the corresponding diaxial com-pounds. cis-1,2-Compounds (in which one substituent must be axial and the other equatorial) undergo elimination reactions slowly.

The steric course of E1 reactions is more difficult to study than that of E2 reactions because of the two-stage mechanism. This makes it difficult to ascertain the geometry of the intermediates involved. The formation of the carbonium ion will be sterically accelerated if the ionising group is axial and, if a second group is eliminated to form a double bond, this second stage will also be sterically ac-celerated if the second group is axial (see below).

The arguments used above are satisfactory so long as we know whether the group under dis-cussion is axial or equatorial. Since, however, the two chair forms are readily interconvertible and in equilibrium, to study these predictions experimentally it is necessary to deal with rigid conforma-tions. The t-butyl group, because of its large size, is far more stable in the e- than in the a-position (the energy difference between the two forms is about 23·4 kJ mol⁻¹; Winstein et al., 1955). Thus almost only the e-form is present and consequently this position is 'locked'. Alternatively, the t-butyl group is referred to as an 'anchor' or 'anchoring group', and the compounds are said to be conformationally 'biased'. Hence, on the basis that the t-butyl group is equatorial, 4-substituents must be axial when cis to the t-butyl group and equatorial when trans to this group (§11a). Working with different substituents in the 4-position with respect to the t-butyl group, various workers have confirmed the above predictions experimentally, e.g., it has been shown that cis-4-t-butylcyclo-hexanol forms esters more slowly than the trans-isomer, and similarly cis-4-t-butylcyclohexane-1-carboxylic acid is more slowly esterified and the ester more slowly hydrolysed than the trans-isomer.

Another interesting example is the case of 4-t-butylcyclohexyl tosylate. Two forms are possible, *cis* and *trans*, but because of the large bulk of the t-butyl group, this group is always equatorial. Under the same conditions (sodium ethoxide in ethanol at 70°C), the *cis*-form readily undergoes

OTs

Bu^t Bu^t OTs

H   H
cis-   *trans*-

bimolecular-elimination (E2), but the *trans*- does not. Actually, the latter does undergo bimolecular elimination, but this is so slow that it is virtually undetectable in the presence of the concurrent E1 reaction (Winstein *et al.*, 1955; but see also **8** §16).

Some examples of neighbouring group participation in cyclohexane systems have been described in Ch. 3 (§§6b–6e). These examples clearly show the effect of conformation on rates of reaction when anchimeric assistance is possible.

Not only does conformation control the rate of reactions, but it also may affect the course of a reaction. An example is the action of nitrous acid on amines. Mills (1953) has proposed the following generalisation: When the amino-group is equatorial, the product is an alcohol with an equatorial conformation; but when the amino-group is axial, the main product is an alkene together with some equatorial alcohol. The basis of this generalisation is as follows. The diazonium ion produced undergoes unimolecular decomposition, and if the amino group is axial, then the diazo group is axial and the carbonium ion readily undergoes elimination if there is an axial hydrogen atom on the adjacent carbon atom. At the same time a small amount of equatorial alcohol is also formed. When the amino

N$_2^+$

H $-N_2$ →   [+   ] $-H^+$ →

H

H$_2$O ↓

OH

group is equatorial, the leaving diazo group is equatorial. Since the adjacent hydrogen atoms are no longer suitably placed for attack at the back of the receding diazo group, the result is formation of equatorial alcohol only (see also below).

$-N_2$ →   + $\xrightarrow{H_2O}$

N$_2^+$ OH

There are, however, exceptions to the above generalisation, *e.g.*, *trans*-4-t-butylcyclohexylamine (e-t-Bu:e-NH$_2$) gives mainly the *trans*-alcohol, but only 13 per cent of the *cis*-alcohol (e-t-Bu:a-OH) and 10 per cent of alkene. Also, *cis*-4-t-butylcyclohexylamine (e-t-Bu:a-NH$_2$) gives a mixture of the corresponding alcohols and predominantly the alkene (Hückel *et al.*, 1963). The explanation for these results is uncertain.

As we have seen, although there is a preferred form in cyclohexane derivatives, the energy barrier of interconversion between the preferred and less stable form is too low to permit their being distinguished by the classical methods of stereochemistry. This predominance of the preferred form holds good at room temperature (or below). At higher temperatures, or during the course of a chemical reaction, the preponderance of the preferred form may be reduced. In chemical reactions, it may be possible for the reaction to proceed more readily through the less stable conformation because it is this one which more closely approaches the geometry of the transition state. An example of this type is chlorocyclohexane. As we have seen, the preferred form is the equatorial conformation. This compound, on treatment with ethanolic potassium hydroxide, undergoes dehydrohalogenation to form cyclohexene. Since *trans* elimination is preferred, and since the rate of interconversion of the conformers is much faster than the rate of the elimination, elimination can be expected to occur *via* the axial conformation (see the Curtin–Hammett principle, §5m).

Systems of this type, *i.e.*, conformers of cyclohexane derivatives in equilibrium, have been studied from the point of view of determining the conformational equilibrium constant and the reactivities of both conformations. One example is the acetylation of cyclohexanol with acetic anhydride in pyridine at 25°C (Eliel *et al.*, 1957).

If k is the overall observed rate of acetylation and k_e and k_a are the rates of acetylation of the equatorial and axial conformers, respectively, then (Winstein *et al.*, 1955):

$$k = k_e N_e + k_a N_a$$

where N_e and N_a are the mole fractions in the equatorial and axial conformations, respectively. Also:

$$N_e + N_a = 1 \quad \text{and} \quad K = N_e/N_a$$

where K is the conformational equilibrium constant. The value of k can be readily obtained but the difficulty is to obtain the values of k_e and k_a because the two conformations are too readily inter-convertible to be studied separately. However, the required values of k_e and k_a have been determined by using *cis*- and *trans*-4-t-butylcyclohexane derivatives, the assumption being made that the t-butyl group is *exclusively* equatorial. This is essentially true provided the other group is not comparable in size with the t-butyl group; this is usually the case. In this way, the conformations of the *cis*- and *trans*-isomers are known and are therefore fixed.

According to Eliel, k for cyclohexanol is $8{\cdot}37 \times 10^{-5}$, k_a for *cis*-4-t-butylcyclohexanol (*e*-t-Bu, *a*-OH; $N_a = 1$, $N_e = 0$) is $2{\cdot}89 \times 10^{-5}$, and k_e for *trans*-4-t-butylcyclohexanol (*e*-t-Bu, *e*-OH; $N_a = 0$, $N_e = 1$) is $10{\cdot}65 \times 10^{-5}$ (1 mol^{-1} s^{-1}). Hence:

$$8{\cdot}37 = 10{\cdot}65 N_e + 2{\cdot}89 N_a$$
$$= 10{\cdot}65 N_e + 2{\cdot}89(1 - N_e)$$
$$= N_e(10{\cdot}65 - 2{\cdot}89) + 2{\cdot}89$$

$$\therefore \quad 7\cdot76 N_e = 5\cdot48$$
$$\therefore \quad\quad N_e = 5\cdot48/7\cdot76 = 0\cdot71$$
$$\therefore \quad\quad N_a = 0\cdot29$$

Hence $K = 0\cdot71/0\cdot29 = 2\cdot45$

Also, since $\Delta G^\circ = -RT \ln K$

$$\therefore \quad \Delta G^\circ = -2\cdot2 \text{ kJ mol}^{-1}$$

i.e., the free-energy difference between equatorial and axial hydroxyl is $-2\cdot2$ kJ mol^{-1} (the equatorial form is more stable than the axial).

Eliel (1960), independently of Winstein, derived the equivalent relationship:

$$k = (k_e K + k_a)/(K + 1)$$

This equation, when solved for K, gives:

$$K = (k_a - k)/(k - k_e)$$

The equivalence of the Winstein and Eliel relationships is readily established as follows:

$$K = N_e/N_a$$
$$K + 1 = (N_e + N_a)/N_a = 1/N_a$$

Substituting these values in Eliel's equation, we get

$$k = (k_e N_e/N_a + k_a)/(1/N_a)$$
$$= k_e N_e + k_a N_a$$

Conformational equilibrium constants (and hence free-energy differences) may be calculated more directly from equilibrium reactions. These reactions can occur for various types of cyclohexane derivatives, the most important group being that involving the interconversion of isomers *via* an enol or enolate ion. Thus, for example, either *cis*- or *trans*-4-t-butyl-2-methylcyclohexanone is converted into an equilibrium mixture of the two isomers in which the *cis*-isomer predominates. This is to be expected on the basis that the *e*-methyl conformation is more stable than the *a*-form.

Similarly, *cis*-decal-1-one is converted, by means of alkali, into an equilibrium mixture of the *cis*- and *trans*-isomers, with the latter being present almost exclusively.

Ethyl *cis*-4-t-butylcyclohexanecarboxylate or the *trans*-isomer is converted into the same equilibrium mixture of the two isomers when heated with ethanolic sodium ethoxide. The *trans*-isomer (e-CO$_2$Et) predominates.

Not only do the values of free-energy differences show which is the more stable conformer, they also give some indication of the 'size' of the groups, since it can be anticipated that the larger the size, the higher will be the free-energy difference. These values, however, depend on temperature and the nature of the solvent. Some values are (kJ mol^{-1}): halogen, 0–2; OH, OR, 2–4; CO_2H, CO_2R, 4–6·2; Me, Et, NH_2, 6·2–8·3; Pr, isoPr, NMe_2, 8·3–10·4; Ph, 13; t-Bu, >16·7.

Doubts have been expressed about the validity of conformational energies computed by means of the kinetic methods (*inter alia*, Kwart *et al.*, 1964, 1967).

Conformational equilibrium constants may also be determined by physical methods: i.r., u.v., NMR, ORD, etc. Thus, *e.g.*, in the infrared method it is necessary to find an absorption frequency characteristic of the equatorial and the axial conformation. This may be done by using *cis*- and *trans*-t-butyl derivatives containing the group under investigation (see above). Then, on the assumption that the molar extinction coefficients are the same in the compound being investigated and its corresponding t-butyl derivative, the ratio of the intensities of the bands in these two compounds gives the mole fraction of the equatorial or axial conformation. In the NMR method, if δ is the chemical shift of the proton of the CHOH group in cyclohexanol and δ_e (axial proton) and δ_a (equatorial proton), those of the corresponding *trans*- and *cis*-4-t-butyl derivatives (*e*-OH and *a*-OH, respectively), then, on the assumption that the 4-t-butyl group has no effect on the chemical shift:

$$\delta = N_e\delta_e + N_a\delta_a$$

From this the ratio $N_e/N_a = K$ can be calculated.

An alternative approach uses the fact that the values of coupling constants vary with the dihedral angle between the coupled protons (see also 1 §12e).

Rearrangements involving cyclohexanes. Most cyclohexane derivatives can undergo 1,2-shifts, but the course of the reaction depends on a number of factors. If the leaving group Z is *axial* and there is a group Y attached to an *adjacent carbon atom which is also axial, i.e., trans*, and capable of migration, *e.g.*, methyl, hydrogen, then the spatial requirements are satisfied and so a 1,2-shift can occur with the formation of a *cyclohexane* derivative (see III). If the leaving group Z is equatorial

(III)

(IV)

and Y axial (*i.e., cis*), then these two groups no longer satisfy the spatial requirements. However, *an adjacent carbon atom of the ring system* does satisfy the spatial requirements of the 1,2-shift, and this occurs with the formation of a cyclopentane derivative (see IV). These rearrangements are also examples of neighbouring group participation, but this may be absent in certain cases.

These principles may be illustrated by the deamination of 2-aminocyclohexanol (McCasland, 1951). Thr *trans*-isomer, on treatment with nitrous acid, forms cyclopentanecarboxaldehyde. Both groups are equatorial and since this conformer is much more favoured than the diaxial conformer, the molecule reacts in the former conformation. Thus:

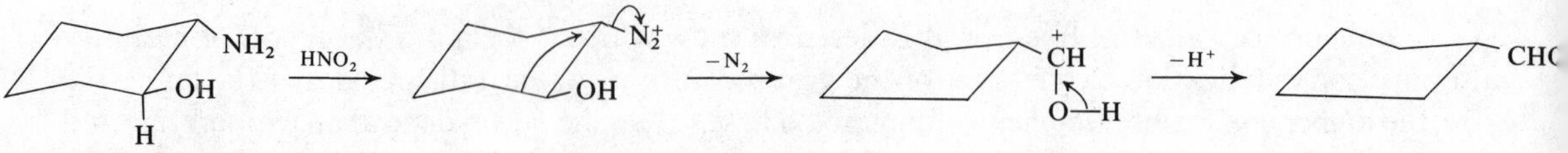

trans

On the other hand, the *cis*-isomer gives cyclopentanecarboxaldehyde and cyclohexanone under the same conditions. In this isomer, the two *e,a*-conformations contain about the same amount of energy and hence are in equilibrium of approximately equal populations. Thus:

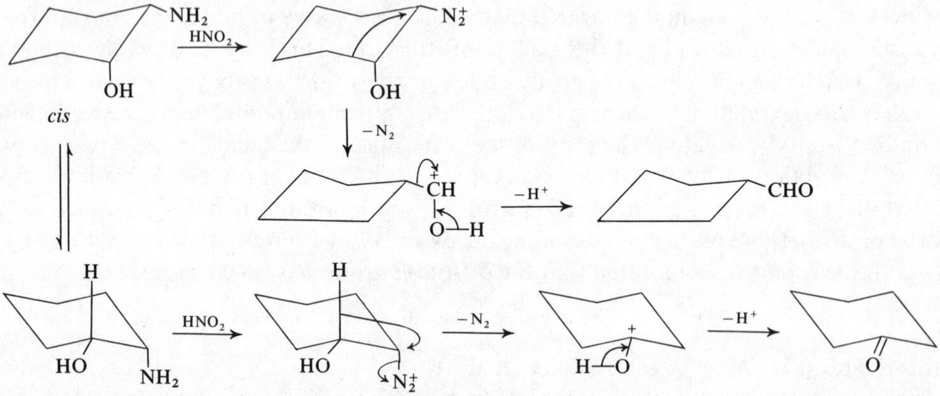

cis

§13. Cycloalkenes

A very important problem in connection with elimination reactions is the conformation of cyclohexene. The presence of the double bond causes the ring to assume the half-chair conformation (atoms 1, 2, 3 and 6 are in one plane). This has been demonstrated by means of X-ray and electron-diffraction studies of some cyclohexene derivatives, *e.g.*, 3,4,5,6-tetrachlorocyclohexene.

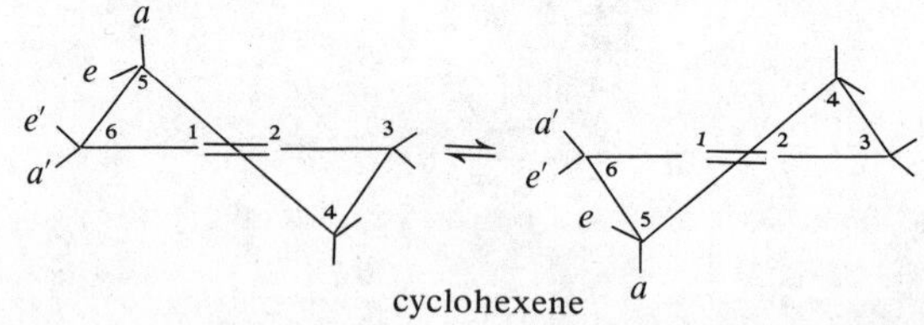

cyclohexene

The hydrogen atoms at positions 4 and 5 are the normal axial and equatorial types, but those at 3 and 6 are referred to as quasi-axial (pseudo-axial) (*a'*) and quasi-equatorial (pseudo-equatorial) (*e'*); the latter is the more stable.

Since the addition of halogen and halogen acids (by the polar mechanism) normally produces the *trans*-product, it can be anticipated that the predominant product will be the diaxial one in a rigid system. In a mobile system, however, if the diaxial is less stable than the diequatorial form, then the equilibrium will shift to the latter, *e.g.*, when bromine adds to cyclohexene, the product is *trans*-1,2-dibromocyclohexane, and the diaxial and diequatorial forms are present in about equal amounts (Hassel *et al.*, 1947). The two C—Br bonds produce strong dipole-dipole interactions and so partly offset the 1,3-interactions. An interesting point in this connection is that Berti *et al.* (1963) have shown that the addition of bromine to cyclohexene in the presence of cinchonine or cinchonidine gives optically active *trans*-1,2-dibromocyclohexane (*cf.* **3** §7).

Epoxidation occurs by a *cis*-mechanism (§5l), and it has been shown by electron diffraction measurements that the half-chair conformation in cyclohexene is retained in 1,2-epoxycyclohexane (Ottar, 1947).

trans-cyclo-octene

A particularly interesting case of the conformation of a cycloalkene is cyclo-octene. The *trans*-isomer is not superimposable on its mirror image, and has been resolved by Cope *et al.* (1963). It is the first cyclic alkene that has been found to contain molecular asymmetry.

§14. Small rings

We have already discussed the six-membered ring, and the principles described may be applied to the other rings. Cyclopropane, since it is a three-point system, *must* be planar. Large rings are puckered, contain very little strain, and the chemistry of their derivatives closely resembles that of the aliphatic analogues.

Cyclobutane is a four-point system and so could be either planar or puckered. If it were planar then, apart from angle strain, there could be strain due to eclipsing of adjacent hydrogen atoms and to bond opposition (I). On the other hand if the ring were puckered, then eclipsing and bond

(I)   (II)   (III)

opposition strains would be diminished, but angle strain would be increased. As we saw in **2** §4a, bond angle deformation is brought about comparatively easily, and so the puckered form might therefore be more stable than the planar. This has actually been shown to be the case; electron diffraction (Bastiansen *et al.*, 1961) and spectroscopic and thermodynamic measurements (Pitzer *et al.*, 1953) have shown that cyclobutane is puckered. Allinger *et al.* (1962) showed, by thermo-dynamic calculations, that methyl *cis*-3-methylcyclobutanecarboxylate (II) is more stable than the *trans*-isomer by $1 \cdot 3$ kJ mol^{-1}. This is in agreement with a puckered structure, but Allinger *et al.* (1965) found that dimethyl *trans*-cyclobutane-1,3-dicarboxylate (III) is more stable than the *cis*-isomer by $0 \cdot 42$ kJ mol^{-1}. The greater stability of the *trans*-isomer appears to be due to dipole-dipole interactions. On the other hand, the *trans*-isomer of cyclobutane-1,3-dicarboxylic acid has been shown, by X-ray analysis, to have a planar ring in the solid state, whereas the *cis*-isomer has a puckered ring (Margulis *et al.*, 1967). However, it should be noted that X-ray analysis on single crystals may give a shape of the molecule dominated by packing effects within the crystal and not the shape of the molecule in different circumstances, *e.g.*, in solution.

Common rings. **Cyclopentane** could be planar or puckered, and the arguments used for cyclo-butane suggest that the puckered form might be the more stable one. However, since cyclopentane is a five-point system, it can have four carbon atoms in one plane and the remaining one outside (*envelope* or C_s form) or three in one plane and the other two outside (*half-chair* or C_2 form).

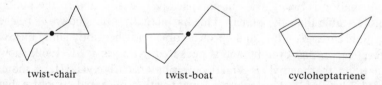

envelope   half-chair   *cis*-1,3-dimethyl-
cyclopentane

Electron diffraction measurements of cyclopentane indicate puckering (Bastiansen *et al.*, 1961). The puckering is not fixed, but 'rotates' round the ring, *i.e.*, each carbon atom oscillates in a direction perpendicular to the average plane of the ring, *i.e.*, no particular carbon atom is *always* out of plane, but each one takes up this conformation. This effect is called **pseudorotation**. Pseudorotation occurs in cyclopentane because the potential energy barriers are very low, but when the ring carries one or more substituents, the energy barriers may now be high enough to inhibit pseudorotation.

The projected angle for *cis*-1,2,-substituents in cyclohexane is 60°, whereas that for *cis*-1,2 (and 1,5) is about 46° and that for *cis*-2,3 (and 4,5) is about 29° in the envelope form of cyclopentane (Pitzer *et al.*, 1959). Also, since *cis*-3,4 substituents are eclipsed, instability due to this eclipsing can be relieved by the compound assuming the half-chair conformation. For cyclopentane itself the two conformations differ very little in energy content (Pitzer *et al.*, 1959). The conformation of the ring, however, in cyclopentane derivatives depends on the nature of the substituents. Calculations by Pitzer *et al.* (1949) have shown that *cis*-1,3-dimethylcyclopentane is more stable by 2·1 kJ mol⁻¹ than the *trans*-isomer; this is in agreement with the envelope conformation. On the other hand, cyclopentanone is more stable in the half-chair form; the remaining hydrogens possess a minimum of steric repulsions (due to maximum staggering in this form).

Pitzer *et al.* (1959) have also carried out calculations on heterocyclic 5-membered rings, *e.g.*, pyrrolidine, tetrahydrofuran, etc., and conclude that these compounds are also in the half-chair form (the hetero-atom replaces the CO group in cyclopentanone).

Cycloheptane has, according to the calculations of Hendrickson (1961), two stable conformations, the twist-chair and the slightly less favoured twist-boat conformation, both of which are flexible,

twist-chair   twist-boat   cycloheptatriene

and interconversion of the equatorial and axial bonds in the twist-chair can be achieved by pseudo-rotation. Cycloheptatriene, a compound obtained from tropine, exists in a boat-shaped conformation (Traetterberg, 1964).

Medium rings. Several conformations have been proposed for **cyclo-octane**: the extended crown (IV) (Mez, 1960) and the 'saddle' conformation (V) (Dale *et al.*, 1964). Strain energy minimisation calculations by Hendrickson (1964) and Wiberg (1965) suggest that neither form is clearly favoured energetically. Dunitz *et al.* (1966) have examined, by X-ray analysis, cyclo-octane-1,2-*trans*-dicarboxylic acid, and showed that the conformation of this molecule is (VI), the 'boat-chair' form (so named by Hendrickson). Cyclo-octatetraene (VII) exists in the tub form (Treibs, 1950). This

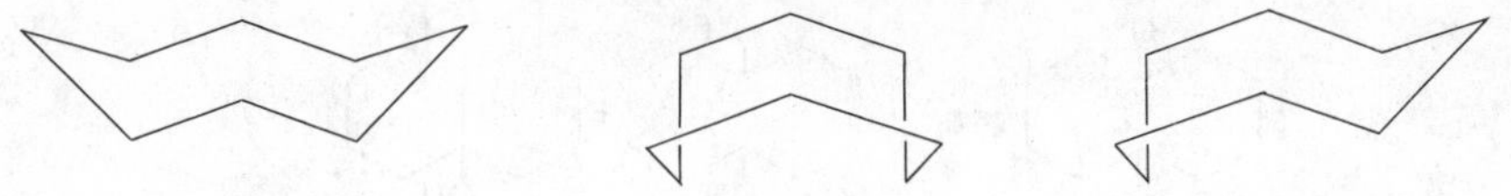

(IV)　　　　　　　(V)　　　　　　　(VI)

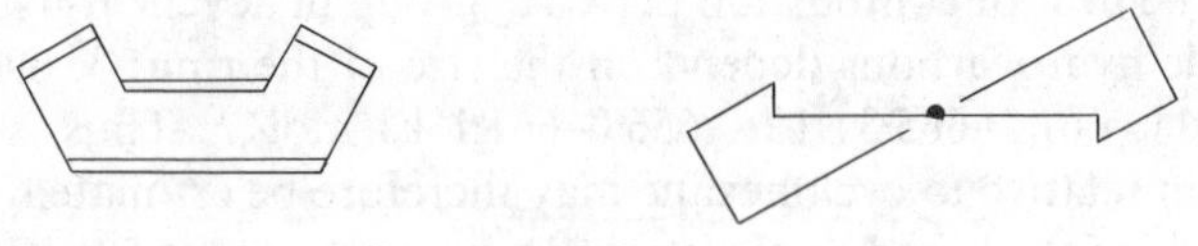

(VII)　　　　　　　　　　　(VIII)

compound is of particular interest because bond fluctuation, called **fluxionalism,** has been observed and measured by NMR spectroscopy in, *e.g.*, fluorocyclo-octatetraene (*cf.* Kekulé's dynamic structure for benzene, Vol. 1, Ch. 20). Its NMR spectrum shows a broad band at room temperature

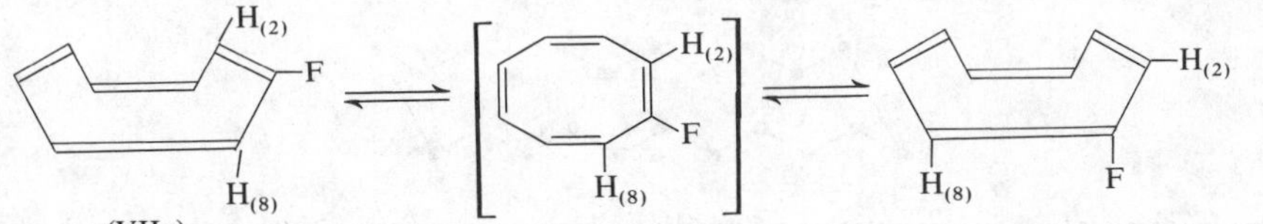

(VIIa)　　　　　　　　　　　　　　　　　　　　　(VIIb)

because, at this temperature, bond fluctuation and ring inversion occur rapidly. At $-65°C$, however, these processes are sufficiently slowed down for the spectrum to show a doublet due to coupling of $H_{(2)}$ with F in (VIIa) or $H_{(8)}$ with F in (VIIb).

Cyclononane has the flexible symmetrical form (VIII) (Hendrickson, 1964).

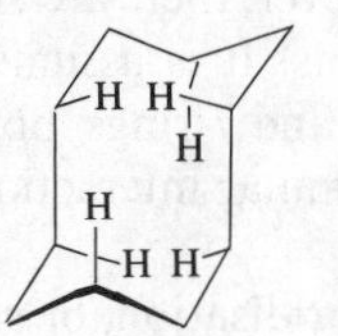

(IX)

Cyclodecane. X-ray analysis studies on some cyclodecane derivatives have shown that the conformation is (IX) (Dunitz *et al.*, 1960). This is derived from two chair conformations of cyclohexane joined by 1,3-axial bonds. It is these more complicated conformations which make the medium rings so different from large rings in many chemical and physical properties. The anomalous behaviour has been explained in terms of bond opposition strain, angle strain, and steric strain, in the last of which a very important contributing factor is the interactions between atoms on *opposite* sides of the ring (see (IX)). This type of interaction has been designated *transannular interaction*, and this produces *transannular strain*.

Examples of anomalous reactions are, *e.g.*, the formolysis of epoxycyclodecane (from *trans*-cyclodecene) to give *trans*-cyclodecane-1,6-diol (Prelog *et al.*, 1952). The structures have been written in the conventional manner; the reaction occurs by a transannular hydride shift:

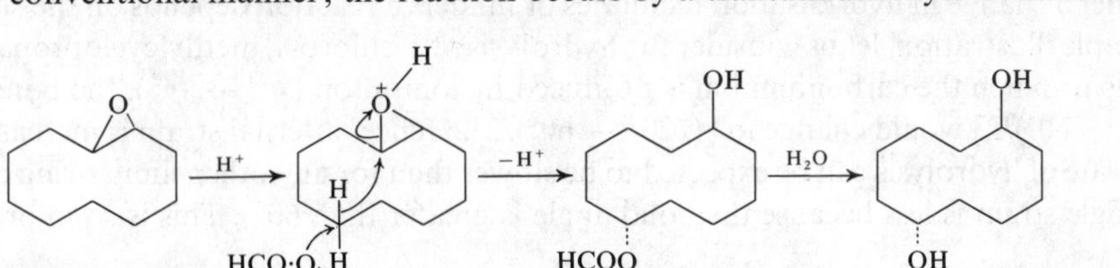

Addition of bromine to *cis*- and *trans*-cyclodecene gives, respectively, *cis*- and *trans*-1,6-dibromo-cyclodecane (Sicher *et al.*, 1961). Another example is the catalytic reduction of cyclodecane-1,6-dione (Kosover *et al.*, 1961).

Large rings. It is also of interest to discuss strain in alicyclic compounds in the following way (see also Vol. I, Ch. 19). The heat of combustion per CH_2 group in acyclic n-hydrocarbons is 659·0 kJ. The values for alicyclic hydrocarbons depend on the size of the ring: 3, 696·6; 4, 685·3; 5, 664·0; 6, 659·0; 7, 661·9; 8–11, 661·1–665·3; 12–, 656·0–661·1 kJ mol^{-1}. Thus, strain is a minimum in cyclohexane, and strain relative to cyclohexane may therefore be estimated, *e.g.*, the difference per CH_2 for 5- and 6-rings is 5·0 kJ, and so the strain in cyclopentane is $5 \times 5·0 = 25$ kJ mol^{-1}. The strains in medium rings may also be calculated in this way. The values are about 25·1 kJ mol^{-1} for cycloheptane, about 37·7–41·8 for cyclo-octane, and about 50·2–54·4 for cyclononane to cyclo-undecane. From cyclododecane onwards, the value of CH_2 groups is close to that of the acyclic hydrocarbons, *i.e.*, these large rings are strainless and have been shown (by X-ray analysis) to consist of two parallel chains which are puckered.

I-Strain. In general, many reactions of medium rings are either faster or slower than those of the other ring systems, *e.g.*, the rate of hydrolysis of medium-ring chlorides and *p*-toluenesulphonates is faster, reduction of medium-ring ketones by sodium borohydride slower, dissociation of these ketone cyanohydrins greater, etc. Many of these differences in reactivity can be explained in terms of steric strain. The total ring strain in cyclic systems has been called **I-strain** (*internal strain*; Brown, 1951, 1956). The contributing factors to strain in alicyclic hydrocarbons, as we have seen, are steric repulsion, bond opposition forces, and angle deformation. In medium rings, however, there are also transannular interactions. The difficulty is the estimation of these contributions. It is assumed, however, that in small rings, the major source of strain is angle distortion; in 5- and 7-rings, bond opposition forces; and medium rings all four factors play a part, with transannular interactions particularly prominent.

Changes in I-strain may be considered in terms of changes from sp^2 to sp^3 hybridisation, or *vice versa*, at the site of reaction. Brown assumed that if the change $sp^2 \rightarrow sp^3$ is accompanied by a decrease in I-strain, reactions involving this change are facilitated. Also, reactions involving the change $sp^3 \rightarrow sp^2$ are hindered. On the other hand, in those situations where the change $sp^2 \rightarrow sp^3$ is accompanied by an increase in I-strain, reactions are hindered, and those for $sp^3 \rightarrow sp^2$ are facilitated.

Whether a change in hybridisation facilitates or hinders a reaction depends on the size of the ring. For a simple illustration, let us consider the hydrolysis of 1-chloro-1-methylcyclopropane by the S_N1 mechanism. When the carbonium ion is produced by ionisation ($sp^3 \rightarrow sp^2$), the bond angle strain $[(109·5° - 60°)/2]$ would change to $[(120° - 60°)/2]$. Hence, internal strain is increased and therefore the rate of hydrolysis can be expected to be slower than for any other similar ring compound (in which angle strain is less because the bond angle is greater than 60°). This is so in practice.

§15. Bridged-ring systems

A number of these systems occur in various bicyclic terpenes (see Ch. 8). On the other hand, many complicated bridged-ring systems have been synthesised recently. Tamelen *et al.* (1963) have prepared bicyclo[2,2,0]hexadiene (I); this is the 'Dewar benzene'. It has a half-life in pyridine of two days at room temperature, and when heated to 90°C it is converted into benzene. *Adamantane* (II) was first isolated from petroleum (Landa *et al.*, 1933), but it has now been synthesised in various ways, *e.g.*, dicyclopentadiene is hydrogenated and the product isomerised by aluminium chloride

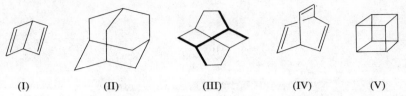

| (I) | (II) | (III) | (IV) | (V) |

(Schleyer, 1957). It is composed of three fused cyclohexane chair conformations; its structure is rigid but strainless. *Twistane* (III), the twist-boat isomer of adamantane, has been synthesised by Whitlock, Jr. (1962). Other compounds which have been prepared are, *e.g.*, *barrelene* (IV) [Zimmerman *et al.*, 1960] and *cubane* (V) [Eaton *et al.*, 1964].

§16. Catenanes

These are large ring compounds consisting of two interlocked rings (see also Vol. I, Ch. 19). Wasserman (1960) prepared (I), and this compound, in the form of a hydrocarbon, may be represented as (II).

$(C_{34}H_{65}D_3)$ —CO— CHOH —(CH$_2$)$_{32}$

| (I) | (II) | (III) |

Each ring can be described independently of the other, and since they share no bonds, they are chemically independent. To convert the catenane into the corresponding non-interlocked pair of rings, it is necessary to break a bond in one of the rings. This bond is not a property of a particular pair of atoms in a catenane hydrocarbon, since all atoms are equivalent in each ring. Thus the bond to be broken is a property of the two complete rings. This bond is called a *topological bond*, and the relationship of the catenane to its pair of 'unlocked' rings is called *topological isomerism*. DNAs have been shown to exist as catenanes (see **16** §15).

(III), which is a trefoil, is an example of a single chain that is knotted. It is a topological isomer of the corresponding unknotted cyclohexane, and the two isomers can be interconverted only by breaking a C—C bond.

The trefoil (IV) has been synthesised by Schill (1969).

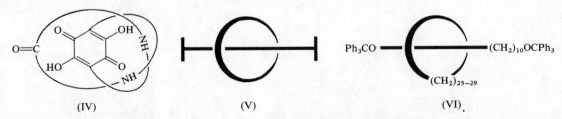

| (IV) | (V) | (VI). |

Rotaxanes. These are circular macromolecules which are threaded by a spindle whose ends consist of groups of such bulk that the 'ring' cannot 'fall off' the spindle (see V). Various rotaxanes have now been synthesised, *e.g.*, (VI) (Harrison, 1972).

A very interesting example of chemical topology is 3-methyl-5-bromoadamantanecarboxylic acid (VII). This may be regarded as the formal analogue of 2-bromopropionic acid (VIII) in which the

$$
\text{(VII)} \qquad\qquad \text{(VIII)}
$$

centre of chirality (denoted by the dot) is at the 'unoccupied' centre of (VII). This compound has been resolved by McKervey *et al.* (1969).

REFERENCES

INGOLD, *Structure and Mechanism in Organic Chemistry*, Bell and Sons (1969, 2nd edn.). Ch. 13. 'Additions and their Retrogressions'.

DOLBIER, 'Electrophilic Addition to Alkenes', *J. Chem. Educ.*, 1969, **46**, 342.

BANTHORPE, *Elimination Reactions*, Elsevier (1963).

MCLENNAN, 'The Carbanion Mechanism of Olefin-forming Elimination', *Quart. Rev.*, 1967, **21**, 490.

FRY, 'Isotope Effect Studies of Elimination Reactions', *Chem. Soc. Rev.*, 1972, **1**, 163.

KLYNE (ed.), *Progress in Stereochemistry*, Butterworth.

BARTON and COOKSON, 'The Principles of Conformational Analysis', *Quart. Rev.*, 1956, **10**, 44.

NEWMAN, (ed.), *Steric Effects in Organic Chemistry*, Wiley (1956). Ch. 1. 'Conformational Analysis.'

ELIEL, *Stereochemistry of Carbon Compounds*, McGraw-Hill (1962).

HANACK, *Conformation Theory*, Academic Press (1965). Translated by Neumann.

ELIEL, ALLINGER, ANGYAL, and MORRISON, *Conformational Analysis*, Interscience (1965).

MCKENNA, 'Conformational Analysis of Organic Compounds', *Roy. Inst. Chem.*, Lecture Series, 1966. No. 1.

FERGUSON, *The Modern Structural Theory of Organic Chemistry*, Prentice-Hall (1963).

LLOYD, *Alicyclic Compounds*, Arnold (1963).

WHITHAM, *Alicyclic Chemistry*, Oldbourne Press (1963).

MCQUILLIN, *Alicyclic Chemistry*, Cambridge University Press (1972).

ANDERSON, 'The Study of Ring Inversions by Nuclear Magnetic Resonance Spectroscopy,' *Quart. Rev.*, 1965, **19**, 426.

COPE, MARTIN, and MCKERVEY, 'Transannular Reactions in Medium-Sized Rings', *Quart. Rev.*, 1966, **20**, 119.

FRISCH and WASSERMAN, 'Chemical Topology', *J. Amer. Chem. Soc.*, 1961, **83**, 3789.

SCHILL, *Catenanes, Rotaxanes, and Knots*, Academic Press (1971). Translated by Boeckmann.

Stereochemistry of biphenyl compounds

§1. Configuration of the biphenyl molecule

If we assume that the benzene ring is planar, then the biphenyl molecule will consist of two planar rings; but without any further information we cannot say how these two rings are arranged spatially. Kaufler (1907) proposed the 'butterfly' formula (I) in order to account for the chemical behaviour of various biphenyl derivatives, *e.g.*, Michler and Zimmermann (1881) had condensed benzidine with

(I)   (II)   (III)   (IV)

carbonyl chloride and obtained a product to which Kaufler assigned structure (II). According to Kaufler, the co-axial structure (III) was impossible, since the two amino-groups are too far apart to react simultaneously with carbonyl chloride; it should be noted that this *simultaneous* reaction at both ends was assumed by Kaufler. Simultaneous reaction, however, is reasonable (according to Kaufler) on the folded structure (II).

Now Schultz (1880) had prepared a dinitrodiphenic acid by the nitration of diphenic acid, and Schmidt *et al.* (1903), from their work on this acid, believed it to be 6,6′-dinitrodiphenic acid (IV); these workers, it should be noted, did not synthesise the acid. In 1921, however, Kenner *et al.* synthesised 6,6′-dinitrodiphenic acid by means of the Ullmann reaction (see Vol. I) on the ethyl ester of 2-chloro-3-nitrobenzoic acid, and hydrolysing the product. This acid (V) (written with the two benzene rings co-axial), did not have the same melting point as Schultz's acid, and so Kenner, believing that his and Schultz's acid were both 6,6′-dinitrodiphenic acid, suggested that the two were stereoisomers. Then Christie and Kenner (1922) showed that Kenner's acid was resolvable, and pointed out that this could be explained on the Kaufler formula (IV), since this structure has no elements of symmetry. These authors, however, also pointed out that the optical activity could also

$$CO_2C_2H_5 \quad \xrightarrow{Cu} \quad CO_2C_2H_5 \; NO_2 \quad \longrightarrow \quad CO_2H \; NO_2$$

(V)

be accounted for by the co-axial structure (V), provided that the two benzene rings do not lie in one plane (see also §2).

Kaufler's formula, as we have seen, was based on the assumption that the two amino-groups in benzidine react *simultaneously* with various reagents. Re-investigation of these reactions showed that this was not the case, *e.g.*, Turner and Le Fèvre (1926) found that the compound produced from benzidine and carbonyl chloride was not as originally formulated (see II or III), but had a free amino-group, *i.e.*, the compound was

$$[NH_2C_6H_4C_6H_4NH]_2CO$$

Hence Kaufler's *reason* for his butterfly formula is incorrect, and although it does not necessarily follow that the *formula* is incorrect, nevertheless Turner's work weakened Kaufler's claim. One of the strongest bits of chemical evidence for rejecting Kaufler's formula is that of Barber and Smiles (1928). These workers prepared the three dimercaptobiphenyls, (VI), (VII) and (VIII), and oxidised each one. Only one of them, the 2,2'-derivative (VI), gave the intramolecular disulphide (diphenylene

(VI)   (VII)   (VIII)   (IX)

disulphide, IX). On the Kaufler formula, all three dithiols would be expected to give the intramolecular disulphides, since the two thiol groups are equally distant in all three compounds.

Physico-chemical methods have also been used to determine the configuration of the biphenyl molecule, *e.g.*, the crystal structure of 4,4'-biphenyl derivatives shows a centre of symmetry; this is only possible for the co-axial formula. Dipole moment measurements also confirm this configuration, *e.g.*, the dipole moment of 4,4'-dichlorobiphenyl is zero; this again is only possible if the two benzene rings are co-axial.

§2. Optical activity of biphenyl compounds

Christie and Kenner's work (see above) has been extended by other workers, who showed that compounds in which at least *three* of the four *ortho*-positions in biphenyl are occupied by certain groups could be resolved. It was then soon found that two conditions were necessary for biphenyl compounds to exhibit optical activity:

(i) Neither ring must have a vertical plane of symmetry. Thus (I) is not resolvable, but (II) is.

(I)   (II)

(ii) The substituents in the *ortho*-positions must have a large size, *e.g.*, the following compounds were resolved: 6-nitrodiphenic acid, 6,6'-dinitrodiphenic acid, 6,6'-dichlorodiphenic acid, 2,2'-diamino-6,6'-dimethylbiphenyl (see also §4).

The earlier work showed that three groups had to be present in the *ortho*-positions. This gave rise to the theory that the groups in these positions impinged on one another when free rotation was attempted, *i.e.*, the steric effect prevented free rotation. This theory of restricted rotation about the single bond joining the two benzene rings (in the co-axial formula) was suggested simultaneously in 1926 by Turner and Le Fèvre, Bell and Kenyon, and Mills. Consider molecule (III) and its mirror image (IV). Provided that the groups A, B and C are large enough to 'interfere mechanically', *i.e.*, to behave as 'obstacles', then free rotation about the single bond is restricted. Thus the two benzene

(III)   (IV)

rings cannot be coplanar and consequently (IV) is not superimposable on (III), *i.e.*, (III) and (IV) are enantiomers. In molecule (III) there is no chiral centre; it is the molecule *as a whole* which is chiral, due to the restricted rotation.

In biphenyl the two benzene rings are co-axial, and in optically active biphenyl derivatives the rings are inclined to each other due to the steric and repulsive effects of the groups in the *ortho*-positions. The actual angle of inclination of the two rings depends on the nature of the substituent groups, but it appears to be usually in the vicinity of 90°, *i.e.*, the rings tend to be approximately perpendicular to each other. Thus, in order to exhibit optical activity, the substituent groups in the *ortho*-positions must be large enough to prevent the two rings from becoming coplanar, in which

(V)   (VI)

case the molecule would possess a plane or a centre of symmetry, *e.g.*, diphenic acid is not optically active. In configuration (V) the molecule has a plane of symmetry, and in configuration (VI) a centre of symmetry; of these two, (VI) is the more likely because of the repulsion between the two carboxyl groups (*cf.* **2** §4).

If restricted rotation in biphenyl compounds is due entirely to the spatial effect, then theoretically we have only to calculate the size of the group in order to ascertain whether the groups will impinge and thereby give rise to optical activity. The 'size' of the group, however, must be calculated from van der Waals radii (**1** §2); the results are in good agreement with experiment.

Later work has shown that if the substituent groups are large enough, then only *two* in the *o*- and *o'*-positions will produce restricted rotation, *e.g.*, Lesslie and Turner (1932) resolved biphenyl-2,2'-disulphonic acid (VII). In this molecule the sulphonic acid group is large enough to be impeded by the *ortho*-hydrogen atoms. This molecule was readily racemised on heating, but Lesslie *et al.* (1962) prepared the enantiomers of 2,2'-di-t-butylbiphenyl from the corresponding optically active 6,6'-di-t-butylbiphenyl-3,3'-dicarboxylic acids. These were found to be highly optically stable (the

(VII)   (VIII)

t-butyl group is very large). Lesslie and Turner (1933) have also shown that the (+)-camphor-sulphonate of 3'-bromobiphenyl-2-trimethylarsonium iodide (VIII) undergoes mutarotation. The trimethylarsonium group is large enough to be impeded by the *ortho*-hydrogen atoms (the bromine atom in the *meta*-position gives asymmetry to this ring). Attempts to isolate the active biphenyl compound failed because it racemised rapidly. This mutarotation indicates that the biphenyl is optically active and that the two enantiomers are readily interconvertible.

Since one phenyl group can rotate with respect to the other (about the interannular bond), the various positions would correspond to different conformations. In acyclic compounds, although there are preferred conformations the energy barriers are very low, and so the various conformations (staggered, eclipsed, and skew) are interconvertible (**2** §4a). In the case of the biphenyls, however, because of steric hindrance, the molecules have large energy barriers separating the two forms, and these barriers are large enough (75–105 kJ mol^{-1}) to produce *separable* rotational isomers. Such isomers are called **atropisomers**, and the two conditions for **atropisomerism** have been given above (see also **5** §3).

It has already been pointed out that diphenic acid is not optically active, and that its configuration is most probably (VI). Now calculation shows that the effective diameter of the carboxyl group is large enough to prevent configuration (V) from being planar, and consequently, if the two rings could be held more or less in this configuration, the molecule would not be coplanar and hence would be resolvable. Such a compound, (IX), was prepared and resolved by Adams and Kornblum (1941). The two benzene rings are not coplanar and are held fairly rigid by the large methylene bridge.

Many biphenyls have been studied from the point of view of the effect of a 2,2'-bridge on the optical activity of molecules of the type (X). When *n* = 1, the molecule is a disubstituted fluorene. Since this molecule is flat, it is not resolvable (but see also §3a). When *n* = 2, the molecule is a disubstituted 9,10-dihydrophenanthrene. Such compounds have been resolved, *e.g.*, (XVI) and (XVII) (see below). When *n* = 3, the molecules are resolvable and are highly optically stable. Iffland *et al.* (1956) prepared the optically active biphenyl (XI) which has two amino-groups in the 6,6'-positions. On the other hand, these authors have also prepared (XII) in optically active forms. Mislow (1957) has also obtained the dibenzocyclo-octadiene acids (XIII) in optically active forms;

both forms were highly optically labile. Similar to (XIII) is (XIV) which has been resolved by Bell (1952). Mislow *et al.* (1961) have also resolved the biphenyl derivative (XV), and in 1962, prepared the (−)-form of (XVI). Turner *et al.* (1955) had prepared (XVII), and Mislow, on comparing the

(XV)   (XVI)   (XVII)

optical stability of (XVI) with (XVII), found that the latter was the more stable one. In (XVI), the two methyl groups can slip past each other comparatively easily by bending out of the ring plane, but in (XVI) the second benzene ring in each naphthalene nucleus behaves as a large group and is also rigid, and consequently bending is very difficult.

(XVIII)   (XIX)

Mislow *et al.* (1961) have also prepared the (−)-form of dibenzocyclononadienecarboxylic acid (XVIII), and Hall *et al.* (1959) prepared the piperidinium salt (XIX) as the picrate and found it was optically labile.

Apart from the resolution of 2,2′-biphenyls, the stereochemistry of these compounds has been studied by u.v. and NMR spectroscopy and by X-ray analysis. In this way, a more detailed three-dimensional structure of these molecules has been obtained, *e.g.*, Wahl, jun. *et al.* (1972) have

(XX)   (XXI)   (XXII)

carried out an X-ray diffraction study of (XX) and have shown that this molecule exists in the pseudo-chair form (XXI). (XX) had been prepared and resolved chromatographically (on cellulose acetate) by Lüttringhaus *et al.* (1967). These latter authors had, on the basis of consideration of bond angles, predicted that the pseudo-tub conformation (XXII) was the more likely one.

A point of interest in connection with optically active biphenyls is that Schmidt *et al.* (1957) have shown that 4,4′,5,5′,6,6′-hexahydroxydiphenic acid occurs naturally in an optically active form.

§2a. Absolute configurations of biphenyls.   Since biphenyls owe their asymmetry to the molecule being asymmetric, the methods used for correlating configurations of compounds containing asymmetric carbon atoms cannot be applied (*cf.* **2** §§5a–5c). However, Mislow *et al.* (1957) used asymmetric synthesis (cf. **3** §7) as a means of establishing the absolute configuration of 6,6'-dinitro-2,2'-diphenic acid. Their method was chemical; assignment of absolute configuration has been obtained from a consideration of the transition states in the Meerwein–Ponndorf–Verley reduction of a dissymmetric diphenylic ketone by asymmetric alcohols of known absolute configuration. The (+)- and (−)-ketones (I) were partially reduced with (*S*)-(+)-methyl-t-butylmethanol in the presence of aluminium t-butoxide. The products were unchanged ketone with the (+)-form predominating, and the (+)- and (−)-alcohols, (II), with the (−)-form predominating. Thus, as far as the unchanged ketone is concerned, this reaction is a kinetic resolution (**2** §10.vii), since the ketone is now enriched in the (+)-form, and at the same time, the alcohol has become enriched in the (−)-form. Examination of models showed that, in the single conformation possible for the (*S*)-enantiomer (of the ketone), hydride transfer to either side of the carbonyl group is hindered by steric repulsion between the t-butyl group and a phenyl group, whereas for the (*R*)-enantiomer, the repulsion is only between the methyl group and a phenyl group. Thus the (+)-ketone

is (*S*)-(+) and the (−)-alcohol is (*R*)-(−). Furthermore, the (*S*)-(+)-ketone had been prepared from (−)-6,6'dinitro-2,2'-diphenic acid (*via* the dimethyl ester), and so this (−)-enantiomer is the (*S*)-(−)-acid. This assignment of absolute configuration has been confirmed by X-ray diffraction (Akimoto *et al.*, 1968).

The method of chemical correlation is reliable only if there is no change in configuration during the transformation (*cf.* **2** §5b), or if the change in configuration occurs in a predictable manner (*cf.* **3** §4). Thus, using the (*S*)-(−)-acid as absolute standard, Mislow *et al.* carried out a number of chemical correlations, *e.g.*,

$(S)-(-)$ $(S)-(-)$

(i) H$^+$; MeOH
(ii) LAH
(iii) HBr

(i) NaBH$_4$—AlCl$_3$
(ii) H$_2$—Pd

(i) NaNO$_2$/H$_2$SO$_4$
(ii) CuCl

$(S)-(-)$ $(S)-(-)$

Mislow *et al.* (1958), using the (S)-$(-)$-acid as the absolute standard, also correlated configurations in the biphenyl series by the quasi-racemate method (**2** §9a). In this way these authors determined the configurations of 6,6′-dichloro- and 6,6′-dimethyl-2,2′-diphenic acid. Mislow *et al.* (1960) have also confirmed absolute configurations in the biphenyl series by the rotatory dispersion method. The authors showed that the shapes of the ORD curves (**1** §12a) depended on the configuration and conformation of the biphenyl compounds; these compounds contain inherently dissymmetric chromophores (**2** §11).

The specification of absolute configuration of biphenyl compounds is carried out as follows. Since biphenyls do not owe their asymmetry to the presence of asymmetric carbon atoms (which are chiral centres; **2** §3a), the criterion now is the presence of a *chiral axis* (*i.e.*, an *axis of asymmetry*). This chiral axis may be derived from a chiral centre Z, (III), by 'extending' the point into a line AB which now passes through an elongated tetrahedron, (IV). For Z to be a chiral centre in (III), a, a', b, and b' must all be different, but for AB to be a chiral axis in (IV), it is sufficient that a and b be different, and a' and b' be different; it is not necessary that a should be different from a', or b from b'.

To apply the sequence rule (**2** §5d) to axial chirality (or axial asymmetry), it is necessary to use an additional rule, *viz.* with respect to an external point on the chiral axis, groups at the near end of the axis are given precedence over groups at the far end. If (IV) is viewed from point A, then the pair a–b, being nearer A, precedes the pair a'–b'; and in (V), pair a–b precedes pair c–d. If the order of priority is $a > b$ and $a' > b'$ (for IV), and $a > b$ and $c > d$ (for V), then both of these models give the final order of priority shown in (VI). If now, in accordance with the conversion rule, (VI) is viewed from the side remote from 4, then (VII) is obtained. This, by two interchanges gives (VIIa), and since the sequence $1 \rightarrow 2 \rightarrow 3$ is clockwise, (IV) and (V) are (R)-configurations. Had (IV) and (V) been viewed from point B on the chiral axis, then pairs a'–b' and c–d will be 1 and 2, and the pair a–b

(III) (IV) (IVa)

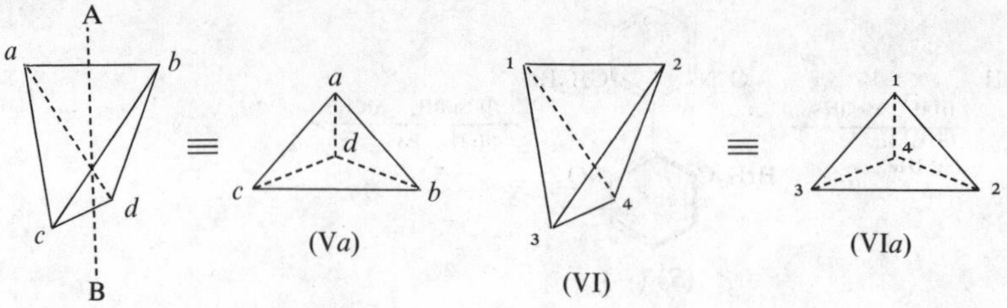

(V)   (Va)   (VI)   (VIa)

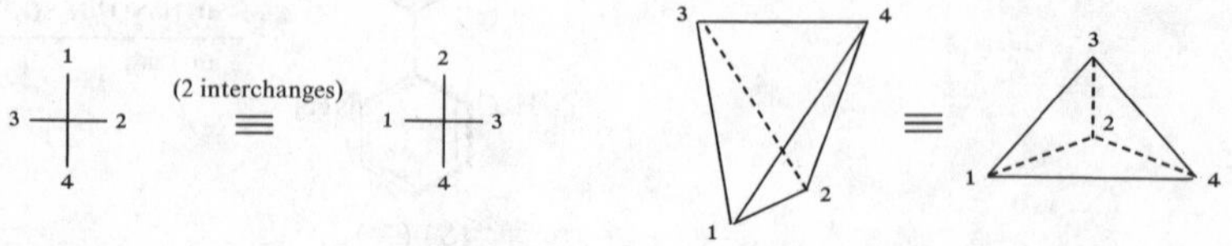

(VII)   (VIIa)   (VIII)   (VIIIa)

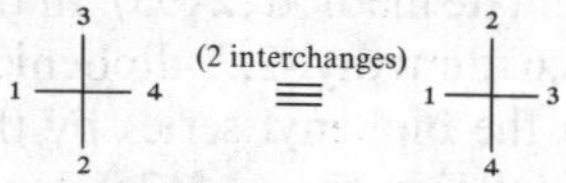

(IX)   (IXa)

will be 3 and 4. This gives (VIII), which in turn gives (IX), and this, by two interchanges, gives (IXa), which is still the (R)-configuration.

Let us now consider some substituted biphenyls. First, the four *ortho*-substituent groups are inspected. If they are different, as pairs (2–6 and 2'–6'), then they are used. Thus, in (X), $NO_2 = a$,

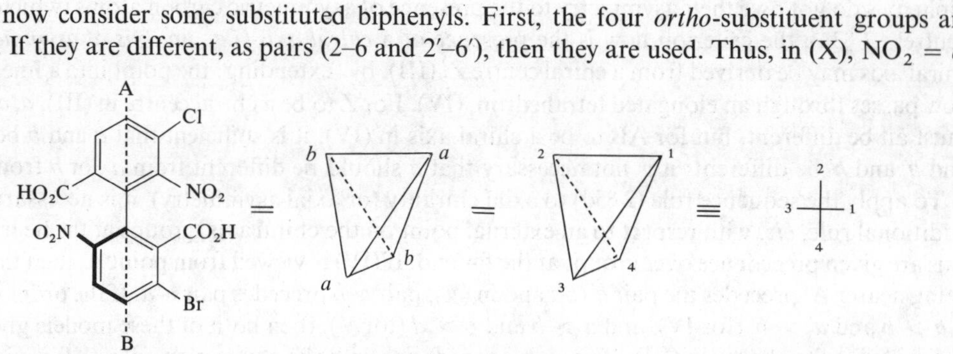

(X) (S)-form

and $CO_2H = b$ (priority $a > b$), and this molecule is therefore the (S)-form (the last diagram has $1 \rightarrow 2 \rightarrow 3$ anticlockwise). In (XI), since the upper ring has Cl in both *ortho*-positions, groups H and

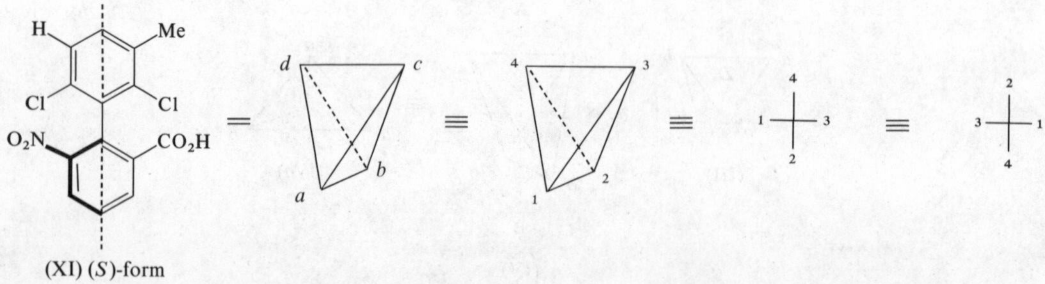

(XI) (S)-form

Me are therefore selected; $NO_2 = a$, $CO_2H = b$, Me $= c$, and H $= d$. Hence, (XI) is the (S)-form (two interchanges in the last diagram give $1 \rightarrow 2 \rightarrow 3$ in an anticlockwise direction).

Compound (I) is the ($+$)-ketone described above; $NO_2 = a$, $-CH_2CO = b$, and so (I) is the (S)-form.

(I) (S)-form

§3. Other examples of atropisomerism

In addition to the biphenyl compounds, there are many other examples where optical activity in the molecule is produced by restricted rotation about a single bond which may or may not be one that joins two rings. The following examples are only a few out of a very large number of compounds that have been resolved.

(i) Adams *et al.* (1931) have resolved the following *N*-phenylpyrrole and *N,N'*-bipyrryl.

Adams *et al.* (1932) have also resolved the 3,3'-bipyridyl

(ii) 1,1'-Binaphthyl-8,8'-dicarboxylic acid has been obtained in optically active forms by Stanley (1931).

This compound gives rise to asymmetric transformation (**2** §10iv); resolution with brucine gave 100 per cent of either the ($+$)- or ($-$)-compound.

Other compounds similar to the binaphthyl which have been obtained in optically active forms are 1,1'-binaphthyl-5,5'-dicarboxylic acid (I) (Bell *et al.*, 1951), the bianthryl derivatives, (II) and (III) (Bell *et al.*, 1949), and the 4,4'- and 5,5'-biquinolyls, (IV) and (V) (Crawford *et al.*, 1952).

(iii) Mills and Elliott (1928) obtained N-benzenesulphonyl-8-nitro-1-naphthylglycine (VI) in optically active forms; these were optically unstable, undergoing asymmetric transformation with

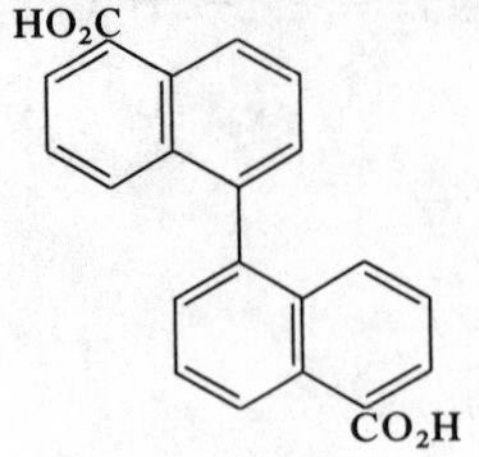

(I) 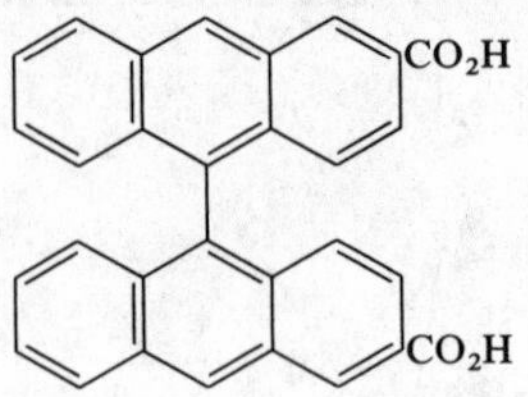   (II)

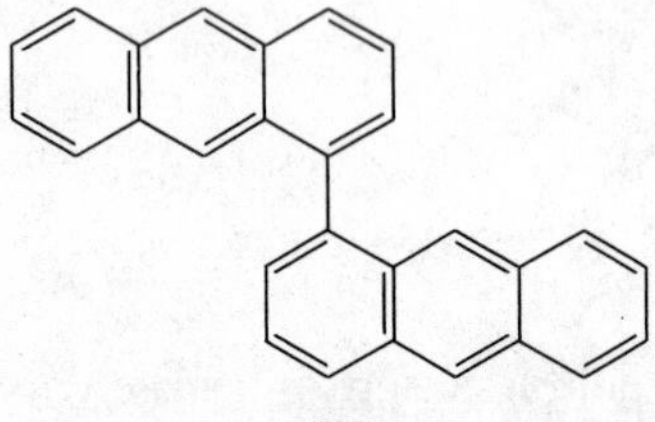

(III) 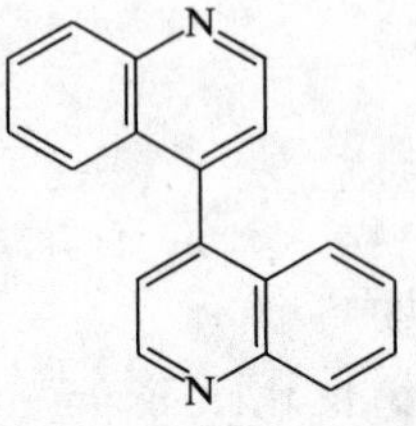   (IV) 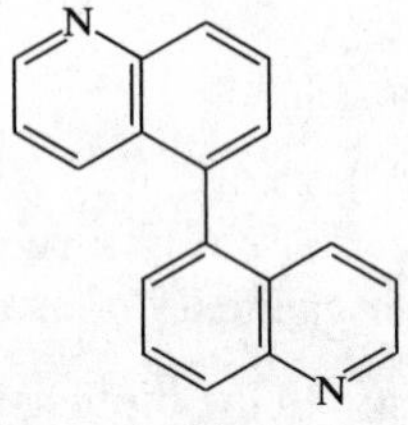   (V)

brucine. Mills and Kelham (1937) also resolved N-acetyl-N-methyl-p-toluidine-3-sulphonic acid (VII) with brucine, and found that it racemised slowly on standing. In both (VI) and (VII) the optical activity arises from the restricted rotation about the C—N bond (the C being the ring carbon to

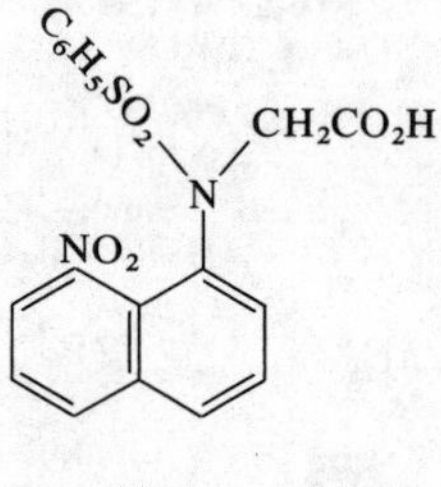

(VI) 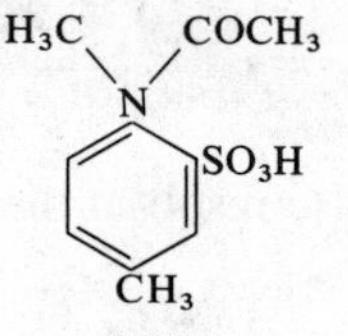   (VII)

which the N is attached). Asymmetry arising from the same cause is also shown by 2-acetomethyl-amido-4′,5-dimethyldiphenylsulphone (VIII); this was partially resolved by Buchanan et al. (1950; see also 2 §10iv). It is also interesting to note in this connection that Adams et al. (1950) have isolated pairs of *geometrical* isomers of compounds of the types (IX) and (X); here geometrical isomerism is possible because of the restricted rotation about the C—N bonds.

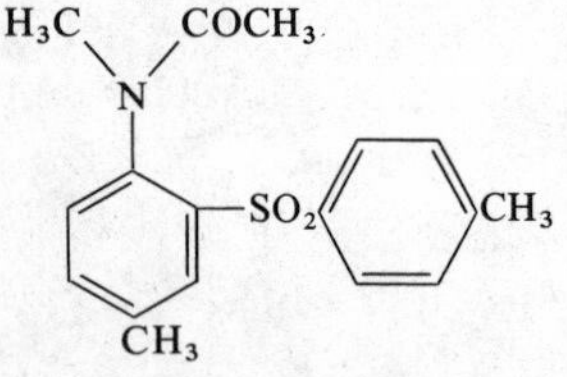

(VIII) 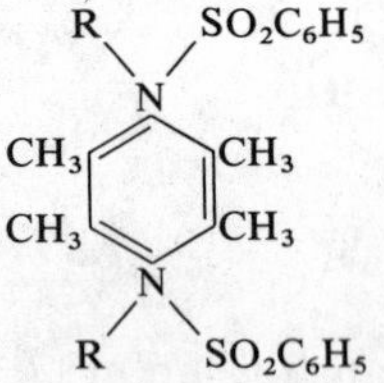   (IX) 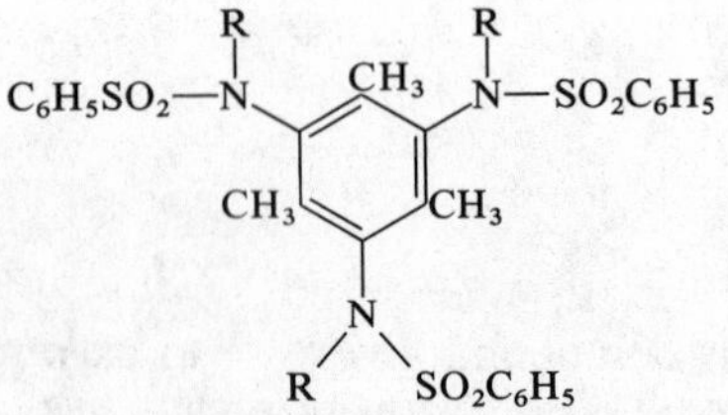   (X)

(iv) Lüttringhaus et al. (1940, 1947) isolated two optically active forms of 4-bromogentisic acid decamethylene ether (XI). This belongs to the group known as 'ansa' compounds, and the methylene ring is perpendicular to the plane of the benzene ring; the two substituents, Br and CO_2H, prevent the rotation of the benzene nucleus inside the large ring. Cram *et al.* (1955) have obtained paracyclophanes in optically active forms, *e.g.*, (XII). In this molecule, the planes of the two benzene rings are

(XI)   (XII)   (XIII)

approximately parallel (and the carboxyphenyl ring cannot rotate to give the enantiomer). When the bridges each contained four methylene groups, the compound could not be resolved (the carboxyphenyl ring can now rotate to give the enantiomers). On the other hand, Blomquist *et al.* (1961) have resolved the simple paracyclophane (XIII).

(v) Terphenyl compounds can exhibit both geometrical and optical isomerism when suitable substituents are present to prevent free rotation about single bonds, *e.g.*, Shildneck and Adams (1931) obtained (XIV) in both the *cis*- and *trans*-forms. Interference of the methyl and hydroxyl groups in the *ortho*-positions prevents free rotation and tends to hold the two outside rings perpendicular to the centre ring. Inspection of these formulae shows that if the centre ring does not possess a vertical plane of symmetry, then optical activity is possible. Thus, Browning and Adams (1930)

cis- (XIV)   trans-(XIV)

prepared the dibromo *cis*- and *trans*-forms of (XV) and resolved the *cis*-isomer; the *trans*-isomer is not resolvable since it has a centre of symmetry.

cis-(XV)   trans-(XV)

It can be seen from the terphenyl compounds discussed that atropisomerism (§2) does not necessarily imply enantiomerism. The different forms may be related to each other as diastereoisomers, but whether optical isomerism is also exhibited depends on the substitution pattern.

(vi) A very interesting case of restricted rotation about a single bond is afforded by the compound 10-*m*-aminobenzylideneanthrone (XVI). This was prepared by Ingram (1950), but he failed to resolve it. He did show, however, that it was optically active by the mutarotation of its camphorsulphonate salt, and by the preparation of an active hydriodide. Thus the molecule is asymmetric, and this asymmetry can only be due to the restricted rotation of the phenyl group about the C—phenyl bond, the restriction being brought about by *hydrogen* atoms in the *ortho*-positions. The two hydrogen atoms labelled H̆ overlap in space, and consequently the benzene ring cannot lie in the same plane as the 10-methyleneanthrone skeleton. Another example is the substituted cinnamic acids (XVII) (R = Cl, Me, OMe) [Adams *et al.*, 1940, 1941]. The benzene ring and the ethylenic double bond cannot become coplanar, and it was found that the order of stability to racemisation was Cl > Me > OMe (*cf.* §4).

(XVI)   (XVII)

§3a. **Molecular overcrowding.** All the cases discussed so far owe their asymmetry to restricted rotation about a single bond. There is, however, another way in which steric factors may produce molecular asymmetry. It has been found that, in general, non-bonded carbon atoms cannot approach

(I)   (II)   (III)

closer to each other than about 3·0 Å. Thus, if the geometry of the molecule is such as to produce 'intramolecular overcrowding', the molecule becomes distorted. An example of this type is 4,5,8-trimethyl-1-phenanthrylacetic acid (I). The phenanthrene nucleus is planar and substituents lie in this plane. If, however, there are fairly large groups in positions 4 and 5, then there will not be enough room to accommodate both groups in the plane of the nucleus. This leads to strain being produced by intramolecular overcrowding, and the strain may be relieved by the bending of the substituents out of the plane of the nucleus, or by the bending (buckling) of the aromatic rings, or by both. Thus the molecule will not be planar and consequently will be asymmetric and therefore (theoretically) resolvable. Newman *et al.* (1940, 1947) have actually resolved it, and have also resolved (II). Bell *et al.* (1949) resolved (III), and it was these authors who introduced the term 'intramolecular overcrowding'.

Theilacker *et al.* (1953) resolved (IV), a heterocyclic analogue of phenanthrene. All of these compounds were found to have low optical stability, but Newman *et al.* (1955, 1956) have prepared (V)

(IV)   (V)   (VI)

and (VI; hexahelicene) which, so far, are the most optically stable compounds of the intramolecular overcrowding type.

It will be noticed that in (VI) the only way in which out-of-plane distortion can occur is through buckling of the molecule. The simplest molecule exhibiting overcrowding and consequent *out-of-plane buckling* of the molecule is 3,4-benzophenanthrene (VII); this has been shown to be non-planar by X-ray analysis (Schmidt *et al.*, 1954). Similarly, Robertson *et al.* (1954) have shown that (VIII) exhibits out-of-plane buckling.

Another point to note in connection with out-of-plane buckling is that the buckling is distributed over all the rings in such a manner as to cause the minimum distortion in any one ring. This distortion,

(VII)   (VIII)   (IX)

which enables non-bonded carbon atoms to avoid being closer together than 3·0 Å (marked with dots in VII and VIII), forces some of the other carbon atoms to adopt an almost tetrahedral valency arrangement (the original hybridisation is trigonal), and this affects the physical and chemical properties of the molecule, *e.g.*, Coulson *et al.* (1955) have calculated that the deformation in (VIII) produces a loss of resonance energy of about 75 kJ mol^{-1}.

We may now summarise the problem of molecular overcrowding as follows. A molecule is said to be overcrowded if, when the standard values are assigned to the bond lengths and bond angles, at least one pair of non-bonded atoms are closer to each other than the sum of their accepted van der Waals radii. If these atoms were to remain very close to each other and the rest of the molecule remained unchanged, there would be a large steric strain. If, however, the molecule were deformed (buckled) so that the overcrowded atoms became separated to the sum of their van der Waals radii. there would now be a considerable strain energy in the molecule. Since a large amount of energy is required to stretch bonds and much less energy is required to bend them (*cf.* **2** §4a), in overcrowded molecules the geometry of the molecule adjusts itself so that the energy is a minimum by mainly bending various bonds, with the bond lengths not much changed from the unstrained analogue. Thus overcrowded molecules are non-coplanar and have the form of a segment of a helix.

Mason *et al.* (1965) have measured the circular dichroism spectra of (−)-(VII*a*) and (+)-(VII*b*) (these are derivatives of VII), and analysis of these spectra led the authors to conclude that (−)-(VII*a*)

(−)-VII*a*   (+)-VII*b*

has the *M*- (minus, left-handed) and (+)-(VII*b*) the *P*- (plus, right-handed) helical configuration viewed in the direction perpendicular to the mean molecular plane.

Helical molecules are those in which the arrangement of the atoms or groups is an imaginary helix. Such molecules are optically active due to the presence of **helical dissymmetry** or **helicity**. Thus, helicity is a particular type of chirality (see also **13** §12a).

Just as benzene rings may suffer distortion, so can a molecule which owes its planarity to the presence of a double bond. Such an example is dianthronylidene (IX). The carbon atoms marked with dots are overcrowded (the distance between each pair is 2·9 Å), and the strain is relieved by a rotation of about 40° around the olefinic double bond (Schmidt *et al.*, 1954). Even in such simple molecules as tiglic acid (X) the two methyl groups give rise to molecular overcrowding with the result that the β-methyl group appears to be displaced from the molecular plane, thereby relieving overcrowding which is also partly relieved by small distortions in bond angles. These results were obtained by Robertson *et al.* (1959) from X-ray studies, and these authors also showed similar distortions in angelic acid (XI).

$$\text{Me} \quad \text{H} \qquad\qquad \text{Me} \quad \text{H}$$
$$\underset{\text{Me}}{\overset{\text{C}}{\big\|}}\quad\qquad$$

(X)   (XI)

In polynuclear aromatic hydrocarbons in which the strain tends to be overcome by out-of-plane displacements of substituents and out-of-plane ring buckling, these effects cause changes in the ultraviolet spectra, but it is not yet possible to formulate any correlating rules. NMR studies by Reid (1957) have shown a shift for the hydrogen atoms in positions 4 and 5 in phenanthrene itself. A similar phenomenon has been detected by Brownstein (1958) in 2-halogenobiphenyls, and the explanation offered is that the shift is due to the steric effect between the 2-halogen and the 2′-hydrogen atom.

Although molecular overcrowding is normally confined in the polynuclear type to systems containing three or more rings, nevertheless various substituted benzenes may also exhibit out-of-plane displacements of the substituents. Electron-diffraction studies of polyhalogenobenzenes suggest that such molecules are non-planar (Hassel *et al.*, 1947), whereas X-ray studies indicate that in the solid state such molecules are very closely or even exactly planar (Tulinsky *et al.*, 1958; Gafner *et al.*, 1960). Ferguson *et al.* (1959, 1961) have examined, by X-ray analysis, polysubstituted benzenes containing not more than one halogen atom, *e.g.*, *o*-chloro- and bromobenzoic acid, and 2-chloro-5-nitrobenzoic acid. In all three molecules the steric strain is relieved by small out-of-plane displacements of the exocyclic valency bonds in addition to the larger in-plane displacements of these bonds away from one another. Ferguson *et al.* (1962) have also shown that in 2-chloro-5-nitro-benzoic acid the carboxyl group is twisted further out of the benzene plane than in *o*-chlorobenzoic acid.

§4. Racemisation of biphenyl compounds

Since the optical activity of biphenyl compounds arises from restricted rotation, it might be expected that racemisation of these compounds would not be possible. In practice, it has been found that many optically active biphenyl compounds can be racemised under suitable conditions, *e.g.*, boiling in solution. The general theory of these racemisations is that heating increases the amplitude of the vibrations of the substituent groups in the 2,2′,6,6′-positions, and also the amplitude of vibration of the two benzene rings with respect to each other, thereby permitting the substituent groups to slip by one another. Thus the nuclei pass through a common plane and hence the probability is that the final product will contain an equimolecular amount of the (+)- and (−)-forms. Westheimer (1946–1950) has assumed, in addition to the above bond-stretchings, that the angles α, β and γ are deformed, and also the benzene rings themselves are deformed during racemisation. Westheimer obtained good agreement between the estimated and measured activation energies of racemisation of some di-*ortho*-substituted biphenyls. His calculations were based on known values of van der Waals radii and stretching and bending-force constants of the various bonds. In the absence of the assumption of deformations, the agreement between estimated and calculated values was very poor. At the same time, these calculations offer very strong evidence for the obstacle theory (see also §5).

These ideas may be represented pictorially by the energy profile shown in Fig. 5.1. The enantiomers (*A*) and (*A'*) have the same energy content, and as they approach the planar configuration (*B*) the energy content increases due to steric repulsion. The larger the groups *a* and *b*, the higher will be the energy barrier, *i.e.*, the slower will be the rate of racemisation.

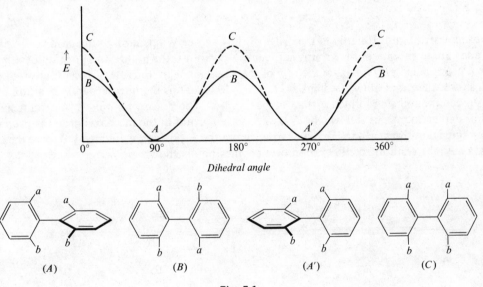

Fig. 5.1

There is, however, a further point that requires consideration. There are two possible planar configurations for the transition state, (*B*) and (*C*). As we have seen earlier, the general principle is that crossed steric interactions between groups of different size are less than the sum of the steric interactions between groups of equal size (**2** §4a). Hence, the transition state for racemisation is more likely to be (*B*) than (*C*).

2,2',6,6'-Tetrasubstituted biphenyl compounds may be classified under three headings according to the nature of the substituent groups.

(i) *Non-resolvable*. These contain any of the following groups: hydrogen, methoxyl or fluorine. The volumes (*effective* volumes) of these groups are too small to prevent rotation about the single bond. Thus, 2,2'-difluoro-6,6'-dimethoxybiphenyl-3,3'-dicarboxylic acid (I) is non-resolvable.

(ii) *Resolvable, but easily racemised*. These must contain at least two amino-groups, or two carboxyl

(I)   (II)

groups, or one amino- and one carboxyl group; the remaining groups may be any of those given in (i) [but not hydrogen]. Thus, 6,6'-difluorodiphenic acid (II) is resolvable, and is readily racemised. (iii) *Not racemisable at all.* Biphenyl compounds which fall in this group are those which contain at least two nitro-groups; the other groups can be any of those given in (i)—but not hydrogen— and (ii). Thus 2,2'-difluoro-6,6'-dinitrobiphenyl (III) is resolvable, and cannot be racemised.

(III)   (IV)   (V)

The order of steric hindrance produced by various groups appears to be:

$$Br \gg Me > Cl > NO_2 > CO_2H \gg OMe > F$$

This order corresponds roughly to the order of the van der Waals radii of the groups.

In addition to the size of the groups in the *ortho*-positions, the nature and position of other substituent groups also play a part in the rate of racemisation, *e.g.*, the rate of racemisation of (IV) is much slower than that of (V) (Adams *et al.*, 1932, 1934). Thus the nitro-group in position 3' has a much greater stabilising influence than in position 5'. The reason for this is uncertain, but one possible explanation is as follows. In (VI), the methyl group of the methoxyl group is probably in the configuration shown. In (VII), the nitro-group in the 3'-position would tend to force the methyl group away, the resulting configuration being somewhat as shown in (VII);

(VI)   (VII)

in this condition there would be greater interference between the methoxyl group and the two groups in the other benzene ring. This buttressing effect of groups is in the order:

$$NO_2 > Br > Cl > Me$$

It is interesting to note that this order is very different from that in which these groups produce steric hindrance in the *o*-position. It has also been found that groups in the 4- and/or 4'-positions affect the rate of racemisation. The reason for this is not clear. It has been proposed that the effect of a 4- (and/or 4'-) nitro-group in retarding the racemisation of 6-nitrodiphenic acid is entirely due to a change in entropy of activation (Harris *et al.*, 1957).

Adams *et al.* (1954, 1957) have examined the rate of racemisation of (VIII). The rate is increased when R is an electron-attracting group such as NO_2 or CN, and is decreased when R is an electron-releasing group such as Me or OMe. These results were explained as follows. With, *e.g.*, R = NO_2,

(IX) contributes to the resonance hybrid as well as (VIII). The resonance hybrid therefore has increased C=N double bond character and consequently it is now easier for the molecule to pass through a planar transition state. With, e.g., R = Me, the C—N bond acquires far less double

(VIII)   (IX)   (X)

bond character than in its absence, and so it is more difficult for the molecule to pass through a planar transition state.

Adams et al. (1957, 1961) also examined the optical stability of compounds of type (X); they found that the half-life was in the following order for R: Me < Et < i-Pr < t-Bu. If the effect of R were due merely to the inductive effect, then the unexpected value for t-Bu cannot be explained on this basis. The authors have proposed the following explanation. The t-Bu group, because of its large bulk, displaces the adjacent Me groups out of the plane of the benzene ring, thereby causing molecular overcrowding; this decreases the interference to rotation about the N—C (ring) bond (§3a). A molecular model of this compound showed such an interference. According to Bryan et al. (1960), it is possible that steric repulsion also operates to cause considerable angle distortion.

The racemisation of 2,2′-bridged biphenyls is, in general, easy to effect, since many of them are optically labile. Furthermore, the optical stability of a bridged compound is generally considerably lower than that of the corresponding unbridged biphenyl. If, however, the bridge contains double bonds, it will have additional rigidity and so will be less optically labile, e.g., in §2, (XIII) is more optically stable than (X), (XI) and (XII).

Racemisation of biphenyls is usually effected by heating in a suitable solvent, but Mislow et al. (1963) have racemised (XIa) by irradiation (in ether solution) with ultraviolet light or by heating in

(XIa): Z = CH_2 (XIc)
(XIb): Z = CO

the dark above 200°C. On the other hand, the ketone (XIb) underwent simultaneous racemisation and decarbonylation to (XIc) when irradiated under the same conditions.

Mislow et al. (1963) have also compared the rates of racemisation of (XII) and (XIII), and found that the deutero compound (XIII) racemised 1·13 times as fast as (XII). This is an example of the secondary isotope effect (3 §2a), and has also been referred to as an inverse isotope effect. These results may be explained by the fact that deuterium has a smaller van der Waals radius than hydrogen, and in keeping with this explanation is that Mislow et al. (1964) were unable to detect any optical activity in (XIV) (which was mixed with other deuteromethyl compounds: CD_3,CD_2H; CD_2H,CD_2H; CD_3,CDH_2).

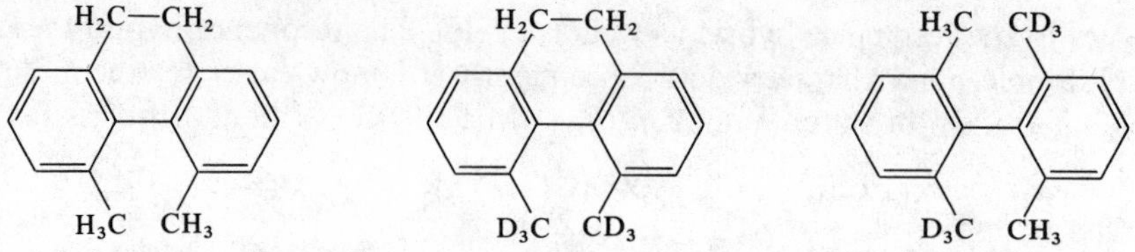

(XII)   (XIII)   (XIV)

§5. Evidence for the obstacle theory

Evidence for the obstacle theory, *i.e.*, interference of groups, amounts to proving that the two benzene rings in optically active biphenyl compounds are not coplanar. A direct chemical proof for the non-coplanar configuration was given by Meisenheimer *et al.* (1927). The method was to unite the 'obstacle groups' in optically active biphenyl compounds, thereby forming five- or six-membered rings. Meisenheimer started with 2,2'-diamino-6,6'-dimethylbiphenyl, resolved it and then carried out the following reactions on one of the enantiomers:

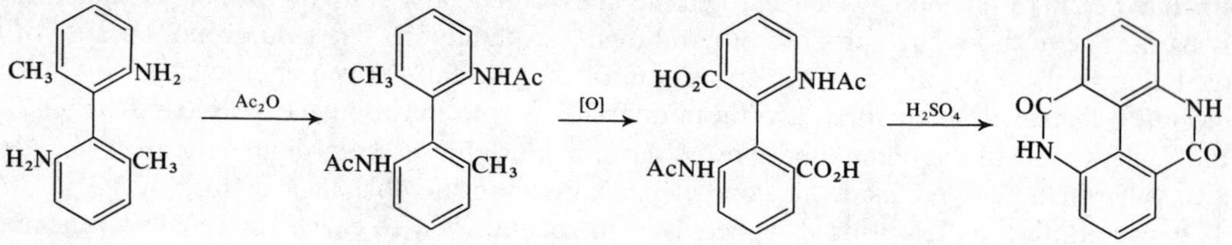

optically active   optically active   optically active   optically inactive
form

In all the optically active compounds, the rings *cannot* be coplanar, since if they were, the molecules would possess a centre or plane of symmetry. If the dilactam, however, is *not* planar, then it would possess no elements of symmetry, and consequently would be optically active. If the dilactam is planar, then it has a centre of symmetry, and consequently cannot be optically active. This compound was, in fact, not optically active, and so must be planar. This planarity is readily explained in terms of resonance; all bonds have double bond character and so the molecule is planar (*cf.* 2,2'-bridged biphenyls, §2).

According to Dhar (1932), X-ray analysis studies have shown that in the solid state the biphenyl molecule is planar. On the other hand, according to Robertson (1961), who also examined crystalline biphenyl by X-ray analysis, the molecule is *not* strictly planar. This non-planarity has been attributed to steric repulsion between the *o*-hydrogen atoms. Gas phase electron-diffraction studies indicated that the two rings are inclined at about 45° to one another (Brockway *et al.*, 1944; Bastiansen, 1949). In the solid state, crystal forces presumably tend to keep the biphenyl molecule almost planar.

Ultraviolet spectra measurements of biphenyl compounds have shown that the two rings in *o*-substituted biphenyls are not coplanar. The ultraviolet spectrum of biphenyl, λ_{max} 248 (19 000) nm, is different from that of benzene, λ_{max} 198 (8 000) nm. This shift to the longer wavelength can be explained on the basis that biphenyl is a resonance hybrid, one of the contributing structures being the extended conjugated form (II). Thus the interannular bond will have some partial double bond

(I)   (II)

character and consequently the molecule will tend to be planar. When o-positions are occupied, the coplanarity is prevented and consequently the spectrum will be different, the maximum absorption shifting to shorter wavelengths (*cf.* **4** §5g). Thus, 2-methylbiphenyl has λ_{max} 236 (10 000) nm and 2,2′-dimethylbiphenyl λ_{max} 224 (~ 700) nm. Also, Pickett *et al.* (1936) have shown that the ultraviolet absorption spectra of bimesityl (III), λ_{max} 267 (545) nm, and mesitylene (IV), λ_{max} 266 (260) nm, were

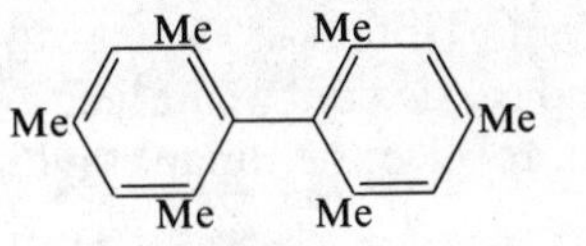

(III) 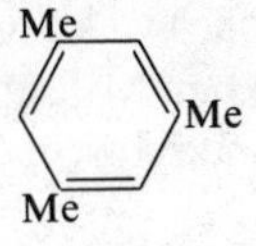   (IV)

almost identical but different from the spectrum of biphenyl. In (III) there is steric inhibition of resonance, and so coplanarity is prevented. Thus ε for (III) is approximately double that of (IV), but λ_{max} remains essentially unchanged.

In 2,2′-bridged biphenyls in which the bridge is saturated (see §2), it is possible to calculate the angle of twist between the two benzene rings from normal bond angles and bond lengths. These values depend on the type of bridge, *i.e.*, the number of atoms and their nature (C, S, O, etc.). The ultraviolet spectra of these compounds have confirmed that the two benzene rings are not coplanar (when the bridge is of the appropriate type).

Other evidence for the obstacle theory is the behaviour of Chichibabin's hydrocarbon. Wheland *et al.* (1952) examined this compound by means of the ESR method and found that it existed in the

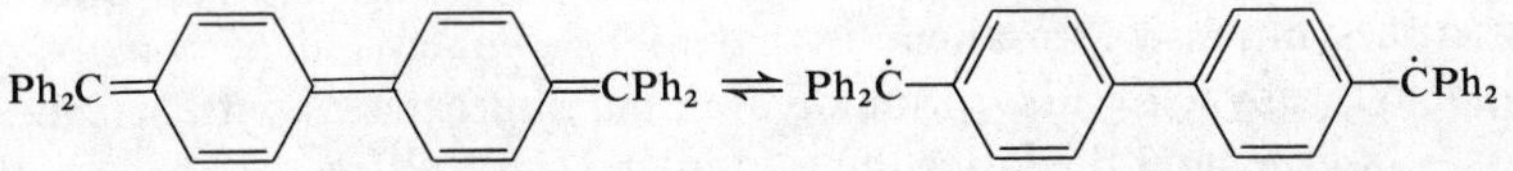

form of the free diradical to the extent of 4–5 per cent. When, however, there were four chlorine atoms in the four o-positions, the amount of free diradical was very much greater. In the latter, the coplanarity of the two rings is now prevented.

Westheimer's calculations of the activation energies of racemisation of some biphenyl compounds are also evidence for the obstacle theory (see §4).

§6. Stereochemistry of the allenes

Allenes are compounds which have the general structure (I).

$$abC{=}C{=}Cde \qquad abC{=}C{=}Cab$$
(I)   (II)

Examination of the space formula of compounds of this type shows that the molecule and its mirror image are not superimposable. The σ–π way of writing (I) is shown in Fig. 5.2. The two end carbon atoms are in a state of trigonal hybridisation, and the centre carbon atom is in the digonal state. Thus the centre carbon atom forms two π-bonds which are perpendicular to each other; in Fig. 5.2

Fig. 5.2

the π_x-bond is perpendicular to the plane of the paper, and the π_y-bond is in the plane of the paper. In the trigonal state, the π-bond is perpendicular to the plane containing the three σ-bonds (see Vol. I, Ch. 2); consequently the groups a and b lie in the plane of the paper, and the groups d and e in the plane perpendicular to the plane of the paper. This molecule does not possess a plane or centre of symmetry: this is also true for molecule (II). Thus (I) and (II) will be resolvable (see also **4** §3).

The resolvability of allenes was predicted by van't Hoff in 1875, but experimental verification was not obtained until 1935, when Mills and Maitland carried out a catalytic asymmetric dehydration on 1,3-di-1-naphthyl-1,3-diphenylprop-2-enol (III), to give the dinaphthyldiphenylallene (IV). When

(III)   (IV)

the dehydration was carried out with an optically inactive dehydrating catalyst, *e.g.*, *p*-toluene-sulphonic acid, the racemic modification of the allene derivative was obtained. When, however, the alcohol (III) was boiled with 1 per cent benzene solution of (+)-camphorsulphonic acid, a dextro-rotatory allene was obtained. Similarly, (−)-camphorsulphonic acid gave a laevorotatory allene. Another asymmetric synthesis of an allene is that of 1,3-diphenylallene. Jacobs *et al.* (1957) re-arranged 1,3-diphenylpropyne by adsorption on alumina impregnated with brucine or quinine; the former gave the (−)-allene, and the latter the (+)-allene (*cf.* **2** §10vi):

$$PhC{\equiv}CCH_2Ph \xrightarrow[\text{alkaloid}]{Al_2O_3} PhCH{=}C{=}CHPh$$

The first successful *resolution* of an allene derivative was carried out by Kohler *et al.*, also in 1935. Lapworth and Wechsler (1910) prepared 3-1-naphthyl-1,3-diphenylallene-1-carboxylic acid (V)

(V)   (VI)

but failed to resolve it; they were unable to crystallise the salts with active bases. Kohler converted this acid into the glycollic acid ester (VI) and was then able to resolve (VI) by means of brucine. Wotiz *et al.* (1951) have also resolved the simpler allenic acid (VII) by means of strychnine.

(VII)

Landor *et al.* (1959) have prepared an optically active allene by a method which correlates it stereochemically with a tetrahedrally asymmetric alcohol. An optically active acetylenic alcohol, on treatment with thionyl chloride, gave an optically active allene; the mechanism is possibly $S_N i'$.

Landor *et al.* (1962) have also deduced the absolute configuration of the (+)-chloride by first determining the absolute configuration of the (+)-alcohol; the (R)-(−)-alcohol gave the (S)-(−)-allene (see also §6a).

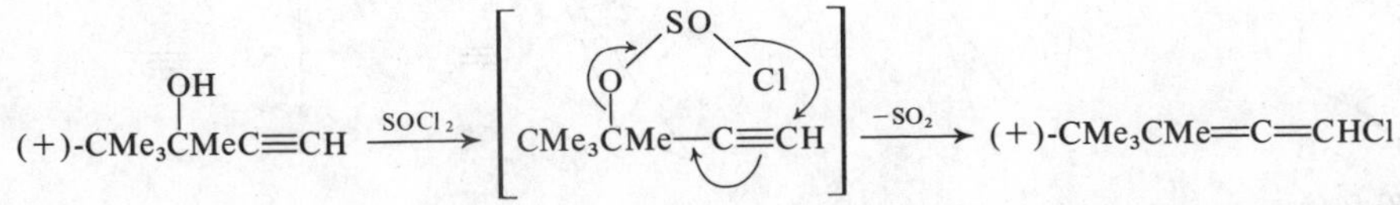

$$(+)\text{-CMe}_3\overset{\displaystyle \text{OH}}{\underset{\displaystyle |}{\text{C}}}\text{MeC}\equiv\text{CH} \xrightarrow{\text{SOCl}_2} \left[\text{CMe}_3\text{CMe}-\text{C}\equiv\text{CH}\right] \xrightarrow{-\text{SO}_2} (+)\text{-CMe}_3\text{CMe}\!=\!\text{C}\!=\!\text{CHCl}$$

It has been previously pointed out (**4** §4) that if the number of double bonds in the cumulene is odd the molecule exhibits geometrical isomerism, but if even, then it exhibits optical isomerism. The allenes discussed above contain two double bonds, but more recently, Nakagawa *et al.* (1961) have prepared the following cumulene with four double bonds, 1,5-di-t-butyl-1,5-di-*p*-chlorophenyl-pentatetraene, in optically active forms.

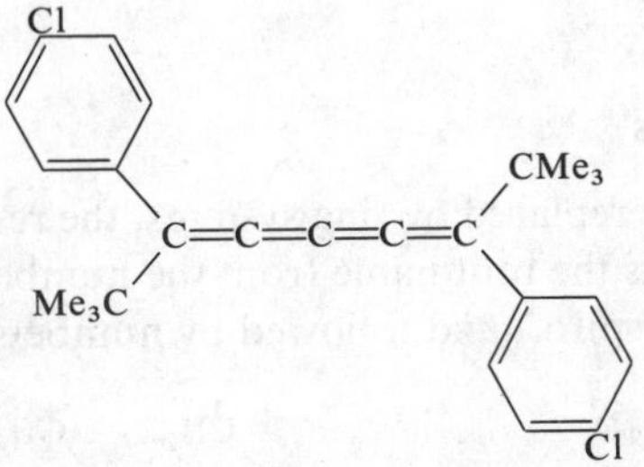

Although allenes were not successfully resolved until 1935, compounds with a *similar* configuration were resolved as early as 1909. In this year, Pope *et al.* resolved 4-methylcyclohexylidene-1-acetic

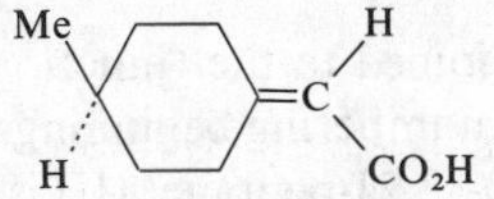

(VIII)

acid (VIII); in this compound one of the double bonds of allene has been replaced by a six-membered ring, and the general shape of the allene molecule is retained.

It is interesting to note, in connection with allenes, that the antibiotic *mycomycin* and other natural polyacetylenes have been shown to contain the allene grouping. Mycomycin is optically active, and owes its optical activity to the presence of this grouping. Celmer and Solomons (1953) have shown that the structure of mycomycin is:

$$\text{CH}\!\equiv\!\text{CC}\!\equiv\!\text{CCH}\!=\!\text{C}\!=\!\text{CHCH}\!=\!\text{CHCH}\!=\!\text{CHCH}_2\text{CO}_2\text{H}$$

§6a. Specification of absolute configuration of allenes.
This is carried out in a similar manner to that used for biphenyls (§2a). For allenes, the chiral axis passes through the double bonds.

The absolute configurations of allenes have been determined by conversion of an optically active molecule of known absolute configuration into an allene (*e.g.*, Landor, above), or by converting a

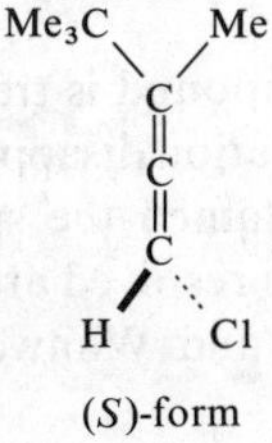

(*S*)-form

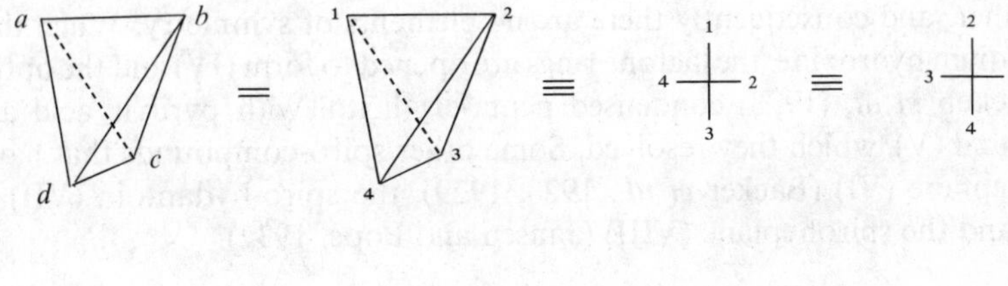

(R)-form

chiral allene into a molecule of known absolute configuration by stereochemically unambiguous reactions. The exception to the above procedures is the work of Mason, who determined the absolute configuration of 1,3-diphenylallene by means of electronic absorption and circular dichroism spectra. Lowe (1965) has now developed a method for predicting the sign of rotation of allenes of known absolute configuration.

§7. Stereochemistry of the spirans

If both double bonds in allene are replaced by ring systems, the resulting molecules are *spirans*. One method of naming spirans obtains the root name from the number of carbon atoms in the *nucleus*; this is then prefixed by the term 'spiro', and followed by numbers placed in square brackets which

indicate the number of carbon atoms joined to the 'junction' carbon atom. The positions of substituents are indicated by numbers, the numbering beginning with the *smaller* ring and ending on the junction carbon atom; *e.g.*, (I) is spiro-[2,2]-pentane, (II) is 1-chlorospiro-[5,3]-nonane.

Examination of these formulae shows that the two rings are perpendicular to each other, and hence suitable substitution will produce molecules with no elements of symmetry, thereby giving rise to optically active forms, *e.g.*, Mills and Nodder (1920, 1921) resolved the dilactone of benzophenone-2,2′,4,4′-tetracarboxylic acid (III). In this molecule the two shaded portions are perpendicular to

each other, and consequently there are no elements of symmetry. When this compound is treated with sodium hydroxide, the lactone rings are opened to form (IV) and the optical rotation disappears.

Böeseken *et al.* (1928) condensed penta-erythritol with pyruvic acid and obtained the spiro-compound (V), which they resolved. Some other spiro-compounds that have been resolved are the spiro-heptane (VI) (Backer *et al.*, 1928, 1929), the spiro-hydantoin (VII) (Pope and Whitworth, 1931), and the spiroheptane (VIII) (Jansen and Pope, 1932).

$$2\ CH_3COCO_2H + C(CH_2OH)_4 \longrightarrow$$

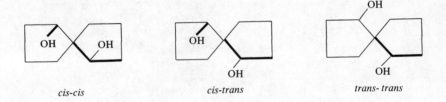

In all the cases so far discussed, the optical activity of the spiran is due to the asymmetry of the molecule as a whole; there is only one pair of enantiomers. If a spiro-compound also contains asymmetric carbon atoms, then the number of optically active forms is increased (above two), the actual number depending on the compound in question, e.g., Sutter and Wijkman (1935) prepared the spiro-compound (IX), which contains two similar asymmetric carbon atoms (*). If we imagine the left-hand ring of (IX) to be horizontal, then the right-hand ring will be vertical; and if we represent them by bold horizontal and vertical lines, respectively, then there are three different geometrical isomers possible, (X), (XI) and (XII) (this can be readily demonstrated by means

of models). Each of these geometrical isomers has no elements of symmetry, and so each can exist as a pair of enantiomers. Three racemic modifications were actually isolated by Sutter and Wijkman, but were not resolved.

Cram *et al.* (1954) have also prepared the following three spiro-[4,4]-nonanediols (as racemates):

cis-cis   *cis-trans*   *trans-trans*

Various spiro-compounds have been prepared in which the spiro-atom is nitrogen (6 §2a), phosphorus (6 §3b), or arsenic (6 §4a).

A spiran compound, acorone, has now been found in nature (8 §28d).

The method of specifying the absolute configuration of spirans is similar to that for allenes (§6a), *e.g.*,

(R)-form

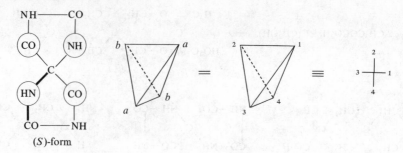

(S)-form

REFERENCES

GILMAN (ed.), *Advanced Organic Chemistry*, Wiley (1943, 2nd edn.). Vol. I. Ch. 4, pp. 337–382.

Progress in Stereochemistry, Butterworth. Vol. II (1958). Ch. I, p. 22. 'Molecular Overcrowding.' Vol. IV (1969). Ch. 1. 'The Stereochemistry of 2,2′- Bridged Biphenyls.'

NEWMAN (ed.), *Steric Effects in Organic Chemistry*, Wiley (1956). Chs. 10, 11, 12.

ELIEL, *Stereochemistry of Carbon Compounds*, McGraw-Hill (1962). Ch. 6.

GRAY (ed.), *Steric Effects in Conjugated Systems*, Butterworths (1958), p. 22.

GOLD (ed.), *Advances in Physical Organic Chemistry*, Academic Press. Vol. I (1963). 'Planar and Non-Planar Aromatic Systems,' p. 203.

CAHN, 'An Introduction to the Sequence Rule', *J. Chem. Educ.*, 1964, **41**, 116.

LOWE, 'The Absolute Configuration of Allenes,' *Chem. Comm.*, 1965, 411.

CRABBÉ, *Optical Rotatory Dispersion and Circular Dichroism in Organic Chemistry*, Holden-Day (1965). Ch. 8.

Topics in Stereochemistry, Wiley-Interscience. Vol. 5 (1970). 'The Determination of Absolute Configuration of Planar and Axially Dissymmetric Molecules,' p. 31.

6

Stereochemistry of some elements other than carbon

§1. Shapes of molecules

Many elements other than carbon form compounds which exhibit optical isomerism. Since the criterion for optical activity must be satisfied, *viz.* the molecule must not be superimposable on its mirror image, it therefore follows that the configurations of the various molecules can never be planar.

In Vol. I, Ch. 2, the theory of shapes of molecules has been explained on the basis that all electrons (shared and unshared) in the valency shell of the central atom arrange themselves in pairs of opposite spin which keep as far apart as possible. Furthermore, it was assumed that deviations from regular shapes arise from electrostatic repulsions between electron pairs in the valency shell as follows:

lone-pair—lone-pair > lone-pair—bond-pair > bond-pair—bond-pair.

It was also assumed that a double (and triple) bond repels other bond-pairs more than does a single bond. The following two tables illustrate these ideas.

Shapes of molecules containing single bonds

Number of electrons in valency shell	Number of bonding pairs	Number of lone-pairs	Hybrid orbitals used	Shape of molecule	Examples
2	2	0	sp	Linear	$HgCl_2$
3	3	0	sp^2	Triangular plane	BCl_3
4	4	0	sp^3	Tetrahedron	CH_4
	3	1	sp^3	Trigonal pyramid	NH_3
	2	2	sp^3	V-shape	H_2O
5	5	0	sp^3d	Trigonal bipyramid	PCl_5
6	6	0	sp^3d^2	Octahedron	SF_6

When dealing with molecules containing multiple bonds (treated in terms of σ- and π-bonds), the shapes may also be predicted in a similar fashion if it is assumed that the electron-pairs (2 in a double and 3 in a triple bond) occupy only *one* of the positions in the various arrangements described in the above table, *i.e.*, a multiple bond is treated as a 'single' bond. This means that the shape of the molecule is determined by the number of σ-bonds and lone-pairs only; the π-bonds are 'fitted in' afterwards.

§2. Stereochemistry of nitrogen compounds

According to the electronic theory of valency, nitrogen can be tercovalent or quadricovalent unielectrovalent; in both of these states nitrogen, as the 'central' atom, can exhibit optical activity.

§2a. Quaternary ammonium salts. Originally, the valency of nitrogen in quaternary ammonium salts was believed to be quinquevalent; later, however, it was shown that one valency was different

Shapes of molecules containing multiple bonds

Total number of σ-bonds and lone-pairs	Number of σ-bonds	Number of lone-pairs	Shape of molecule	Examples
2	2	0	Linear	$O=C=O$; $H-C\equiv N$
3	3	0	Triangular plane	
	2	1	Triangular plane	
4	4	0	Tetrahedron	
	3	1	Trigonal pyramid	

from the other four. Thus, using the formula, $[Nabcd]^+X^-$, for quaternary ammonium salts, and assuming that the charge on the nitrogen atom has no effect on the configuration of the cation, the cation may be considered as a five-point system similar to that of carbon in compounds of the type *Cabde*. This similarity is based on the assumption that the four valencies in the ammonium ion are equivalent, and this assumption is well substantiated experimentally and also theoretically. Hence there are three possible configurations for the cation $[Nabcd]^+$, (I), (II) and (III) (*cf.* **2** §3a). If the

(I)   (II)   (III)

cation is planar (I), then it would not be resolvable; it would be resolvable, however, if the configuration is pyramidal (II) or tetrahedral (III). Le Bel (1891) claimed to have partially resolved isobutyl-ethylmethylpropylammonium chloride, (IV), by means of *Penicillium glaucum* (*cf.* **2** §10iii), but later work apparently showed this was wrong. The first definite resolution of a quaternary ammonium salt was that of Pope and Peachey (1899), who resolved allylbenzylmethylphenylammonium iodide, (V) by means of (+)-bromocamphorsulphonic acid. This was the first case of optical activity due to a 'central' atom other than carbon. This resolution was then followed by the work of Jones (1905), who resolved benzylethylmethylphenylammonium iodide, Thus the ammonium ion cannot be

$$\left[CH_3CH_2CH_2-\underset{\underset{C_2H_5}{|}}{\overset{\overset{CH_3}{|}}{N}}-CH_2CH(CH_3)_2 \right]^+ Cl^- \qquad \left[CH_2{=}CHCH_2-\underset{\underset{C_6H_5}{|}}{\overset{\overset{CH_3}{|}}{N}}-CH_2C_6H_5 \right]^+ I^-$$

$$\text{(IV)} \qquad\qquad\qquad \text{(V)}$$

planar, but must be either pyramidal or tetrahedral. Bischoff (1890) had proposed a pyramidal structure, and this configuration was supported by Jones (1905) and Jones and Dunlop (1912). On the other hand, Werner (1911) had suggested the tetrahedral configuration, and this was supported by Neagi (1919) and Mills and Warren (1925). It was, however, Mills and Warren who gave the most conclusive evidence that the configuration is tetrahedral. Their evidence is based on the following argument. Compounds of the type $abC{=}C{=}Cab$ are resolvable since carbon is 'tetrahedral' (see allenes, 5 §6), and if nitrogen is also 'tetrahedral', then the compound $abC{=}N{=}Cab$ should be resolvable, but will not be resolvable if the nitrogen is pyramidal. Mills and Warren prepared 4-carbethoxy-4'-phenylbispiperidinium-1,1'-spiran bromide, and resolved it. If the configuration of this molecule is (VI), *i.e.*, a spiran, then it possesses no elements of symmetry, and hence will be resolvable; if the configuration is (VII) (*i.e.*, pyramidal), then it will possess a vertical plane of symmetry, and hence will be optically inactive. Since the compound was resolved, the configuration

$$\text{(VI)} \qquad\qquad\qquad \text{(VII)}$$

must be tetrahedral, *i.e.*, (VI). This tetrahedral configuration has been confirmed by physicochemical studies (see §2b). Later, Hanby and Rydon (1945) have shown that the diquaternary salts of dimethylpiperazine exhibit geometrical isomerism, and this is readily explained on the tetrahedral configuration of the four nitrogen valencies.

$$\text{cis} \qquad\qquad\qquad \text{trans}$$

Further support for the tetrahedral configuration comes from the X-ray analysis of crystalline tetramethylammonium chloride; each nitrogen atom has a tetrahedral arrangement of four methyl groups around it. Thus, quadrivalent nitrogen $(2p^3)(3s)$ is tetrahedrally hybridised (sp^3).

It has already been mentioned (2 §6) that McCasland and Proskow (1956) prepared a spironitrogen compound which contained no plane or centre of symmetry, but was nevertheless optically inactive because it contained an alternating axis of symmetry. We shall now examine this compound (VIII; Y^- is the *p*-toluenesulphonate ion) in more detail. This molecule can exist in four diastereoisomeric forms, three active and one *meso*. All four have been prepared, and are depicted as shown in (IX), (X), (XI) and (XII). The co-axis of each spiran is assumed to be perpendicular to the plane of the paper, and the intersecting lines represent the two rings. The short appendages show whether the two substituents (methyl) are *cis* or *trans*. The ring nearer the observer's eye is indicated by the heavy line and a uniform orientation has been adopted: the front ring is always vertical, and the back horizontal ring with at least one substituent directed upwards and the *cis* ring placed at the back in the case of the *cis*/*trans* ring combination.

(VIII)

(+)	(−)	(+)	(−)
	cis-cis		*cis-trans*
	(IX)		(X)

(+)	(−)	*meso*
	trans-trans	*trans-trans*
	(XI)	(XII)

Racemisation of optically active quaternary ammonium salts is far more readily effected than that of carbon compounds containing a chiral centre, *i.e.*, compounds of the type *Cabde*. The mechanism of the racemisation of the ammonium salts is believed to take place by dissociation into the amine, which then rapidly racemises (§2c):

$$N abcd\} \ ^+X^- \rightleftharpoons Nabc + dX$$

Recombination of the racemised amine with *d*X results in the racemisation of the quaternary compound (see §4a). This is in keeping with the fact that quaternary ammonium sulphates and nitrates are difficult to racemise. These anions are poor nucleophiles and so formation of *d*X (X = $\bar{O}SO_2H, \bar{O}NO_2$) is very slow.

§2b. Tertiary amine oxides.   In tertiary amine oxides, *abc*NO, the nitrogen atom is joined to four different groups, and on the basis that the configuration is tetrahedral, such compounds should be resolvable. In 1908, Meisenheimer resolved ethylmethylphenylamine oxide (I) and this was then

(I)   (II)   (III)

followed by the resolution of other amine oxides, *e.g.*, ethylmethyl-1-naphthylamine oxide (II) and kairoline oxide (III).

Bennett and Glynn (1950) have obtained two geometrical isomers of 1,4-diphenylpiperazine dioxide; this is readily explained on the tetrahedral configuration of nitrogen (*cf.* §2a).

cis   *trans*

§2c. Amines. If the tertiary amine molecule, Nabc, is planar, it will be superimposable on its mirror image, and therefore cannot be optically active. All attempts to obtain tertiary amines in optically active forms have failed up to the present time, *e.g.*, Kipping and Salway (1904) treated secondary amines, R^1NHR^2, with ($\pm$)-benzylmethylacetyl chloride; if the three valencies of the nitrogen atom are not planar, then the base will be a racemic modification, and on reaction with the acid chloride, the following four substituted amides should be formed: B_+A_+, B_-A_-, B_+A_-, B_-A_+, *i.e.*, a mixture of two pairs of enantiomers. Experiments carried out with, *e.g.*, methylaniline and benzylaniline gave *homogeneous* products. Meisenheimer *et al.* (1924) attempted to resolve N-phenyl-N-*p*-tolylanthranilic acid (I) and also failed. In view of these failures, it would thus appear

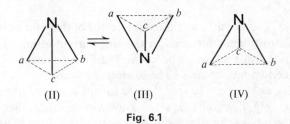

(I)

that the tertiary amine molecule is planar. Physico-chemical methods, *e.g.*, dipole moment measurements, infrared absorption spectra studies, etc., have, however, shown conclusively that the configuration of ammonia and of tertiary amines is tetrahedral. Thus ammonia has been shown to have a dipole moment of 1·5 D; had the molecule been planar, the dipole moment would have been zero. Furthermore, the nitrogen valency angles in, *e.g.*, trimethylamine have been found to be 108°, thus again showing that the amine molecule is not planar. Why, then, cannot tertiary amines be resolved? Is it a question of experimental technique, or is there something inherent in the tertiary amine molecule that makes it impossible to be resolved? Meisenheimer (1924) explained the failure to resolve as follows. In the tertiary amine molecule, the nitrogen atom oscillates rapidly at right angles above and below the plane containing the groups a, b and c (see Fig. 6.1); (II) and (III) are

(II)   (III)   (IV)

Fig. 6.1

the two extreme forms, and they are mirror images and not superimposable ((IV) is (III) 'turned over', and it can be seen that (IV) is the mirror image of (II)). Thus this oscillation brings about very rapid optical inversion. This oscillation theory is supported by evidence obtained from the absorption spectrum of ammonia (Barker, 1929; Badger, 1930), and the frequency of the oscillation (and therefore the inversion) has been calculated to be $2\cdot3 \times 10^{10}$ per second (Cleeton *et al.*, 1934). This inversion of amines is best represented as an 'umbrella' switch of bonds, *i.e.*, the bond lengths remain unaltered and only the nitrogen valency angles change. This interpretation is more in keeping with the facts, *e.g.*, as the groups a, b and c increase in weight, the frequency of the inversion of the molecule decreases (*cf.* **2** §4a).

Theoretical calculations have shown that an optically active compound will not racemise spontaneously provided that the energy of activation for the change of one enantiomer into the other is greater than 50–63 kJ mol^{-1}. The two forms, (II) and (III), have been shown to be separated by an energy barrier of about 25 kJ mol^{-1}, and consequently the two forms are readily interconvertible.

In view of what has been said above, it would appear that tertiary amines of the type Nabc could never be resolved. Now, Kincaid and Henriques (1940), on the basis of calculations of the energy of activation required for the inversion of the amine molecule, arrived at the conclusion that tertiary amines are incapable of resolution because of the ease of racemisation, but if the nitrogen atom formed a part of a *ring* system, then the compound would be sufficiently optically stable to be isolated.

This prediction was confirmed by Prelog and Wieland (1944), who resolved Tröger's base (V) by chromatographic adsorption on D-lactose (*cf.* **2** §10vi). In this compound, the nitrogen is tervalent, but the frequency of oscillation has been brought to zero by having the three valencies of nitrogen as

(V)   (VI)

part of the ring system (see also below). As a result of their CD studies, Mason *et al.* (1967) believe that Tröger's base has predominantly the folded structure (V) and that this is the (+)-isomer and has the (1*R*, 3*R*) configuration.

Roberts *et al.* (1958) have examined *N*-substituted aziridines (ethyleneimines) (see Vol. I) by NMR spectroscopy. Their results support the 'umbrella' switch of bonds, and these authors believe that optical resolution of this type of compounds may be possible below −50°C. *N*-Ethylaziridine (VI) at room temperature showed two chemical shifts for the protons, one being due to hydrogens *cis* and the other to hydrogens *trans* to the ethyl group. At 110°C only one broad band was observed. At this temperature, the rate of inversion is fast enough for the protons to now exhibit a 'single environment' (*cf.* **1** §12e).

The rate of inversion in *N*-substituted aziridines is affected both by the nature of the *N*-substituent and by the presence of substituents attached to the ring-carbon atoms. Thus, *e.g.*, in *N*-t-butyl-aziridine, the inversion rate is accelerated, whereas in *N*-chloro-2-methylaziridine the inversion rate is sufficiently slow for the two invertomers to be separated (Brois, 1967, 1968).

From the foregoing discussion it can be seen that the rate of inversion of nitrogen in aziridines can be slowed down considerably. If it could be slowed down completely, then it might be possible to obtain a chiral compound whose chirality is due to the tervalent nitrogen atom (*cf.* Tröger's base). Montanari *et al.* (1968) have prepared such a compound, 2-methyl-3,3-diphenyloxaziridine (VII) by an asymmetric synthesis, *e.g.*, *N*-diphenylmethylenemethylamine (VIII) has been oxidised with (1*S*)-(+)-peroxycamphoric acid to give (−)-(VII).

Ph$_2$C=NMe $\longrightarrow$

(VIII)   (−)-(VII)

In general, the inversion rate in solution of amines of the type R$_3$N is too fast to be measured by NMR spectroscopy. Saunders *et al.* (1963), however, examined the inversion rate of *N,N*-dibenzyl-methylamine in aqueous hydrochloric acid, basing their method on the assumption that a pro-tonated tertiary amine cannot undergo inversion. In acid solution, protonation and deprotonation are extremely fast and consequently the averaged rate of inversion of amine molecule is reduced sufficiently for the inversion rate to be measured.

A point worth recalling here is that resolution has been carried out with substituted amines of the type ArNR^{1}R^2, where Ar is an aromatic nucleus containing at least one *ortho*-substituent and R^1 and R^2 are different groups (see (VI)–(VIII), **5** §3). The optical activity of these compounds is not due to the asymmetry of the nitrogen atom; it is due to the asymmetry of the molecule as a whole, arising from restricted rotation and about the N—C (aryl) bond. Although the nitrogen atom is in a state of oscillation, there is *always* restricted rotation; the relative positions of Ar, R^1 and R^2 remain unchanged throughout these oscillations (*cf*. Fig. 6.1).

Tertiary amines are an example of a group of compounds in which the central atom is bonded to three groups in a pyramidal geometry and possesses one lone pair of electrons, *i.e.*, tertiary amines are of the type $:MY_3$. Such compounds, in which the central atom belongs to Groups IV to VI of the Periodic Table, may undergo spontaneous inversion of configuration—**pyramidal (atomic) inversion** —the process involving a transition state in which the bonds (from the central atom) are sp^2 hybridised and the lone pair has pure *p*-character. Pyramidal inversion has been observed for nitrogen, phosphorus (§3a), and arsenic (§4b). In analogous sulphur compounds (§5a), however, because of the configurational stability of the sulphur atom in these compounds, optical isomers have been isolated. Even so, pyramidal inversion has been observed in certain cases, *e.g.*, $Me_3\ddot{S}^+$.

Carbanions, *i.e.*, species of the type $:CY_3^-$, are also an example of pyramidal inversion.

§2d. **Oximes.** In 1883, Goldschmidt found that benzil dioxime,

$$C_6H_5C(\!\!=\!\!NOH)C(\!\!=\!\!NOH)C_6H_5$$

could be converted into an isomeric form by boiling it in ethanolic solution; and then, in 1889, Meyer *et al.* isolated a third isomer of this compound. Beckmann, also in 1889, found that benzald-oxime existed in two isomeric forms, and from that time many aromatic oximes were shown to exist in two isomeric forms. The existence of isomerism in aromatic oximes was first explained by structural isomerism, two of the following four structures corresponding to the two isomers (where R is an alkyl or an aryl group). Hantzsh and Werner (1890), however, suggested that the isomerism

oxime   nitrone

(I)   (II)   (III)   (IV)

of the oximes was geometrical and not structural. According to these authors, nitrogen is tervalent (in oximes), and is situated at one corner of a tetrahedron with its three valencies directed towards the other three corners; consequently the three valencies are not coplanar (see also below). These authors also assumed that there is no free rotation about the $C\!\!=\!\!N$ double bond (*cf.* 4 §2), and there-fore proposed configurations (V) and (VI) for the two isomers:

(V)   (VI)

Many facts are in favour of geometrical isomerism, *e.g.*,

(i) If Ar = R, then isomerism disappears.

(ii) (III) and (IV) would be optically active; this is not found to be so in practice.

(iii) Absorption spectra measurements show that the two isomers have identical structures.

As pointed out above, Hantzsch and Werner chose structure (I) as the formula for the oximes, but examination of (II) shows that this would also satisfy the requirements for geometrical isomerism; structure (I) was chosen because oximes were known to contain the group $>\!C\!\!=\!\!NOH$. Later work, however, has shown that the problem is not so simple as this; methylation of an oxime (with methyl sulphate) usually produces a mixture of two compounds, one of which is the *O*-methyl ether, (VII), and the other the *N*-methyl ether, (VIII). These two are readily distinguished by the fact that on heating with hydriodic acid, (VII) gives methyl iodide, whereas (VIII) gives methylamine. Thus,

$$
\begin{array}{cc}
\mathrm{Ar}\diagdown \\
\quad\quad\mathrm{C}=\mathrm{NOCH_3} \\
\mathrm{R}\diagup \\
\text{(VII)}
\end{array}
\qquad
\begin{array}{cc}
\mathrm{Ar}\diagdown\quad\mathrm{CH_3} \\
\quad\;\mathrm{C}=\overset{+}{\mathrm{N}} \\
\mathrm{R}\diagup\quad\diagdown\mathrm{O^-} \\
\text{(VIII)}
\end{array}
$$

Semper and Lichtenstadt (1918) obtained *four* methyl derivatives of phenyl *p*-tolyl ketoxime, (IX)–(XII). On treatment with concentrated hydriodic acid, two of these compounds gave methyl iodide, and therefore correspond to the *O*-methyl derivatives, (IX) and (X); the other two compounds gave methylamine, and therefore correspond to the *N*-methyl derivatives, (XI) and (XII).

$$
\begin{array}{cccc}
p\text{-}\mathrm{CH_3C_6H_4}\diagdown\quad\diagup\mathrm{C_6H_5} & p\text{-}\mathrm{CH_3C_6H_4}\diagdown\quad\diagup\mathrm{C_6H_5} & p\text{-}\mathrm{CH_3C_6H_4}\diagdown\quad\diagup\mathrm{C_6H_5} & p\text{-}\mathrm{CH_3C_6H_4}\diagdown\quad\diagup\mathrm{C_6H_5} \\
\mathrm{C} & \mathrm{C} & \mathrm{C} & \mathrm{C} \\
\| & \| & \| & \| \\
\mathrm{N} & \mathrm{N} & \overset{+}{\mathrm{N}} & \overset{+}{\mathrm{N}} \\
\diagdown\mathrm{OCH_3} & \diagdown\mathrm{CH_3O} & \mathrm{H_3C}\diagup\;\diagdown\mathrm{O^-} & ^-\mathrm{O}\diagup\;\diagdown\mathrm{CH_3} \\
\text{(IX)} & \text{(X)} & \text{(XI)} & \text{(XII)}
\end{array}
$$

Thus it appears that oximes can exist in forms (I) and (II). Brady (1916) considered that oximes in solution are a tautomeric mixture of (I) and (II) (*oximino-nitrone diad system*). Ultraviolet absorption spectra studies show that the spectra of the oximes are the same as those of the *O*-methyl ethers, whereas those of the *N*-methyl ethers are entirely different. Hence, if oximes are tautomeric mixtures of (I) and (II), the equilibrium must lie almost completely on the oxime side, *i.e.*,

$$
\begin{array}{ccccc}
\mathrm{Ar}\diagdown\;\diagup\mathrm{R} & \mathrm{Ar}\diagdown\;\diagup\mathrm{R} & & \mathrm{Ar}\diagdown\;\diagup\mathrm{R} & \mathrm{Ar}\diagdown\;\diagup\mathrm{R} \\
\mathrm{C} & \mathrm{C} & & \mathrm{C} & \mathrm{C} \\
\| & \| & \text{and} & \| & \| \\
\mathrm{N} & \overset{+}{\mathrm{N}} & & \mathrm{N} & \overset{+}{\mathrm{N}} \\
\diagdown\mathrm{OH} & \mathrm{H}\diagup\;\diagdown\mathrm{O^-} & & \mathrm{HO}\diagup & ^-\mathrm{O}\diagup\;\diagdown\mathrm{H}
\end{array}
$$

It is possible, however, that none of the nitrone form is present, but its methyl derivative is formed during the process of methylation. If we assume that methyl sulphate provides methyl carbonium ions, then it is possible that these ions attack the nitrogen atom (with its lone-pair) or the oxygen atom (with its two lone-pairs). This would result in the formation of the *N*- and *O*-methyl ethers, without having to postulate the existence of the oximino-nitrone tautomeric system.

$$\mathrm{CH_3}\!\!-\!\!\overset{\frown}{\mathrm{O}}\mathrm{SO_2OCH_3} \longrightarrow \mathrm{CH_3^+} + {}^-\mathrm{OSO_2OCH_3}$$

$$
\begin{array}{ccc}
\mathrm{Ar}\diagdown\;\diagup\mathrm{R} & \mathrm{Ar}\diagdown\;\diagup\mathrm{R} & \mathrm{Ar}\diagdown\;\diagup\mathrm{R} \\
\mathrm{C} & \mathrm{C} & \mathrm{C} \\
\| & \| & \| \\
:\!\mathrm{N} \quad +\,\mathrm{CH_3^+}\longrightarrow & \overset{+}{\mathrm{N}} \quad\xrightarrow{-\,\mathrm{H^+}} & \overset{+}{\mathrm{N}} \\
\diagdown\overset{..}{\mathrm{O}}\!\!-\!\!\mathrm{H} & \mathrm{H_3C}\diagup\;\diagdown\overset{..}{\mathrm{O}}\!\!-\!\!\mathrm{H} & \mathrm{H_3C}\diagup\;\diagdown\mathrm{O^-}
\end{array}
$$

$$
\begin{array}{ccc}
\mathrm{Ar}\diagdown\;\diagup\mathrm{R} & \mathrm{Ar}\diagdown\;\diagup\mathrm{R} & \mathrm{Ar}\diagdown\;\diagup\mathrm{R} \\
\mathrm{C} & \mathrm{C} & \mathrm{C} \\
\| & \| & \| \\
:\!\mathrm{N} \quad +\,\mathrm{CH_3^+}\longrightarrow & :\!\mathrm{N} \quad\xrightarrow{-\,\mathrm{H^+}} & :\!\mathrm{N} \\
\diagdown\overset{..}{\mathrm{O}}\!\!-\!\!\mathrm{H} & \diagdown\overset{+}{\underset{|}{\mathrm{O}}}\!\!-\!\!\mathrm{H} & \diagdown\mathrm{OCH_3} \\
& \mathrm{CH_3} &
\end{array}
$$

In terms of modern valency theory, both the carbon and nitrogen atoms in oximes are sp^2-hybridised. This is analogous to the hybridisation of the carbon atoms in ethylene. Hence, the C=N double bond consists of one σ- and one π-bond, and the third sp^2 orbital of the nitrogen atom is occupied by a lone pair of electrons. Thus, the oxime molecule is coplanar about the double bond and can exhibit geometrical isomerism (diastereoisomerism). This geometry is in agreement with the facts described above, and further proof for this configuration is obtained from the examination of the oxime of 4-oxocyclohexane-1-carboxylic acid (XIII*a* or *b*). If the N—O bond is not collinear with

(XIII*a*)   (XIII*b*)

the C=N double bond), the configuration is (XIII*a*), and it will therefore be optically active. If, however, the three nitrogen valencies are coplanar and symmetrically placed, then the configuration will be (XIII*b*), and this will not be optically active, since it possesses a plane of symmetry. Mills and Bain (1910) prepared this oxime and resolved it; hence its configuration must be (XIII*a*).

The problem of geometrical enantiomerism has already been discussed for ethylenic compounds (4 §4), and Lyle *et al.* (1959) have shown that oximes of ketones of the type Z^+COZ^- can also exhibit this phenomenon. Thus, these authors obtained the (+)-form of 2,6-diphenyl-1-methylpiperid-4-one oxime, (XIV); attempts to isolate the (−)-form failed.

meso-isomer   (±)
                                        (XIV)

The mechanism of the interconversion of oximes has been the subject of much debate. A current theory is that the isomerisation involves a 'lateral shift'. The sp^2-hybridised nitrogen atom becomes sp-hybridised in the transition state. In this conversion, the lone pair which originally occupied an sp^2-orbital now occupies an in-plane p-orbital. The C=N—OH bond angle is 180° and the C, N, and OH remain in the same plane (in the T.S.).

sp^2 sp sp^2
                  (T.S.)

§2e. Nomenclature of the oximes. In oxime chemistry the terms *syn* and *anti* are used instead of the terms *cis* and *trans*. When dealing with aldoximes, the *syn*-form is the one in which both the hydrogen atom and the hydroxyl group are on the same side; when these groups are on opposite sides, the configuration is *anti*. Thus (I) is *syn*- and (II) is *anti*-benzaldoxime. With ketoximes, the prefix

(I)   (II)   (III)
syn   *anti*

indicates the spatial relationship between the *first* group named and the hydroxyl group (*cf.* **4** §4). Thus III may be named as *syn-p*-tolyl phenyl ketoxime or *anti*-phenyl *p*-tolyl ketoxime.

The *E—Z* system of nomenclature (**4** §4) is also applied to oximes. Thus, the *syn*-oxime (I) is named benzaldehyde (*E*)-oxime or (*E*)-benzaldehyde oxime; (II) is the corresponding (*Z*)-oxime. The group with the greater priority (phenyl) is taken as being *cis*-with respect to the hydroxyl group. Since *p*-tolyl has priority over phenyl, (III) is (*Z*)-*p*-tolyl phenyl ketoxime.

§2f. Determination of the configuration of aldoximes.   As we have seen, aromatic aldoximes can be obtained in two geometrical isomeric forms, the *syn* and the *anti*. Aliphatic aldoximes, however, appear to occur in one form only, and this is, apparently, the *anti*-form. The problem, then, with aromatic aldoximes is to assign configurations to the stereoisomeric forms. The two forms (of a given aldoxime) resemble each other in many ways, but differ very much in the behaviour of their acetyl derivatives towards aqueous sodium carbonate. The acetyl derivative of one isomer regenerates the aldoxime; this form is known as the α-isomer. The other isomer, however, eliminates a molecule of acetic acid to form an aryl cyanide; this form is known as the β-isomer. Hantzsch and Werner (1890) suggested that the β-form readily eliminates acetic acid because the hydrogen atom and the acetoxy-group are close together, *i.e.*, the β-isomer is the *syn*-form. Such a view, however, is contrary to many experimental results (*cf.* **4** §5k), *i.e.*, the experimental results are:

syn- (or *E*-)

anti- (or *Z*-)

Brady and Bishop (1925) found that only one of the two isomers of 2-chloro-5-nitrobenzaldoxime readily gave ring closure on treatment with sodium hydroxide. It therefore follows that this form is the *anti*-isomer (*cf.* method of cyclisation, **4** §5a). It was also found that it was this isomer that gave

the cyanide on treatment with acetic anhydride followed by aqueous sodium carbonate. Thus *anti*-elimination must have occured, *i.e.*, the β-isomer is the *anti*-form. Actually, the ring compound produced, the 5-nitrobenzisoxazole, is unstable, and rearranges to nitrosalicylonitrile.

In a similar manner, Meisenheimer (1932) found that of the two isomeric 2,6-dichloro-3-nitrobenzaldoximes, it was the *anti*-isomer that gave ring closure, and was also the one that gave the cyanide. Hence, if *anti*-elimination is used as the criterion for these reactions, the configurations

of the *syn*- and *anti*-forms can be determined. It might be noted here, in passing, that since the *syn*-form was originally believed to form the cyanide, the configurations of the isomers in the literature up to 1925 (*i.e.*, before Brady's work) are the reverse of those accepted now.

§2g. Determination of the configuration of ketoximes.   The configurations of ketoximes have been mainly determined by means of the **Beckmann rearrangement** (1886). Aromatic ketoximes, *i.e.*, ketoximes containing at least one aromatic group, occur in two forms; aliphatic ketoximes appear to occur in one form only. When treated with reagents such as sulphuric acid, acid chlorides, acid anhydrides, phosphorus pentachloride, etc., ketoximes undergo a molecular rearrangement, resulting in the formation of an acid amide:

$$\begin{array}{c} Ar \\ \diagdown \\ \diagup \\ Ar \end{array} C{=}NOH \longrightarrow ArCONHAr$$

This rearrangement is known as the *Beckmann rearrangement*. The best method is to treat an ethereal solution of the oxime with phosphorus pentachloride at a temperature below $-20°C$. On the other hand, Horning *et al.* (1952) have found that a very good method for effecting the Beckmann rearrangement is to heat the oxime in polyphosphoric acid at 95° to 130°C, and more recently, van Es (1965) has shown that refluxing a solution of the ketoxime in formic acid gives the amide in good yield.

   Hantzsch (1891) suggested that the course of the rearrangement indicated the configuration of the oxime, and assumed that the *syn*-exchange of groups occurred since they were closer together in this isomer. This, again, was shown experimentally to be the reverse, *i.e.*, it is the *anti*-rearrangement that occurs, and not the *syn*; thus:

Meisenheimer (1921) subjected triphenylisoxazole, (I), to ozonolysis, and thereby obtained the benzoyl-derivative of *anti*-phenyl benzil monoxime, (II). This configuration is based on the reasonable assumption that the ozonolysis proceeds without any change in configuration. Furthermore, the monoxime designated the β-isomer gave (II) on benzoylation, and so the configuration of the

$$
\begin{array}{ccccc}
\underset{\text{(I)}}{
\begin{array}{c}
C_6H_5C\!-\!\!-\!\!CC_6H_5 \\
\parallel \quad\quad \parallel \\
N \quad\; CC_6H_5 \\
\diagdown\!O\!\diagup
\end{array}
} &
\xrightarrow{\text{ozonolysis}} &
\underset{\text{(II)}}{
\begin{array}{c}
C_6H_5C\!-\!\!-\!\!CC_6H_5 \\
\parallel \quad\quad \parallel \\
N \quad\; O \\
\diagdown \text{OCOC}_6H_5
\end{array}
} &
\xleftarrow{C_6H_5COCl} &
\underset{\text{(III)}}{
\begin{array}{c}
C_6H_5C\!-\!\!-\!\!CC_6H_5 \\
\parallel \quad\quad \parallel \\
N \quad\; O \\
\diagdown \text{OH}
\end{array}
}
\end{array}
$$

β-isomer, (III), is determined. These assigned configurations have been confirmed by X-ray analysis (Robertson *et al.*, 1967). Meisenheimer then subjected this β-oxime (*i.e.*, the *anti*-phenyl oxime) to the Beckmann rearrangement, and obtained the anilide of benzoylformic acid, (IV); thus the exchange of groups must occur in the *anti*-position. The configuration of the β-monoxime, (III), is

$$
\underset{\text{(III)}}{
\begin{array}{c}
C_6H_5 \quad COC_6H_5 \\
\diagdown\; C \;\diagup \\
\parallel \\
N \\
\diagdown \text{OH}
\end{array}
}
\xrightarrow{PCl_5}
\underset{\text{(IV)}}{
\begin{array}{c}
O \quad\;\; COC_6H_5 \\
\diagdown\; C \;\diagup \\
\mid \\
NHC_6H_5
\end{array}
}
$$

confirmed by the fact that it may be obtained directly by the ozonolysis of 3,4-diphenyliso-oxazole-5-carboxylic acid, (V) (Kohler, 1924). Meisenheimer *et al.* (1925) also demonstrated the *anti*-rearrangement as follows.

$$
\underset{\text{(V)}}{
\begin{array}{c}
C_6H_5C\!-\!\!-\!\!CC_6H_5 \\
\parallel \quad\quad \parallel \\
N \quad\; CCO_2H \\
\diagdown\!O\!\diagup
\end{array}
}
\xrightarrow{\text{ozonolysis}}
\underset{\text{(III)}}{
\begin{array}{c}
C_6H_5 \quad COC_6H_5 \\
\diagdown\; C \;\diagup \\
\parallel \\
N \\
\diagdown \text{OH}
\end{array}
}
$$

The α-oxime of 2-bromo-5-nitroacetophenone is unaffected by sodium hydroxide, whereas the β-isomer undergoes ring closure to form 3-methyl-5-nitrobenziso-oxazole; thus the α-oxime is the *syn*-methyl isomer (VI) and the β-oxime the *anti*-methyl isomer (VII). When treated with sulphuric acid or phosphorus pentachloride, the α-oxime underwent the Beckmann rearrangement to give the *N*-substituted acetamide; thus the exchange occurs in the *anti*-positions.

Further evidence for the *anti*-exchange of groups in the Beckmann rearrangement has been obtained by studying the behaviour of compounds exhibiting restricted rotation about a single bond, *e.g.*, Meisenheimer *et al.* (1932) prepared the two isomeric oximes of 1-acetyl-2-hydroxy-naphthalene-3-carboxylic acid, (VIII) and (IX), and of these two forms only one was resolvable. This resolvable isomer must therefore be (IX), since asymmetry due to restricted rotation is possible

(VIII)   (IX)

only with this form (*cf.* **5** §3). Meisenheimer found that the ethyl ester of (IX), on undergoing the Beckmann rearrangement, gave the amide $ArCONHCH_3$ (where Ar is the naphthalene part of the molecule), whereas the ethyl ester of (VIII) gave the amide $CH_3CONHAr$. These results are in agreement with the *anti*-exchange of groups in each case.

Another method used for examining which groups exchange has been dipole measurements. Sutton *et al.* (1931) measured the dipole moments of the two isomeric *N*-methyl ethers of *p*-nitro-benzophenone oxime and obtained the values shown. These clearly indicate the configurations, and

$\mu = 6\cdot60D$ $\mu = 1\cdot09D$

since the oxime corresponding to the nitrone with the higher dipole moment gives *p*-nitrobenz-anilide on undergoing the Beckmann rearrangement, and the other isomer gives benzo-*p*-nitranilide, it follows that the rearrangement occurs by the *anti* exchange of groups.

Thus the evidence is all in favour of the *anti*-exchange of groups in the Beckmann rearrangement, and hence by using this principle, the Beckmann rearrangement may be used to determine the configuration of ketoximes.

An interesting application of the Beckmann rearrangement is in the formation of heterocyclic rings, *e.g.*, when cyclopentanonoxime is subjected to the Beckmann rearrangement, the nitrogen atom enters the ring (thus producing ring expansion) to form 2-piperidone (see also §2h).

On the other hand, Hill *et al.* (1956) have shown that the oximes of some spiro-ketones undergo abnormal Beckmann rearrangements in the presence of polyphosphoric acid, *e.g.*, spiro-[4,4]-nonanone-1-oxime gives hydrind-8,9-en-4-one:

Although aliphatic ketoximes are not known in two isomeric forms, some may produce two products when subjected to the Beckmann rearrangement, *e.g.*, the oxime of pentan-2-one gives *N*-propylacetamide and *N*-methylbutyramide. The reason for this is uncertain; possibly oximes of this type are actually a mixture of the two forms; or alternatively, they exist in one stable form which,

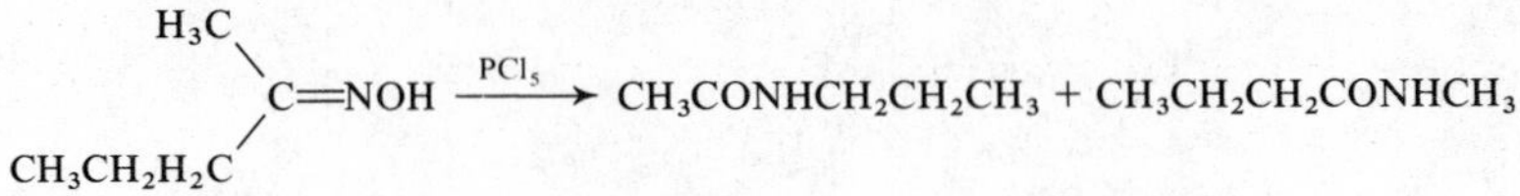

$$
\begin{array}{c}
H_3C \\
 \\
C{=}NOH \xrightarrow{\ PCl_5\ } CH_3CONHCH_2CH_2CH_3 + CH_3CH_2CH_2CONHCH_3 \\
 \\
CH_3CH_2H_2C
\end{array}
$$

during the Beckmann rearrangement, is partially converted into the labile form which then undergoes the rearrangement (*cf.* benzaldoxime, below).

In an attempt to prepare quinoline by the dehydration of cinnamaldoxime with phosphorus pentoxide, Bamberger and Goldschmidt (1894) actually obtained isoquinoline; the formation of the latter compound and not the former can only be reasonably explained on the assumption that the oxime first undergoes the Beckmann rearrangement, and the rearranged product then undergoes ring closure to form isoquinoline. Later, Horning *et al.* (1952) have shown that aldoximes can be

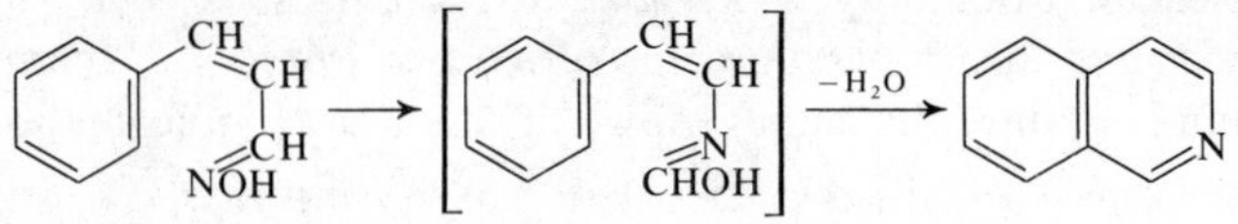

$$
\text{(structures)} \xrightarrow{} \left[\text{(structures)} \right] \xrightarrow{-H_2O} \text{(structure)}
$$

made to undergo the Beckmann rearrangement under the influence of polyphosphoric acid, *e.g.*, *syn*-benzaldoxime gives a mixture of formanilide and benzamide, the latter being produced by the

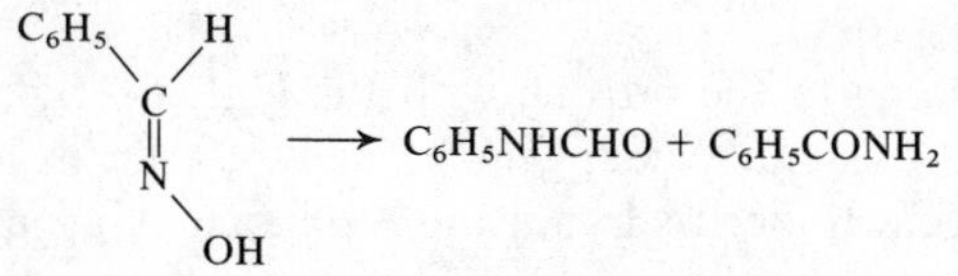

$$
\begin{array}{c}
C_6H_5 \qquad H \\
C \\
\| \\
N \\
OH
\end{array}
\longrightarrow C_6H_5NHCHO + C_6H_5CONH_2
$$

syn- (or *E*-) isomer

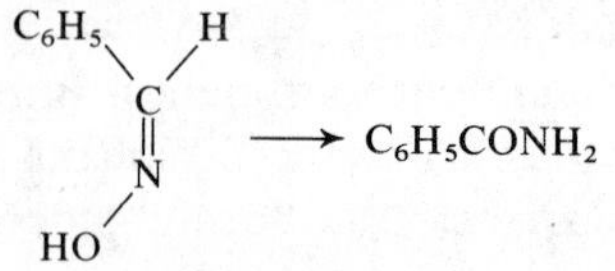

$$
\begin{array}{c}
C_6H_5 \qquad H \\
C \\
\| \\
N \\
HO
\end{array}
\longrightarrow C_6H_5CONH_2
$$

anti- (or *Z*-) isomer

conversion of the *syn*-form into the *anti*; *anti*-benzaldoxime gives benzamide only. These results are in agreement with the configurations obtained by other methods (see §2f).

§2h. Mechanism of the Beckmann rearrangement.   This rearrangement is an example of the 1,2-shift in which the migration origin is carbon and the migration terminus is nitrogen (see also 1,2-shifts, Vol. I, Ch. 5). As we have seen above (§2g), an integral part of the rearrangement is the *anti* migration of the group. Since the oxime itself does not rearrange, it is reasonable to suppose that some intermediate is formed between the oxime and the reagent used to effect the rearrangement, and it is this intermediate which then rearranges. Kuhara *et al.* (1914, 1916) prepared the benzenesulphonate of benzophenone oxime and showed that this readily underwent rearrangement in neutral solvents in the absence of any acid catalyst to give an isomeric compound which, on hydrolysis, gave benzanilide and benzenesulphonic acid; thus:

$$\underset{\overset{\displaystyle |}{OSO_2Ph}}{Ph-\overset{\displaystyle \overset{Ph}{|}}{C}=N} \longrightarrow \underset{\overset{\displaystyle |}{OSO_2Ph}}{Ph-\overset{\displaystyle \overset{Ph}{|}}{C}=N} \xrightarrow{\text{hydrolysis}} \begin{array}{c} PhCONHPh \\ + \\ PhSO_3H \end{array}$$

$$(I)$$

Kuhara assigned structure (I) to this intermediate on the fact that its absorption spectrum was almost identical with that of the compound prepared by reaction between *N*-phenylbenzimidoyl chloride and silver benzenesulphonate:

$$PhCCl{=}NPh + AgOSO_2Ph \longrightarrow (I) + AgCl$$

Kuhara (1926) also showed that the rate of rearrangement of the benzophenone oxime ester is faster the stronger the acid used to form the ester; the order obtained was:

$$PhSO_3H > CH_2ClCO_2H > PhCO_2H > MeCO_2H$$

Chapman (1934) showed that the rate of rearrangement of benzophenone oxime picryl ester is faster in polar than in non-polar solvents. Thus the work of Kuhara and Chapman is strong evidence that the rate-determining step in the rearrangement is the ionisation of the intermediate.

Now let us consider the migration of the R or Ar group. This could be either intermolecular or intramolecular, but Kenyon *et al.* have shown it to be the latter; *e.g.*, in 1946, Kenyon *et al.* showed that when (+)-α-phenylethyl methyl ketoxime is treated with sulphuric acid the product, *N*-α-phenylethylacetamide, is almost 100 per cent optically pure. Thus the migrating group never separates during the rearrangement, since if it did a racemised product would have been obtained. Furthermore, this retention of optical activity might be cited as evidence for the formation of a bridged-ion during the migration, since in such an ion the migrating group is not free and the 'new partial' bond is formed on the *same* side as the bond which is breaking (see below).

$$\underset{\overset{\displaystyle ||}{NOH}}{PhMeCH-\overset{\displaystyle }{C}-Me} \xrightarrow{H_2SO_4} \underset{\overset{\displaystyle |}{HNCHMePh}}{O{=}\overset{\displaystyle }{C}-Me}$$

Another problem that arises here is: Does the anion separate completely during the ionisation or does it also migrate intramolecularly? The work of Kuhara and Chapman strongly suggests complete separation, and this is supported by the work of Brodskii *et al.* (1941), who found that when benzophenone oxime was treated with phosphorus pentachloride and then with water enriched with the isotope ^{18}O, the benzanilide obtained contained some of this isotope. Thus the oxygen atom of the oxime group must have been completely removed in the ionisation stage (see below). The following mechanism is in agreement with all of the above facts (Y is PCl_4, MeCO, etc.); the lower set of equations is the alternative route *via* a bridged-ion. It might also be noted that when acid is used as

the rearranging reagent, OY is possibly OH_2^+ (but see below). Support for this mechanism is the evidence obtained for the intermediate formation of the imidoyl ester (RN = CROY); compound

(II) was obtained by Heard *et al.* (1959), who examined the rearrangement of a 17-keto-16-oxime (a steroid; Ch. 11):

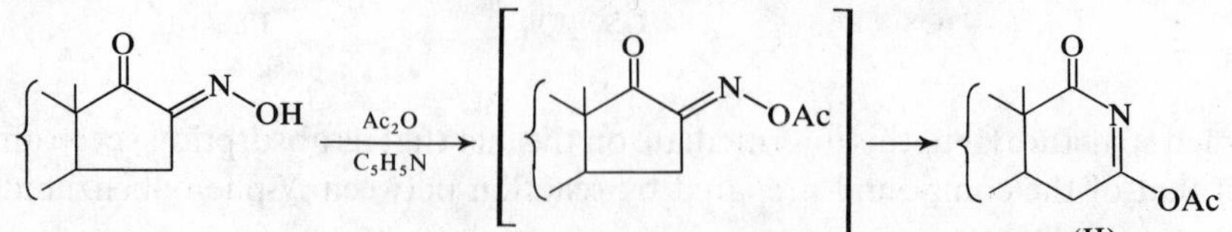

It has been shown that when the migrating group is aryl, the rate of the rearrangement is accelerated when there is an electron-releasing group, *e.g.*, Me, in the *p*-position. This may be cited as evidence to support the formation of a bridged-ion (at least for migrating aryl groups).

Another mechanism has been proposed by Grob *et al.* (1964) who studied the Beckmann rearrangement of various tosylates. According to these authors, the rearrangement proceeds *via* a nitrilium salt (Y = OTs).

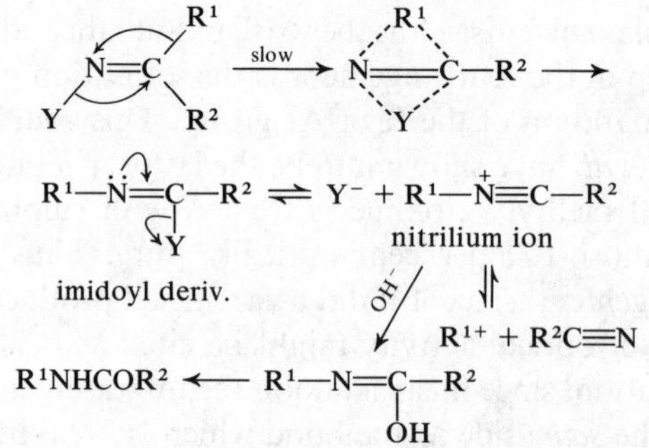

The existence of the nitrilium ion was demonstrated by infrared spectroscopy. This mechanism has been supported by other workers, *e.g.*, Schofield *et al.* (1970) carried out the Beckmann rearrangement of *ortho*-substituted acetophenone oximes in the presence of sulphuric acid and detected, by infrared spectroscopy, the nitrilium ion as an intermediate.

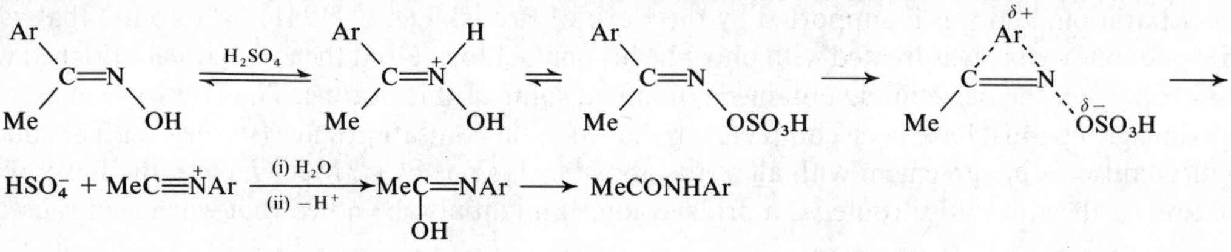

These workers did not detect the oxime *O*-sulphonic acid, but this has been done by Yukawa *et al.* (1971) who used NMR spectroscopy. This mechanism can also be used to explain the course of the rearrangement under the influence of phosphorus pentachloride.

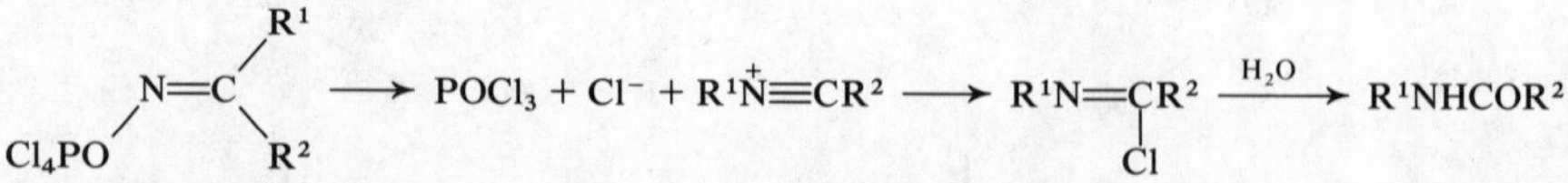

Since phosphoryl chloride can catalyse the Beckmann rearrangement, it is not necessary to use phosphorus pentachloride in molar amount. Actually, Stephen *et al.* (1956) have shown that *one* molecule of phosphorus pentachloride, phosphoryl chloride, thionyl chloride, or benzenesulphonyl chloride rearranges *two* molecules of the ketoxime to yield the corresponding amide and imidoyl chloride in approximately equimolecular amounts, *e.g.*,

$$2R_2C\!\!=\!\!NOH + PCl_5 \longrightarrow RCONHR + RCCl\!\!=\!\!NR + POCl_3 + HCl$$

It has also been shown that hydrogen chloride is essential during the rearrangement, but that it does not itself cause the rearrangement of the oxime. On the basis of these results, Stephen *et al.* have proposed the following mechanism for the Beckmann rearrangement of ketoximes. The reagent first produces some acid amide and imidoyl chloride, and the latter then dehydrates unchanged ketoxime to the anhydride which then reacts as shown:

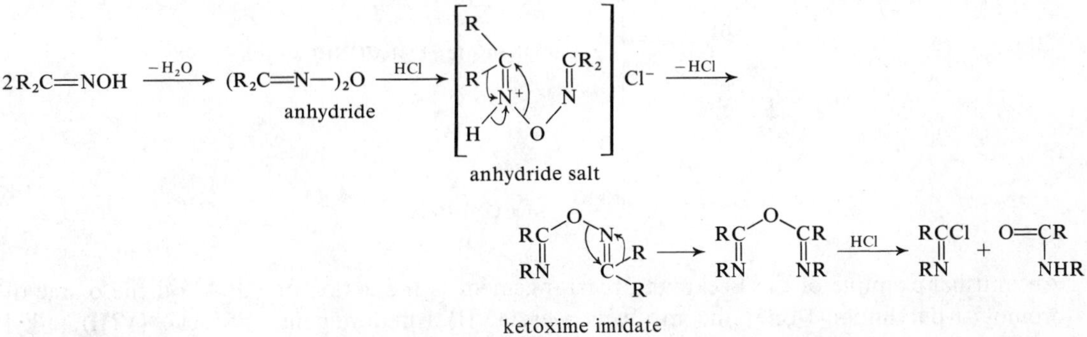

It was also suggested that other reagents which effect the Beckmann rearrangement may function as dehydrating agents for the formation of the ketoxime anhydride.

When a *trace* of the reagent is used, a large yield of amide is obtained. The mechanism is believed to be the same as that given above, provided that in the initial stage there is sufficient to form a trace of the ketoxime anhydride in the presence of hydrogen chloride. Rearrangement of the anhydride will now take place as above with the formation of the imidoyl chloride which can then dehydrate ketoxime to anhydride, itself being converted into the amide:

$$2R_2C\!\!=\!\!NOH + RCCl\!\!=\!\!NR \longrightarrow (R_2C\!\!=\!\!N\!\!-\!\!)_2O + RCONHR + HCl$$

Thus the yield of amide increases at the expense of the imidoyl chloride.

It can be seen from the foregoing account that several mechanisms appear possible for the Beckmann rearrangement. These are intramolecular, but now an intermolecular mechanism has also been proposed by Hill *et al.* (1962) who have reported an example in which the migrating group had the *inverted* configuration in the amide. These authors examined the rearrangement of 9-acetyl-*cis*-decalin oxime and have suggested the following mechanism:

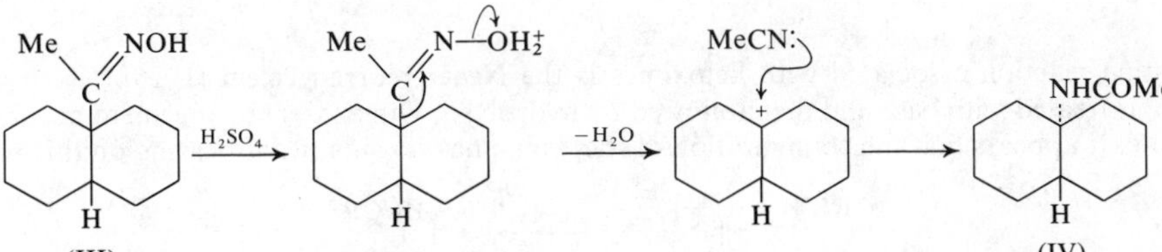

The authors identified methyl cyanide as a product of the reaction of (III) with phosphorus pentachloride, and also showed that methyl cyanide and *cis*-β-decalol in sulphuric acid gave (IV).

Further evidence for the intermolecular mechanism is afforded by the work of Conley (1963), who showed that cleavage of an oxime which is completely substituted at the α-carbon atom appears to be a general process. When a mixture of phenyl 2-phenylisopropyl ketoxime and pinacone oxime are heated in polyphosphoric acid, the product is a mixture of four secondary amides. Each oxime, on rearrangement under the same conditions, gives only one secondary amide. The formation of the crossed-product from the mixture of oximes indicates a fragmentation-recombination mechanism.

An unusual example of the Beckmann rearrangement is the action of P.P.A. on the oxime of 4-bromo-7-t-butylindan-1-one; the products were (VII) (predominant product), (VIII) (alkyl migration), and (IX) (aryl migration), with (VIII) being formed to a much greater extent than (IX)

(Lansbury *et al.*, 1964). On the other hand, Lansbury *et al.* (1966) found that the oxime of 8-t-butyl-5-bromotetral-1-one underwent ring expansion (aryl migration) with the *loss* of the t-butyl group.

An interesting reaction associated with ketoximes is the **Neber rearrangement** (1926). When a ketoxime *O*-sulphonate is treated with base and then followed by hydrolysis with acid, rearrangement occurs to give an α-aminoketone. It appears that the configuration of the oxime has no significant bearing on this reaction.

§2i. Stereoisomerism of some other tervalent nitrogen compounds containing a double bond. There are several other types of compounds besides the oximes in which the nitrogen atom is linked by a double bond. The other atom joined by this double bond may be a carbon atom (as in the oximes), or another nitrogen atom, and in both cases stereoisomerism is possible; *e.g.*, Krause (1890) obtained two isomeric forms of the phenylhydrazone of *o*-nitrophenylglyoxylic acid, (I), and Hopper (1925) isolated two isomers of the monosemicarbazone of benzil, (II). Mills and Bain (1914) resolved (III); this is resolvable because of the non-planar configuration of the three nitrogen valencies (*cf.* the oximes, §2d). Karabatsos *et al.* (1962) have examined the NMR spectra of a

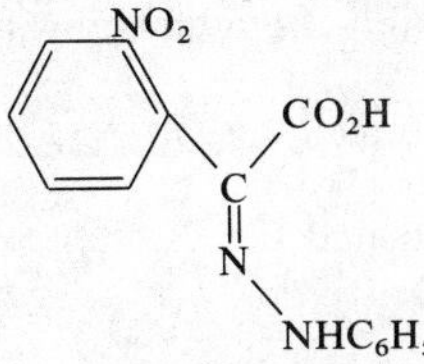

NO₂

CO₂H

C

N

NHC₆H₅

(I)

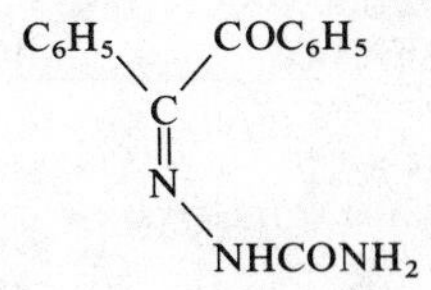

C₆H₅ COC₆H₅

C

N

NHCONH₂

(II)

H

HO₂C

=N C₆H₅

N

COC₆H₅

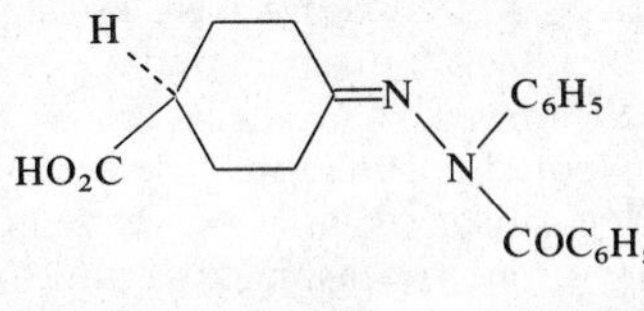

(III)

number of ketone dinitrophenylhydrazones and semicarbazones, and have distinguished between the *syn-* and *anti-*forms, and have also calculated the amounts of each in solution. Phillips (1958) had already examined aldoximes by means of their NMR spectra.

Many cases of geometrical isomerism are known in which the two forms are due to the presence of a nitrogen–nitrogen double bond. Examples of this type which have been most extensively studied are the diazoates, (IV), the diazosulphonates, (V), and the diazocyanides, (VI) (see Vol. I, Ch. 24, for an account of these compounds).

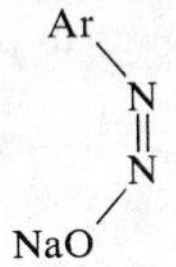

Ar

N

N

NaO

(IV)

syn- (or *Z-*) form

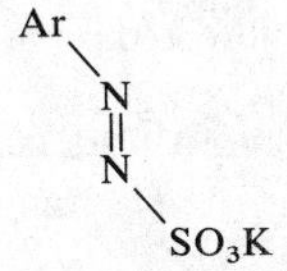

Ar

N

N

SO₃K

(V)

anti- (or *E-*) form

Ar

N

N

CN

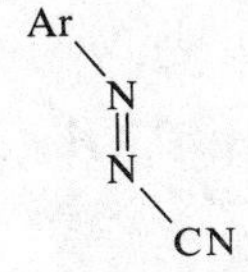

(VI)

anti- (or *E-*) form

Azobenzene is also an example of this type, and according to Hartley (1938), 'ordinary' azobenzene is the *anti-*form.

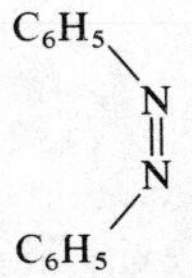

C₆H₅

N

N

C₆H₅

syn- (or *Z-*) azobenzene
m.p. 71·4°C

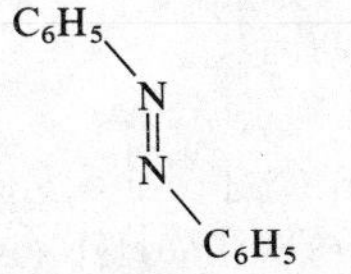

C₆H₅

N

N

C₆H₅

anti (or *E-*) azobenzene
m.p. 68°C

Azoxybenzene (in which one nitrogen atom is tercovalent and the other quadricovalent) also exists in two geometrical isomeric forms, the *anti-*isomer being 'ordinary' azoxybenzene.

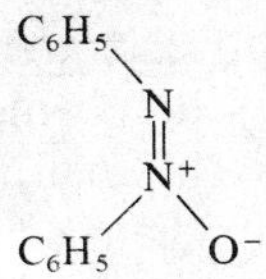

C₆H₅

N

N⁺

C₆H₅ O⁻

syn- (or *E-*) azoxybenzene
m.p. 86°C

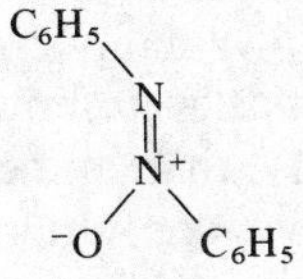

C₆H₅

N

N⁺

⁻O C₆H₅

anti- (or *Z-*) azoxybenzene
m.p. 36°C

Aliphatic nitroso compounds are dimers in the solid state, and Chilton *et al.* (1955) and Gowenlock *et al.* (1955) have examined the ultraviolet absorption spectra of the two solid forms of nitrosomethane and conclude

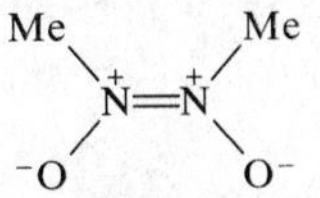

Me Me

N⁺=N⁺

⁻O O⁻

cis (or *Z*)

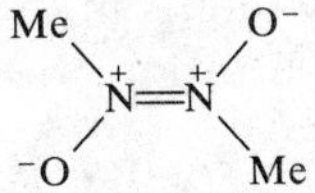

Me O⁻

N⁺=N⁺

⁻O Me

trans (or *E*)

R

N

N

NHR

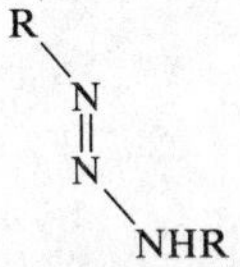

(VII)

that they are geometrical isomers. This has been confirmed by Lüttke (1956, 1957) from his infrared spectra studies.

Recently, Le Fèvre *et al.* (1951) have measured the dipole moments and the ultraviolet absorption spectra of a number of triazens, and have concluded that these compounds exist in the *anti*-configuration about the nitrogen–nitrogen double bond, *i.e.*, the configuration is (VII).

These authors also believe that this *anti*-form is converted into an equilibrium mixture of the *anti*- and *syn*-forms when exposed to sunlight.

Harley-Mason *et al.* (1961) have offered evidence to show that they have isolated the three theoretically possible geometrical isomers of *o*-nitroacetophenone azine (Ar = *o*-NO$_2$C$_6$H$_4$-):

Their evidence was based on infrared, ultraviolet and NMR spectra. This compound appears to be the first example of the isolation and characterisation of all three possible geometrical isomers of an azine.

§2j. Conformational analysis of ring systems containing nitrogen.   The stereochemistry of aziridines has already been discussed (see §2c). Pyrrolidine (I) has been shown, from spectroscopic data and

X-ray analysis, to be a puckered ring similar to cyclopentane and also, like cyclopentane, undergoes pseudorotation (**4** §14). Piperidine (II) has been shown to exist in the chair form (*cf.* cyclohexane) and was believed to be predominantly in conformation (II*b*), *i.e.*, with the hydrogen of the NH group in the axial position. One explanation offered is that the spatial requirements of a lone pair of electrons are greater than those of a hydrogen atom. There are, however, objections to this explanation, *e.g.*, it is to be expected that in *N*-methylpiperidine the methyl group, because of the 'large bulk' of a lone pair of electrons, would be present in the equatorial form in smaller amount than the corresponding methyl group in methylcyclohexane. In practice, by the use of dipole measurements,

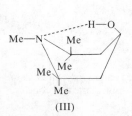

(III)

it has been shown that hydrogen is slightly more in the equatorial position (II*a*) than in the axial (II*b*), and methyl is predominantly in the equatorial position. It therefore appears that in heterocyclic ring systems the effect of the lone pair of electrons may be ignored. In certain circumstances, however, the effect of the lone pair must be taken into consideration. This is the case when there is a *polar* substituent on an adjacent carbon atom (see pyranose sugars, **7** §7a).

As we have seen (**4** §11b), because of intramolecular hydrogen bonding, cyclohexane-1,4-diol is in the boat form (or twist-boat). In some highly substituted 4-hydroxypiperidines the boat form is also present, *e.g.*, (III).

§3. Stereochemistry of phosphorus compounds

Nitrogen, as we have seen, can exhibit covalencies of 3 and 4; phosphorus (and arsenic), however, can exhibit covalencies of 3, 4, 5 and 6, and consequently gives rise to more possible configurations than nitrogen. In tercovalent compounds the valency disposition is tetrahedral (*sp*^{3}), one orbital being occupied by a lone-pair; and in quinquevalent compounds the valency disposition is trigonal bipyramidal (sp^3d). In quadricovalent unielectrovalent compounds one electron is transferred from the phosphorus or arsenic atom to the anion and the valency disposition is tetrahedral (sp^3) (see also §4b). When there are double bonds present, one is a σ- and the other is a p_π-d_π-bond; thus, in $POCl_3$, the shape is tetrahedral (see also §1).

§3a. Tercovalent phosphorus compounds.   Since the electronic configuration of phosphorus is $(1s^2)(2s^2)(2p^6)(3s^2)(3p^3)$, it might be expected that suitable tercovalent compounds, R_3P, could be resolved, since the configuration would be a trigonal pyramid (*cf.* §2c). However, the phosphorus atom is in a state of oscillation. Calculation has shown that the frequency of this oscillation in phosphine is 5×10^6; this is slower than that of nitrogen ($2 \cdot 3 \times 10^{10}$), and if it could be brought to zero, then tertiary phosphines would be resolvable. Increasing the weight of the groups slows down the oscillation in phosphorus compounds, *e.g.*, replacement of the three hydrogen atoms by deuterium atoms changes the frequency to 6×10^3. It seems possible, therefore, that very large groups might produce phosphines which would be resolvable. This has been shown to be the case in practice, *e.g.*, Horner *et al.* (1961) resolved EtMePhP, MePhPrP, etc., and (1966) obtained the optically active diphosphine, MePhPCH$_2$CH$_2$PPhMe. Horner was also able to determine the absolute configuration of MePhPrP as follows. When an enantiomer of an optically active phosphine is treated with benzyl bromide, the phosphonium bromide is obtained with retention of configuration. This salt, on electrolytic reduction, regenerates the original phosphine without loss of optical activity. Now, the absolute configuration of (+)-benzylmethylphenylpropylphosphonium bromide has been shown to be (S) [see 8 §3b]. Hence, the phosphine obtained also has the (S)-configuration.

$$\text{MePrPhP} \underset{2e\,;\ H^+}{\overset{PhCH_2Br}{\rightleftharpoons}} \text{MePrPhP}\overset{+}{P}CH_2Ph\}Br^-$$

$$(S)\text{-}(+) \qquad\qquad\qquad\qquad (S)\text{-}(+)$$

Optically active phosphines are fairly stable (optically); they are racemised on heating (probably through oscillation).

§3b. Quadricovalent and quinquevalent phosphorus compounds.   The earliest phosphorus compounds to be resolved were the phosphine oxides, *e.g.*, Meisenheimer *et al.* (1911) resolved ethylmethylphenylphosphine oxide (I) and benzylmethylphenylphosphine oxide (II).

$$\begin{array}{cc}
\underset{\displaystyle \text{C}_2\text{H}_5}{\overset{\displaystyle \text{CH}_3}{\text{C}_6\text{H}_5-\text{P}=\text{O}}} & \underset{\displaystyle \text{CH}_2\text{C}_6\text{H}_5}{\overset{\displaystyle \text{CH}_3}{\text{C}_6\text{H}_5-\text{P}=\text{O}}} \\
(\text{I}) & (\text{II})
\end{array}$$

Many optically active compounds containing quinquevalent phosphorus of the type $R_3P{=}Z$ have now been prepared, *e.g.*,

$$\begin{array}{ccccc}
\overset{\displaystyle \text{OMe}}{\underset{\displaystyle \text{O}}{\text{Me}-\text{P}-\text{C}_6\text{H}_4\overset{+}{\text{N}}\text{Me}_3\text{-}p\}\text{I}^-}} &
\overset{\displaystyle \text{Ph}}{\underset{\displaystyle \text{O}}{\text{Me}-\text{P}-\text{NHPh}}} &
\overset{\displaystyle \text{OEt}}{\underset{\displaystyle \text{O}}{\text{Et}-\text{P}-\text{SH}}} &
\overset{\displaystyle \text{OEt}}{\underset{\displaystyle \text{S}}{\text{Et}-\text{P}-\text{OH}}} &
\overset{\displaystyle \text{OEt}}{\underset{\displaystyle \text{Se}}{\text{Et}-\text{P}-\text{SH}}}
\end{array}$$

Optically active phosphine oxides are racemised by acids. A possible mechanism is *via* the formation of the symmetrical compound which has a trigonal bipyramid configuration (sp^3d; see also §4b). This is supported by the fact that when the aqueous solution contained $H_2{}^{18}O$, ^{18}O was incorporated in the product (Denney *et al.*, 1964).

$$\underset{\displaystyle R^3}{\overset{\displaystyle R^1}{R^2-\text{P}=\text{O}}} \underset{-H^+}{\overset{+H^+}{\rightleftharpoons}} \underset{\displaystyle R^3}{\overset{\displaystyle R^1}{R^2-\overset{+}{\text{P}}-\text{OH}}} \underset{-H_2O}{\overset{+H_2O}{\rightleftharpoons}} \underset{\displaystyle \text{OH}}{\overset{\displaystyle \text{OH}}{R^1-\text{P}\overset{\displaystyle R^2}{\underset{\displaystyle R^3}{\big\langle}}}} + H^+$$

Another interesting phosphorus compound from the point of view of optical isomerism is ethyl triphenylmethylpyrophosphonate (III). If the two phosphorus atoms are asymmetric, then (III) contains two similar asymmetric carbon atoms, and so its structure corresponds to the molecule *CabdCabd*.

(III)   (IV)   (V)

Thus there will be one racemic modification (composed of the pair of enantiomers) and one *meso*-form (*cf.* **2** §7d). Hatt (1933) obtained two forms of compound (III); both were inactive and so correspond to the racemic modification and the *meso*-form, but it was not possible to tell which was which.

Many attempts have been made to resolve quaternary phosphonium compounds, but until recently, all these attempts failed. This failure is attributed to the occurrence in solution of a 'dissociation-equilibrium', which causes very rapid racemisation (see §4a).

$$[abcdP]^+X^- \rightleftharpoons abcP + dX$$

The earlier attempts to resolve phosphonium compounds were always carried out on compounds containing at least one alkyl group; consequently dissociation in solution could occur, thereby resulting in racemisation. Holliman and Mann (1947) overcame this difficulty by preparing a much more stable type of phosphonium compound; these workers prepared a salt in which the phosphorus atom was in a ring, *viz.*, 2-*p*-hydroxyphenyl-2-phenyl-1,2,3,4-tetrahydro-isophosphinolinium bromide, (IV), and resolved it. The resolution of 4-covalent compounds of phosphorus does not *prove* that the phosphorus atom has a tetrahedral configuration; it only proves that the phosphorus atom cannot be in the same plane as the other four groups attached to it. Mann *et al.* (1955), however have now synthesised P-spirobis-1,2,3,4-tetrahydrophosphinolinium iodide (V) and resolved it into (+)- and (−)-forms which have high optical stability. The phosphorus atom is not asymmetric in this compounds; it is the *tetrahedral* disposition of the four valencies which produces the dissymmetric cation (*cf.* nitrogen, §2a; see also §4b).

It is interesting to note, in view of what has been said above about the dissociation of phosphonium

(VI)   (VII)

salts containing at least one alkyl group, that McEwen *et al.* (1959) have resolved benzylethylmethyl-phenylphosphonium iodide (VI). Also, McEwen *et al.* (1964) have shown that this compound, on treatment with sodium hydroxide, undergoes inversion to give ethylmethylphenylphosphine oxide (VII) and toluene. Horner *et al.* (1965) have prepared (VIII) in its optically active forms and showed, by X-ray analysis, that the (+)-enantiomer has the (*S*)-configuration.

Phosphines are readily oxidised to phosphine oxides by hydrogen peroxide with retention of configuration. Hence it is possible to prepare an enantiomer of a phosphine oxide with a known absolute configuration, *e.g.* (see also §3a):

$$\text{MePrPhP} \xrightarrow{\text{H}_2\text{O}_2} \text{MePrPhP=O}$$

(*S*)-(+)   (*S*)-(+)

Since phosphines combine directly with sulphur to form phosphine sulphides (with retention of configuration), the absolute configurations of these sulphides may also be determined.

Campbell *et al.* (1960) have prepared a series of azophosphaphenanthrens ((IX); *e.g.*, R^1 = H, R^2 = NMe_2), but could not resolve them. When the phosphine (IX) was oxidised with hydrogen

peroxide, the phosphine oxide obtained, (X), was resolved. Reduction of the (+)-oxide with lithium aluminium hydride gave the (−)-phosphine (IX), and in the same way the reduction of the (−)-oxide gave the (+)-phosphine (IX). It is not certain whether the optical activity in (IX) is due to an asymmetric tervalent phosphorus atom or to a rigid puckering of the molecular framework, which is a 2,2′-bridged biphenyl.

A tercovalent phosphorus compound which does not exhibit optical isomerism, but exists as geometrical isomers is 5,10-diethyl-5,10-dihydrophosphanthren, (XI). It is folded about the P—P

axis, and Mann *et al.* (1962) isolated two forms (see the corresponding arsenic compounds, (X)–(XII), §4b, for further discussion).

Hellwinkel (1965) has resolved salts of (XII). The anion contains hexavalent phosphorus and has an octahedral configuration (sp^3d^2; see also §4b).

§4. Stereochemistry of arsenic compounds

Arsenic, like phosphorus, can exhibit covalencies of 3, 4, 5 and 6; consequently these two elements show a great similarity to each other, and differ from nitrogen which has a maximum valency of 4.

§4a. Quadricovalent and quinquevalent arsenic compounds.   The first resolution of an arsonium compound was carried out by Burrows and Turner (1921). These workers obtained a solution of benzylmethyl-1-naphthylphenylarsonium iodide, (I), that had a rotation of $+12°$, but racemised rapidly (in solution). Similarly, Kamai (1933) isolated the $(+)$-form of benzylethyl-1-naphthyl-n-propylarsonium iodide, (II), which also racemised rapidly in solution. This rapid racemisation is believed to be due to a 'dissociation-equilibrium' in solution. This explanation was suggested by Pope and Harvey (1901) to account for the racemisation of certain ammonium salts, but definite evidence for this theory was provided by Burrows and Turner (1921) in their work on arsonium salts. If this dissociation-equilibrium occurs, then in solution there will be:

$$[abcdAs]^+I^- \rightleftharpoons abcAs + dI$$

Burrows and Turner showed that when dimethylphenylarsine is treated with ethyl iodide, the expected ethyldimethylphenylarsonium iodide is obtained, but at the same time a considerable amount

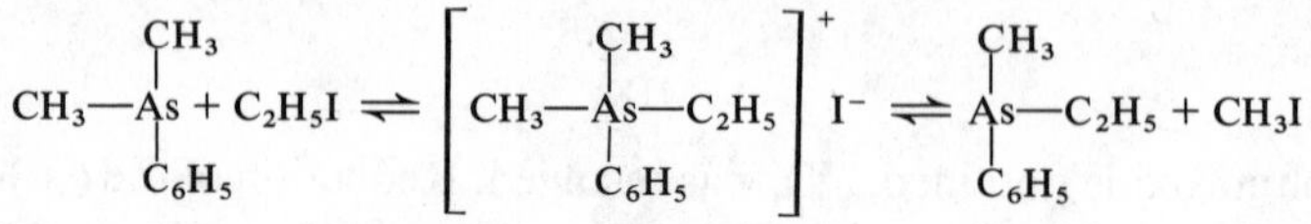

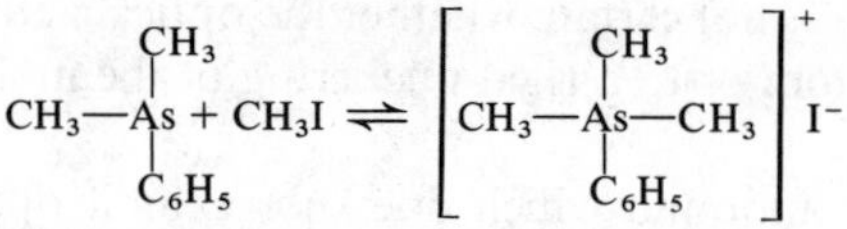

of trimethylphenylarsonium iodide is also formed. These results are readily explained by the dissociation-equilibrium theory.

Since all the arsonium compounds investigated contained at least one alkyl group, Holliman and Mann (1943) prepared an arsonium compound with the arsenic atom in a ring, in the hope of stabilising the compound (*cf.* phosphorus, §3b). These authors prepared 2-*p*-chlorophenacyl-2-phenyl-1,2,3,4-tetrahydro-isoarsinolinium bromide, (III), resolved it, and found that it did not racemise in solution at room temperature.

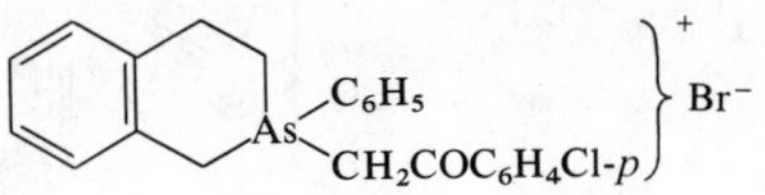

(III)

Although phosphine oxides of the type *abc*PO have been resolved (§3b), similar arsine oxides have not; the reason for this is obscure. On the other hand, arsine sulphides have been resolved, *e.g.*, Mills and Raper (1925) resolved *p*-carboxyphenylmethylethylarsine sulphide (IV). Horner *et al.* (1962) have prepared optically active forms of (V) and (VI) by direct combination between the optically active arsine and sulphur (see also §4b).

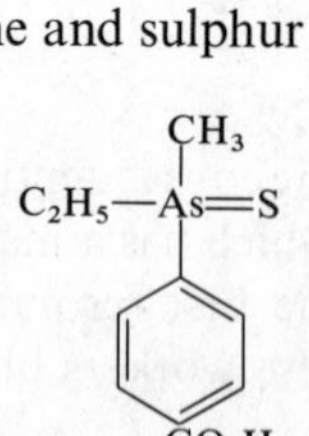

(IV) 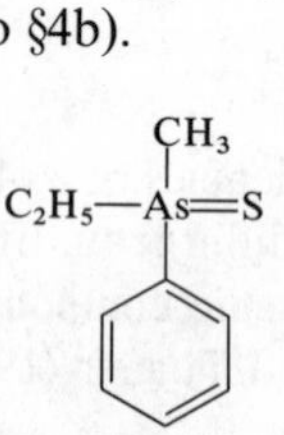   (V) 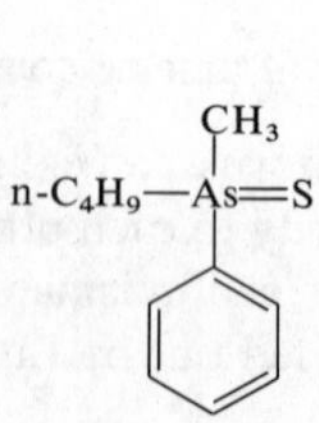   (VI)

It has already been pointed out above that Mann prepared the optically stable arsonium compound (III). These authors, in 1945, also resolved an arsonium compound of the spiran type, *viz.*,

(VII)   (VIII)

As-spiro-bis-1,2,3,4-tetrahydro-isoarsinolinium bromide, (VII). This does not contain an asymmetric arsenic atom; the optical activity is due to the asymmetry of the molecule (the two rings are perpendicular to each other). Mann *et al.* (1960) have also resolved compound (VIII), and in 1963, Mann *et al.* resolved the cyclic quaternary diarsonium dibromides (IX) and (X).

(IX): $n = 1, 2,$ or 3   (X)

§4b. Tercovalent arsenic compounds. The electronic configuration of arsenic is $(1s^2)(2s^2)(2p^6)$-$(3s^2)(3p^6)(3d^{10})(4s^2)(4p^3)$. Thus the configuration of tercovalent arsenic compounds will be a trigonal pyramid (*cf.* phosphorus, §3a). Physico-chemical evidence (X-ray analysis, spectroscopy and electron diffraction) has shown that in tercovalent compounds the arsenic atom is at the apex of a tetrahedron, and that the intervalency angle is $100 \pm 4°$. It has also been shown that the arsenic is in a state of oscillation, the frequency of this oscillation through the plane of the three hydrogen atoms in arsine being 16×10^4. This is slower than that of phosphorus (5×10^6), and very much slower than that of nitrogen ($2\cdot3 \times 10^{10}$). Thus, preventing the oscillation of the arsenic atom, possibly by attachment to very large groups, should lead to the isolation of optically active tercovalent compounds. In fact, calculations by Weston (1954) led him to the conclusion that tervalent arsenic (and antimony and sulphur) compounds should be stable to inversion at room temperature. Horner *et al.* (1962) have prepared the optically active arsines EtMePhAs and n-BuMePhAs by removal of the benzyl group from the corresponding optically active arsonium compound (*cf.* phosphines, §3a), and Mislow *et al.* (1963) have resolved (I). Chan (1968) has also prepared optically active t-BuMePhAs *via* a chiral platinum (II) complex.

Heterocyclic 9,10-dihydroanthracenes have been resolved. Thus, Lesslie *et al.* (1934) resolved 10-methylphenoxarsine-2-carboxylic acid, (II). These authors suggested that the asymmetry of the molecule is due to a 'butterfly' configuration, *i.e.*, the molecule is folded about the O—As axis (see IV). The authors also pointed out that there was the possibility that the asymmetry might be due to the presence of a stable 'asymmetric' arsenic atom, but preferred the former explanation. Molecules of the type (II) cannot be coplanar unless the oxygen and arsenic valency angles are both 120°. Since this is not the case ($\angle$ COC is approximately 104°), the butterfly configuration is reasonable. There are, however, some difficulties, *e.g.*, the corresponding thianthren compounds (§5c), phenoxathiin (replace As by S) and phenoxaselinin (replace As by Se) cannot be resolved. Dipole moment measurements of these compounds showed that they have a folded structure and consequently the failure to resolve them was ascribed to instability of the folded structure, this readily undergoing rapid racemisation by 'fluttering' through the planar conformation. Since (II) and also [(III);

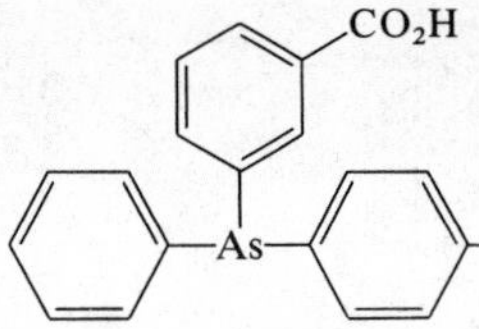

(I)

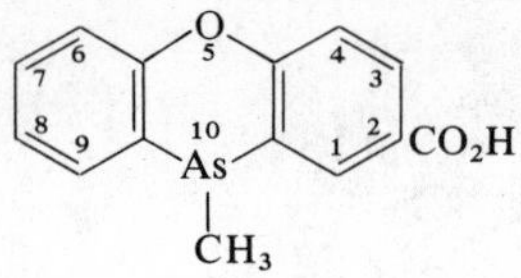

(II)

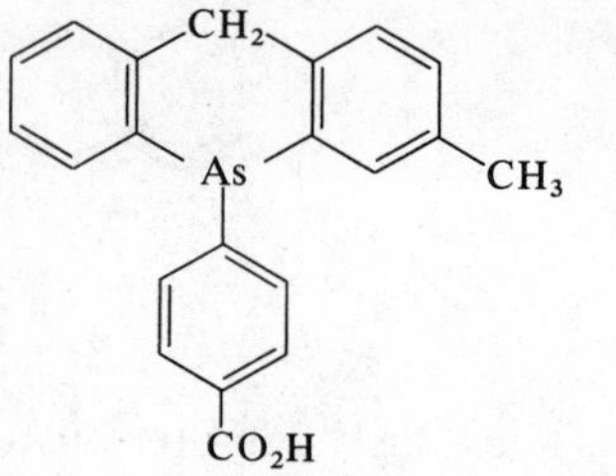

(III)

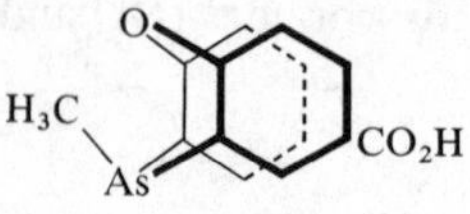

(IV)

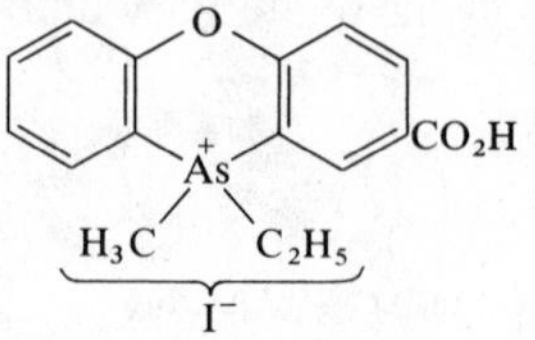

(V)

Mislow *et al.*, 1963] have been resolved, it might appear that in such arsenic compounds the folded conformation is stable. This could be supported by the argument that optically active acyclic arsines have now been prepared (and also the isolation of the two forms (X) and (XI); see below). Mislow, however, has presented evidence that the folded conformation of phenoxarsines is highly flexible, and Campbell (1968) has pointed out that if the folded conformation were stable, then two racemates are possible. Since only one has been isolated, this supports the presence of a stable 'asymmetric' arsenic atom in an unstably folded molecule in which the butterfly wings can flutter. According to Mislow, resolvable phenoxarsines are most correctly pictured as separable configurationally stable enantiomers which individually exist in solution as mixtures of rapidly interconverting diastereoisomeric folded conformations (the term configuration refers to the arsenic pyramid).

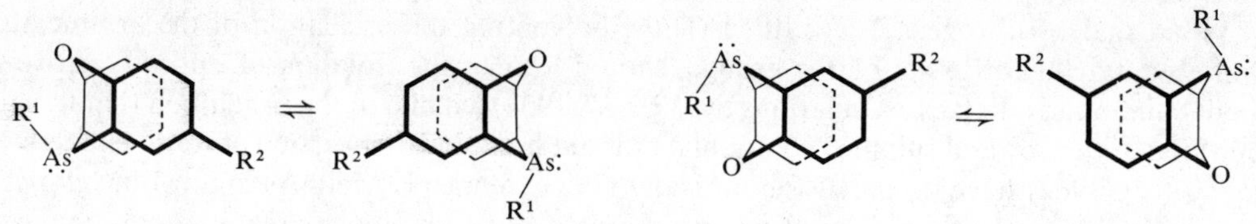

When each enantiomer of (IV) is treated with ethyl iodide, the *same* racemised product is obtained. This is due to the fact that when the arsonium compound, (V), is formed, the asymmetric quaternary arsenic atom is racemised owing to the dissociation-equilibrium.

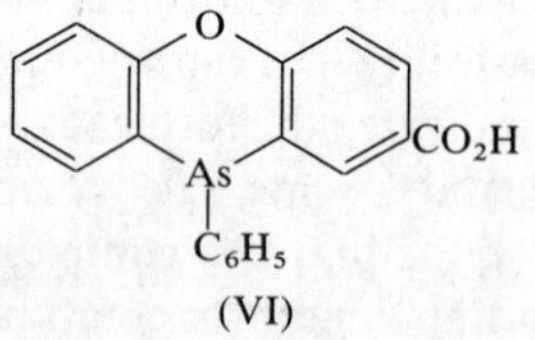

(VI)

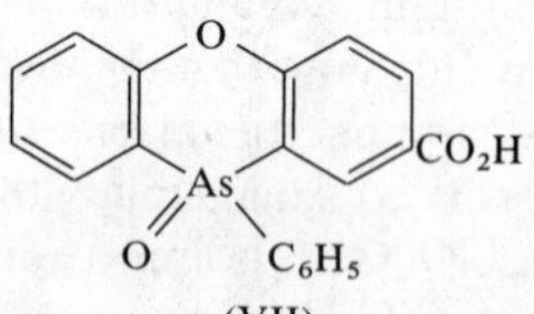

(VII)

Lesslie and Turner (1936) also resolved 10-phenylphenoxarsine-2-carboxylic acid, (VI). This compound was very stable, and oxidation to the arsine oxide, (VII), gave a completely racemised product.

Campbell *et al.* (1956) have resolved some substituted 9-arsafluorenes, *e.g.*, 9-*p*-carboxyphenyl-2-methoxy-9-arsafluorene (VIII). Campbell (1956) has also resolved 2-*p*-carboxyphenyl-5-methyl-1,3-dithia-2-arsaindane (IX). This compound is optically stable in chloroform solution, but is racemised in aqueous sodium hydroxide. Campbell believed that this racemisation is due to the fission of the As—S bonds by aqueous alkali, and subsequent reversal of the reaction by acid, a type

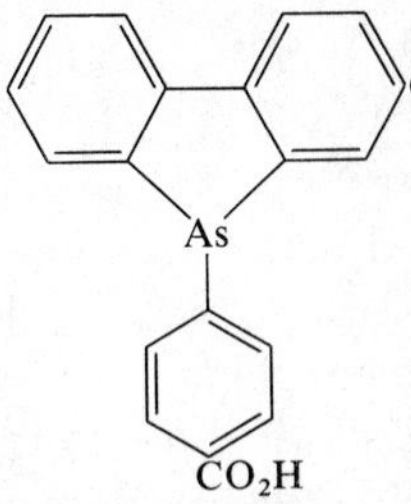

(VIII) 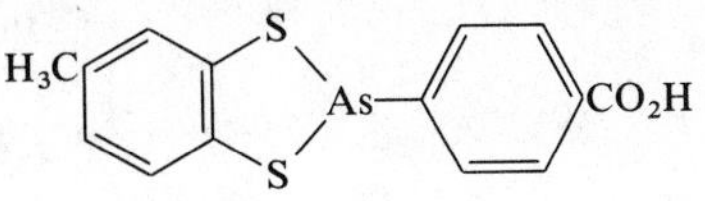   (IX)

of behaviour observed in triaryl thioarsenites (Klement *et al.*, 1938). Furthermore, Cohen *et al.* (1931) have shown that in sodium hydroxide solution, alkyl thioarsenites exist in equilibrium with thiol and arsenoxide:

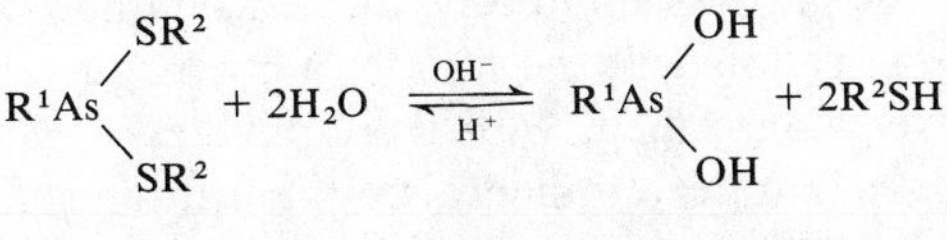

Chatt and Mann (1940) prepared 5,10-di-*p*-tolyl-5,10-dihydroarsanthren, and pointed out that if the valency angle of arsenic remains constant at its normal angle (of approximately 100°), then the structure will be folded, and consequently the three geometrical isomers, (X), (XI) and (XII), are apparently possible (T represents the *p*-tolyl group). Chatt and Mann also pointed out that evidence

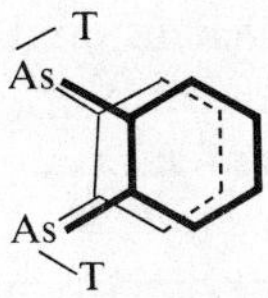

(X) 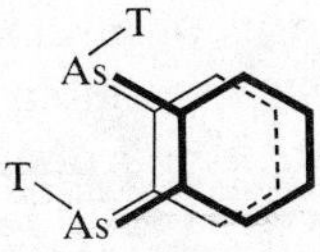   (XI) 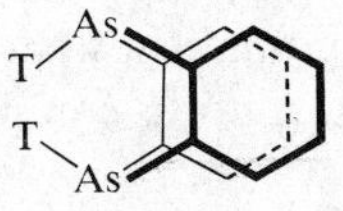   (XII) 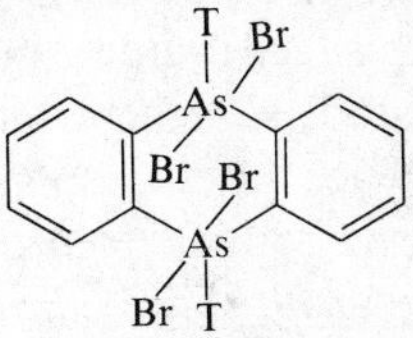   (XIII)

obtained from models constructed to scale showed that the two *p*-tolyl groups (T) in (XII) would almost be coincident, and hence this isomer cannot exist. These authors isolated two optically inactive forms, but were unable to say which was which. When each compound was treated with bromine, both gave the *same* tetrabromide which, on hydrolysis, gave only one tetrahydroxide. The loss of isomerism in the tetrabromide (and in the tetrahydroxide) may be explained as follows. Bromination of (X) and (XI) converts tercovalent arsenic into quinquecovalent arsenic, and in the latter state the ring valency angles of the arsenic become 120°, and so the arsanthren nucleus is *now* planar. Thus both the forms (X) and (XI) would give the same tetrabromide (XIII) (the same is true for the tetrahydroxide); the tetrabromide should thus be planar, the configuration of each arsenic atom being trigonal bipyramidal in the 5-covalent state (Fig. 6.2).

Quinquevalent phosphorus and arsenic can make use of the 3*d* or 4*d* orbitals, respectively (*cf.* nitrogen, §2b). Thus nitrogen has a maximum covalency of 4, whereas that of phosphorus and arsenic is 5 or 6, *e.g.*, the covalency of 6 is exhibited by phosphorus in *solid* phosphorus pentachloride; X-ray diffraction shows this 'molecule' (in the solid state) is $PCl_4^+ PCl_6^-$.

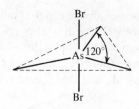

Fig. 6.2

Phosphorus, which is $(1s^2)(2s^2)(2p^6)(3s^2)(3p^3)$ in the ground state, may become $(1s^2)(2s^2)$-$(2p^6)(3s)(3p^3)(3d)$ in its 'valence state', since the $3s$ and $3d$ orbitals have energy levels which are close together. Kimball (1940) showed, by calculation, that this arrangement, *i.e.*, sp^3d, could give rise to the stable trigonal bipyramidal configuration. This consists of three equivalent coplanar orbitals pointing towards the corners of an equilateral triangle, and two orbitals perpendicular to this plane (see Fig. 6.2). Electron diffraction studies of the vapours of phosphorus pentachloride and pentafluoride indicate the trigonal bipyramidal configuration in these molecules. The phosphonium ion might possibly be formed from this trigonal bipyramid by the transference of one of the electrons, or by the transference of a $3s$ electron and hybridisation of the $(3s)(3p^3)$ orbitals; in either case the tetrahedral configuration of the phosphonium ion can be asymmetric, but only in the case of the hybridisation of the $(3s)(3p^3)$ orbitals will the four bonds be equivalent. Since the properties of phosphonium compounds are in agreement with the equivalence of the four bonds, it therefore appears, on theoretical grounds, that the tetrahedral configuration with the phosphorus atom at the centre is the probable one.

From the experimental side, the preparation of optically active spiro-compounds of phosphorus (§3b) and of arsenic (§4a) proves the tetrahedral configuration of these atoms. Earlier work by Mann *et al.* (1936, 1937) has also definitely established this configuration. These authors prepared compounds of the type $[R_3As—CuI]_4$ by combination of tertiary arsines or phosphines with cuprous iodide (or silver iodide); in these compounds the phosphorus or arsenic is 4-covalent, and X-ray analysis studies of the arsenic compound showed that the arsenic atom is at the centre of a tetrahedron. Since the corresponding phosphorus compounds are isomorphous, the configuration of the phosphorus is also tetrahedral.

Horner *et al.* (1965) have been able to assign absolute configurations to benzylmethylphenyl-propylarsonium salts by means of the quasi-racemate method (with the corresponding phosphonium compounds; Formula (VIII), §3b).

In the *solid* state, phosphorus and arsenic compounds may contain a negatively charged phosphorus or arsenic atom, *e.g.*, $PCl_4^+ PCl_6^-$ (see above). In this condition, the phosphorus acquires an electron to become $-\!-\!-(3s)(3p^3)(3d^2)$, and the arsenic also acquires an electron to become $-\!-\!-(4s)(4p^3)(4d^2)$. In both cases the configuration is octahedral (six sp^3d^2 bonds), *e.g.*, the following compound has been resolved (Rosenheim *et al.*, 1925); see also the P (VI) compound (XII), §3b.

$$\left[As \left(\begin{array}{c} O \\ \\ O \end{array} \right)_3 \right]^-$$

§4c. **Stereochemistry of antimony compounds.**   Some optically active tervalent antimony compounds have been prepared, the phenoxastibine (I) and the stibiafluorene (II; Campbell, 1947, 1950). The asymmetry in (I) is probably due to the presence of a stable 'asymmetric' antimony atom (*cf.* phenoxarsines, §4b). Campbell *et al.* (1958) have also resolved the stibine (III).

(I)

(II)

(III)

§5. Stereochemistry of sulphur compounds

Various types of sulphur compounds have been obtained in optically active forms.

§5a. Sulphonium salts. Pope and Peachey (1900) prepared carboxymethylethylmethylsulphonium bromide by the reaction between ethyl methyl sulphide and bromoacetic acid. Since sulphur is tercovalent unielectrovalent in sulphonium salts (sp^3 hybridisation), the reaction may be formulated

$$\begin{array}{c} H_3C \\ \diagdown \\ \qquad S + BrCH_2CO_2H \longrightarrow \\ \diagup \\ C_2H_5 \end{array} \qquad CH_3 \overset{\overset{\textstyle :\overset{+}{S}}{|}}{\underset{C_2H_5}{|}} CH_2CO_2H \quad Br^-$$

as shown. This molecule is not superimposable on its mirror image, and hence can, at least theoretically, exist in two optically active forms. This bromide was treated with silver (+)-camphorsulphonate and the salt obtained was fractionally crystallised from a mixture of ethanol and ether. Pope and Peachey found that the (+)-sulphonium camphorsulphonate was the less soluble fraction, and had an M_D of $+68°$. Since the rotation of the (+)-camphorsulphonate ion is about $+52°$, this leaves $+16°$ as the contribution of the sulphonium ion to the total rotation (see **1** §9). Although this does not prove conclusively that the sulphur compound is optically active, it is certainly strong evidence in its favour. Final proof was obtained by replacement of the camphorsulphonate ion by the platinichloride ion to give $[CH_3(C_2H_5)SCH_2CO_2H]_2^+ PtCl_6^=$; this compound had an $[\alpha]_D$ of $+4\cdot5°$ in water. In a similar way, Smiles (1900) prepared ethylmethylphenacylsulphonium picrate, (I), in two optically active forms, one with an $[\alpha]_D$ of $+8\cdot1°$ and the other $-9\cdot2°$. A more recent

$$\left[\begin{array}{c} H_3C \\ \diagdown \\ \quad S{-}CH_2COC_6H_5 \\ \diagup \\ C_2H_5 \end{array} \right]^+ \left[\begin{array}{c} O_2N \diagup\!\!\diagdown NO_2 \\ \text{NO}_2 \end{array} \right]^-$$

(I)

$$\left\{ \quad {}^+S{-}CH_2COC_6H_4Cl\text{-}p \right\} Br^-$$

(II)

example of an optically active sulphonium salt is one with the sulphur atom in a ring; this compound, (II), was obtained as the optically active ion with the picrate (Mann and Holliman, 1946).

Optically active sulphonium salts have been prepared from optically active sulphoxides, *e.g.* (Anderson, 1971; see also §5c).

$$p\text{-MeC}_6H_4{-}\overset{\overset{\textstyle O}{\|}}{S}{-}Me \xrightarrow{Et_3O^+BF_4^-} \left[p\text{-MeC}_6H_4{-}\overset{\overset{\textstyle OEt}{|}}{S}{-}Me \right]^+ BF_4^- \xrightarrow[\text{(ii) HBr}]{\text{(i) Et}_2\text{Cd}} \left[p\text{-MeC}_6H_4{-}\overset{\overset{\textstyle Et}{|}}{S}{-}Me \right]^+ Br^-$$

(+)   (−)

It can be seen that these sulphur compounds do not undergo pyramidal inversion (*cf.* §2c).

§5b. Sulphinic esters. Phillips (1925) partially resolved sulphinic esters, $R^1SO_2R^2$, by means of the kinetic method of resolution (**2** §10vii). Two molecules of ethyl *p*-toluenesulphinate were heated with one molecule of (−)-menthyl alcohol or (−)-*s*-octyl alcohol, *i.e.*, the sulphinate was subjected to alcoholysis. Now, if the sulphinate is a racemic modification, then the (+)- and (−)-forms will react at *different* rates with the optically active alcohol (see **2** §§2, 7b). Phillips actually found that the (+)-ester reacted faster than the (−)-ester. If we represent the ester by E, the alcohol by A, and unchanged ester by E$_r$, then the following equation symbolises the alcoholysis:

$$(+)E + (-)E + (-)A \rightarrow [(+)E(-)A] + [(-)E(-)A] + (+)E_r + (-)E_r$$

Since $[(+)E(-)A]$ is greater than $[(-)E(-)A]$, it therefore follows that $(+)E_r$ is less than $(-)E_r$; thus a partial resolution has occurred. The unchanged ester, having a lower boiling point than the new ester, distilled off first; this contained more of the (−)-form. The residual ester (the higher boiling fraction) was then heated with a large excess of ethanol; alcoholysis again occurred, this time the (−)-alcohol (menthol or octyl) being displaced to regenerate the original ethyl *p*-toluene-sulphinate. This resulted in a fraction containing more of the (+)-form.

The optical activity of sulphinates is readily explained if their structure is (I), in which the sulphur atom is sp^3-hybridised (*cf.* sulphonium salts, above).

(I)

§5c. Sulphoxides. Sulphoxides of the type R^1SOR^2 have also been resolved; sulphoxides (I) and (II) were resolved by Phillips *et al.* (1926), and Karrer *et al.* (1951) obtained (III) in the (−)-form and the racemic modification.

Bell and Bennett (1927) investigated disulphoxides of the type

$$CH_3SOCH_2CH_2SOCH_3$$

This molecule contains two similar asymmetric sulphur atoms and so is of the type *CabdCabd*. Thus it should exist in one racemic modification and one *meso*-form. Bell and Bennett failed to resolve this compound, but succeeded in resolving the following disulphoxide.

If the former disulphoxide (the dioxide of a 1,4-dithian) is converted into the corresponding ring compound (*i.e.*, into a cyclic 1,4-dithian), then two geometrical isomers are possible, neither of which is resolvable; these two forms have been isolated by Bell and Bennett (1927, 1929). Shearer

(1959) has examined the *trans*-form by X-ray analysis and showed that the ring is in the chair form with the S=O groups in *trans* and axial positions.

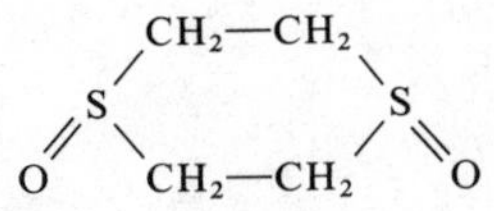

cis 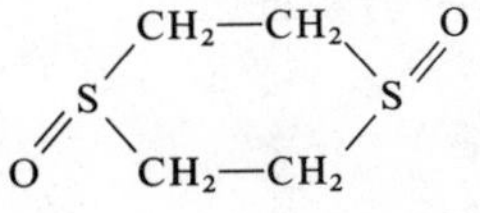   *trans*

Thianthren dioxide (IV) also exists in two geometrical isomeric forms, α, m.p. 284°C, $\mu = 1\cdot7$ D; and β, m.p. 249°C, $\mu = 4\cdot2$ D (Bergmann *et al.*, 1932). Hosoya *et al.* (1957) have examined the α-form by X-ray analysis and showed it was boat-shaped (only this part of the molecule is shown in the diagrams), with the molecule folded along the S—S axis (*cf.* the dithian dioxides above). These authors also showed that this α-form has the *anti-cis*-configuration of the two S=O bonds. The β-form is therefore assumed to be a *trans*-form.

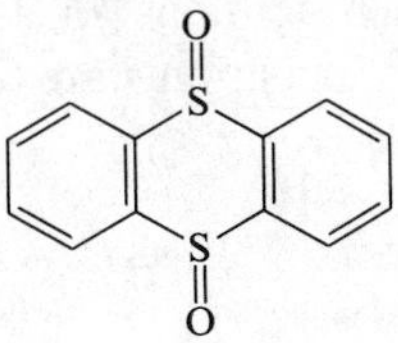

(IV) 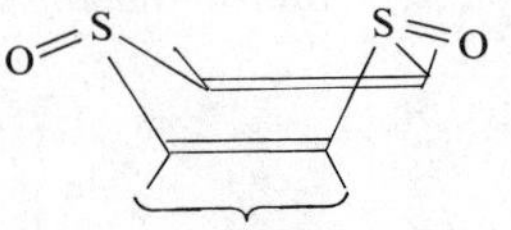   α-form 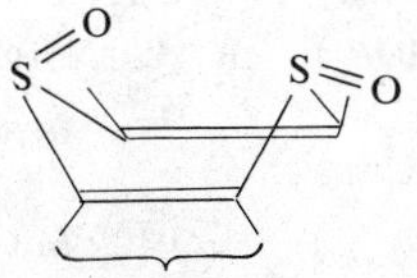   β-form

When either of these disulphoxides is oxidised to the disulphone, both give the same compound (Hosoya, 1958).

The sulphoxides described above have been obtained in optically active forms by resolution of their racemates. However, optically active sulphoxides have also been prepared by asymmetric synthesis, which has been carried out by oxidation of unsymmetrically substituted sulphides, R^1SR^2, by optically active peroxy-acids, *e.g.*, α-substituted monoperoxyglutaric acids (Balenovic *et al.*, 1960, 1961). Montanari *et al.* (1968) have oxidised racemic alkyl aryl sulphoxides with 0·5 molar equivalents of optically active peroxy-acids and obtained mixtures of sulphones and optically active sulphoxides. This method is based on the preferential oxidation of one enantiomer of the sulphoxide (see below). On the other hand, Savige *et al.* (1965) have carried out an asymmetric synthesis of disulphoxide monoxides (thiosulphinates) of the type ArSOSAr by oxidation of the diaryl disulphide with peroxycamphoric acid (Ar = Ph, *p*-Cl—C_6H_4, *p*-Me—C_6H_4, or 2-naphthyl).

Since a chiral reagent (asymmetric peroxy-acid) has been used in all of these oxidations, if we treat the two lone pairs of electrons on the sulphur as enantiotopic 'groups', then different amounts of the enantiomeric sulphoxides can be expected (see **2** §7a).

Cram *et al.* (1963) have prepared diastereoisomeric sulphoxides by the oxidation of (−)-2-octyl phenyl sulphide (V) with t-butyl hydroperoxide (an achiral reagent). Using modified Newman formulae, with the sulphur in *front*, we can represent the reaction as shown.

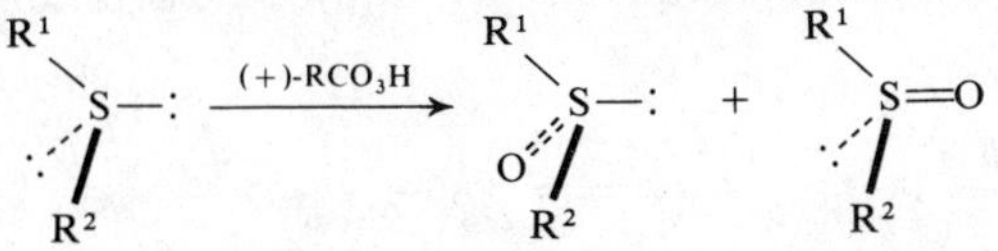

Cram assumed that oxidation occurs more rapidly at the less hindered electron pair on the sulphur atom. Hence, the predominant product is (VI). The different rates of reaction to form diastereo-isomers in unequal amounts is to be expected, since the two electron pairs may be regarded as diastereotopic 'groups' (see **2** §7b).

$$n\text{-}C_6H_{13} \overset{S}{\underset{H}{\diagdown}} \begin{matrix} Me \\ Ph \end{matrix} \quad \xrightarrow{t\text{-BuOOH}} \quad n\text{-}C_6H_{13} \overset{S}{\underset{H}{\diagdown}} \begin{matrix} Me \\ Ph \end{matrix} \quad + \quad n\text{-}C_6H_{13} \overset{S}{\underset{H}{\diagdown}} \begin{matrix} Me \\ Ph \end{matrix}$$

(V) $(-)$-(VI) $(+)$-(VII)

Henbest *et al.* (1966) have shown that alkyl aryl sulphides may be stereoselectively oxidised to sulphoxides in the presence of growing aerobic cultures of *Aspergillus niger* (4–98 per cent optical purity).

An interesting example of an optically active sulphoxide is its preparation by transfer of a chiral centre at a carbon atom in the molecule to a sulphur atom. Mislow *et al.* (1968) prepared (*S*)-α-methylallyl *p*-toluenesulphenate (which contains an asymmetric carbon atom) and found that it spontaneously rearranged to (*S*)-*trans*-crotyl *p*-tolyl sulphoxide (which contains an asymmetric sulphur atom). The rearrangement was shown to take place *via* a cyclic transition state (*cf.* **4** §5m).

(S) → [transition state] → (S)

Racemisation of optically active sulphoxides has not been studied very much, but recently, Henbest *et al.* (1964) have shown that the sulphoxide group in certain compounds can be inverted by heating. (+)-Benzyl *p*-tolyl sulphoxide is racemised by heating in, *e.g.*, decalin solution at 162°C. The authors also showed that *cis*- and *trans*-cyclic sulphoxides, (VIII), when heated separately in decalin at 190°C, give the same *cis-trans* mixture (in the ratio 1 : 4). It should be noted that the t-butyl group is always equatorial and that the 1*e*,4*e* form (*trans*) is more stable than the 1*a*,4*e* (*cis*).

$$Me_3C \diagup\!\!\!\diagdown\!\!\!\diagup\!\!\!\diagdown S{=}O \quad \rightleftharpoons \quad Me_3C \diagup\!\!\!\diagdown\!\!\!\diagup\!\!\!\diagdown S{=}O$$

cis   trans

(VIII)

Mislow *et al.* (1964) have shown that optically active sulphoxides are rapidly racemised at room temperature by solutions of hydrogen chloride in organic solvents such as benzene, dioxan, etc. The mechanism is believed to occur by nucleophilic attack of the halide ion on the protonated sulphoxide. Montanari *et al.* (1968) have also investigated this racemisation process (and reduction of the sulphoxide to sulphide) by iodide ion in aqueous perchloric acid solution. The mechanism proposed for the racemisation is:

$$\diagdown\!\!\!\!SO + H^+ \rightleftharpoons \diagdown\!\!\!\!\overset{+}{S}OH \xrightarrow[\text{slow}]{I^-;\,H^+} I{-}\overset{+}{\underset{\diagdown}{S}}\diagup + H_2O \rightleftharpoons \diagdown\!\!\!\overset{+}{\underset{}{S}}{-}I + H_2O \longrightarrow H^+ + I^- + HO{-}\overset{+}{\underset{\diagdown}{S}}\diagup \rightleftharpoons OS\diagup + H^+$$

Also, Hammond *et al.* (1965) have racemised sulphoxides photochemically, *e.g.*, (+)-methyl *p*-tolyl sulphoxide, on irradiation with a mercury vapour lamp, gave the racemised product.

Johnson *et al.* (1965) have *inverted* sulphoxides by chemical means. The sulphoxide is treated with triethyloxonium borofluoride followed by alkali.

The mechanism is uncertain, but the authors believe that inversion occurs by an S_N2 mechanism in the stage involving the hydroxide ion, *i.e.*,

$$EtO\overset{+}{\text{---}}\overset{}{S}< + OH^- \longrightarrow EtO\overset{\delta-}{\text{---}}S\overset{\delta-}{\text{---}}OH \longrightarrow EtO^- + >\overset{+}{S}\text{---}OH \xrightarrow{-H^+} >S{=}O$$

It is of interest to note, in connection with optically active sulphoxides, that Schmid and Karrer (1948) have isolated *sulphoraphen* from its glycoside which occurs in radish seed. These authors showed that sulphoraphen is a laevorotatory oil which owes its optical activity to the presence of a sulphoxide group.

$$CH_3SOCH{=}CHCH_2CH_2NCS$$
sulphoraphen

The absolute configurations of a number of optically active sulphoxides have now been determined by Mislow *et al.* (1963–66). The method is based on asymmetric synthesis, the first step being the preparation of a mixture of, *e.g.*, diastereoisomeric menthyl sulphinates enriched in one form (prepared by the action of (−)-menthyl alcohol on *p*-toluenesulphinyl chloride in the presence of pyridine at − 78°C). This ester was then subjected to the Grignard reaction, and in this way the menthyloxy group is displaced by an alkyl or aryl group, the product being a mixture of enantiomers of the sulphoxide enriched in one form.

The sign of the predominant enantiomer is related to the absolute configuration of the 'inducing' alcohol. Alcohols conforming to the stereoformula shown produce an excess of the (−)-(*S*)-enantiomer. Thus terpene alcohols which have the (*R*)-configuration fit the stereoformula, *e.g.*, (−)-menthol, (−)-borneol, etc., induce the formation of the (−)-(*S*)-sulphoxide. On the other hand, (+)-butan-2-ol has the (*S*)-configuration, and preferentially induces the formation of the (+)-(*R*)-sulphoxide. This series of reactions therefore offers a means of configurational correlation of optically active alcohols.

$$\begin{array}{c} M \\ | \\ S\text{---}C\text{---}L \\ | \\ OH \end{array}$$

Mislow *et al.* (1965) have also established the absolute configurations of sulphoxides by means of the ORD method (**1** §9a).

In view of the previous discussion, it can be seen that the configuration of groups attached to sulphur in organic sulphites is also pyramidal. Pritchard *et al.* (1968) have isolated these optically active sulphites and optically active diastereoisomers containing one asymmetric carbon atom and one asymmetric sulphur atom (*cf.* Cram's work, above).

One other point of interest that may be mentioned here is the stereochemistry of sulphones, $R^1SO_2R^2$. It can be seen from the formula that such compounds cannot be optically active unless the two oxygen atoms are 'different'. This has been accomplished by Stirling (1963), who synthesised $(-)$-benzyl *p*-tolyl $[^{16}O^{18}O]$sulphone ($[\alpha_D]$ $=$ $-0.16°$). This is the first case of isotopic asymmetry for a central atom other than carbon (**2** §3a).

§5d. Sulphilimines. Chloramine T reacts with alkyl sulphides to form sulphilimines (iminosulphuranes), *e.g.*,

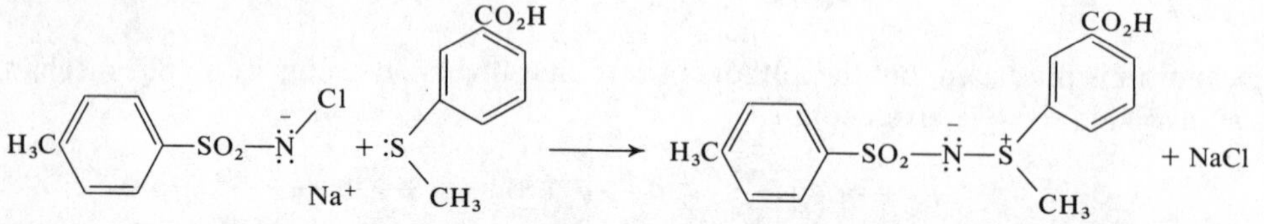

The electronic structure of this molecule appears to be uncertain; one possibility has been given above, and in this one the sulphur atom is asymmetric (it is of the type that occurs in the sulphonium salts). An alternative electronic structure is:

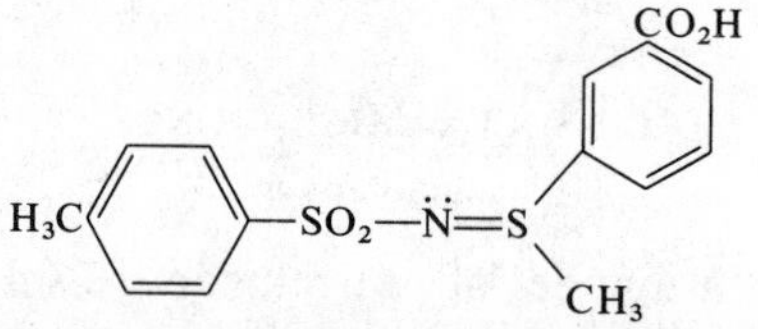

In this structure, the sulphur atom can still be asymmetric. This sulphilimine has been resolved by Kenyon *et al.* (1927).

It seems likely that sulphilimines are resonance hybrids of the above two contributing structures.

Lambert *et al.* (1971) have prepared the cyclic six-membered sulphilimine, thian 1-imine, and were able to show from NMR spectroscopic studies that the parent compound is preferentially in the

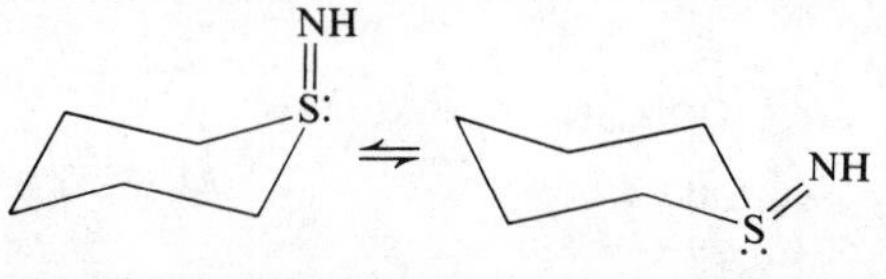

equatorial position, whereas its *N*-benzenesulphonyl and *N*-tosyl derivatives are preferentially in the axial position (*cf.* §2j).

§5e. Sulphines. NMR spectroscopic studies have led to the conclusion that the $C{=}S{=}O$ system in sulphines is a rigid non-linear group. Because of this, *syn* and *anti* isomers are possible. Mangini *et al.* (1969) have shown, from their NMR studies, that the sulphine (I)—prepared by oxidation of

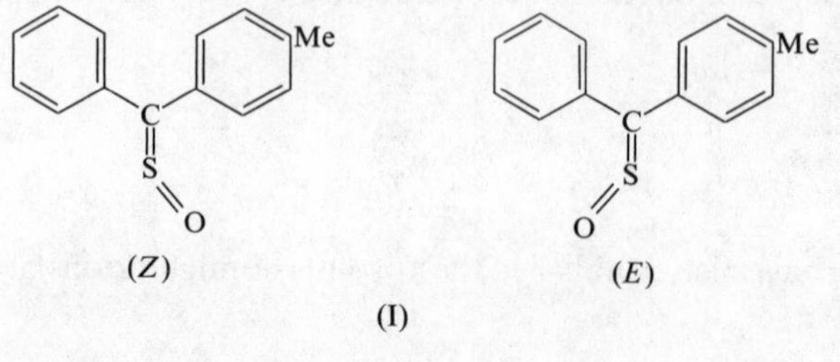

(Z)   (E)

(I)

the thioketone with peroxy-acid—exists in two isomeric forms in about equal amounts. The authors also believe they have isolated the *syn-p*-tolyl (or the *Z*) form; they used column chromatography.

§6. Stereochemistry of silicon compounds

Kipping (1907) prepared benzylethylpropylsilicyl oxide (I) and isolated one form of it. If the silicon atom has a tetrahedral configuration, this molecule is of the type *CabdCabd*, *i.e.*, it should exist in

(I)   (II)

(III)

($+$)-, ($-$)- and *meso*-forms. When (I) was sulphonated to give (II), the latter compound was resolved. Challenger and Kipping (1910) also resolved the silane (III), and Eaborn *et al.* (1958) have resolved the silane (IV).

X = H, Cl, Br, F, OH.

(IV)   (V)

More recently, Sommer *et al.* (1964) have prepared a number of optically active silicon compounds of type (V).

Many other optically active silicon compounds have been prepared by a series of chemical transformations (see also §8).

The relative configurations of the various silanes have been elucidated by the method of quasi-racemates and by ORD measurements. The absolute configurations of 1-NpPhMeSiH and 1-NpPhMeSiF have been determined by X-ray analysis (Okaya *et al.*, 1966).

An interesting point about the chemistry of optically active silanes, $R^1R^2R^3SiZ$, is that substitution reactions (of Z) may take place with inversion or retention of configuration. Which of these occurs depends on the nature of Z and the incoming group (Y). If Z is a good leaving group and Y is more basic than Z, then reaction occurs with inversion. Hence it is possible to carry out Walden inversions with silanes, *e.g.* (1-Np = 1-naphthyl):

It is possible that reactions that occur with retention proceed *via* a four-centre mechanism (*cf.* **3** §5), *e.g.* (Attridge *et al.*, 1966):

$$\underset{\underset{Me}{|}}{\overset{\overset{1\text{-Np}}{|}}{Ph\!-\!Si\!-\!H}} \xrightarrow{BCl_3} \underset{\underset{Ph\;\;Me}{\diagdown\;\diagup}}{\overset{\overset{1\text{-Np}\;\;H\cdots BCl_2}{\diagdown\quad\vdots}}{Si\cdots Cl}} \longrightarrow \underset{\underset{Me}{|}}{\overset{\overset{1\text{-Np}}{|}}{Ph\!-\!Si\!-\!Cl}}$$

§7. Stereochemistry of tin compounds

Pope and Peachey (1900) obtained ethylmethyl-n-propylstannonium iodide in the dextrorotatory form by means of silver (+)-camphorsulphonate. Concentration of the mother liquor also gave this (+)-form. Thus we have an example of asymmetric transformation (**2** §10iv).

$$\underset{n\text{-}C_3H_7\qquad I}{\overset{CH_3\qquad C_2H_5}{\underset{\diagdown\;\diagup}{Sn}\diagup\;\diagdown}}$$

Attempts to repeat this work, however, have failed. Also, all attempts to prepare other optically active organotin halides have been unsuccessful. One explanation for these failures is that tin readily forms 5-co-ordinate compounds.

$$\underset{R^2\;\;R^3\quad\;\;R^2\;\;R^3}{\overset{R^1\qqu\qquad R^1}{-\!Sn\!-\!X\!-\!Sn\!-\!X\!-}}$$

Dissociation would result in racemisation due to halide exchange; a given halide atom (X) can either remain with its 'original' tin atom (retention) or become attached to the adjacent tin atom (inversion).

§8. Stereochemistry of germanium compounds

Schwarz and Lewinsohn (1931) obtained the (+)-form of ethylphenylisopropylgermanium bromide, but failed to get the (−)-form; this latter form appears to racemise in the mother liquor.

$$\underset{C_2H_5\qquad Br}{\overset{(CH_3)_2CH\qquad C_6H_5}{\underset{\diagdown\;\diagup}{Ge}\diagup\;\diagdown}}$$

On the other hand, several workers have now synthesised a number of optically active germanium compounds by a series of chemical transformations starting from the resolved (+)- and (−)-forms of 1-NpPhMeGeH (Peddle *et al.*, 1963; Eaborn *et al.*, 1963, 1966). For Example (R = retention; I = inversion; R_3GeH = 1-NpPhMeGeH):

$$(-)\text{-}R_3GeH \xrightarrow[R]{Cl_2} (+)\text{-}R_3GeCl \xrightarrow[I]{LiAlH_4} (+)\text{-}R_3GeH$$
$$R \downarrow n\text{-BuLi}$$
$$R_3GeLi \xrightarrow[R]{CO_2} (+)\text{-}R_3GeCO_2H \xrightarrow{CH_2N_2} (+)\text{-}R_3GeCO_2Me$$

Eaborn *et al.* (1968) have also examined various reactions starting with optically active 1-NpPhEtGeH, and their stereochemical assignments are based on Brewster's rules (see **2** §12). These rules have also been applied to silicon compounds (§6).

§9. Stereochemistry of selenium compounds

Pope *et al.* (1902) resolved carboxymethylmethylphenylselenonium bromide in the same way as the corresponding sulphonium salts (§5a); they obtained the active platinichloride (I). Mann *et al.* (1945) also resolved selenonium salt (II). So far, attempts to resolve selenoxides have failed.

$$\left[\begin{array}{c} CH_3 \\ \ddot{S}e-CH_2CO_2H \\ C_6H_5 \end{array}\right]_2^+ PtCl_6^=$$

(I)

$$\left\{ \text{(tetralin)} \overset{+}{S}e-CH_2CO-\text{(C}_6H_4\text{)}-Cl \right\} Br^-$$

(II)

§10. Stereochemistry of tellurium compounds

Lowry *et al.* (1929) obtained the optically active forms of methylphenyl-*p*-tolytelluronium iodide (I), and Mann *et al.* (1945) have resolved (II).

$$\left[CH_3-\text{(C}_6H_4\text{)}-\overset{CH_3}{\underset{C_6H_5}{\overset{|}{Te}:}} \right]^+ I^-$$

(I)

$$\left\{ \text{(tetralin)} \overset{+}{Te}-CH_2COC_6H_4Cl\,(p) \right\} Br^-$$

(II)

REFERENCES

GILMAN (ed.), *Advanced Organic Chemistry*, Wiley (1943, 2nd edn.). Ch. 4, pp. 400–443. 'Optical Isomerism of Elements other than Carbon.'

GILLESPIE and NYHOLM, 'Inorganic Stereochemistry', *Quart. Rev.*, 1957, **11**, 339.

Organic Reactions, Wiley. Vol. 11 (1960). Ch. 1. 'The Beckmann Rearrangement.'

CAMPBELL and WAY, 'Synthesis and Stereochemistry of Heterocyclic Phosphorus Compounds,' *J. Chem. Soc.*, **1960**, 5034.

ABRAHAMS, 'The Stereochemistry of Sub-group VIB of the Periodic Table', *Quart. Rev.*, 1956, **10**, 407.

MCCASLAND and PROSKOW, 'Synthesis of an Image-Superimposable Molecule which Contains no Plane or Centre of Symmetry', *J. Am. chem. Soc.*, 1956, **78**, 5646.

KLYNE and DE LA MARE (eds.), *Progress in Stereochemistry*, Butterworth. Vol. II (1958). Ch. 6. 'The Stereochemistry of the Group V Elements.'

HAMER and MACALUSO, 'Nitrones', *Chem. Rev.*, 1964, **64**, 473.

DELPIERRE and LAMCHEN, 'Nitrones', *Quart. Rev.*, 1965, **19**, 329.

O'BRIEN, 'The Rearrangement of Ketoxime *O*-Sulphonates to Amino Ketones', *Chem. Rev.*, 1964, **64**, 81.

CAMMARATA, 'Optical Studies in Organophosphorus Chemistry', *J. chem. Educ.*, 1966, **43**, 64.

Topics in Stereochemistry, Interscience. Vol. 3 (1968), p. 1. 'Stereochemical Aspects of Phosphorus Chemistry'.

Topics in Stereochemistry, Wiley-Interscience. Vol. 6 (1971), p. 19. 'Pyramidal Atomic Inversion'.

CAMPBELL, 'Substituted Phenoxaphosphines', *J. chem. Soc.* (*C*), 1968, 3026.

MISLOW *et al.*, 'Folded Conformations of Optically Active Triarylarsines', *J. Am. chem. Soc.*, 1963, **85**, 594.

SOMMER, *Stereochemistry, Mechanism, and Silicon*. McGraw-Hill (1965).

BELLOLI, 'Resolution and Stereochemistry of Asymmetric Silicon, Germanium, Tin, and Lead Compounds', *J. chem. Educ.*, 1969, **46**, 640.

KESSLER, 'Detection of Hindered Rotation and Inversion by NMR Spectroscopy', *Angew. Chem. Int. Edn.*, 1970, **9**, 219.

7

Carbohydrates

This chapter is mainly concerned with the stereochemistry of the carbohydrates and the structures of the disaccharides and polysaccharides. It is assumed that the reader is familiar with the open-chain structures and general reactions of the monosaccharides (for an elementary account of these compounds, see Vol. I, Ch. 18).

§1. Determination of the configuration of the monosaccharides

Aldotrioses. There is only one aldotriose, and that is glyceraldehyde. As we have seen (**2** §5), the enantiomers of this compound have been chosen as the *arbitrary* standards for the D- and L-series in sugar chemistry. At the same time, these configurations also represent (fortuitously) the *absolute* configurations.

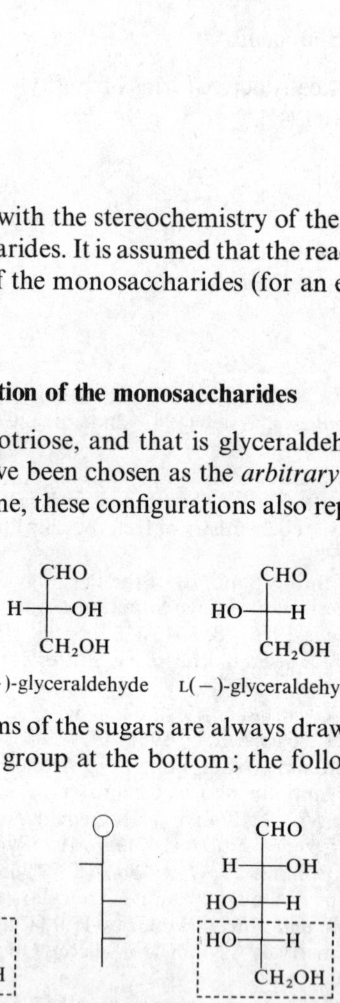

$$
\begin{array}{cc}
\text{CHO} & \text{CHO} \\
\text{H}\!-\!\!-\!\text{OH} & \text{HO}\!-\!\!-\!\text{H} \\
\text{CH}_2\text{OH} & \text{CH}_2\text{OH} \\
\text{D}(+)\text{-glyceraldehyde} & \text{L}(-)\text{-glyceraldehyde}
\end{array}
$$

The conventional planar diagrams of the sugars are always drawn with the CHO (or CH_2OHCO) group at the top and the CH_2OH group at the bottom; the following short-hand notation is also used:

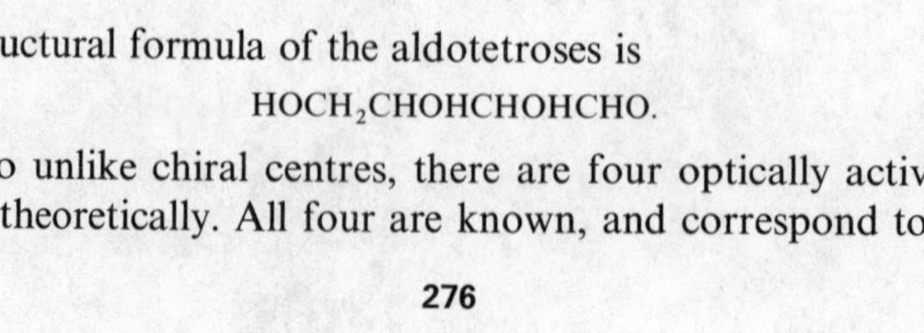

$$
\begin{array}{cccc}
\text{CHO} & & \text{CHO} & \\
\text{HO}\!-\!\text{H} & & \text{H}\!-\!\text{OH} & \\
\text{H}\!-\!\text{OH} & & \text{HO}\!-\!\text{H} & \\
\text{H}\!-\!\text{OH} & & \text{HO}\!-\!\text{H} & \\
\text{CH}_2\text{OH} & & \text{CH}_2\text{OH} & \\
\text{D-series} & & \text{L-series} &
\end{array}
$$

Aldotetroses. The structural formula of the aldotetroses is

$$HOCH_2CHOHCHOHCHO.$$

Since this contains two unlike chiral centres, there are four optically active forms (two pairs of enantiomers) possible theoretically. All four are known, and correspond to D- and L-threose and

276

```
                                        CHO
                                  H ——|—— OH
                                        CH₂OH
```

```
      CO₂H                CHO                    CHO                    CO₂H
 H ——|—— OH    [O]   H ——|—— OH          HO ——|—— H    [O]   HO ——|—— H
 H ——|—— OH   ←——   H ——|—— OH          H ——|—— OH    ——→   H ——|—— OH
      CO₂H                CH₂OH                  CH₂OH                  CO₂H

 meso-tartaric acid    D(−)-erythrose         D(−)-threose        L(−)-tartaric acid
                           (I)                    (II)
```

D- and L-erythrose. D(+)-Glyceraldehyde may be stepped up by the Kiliani reaction to give
D(−)-erythrose and D(−)-threose. The question now is: Which is which? On oxidation, D-erythrose
gives *meso*-tartaric acid, and on reduction gives *meso*-erythritol. Therefore D-erythrose is (I), and
consequently (II) must be D-threose. The configuration of the latter is confirmed by the fact that on
oxidation, D-threose gives L(−)-tartaric acid.

Aldopentoses. These have the structural formula

$$OCHCHOHCHOHCHOHCH_2OH,$$

and since it contains three unlike chiral centres, there are eight optically active forms (four pairs of
enantiomers). All are known, and correspond to the D- and L-forms of ribose, arabinose, xylose and
lyxose. Their configurations may be ascertained by either of the following two methods.

```
        ┌──── D-erythrose ────┐            ┌──── D-threose ────┐
              (I)                                 (II)
             ↓          ↓                        ↓          ↓
           CHO        CHO                      CHO        CHO
       H —|— OH   HO —|— H                 H —|— OH   HO —|— H
       H —|— OH   H —|— OH                 HO —|— H   HO —|— H
       H —|— OH   H —|— OH                 H —|— OH   H —|— OH
           CH₂OH      CH₂OH                    CH₂OH      CH₂OH
      D(−)-ribose  D(−)-arabinose        D(+)-xylose   D(−)-lyxose
         (III)       (IV)                    (V)          (VI)
```

One method starts by stepping up the aldotetroses by the Kiliani reaction. Thus D-erythrose gives
D(−)-ribose and D(−)-arabinose; similarly, D-threose gives D(+)-xylose and D(−)-lyxose. (III) and
(IV) must be ribose and arabinose; but which is which? On oxidation with nitric acid, arabinose
gives an optically active dicarboxylic acid (a trihydroxyglutaric acid), whereas ribose gives an

```
      (III)            (IV)              (V)              (VI)
       ↓[O]             ↓[O]              ↓[O]             ↓[O]
      CO₂H             CO₂H              CO₂H             CO₂H
  H —|— OH        HO —|— H          H —|— OH        HO —|— H
  H —|— OH        H —|— OH          HO —|— H        HO —|— H
  H —|— OH        H —|— OH          H —|— OH        H —|— OH
      CO₂H             CO₂H              CO₂H             CO₂H
    inactive          active          inactive          active
     (IIIa)           (IVa)            (Va)             (VIa)
```

optically inactive dicarboxylic acid. When the terminal groups, *i.e.*, CHO and CH_2OH, of (III) are oxidised to carboxyl groups, the molecule produced (IIIa) possesses a plane of symmetry, and so is inactive. Oxidation of (IV) gives (IVa), and since this molecule has no plane (or any other element) of symmetry, it is optically active. Thus (III) is D-ribose and (IV) is D-arabinose.

   (V) and (VI) must be xylose and lyxose; but which is which? The former sugar, on oxidation, gives an optically inactive dicarboxylic acid, whereas the latter gives an optically active dicarboxylic acid. Therefore (V) is D-xylose and (VI) is D-lyxose.

   The following is the alternative method of elucidating the configurations of the aldopentoses; it is more in keeping with Fischer's solution to the problem. The structural formula of the aldopentoses can give rise to four pairs of enantiomers, the D-forms of which are as follows:

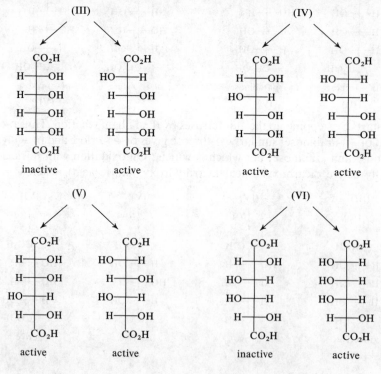

   It should be noted that these four configurations have been obtained from first principles (see **2** §7c); no recourse has been made to the configurations of the aldotetroses. Arabinose and lyxose, on oxidation with nitric acid, produce optically active dicarboxylic acids (trihydroxyglutaric acids). Therefore these two pentoses must be (IV) and (VI), but we cannot say which is which. Xylose and ribose, on oxidation, produce optically inactive dicarboxylic acids (trihydroxyglutaric acids). Therefore these two pentoses must be (III) and (V), and again we say which is which. When each aldopentose is stepped up by one carbon atom (by means of the Kiliani reaction) and then oxidised to the dicarboxylic acid (the terminal groups are oxidised), it is found that arabinose and xylose each give *two* active dicarboxylic acids, whereas ribose and lyxose each give one active and one inactive (*meso*) dicarboxylic acid. The chart shows the dicarboxylic acids obtained from the configurations (III)–(VI).

It therefore follows that D-ribose is (III), D-arabinose is (IV), D-xylose is (V), and D-lyxose is (VI). These configurations are confirmed by the facts that ribose and arabinose give the same osazone, and xylose and lyxose give the same osazone; the only difference between sugars giving the same osazone is the configuration of the second atom, *i.e.*, (III) and (IV) are epimers, as are (V) and (VI).

Aldohexoses. The structural formula of these compounds is

OCHCHOHCHOHCHOHCHOHCH₂OH,

and since it contains four unlike chiral centres, there are sixteen optically active forms (eight pairs of enantiomers). All are known, and may be prepared by stepping up the aldopentoses: D-ribose gives D(+)-allose and D(+)-altrose; D-arabinose gives D(+)-glucose and D(+)-mannose; D-xylose gives D(−)-glucose and D(−)-idose; and D-lyxose gives D(+)-galactose and D(+)-talose.

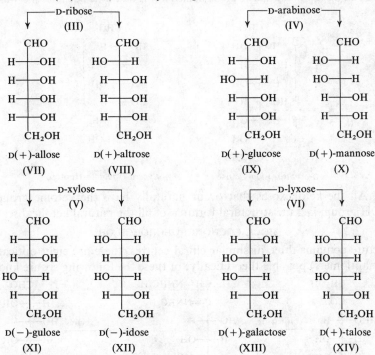

(VII) and (VIII) must be allose and altrose; but which is which? On oxidation with nitric acid, the former gives an optically inactive (allomucic) and the latter an optically active (talomucic) dicarboxylic acid. Therefore allose is (VII) and altrose is (VIII).

(XIII) and (XIV) must be galactose and talose; but which is which? On oxidation with nitric acid, the former gives an optically inactive (mucic) and the latter an optically active (talomucic) dicarboxylic acid. Therefore (XIII) is galactose and (XIV) is talose.

The elucidation of the configurations of the remaining four aldohexoses is not quite so simple, since, on oxidation with nitric acid, glucose and mannose *both* give optically active dicarboxylic acids, as also do gulose and idose; in all four configurations [(IX), (X), (XI), (XII)], replacement of the two terminal groups (CHO and CH₂OH) by carboxyl groups leads to dicarboxylic acids whose structures have no plane (or any other element) of symmetry. It has been found, however, that the dicarboxylic acid from glucose (saccharic acid) is the same as that obtained from gulose (actually the two saccharic acids obtained are enantiomers, D-glucose giving D-saccharic acid and D-gulose L-saccharic acid). Since saccharic acid, $HO_2C(CHOH)_4CO_2H$, is produced by the oxidation of the terminal groups with the rest of the molecule unaffected, it therefore follows that the 'rest of molecule' must be the same for both glucose and gulose. Inspection of formulae (IX), (X), (XI), and (XII) shows that only (IX) and (XI) have the 'rest of the molecule' the same; by interchanging the CHO and CH_2OH groups of (IX), the enantiomer of (XI), i.e., L-gulose, is obtained. Therefore (IX) must be glucose (since we know that glucose is obtained from arabinose), and (XI) must be gulose. Consequently (X) is mannose and (XII) is idose.

Monosaccharides containing more than four asymmetric carbon atoms, e.g., aldoheptose, aldo-octose, etc., are named by using two (or more) prefixes derived from the lower sugars. Thus: **one** asymmetric carbon atom: *glycero*; **two**: *erythro, threo*; **three**: *ribo, arabino, xylo, lyxo*; **four**: *allo, altro, gluco, manno, gulo, ido, galacto, talo*. The name to be assigned to the sugar is given by the prefix denoting *four* asymmetric carbon atoms which occur adjacent to C-1 (aldose) or C-2 (ketose) and by another prefix (or prefixes) denoting the next group of asymmetric carbon atoms (up to four). The prefix named *last* is that which denotes the 4-unit adjacent to the oxo group, e.g.,

D-*erythro*-D-*ido*-Octose   D-*glycero*-L-*galacto*-Heptose

Ketohexoses. All the ketohexoses that occur naturally have the ketonic group adjacent to a terminal CH_2OH group, i.e., the structural formula of all the natural ketohexoses is

$$HOCH_2COCHOHCHOHCHOHCH_2OH.$$

Since this structure contains three dissimilar chiral centres, there are eight optically active forms (four pairs of enantiomers) possible theoretically; of these the following six are known: D(−)- and

D(−)-fructose   osazone   D(+)-glucose
(XV)

osone

L($+$)-fructose, D($+$)- and L($-$)-sorbose, D($+$)-tagatose and L($-$)-psicose. Only D($-$)-fructose, L($-$)-sorbose and D($+$)-tagatose occur naturally.

Fructose. Natural fructose is laevorotatory, and since D-glucose gives the *same* osazone as natural fructose, the latter must be D($-$)-fructose. Furthermore, since osazone formation involves only the first two carbon atoms in a sugar, it therefore follows that the configuration of the rest of the molecule in glucose and fructose must be the same. Hence the configuration of D($-$)-fructose is (XV), and is confirmed by the fact that D($+$)-glucose may be converted into D($-$)-fructose *via* the osazone.

The configurations of the other ketohexoses are:

	CH_2OH			CH_2OH			CH_2OH	
	CO			CO			CO	
H—	—OH		HO—	—H		HO—	—H	
HO—	—H		HO—	—H		HO—	—H	
H—	—OH		H—	—OH		HO—	—H	
	CH_2OH			CH_2OH			CH_2OH	
	D($+$)-sorbose			D($+$)-tagatose			L($-$)-psicose	

The specification of the absolute configurations of the sugars has been discussed in **2** §5d.

Ketoses are named as groups by means of the suffix 'ulose' preceded by a prefix indicating the number of carbon atoms in the chain. Also, the position of the keto group is usually indicated by a number; *e.g.*, fructose is a 2-hexulose. The configuration of a ketose is indicated by a prefix derived from the configuration of the asymmetric carbon atoms in the corresponding aldose, *e.g.*, D-fructose is D-*arabino*hexulose; D-sorbose is D-*xylo*hexulose (*cf.* above).

§1a. Deoxy-sugars.

These are sugars in which one or more hydroxyl groups have been replaced by hydrogen. Some examples are: 2-deoxy-D($-$)-ribose, L($+$)-rhamnose (6-deoxy-L($-$)-mannose), L($-$)-fucose (6-deoxy-L($-$)-galactose), and D($+$)-digitoxose (2,6-dideoxy-D($+$)-allose). All have been obtained from natural sources, but no *free* deoxy sugar has been found in nature (see also §10).

	CHO			CHO			CHO			CHO	
H—	—H		H—	—OH		HO—	—H		H—	—H	
H—	—OH		H—	—OH		H—	—OH		H—	—OH	
H—	—OH		HO—	—H		H—	—OH		H—	—OH	
	CH_2OH		HO—	—H		HO—	—H		H—	—OH	
				CH_3			CH_3			CH_3	
2-deoxy-D($-$)-ribose			L($+$)-rhamnose			L($-$)-fucose			D($+$)-digitoxose		

Deoxy-sugars are named systematically by a configurational prefix representing the system of asymmetric carbon atoms, *e.g.*, 2-deoxy-D-ribose is 2-deoxy-D-*erythro*pentose; L-rhamnose is 6-deoxy-L-*manno*hexose (*cf.* §1).

§2. Ring structure of the monosaccharides

When a monosaccharide is dissolved in water, the optical rotatory power of the solution gradually changes until it reaches a constant value (Dubrunfaut, 1846); *e.g.*, a freshly prepared solution of glucose has a specific rotation of $+111°$, and when this solution is allowed to stand, the rotation falls to $+52.5°$, and remains constant at this value. The final stage can be reached more rapidly either by heating the solution or by adding some catalyst which may be an acid or a base. This change in specific rotation is known as **mutarotation**; all *reducing* sugars (except a few ketoses) undergo mutarotation. In addition to change in optical rotation, mutarotation may be followed by changes in i.r. and NMR spectra, etc.

To account for mutarotation, Tollens (1883) suggested an oxide ring structure for D(+)-glucose, whereby *two* forms would be produced, since, in the formation of the ring, another chiral centre (which can exist in *two* configurations) is produced (*cf.* the Kiliani reaction). Tollens assumed that a five-membered ring (the furanose form) was produced:

```
  H——OH                CHO          HO——H
  H——OH      O  ⇌   H——OH  ⇌   H——OH      O
 HO——H               HO——H         HO——H
  H——               H——OH         H——
  H——OH               H——OH         H——OH
  CH₂OH               CH₂OH         CH₂OH
   (I)              D(+)-glucose       (II)
```

The difficulty of this suggestion was that there was no experimental evidence for the existence of these two forms. Tanret (1895), however, isolated two isomeric forms of D(+)-glucose, thus apparently verifying Tollens' supposition (but see §§7a, 7f). The two forms, (I) and (II), are known respectively as α- and β-D(+)-glucofuranose (see also §7b for the nomenclature of these forms).

Ring formation of a sugar is really hemiacetal formation, one alcoholic group of the sugar forming a hemiacetal with the aldehyde group of the *same* molecule.

Mechanism of mutarotation. According to Lowry (1925), mutarotation is not possible without the presence of an amphiprotic solvent, *i.e.*, a solvent which can function both as an acid and a base, *e.g.*, water. Thus, Lowry and Faulkner (1925) showed that mutarotation is arrested in pyridine solution (basic solvent) and in cresol solution (acidic solvent), but that it takes place in a mixture of pyridine and cresol. It has been assumed that when mutarotation takes place, the ring opens and then recloses in the inverted position or in the original position. There is some evidence for the existence of this open-chain form. The absorption spectra of fructose and sorbose in aqueous solution indicate the presence of open-chain forms; aldoses gave negative results (Bednarczyk *et al.*, 1938). Solutions of glucose and arabinose in 50 per cent sulphuric acid gave an ultraviolet absorption spectrum containing the band characteristic of the oxo (carbonyl) group (Pascu *et al.*, 1948). Aldoses in solution contain a form which is reducible at the dropping mercury electrode (Cantor *et al.*, 1940). Furthermore, a relationship was shown to exist between the amount of this reducible form and the rate of mutarotation. One interpretation of this observation is that the reducible form is an intermediate in mutarotation. Rate constants for the conversion of the ring forms of aldoses to the open-chain form have been calculated from polarographic measurements, and it has also been shown that the energy of activation required to open the pyranose ring is the same for glucose, mannose, galactose, arabinose and xylose (Delahay *et al.*, 1952). The formation of this acyclic intermediate during mutarotation has been confirmed by isotopic evidence (Goto *et al.*, 1941) and by further polarographic evidence (Overend *et al.*, 1957). It is interesting to note in connection with this problem of the existence of the open-chain structure that *aldehydo-sugars*, *i.e.*, aldoses in which the aldehyde group is present, can only be *isolated* if all the hydroxyl groups in the *open-chain form* are 'protected'; *e.g.*, Wolfrom (1929) prepared 2,3,4,5,6-penta-acetylaldehydoglucose as shown in the equations.

The widely accepted view is that monosaccharides in solution exist mainly as an equilibrium mixture of the α- and β-anomeric pyranoses, a small amount of the open-chain form and very small

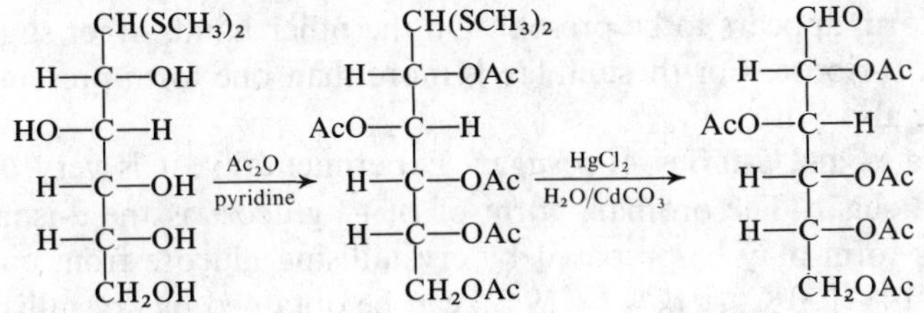

The chemical scheme at top:

$$
\begin{array}{c}
\text{CH(SCH}_3)_2 \\
\text{H—C—OH} \\
\text{HO—C—H} \\
\text{H—C—OH} \\
\text{H—C—OH} \\
\text{CH}_2\text{OH}
\end{array}
\xrightarrow[\text{pyridine}]{\text{Ac}_2\text{O}}
\begin{array}{c}
\text{CH(SCH}_3)_2 \\
\text{H—C—OAc} \\
\text{AcO—C—H} \\
\text{H—C—OAc} \\
\text{H—C—OAc} \\
\text{CH}_2\text{OAc}
\end{array}
\xrightarrow[\text{H}_2\text{O/CdCO}_3]{\text{HgCl}_2}
\begin{array}{c}
\text{CHO} \\
\text{H—C—OAc} \\
\text{AcO—C—H} \\
\text{H—C—OAc} \\
\text{H—C—OAc} \\
\text{CH}_2\text{OAc}
\end{array}
$$

glucose dimethyl
mercaptal

amounts of the α- and β-anomeric furanoses. The presence of the furanose forms has been inferred from the fact that monosaccharides undergo some reactions which lead to the formation of furanose derivatives (see, *e.g.*, §7b). However, NMR studies by Angyal *et al.* (1967) indicated the absence of the furanose form for D-glucose, D-xylose, etc., but its presence in D-allose, D-arabinose, etc.

The problem now is: What is the mechanism of the formation of the open-chain form from the ring-form? Lowry (1925) suggested that it occurred by the simultaneous addition and elimination of a proton, since both an acid and a base must be present (see above). This concerted mechanism would conform to a third-order reaction:

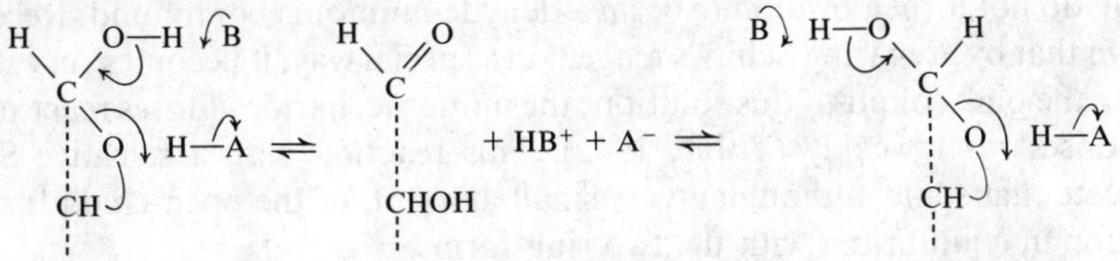

$$+ HB^+ + A^- \rightleftharpoons$$

α-D-   β-D-

Swain *et al.* (1952) have shown that the mutarotation of tetramethylglucose, catalysed by phenol and pyridine in benzene solution, is a third-order reaction; this supports the above mechanism. Furthermore, Swain also showed that a dilute solution of 2-hydroxypyridine in benzene is far more effective as a catalyst than a mixture of phenol and pyridine (at the same concentration as 2-hydroxypyridine). Since the reaction was now second-order (first-order in 2-hydroxypyridine), this is in keeping with the concerted mechanism.

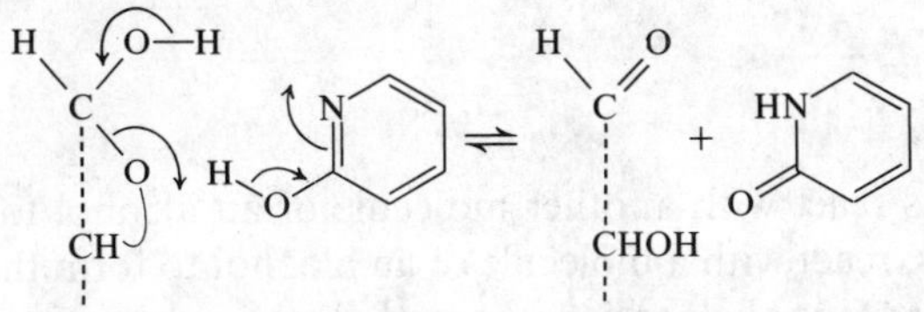

A possible explanation for the increased rate is that the *cyclic* transition state with 2-hydroxypyridine requires a lower energy of activation than the T.S. involving simultaneous attack by phenol and pyridine.

On the other hand, some authors believe that the reaction proceeds in two independent steps, one being the acid-catalysed reaction, and the other the base-catalysed reaction. In this case the mechanism would conform to a second-order reaction. Hill *et al.* (1952) have shown that the mutarotation of glucose in aqueous methanol containing acetate buffers is in better agreement with a second-order reaction than with a third-order.

There are, however, other factors involved in mutarotation. The foregoing account has been confined to work on D-glucopyranose. It has been observed that in freshly prepared solutions some sugars exhibit normal mutarotations, *e.g.*, the pyranose forms of D-glucose, D-lyxose, etc. For these, only the pyranose form appears to be present. On the other hand, other sugars exhibit abnormal mutarotations, *e.g.*, D-ribose. For these, there is more than one form present: pyranose, furanose and open-chain (see also §7h).

Preparation of the α- and β-forms of a sugar. Experimentally, it is very difficult to isolate the α- and β-forms of a sugar. The ordinary form of D(+)-glucose is the α-isomer, m.p. 146°C and $[\alpha]_D = +111°$; this form may be prepared by crystallising glucose from cold aqueous solution. The β-isomer, m.p. 148–150°C, $[\alpha]_D = +19\cdot2°$, can be obtained by crystallising glucose from hot saturated aqueous solution. Thus the α-form may be converted into the β-, and *vice versa*, during the process of crystallisation; this is an example of asymmetric transformation (**2** §10iv). Both forms show mutarotation, the final value of the specific rotation being $+52\cdot5°$; this corresponds to a mixture containing about 38 per cent of the α-isomer, and 62 per cent of the β-. The two stereo-isomeric ring-forms of a sugar are often referred to as *anomers*.

Summary of the evidence for the ring structures of sugars. The cyclic structure of the sugars accounts for the following facts:

(i) The existence of two anomers of a given sugar, *e.g.*, α- and β-glucose.

(ii) Mutarotation.

(iii) Glucose and other aldoses do not give certain characteristic reactions of aldehydes, *e.g.*, Schiff's reaction, do not form a bisulphite or an aldehyde-ammonia compound. Recently, however, it has been shown that by preparing Schiff's reagent in a special way, it becomes very sensitive, simple aldoses restoring the pink colour to this solution; the monosaccharide aldoses react strongly, but the disaccharide aldoses react weakly (Tobie, 1942). This reaction with a sensitive Schiff's reagent appears to indicate that some, although a very small amount, of the open-chain form of a sugar is present in solution in equilibrium with the two ring-forms.

(iv) Glucose penta-acetate does not react with hydroxylamine; this indicates that the aldehyde group is absent in this derivative (glucose itself does form an oxime).

(v) Aldehydes normally form acetals by combination with two molecules of a monohydric alcohol; aldoses (and ketoses) combine with only one molecule of an alcohol. It should be noted, however, that aldoses will combine with *two* molecules of a thiol to form a mercaptal (thioacetal).

(vi) X-ray analysis definitely proves the existence of the ring structure, and at the same time indicates the size of the ring (see §7f).

§3. Glycosides

Just as simple hemiacetals react with another molecule of an alcohol to form acetals, so can the sugars, in their ring-forms, react with a molecule of an alcohol to form the acetal derivative, which is known under the generic name of **glycoside**; those of glucose are known as *glucosides*; of fructose, *fructosides*, etc. The hydroxyl group produced at the oxo group by ring formation is known as the *glycosidic hydroxyl group*. This group can be acetylated and methylated, as can all the other hydroxyl groups in the sugar, but the glycoside derivatives are far more readily decomposed by various reagents.

E. Fischer (1893) refluxed glucose in methanol solution in the presence of one-half per cent hydrochloric acid, and thereby obtained a white crystalline product which contained *one* methyl group (as shown by analysis), and which did not reduce Fehling's solution or mutarotate, and did not form an osazone. Thus the hemiacetal structure is no longer present in this compound; in fact, this compound appears to be an acetal since it is stable in alkaline solution (Fehling's solution). Furthermore, on boiling with dilute inorganic acids the compound regenerated the original sugar, a reaction again typical of acetals. Ekenstein (1894) isolated a second isomer from the reaction mixture when he repeated Fischer's work, and Fischer explained the existence of these two isomers by suggesting ring structures for the two methyl glucosides.

methyl α-D-glucoside	methyl β-D-glucoside

Fischer assumed that these methyl glucosides were five-membered ring systems, basing his assumption on Tollens' suggestion (§2). As we shall see later (§7a), Fischer's assumption is incorrect (see also §7h).

The non-sugar part of a glycoside is known as the *aglycon* (or *aglycone*), and in many glycosides that occur naturally, the aglycon is often a phenolic compound (see §24).

Fischer (1894) found that methyl α-D-glucoside was hydrolysed by the enzyme maltase, and the β-D-glucoside by the enzyme emulsin. Furthermore, Fischer also found that maltase would not hydrolyse the β-glucoside, and that emulsion would not hydrolyse the α-glucoside. Thus the two isomers can be distinguished by the specificity of action of certain enzymes (see also **13** §16). Armstrong (1903) followed these enzymic hydrolyses polarimetrically, and showed that methyl α-D-glucoside liberates α-D-glucose, and that the β-glucoside liberates β-D-glucose; Armstrong found that hydrolysis of the α-glucoside produced a 'downward' mutarotation, whereas that of the β-glucoside produced an 'upward' mutarotation. It therefore follows that α-D-glucose is stereo-chemically related to methyl α-D-glucoside, and β-D-glucose to methyl β-D-glucoside. Further support for these assignments of configurations comes from the fact that acetylation of α- and β-D-glucopyranose by pyridine-acetic anhydride at 0°C gave respectively the α- and β-pyranose penta-acetate (Behrend *et al.*, 1904).

§4. Configuration of C_1 in glucose

The configurations of C-1 in α- and β-D-glucose have been written, in the foregoing account, as:

α-isomer	β-isomer
(I)	(II)

The question now is: What justification is there for this choice, *i.e.*, what is the evidence that enables us to say that the α-isomer (characterised by certain physical constants) actually has the hydrogen atom to the left and the hydroxyl group to the right? Hudson (1909) proposed the *empirical* rule that of an α, β pair of sugars in the D-series, the α-anomer, which has the *higher* dextrorotation (*i.e.*, this physical constant decides which of the two is to be designated α-), has the hydrogen to the left (*i.e.*, I); the β-anomer consequently has the hydrogen atom to the right (II). Thus, α-D(+)-glucose is the anomer with the specific rotation +111°, and β-D(+)-glucose is the anomer with the specific rotation +19·2°. If the D-sugar has a negative rotation, then, according to the empirical rule, the β-anomer has the higher negative rotation (*i.e.*, the less positive rotation), *e.g.*, α-D(−)-fructose is the anomer with the specific rotation −20°, and the β-anomer −133°. In the L-sugars, the α-anomer is the one with the *higher* laevorotation, and the other is the β-anomer; thus the α-forms (and the

β-forms) of the D- and L-series are enantiomeric. These configurations have been confirmed by further work, *e.g.*, Rüber (1931) found that, in general, *trans*-compounds have a higher molecular refraction than the corresponding *cis*-; the molecular refraction of β-D-glucose is greater than that of the α-anomer. The strongest bit of evidence for the configurations of the α- and β-anomers, however, has been obtained from X-ray studies of α-D-glucose (see §7f).

It has been pointed out above that the two anomers of a D-sugar are enantiomers of the corresponding two anomers of the L-sugar. This means that the configurations at C-1 are also mirror images, and consequently the configuration of C-1 in an α-D-aldose (C_1—H to the *left*) is identical with that of the β-L-aldose (C_1—H also to the *left*).

| α-D- | α-L- | β-D- | β-L- |

and

§5. Hudson's lactone rule

Hudson (1910) studied the rotation of the lactones derived from the aldonic acids. If we use the usual projection formulae, the lactone ring will be on the right or left according as the hydroxyl group on C-4 (*i.e.*, the γ-hydroxyl group) is on the right or left, *i.e.*, according as C-4 has a *dextro* or *laevo* configuration:

dextrorotatory　　　　laevorotatory

From an examination of 24 lactones derived from aldonic acids, and assuming that they were γ-lactones, Hudson concluded that if the lactone ring was on the right, the compound was dextrorotatory; if the ring was on the left, then laevorotatory.

This rule also applies to δ-lactones.

§6. Hudson's isorotation rules

Hudson (1909, 1930) applied the rule of optical superposition (**1** §9) to carbohydrate chemistry, and his first application was to the problem of the configuration of C-1 in the anomers of aldoses. Hudson pointed out that the only structural difference between the α- and β-anomers (of sugars and glycosides) is the configuration of C-1. Thus, representing the rotation of this terminal group as A and that of the rest of the molecule as B, and then taking the α-anomer as the one with the higher positive rotation (in the D-series) we have:

Molecular rotation of the α-anomer $= + A + B$
Molecular rotation of the β-anomer $= - A + B$

Thus in every pair of α- and β-anomers the following rules will hold:

Rule 1. The sum of the molecular rotations (2B) will be a constant value characteristic of a particular sugar and independent of the nature of R.

Rule 2. The difference of the molecular rotations (2A) will be a constant value characteristic of R.

As we have seen, the rule of optical superposition does not hold exactly (due to neighbouring action, etc.; see 1 §9). In the sugars, however, the rotation of C-1 is affected only to a small extent by changes in the rest of the molecule, and *vice versa.* This is illustrated in the following table, from which it can be seen that the sum of the molecular rotations (2B) for various pairs of glucopyranoside anomers is fairly constant.

C-1 *substituent*	M_α	M_β	$M_\alpha + M_\beta = 2B$
OH	$+202$	$+34$	$+236$
OCH$_3$	$+309$	-66	$+243$
OC$_2$H$_5$	$+314$	$-69 \cdot 5$	$+245 \cdot 5$

These isorotation rules have been used to ascertain which of an anomeric pair of glycosides is α and which is β, and to determine the type of glycosidic link in disaccharides and polysaccharides.

§6a. Hudson's amide rule. Hudson (1918, 1919) proposed a generalisation for ascertaining the configuration of the α-carbon atom in α-hydroxy-acids. In carbohydrate chemistry, this may be applied to aldonic acids and, according to the rule (based on the rule of shift; **1** §9), the Δ value for (CONH$_2$—CO$_2$H) is *positive* if C-2 has a D-hydroxyl group and *negative* if it has an L-hydroxyl group. Inspection of the formulae in §1 shows that the following aldonic acids have a D-hydroxyl group at C-2: D-ribonic (III), L-arabonic (IV), D-gluconic (IX), L-mannonic (X), D-gulonic acid (XI), etc. The value of Δ (amide—acid) is positive for all of these acids, *e.g.,* (III): $(+27) - (-29) = +56$; (IX): $(+61) - (-13) = +74$; etc.

§7. Methods for determining the size of sugar rings

As pointed out previously, Fischer followed Tollens in proposing the γ-oxide ring. There was, however, no experimental evidence for this; the γ-hydroxyl group was chosen as being involved in ring formation by analogy with the ready formation of γ-lactones from γ-hydroxyacids. The problem was further complicated by the fact that Hudson *et al.* (1915) isolated four galactose penta-acetates, none of which had a free aldehyde group. Furthermore, these four compounds were related to each other as pairs, *i.e.,* there were two α- and two β-isomers. The only reasonable explanation for this was that there are *two* ring systems present, but once again there is no evidence to decide the actual sizes of the rings.

The original experimental approach to the problem of determining the size of the ring present in sugars consisted essentially in studying the methylated sugars. A more recent method uses the methyl glycosides (for this method, see §7g). Since methylation is so important in the original method, the following account describes briefly the methods used.

(i) *Purdie's method* (1903). The sugar is first converted into the corresponding methyl glycoside (methanol and hydrochloric acid), and this is then heated with methyl iodide in the presence of *dry* silver oxide; thus:

Purdie's method is only applicable to glycosides and other derivatives in which the *reducing group* is missing or has been protected by substitution. Methylation of a free reducing sugar by this method would result in the oxidation of that sugar by the silver oxide.

In certain cases, thallous hydroxide may be used instead of silver oxide (Fear *et al*., 1926).

(ii) *Haworth's method* (1915). In this method methyl sulphate and aqueous sodium hydroxide are added to a well-stirred sugar solution at such a rate that the liquid remains practically neutral:

$$\overset{|}{\underset{|}{C}}HOH + (CH_3)_2SO_4 + NaOH \longrightarrow \overset{|}{\underset{|}{C}}HOCH_3 + CH_3NaSO_4 + H_2O$$

This method is directly applicable to all reducing sugars.

(iii) More recent methods of methylation use sodium and methyl iodide in liquid ammonia, or diazomethane in the presence of moisture.

The fully methylated methyl glycoside is hydrolysed with dilute hydrochloric acid, whereby the glycosidic methyl group is eliminated. A study of the oxidation products of the methylated sugar then leads to the size of the ring. It should be noted that throughout the whole method the assumption is made that no methyl groups migrate or that any change in the position of the oxide ring occurs (see, however, later). The number of methyl groups present in the methylated sugar and the various oxidation products are determined by the Zeisel method (see Vol. I; see also §7h and §21). It might also be noted here that many partially methylated sugars occur naturally (see §20).

§7a. **Pyranose structure.** This structure has also been referred to as the δ-oxide or amylene oxide ring. As an example of the method used, we shall consider the case of D($+$)-glucose (Haworth and Hirst, 1927). D($+$)-Glucose (I) was refluxed in methanol solution in the presence of a small amount of hydrochloric acid, and the methyl D-glucoside (II) so produced was methylated with methyl sulphate in the presence of sodium hydroxide to give methyl tetramethyl-D-glucoside (III) and this, on hydrolysis with dilute hydrochloric acid, gave tetramethyl-D-glucose (IV). When this was dissolved in water and then oxidised by heating with excess of bromine at 90°C, a lactone (V) was isolated, and this, on further oxidation with nitric acid, gave xylotrimethoxyglutaric acid (VI). The structure of this compound is known, since it can be obtained directly by the oxidation of methylated xylose; thus its structure is (VI) (see also §7d). The structure of this compound is the key to the determination

$$\begin{array}{c} CO_2H \\ H\text{---}\!\!\!\!\!-OCH_3 \\ CH_3O\text{---}\!\!\!\!\!-H \\ H\text{---}\!\!\!\!\!-OCH_3 \\ CO_2H \end{array}$$

(VI)

of the size of the ring in the sugar. One of the carboxyl groups in (VI) must be that which is combined in the formation of the lactone ring in the tetramethylgluconolactone (V). The other carboxyl group is almost certainly the one that has been derived from the non-methylated carbon atom, *i.e.*, from the CHOH group that is involved in the ring formation in the sugar. Therefore there must be *three* methoxyl groups in the lactone ring. Thus the lactone *cannot* be a γ-lactone, and consequently C-5 must be involved in the ring formation. It therefore follows that the lactone (V) must be 2,3,4,6-tetra-*O*-methyl-D-gluconolactone. Working *backwards* from this compound, then (IV) must be 2,3,4,6-tetra-*O*-methyl-D-glucose, (III) methyl 2,3,4,6-tetra-*O*-methyl-D-glucoside, (II) methyl D-glucopyranoside, and (I) D-glucopyranose (see §7f for the significance of the term pyranose). It should be noted that the question as to whether the sugar is α or β has been ignored; starting with either leads to the same final results. The foregoing experimental results can now be represented by the following equations:

$$\begin{array}{c}
\text{CHOH} \\
\text{H}-\text{OH} \\
\text{HO}-\text{H} \\
\text{H}-\text{OH} \\
\text{H}- \\
\text{CH}_2\text{OH}
\end{array}\ \text{O} \quad \xrightarrow[\text{reflux}]{\text{CH}_3\text{OH/HCl}} \quad
\begin{array}{c}
\text{CHOCH}_3 \\
\text{H}-\text{OH} \\
\text{HO}-\text{H} \\
\text{H}-\text{OH} \\
\text{H}- \\
\text{CH}_2\text{OH}
\end{array}\ \text{O} \quad \xrightarrow[\text{NaOH}]{(\text{CH}_3)_2\text{SO}_4} \quad
\begin{array}{c}
\text{CHOCH}_3 \\
\text{H}-\text{OCH}_3 \\
\text{CH}_3\text{O}-\text{H} \\
\text{H}-\text{OCH}_3 \\
\text{H}- \\
\text{CH}_2\text{OCH}_3
\end{array}\ \text{O} \quad \xrightarrow{\text{HCl}} \quad
\begin{array}{c}
\text{CHOH} \\
\text{H}-\text{OCH}_3 \\
\text{CH}_3\text{O}-\text{H} \\
\text{H}-\text{OCH}_3 \\
\text{H}- \\
\text{CH}_2\text{OCH}_3
\end{array}\ \text{O} \quad \xrightarrow[\text{90}^\circ\text{C}]{\text{Br}_2/\text{H}_2\text{O}}$$

   (I)   (II)   (III)   (IV)

$$\begin{array}{c}
\text{CO} \\
\text{H}-\text{OCH}_3 \\
\text{CH}_3\text{O}-\text{H} \\
\text{H}-\text{OCH}_3 \\
\text{H}- \\
\text{CH}_2\text{OCH}_3
\end{array}\ \text{O} \quad \xrightarrow{\text{HNO}_3} \quad
\left[\begin{array}{c}
\text{CO}_2\text{H} \\
\text{H}-\text{OCH}_3 \\
\text{CH}_3\text{O}-\text{H} \\
\text{H}-\text{OCH}_3 \\
\text{H}-\text{OH} \\
\overline{} \\
\text{CH}_2\text{OCH}_3
\end{array}\right] \quad \xrightarrow{\text{HNO}_3} \quad
\begin{array}{c}
\text{CO}_2\text{H} \\
\text{H}-\text{OCH}_3 \\
\text{CH}_3\text{O}-\text{H} \\
\text{H}-\text{OCH}_3 \\
\text{CO}_2\text{H}
\end{array}$$

    (V)   (VI)

There is a slight possibility that the ring might have been an ε-ring, *i.e.*, the oxide ring involves C-1 and C-6, and that C-5 is converted to the carboxy group with loss of C-6. Haworth, however, made certain that this was not the case by the following method. Had the ring been 1,6-, then 2,3,4,5-tetramethylgluconic acid (VII) would have been obtained (instead of V). (VII) was obtained by Haworth *et al.* (1927) from melibiose and gentiobiose (see §§18, 19) and, on oxidation, gave tetra-methylsaccharic acid (VIII) and not the dicarboxylic acid (VI).

$$\begin{array}{c}
\text{CO}_2\text{H} \\
\text{H}-\text{OCH}_3 \\
\text{CH}_3\text{O}-\text{H} \\
\text{H}-\text{OCH}_3 \\
\text{H}-\text{OCH}_3 \\
\text{CH}_2\text{OH}
\end{array} \quad \longrightarrow \quad
\begin{array}{c}
\text{CO}_2\text{H} \\
\text{H}-\text{OCH}_3 \\
\text{CH}_3\text{O}-\text{H} \\
\text{H}-\text{OCH}_3 \\
\text{H}-\text{OCH}_3 \\
\text{CO}_2\text{H}
\end{array}$$

     (VII)   (VIII)

Thus there is a 1,5-ring in the tetramethylgluconolactone, tetra-*O*-methylglucose, methyl tetra-*O*-methylglucoside, methyl glucoside, *and therefore in glucose itself*. This conclusion is based on the assumption that no change in the ring position occurs during the methylation of glucose. Thus glucose is a δ- or pyranose sugar (see also §7h).

By similar methods it has been shown that hexoses and pentoses all possess a pyranose structure.

§7b. Furanose structure. This structure has also been called the γ-oxide or butylene oxide ring. Fischer (1914) prepared methyl D(+)-glucoside by a slightly modified method, *viz.*, by dissolving D(+)-glucose in methanol, adding 1 per cent hydrochloric acid, and then allowing the mixture to stand at 0°C (instead of refluxing, as in his first procedure; see also §7h). On working up the product, he obtained a syrup (a crystalline compound was obtained by the first procedure). Fischer called this compound methyl γ-glucoside, and believed it was another isomer of the α- and β-forms; this is the significance of the symbol γ is used by Fischer. This syrup, however, was subsequently shown to be a mixture of methyl α- and β-glucofuranosides, *i.e.*, this glucoside contained a γ- or 1,4-ring

(Haworth *et al.*, 1927). This syrup (I), when completely methylated (methyl sulphate method), gave a methyl tetra-*O*-methyl-D-glucoside (II) and this, on hydrolysis with dilute hydrochloric acid, gave tetra-*O*-methyl-D-glucose (III). On oxidation with bromine water at 90°C, (III) gave a crystalline lactone (IV) and this, when oxidised with nitric acid gave dimethyl-D-tartaric (dimethoxysuccinic) acid (V). This compound (V) is the only compound of known structure, and is therefore the key to the determination of the size of the ring in the sugar. Working *backwards* from (V), then (IV) is 2,3,5,6-tetra-*O*-methyl-D-gluconolactone, (III) is 2,3,5,6-tetra-*O*-methyl-D-glucose, (II) is methyl 2,3,5,6-tetra-*O*-methyl-D-glucoside, and (I) is methyl D-glucofuranoside. If we write D-glucose as D-glucofuranose, then the foregoing reactions may be formulated as shown below (see §7f for the meaning of furanose).

These reactions prove that (I), (II), (III) and (IV) all contain a γ-oxide ring, *i.e.*, the methyl glucoside (I) *prepared at* 0°C, has a 1,4-ring. This then raises the question: What is the size of the ring in glucose itself? Is it 1,4 or 1,5? Preparation of the methyl glucoside at reflux temperature gives the 1,5-compounds (see §7a); preparation at 0°C gives the 1,4-compounds. It is therefore not possible to say from these experiments whether glucose itself exists in the pyranose (1,5-) or furanose (1,4-) forms originally, or whether these two forms are in equilibrium. Further information is necessary to supply an answer to these questions. As we shall see later, the normal form of a sugar is the pyranose structure (see §7f); pyranosides are often referred to as the 'normal' glycosides.

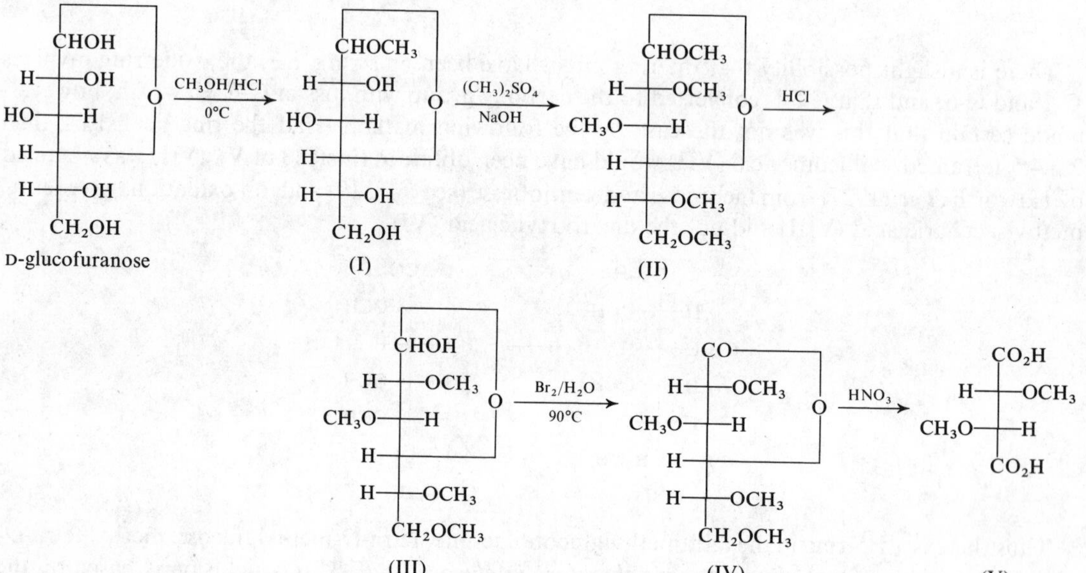

By similar methods it has been shown that hexoses and pentoses give methyl glycosides possessing a furanose structure when prepared at 0°C (or at room temperature).

§7c. **Determination of ring size by means of lactone formation.** As we have seen, glycoside formation at *reflux* temperature leads ultimately to a methylated δ-lactone, whereas at 0°C a methylated γ-lactone is obtained. Haworth (1927) examined the rates of hydration of these two types of lactones to the open-chain acids; the rates were measured by changes in the rotation or conductance. Haworth found that the rate of hydration was much faster in one series than in the other; the δ-lactones were converted almost completely to the acids, whereas the γ-lactones were converted at a much slower rate (see Fig. 7.1). Thus, by comparing the stabilities (to hydration) of the various methylated lactones, it is possible to say whether the lactone under investigation is γ- or δ-. It is very important to note that this method easily distinguishes a γ- from a δ-lactone, but it does not *prove* one to be γ- and the other δ-. The actual nature of the lactone was proved *chemically*; the fast-changing

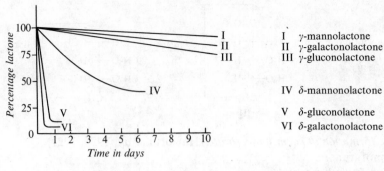

Fig. 7.1

I   γ-mannolactone
II   γ-galactonolactone
III γ-gluconolactone

IV   δ-mannonolactone

V   δ-gluconolactone
VI   δ-galactonolactone

lactone was shown to be the δ-lactone, and the slow-changing one the γ- (the chemical evidence was obtained by the degradative oxidation already described). However, having once established the relationship between the rate of hydration and the nature of the lactone, *e.g.*, in the case of glucose, mannose, galactose and arabinose, the property can *then* be used to determine the size of the ring in an unknown lactone of a sugar acid (see also §7h).

$$
\begin{array}{c}
\text{CHO} \\
\text{H}\!-\!^{\alpha}\!-\!\text{OH} \\
\text{HO}\!-\!^{\beta}\!-\!\text{H} \\
\text{HO}\!-\!^{\gamma}\!-\!\text{H} \\
\text{H}\!-\!^{\delta}\!-\!\text{OH} \\
\text{CH}_2\text{OH}
\end{array}
$$

D-galactose
(open-chain)

$$
\begin{array}{c}
\text{CO} \\
\text{H}\!-\!\text{OCH}_3 \\
\text{CH}_3\text{O}\!-\!\text{H} \\
\text{CH}_3\text{O}\!-\!\text{H} \\
\text{H}\!-\! \\
\text{CH}_2\text{OCH}_3
\end{array}
$$

(+)-lactone;
δ-lactone

$$
\begin{array}{c}
\text{CO} \\
\text{H}\!-\!\text{OCH}_3 \\
\text{CH}_3\text{O}\!-\!\text{H} \\
\text{H}\!- \\
\text{H}\!-\!\text{OCH}_3 \\
\text{CH}_2\text{OCH}_3
\end{array}
$$

(−)-lactone;
γ-lactone

Correlation between the above scheme and Hudson's lactone rule has been demonstrated in certain cases, *e.g.*, galactose. Preparation of the methyl galactoside at reflux temperature, then methylation, hydrolysis, and finally oxidation with bromine water, leads to the formation of a methylated lactone which is dextrorotatory (and so the ring will be to the right and is therefore a δ-lactone), and since it is a rapidly hydrated lactone, it must be δ-. Preparation of the methyl galactoside at 0°C, etc., leads to the formation of a methylated lactone which is laevorotatory and is very stable to hydration. Thus, this lactone will have the ring to the left, and hence must be a γ-lactone; at the same time, since it is a slowly hydrated lactone, it must be γ- (see the above formulae).

§7d. Pyranose and furanose structures of pentoses.
The methods used for determining the size of sugar rings have been described with glucose (an aldehexose) as the example. It is also instructive to apply these methods to the aldopentoses. L(+)-Arabinose has been chosen as the example, and the following equations and footnotes explain the method.

(i) *Glycoside formation at reflux temperature* (Haworth *et al.*, 1927).

(I) is L(+)-arabinopyranose, and since it is *dextrorotatory*, the ring has been drawn to the *right*. This way of drawing the projection formula is based on the observation of Haworth and Drew (1926), who pointed out that if a ring in a sugar is 1,5- (*i.e.*, δ-), then Hudson's lactone rule holds good for sugars as for γ- and δ-lactones.

(II) is 2,3,4-tri-*O*-methyl-L-arabinose.

(III) is 2,3,4-tri-*O*-methyl-L-arabinolactone; it is a δ-lactone as shown by oxidation to (IV) and also by the fact that it is of the type that is readily hydrated.

(IV) is 2,3,4-L-arabinotrimethoxyglutaric acid (this is the key compound).

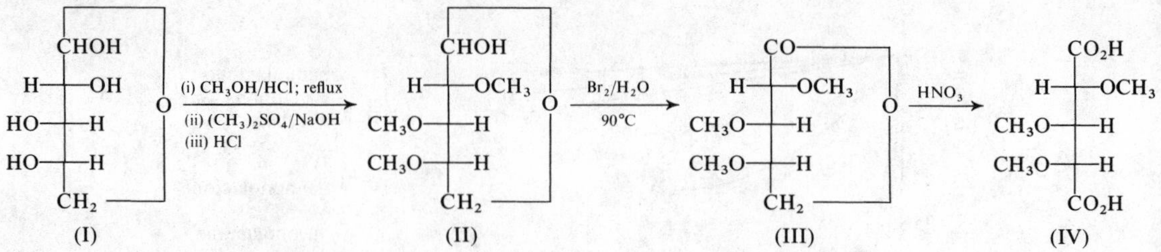

```
    CHOH                              CHOH                             CO                             CO2H
 H——OH                            H——OCH3                          H——OCH3                        H——OCH3
HO——H    O  (i) CH3OH/HCl; reflux  CH3O——H   O  Br2/H2O  CH3O——H   O   HNO3  CH3O——H
HO——H       (ii) (CH3)2SO4/NaOH    CH3O——H       90°C    CH3O——H                CH3O——H
    CH2        (iii) HCl               CH2                          CH2                            CO2H
    (I)                               (II)                          (III)                           (IV)
```

(ii) *Glycoside formation at room temperature* (Haworth *et al.*, 1925, 1927).
(V) is L-arabinofuranose.
(VI) is 2,3,5-tri-*O*-methyl-L-arabinose.
(VII) is 2,3,5-tri-*O*-methyl-L-arabinolactone (Hudson's lactone rule, and is slow-changing type).
(VIII) is dimethyl-D-tartaric acid (this is the key compound).

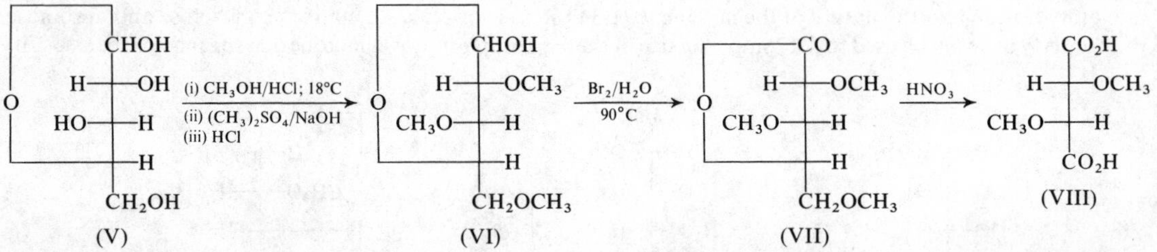

```
        CHOH                              CHOH                             CO                             CO2H
     H——OH                            H——OCH3                          H——OCH3                        H——OCH3
O   HO——H   (i) CH3OH/HCl; 18°C  O  CH3O——H   Br2/H2O  O  CH3O——H   HNO3  CH3O——H
        H——      (ii) (CH3)2SO4/NaOH       H——      90°C       H——               CO2H
     CH2OH         (iii) HCl             CH2OCH3                      CH2OCH3                        (VIII)
      (V)                               (VI)                          (VII)
```

§7e. Ketose ring structures. Only D-fructose will be considered; the method is essentially the same as that for the aldoses, but there is one important variation, and that is in the oxidation of the tetramethylfructose. This cannot be oxidised by bromine water as can the tetramethylaldose; the fructose derivative is first oxidised with dilute nitric acid and then with acid permanganate, and by this means the lactone is obtained. The lactone is then further oxidised by moderately concentrated nitric acid. The following equations and footnotes explain the method, but before giving these, let us first

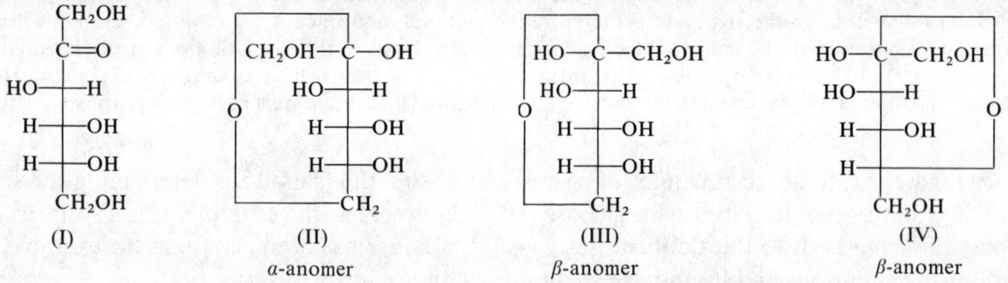

```
    CH2OH
    C═O             CH2OH—C—OH         HO—C—CH2OH          HO—C—CH2OH
 HO——H          HO——H              HO——H               HO——H
  H——OH      O   H——OH         O    H——OH          O    H——OH          O
  H——OH           H——OH              H——OH                H——
    CH2OH            CH2                 CH2                 CH2OH
     (I)             (II)                (III)               (IV)
                   α-anomer            β-anomer            β-anomer
```

consider the way of writing the projection formula of the ring structure of fructose. The usual open-chain formula is (I), and to form the ring the ketone group is involved with C-6 in the pyranose form, and with C-5 in the furanose form; each of these can exist as the α- and β-anomers. When the ring is closed, then if the hydroxyl group is drawn on the right, this will be the α-anomer (the CH₂OH group now replaces a hydrogen atom in the aldoses). Furthermore, since D-fructopyranose is laevo-rotatory, the oxide ring is drawn to the left (see the comments on L(+)-arabinopyranose, §7d). Thus α-D(−)-fructopyranose is (II) and β-D(−)-fructopyranose is (III). The furanose forms are obtained in a similar manner, but in this case the ring must be written to the right since the hydroxyl group on C-5 is on the right; thus β-D-fructofuranose is (IV) (see also sucrose, §13).

(i) *Glycoside formation at reflux temperature* (Haworth *et al.*, 1926, 1927).
(V) is β-D(−)-fructopyranose.
(VI) is methyl β-D-fructopyranoside.
(VII) is methyl 1,3,4,5-tetra-*O*-methyl-β-D-fructoside.
(VIII) is 1,3,4,5-tetra-*O*-methyl-β-D-fructose.
(IX) is 3,4,5-tri-*O*-methyl-β-D-fructuronic acid.
(X) is 2,3,4-tri-*O*-methyl-D-arabinolactone; this is a quick-changing lactone, and is therefore a δ-lactone.
(XI) is D-arabinotrimethoxyglutaric acid.

(V) → [CH₃OH/HCl, reflux] → (VI) → [(CH₃)₂SO₄, NaOH] → (VII) → [HCl] →
(VIII) → [HNO₃] → (IX) → [KMnO₄, H₂SO₄] → (X) → [HNO₃] → (XI)

(ii) *Glycoside formation at room temperature* (Haworth *et al.*, 1927).
(XII) is β-D-fructofuranose.
(XIII) is 1,3,4,6-tetra-*O*-methyl-β-D-fructose.
(XIV) is 3,4,6-tri-*O*-methyl-β-D-fructuronic acid.
(XV) is 2,3,5-tri-*O*-methyl-D-arabinolactone; this is a slow-changing lactone, and so is γ-.
(XVI) is dimethyl-L-tartaric acid.

(XII) → [(i) CH₃OH/HCl; 18°C; (ii) (CH₃)₂SO₄/NaOH; (iii) HCl] → (XIII) → [HNO₃] →
(XIV) → [KMnO₄, H₂SO₄] → (XV) → [HNO₃] → (XVI)

§7f. **Conclusion.**   From the foregoing account it can be seen that the sugars exist as ring structures and not as open chains. Haworth (1926) therefore proposed a hexagonal formula for δ-sugars based on the pyran ring (I). The problem now is to convert the conventional plane-diagrams that we have been using into the *pyranose* formula. Let us take α-D-glucopyranose (II) as our example. The conventional tetrahedral diagram of (II) is (III) (see **2** §5). Examination of (III) shows that the point of attachment of the oxide ring at C-1 is *below* the plane of the paper, and that at C-5 it is *above* the plane of the paper. If the tetrahedron with C-5 at its centre is rotated so that the point of attachment of the oxide ring is placed *below* the plane of the paper, (III) will now become (IV) and the oxide ring will now be *perpendicular* to the plane of the paper, *i.e.*, perpendicular to the plane containing all the other groups (these all lie in a plane above the plane of the paper). The conventional plane-diagram of (IV) is (V), but in order to emphasise the fact that the oxide ring is actually perpendicular to the plane of the paper, the part of the ring lying below the plane of the paper is shown by a broken line (the true plane-diagram should have a normal line drawn as in (II)). Comparison of (V) with (II) shows that where the CH_2OH was originally is now the point of attachment of the oxide ring, the CH_2OH occupying the position where the H atom was, and the latter now where the oxide ring was. Thus, if we consider the conversion of (II) into (V) without first drawing (III) and (IV), then in effect *two* Walden inversions have been effected, and consequently the original configuration is retained. (V) is now transformed into the perspective formula (VI) by twisting (V) so that the oxide ring is perpendicular to the plane of the paper and all the other groups

(I)   (II)   (III)   (IV)

(V)   (VI) (α-D)   (VII)   (VIII) (α-L)

are joined to bonds which are parallel to the plane of the paper. By convention, C-1 is placed to the right and the oxygen atom at the right-hand side of the part of the ring furthest from the observer. Sometimes the lower part of the ring, which represents the part nearest to the observer, is drawn in thick lines. Thus, to change (V) into (VI), first draw the hexagon as shown in (VI) and then place all the groups on the left-hand side in (V) above the plane of the ring in (VI); all those on the right-hand side in (V) are placed below the plane of the ring in (VI). (VII) represents a 'short-hand representation' of D-glucose.

The pyranose forms of the L-sugars are obtained by the same process. The result is the mirror image of the corresponding D-sugar, *e.g.*, α-L-glucopyranose is (VIII) [note that every asymmetric carbon atom has been inverted; see §4].

In a similar manner, Haworth proposed a five-membered ring for γ-sugars based on the furan ring (VIII). If we use the above scheme of transformation, the plane-diagram of methyl β-D(+)-glucofuranoside (IX) is first changed into (X) (*two* changes are carried out), and then (X) is twisted so as to be represented by (XI), in which the oxygen atom is furthest from the observer.

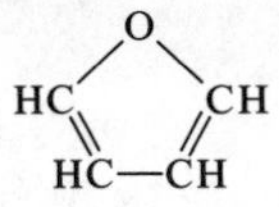

(VIII) 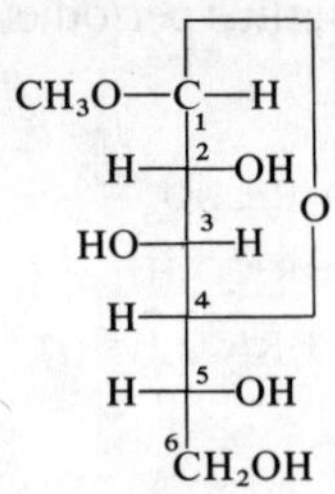 (IX) 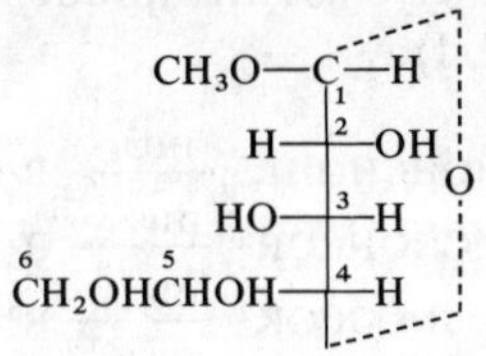 (X) 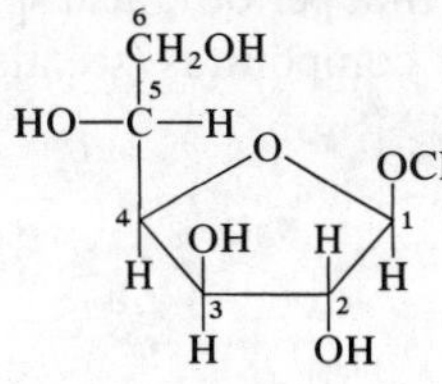 (XI)

Two other examples which illustrate the conversion into the perspective formula are:

(i) **α-D(−)-fructopyranose.**

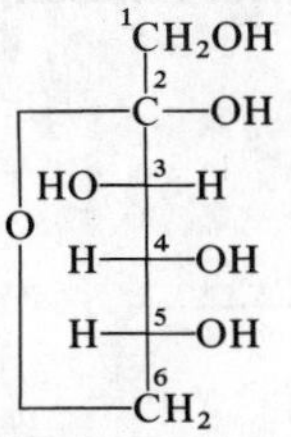

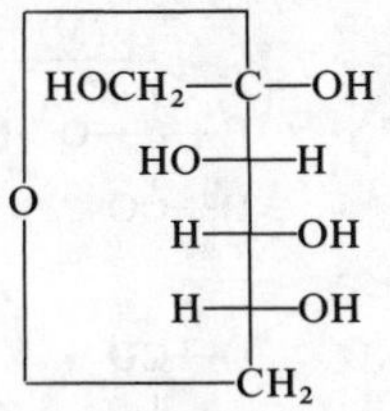

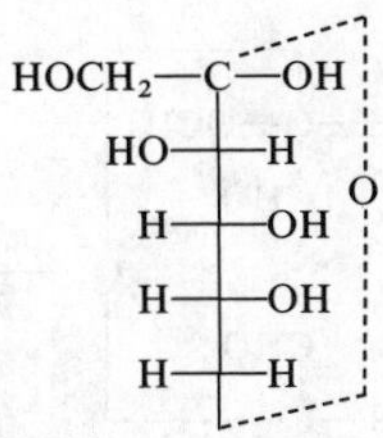

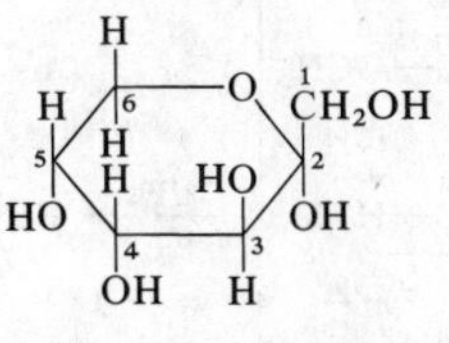

(ii) **Methyl β-D(+)-fructofuranoside.**

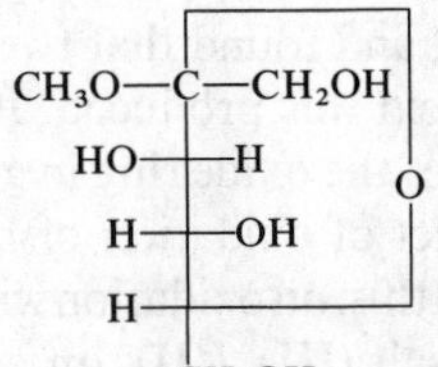

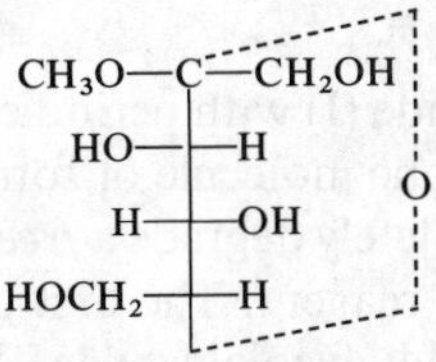

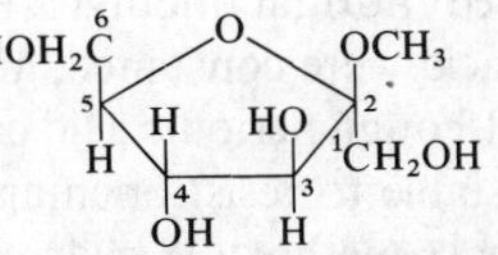

The perspective formulae better represent the relative spatial positions of the atoms or groups than do the projection formulae, but best of all are the conformational representations, since these give a much clearer picture of the details of reactions undergone by the sugars (see §7h).

Actual size of sugar rings. Since glycoside formation under different conditions gives compounds containing different sized rings, the important question then is: What is the size of the ring in the original sugar? Oxidation of an aldose with hypobromite produces an unstable δ-lactone; this is the first product, but slowly changes into the stable γ-lactone (Hudson, 1932). It therefore follows that the size of the ring in *normal* sugars is pyranose. By analogy, ketoses are also believed to exist normally as pyranose compounds. This pyranose structure has been confirmed by X-ray analysis of various crystalline monosaccharides (Cox, 1935). McDonald *et al.* (1950) examined α-D-glucose by X-ray analysis, and confirmed the presence of the six-membered ring, the configuration as found chemically, and also the *cis* arrangement of the 1,2-hydroxyl groups in the α-form. The configuration at C-1 of β-D-glucose has been confirmed by NMR spectroscopy (Furberg *et al.*, 1963). Eiland *et al.* (1950) subjected difructose strontium chloride dihydrate to X-ray analysis, and showed the presence of a six-membered ring, and confirmed the configuration found chemically. It might be noted here that furanose sugars have not yet been isolated, but some furanosides have. It is also interesting to note that apparently fructose and ribose *always* occur in compounds as the furanose structure.

§7g. Oxidation methods for determining the size of the ring in sugars.   These methods make use of the fact that periodic acid splits 1,2-glycols (Malaprade, 1928); thus periodic acid splits the following types of compounds (see also Vol. I):

$$R^1CHOHCHOHR^2 \xrightarrow{1HIO_4} R^1CHO + R^2CHO$$

$$R^1CHOHCOR^2 \xrightarrow{1HIO_4} R^1CHO + R^2CO_2H$$

$$R^1COCOR^2 \xrightarrow{1HIO_4} R^1CO_2H + R^2CO_2H$$

Thus a *free* sugar is broken down completely, *e.g.*,

$$HOCH_2CHOHCHOHCHOHCHO \xrightarrow{4HIO_4} HCHO + 4HCO_2H$$

In all these reactions, one molecule of periodic acid is used for each pair of adjacent alcoholic groups (or oxo groups). Thus, by estimating the periodic acid used, and the formic acid and formaldehyde formed, the number of *free* adjacent hydroxyl groups in a sugar can be ascertained. Hudson (1937,

1939) oxidised 'normal' methyl α-D-glucoside (I) with periodic acid, and found that two molecules of periodic acid were consumed, and that one molecule of formic acid was produced. It should be noted that although periodic acid can completely degrade a *free* sugar, the oxide ring in glycosides is sufficiently stable to resist opening by this reagent. The first product of oxidation of methyl α-D-glucoside was D'-methoxy-D-hydroxymethyldiglycolaldehyde (II) and this, on oxidation with bromine water in the presence of strontium carbonate, gave the crystalline salt (III). (III), on acidification with sulphuric acid (for hydrolysis), followed by further oxidation with bromine water, gave oxalic acid (IV) and D(−)-glyceric acid (V). Isolation of (II), (III), (IV) and (V) indicates that the ring in (I) is δ-; this is also supported by the fact that only one carbon atom was eliminated as formic acid, and that two molecules of periodic acid were consumed. By similar experiments, it has been shown that all methyl α-D-hexosides of the 'normal' type consume *two* molecules of periodic acid and produce *one* molecule of formic acid, and all also give products (II), (III), (IV) and (V). Thus all these hexosides must be six-membered rings, and also it follows that all 'normal' methyl α-pyranosides have the same configuration for C-1; this has already been shown to be (VI).

Similarly, all β-compounds, on oxidation with periodic acid, give the stereoisomer of (II), *i.e.*, L'-methoxy-D-hydroxymethyldiglycolaldehyde.

Aldopentopyranosides also give similar products as those obtained from the aldohexopyranosides, *e.g.*, methyl α-D-arabinopyranoside (VII) gives D'-methoxydiglycolaldehyde (VIII). Since all methyl α-D-aldopentopyranosides give the *same* diglycolaldehyde, they too have the same configuration for C-1, *viz.*, (VI).

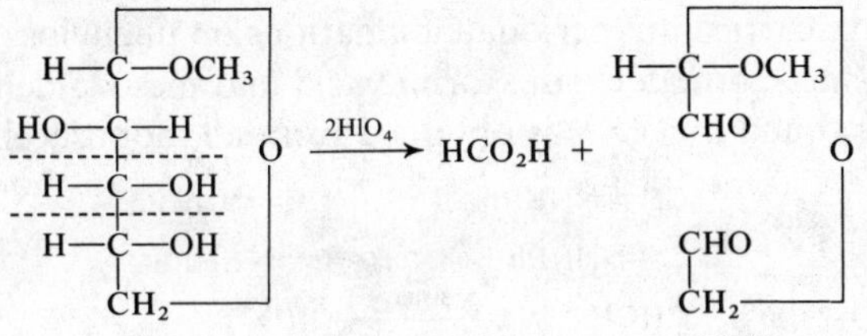

$$
\begin{array}{c}
\text{H—C—OCH}_3 \\
\text{HO—C—H} \\
\text{H—C—OH} \\
\text{H—C—OH} \\
\text{CH}_2\text{—}
\end{array} \; \text{O} \quad \xrightarrow{\;2\text{HIO}_4\;} \quad \text{HCO}_2\text{H} \; + \quad
\begin{array}{c}
\text{H—C—OCH}_3 \\
\text{CHO} \\
\; \\
\text{CHO} \\
\text{CH}_2\text{—}
\end{array} \; \text{O}
$$

(VII)   (VIII)

When hexofuranosides, *i.e.*, the 'abnormal' glycosides, are oxidised with periodic acid, *two* molecules of acid are consumed and one molecule of *formaldehyde* is formed. These results are in keeping with the presence of a five-membered ring, *e.g.*, methyl α-D-glucofuranoside.

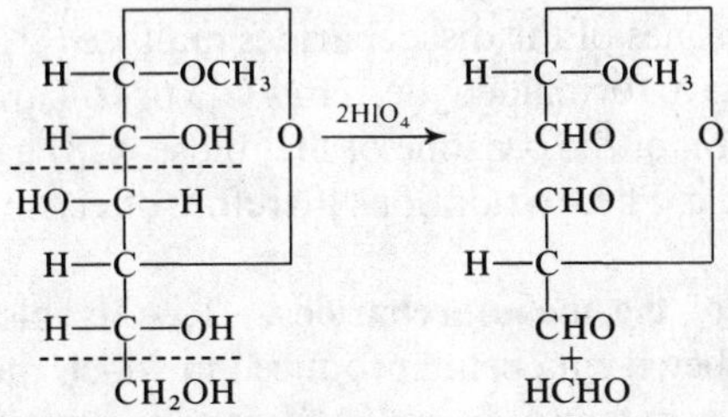

$$
\begin{array}{c}
\text{H—C—OCH}_3 \\
\text{H—C—OH} \\
\text{HO—C—H} \\
\text{H—C} \\
\text{H—C—OH} \\
\text{CH}_2\text{OH}
\end{array} \; \text{O} \quad \xrightarrow{\;2\text{HIO}_4\;} \quad
\begin{array}{c}
\text{H—C—OCH}_3 \\
\text{CHO} \\
\text{CHO} \\
\text{H—C} \\
\text{CHO} \\
+ \\
\text{HCHO}
\end{array} \; \text{O}
$$

Oxidation of methyl α-D-arabinofuranoside (IX) consumes *one* molecule of periodic acid, and no carbon atom is eliminated (either as formaldehyde or formic acid); thus the ring is five-membered. Furthermore, since the dialdehyde (II) obtained is the same as that from methyl α-D-glucopyranoside (I), the configuration of C-1 is the same in both (I) and (IX).

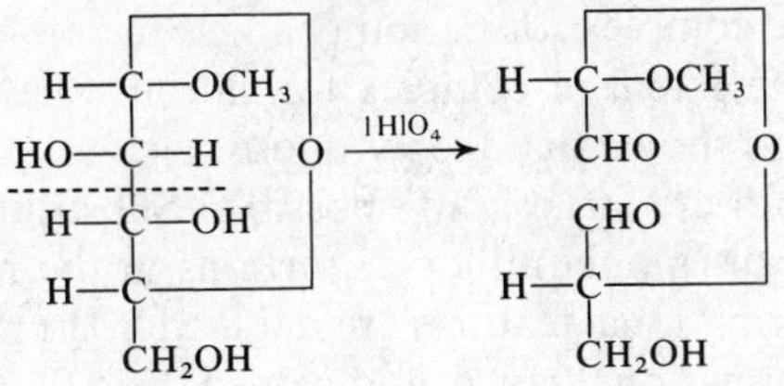

$$
\begin{array}{c}
\text{H—C—OCH}_3 \\
\text{HO—C—H} \\
\text{H—C—OH} \\
\text{H—C} \\
\text{CH}_2\text{OH}
\end{array} \; \text{O} \quad \xrightarrow{\;1\text{HIO}_4\;} \quad
\begin{array}{c}
\text{H—C—OCH}_3 \\
\text{CHO} \\
\text{CHO} \\
\text{H—C} \\
\text{CH}_2\text{OH}
\end{array} \; \text{O}
$$

(IX)   (II)

There is evidence that (II) is not an acyclic compound but is a dioxan derivative, (II*a*), or more probably a dimer of this, (II*b*), arising by intermolecular hemiacetal formation.

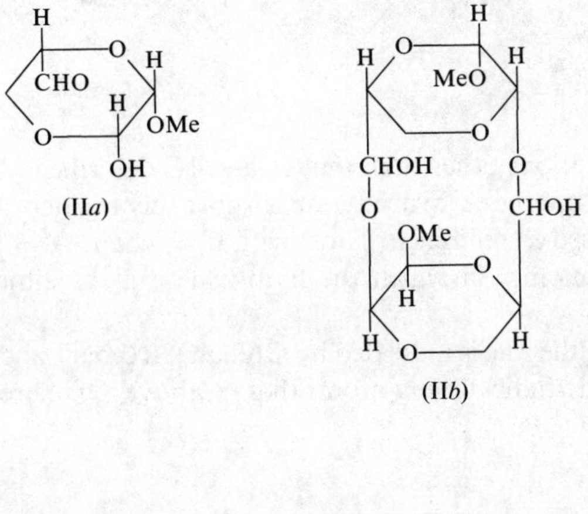

(II*a*)

(II*b*)

Hough *et al.* (1956) have carried out periodate oxidations on phenylosazones of reducing mono-saccharides (X) and obtained formaldehyde, formic acid and mesoxaldehyde 1,2-bisphenylhydra-zone (XI). These authors found that (XI) is obtained from all monosaccharides in which C-3 and

$$
\begin{array}{ccc}
CH = NNHPh & & CH = NNHPh \\
| & & | \\
C = NNHPh & & C = NNHPh \\
| & \xrightarrow{3HIO_4} & | \\
CHOH & & CHO \\
\text{----}| \text{----} & & \quad (XI) \\
CHOH & & \\
\text{----}| \text{----} & & + \\
CHOH & & 2HCO_2H \\
\text{----}| \text{----} & & + \\
CH_2OH & & CH_2O \\
(X) & &
\end{array}
$$

C-4 are free, and 1 molecule of formaldehyde from the terminal CH_2OH group when this is free. They also showed that the osazones of the disaccharides maltose (§15), cellobiose (§16), and lactose (§17) did not give (XI) but did give formaldehyde. Thus C-3 or C-4 are linked in these disaccharides. On the other hand, the oxidation of the osazone of melibiose (§18) gave (XI) but no formaldehyde; thus C-6 is linked in this molecule. These oxidations therefore offer a means of differentiating between the two types of disaccharides.

§7h. Conformational analysis of the monosaccharides.   1,2-Glycols form complexes in cupram-monium solutions, a five-membered ring being produced in which the copper atom is linked to two oxygen atoms. Furthermore, the extent of complex formation depends on the spatial arrangement of the two adjacent hydroxyls, the most favoured position being that in which the two groups and the two carbon atoms to which they are attached lie in one plane. In six-membered rings, the hydroxyl groups of 1,2-diols, if *cis*, are *a,e* and if *trans* are *e,e* or *a,a*. Now, the projection angle between $1a,2e$ or $1e,2e$ substituents is 60° and that for $1a,2a$ is 180° (see **4** §11). Reeves (1946) showed that complex formation occurred only if the projection angle was 0° (the most favoured position mentioned above) or 60°. Since complex formation changes the molecular rotation, the molecular rotational shift will indicate the extent of complex formation. Reeves (1950), using this cupram-monium complex formation, has shown that the pyranose sugars assume a chair form in preference to any boat form wherever both are structurally possible. Substitution of an oxygen atom for a carbon atom in cyclohexane causes only minor distortions in the ring (Hassel *et al.*, 1947), and consequently the general conformational features are retained in the pyranose sugars. Reeves (1951) proposed the two regular conformations shown, and named them C1 (the normal chair) and 1C (the reverse chair). Reeves (1958) pointed out that there is an infinite number of skew conformations in which angle strain is absent. It is still usual, however, to use the regular conformations of Reeves since these are readily related to the Haworth formulae.

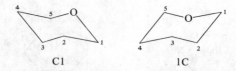

C1   1C

There are various descriptions other than the C1 and 1C described above, *e.g.*,

(*a*) The position of the anomeric hydroxyl or a substituent group (C-1 in aldoses and C-2 in ketoses) in α-anomers is used as reference. Thus, with C = chair, A = axial, and E = equatorial, CA and CE refer to the anomer in which the hydroxyl or a substituent is respectively axial or equatorial.

(*b*) The conformation of the ring is indicated by **C** (chair), **B** (boat), and **HC** (half-chair). Numbers are then used, superscripts to indicate ring-atoms that lie above the reference plane (which is defined by the plane containing atoms 2,3,5 and the ring-oxygen) and subscripts to indicate ring-atoms which lie below the reference plane.

Descriptions (*a*) and (*b*) may be illustrated with D-glucopyranose (Z = OH or a substituent group):

$$\alpha\text{-D-C1}$$
$$\text{CA}$$
$$\text{CA(D-C1)}$$
$$\alpha\text{-C}_1^4$$

$$\alpha\text{-D-1C}$$
$$\text{CE}$$
$$\text{CE(D-1C)}$$
$$\alpha\text{-C}_4^1$$

It might also be noted that there are six possible boat forms (B1–B3 and 1B–3B), but since the chair forms are preferred, no discussion of the boat forms has been given here.

Let us now first summarise some useful points in writing conformations of the monosaccharides (see also **4** §11a).

(i) 1,2-*cis*-Groups in the projection and perspective formulae are *a,e* (or *e,a*) in the conformational representation.

(ii) 1,2-*trans*-Groups in the projection and perspective formulae are *e,e* (or *a,a*) in the conformational representation.

(iii) For D-aldohexoses in the normal chair form (C1), the α-form has the anomeric hydroxyl group in the axial position; in the reverse chair form (1C) the α-form has the anomeric hydroxyl group in the equatorial position (see below).

(iv) Epimerisation of a hydroxyl group involves the conversion of the axial position into the equatorial or *vice versa*.

Various methods are used to study conformational analysis of the monosaccharides. One method involves the estimation of the **instability rating** of the various conformations. This is done by the use of **instability factors**, which were introduced by Reeves (1951) and later modified by Kelly (1957). The application of these rules has led to predictions which are in good agreement with the experimental results.

(i) The chair conformation is usually preferred to the boat (or twist-boat) whenever both are structurally possible.

(ii) Axial hydroxyl groups (or any substituent other than hydrogen) increase the instability of the molecule. Each axial hydroxyl group results in one instability unit.

(iii) 1,3-Interactions involving axial hydroxyl result in 0·5 instability unit.

(iv) An axial CH_2OH group (at C-5) results in two instability units if only axial hydrogens are on C-1 and C-3. If an axial substituent other than hydrogen is on C-1 or C-3, the instability factor is 2·5 units. Because of this large value, it is unusual to have conformations with an axial CH_2OH group.

(v) If the hydroxyl group (*i.e.*, an oxygen atom) on C-2 is axial and the oxygen atom on C-1 is equatorial, this results in 2·5 instability units. This situation is referred to as the **Delta-2 (Δ2) condition** or the **Δ2 instability factor**. Its origin is not fully understood, but it appears to be due to dipole interaction.

In addition to this method (instability rating), physical methods are used in conformational analysis and also to identify and elucidate structures of the monosaccharides.

X-ray analysis. This is limited to studies on the *solid* compound, and consequently the results may not apply to conformations when the compound is in solution. The X-ray analysis of the *p*-bromo-phenylhydrazones of D-arabinose and D-glucose has shown that these are pyranose forms, whereas those of D-ribose and D-mannose are open-chain derivatives, as are also the *p*-bromophenyl-osazones of D-ribose and D-glucose.

Infrared spectroscopy. By means of this technique, it is possible to identify monosaccharides and, to some extent, determine structure, configuration and conformation. Thus, for example, the identification of various groups is readily carried out, and the α- and β-anomers may be differentiated. The validity of the results obtained for the differentiation of the α- and β-anomers has been questioned.

NMR spectroscopy. NMR spectroscopic studies of monosaccharides and their derivatives have led to a number of generalisations which are used for the purpose of identification and assignment of configuration and conformation. Deuterium oxide is a very useful solvent (in these NMR studies) since it permits the examination of all C—H protons. On the other hand, dimethyl sulphoxide (preferably deuterated) as solvent permits the examination of hydroxylic protons (in this case, no exchange reaction can occur).

(i) Anomeric protons (C_1—H) almost always occur at lower field than any other ring-hydrogens (due to the deshielding effect of *two* oxygen atoms attached to C-1). Anomeric protons also show characteristic coupling constants with the proton on C-2. For α-glucopyranose derivatives, $J_{1,2}$ for eH_1, aH_2 is 3–3·6 Hz (this is also the case for other sugars with eH_1, aH_2); and for α-manno-pyranose, $J_{1,2}$ for eH_1, eH_2 is 1·0–1·5 Hz (and is the case for other sugars with eH_1, eH_2).

(ii) Axial ring-hydrogens usually appear upfield with respect to equatorial hydrogens.

(iii) Axial hydroxylic protons (in pyranoses) usually appear upfield (0·3 p.p.m.) with respect to equatorial hydroxylic protons. This is also the case for the anomeric hydroxylic proton.

Long-range coupling is observed at 100 MHz between hydroxyl groups and axial vicinal ring-hydrogens. For example, α-glucopyranose shows a signal that is a quartet: C_1—OH and C_1—H splitting, J 4·5 Hz; C_1—OH and C_2—H splitting, J 0·7 Hz. The β-anomer, on the other hand, shows a doublet: C_1—OH and C_1—H splitting, J 6·4 Hz.

(iv) Vicinal *trans* diaxial protons in pyranose rings have large coupling constants (5–12 Hz). Vicinal *e,e* (*trans*) and *e,a* (*cis*) protons cannot be differentiated; J for both of these is 1–3·6 Hz. Generally, J for axial and equatorial protons attached to the same carbon atom is about 2 Hz. Also, because the CH_2OH group (on C-5 of the ring) is almost always equatorial, this fixes the proton on C-5 as axial. With this as a 'standard', it may be possible to deduce the positions (*a* or *e*) of the other ring protons.

(v) For acetylated pyranosides, the methyl group on an axial secondary hydroxyl group occurs downfield with respect to that on an equatorial secondary hydroxyl group. Thus: τ: axial, 7·80–7·90; equatorial, 7·88–8·03. These relative positions of the signals also hold for the acetamido group. Thus: τ: axial, 7·92–8·04; equatorial, 8·03–8·12.

(vi) For methylated pyranosides, the methyl group on an axial hydroxyl group occurs upfield with respect that on an equatorial hydroxyl group. Thus: τ: axial, 6·54–6·64; equatorial, 6·46–6·47. Many exceptions, however, are known. An equatorial C—Me group has a τ 8·76–8·84.

These generalisations are useful, but may lead to wrong conclusions in rings which have been deformed by, *e.g.*, steric effects.

The use of these relationships may be illustrated by the elucidation of the configuration and conformation of *desosamine*, a 3-aminohexose that has been isolated from a series of antibiotics.

desosamine

A *freshly* prepared solution of this compound showed the presence of only an axial anomeric proton. Hence crystalline desosamine is the β-anomer (Woo *et al.*, 1962). Also, the values of the coupling constants $J_{2,3}$, $J_{3,4}$ and $J_{4,5}$ were all between 10 and 12 Hz, and consequently there are axial protons on C-2, C-3, (C-4) and C-4 (see also §20).

Mass spectrometry. This is now sufficiently developed to be used as a means of determining, *e.g.*, the size of a ring of a monosaccharide (pyranose of furanose), the number and position of methyl ether and acetyl groups in a methylated sugar, position of linking in a disaccharide, etc.

The mass spectrum of β-D-glucopyranose penta-acetate has been examined in great detail, and this spectrum contains features common to most aldopyranoses. The molecular ion ($M = 390$) is absent; this is due to the ready elimination of the glycosidic acetyl group as a free radical ($CH_3CO \cdot$; m/e 43). Hence the highest mass recorded is m/e 347 (390 − 43), and is a very weak peak.

Three ions are always observed (and also in all fully acetylated sugars) provided acetoxy groups are in the 1,2- or 1,3-positions. These ions are the acetylium ion (m/e 43), the diacetyl oxonium ion (m/e 103), and the tracetyl oxonium ion (m/e 145).

$$CH_3CO^+ \qquad (CH_3CO)_2\overset{+}{O}\text{---}H \qquad (CH_3CO)_3O^+$$
$$m/e \qquad 43 \qquad\qquad 103 \qquad\qquad\qquad 145$$

Another common feature is the elimination of acetic acid followed by the elimination of keten. This results in the overall loss of 102 units to give a very strong peak at m/e M − 102 (*i.e.*, 288 in our example). The fragmentation paths proposed are:

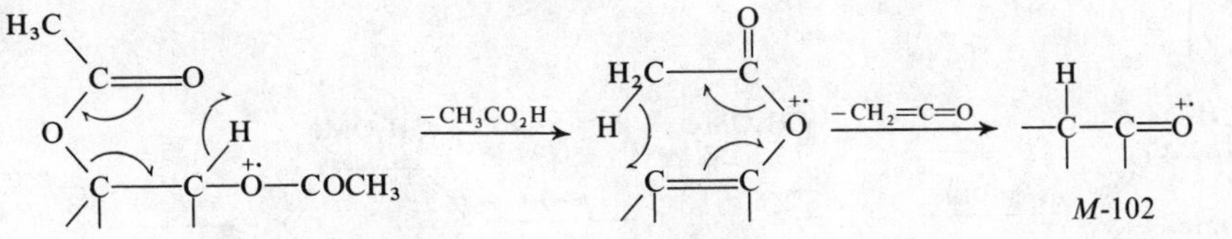

$$M \qquad\qquad\qquad M\text{-}60 \qquad\qquad\qquad M\text{-}102$$

The spectrum is complicated; strong peaks include m/e *43*, 73, 98, *103*, 115, *140*, *145*, 157, 200, 242, *288*; and weak peaks m/e *330*, 331, 347 (masses in italics have been accounted for in the above discussion). The peaks given are believed to be produced by paths (i) and (ii).

(i)

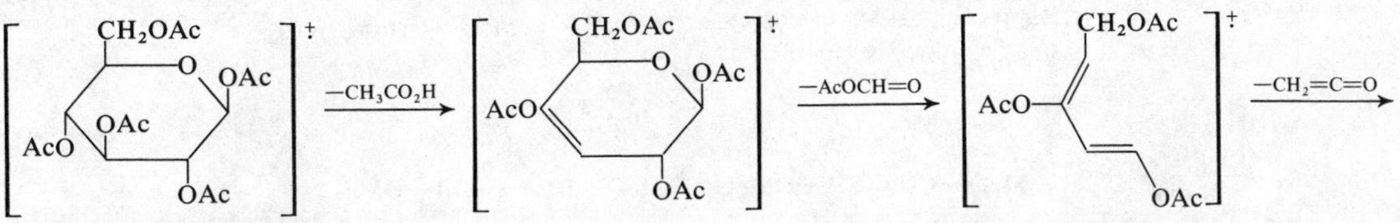

$$[M\ 390] \qquad\qquad m/e\ 330 \qquad\qquad m/e\ 242$$

$$[C_9H_{12}O_5]^+ \xrightarrow{-CH_3CO_2H} [C_7H_8O_3]^{+} \xrightarrow{-CH_2=C=O} [C_5H_6O_2]^{+}$$
$$m/e\ 200 \qquad\qquad m/e\ 140 \qquad\qquad m/e\ 98$$

(ii)

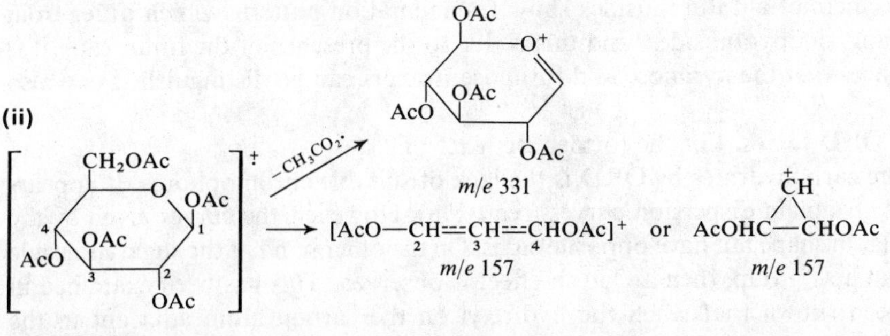

$$m/e\ 331$$

$$\longrightarrow [AcO\text{---}\underset{2}{C}H\!=\!\!=\!\!=\!\underset{3}{C}H\!=\!\!=\!\!=\!\underset{4}{C}HOAc]^+ \quad \text{or} \quad AcOHC\text{---}CHOAc$$
$$m/e\ 157 \qquad\qquad\qquad m/e\ 157$$

$$\xrightarrow{-CH_2=C=O} [C_5H_7O_3]^+ \xrightarrow{-CH_2=C=O} [C_3H_5O_2]^+$$
$$m/e\ 115 \qquad\qquad m/e\ 73$$

Now let us consider fully methylated glycosides, *e.g.*, methyl 2,3,4,6-tetra-*O*-methyl-α-D-gluco-pyranoside. The fragmentation paths of this compound show some similarities to those of the penta-acetates: (i) no molecular ion ($M = 250$) is observed because of the ready elimination of the glycosidic methoxy-group as a free radical ($CH_3O \cdot$; m/e 31). Hence the highest mass recorded is m/e 219 (250 − 31), and is a very weak peak. (ii) Methanol is now eliminated (the methoxy-group at position 3 is lost preferentially). (iii) Ethylene oxide is eliminated finally.

Strong peaks include m/e 75, 88, 101, 187, and weak peaks m/e 71, 73, 111, 155, 173, 205, 219. It is not certain how all of these are produced.

The other ions are:

$$CH_2{=}CH{-}CH{=}\overset{+}{O}Me \qquad Me\overset{+}{O}{=}CH{-}CHO \qquad MeO{-}CH{=}CH\overset{+}{O}H_2$$
$$m/e\ 71 \qquad\qquad m/e\ 73 \qquad\qquad m/e\ 75$$

$$[MeO{-}CH{=}CH{-}OMe]^{\ddagger} \qquad MeO{-}HC\overset{\overset{+}{C}H}{\diagup\diagdown}CH{-}OMe$$
$$m/e\ 88 \qquad\qquad\qquad m/e\ 101$$

Acetates of partially methylated sugars (pyranosides) behave like fully acetylated sugars if only one or two methyl ether groups are present, or like the fully methylated sugars if four methyl ether groups are present.

Acetates and methyl ethers of aldofuranosides show fragmentation patterns which differ from those of the corresponding aldopyranosides, and this is due to the presence of the furan ring. It is because of these differences that the pyranose and furanose isomers can be distinguished (see also §20).

Optical rotations and ORD curves. For the former see, *e.g.*, §6.

A difficulty in studying carbohydrates by ORD is the lack of suitable chromophores. It appears that most simple sugars give plain dispersion curves (see **1** §9a). However, the curves given by the D- and L-sugars are similar in shape but have opposite signs. On the other hand, if the sugar molecule contains a carboxyl or an acyl group, then a Cotton effect is observed. This has been examined in γ-lactones and it has been shown that when the hydroxyl on the carbon atom adjacent to the carbonyl group (of the lactone) has the *S*-configuration, the ORD curve (at about 220–230 nm) is positive; and *vice versa*, *i.e.*, the *R*-configuration leads to a negative curve (Okuda *et al.*, 1964).

Examples are **(A)**, D-arabino-γ-lactone (C-2, *S*; positive) and **(B)**, D-glucono-γ-lactone (C-2, *R*; negative).

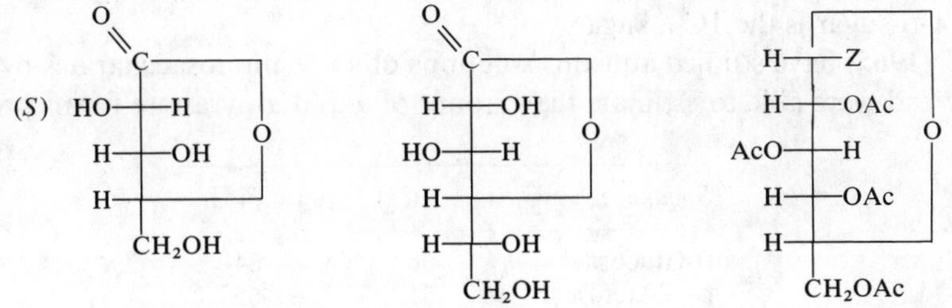

(A)   (B)   (C)

A particularly useful derivative of alcohols that shows the Cotton effect is the xanthate; this has been applied to sugar acetates, *e.g.*, **(C)** [Z = —S—CO—OEt]. The ORD curves of the two anomers are different and so may be distinguished.

Chromatography. This is used for the separation, estimation and identification of mono-saccharides (see §21).

Chemical methods. These are still used to determine structure and configuration, especially in the latter case where several chiral centres are involved (see also **2** §5a).

We shall now consider the application of some of these methods. As we have seen (§2), D-gluco-pyranose is an equilibrium mixture (in solution) of the α- and β-anomers: the conformations of these are:

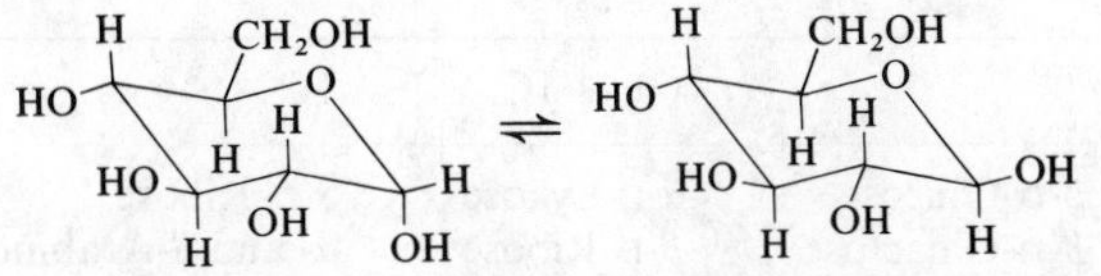

α-(36%)   β-(64%)

These conformations are of the C1 type and, for reasons that are discussed later, the C1 conformation (for D-sugars) is usually more stable than the 1C. The corresponding 1C conformations of α- and β-D-glucopyranose are as shown (these are obtained by changing into the 'other' form, with all equatorial groups now axial, and vice versa):

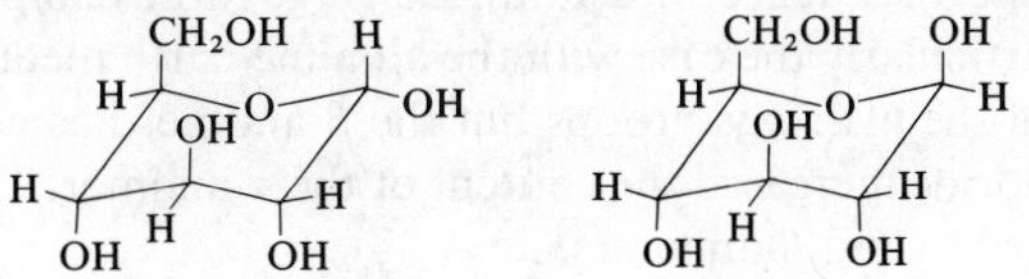

α-   β-

D-glucopyranose (1C form)

It was pointed out in §4 that the configuration at C-1, as well as all the other asymmetric carbon atoms, is reversed in the L-form. Thus, in the α-anomer of an L-sugar, the C_1 hydroxyl group is equatorial (C1 form) and in the β-anomer it is axial, *e.g.*, the conformations of α- and β-L-glucopyranose (C1 form) are:

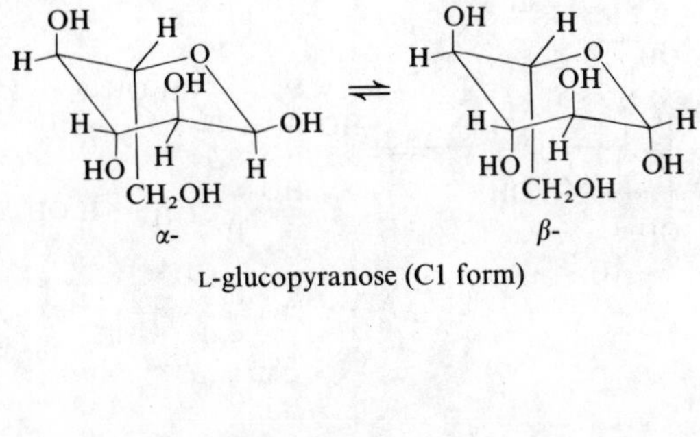

α-   β-

L-glucopyranose (C1 form)

These would be expected to be less stable than the corresponding 1C forms (see later). It might also be noted that the L-sugar may be drawn as the *mirror image* of the D-sugar, but now the mirror image of a C1-D-sugar is the 1C-L-sugar.

Shaw *et al.* (1965) have studied aqueous solutions of some monosaccharides by means of NMR spectroscopy and were able to estimate the amount of α-and α-pyranose forms present.

Sugar	α(%)	β(%)
D-Glucose	36	64
D-Galactose	35	65
D-Mannose	64	36
D-Xylose	29	71
L-Arabinose	63	37
D-Lyxose	69	31
D-Ribose	18	54

The authors also showed that the following were in conformational equilibrium in solution. According to Lemieux *et al.* (1965), β-D-ribopyranose is in the C1 conformation and the α-anomer is *not* in a chair conformation. On the other hand, Bhacca *et al.* (1967) have shown from NMR studies that tetra-*O*-acetyl-β-D-ribopyranose is, at room temperature, in continuous motion between the two chair conformations.

C1	C1 + 1C	1C
α- and β-D-Glucose	α-D-Lyxose	α-D-Ribose
α- and β-D-Galactose	β-D-Ribose	α- and β-Arabinose
α- and β-D-Mannose		
α- and β-D-Xylose		
β-D-Lyxose		

Angyal *et al.* (1971) have shown that sugars containing an *a-e-a* sequence of three hydroxyl groups in a pyranose ring, or a *cis-cis* sequence in a furanose ring, form complexes with metal ions in aqueous solution. This is particularly the case with the alkaline-earth metals. α-D-Allopyranose has the required arrangement of the hydroxyl groups but the β-anomer has not. These workers found that addition of calcium chloride increased the content of the α-anomer. Thus, it is possible to shift the position of equilibrium of α- and β-anomers.

Investigation of the ring-size of sugars from the point of view of conformational analysis has resulted in some interesting conclusions. Let us consider the furanose (I) and pyranose (II) forms of D(+)-glucose (R = CHOHCH$_2$OH) in solution. In (I) (envelope conformation; see **4** §14), the 2- and 3-hydroxyl groups are axial, but in (II) all the large groups, OH and CH$_2$OH, are equatorial. Hence it can be anticipated that the furanose form will be less stable than the pyranose (chair) form, and so the equilibrium will lie far to the right. Ferrier (1963) has examined crystalline β-D-glucose

(I)   (II)

by means of X-ray analysis and has shown that the molecule has the pyranose ring in the chair form with all the substituents in the equatorial positions.

Glucose, mannose, xylose and lyxose show normal mutarotation, and this is readily explained in terms of the equilibrium described, *i.e.*, that there are essentially two forms present, α- and β-pyranose. Also, it has been shown for these four sugars that the amount present as the β-anomer is: glucose, 64; mannose, 36; xylose, 71; lyxose, 31 per cent. This may be explained as follows. In the α-anomers of D-xylose and D-glucose, (III), which are configurationally related, the 1-OH group is

(III); α-anomer   (IV); β-anomer

D-xylose (R = H); D-glucose (R = CH_2OH)

axial, whereas in the corresponding β-anomers, (IV), it is equatorial. Consequently, the β-anomers will be more stable than the α- (the latter contains one instability unit). In fact, since β-D-gluco-pyranose is the only hexopyranose which has no instability units, it would be expected to be the most stable D-aldohexose; this is the case in practice. It might be noted here that sugars which have the same configurations in the ring form are said to be *homomorphous*. In D-lyxose and D-mannose, which are also configurationally related (*i.e.*, are homomorphous), the 2-OH group is axial in both α- (V) and β-anomers (VI), but since the β-anomer (VI) is in the Delta-2-condition, this form is less stable than the α-anomer (V) (by two instability units), and so the latter predominates.

Ribose, arabinose, galactose and talose differ from the sugars described above in that they show abnormal mutarotation curves. This requires the presence of three or more different components in appreciable amounts at equilibrium (see §2). Let us consider arabinose and galactose. Inspection

(V); α-form   (VI); β-form

D-lyxose (R = H); D-mannose (R = CH_2OH)

of formulae (IV) and (XIII) in §1 shows that the *furanose* forms of L(+)-arabinose and D(+)-galactose are configurationally related (*i.e.*, are homomorphous). Thus, we may write these sugars as (VII) and (VIII), and it can be seen that in (VII) all the large groups at 2, 3 and 4 are equatorial,

(VII)   (VIII)

L(+)-arabinose (R^1 = CH_2OH; R^2 = H);

D(+)-galactose (R^1 = $CHOHCH_2OH$; R^2 = CH_2OH)

whereas in (VIII) the 4-OH group is axial. Hence (VII) will be much more stable than (I), and so (VII) can be expected to make some contribution to the equilibrium (VII) ⇌ (VIII).

In view of what has been said above, it might have been anticipated that δ-lactones would be more stable than γ-lactones but, as we have seen (§7c), the reverse is true in practice. The reason for this is not certain, but one explanation offered involves the electrostatic repulsions that can operate between the C—O bond of the carbonyl group and a p-orbital of a lone pair of electrons on the ring-oxygen atom. In (IX) the C=O is almost eclipsed with the 2-e-H, and is staggered with the p-orbitals on the ring-oxygen atom, whereas in (X) the latter interaction will be from the eclipsed conformation. As we have seen (**4** §11b), electrostatic forces can play a very important part in stabilities of conformations and so, if we assume that these electrostatic repulsions are considerable in (X), then

(IX)   (X)

(IX) will be the more stable lactone. This argument has been applied to unsubstituted lactones, but when we consider the lactones of the methylated sugars, we must take into account the 1,3-interactions that may also operate, *i.e.*, all γ-lactones will not have the same stability, nor will all δ-lactones, *e.g.*, comparison of methylated δ-gluconolactone (methylated (II); 1-CHOH → CO) with methylated δ-galactonolactone (methylated (VIII); 1-CHOH → CO) indicates that the former will be more stable than the latter (*cf.* Fig. 7.1; §7c). Also, in 2,3,5-trimethylxylonolactone (γ-lactone) there are two methoxyl groups (2 and 3) axial, whereas in 2,3,4-trimethylxylonolactone (δ-lactone) all methoxyl groups are equatorial (*cf.* (III)). Thus the δ-lactone might be more stable than the γ-; this has been found to be so in practice.

Let us now consider the open-chain (*aldehydo*) sugars. Their conformations are zig-zag and their stabilities depend on the number of hydroxyl groups which lie on the same side of the chain. Since

1,3-interactions are the cause of greatest strain, the larger the number of hydroxyl groups on the same side, the lower is the stability of that sugar.

Anomeric effect. Except for the hydroxyl group, a polar aglycon group tends to assume the axial orientation rather than the equatorial, *e.g.*, Lemieux *et al.* (1958) showed, by means of NMR spectroscopy, that this was the case for aldopyranosides in which the 1-OH group had been replaced by OMe, OAc, and Cl. This has been called the **anomeric effect**, and is believed to be due to the interaction between lone pairs of the ring-oxygen atom and those of the substituent at C-1; this interaction is less for an axial than for an equatorial substituent. When Z is OR or OAc, there are only two lone pairs on the oxygen atom (see also **6** §2j).

equatorial

axial

In accordance with this explanation, it would be expected that the anomeric effect should vary inversely with the dielectric constant of the solvent. Thus, in aqueous solution, the anomeric effect will be small because of the high dielectric constant of water; hence the exception for C_1—OH (since the equilibrium is measured in aqueous solutions). Furthermore, in solvents with smaller dielectric constants than water, the anomeric effect of the OH group should be greater. This has been shown to be the case, e.g., in anhydrous methanol, there is 50 per cent of α-D-glucose.

As we have seen (4 §12), rates of reaction may depend on conformation. Since the anomeric hydroxyl group is more reactive than any other hydroxyls in the ring, the reactions which have been most widely studied are those involving the anomeric groups. Mechanisms have been proposed for the various types of reactions, but in most cases, although the overall picture appears to be reasonably clear, details are still the subject of discussion.

For the Fischer glycoside synthesis (§3), although the mechanism is not settled, it appears that in a number of cases the furanosides are formed first and then these equilibrate with pyranosides, e.g., D-glucose, D-ribose. In other cases, however, the furanosides and pyranosides are formed simultaneously, e.g., D-mannose, D-lyxose. These observations now lead to the problem of the mechanism for the ring expansion of furanosides to pyranosides, and the reverse, i.e., ring contraction of pyranosides to furanosides. A favoured mechanism for ring expansion and contraction is shown in the chart (the bond drawn as a wavy line indicates that the group can be either axial or equatorial; methyl α-D-glucoside is the example).

The mechanism of acid-catalysed hydrolysis of glycosides falls into two distinct groups: aldopyranosides undergo hydrolysis by an A-1 mechanism, whereas aldofuranosides undergo hydrolysis by an A-2 mechanism.

Aldopyranosides (A-1).

This appears to be the favoured mechanism; an alternative uses the formation of an acyclic intermediate. β-anomers of D-sugars are often hydrolysed faster than the corresponding α-anomers; the reverse is true for the L-sugars (α-D ≡ β-L). The reason for these observations is uncertain; the rate of hydrolysis depends on the nature of the aglycon. One contributing factor could be the steric effect, a large group experiencing greater 1,3-interactions in the axial position and consequently hydrolysis is accelerated. This argument may be supported by the fact that when the aglycon is phenyl the rate of hydrolysis is faster for the α-anomer (this is the reverse for the methyl glycosides). Further support for this argument is the fact that for disaccharides composed of two glucose units (1 → 2, 1 → 3, and 1 → 4; see §12), the α-anomers are hydrolysed faster than the β-. On the other hand, for (1 → 6)-disaccharides, the β-anomer is hydrolysed faster than the α-.

Aldofuranosides (A-2).

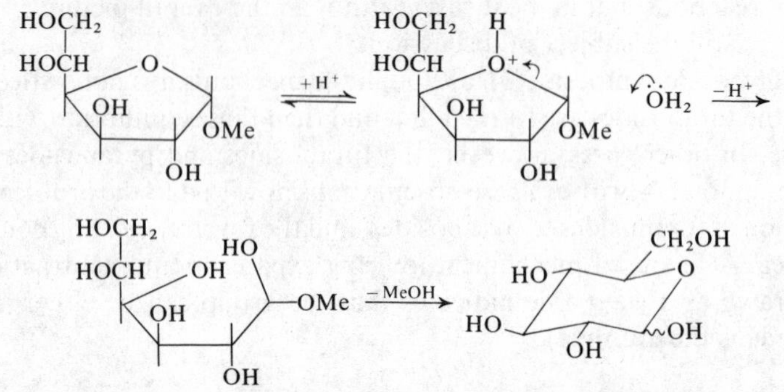

Several possible mechanisms have been proposed; the one given here is a highly favoured one and it should be noted that the product is in the pyranose form and is produced *via* an acyclic intermediate (*cf.* glycoside synthesis, above). Also, furanosides are hydrolysed much faster than the corresponding pyranosides.

The hydrolysis of glycosides can also be effected by enzymes. Enzyme-catalysed hydrolysis is stereospecific, *e.g.*, α-amylases hydrolyse only α-glycosides and β-amylases only β-glycosides. It appears that the enzyme forms an enzyme–glycoside complex and the glycoside is hydrolysed by an acidic group in the enzyme (see also Enzymes, Ch. 13).

The oxidation of aldoses with bromine has been studied in some detail but again the mechanism is not settled. It is accepted that the reaction proceeds to the 1,5-lactone by direct oxidation of the pyranose form, and that the β-D-anomers are oxidised more rapidly than the corresponding α-D-anomers. It also appears that the α-anomer is first converted into the β-anomer, which then undergoes rapid oxidation. One mechanism proposed is (the rate-determining step is the anomerisation of the α- to the β-anomer):

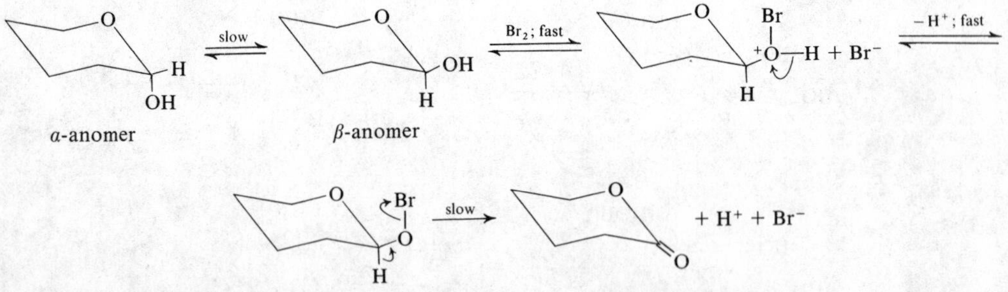

The faster oxidation of the β-anomer is in keeping with the more ready attack at an equatorial group, and also the elimination of the proton from the axial position would be more favourable than from an equatorial position.

Provided that the forms present in equilibrium are pyranose and are stable, then comparison of rates of oxidation with bromine affords a means of determining the relative amounts of anomeric pyranoses (see also §24 for other reactions at C-1).

§8. Isopropylidene derivatives of the monosaccharides

Sugars condense with anhydrous acetone in the presence of hydrogen chloride, sulphuric acid, etc., at room temperature to form mono- and di-isopropylidene (or acetone) derivatives. These are stable towards alkalis, but are readily hydrolysed by acids. In the di-isopropylidene derivatives, one iso-propylidene group is generally removed by hydrolysis more readily than the other, and thus by controlled hydrolysis it is possible to isolate the mono-isopropylidene derivative, *e.g.*, di-isopropyl-ideneglucose may be hydrolysed by acetic acid to the mono-derivative.

The structures of these isopropylidene derivatives have been determined by the methods used for the sugars themselves, *i.e.*, the compound is first methylated, then hydrolysed to remove the acetone groups, and the product finally oxidised in order to ascertain the positions of the methyl groups. Let us consider D-glucose as an example. This forms a di-isopropylidene derivative (I), which is non-reducing; therefore C-1 is involved in the formation of (I). On methylation, (I) forms a mono-methyldi-isopropylideneglucose (II) and this, on hydrolysis with hydrochloric acid, gives a mono-methylglucose (III). Hydrolysis of (I) with acetic acid produces a mono-isopropylideneglucose (IV) which is also non-reducing. Thus C-1 in (IV) must be combined with the isopropylidene group.

Methylation of (IV), followed by hydrolysis gives a trimethylglucose (V): Methylation of (V) gives a methyl tetramethylglucoside, and this, on hydrolysis, gives 2,3,5,6-tetra-O-methyl-D-glucose (VI), a *known* compound (see §7b). Thus (V) must be 2,3,5-, 2,3,6-, or 3,5,6-tri-O-methyl-D-glucose. Now (V) forms an osazone without loss of any methyl group; therefore C-2 cannot have a methoxyl group attached to it, and so (V) must be 3,5,6-tri-O-methyl-D-glucose. Thus one isopropylidene group in di-isopropylideneglucose (I) must be 3,5-, 3,6- or 5,6-. Monomethyl-glucose (III), on methylation followed by hydrolysis, gives 2,3,4,6-tetra-O-methyl-D-glucose (VII), a *known* compound (see §7a). Hence (III) must be 2-, 3-, 4- or 6-O-methyl-D-glucose. Since (III) gives sodium cyanate when subjected to the Weerman test (see §11), it therefore follows that C-2 has a free hydroxyl group. Oxidation of (III) with nitric acid produces a monomethylsaccharic acid; therefore C-6 cannot have a methoxyl group attached to it. This monomethylsaccharic acid forms a lactone which behaves as a γ-lactone; therefore a methoxyl group cannot be at C-4. Thus, by the process of elimination, this monomethylglucose, (III), must be 3-O-methyl-D-glucose. It therefore follows that the two isopropylidene groups in the di-isopropylidene derivative must be 1,2- and 5,6-, the ring being furanose, and the mono-isopropylidene derivative being 1,2-. The foregoing reactions can be written as shown. The furanose form has been given as the isomer involved (see above).

As a result of much experimental work (of the foregoing type), it has been found that acetone usually condenses with *cis*-hydroxyl groups on *adjacent* carbon atoms, the condensation occurring in such a way as to favour the formation of the di-isopropylidene derivative. Because of this, the majority of aldoses form furanose rather than pyranose derivatives. The reason for this is not certain, but a widely accepted explanation is that the strain in two fused five-membered rings is less than that in the fusion of a five- with a six-membered ring. However, aldoses with the D- (or L-) *arabino*-configuration at atoms C-2, C-3 and C-4, do react to give pyranose derivatives. Thus, *e.g.*, in α-D-galactopyranose (VIII), the hydroxyl groups on C-1 and C-2 are in the *cis* position, as are also the hydroxyl groups on C-3 and C-4. Thus galactose forms the 1,2–3,4-di-O-isopropylidene-D-galactopyranose (IX). On the other hand, in α-D-glucopyranose, only the two hydroxyl groups on C-1 and C-2 are in the *cis* position, and thus, in order to form the di-isopropylidene derivative, the furanose ring (present in the equilibrium mixture; see §2) undergoes reaction to produce 1,2–5,6-di-O-isopropylidene-D-glucofuranose (I); the final result is that D-glucose behaves completely as D-glucofuranose. The mono-derivative is 1,2-O-isopropylidene-D-glucofuranose (IV).

(VIII)

(IX)

Fructose can form *two* di-isopropylidene derivatives which both contain the pyranose ring.

1,2-4,5-

2,3-4,5-

§9. Other condensation products of the sugars

Not only does acetone condense with sugars, but so do other oxo compounds such as formaldehyde, acetaldehyde and benzaldehyde. Benzaldehyde condenses with two *cis* hydroxyl groups on *alternate* carbon atoms, *e.g.*, glucose forms 4,6-*O*-benzylidene-D-glucopyranose (I).

Triphenylmethyl chloride reacts with sugars to form triphenylmethyl ethers; these are usually known as *trityl* derivatives. Trityl ethers are formed much faster with primary alcoholic groups than

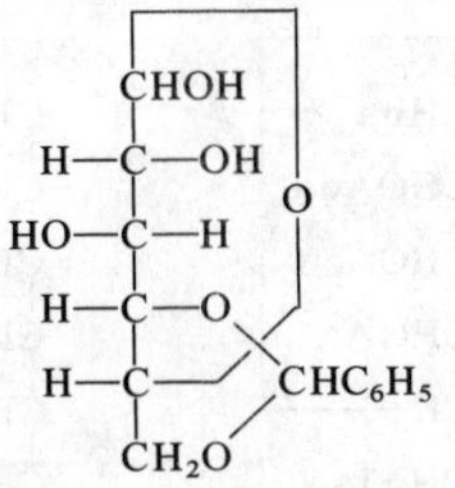

$$
\begin{array}{ll}
\text{CHOH} & \\
\text{H—C—OH} & \\
\text{HO—C—H} \quad \text{O} & \\
\text{H—C—O} & \\
\text{H—C} \quad \text{CHC}_6\text{H}_5 & \\
\text{CH}_2\text{O} & \\
\quad\quad\text{(I)}
\end{array}
\qquad
\begin{array}{ll}
\text{CHOCH}_3 & \\
\text{H—C—OH} & \\
\text{HO—C—H} \quad \text{O} & \\
\text{H—C—OH} & \\
\text{H—C} & \\
\text{CH}_2\text{OC(C}_6\text{H}_5)_3 & \\
\quad\quad\text{(II)}
\end{array}
$$

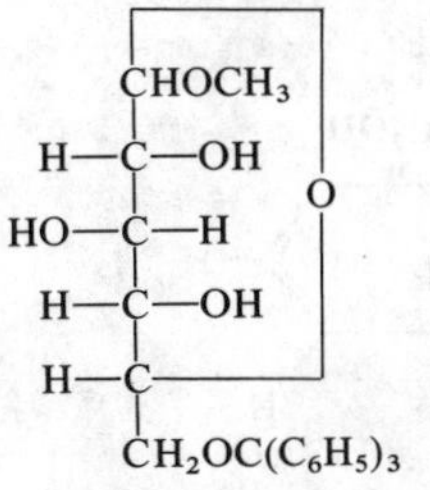

with secondary, but at the same time, because the hydroxyl of the CH_2OH group is the only exocyclic alcoholic group (in hexapyranoses), it is far more reactive than any alcoholic group in the ring, *e.g.*, methyl glucopyranoside reacts with triphenylmethyl chloride in pyridine solution to form methyl 6-tritylglucopyranoside (II).

§10. Some sugar derivatives

Glycals are sugar derivatives which have a pyranose ring structure and a double bond between C-1 and C-2, *e.g.*, D-glucal is (I). Glycals may be prepared by reducing acetobromo compounds (see §24) with zinc dust and acetic acid, *e.g.*, D-glucal from tetra-*O*-acetyl-D-glucopyranosyl bromide (II), followed by hydrolysis of the acetyl groups. Glycals are of interest because of their ready conversion

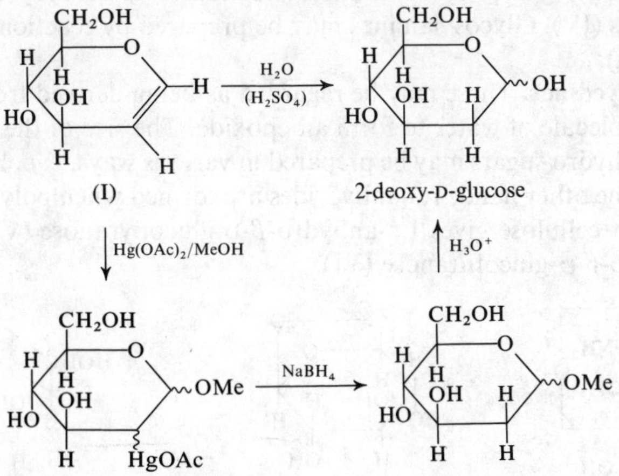

into 2-deoxy-sugars (§1a) by dilute inorganic acids, *e.g.*, D-glucal (I) forms 2-deoxy-D-glucose. The yield is poor but is very much improved by using the process of methoxymercuration of the double bond (see also Vol. I). On the other hand, 6-deoxy-sugars are readily prepared from the 6-tosyl derivatives as shown:

Glycosamines are amino-sugars in which a hydroxyl group has been replaced by an amino-group, *e.g.*, glucosamine is 2-aminoglucose (III). Its systematic name is 2-amino-2-D-deoxyglucose, *i.e.*, it is a derivative of 2-deoxyglucose.

2-Amino-2-deoxyaldoses occur in nature, *e.g.*, in chitin (see §23), and are involved in various physiological processes. 3-Amino-sugars occur in many antibiotics. 2-Amino-sugars may be prepared in several ways, *e.g.*,

2-Amino-sugars differ from the other amino-sugars in that they do *not* give the Molisch test (characteristic of carbohydrates).

Glycosylamines. These are *N*-glycosides; they are derived from monosaccharides by replacement of the glycosidic hydroxyl group by a primary, secondary, or tertiary amino-group, *e.g.*, α-D-glucopyranosylamine is (IV). Glycosylamines may be prepared by reaction between an aldose and an amine (or ammonia).

Anhydro sugars or glycosans. These may be regarded as being derived from monosaccharides by the elimination of a molecule of water to form an epoxide. The size of the oxiran ring varies from 1,2- to 1,6-. The 1,2-anhydro sugars may be prepared in various ways, *e.g.*, by heating a sugar under reduced pressure. On the other hand, 1,6-anhydrides are formed when polysaccharides are distilled *in vacuo*, *e.g.*, starch or cellulose gives 1,6-anhydro-β-D-glucopyranose (V), together with a small amount of 1,6-anhydro-β-D-glucofuranose (VI).

The *epoxides* of the sugars are a special class of anhydro sugars; they do not involve the glycosidic hydroxyl group. They may be prepared by the action of a base on a suitable sugar derivative, *e.g.*, tosyl esters. These esters usually produce **epoxy-sugars** when hydrolysed with sodium methoxide in the cold, provided that there is a free hydroxyl group on an adjacent carbon atom and that this hydroxyl and the tosyl group are *trans* to each other. This is an example of neighbouring hydroxyl group participation (3 §6c), and the mechanism is:

$$H-\underset{HO-\underset{|}{C}-H}{\overset{|}{C}}-OH \xrightarrow[C_6H_5N]{TsCl} H-\underset{HO-\underset{|}{C}-H}{\overset{|}{C}}-OTs \xrightarrow{OMe^-} H-\underset{O-\underset{|}{C}-H}{\overset{|}{C}}-OTs \xrightarrow{-OTs^-} O\underset{\overset{|}{C}-H}{\overset{\overset{|}{C}-H}{\diagdown}}$$

On hydrolysis with alkali, these epoxy-sugars form a mixture of *two* sugars, inversion occurring at either carbon when the epoxide ring opens (see 4 §5l).

$$H-\underset{HO-\underset{|}{C}-H}{\overset{|}{C}}-OH \xleftarrow[O]{NaOH} O\underset{\overset{|}{C}-H}{\overset{\overset{|}{C}-H}{\diagdown}} \xrightarrow[O]{NaOH} HO-\underset{H-\underset{|}{C}-OH}{\overset{|}{C}}-H$$

$$(VII) \qquad\qquad\qquad (VIII)$$

In (VII) the configurations of the two carbon atoms are the same as in the original sugar, but in (VIII) *both* configurations are inverted (to form a new sugar).

When the tosyl group is *trans* to two hydroxyl groups (on adjacent carbon atoms), *two* epoxy-sugars are formed. At the same time, however, *larger* epoxide rings may be produced *without* inversion, e.g., Peat et al. (1938) treated methyl 3-tosyl-β-D-glucopyranoside (IX) with sodium methoxide and obtained a mixture of 2,3-anhydroalloside (X; with inversion), 3,4-anhydroalloside (XI; with inversion), and 3,6-anhydroglucoside (XII; no inversion).

(IX) → MeONa → (X) (60%) + (XI) (25%) + (XII) (15%)

It is possible, however, by using suitable derivatives of a tosyl ester to obtain only one epoxy-sugar, e.g., methyl 2-benzoyl-3-tosyl 4,6-benzylidene α-D-glucopyranoside (XIII), on treatment with sodium methoxide, forms methyl 2,3-anhydro 4,6-benzylidene α-D-allopyranoside (XIV).

(XIII) → MeONa → (XIV)

For the formation of the epoxide to proceed easily, it is necessary that the *trans* OH and Ts groups should be diaxial. In the majority of tosyl derivatives, however, both the tosyl group and the vicinal *trans*-hydroxyl group are equatorial (*cf.* §7h). Nevertheless, these tosyl derivatives are still easily converted into epoxides. This may be explained on the basis that the normal chair form (C1) readily changes into the reverse chair form (1C); consequently both groups are now axial and so epoxide formation proceeds readily (*cf.* 4 §5m).

Monosaccharide esters. Acetates and benzoates are particularly useful for characterising sugars and for the protection (and estimation) of hydroxyl groups (see also §24). p-Nitrobenzoates are also used for characterising sugars. Esters are readily prepared by reaction between the sugar and the acid anhydride or acid chloride in the presence of pyridine (as solvent and catalyst). A characteristic feature of partially acylated sugars is the migration of an acyl group from one hydroxyl group to another under the influence of a base. This may be illustrated by the conversion of 1,2,3,4-tetra-*O*-acetyl-β-D-glucopyranose into the corresponding 1,2,3,6-derivative. The mechanism is intra-molecular and is believed to involve the formation of a cyclic intermediate (cyclic ortho-ester). The details, however, appear to be uncertain; a possibility is:

These migrations usually occur from a secondary alcoholic group to the less hindered primary alcoholic group.

Tosyl esters have been discussed above. The tosyloxy group is readily removed by sodium amal-gam. This is an example of *reductive desulphonylation*, and usually occurs *without* inversion.

Sugar sulphates of the type $ROSO_2OH$ occur in polysaccharides. By the use of suitably substituted derivatives, it is possible to sulphate aldoses selectively with sulphur trioxide or chlorosulphonic acid in pyridine, *e.g.*, D-glucose 3-sulphate may be prepared by the sulphation of the 1,2-5,6-di-*O*-isopropylidene derivative, followed by hydrolysis with dilute acid. Cyclic sulphates (vicinal type) may be prepared by the action of sulphuryl chloride on suitable sugar derivatives in pyridine solution.

Phosphate esters of the monosaccharides are particularly important because of the role they play in metabolic processes (see §24 for their preparation).

§11. Vitamin C or L(+)-ascorbic acid

Ascorbic acid is very closely related to the monosaccharides, and so is conveniently dealt with here. Hawkins (1593) found that oranges and lemons were effective for treating scurvy, a disease parti-cularly prevalent among seamen. The first significant step in elucidating the nature of the compound, the absence of which from the diet caused scurvy, was that of Holst and Frölich (1907), who pro-duced experimental scurvy in guinea-pigs. Then Szent-Györgi (1928) isolated a crystalline substance from various sources, *e.g.*, cabbages, paprika, etc., and found that it had antiscorbutic properties. This compound was originally called *hexuronic acid*, and later was shown to be identical with vitamin C, m.p. 192°C, $[\alpha]_D$ of +24°.

The structure of vitamin C was elucidated by Haworth, Hirst and their co-workers (1932, 1933). The molecular formula was shown to be $C_6H_8O_6$, and since the compound formed a monosodium and monopotassium salt, it was thought that there was a carboxyl group present (hence the name hexuronic acid). Vitamin C behaves as an unsaturated compound and as a strong reducing agent; it also forms a phenylhydrazone and gives a violet colour with ferric chloride. All this suggests that a keto-enol system is present, *i.e.*,

$$-CO-CH- \rightleftharpoons -C(OH)=C-$$

Now, when boiled with hydrochloric acid, ascorbic acid gives a quantitative yield of furfuraldehyde:

$$C_6H_8O_6 \xrightarrow{\text{HCl}} \begin{array}{c} HC\text{-----}CH \\ \parallel \qquad \parallel \\ HC \diagdown_{O}\diagup CCHO \end{array} + CO_2 + 2H_2O$$

This reaction suggests that ascorbic acid contains at least five carbon atoms in a straight chain, and also that there are a number of hydroxyl groups present (*cf.* the pentoses). Aqueous iodine solution oxidises ascorbic acid to dehydroascorbic acid, two atoms of iodine being used in the process and two molecules of hydrogen iodide are produced; the net result is the removal of two hydrogen atoms from ascorbic acid. Dehydroascorbic acid is neutral and behaves as the lactone of a monobasic hydroxy-acid; and on reduction with hydrogen sulphide, dehydroascorbic acid is reconverted into ascorbic acid. Because this oxidation-reduction process may be carried out with 'mild' reagents, it leads to the suggestion that since the oxidation product, dehydroascorbic acid, is a lactone, then ascorbic acid itself is a lactone and *not* an acid as suggested previously. Since, however, ascorbic acid can form salts, this property must still be accounted for. One reasonable possibility is that the salt-forming property is due to the presence of an *enol* group, the presence of which has already been indicated. Thus all the preceding reactions can be explained by the presence of an α-hydroxyketone grouping in ascorbic acid:

$$\begin{array}{c} | \\ HCOH \\ | \\ C{=}O \\ | \end{array} \rightleftharpoons \begin{array}{c} | \\ C\text{---}OH \\ | \\ C\text{---}OH \\ | \end{array} \xrightarrow{I_2 + 2H_2O} \left[\begin{array}{c} | \\ C(OH)_2 \\ | \\ C(OH)_2 \\ | \end{array} \right] + 2HI \xrightarrow{-2H_2O} \begin{array}{c} | \\ C{=}O \\ | \\ C{=}O \\ | \end{array}$$

Reducing;   Unsaturated;
forms a   colour with
phenylhydrazone   ferric chloride;
                           sodium enolate

The final result is the removal of two hydrogen atoms to form dehydroascorbic acid.

$$C_6H_8O_6 + I_2 \longrightarrow C_6H_6O_6 + 2HI$$

Although all these reactions may appear to be speculative, they are known to occur with dihydroxymaleic acid; hence by analogy with this compound, the explanation offered for the reactions of ascorbic acid is very strongly supported.

$$\begin{array}{c} HO \diagdown \quad \diagup CO_2H \\ C \\ \parallel \\ C \\ HO \diagup \quad \diagdown CO_2H \end{array}$$

dihydroxymaleic acid

When dehydroascorbic acid is oxidised with sodium hypoiodite, oxalic and L-threonic acids are produced in quantitative yields (Hirst, 1933). L-Threonic acid (IV) was identified by methylation and then conversion into the crystalline amide; this compound was shown to be identical with tri-*O*-methyl-L-threonamide (obtained from L-threose). Further evidence for the nature of product (IV) is given by the fact that on oxidation with nitric acid it gives D(+)-tartaric acid. The formation of oxalic and L-threonic acids suggests that dehydroascorbic acid is (III), the lactone of 2,3-diketo-L-gulonic acid. Hence, if we assume that (I) is the structure of ascorbic acid, the foregoing reactions may be formulated as follows, dehydroascorbic acid being formed *via* (II).

$$
\text{(I)} \quad
\begin{array}{l}
\text{CO}\!-\!\\
\text{HO}\!-\!\text{C}\\
\quad\quad\; \| \quad\quad \text{O}\\
\text{HO}\!-\!\text{C}\\
\text{H}\!-\!\text{C}\\
\text{HO}\!-\!\text{C}\!-\!\text{H}\\
\text{CH}_2\text{OH}
\end{array}
\xrightarrow[2\text{H}_2\text{O}]{\text{I}_2}
\text{(II)}\quad
\left[
\begin{array}{l}
\text{CO}\!-\!\\
\text{C(OH)}_2\\
\quad\quad\quad \text{O}\\
\text{C(OH}_2)\\
\text{H}\!-\!\text{C}\\
\text{HO}\!-\!\text{C}\!-\!\text{H}\\
\text{CH}_2\text{OH}
\end{array}
\right]
\xrightarrow{-2\text{H}_2\text{O}}
\text{(III)}\quad
\begin{array}{l}
\text{CO}\!-\!\\
\text{CO}\\
\quad\quad\quad \text{O}\\
\text{CO}\\
\text{H}\!-\!\text{C}\\
\text{HO}\!-\!\text{C}\!-\!\text{H}\\
\text{CH}_2\text{OH}
\end{array}
\xrightarrow{\text{NaOI}}
\text{(IV)}\quad
\begin{array}{l}
\text{CO}_2\text{H}\\
\text{CO}_2\text{H}\\
+\\
\text{CO}_2\text{H}\\
\text{H}\!-\!\text{C}\!-\!\text{OH}\\
\text{HO}\!-\!\text{C}\!-\!\text{H}\\
\text{CH}_2\text{OH}
\end{array}
$$

The ring in ascorbic acid has been assumed to be five- and not six-membered, because the lactone (*i.e.*, ascorbic acid) is stable towards alkali (*cf.* §7c). In actual fact, however, the same final products would also have been obtained had the ring been six-membered. It must therefore be admitted that the weakness of the above proof of structure lies in the evidence used for ascertaining the size of the ring. Structure (I), however, has been amply confirmed by other analytical evidence. Diazomethane converts ascorbic acid into dimethylascorbic acid (V); these two methoxyl groups are most likely on C-2 and C-3, since diazomethane readily methylates acidic (in this case, enolic) hydroxyl groups. This dimethyl derivative is neutral, and dissolves in aqueous sodium hydroxide to form a sodium salt without the elimination of a methyl group; thus there cannot be a carbomethoxy group present, and so it is most likely that two enolic hydroxyl groups are present (Hirst, 1933). Furthermore, the formation of the sodium salt from the neutral compound suggests the opening of a lactone ring (the two enolic groups are now methylated and so cannot form a sodium salt). The similarity in structure between ascorbic acid and its dimethyl derivative is shown by the fact that the absorption spectra of both are similar. When this dimethyl derivative is methylated with methyl iodide in the presence of dry silver oxide (Purdie method; see §7), two further methyl groups are introduced to give (VI), and since all four methyl groups behave as methyl ethers, it therefore follows that two alcoholic groups are present in dimethylascorbic acid. Ozonolysis of this tetramethyl compound produces *one* neutral substance containing the *same* number of carbon atoms as its precursor. Since ozonolysis of a carbon–carbon double bond results in scission of that bond, there must be a ring system present in the tetramethyl compound to hold together the two fragments (VII). This ozonised product, on hydrolysis with barium hydroxide, gives oxalic acid and dimethyl-L-threonic acid (VIII). These products contain three carboxyl groups in all, and since ozonolysis of a double bond produces only two, the third carboxyl group must have already been present *as a lactone* in order that ascorbic acid should behave as a neutral compound.

The key to the size of the ring in ascorbic acid is the structure of this dimethyl-L-threonic acid, the nature of which has been ascertained as follows. On methylation, followed by conversion to the amide, dimethyl-L-threonic acid gives trimethyl-L-threonamide. Thus this dimethyl compound, which was unknown when isolated, is a dimethyl-L-threonic acid; but where are the two methoxyl groups? Their positions were ascertained by means of the **Weerman test**. This test is used for showing the presence of a *free* hydroxyl group in the α-position to an amide group, *i.e.*, in an α-hydroxy-amide. Treatment of a methylated hydroxy-amide with alkaline sodium hypochlorite gives an

$$
\begin{array}{l}
\text{CONH}_2\\
\text{CHOH}\\
\text{R}
\end{array}
\xrightarrow{\text{NaOCl}}
\left[
\begin{array}{l}
\text{CNO}\\
\text{CHOH}\\
\text{R}
\end{array}
\right]
\xrightarrow{\text{NaOH}}
\begin{array}{l}
\text{CHO} + \text{NaNCO}\\
\text{R}
\end{array}
$$

aldehyde and *sodium cyanate* if there is a *free* hydroxyl group on the α-carbon atom. If there is no free hydroxyl group on the α-carbon atom, *i.e.*, this atom is attached to a methoxyl group, then treatment with alkaline sodium hypochlorite produces an aldehyde, methanol, ammonia and carbon dioxide.

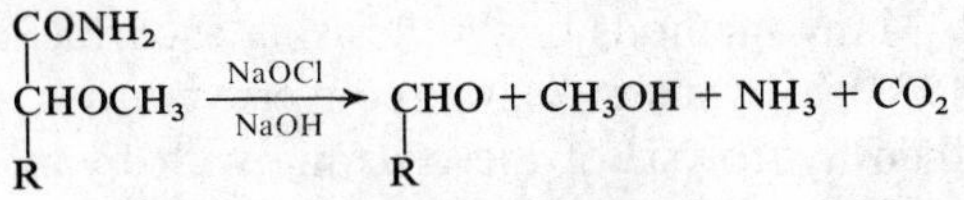

$$\underset{R}{\overset{\overset{\displaystyle CONH_2}{|}}{\underset{|}{CHOCH_3}}} \xrightarrow[\text{NaOH}]{\text{NaOCl}} \underset{R}{\overset{|}{CHO}} + CH_3OH + NH_3 + CO_2$$

The dimethylthreonic acid obtained from the ozonised product was converted into the amide (IX), and this, when subjected to the Weerman test, gave sodium cyanate as one of the products. Thus this dimethylthreonic acid contains a free α-hydroxyl group, and consequently must be 3,4-di-*O*-methyl-L-threonic acid (VIII). Therefore the lactone ring in ascorbic acid must be γ-, since a δ-lactone could not have given (VIII) (actually, 2,4-di-*O*-methyl-L-threonic acid would have been obtained). The amide (IX) was also obtained, together with oxamide, by the action of ammonia in methanol on the ozonised product (VII). All the foregoing facts can be represented by the following equations:

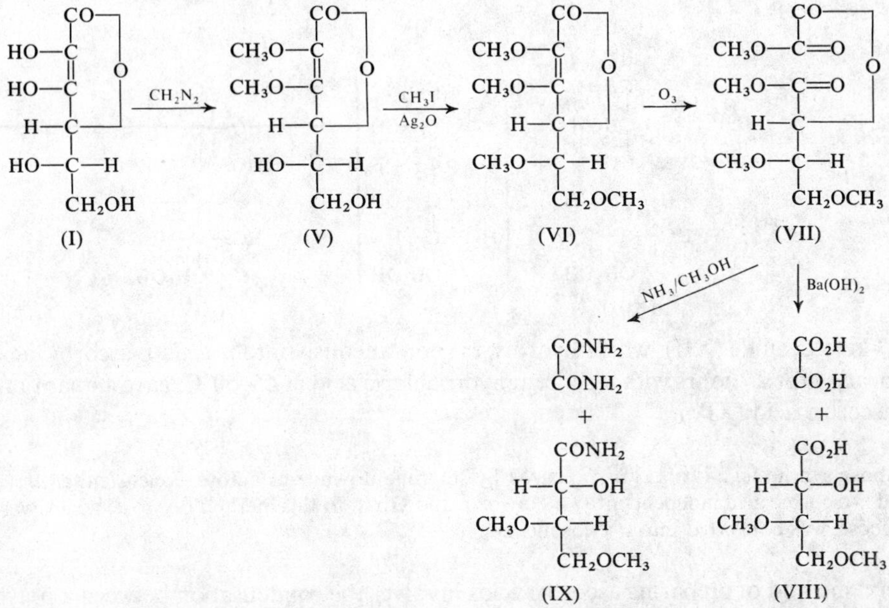

X-ray analysis of L-ascorbic acid has shown that it is almost a flat molecule, and at the same time, supports the structure obtained from chemical evidence. An aqueous solution of ascorbic acid has a *p*H of 3·0, and it is the hydrogen atom of the C_3-enol group which has ionised. In alkaline solution, however, it is the hydrogen atom of the C_2-enol group that ionises and is replaced by the metal. Ascorbic acid has a λ_{max} at 265 nm and a weak band between 350 and 400 nm.

An interesting point about ascorbic acid is that it is *not* reduced by lithium aluminium hydride (Petuely *et al.*, 1952). Thus ascorbic acid does not contain a 'normal' carbonyl group. It has now been shown that all **reductones**

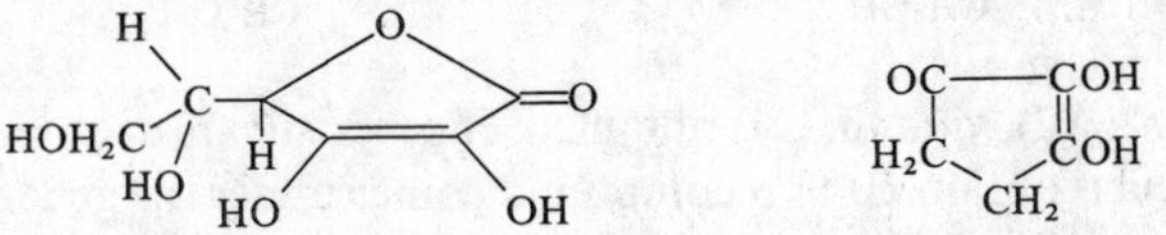

L-ascorbic acid   reductic acid

are not reduced by lithium aluminium hydride. Reductones are compounds which contain the ene-α-diol-α-carbonyl grouping

$$-CO-C(OH)=C(OH)-,$$

and examples of reductones are ascorbic and reductic acids.

Synthesis of ascorbic acid. Many methods of synthesising ascorbic acid are now available, *e.g.*, that of Haworth and Hirst (1933), L-Lyxose, (X), was converted into L(−)-xylosone (XI) (treatment with phenylhydrazine and then hydrolysis of the osazone with hydrochloric acid), and (XI), on treatment in an atmosphere of nitrogen with aqueous potassium cyanide containing calcium chloride,

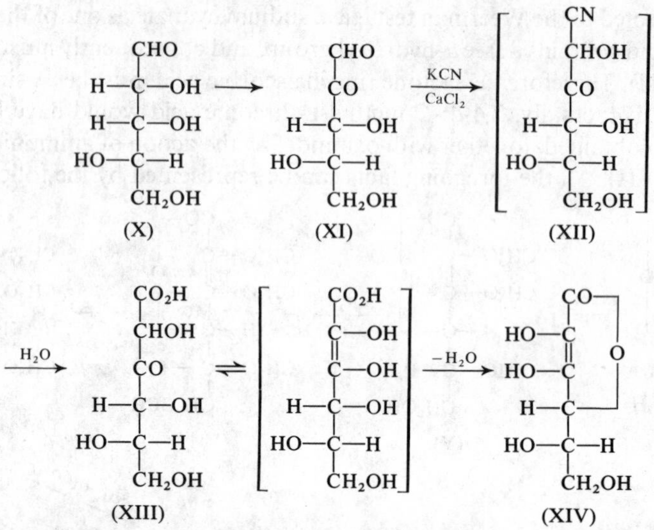

```
    CHO              CHO                   ⎡  CN   ⎤
 H—C—OH              CO         KCN        ⎢ CHOH  ⎥
 H—C—OH           H—C—OH       ————→       ⎢  CO   ⎥
HO—C—H           HO—C—H        CaCl₂       ⎢H—C—OH ⎥
  CH₂OH             CH₂OH                  ⎢HO—C—H ⎥
                                           ⎣ CH₂OH ⎦
   (X)              (XI)                    (XII)
```

```
          CO₂H            ⎡  CO₂H  ⎤             CO——
          CHOH            ⎢  C—OH  ⎥          HO—C   |
   H₂O     CO       ⇌     ⎢  C—OH  ⎥   −H₂O   HO—C    O
  ———→  H—C—OH            ⎢ H—C—OH ⎥  ———→    H—C   |
       HO—C—H            ⎢ HO—C—H ⎥          HO—C—H
          CH₂OH           ⎣  CH₂OH ⎦            CH₂OH
        (XIII)                                 (XIV)
```

gave the β-keto-cyanide (XII), which hydrolyses spontaneously into *pseudo*-L-ascorbic acid (XIII). This, on heating for 26 hours with 8 per cent hydrochloric acid at 45–50°C, gave a quantitative yield of L(+)-ascorbic acid (XIV).

In the above synthesis, L-lyxose was prepared by stepping down D-galactose. Reichstein *et al.* (1932) also synthesised L-ascorbic acid independently of Haworth and Hirst. In this method L-xylose, which was prepared from D-glucose, was converted into L-xylosone, etc.

A general method of preparing ascorbic acids involves the condensation between a polyhydroxy-aldehyde and ethyl glyoxylate in the presence of sodium cyanide (benzoin-type condensation). The intermediate 3-oxo-derivative (not isolated) is then hydrolysed with acid.

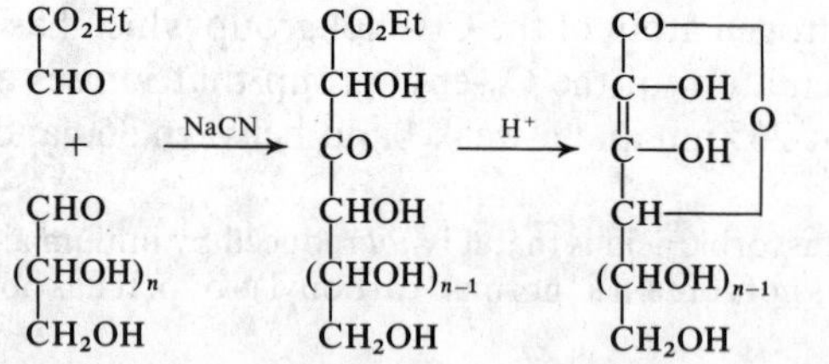

```
   CO₂Et              CO₂Et                 CO——
   CHO               CHOH                   C—OH  |
    +       NaCN      CO          H⁺        C—OH    O
   CHO    ————→      CHOH        ———→       CH—  |
 (CHOH)ₙ           (CHOH)ₙ₋₁            (CHOH)ₙ₋₁
   CH₂OH              CH₂OH                 CH₂OH
```

Thus, with L-threose ($n = 2$), vitamin C is obtained. If other sugars are used, *e.g.*, D-xylose ($n = 3$), D-gulo ido-ascorbic acid is obtained. This compound comes under the general term 'ascorbic acids'.

Ascorbic acid is now synthesised commercially by several methods, *e.g.*, D-glucose is catalytically hydrogenated to (+)-sorbitol which is then converted into (−)-sorbose by microbiological oxidation (using *Acetobacter suboxydans* or *Acetobacter xylinum*). (−)-Sorbose can be oxidised directly to 2-keto-(−)-gulonic acid with nitric acid, but the yield is less than when the oxidation is carried out as shown above. Nitric acid oxidises other alcohol groups besides the first, but by protecting these by means of 2,3–4,6-di-isopropylidene formation (§8), the yield of the gulonic acid is higher.

Görlich (1955) has found that oxygen, in the presence of a Pt—C catalyst, oxidises the di-isopropylidene derivative quantitatively to di-isopropylidene-2-keto-(−)-gulonic acid. The gulonic acid is then dissolved in mixed solvents (of which chloroform is the main constituent) and hydrogen chloride passed in. The product, L-ascorbic acid, is then finally purified by charcoaling.

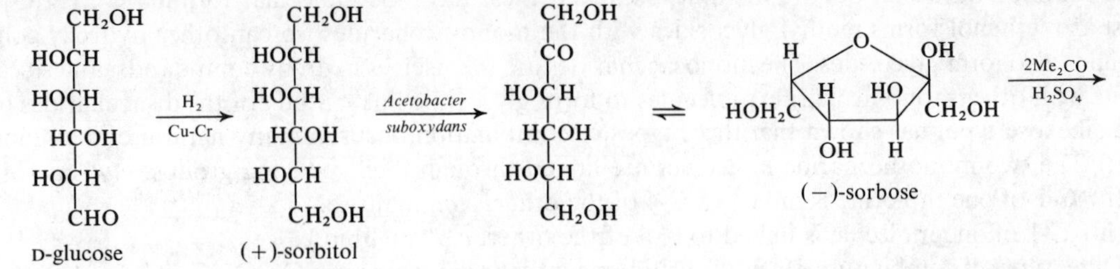

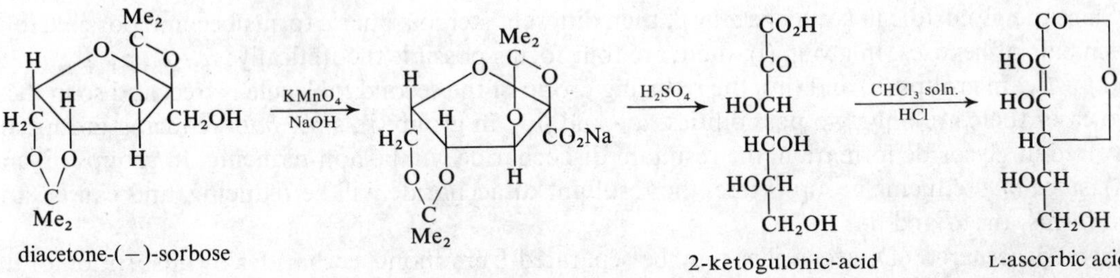

D-glucose   (+)-sorbitol   (−)-sorbose

diacetone-(−)-sorbose   2-ketogulonic-acid   L-ascorbic acid

Bakke *et al.* (1971) have introduced a much shorter synthesis of L-ascorbic acid, starting from D-glucose. 1,2-*O*-Isopropylidene-α-D-glucofuranose is oxidised by platinum-oxygen in acid solution, the product treated with dilute sulphuric acid followed by reduction with sodium borohydride at pH *ca.* 7.

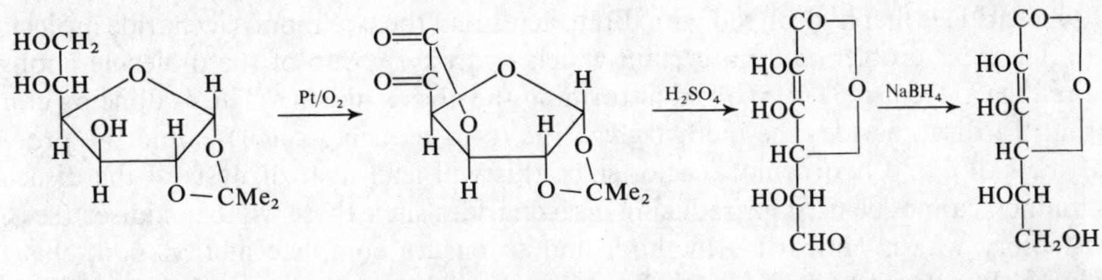

Since it is derived from L-xylohexulosonic acid (2-ketogulonic acid), vitamin C is often referred to as L-xyloascorbic acid. Many ascorbic acids (see above) have been synthesised, but all have much less antiscorbutic property than the natural vitamin.

Biosynthesis of ascorbic acid (see also **8** §34). Horowitz *et al.* (1952) and Burns *et al.* (1956) have shown that rat and plant tissues can convert D-glucose into ascorbic acid. A very interesting observation is that glucose labelled at C-1 (with ^{14}C) produces the vitamin labelled at C-6. In this way, the glucose molecule is 'turned upside down' to form the glucose derivative (*cf.* the stereochemistry of glucose and gulose, §1).

One possible pathway for the biosyntehsis of L-ascorbic acid is:

D-glucose $\xrightarrow[\text{lactonisation}]{\text{oxidn. at C-6}}$ D-glucurono-γ-lactone $\xrightarrow{\text{redn. at C-1}}$ L-gulono-γ-lactone $\xrightarrow[\text{of C-3}]{\text{inversion}}$

L-galactono-γ-lactone $\xrightarrow[\text{enolisation}]{\text{oxidn. at C-2}}$ L-ascorbic acid

There appears to be some doubt about L-galactonolactone being an intermediate.

Disaccharides

§12. Introduction

The common disaccharides are the dihexoses, and these have the molecular formula $C_{12}H_{22}O_{11}$. Just as methanol forms methyl glycosides with the monosaccharides, so can other hydroxy compounds also form glycosides. The monosaccharides are themselves hydroxy compounds, and so can unite with other monosaccharide molecules to form glycosidic links. Study of the disaccharides (of the dihexose type) has shown that three types of combination occur in many natural compounds:

(i) The two monosaccharide molecules are linked through their reducing groups, *e.g.*, sucrose.

(ii) C-1 of one molecule is linked to C-4 of the other, *e.g.*, maltose.

(iii) C-1 of one molecule is linked to C-6 of the other, *e.g.*, melibiose.

Other types of combination (in natural and/or synthetic dihexoses) are C_1–C_2, C_1–C_3, and C_1–C_5.

Since the glycosidic link may be α or β, then different stereoisomeric forms become possible for a given pair of hexoses. In group (i), there are four forms possible theoretically: α_1–α_2, α_1–β_2, β_1–α_2 and β_1–β_2. In groups (ii) and (iii), the reducing group of the second molecule is free, and so in these two cases there are only two possibilities: α_1- and β_1-. In group (i), since *both* reducing groups are involved in glycoside formation, the resultant disaccharide will be non-reducing. In groups (ii) and (iii), since *one* reducing group is free, the resultant disaccharide will be reducing, and can exist in two forms, the α- and β-.

General procedure.   Disaccharides may be separated from monosaccharides by adsorption of the mixture on a column of activated carbon and Celite (1:1), and the column then eluted with water. This removes the monosaccharides, and if elution is now carried out with aqueous ethanol, the disaccharides are removed. By varying the ratio of water to ethanol, it is possible to separate di-, tri-, and higher oligosaccharides. Different disaccharides may be separated by chromatographic separation of their acetates (on hydrated magnesium silicate-Celite columns).

The disaccharide is first hydrolysed with dilute acids and the two monosaccharide molecules then identified. The next problem is to ascertain which hydroxyl group of the molecule acting as the alcohol (*i.e.*, the aglycon; §3) is involved in forming the glycosidic link. This is done by completely methylating the disaccharide; the methyl glycoside (of a reducing sugar) cannot be prepared by means of methanol and hydrochloric acid, since this will lead to hydrolysis of the disaccharide. Purdie's method cannot be used for reducing disaccharides since these will be oxidised (see §7). The only satisfactory way is Haworth's method, and to ensure complete methylation, this may be *followed* by the Purdie method. The methylated disaccharides are then hydrolysed, and the methylated monosaccharides so obtained are investigated by the oxidation methods described previously (see §§7a, 7b, 7e). Reducing disaccharides are also oxidised to the corresponding bionic acid, this is then fully methylated, hydrolysed, and the methylated monosaccharide molecules examined. By this means the hydroxyl group involved in the glycosidic link and the size of the oxide ring are ascertained.

Another method for determining the position of the glycosidic linkage is the periodate oxidation (see §§7g, 13).

The final problem is to decide whether the glycosidic link is α or β. This is done by means of enzymes, maltase hydrolysing α-glucosides and emulsin β-glycosides (*cf.* §3). In non-reducing sugars, the problem is far more difficult since the links α_1–α_2, α_1–β_2, β_1–α_2 would *all* be hydrolysed by maltase. Consideration of the optical rotations has given information on the nature of the link (*cf.* §6). The different types of linkages have also been elucidated by graded oxidation with lead tetra-acetate followed by reduction with sodium borohydride. In this way, only the reducing residue of the disaccharide is degraded to a glycoside of glycerol, the configuration of which has been obtained by other means. NMR spectroscopy has also been used to determine the configuration of the linkage (see also §20).

Many disaccharides have been synthesised, the acetobromo-sugars usually being the best starting materials (see §24). A point of interest in connection with the synthesis of disaccharides is that, although dilute acid has little effect on dilute aqueous solutions of monosaccharides at room temperature, at higher temperatures with more concentrated solutions condensation can occur to give disaccharides, etc. This reaction is referred to as *reversion*, *e.g.*, D-glucose gives predominantly the $(1 \rightarrow 6)$-disaccharide, and L-arabinose gives predominantly the $(1 \rightarrow 3)$-disaccharide (Whelan, 1960).

Nomenclature. Since disaccharides are monosaccharide glycosides (§3), non-reducing disaccharides are glycosyl glycosides. On the other hand, reducing disaccharides (in which one glycosidic hydroxyl group is still present) are *O*-glycosyl-glycoses. This systematic nomenclature of disaccharides is illustrated in the text. There is, however, an alternative scheme in which the sites of linkage of the two monosaccharide residues are indicated by an arrow pointing from the glycosidic group of the non-reducing residue to the site of attachment in the reducing residue, *e.g.*, maltose may be designated as 4-*O*-α-D-glucopyranosyl-D-glucopyranose or as *O*-α-D-glucopyranosyl-$(1 \rightarrow 4)$-D-glucopyranose. The latter designation is preferred for naming tri- and higher oligosaccharides.

§13 Sucrose

This exists in two crystalline forms, a stable form, *sucrose A*, m.p. 184–185°C, and the unstable form, *sucrose B*, m.p. 169–170°C (this is obtained by recrystallisation from methanol). Sucrose has been shown to be α-D-glucopyranosyl-β-D-fructofuranoside. It is hydrolysed by dilute acids or by the enzyme invertase to an equimolecular mixture of D(+)-glucose and D(−)-fructose. Methylation of sucrose (Haworth method) gives octa-*O*-methylsucrose and this, on hydrolysis with dilute hydrochloric acid, gives 2,3,4,6-tetra-*O*-methyl-D-glucose and 1,3,4,6-tetra-*O*-methyl-D-fructose. The structures of these compounds were determined by the oxidation methods previously described (see §§7a, 7e). Thus glucose is present in the pyranose form, and fructose as the furanose.

Since sucrose is a non-reducing sugar, both glucose and fructose must be linked *via* their respective reducing groups. The stereochemical nature of the glycosidic link may be any one of the four possibilities discussed (see §12), but the evidence indicates that it is α-glucose linked to β-fructose. Maltase hydrolyses sucrose; therefore an α-link is present. Furthermore, since the mutarotation of the glucose produced is in a downward direction, it therefore follows that α-glucose is liberated at first. The mutarotation of fructose is too rapid to be followed experimentally, and hence the nature of the link in this component remains to be determined. There is, however, an enzyme which hydrolyses methyl β-fructofuranosides, and it has been found that it also hydrolyses sucrose. This suggests that fructose is present in sucrose in the β-form, and is supported by calculations of the optical rotation of the fructose component. The following structure for sucrose accounts for all of the above facts:

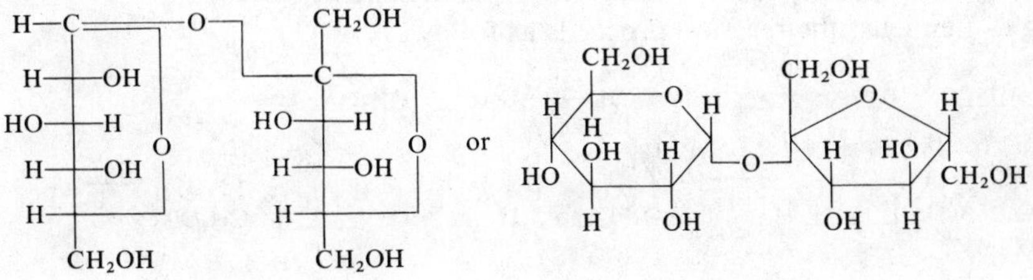

Oxidation of sucrose with periodic acid confirms this structure (but not the nature of the glycosidic link). Three molecules of periodic acid are consumed, and one molecule of formic acid is produced. Subsequent oxidation with bromine water, followed by hydrolysis, gives glyoxylic, glyceric and hydroxypyruvic acids (Fleury *et al.*, 1942).

Beevers *et al.* (1947) examined sucrose sodium bromide dihydrate by X-ray analysis, and confirmed the stereochemical configuration found chemically, and also showed that the fructose ring is five-membered.

Sucrose has now been synthesised by Lemieux *et al.* (1953, 1956). Brigl (1921) prepared the sugar epoxide, 3,4,6-tri-*O*-acetyl-1,2-anhydro-α-D-glucose (II) from tetra-*O*-acetyl-β-D-glucose (I) (*cf.* §9; see also §24).

Brigl also showed that (II) reacted with methanol to give methyl β-D-glucopyranoside triacetate (III), whereas with phenol, the α-glucopyranoside was the main product. Other workers showed that secondary alcohols gave α,β-mixtures. Lemieux was therefore led to believe that fructofuranose, a hindered secondary alcohol, would react with anhydroglucopyranose to form an α-glucose linkage. 1,2-Anhydro-α-D-glucopyranose triacetate and 1,3,4,6-tetra-*O*-acetyl-D-fructofuranose were heated in a sealed tube at 100°C for 104 hours. The product, sucrose hepta-acetate, was acetylated to the octa-acetate by means of acetic anhydride-sodium acetate in benzene solution. The benzene was evaporated off and the residue deacetylated with methanolic sodium methoxide. The sucrose fraction was isolated by paper chromatography and acetylated and the octa-acetate isolated by column chromatography and de-acetylated to sucrose (5·5 per cent yield).

According to Lemieux, the reaction proceeds as follows:

The CH$_2$OAc group at position 6 in the glucopyranose molecule enters into neighbouring group participation in the opening of the oxide ring, and consequently shields this side from attack. Thus the fructofuranose molecule is forced to attack from the other side and this produces the desired α-glucopyranose linkage.

One other point that is of interest is the 'inversion' of sucrose on hydrolysis. Hydrolysis of sucrose gives first of all α-D(+)-glucopyranose and β-D(+)-fructofuranose (this is believed to be dextrorotatory), but the latter is unstable and immediately changes into the stable form, D(−)-fructopyranose (the rotation of (−)-fructose is much greater than that of (+)-glucose).

§14. Trehalose, m.p. 203°C

This is α-D-glucopyranosyl-α-D-glucopyranoside. It is a non-reducing sugar which occurs in yeasts and fungi. It is hydrolysed by hydrochloric acid to two molecules of D-glucose; methylation of trehalose gives octa-O-methyltrehalose which, on hydrolysis, produces two molecules of 2,3,4,6-tetra-O-methyl-D-glucose (see §7a). The nature of the glycosidic link has been shown to be α,α, e.g., by its high positive rotation. Thus trehalose may be written:

§14a. Isotrehalose, m.p. 130–135°C.   This is β-D-glucopyranosyl-β-D-glucopyranoside and has been synthesised, *e.g.*, from tetra-O-acetyl-α-D-glucopyranosyl bromide and silver carbonate (Fischer *et al.*, 1909).

§14b. Neotrehalose.   This is α-D-glucopyranosyl-β-D-glucopyranoside, and has been synthesised from 1,2-anhydro-3,4,6-tri-O-acetyl-D-glucose and 2,3,4,6-tetra-O-acetyl-D-glucose (Haworth *et al.*, 1931).

§15. Maltose, m.p. 102–103°C

This is 4-O-α-D-glucopyranosyl-D-glucopyranose. It is hydrolysed by dilute acids to two molecules of D-glucose, is a reducing sugar, undergoes mutarotation, and forms an osazone. Thus there is one free reducing group present, and since maltose is hydrolysed by maltase, the glycosidic link of the non-reducing half of the molecule is therefore α-. Complete methylation of maltose gives an octa-methyl derivative which is non-reducing, and this, on hydrolysis with very dilute cold hydrochloric acid, is converted into heptamethylmaltose, which has reducing properties. Thus, the original octa-methyl derivative must be methyl hepta-O-methyl-D-maltoside; this is further evidence that only *one* free reducing group is present in maltose. Hydrolysis of hepta-O-methylmaltose with moderately concentrated hydrochloric acid produces 2,3,6-tri-O-methyl-D-glucose and 2,3,4,6-tetra-O-methyl-D-glucose. The structure of the latter is known (see §7a), but that of the former was elucidated as follows. Analysis of the compound showed that it was a trimethyl derivative, and since it formed a phenylhydrazone but not an osazone, C-2 must therefore be attached to a methoxyl group. On further methylation, this trimethylglucose gave 2,3,4,6-tetra-O-methyl-D-glucose, and so the tri-methyl compound must be one of the following: 2,3,4-, 2,3,6- or 2,4,6-tri-O-methyl-D-glucose. Now, on careful oxidation with nitric acid, the trimethylglucose forms a dimethylsaccharic acid. This acid contains two terminal carboxyl groups; one has been derived from the free 'aldehyde' group, and the other by oxidation at C-6, and since in its formation one methyl group is lost, this dimethylsaccharic acid must have been derived from a trimethylglucose having a methoxyl group at C-6. Thus the trimethylglucose must be either 2,3,6- or 2,4,6-tri-O-methyl-D-glucose. On further oxidation, the dimethylsaccharic acid forms dimethyl-D-tartaric acid; this can only arise from a precursor with two methoxyl groups on *adjacent* carbon atoms, and so it follows that the trimethyl-glucose must be 2,3,6-tri-O-methyl-D-glucose. This is confirmed by the fact that the other two possible compounds, *viz.*, 2,3,4- and 2,4,6-tri-O-methyl-D-glucose, have been synthesised, and were shown to be different from the trimethylglucose obtained from maltose. The foregoing reactions may therefore be written:

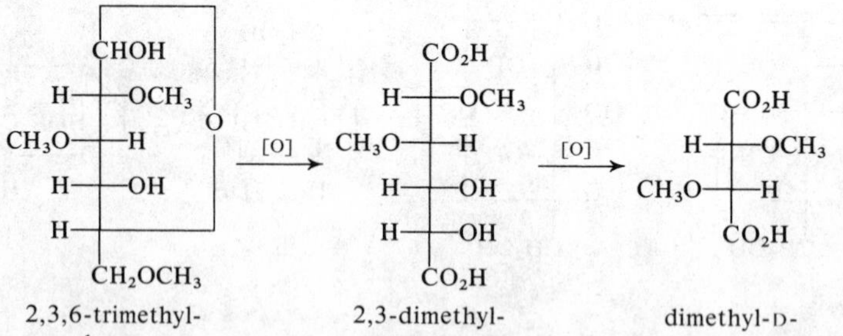

2,3,6-trimethyl-   2,3-dimethyl-   dimethyl-D-
glucose   saccharic acid   (+)-tartaric acid

From this it can be seen that structure (I) for maltose satisfies all the above facts. This structure, however, is not the only one that satisfies all the facts. The structure of the non-reducing half is certain, but that of the reducing half need not necessarily be pyranose as shown in (I), since a furanose structure (II) would also give 2,3,6-tri-O-methyl-D-glucose. To decide whether C-4 (as in (I)) or C-5 (as in (II)) was involved in the glycosidic link, Haworth *et al.* (1926) oxidised maltose with bromine water to maltobionic acid (III), and this, on methylation, gave the methyl ester of octamethyl-maltobionic acid (IV) which, on vigorous hydrolysis gave 2,3,5,6-tetra-O-methyl-D-gluconic acid

(V) (as lactone), and 2,3,4,6-tetra-O-methyl-D-glucose (VI). (V) can be obtained only if maltose has structure (I); structure (II) would have given 2,3,4,6-tetra-O-methyl-D-gluconic acid. Thus maltose is (I) and not (II). Confirmation of the α-glycosidic linkage is afforded by the agreement of the specific

rotation of maltose with that calculated for structure (I), and further evidence for the linkage at C-4 is as follows. Since maltose is a reducing sugar, C-1 (of the reducing half) is free, and since maltose forms an osazone, C-2 is also free, *i.e.*, not combined with an alkoxyl group. Zemplen (1927) degraded maltose by one carbon atom (see Vol. I), and obtained a compound which still formed an osazone; therefore C-3 is free. On further degrading by one carbon atom, a compound was obtained which did *not* form an osazone; therefore C-4 in maltose is not free (see also §7g).

Lemieux *et al.* (1953) have synthesised octa-*O*-acetyl-β-D-maltose by reaction between 3,4,6-tri-*O*-acetyl-1,2-anhydro-α-D-glucopyranose and 1,2,3,6-tetra-*O*-acetyl-β-D-glucose, followed by acetylation and then separation of the products by chromatography (*cf.* sucrose, §13).

§15a. Isomaltose, m.p. 120°C.   This is 6-*O*-α-D-glucopyranosyl-D-glucopyranose (*cf.* gentiobiose, §19), and has been isolated from the products of the partial hydrolysis of amylopectin (§22).

§15b. Turanose, m.p. 157°C.   This is 3-*O*-α-D-glucopyranosyl-D-fructose. This disaccharide is obtained from melezitose by acid hydrolysis (see §20). A particular point of interest about turanose is the way its structure has been elucidated.

Pascu *et al.* (1939) catalytically hydrogenated the keto form of turanose octa-acetate and acetylated the product, thereby obtaining the nona-acetates of 3-*O*-α-D-glucopyranosyl-D-sorbitol and 3-*O*-α-D-glucopyranosyl-D-mannitol (two epimeric alcohols are produced when the keto group is reduced). These names were given to the products by Pascu based on some evidence that turanose is 3-*O*-α-D-glucopyranosyl-D-fructose.

Hudson (1944) argued from theoretical considerations that 4-*O*-α-D-glucopyranosyl-D-mannitol must be identical with the 3-*O*-α-D-glucopyranosyl-D-mannitol prepared by Pascu if turanose has the structure assigned to it. This identity arises from the fact that positions 3 and 4 are equivalent in mannitol, *i.e.*, the 3- and 4-derivatives of mannitol are identical because of the special symmetry of the mannitol molecule. This identity may be shown by rotating (I), the 3-derivative (G = glucose residue, $C_6H_{11}O_5$) through 180° in the plane of the paper; this gives (II), the 4-derivative.

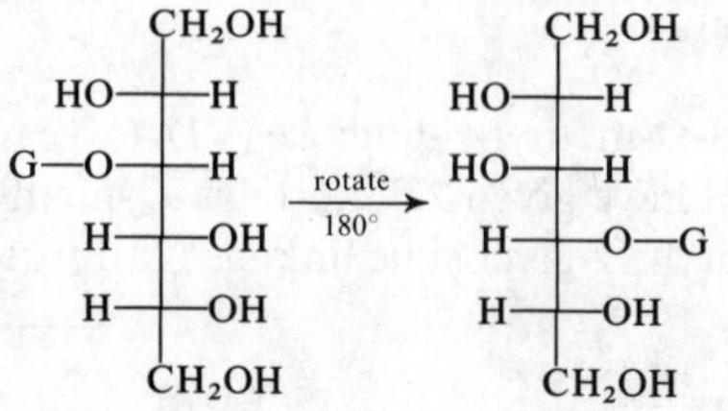

(I)   (II)

Hudson prepared 4-*O*-α-D-glucopyranosyl-β-D-mannose (III) from octa-*O*-acetyl-β-D-maltose *via* the acetobromomaltose (see also §24).

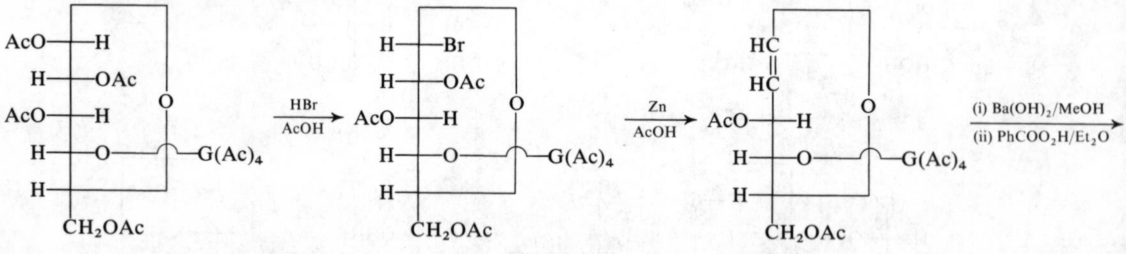

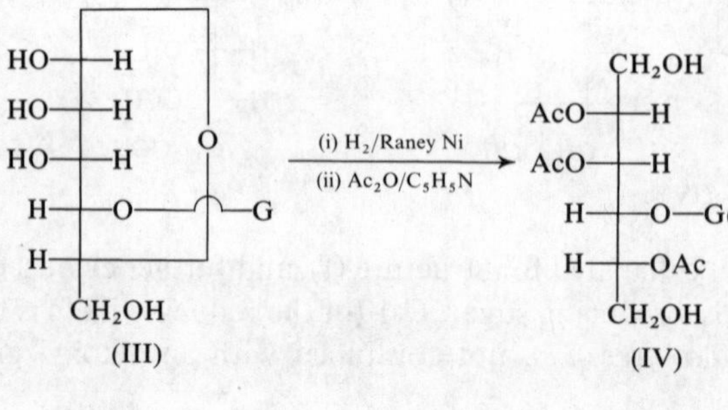

(III)   (IV)

(III) was then converted into (IV), the nona-acetate of the corresponding 4-mannitol derivative, which was shown to be identical with the compound produced from ketoturanose octa-acetate by Pascu (see above). Hence, turanose must be O-α-D-glucose (1 → 3 or 1 → 4)-D-fructose. The 1 → 4 linkage is eliminated by the fact that the osazone of turanose is not identical with that of maltose. Therefore turanose is:

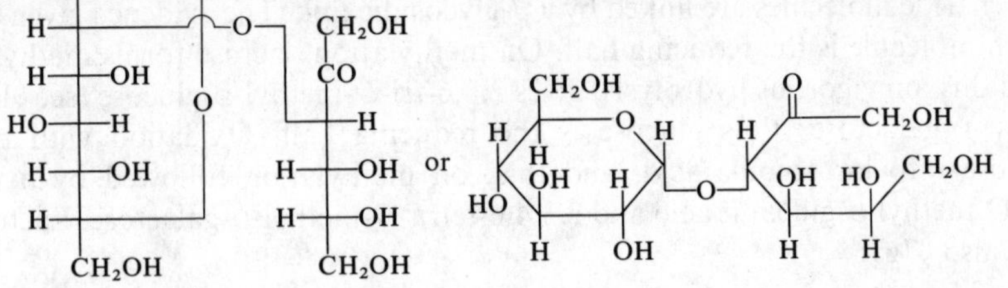

turanose

There is no direct evidence of the nature of the ring in the fructose residue in turanose; it is furanose in melezitose (see §20).

§16. Cellobiose, m.p. 252°C

This is 4-O-β-D-glucopyranosyl-D-glucopyranose. It is obtained as the octa-acetate by the acetolysis of cellulose (see §21a). Cellobiose is hydrolysed by dilute acids to two molecules of D(+)-glucose; since this hydrolysis is also effected by emulsin, the glycosidic link must be β. Cellobiose is a reducing sugar, and so one reducing group is free. Methylation, followed by hydrolysis, gives 2,3,6-trimethyl-D-glucose and 2,3,4,6-tetramethyl-D-glucose (these are the same products obtained from maltose, §15). Oxidation with bromine water converts cellobiose into cellobionic acid, and this, on methylation followed by hydrolysis, gives 2,3,5,6-tetramethylgluconic acid and 2,3,4,6-tetramethylglucose (again the same products as for maltose). Therefore cellobiose and maltose differ only in that the former has a β-glycosidic link, whereas the latter has an α-. Thus cellobiose is (α-form):

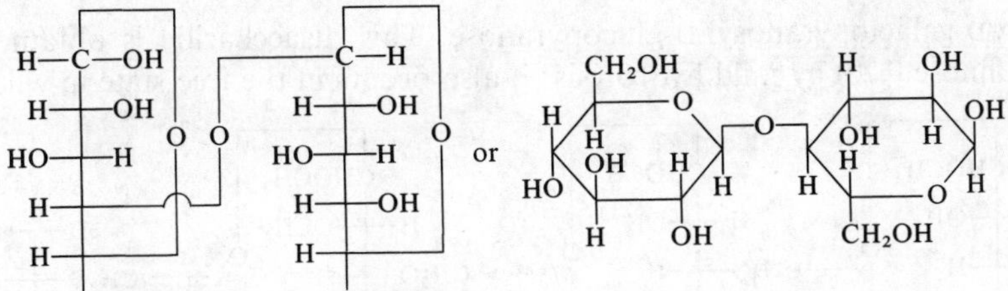

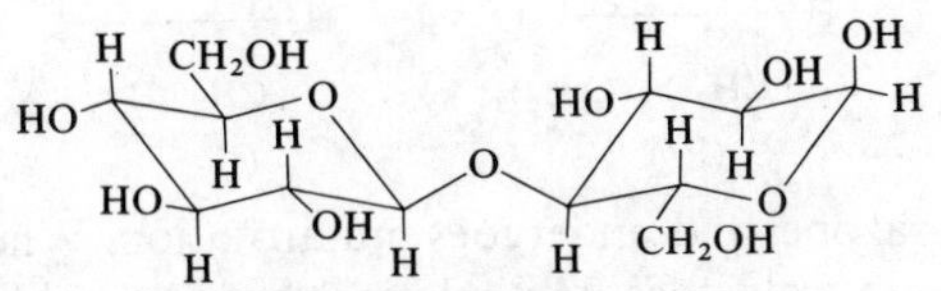

Degradation experiments confirm the C-4 linkage (see also §7g), and the structure has also been confirmed by synthesis, e.g., the condensation between 2,3,4,6-tetra-O-acetyl-α-D-glucopyranosyl bromide and 1,2,3,6-tetra-O-acetyl-4-O-sodium-D-glucose (Stacey et al., 1946).

§17. Lactose, m.p. 252°C

This is 4-*O*-β-D-galactopyranosyl-D-glucopyranose. It is a reducing sugar, and is hydrolysed by dilute acids to one molecule of D(+)-glucose and one molecule of D(+)-galactose. Since lactose is hydrolysed by lactase (which has been shown to be identical with the β-glycosidase in emulsin), the two monosaccharide molecules are linked by a β-glycosidic link. The evidence given so far does not indicate which molecule is the reducing half. On methylation, lactose forms methyl heptamethyl-lactoside, and this, on vigorous hydrolysis, gives 2,3,6-tri-*O*-methyl-D-glucose (see §15) and 2,3,4,6-tetra-*O*-methyl-D-galactose; thus glucose is the reducing half. Oxidation with bromine water converts lactose into lactobionic acid, and this, on methylation followed by hydrolysis, gives 2,3,5,6-tetra-*O*-methyl-D-gluconic acid and 2,3,4,6-tetra-*O*-methyl-D-galactose. Lactose is therefore (β-form) [see also §7g]:

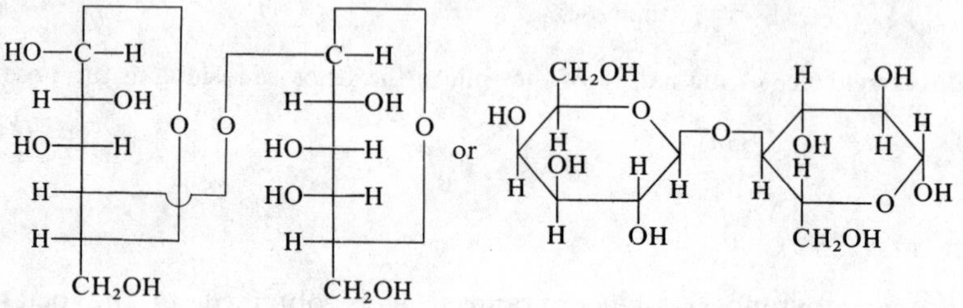

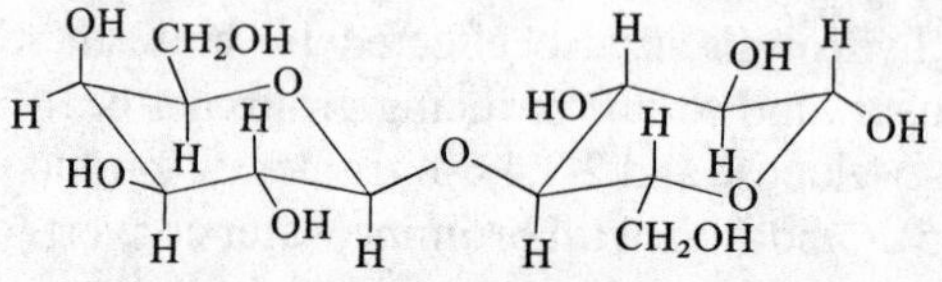

Lactose has been synthesised by, *e.g.*, the condensation between 2,3,4,6-tetra-*O*-acetyl-α-D-galactopyranosyl bromide and 2,3–5,6-di-*O*-isopropylidene-D-glucose diethyl acetal.

§18. Melibiose, m.p. 85°C

This is 6-*O*-α-D-galactopyranosyl-D-glucopyranose. This disaccharide is obtained from the trisaccharide raffinose (§20) by mild hydrolysis; it also occurs in the free state in wild mallow. It is a

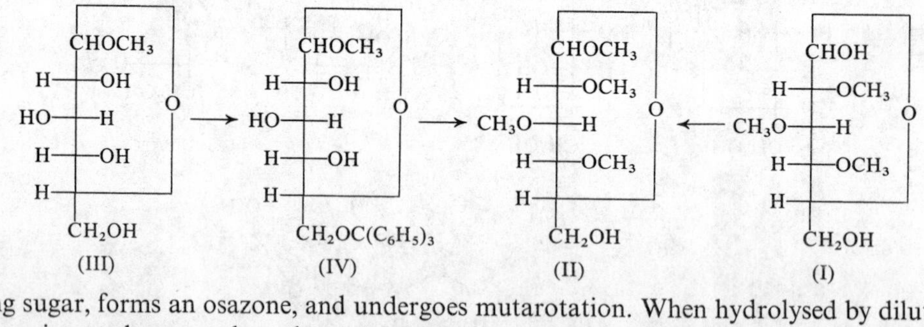

reducing sugar, forms an osazone, and undergoes mutarotation. When hydrolysed by dilute acids, melibiose gives D-glucose and D-galactose. Methylation converts melibiose into methyl heptamethyl-melibioside, and this, on hydrolysis, forms 2,3,4-trimethyl-D-glucose and 2,3,4,6-tetramethyl-D-galactose. The structure of the former has been established as follows. The trimethylglucose (I) readily forms a crystalline methyl trimethylglucoside (II). Now methyl glucopyranoside (III) can be converted into the 6-trityl derivative (IV) (see §9), and this, on methylation followed by removal of the trityl group, gives (II). Thus (II) must be methyl 2,3,4-tri-*O*-methyl-D-glucopyranoside, and consequently (I) is 2,3,4-tri-*O*-methyl-D-glucose. From the foregoing facts, it can be seen that galactose is the non-reducing half of melibiose, and that its reducing group is linked to C-6 of glucose, the reducing half. This has been confirmed by oxidation of melibiose with bromine water to melibionic acid, and this, on methylation followed by hydrolysis, gives 2,3,4,5-tetra-*O*-methyl-D-gluconic acid and 2,3,4,6-tetra-*O*-methyl-D-galactose; the structure of the former is shown by the fact that, on oxidation with nitric acid, it forms tetramethylsaccharic acid. There has been some doubt about the nature of the glycosidic link, but the evidence appears to be strongly in favour of α-. Thus the structure of melibiose is (β-form) [see also §7g]:

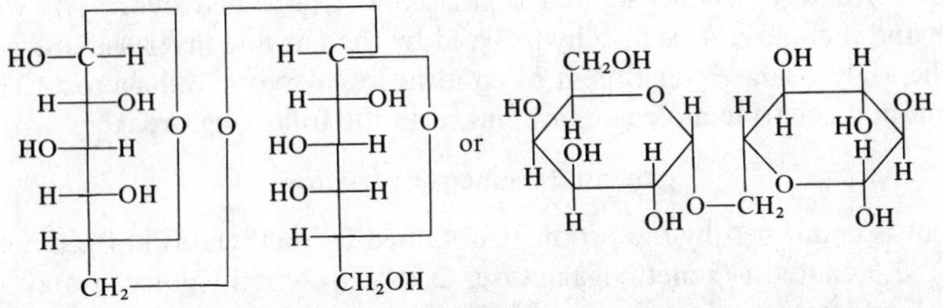

Melibiose has been synthesised by the condensation between 2,3,4,6-tetra-*O*-acetyl-α-D-galacto-pyranosyl bromide and 1,2,3,4-tetra-*O*-acetyl-D-glucose (Helferich *et al.*, 1928).

§19. Gentiobiose, m.p. 190–195°C

This is 6-*O*-β-D-glucopyranosyl-D-glucopyranose. It was originally obtained from the trisaccharide, gentianose (§20), but it also occurs in some glycosides, *e.g.*, amygdalin (§27). Gentiobiose is a reducing sugar, forms an osazone and undergoes mutarotation; hydrolysis with dilute acids produces two molecules of D-glucose. Since this hydrolysis is also effected by emulsin, the glycosidic link must be β-. Methylation, followed by hydrolysis, gives 2,3,4-trimethyl-D-glucose and 2,3,4,6-tetramethyl-D-glucose. Oxidation to gentiobionic acid, this then methylated and followed by hydrolysis, gives 2,3,4,5-tetramethyl-D-gluconic acid and 2,3,4,6-tetramethyl-D-glucose. Thus gentiobiose is (β-form):

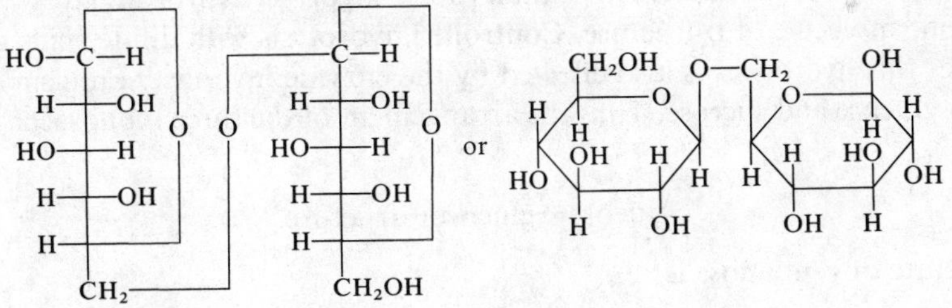

Gentiobiose has been synthesised in the same way as melibiose (§18); the corresponding α-D-gluco-pyranosyl bromide was used (Helferich *et al.*, 1926). Another disaccharide containing the 1,6-glycosidic link is primeverose (§26).

§20. Trisaccharides

The determination of the structure of trisaccharides (and higher oligosaccharides and polysaccharides) is more complicated than that of the disaccharides because more problems are involved: (i) Whether the trisaccharide is a reducing compound or not (Fehling's solution; mutarotation).

(ii) The nature of the three monosaccharide residues. (iii) The order in which they are joined and the points of attachment (methylation; periodic acid oxidation). (iv) The nature of the linkage between pairs of residues (enzymes).

A particularly useful method of determining the structure of trisaccharides is their conversion, by controlled hydrolysis (acids or enzymes), into disaccharides of known structure.

There are two types of trisaccharides, reducing and non-reducing. First we shall discuss only trisaccharides containing three hexose residues; these have the molecular formula $C_{18}H_{32}O_{16}$. Three natural non-reducing trisaccharides are raffinose, gentianose and melezitose.

Raffinose, m.p. 118–120°C, occurs in many plants, particularly beet. Vigorous hydrolysis gives one molecule of D-fructose, D-glucose, and D-galactose. Controlled hydrolysis with dilute acids gives D-fructose and melibiose. It is also hydrolysed by the enzyme invertase to fructose and melibiose, and by the α-glycosidase constituent of emulsin to galactose and sucrose. These facts show that the three monosaccharide molecules are linked in the following order:

galactose—glucose—fructose

This arrangement is confirmed by the products obtained by methylation of raffinose, followed by hydrolysis, viz., 2,3,4,6-tetra-O-methylgalactose, 2,3,4-tri-O-methylglucose and 1,3,4,6-tetra-O-methylfructose. Furthermore, since the structures of sucrose (§13) and melibiose (§18) are known, the structure of raffinose must therefore be:

Thus, raffinose is O-α-D-galactopyranosyl-(1 → 6)-O-α-D-glucopyranosyl-(1 → 2)-β-D-fructofuranoside.

Gentianose, m.p. 209–211°C, occurs in gentian roots. Vigorous hydrolysis gives two molecules of D-glucose and one molecule of D-fructose. Controlled hydrolysis with dilute acids gives D-fructose and gentiobiose; this hydrolysis is also effected by the enzyme invertase. Emulsin also hydrolyses gentianose to D-glucose and sucrose. Thus the arrangement of the three monosaccharide molecules is:

glucose—glucose—fructose

Hence the structure of gentianose is:

Thus, gentianose is O-β-glucopyranosyl-$(1 \rightarrow 6)$-O-α-D-glucopyranosyl-$(1 \rightarrow 2)$-β-D-fructofurano-side.

   Melezitose, m.p. 153–154°C (dihydrate) occurs in the honey-dew of many trees, *e.g.*, poplars, lime, etc. When hydrolysed with dilute acid, melezitose yields D-glucose and the disaccharide turanose (§15b). Hudson *et al.* (1946) established the structure of melezitose by means of the periodic acid oxidation. Four molecules of acid were consumed, two molecules of formic acid were formed, and no formaldehyde could be detected. These results are in agreement with the structure shown.

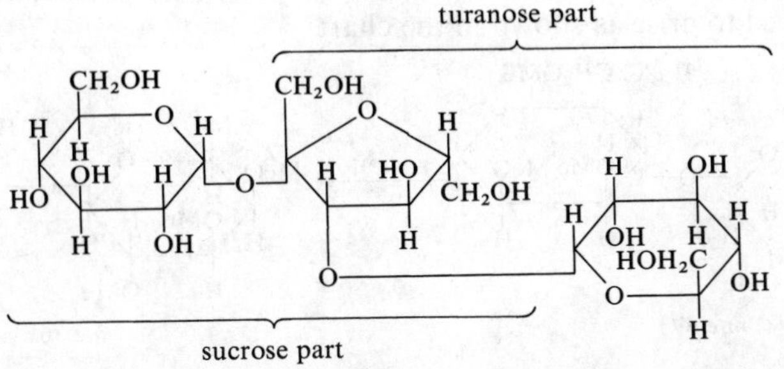

turanose part

sucrose part

The fructose residue is in the furanose form, and this was confirmed by the oxidation of the tetra-aldehyde (from the periodic acid oxidation), followed by hydrolysis to give, among other products, D-fructose, which was identified as its *p*-nitrophenylhydrazone. Hudson was unable to ascertain the nature of the link (α or β) in the 'sucrose part', but believed it was β as in sucrose. Unlike the trisaccharides, melezitose is not hydrolysed by the enzyme invertase. The actual presence of sucrose as a part of the molecule has been established by Hehre *et al.* (1952), who isolated this sugar from the products of the enzymic hydrolysis of melezitose. Thus, melezitose is O-α-D-glucopyranosyl-$(1 \rightarrow 3)$-O-β-D-fructofuranosyl-$(2 \rightarrow 1)$-α-D-glucopyranoside.

   Evertriose is a trisaccharide that has been obtained from **everninomicin D** (an antibiotic) by hydrolysis with dilute acid. It has structure (I) (Ganguly *et al.*, 1970). Its molecular formula was

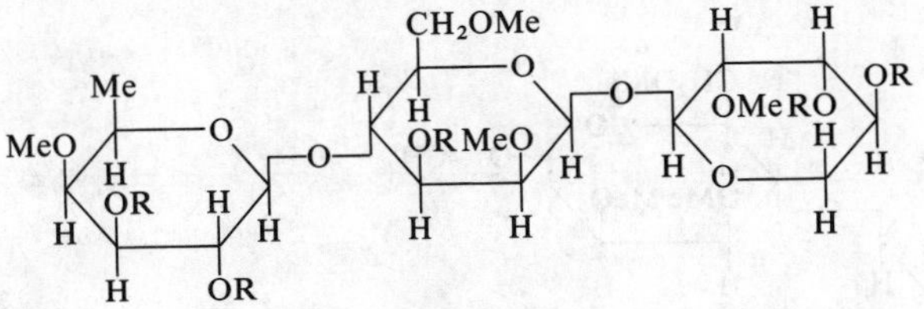

(I) R = H; (IV) R = Me

shown to be $C_{21}H_{38}O_{14}$, and it was found to be non-reducing. Its u.v. spectrum showed no selective absorption and the i.r. spectrum showed the absence of an oxo group. The NMR spectrum (in D_2O) showed the presence of four methoxy-groups, a secondary methyl group (τ 8·7, d; *J* 6·5 Hz), and three anomeric protons at τ 5·69 (*J* 7 Hz), 5·05 (*J* 1·5 Hz), and 4·67 (*J* 2·5 Hz) [note the low values; see NMR, §7h]. On hydrolysis, evertriose gave everninose (II) and D-curacose (III), both of which

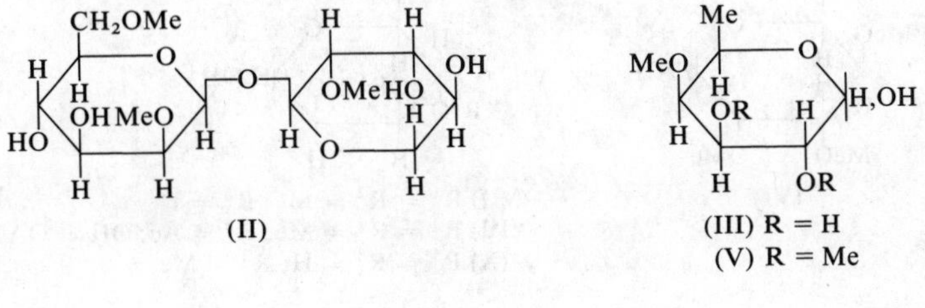

(II)

(III) R = H
(V) R = Me

had known structures (see later). Evertriose, on methylation, gave a permethylated compound (IV), $C_{26}H_{48}O_{14}$. The molecular weight of (IV) was shown to be 584 by mass spectrometry ($M = 584$), and the NMR spectrum showed the presence of nine methoxy-groups, one secondary methyl group (τ 8·67, d; J 6·5 Hz), and three anomeric protons. Two of these anomeric protons at τ 4·70 (d; J 2 Hz) and τ 5·27 (d; J 1·5 Hz) belonged to the everninose part of the molecule, and hence the third anomeric proton at τ 5·64 (d; J 7 Hz) was assigned to the curacose part. This therefore indicates that the two parts are joined by a β-linkage. The mass spectrum of (IV), in addition to showing M 584, showed prominent peaks at m/e 393, 361, 155, 453, 452, 423, 439, 379. Some of these peaks are believed to arise as shown in the chart.

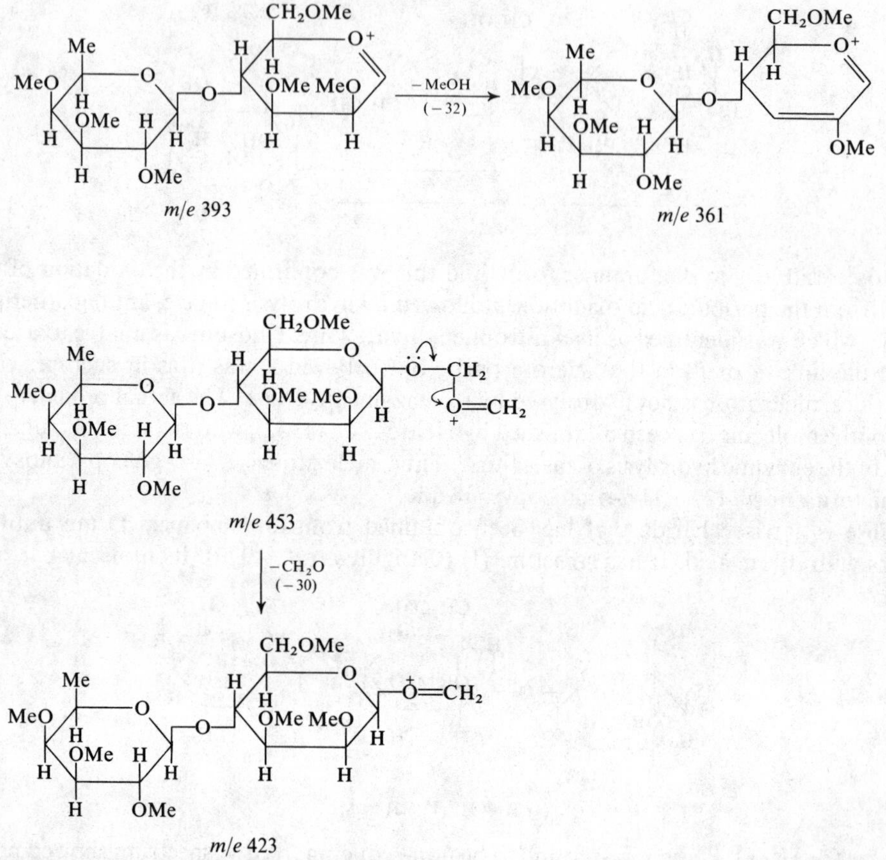

m/e 393   *m/e* 361

m/e 453

m/e 423

It was deduced from this fragmentation pattern that in evertriose (I), D-curacose (III) is linked to the 4-position of the hexose unit in everninose (II). Complete acid-catalysed hydrolysis of (IV) gave, by means of TLC, (V), (VI) and (VII). (VII), which had the molecular formula $C_9H_{18}O_6$, was shown

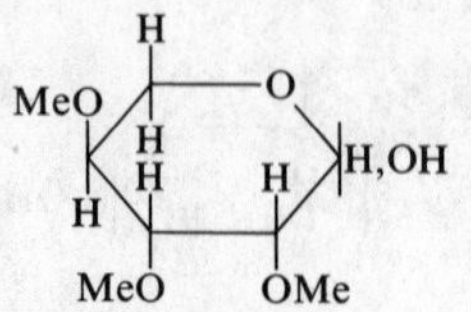

(VI)

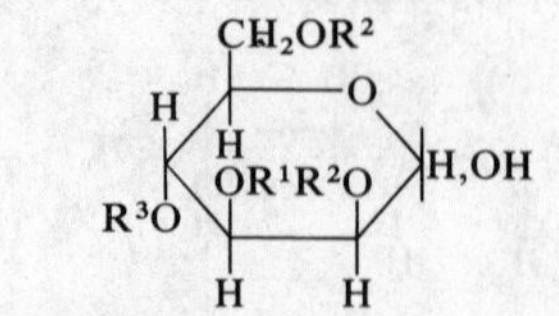

(VII) $R^1 = R^2 = Me; R^3 = H$
(VIII) $R^1 = R^2 = Me; R^3 = Ac; OH = OAc$
(X) $R^1 = R^3 = H; R^2 = Me$

to be 2,3,6-tri-O-methyl-D-mannose by acetylation to give (VIII). The NMR spectrum of (VIII) showed the presence of three methoxy-groups (τ 6·12, 6·44, and 6·55; *cf.* Table 1.9), two acetoxy-groups (τ 7·89 and 7·85; *cf.* Table 1.9), and an anomeric proton at τ 3·72 (J 2 Hz). There was also a triplet at τ 4·72 (J 9 Hz) which was assigned to H-4. All these data are in keeping with (I) being the structure and stereochemistry of evertriose.

In addition to evertriose (I), a disaccharide (IX) was also isolated from the hydrolysis of everninomicin D. This was a reducing sugar, molecular formula $C_{15}H_{28}O_{10}$. The NMR spectrum of

(IX)

(IX) showed the presence of three methoxy-groups (τ 6·64, 6·55, and 6·44), two anomeric protons (τ 4·69, J 2 Hz; τ 5·7, J 7 Hz), and a methyl doublet (τ 8·7, J 6·5 Hz). On hydrolysis with aqueous acid, (IX) gave D-curacose (III) and (X). Hence the structure of the disaccharide (IX) is established.

Now let us consider the structure of everninose (II). This was established by Ganguly *et al.* (1969) as follows. Its molecular formula was found to be $C_{14}H_{26}O_{10}$ and it was shown to be non-reducing, that it consumed two molecules of periodic acid, and did not form a trityl derivative (therefore there is no free CH_2OH group). The NMR spectrum of everninose showed the presence of three methoxy-groups at τ 6·65, 6·5, and 6·35, and two anomeric protons at τ 4·75 (J *ca.* 1·5 Hz) and τ 4·3 (J 2·5 Hz). Everninose formed a tetra-acetate (*cf.* II), the NMR spectrum of which showed the presence of three methoxy-groups, four acetoxy-groups, and two anomeric protons. The mass spectrum of the tetra-O-trimethylsilyl ether of everninose showed a weak molecular-ion peak at m/e 642 and a strong peak at m/e 627 ($M - 15$). There were also strong peaks at m/e 335 and 291; these correspond to ions (XI) and (XII), respectively.

−CHOMe
(−44)

(XI) R = Me_3Si (XII) R = Me_3Si
m/e 335 m/e 291

These observations, together with the fact that everninose is a non-reducing sugar, suggest that everninose is composed of a dimethoxyhexose unit and a monomethoxyhexose unit which are linked by their anomeric hydroxyl groups.

Prolonged heating of everninose with dilute acid produced a mixture of two monosaccharides. These were separated by TLC and were shown to be 2,6-di-O-methyl-D-mannose (XIII) and 2-O-methyl-L-lyxose (XIV) as follows. (XIII) was a reducing sugar (anomeric proton τ 4·7; J 2 Hz),

(XIII) $R^1 = R^2 = H$ (XIV) $R^1 = R^2 = H$
(XV) $R^1 = R^2 = Ac$ (XVI) $R^1 = R^2 = Ac$

contained two methoxy-groups, and formed a triacetate, $C_{14}H_{22}O_9$ (XV). The NMR spectrum of (XV) showed it to be identical with triacetoxycuramicose (a known compound).

The mass spectrum of (XIV) confirmed that it was a 2-methoxypentose, and analysis of the NMR spectrum of (XVI), the triacetate of (XIV), led to the conclusion that (XIV) was 2-methoxylyxose. Its stereochemistry was then established by methylating the methyl glycoside of ((XIV); $R^1 = H$, $R^2 = Me$) and hydrolysing the product to give the trimethyl derivative ((XIV); $R^1 = Me$, $R^2 = H$). This was shown to be identical with 2,3,4-trimethoxy-D-lyxose, except that its sign of rotation was opposite. Hence (XIV) has the L-configuration.

Finally, the stereochemistry of the anomeric linkages in everninose was established to be that shown in (II) by means of the molecular rotations of methylated (II), methyl tetramethyl α- and β-D-mannosides ((XIII); $R^1 = R^2 = Me$), and methyl trimethyl α- and β-L-lyxosides ((XIV); $R^1 = R^2 = Me$) [cf. §6].

Polysaccharides

§21

Polysaccharides are high polymers of the monosaccharides, and may be roughly divided into two groups: those which serve as 'structures' in plants and animals, e.g., cellulose, and those which act as a metabolic reserve in plants and animals, e.g., starch. Structural determination is based on hydrolysis of the polysaccharide and its methylated derivatives.

The analysis of the hydrolytic products is now carried out by chromatography in its various forms: column, paper, GLC, TLC, etc. (1 §15). Column chromatography is used almost exclusively for preparative purposes, and GLC and TLC are particularly useful in analytical (and preparative) work. It appears, however, that it is not always satisfactory to rely on chromatographic behaviour of sugars as a means of their identification. Definite identification is carried out by isolation of the sugars followed by the determination of their physical characteristics and also the preparation of crystalline derivatives. Sufficient amounts for these purposes can generally be obtained from paper chromatography by using large sheets of filter paper, or by column chromatography on cellulose. When the sugars in the hydrolysate have been identified, it is then possible to estimate them quantitatively by means of paper chromatography, GLC, TLC, and zone electrophoresis.

Paper chromatography is particularly useful for the determination of the R_F values (1 §15c) of monosaccharides, and there are now a number of empirical rules connecting R_F values and structure (Isherwood et al., 1951), e.g.,

(i) Furanose sugars have higher R_F values than pyranose sugars.

(ii) Chair-form pyranoses with fewest axial hydroxyl groups have the lowest R_F values.

(iii) Aldopentoses and ketohexoses in the pyranose form have a higher R_F value when the two hydroxyl groups on C-2 and C-3 are cis than when these two hydroxyl groups are trans (in a similar molecule).

The presence of a reducing sugar on a paper chromatogram is carried out by means of various reagents, e.g., spraying with ammoniacal silver nitrate (black spot formation), or the appearance of colours characteristic of the type of reducing sugar when sprayed with a solution of a salt of an aromatic amine, e.g., N,N-dimethylaniline hydrochloride.

GLC requires the stable, volatile derivatives of the sugars. Methyl ethers of the sugars are those most commonly used. Other derivatives used are acetates, acetals or ketals (isopropylidene derivatives), but the best is the poly-O-trimethylsilyl (TMS) ethers.

Since most carbohydrates are non-electrolytes, zone electrophoresis is most frequently carried out on their 'complex' derivatives, e.g., complexes with boric acid.

Methylation of polysaccharides may be carried out by any of the methods described in §7, and a more recent one is that of Srivastava *et al.* (1963), who have methylated lower molecular weight carbohydrates by adding barium oxide and methyl iodide to a solution of the polysaccharide in dimethyl sulphoxide at 20°C (the yield is excellent). Methylation (by any of the methods used) is taken to be complete when the number of methyl groups (determined by the Zeisel method) is not raised by further methylation; or alternatively, by the disappearance of the infrared absorption band of the hydroxyl group. Infrared spectra also give information on the nature of the groups present, *e.g.*, carboxyl, acetamido, etc., and may help in deciding the configuration (α or β) of the glycosidic linkage. Monochromatic optical rotation and ORD studies may also give information about the configuration of the glycosidic linkage.

Hydrolysis of polysaccharides may be carried out with acid, but partial acid hydrolysis is widely used as a method of linkage analysis. Enzymic methods of degradation are also very useful, especially the method of using a series of enzymes which bring about the removal of sugar residues one or more at a time, starting from the reducing end of the polysaccharide. A particularly good method of degrading polysaccharides is the *Smith degradation*. The periodic acid oxidation has been used, but the difficulty is the isolation of the aldehydes after hydrolysis, since in this part of the reaction these aldehydes usually undergo condensation and degradation (*cf.* §7g). Smith *et al.* (1951, 1957) have overcome this difficulty by reducing the carbonyl groups (produced in the periodic acid oxidation) either catalytically (Raney nickel) or by means of sodium borohydride. In this way, polyhydric alcohols are obtained which are not affected by the hydrolysis, *e.g.*,

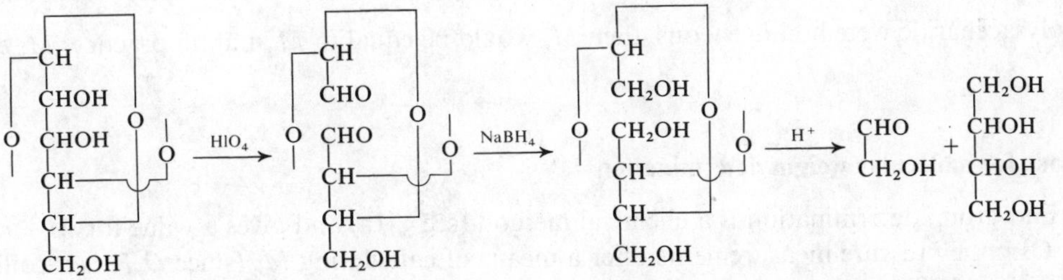

This example illustrates 1,4-linkage, the product being an erythritol. Since a 1,6- or 1,2-linkage would each give glycerol, these may be distinguished by methylation of the reduced product followed by hydrolysis. The 1,6-linkage gives 1-*O*-methylglycerol and the 1,2- gives 1,3-di-*O*-methylglycerol.

Barry *et al.* (1954) have developed an alternative technique for dealing with the periodate-oxidised polysaccharide. Here, the product is first treated with phenylhydrazine acetate and then heated with phenylhydrazine in acetic acid. In this way osazones are produced, *e.g.*, from the 1,4-linkage described above:

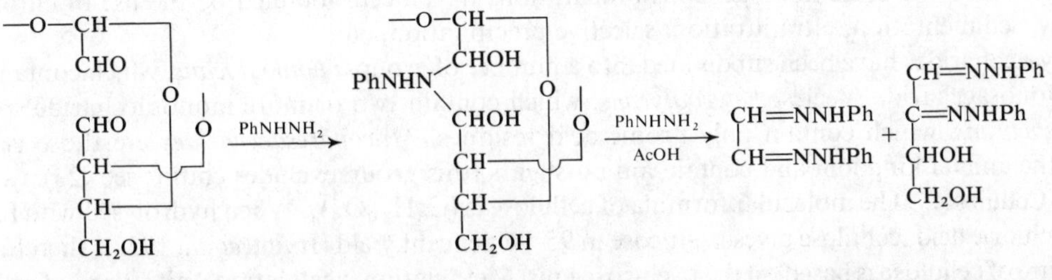

A very important part of structural determination of polysaccharides is their molecular weight. Chemical and physical methods are used, and we shall summarise them here. The *degree of polymer-*

isation, *DP*, of a polysaccharide is the number of monosaccharide units in the molecule. All the work done so far indicates that most polysaccharides are always a mixture of polymers. When these polymers have the same general structure but differ in their *DP* values, the polysaccharides are said to be *polymolecular*. If, however, the polysaccharides contain polymers which differ in detailed structure, they are said to be *polydisperse*.

Polysaccharides are generally isolated from natural sources by solubilisation in aqueous solvents or in aprotic solvents, *e.g.*, dimethyl sulphoxide. Inorganic salts may be removed by dialysis of aqueous solutions, by means of ion-exchange resins, etc., and the polysaccharide is then precipitated by addition of ethanol, acetone, etc.

There are two types of molecular weights that are estimated, M_n and M_w; both are *average* molecular weights. M_n is known as the *number average* molecular weight, and is defined as the weight of sample divided by the total number of molecules, n, present in the mixture, *i.e.*,

$$M_n = \text{Weight}/n$$

If the mixture contains n_1 molecules of molecular weight M_1, n_2 molecules of molecular weight $M_2, \ldots$, then

$$M_n = \frac{n_1 M_1 + n_2 M_2 + \cdots}{n_1 + n_2 + \cdots} = \frac{\sum n_i M}{\sum n_i}$$

On the other hand, M_w is known as the *weight average* molecular weight, and is defined as:

$$M_w = \sum n_i M_i^2 / \sum n_i M_i$$

If a polysaccharide were homogeneous, then M_n would be equal to M_w but, in practice, $M_n > M_w$.

Methods for molecular weight determination

(i) End-group determination is a chemical method (see §21a) and gives a value for M_n.

(ii) Osmotic pressure measurements offer a means of calculating M_n (since *O.P.* is a colligative property; see **1** §2).

(iii) Viscosity measurements lead to a value for M_w (since viscosity depends on the size and shape of the molecule; see **1** §7).

(iv) Sedimentation rate and sedimentation equilibrium give M_w, and at the same time give information on the shape of the molecule.

(v) Other methods are light scattering, diffusion, electrophoresis, and X-ray analysis (for the *solid* state).

The earlier work with these macromolecules was carried out on very inhomogeneous preparations, but now far more homogeneous preparations have been obtained by the use of chromatography, sedimentation, ultrafiltration, selective precipitation, etc.

Polysaccharides have been subdivided into a number of groups: *homoglycans*, which contain only one monosaccharide species; *heteroglycans*, which contain two or more monosaccharide species; and *glycurans*, which contain only uronic acid residues. *Mucopolysaccharides* are those isolated from the animal kingdom and contain amino-sugars (this group excludes chitin; see §23).

§21a. Cellulose.   The molecular formula of cellulose is $(C_6H_{10}O_5)_n$. When hydrolysed with fuming hydrochloric acid, cellulose gives D-glucose in 95–96 per cent yield (Irvine *et al.*, 1922); therefore the structure of cellulose is based on the D-glucose unit. Methylation, acetylation, 'nitration' of cellulose produces a trisubstitution product as a maximum substitution product, and it therefore follows from this that each glucose unit present has *three* hydroxyl groups in an uncombined state. When fully methylated cellulose is hydrolysed, the main product is 2,3,6-tri-O-methyl-D-glucose (90 per cent). Thus the three free hydroxyl groups in each glucose unit must be in the 2, 3 and 6 positions, and positions 4 and 5 are therefore occupied. Now, if we assume that the ring structure is present in each unit, then this would account for position 5 (or alternatively, 4) being occupied. Furthermore, if we also assume that the glucose units are linked by C-1 of one unit to C-4 of the next (or alternatively, C-5), then the following tentative structure for cellulose would account for the facts:

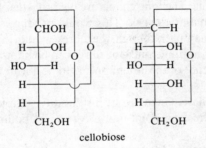

It should be noted, however, that if the linkages at 4 and 5 were interchanged the same trimethyl-glucose would still be obtained on hydrolysis (*cf.* maltose, etc.).

When subjected to *acetolysis*, *i.e.*, simultaneous acetylation and hydrolysis (this is carried out with a mixture of acetic anhydride and concentrated sulphuric acid), cellulose forms cellobiose octa-acetate. Thus the cellobiose unit is present in cellulose, and since the structure of cellobiose is known (see §16), it therefore follows that the glucose units are present in the pyranose form, *i.e.*, C-5 is involved in ring formation, and so the glucose units are linked C_1—C_4. The isolation of cellobiose indicates also that *pairs* of glucose units are joined by β-links, but it does indicate whether the links between the glucose units are the same (all β-) or alternate (α and β), since all the links could

cellobiose

be β-, or each pair of cellobiose units could be joined by α-links; the latter possibility is not likely, but it is not definitely excluded. Very careful acetolysis of cellulose, however, has produced a cellotriose, cellotetraose and a cellopentaose, and in all of these the C_1—C_4 links have been shown to be β- (from calculations of the optical rotations), and so we may conclude that *all* the links in cellulose are β-. This conclusion is supported by other evidence, *e.g.*, the kinetics of hydrolysis of cellulose.

Cellulose forms colloidal solutions in solvents in which glucose is soluble, and so it is inferred that cellulose is a very large molecule. Moreover, since cellulose forms fibres, *e.g.*, rayon, it appears likely that the molecule is linear; X-ray analysis also indicates the linear nature of the molecule, and that the cellulose molecule has a long length. The absence of di-O-methylglucose in the hydrolysis products of fully methylated cellulose (see above) indicates that there is no branching in the chain. Hence, a possible structure for cellulose is:

cellobiose units
(I*a*)
or

(I*b*)

It should be noted that in the structure given for cellulose, the first glucose unit in (I*a*) (*i.e.*, the one on the left-hand side; this unit is on the right-hand side in (I*b*)) has a free reducing group, but since this group is at the end of a very long chain, its properties tend to be masked; thus cellulose does not exhibit the strong reducing properties of the sugars.

The cellulose molecule is not planar, but has a screw-axis, each glucose unit being at right angles to the previous one. Although free rotation about the C—O—C link might appear possible at first sight, it apparently does not occur owing to the steric effect. This and the close packing of the atoms give rise to a rigid chain molecule. The long chains are held together by hydrogen bonding, and thus cellulose has a three-dimensional brickwork. This would produce strong fibres with great rigidity but no flexibility, and consequently, although the fibres would have great tensile strength, they could not be knotted without snapping. Since the fibres can be knotted without snapping, they must possess flexibility, and the presence of the latter appears to be due to the partly amorphous character of cellulose.

The molecular weight of cellulose. Owing to its insolubility, simple methods of molecular weight determination (depression of freezing point and elevation of boiling point) cannot be applied to cellulose.

Chemical methods. Examination of the formula of cellulose shows that on methylation, followed by hydrolysis, the end unit (the non-reducing end) would contain four methoxyl groups, and all the other units three. Hence, by the determination of the percentage of the tetramethyl derivative (2,3,4,6-) it is therefore possible to estimate the length of the chain. This method is known as the **end-group assay**. McGilvray (1953), using chromatographic methods on the hydrolytic products of methylated cellulose, obtained a value of ~ 10 000 units. This is in agreement with the value obtained by physical methods (see below).

Another end-group method for estimating the molecular weight of cellulose is that of Hirst *et al.* (1945); this is based on the periodate oxidation (§7g). Examination of the formula of cellulose shows that the terminal reducing unit would give two molecules of formic acid and one of formaldehyde (this reducing unit, which is left in (I*a*), behaves as the open-chain molecule, since it is *not* a glycoside), whereas the other terminal unit (right in (I*a*)) would give one molecule of formic acid; *i.e.*, one cellulose molecule gives three molecules of formic acid and one of formaldehyde. Estimation of the formic acid produced gives the value of the chain-length as approximately 1 000 glucose units. There appears, however, to be some uncertainty with these results, since 'over-oxidation' as well as normal oxidation with periodic acid results, the former possibly being due to the progressive attack on the chain-molecules from their reducing ends (Head, 1953).

Reduction of cellulose by aqueous sodium borohydride (which reduces the terminal reducing unit), followed by a periodate oxidation may also be used. If the oxidation is carried out at a suitable *p*H, rapid selective oxidation occurs at the terminal glycitol group and over-oxidation is avoided (Belcher *et al.*, 1965).

Physical methods. Ultracentrifuge measurements have given a value of $\sim 5\,000$ glucose units for *native* cellulose (Newman *et al.*, 1953). This is about half the value ($\sim 10\,000$) obtained by use of the light-scattering method (Holtzer *et al.*, 1954). On the other hand, viscosity and light-scattering measurements on the *same* samples of native cellulose have given values in very good agreement ($\sim 10\,000$; Timell, 1957; Goring *et al.*, 1958). Moreover, it appears that the molecular weight of native cellulose is independent of its source.

§22. Starch

The molecular formula of starch is $(C_6H_{10}O_5)_n$. Hydrolysis of starch with acids produces a quantitative yield of D-glucose (*cf.* cellulose); thus the structure of starch is based on the glucose unit. Methylation of starch gives the trimethylated compound (maximum substitution), and this, on hydrolysis, produces 2,3,6-tri-*O*-methyl-D-glucose as the main product, and a small amount (about 4·5 per cent) of 2,3,4,6-tetra-*O*-methyl-D-glucose. Oxidation studies (periodic acid) have also shown the presence of 1,4-linked D-glucopyranose residues. Starch is hydrolysed by the enzyme diastase (*β*-amylase) to maltose (see also below). Thus the maltose unit is present in starch, and so we may conclude that all the glucose units are joined by α-links (*cf.* cellulose). The following structure for starch fits these facts:

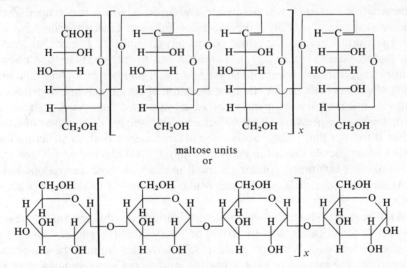

maltose units
or

The Haworth end-group assay (1932) showed that starch is composed of approximately 24–30 glucose units. Thus starch is a linear molecule, at least as far as 24–30 units. Haworth, however, pointed out that this was a *minimum* chain-length, and that starches may differ by having different numbers of this repeating unit (see also below). Viscosity measurements, however, showed the presence of a highly branched structure. Now, it has long been known that starch can be separated into two fractions, but it is only fairly recently that this separation has been satisfactorily carried out; the two fractions are α-amylose (the A-fraction; 17–34 per cent) and β-amylose (amylopectin, or the B-fraction). The fractionation has been carried out in several ways, *e.g.*, n-butanol is added to a hot colloidal solution (aqueous) of starch, and the mixture allowed to cool to room temperature. The A-fraction is precipitated, and the B-fraction is obtained from the mother liquors by the addition of methanol (Schoch, 1942). Haworth *et al.* (1946) have used thymol to bring about selective precipitation.

α-Amylose is soluble in water, and the solution gives a blue colour with iodine. β-Amylose is insoluble in water, and gives a violet colour with iodine. Both amyloses are mixtures of polymers, and the average molecular weight depends on the method of preparation of the starch used.

α-Amylose (A-fraction). The molecular weight of α-amylose extracted from starch granules by water has been shown to be 1×10^6 (Gilbert, 1958). On the other hand, extraction with dimethyl sulphoxide gives α-amylose with a molecular weight of $1 \cdot 9 \times 10^6$ (Killion *et al.*, 1960). Since α-amylose is readily degraded, its extraction from natural sources is carried out in the absence of oxygen.

When α-amylose with a chain-length of about 300 glucose units (as shown by osmotic pressure measurements) was methylated and then hydrolysed, about 0·3 per cent of 2,3,4,6-tetra-*O*-methyl-D-glucose was obtained. This value is to be expected from a straight chain composed of approximately 300 glucose units. From this evidence it would therefore appear that α-amylose is a *linear* polymer, and this is supported by the early work with soya-bean β-amylase (diastase). This enzyme converts α-amylose into maltose in about 100 per cent yield; this indicates that a large number of maltose units are joined by α-links, *i.e.*, amylose is a linear molecule. Further evidence fot the α-linkage is the high positive rotation of α-amylose. Peat *et al.* (1952), however, showed that highly purified soya-bean β-amylase gives only about 70 per cent of maltose, and this has been confirmed by other workers. Since β-amylase only attacks α-1,4-glucosidic linkages, it thus appears that α-amylose contains a small number of other linkages. Careful purification of 'crude' soya-bean β-amylase showed the presence of two enzymes, β-amylase and another which was named Z-enzyme; it is the latter which was shown to hydrolyse the non α-1,4-linkages. Thus unpurified β-amylase (which contains both enzymes) degrades α-amylose completely to maltose. It has also been shown that Z-enzyme has β-glucosidase activity and that emulsin can hydrolyse these 'anomalous' linkages. These observations suggest that α-amylose contains a small number of β-glucosidic linkages.

Another difficulty arises from the fact that the structure of potato amylose depends on its method of preparation, *e.g.*, one sample is completely degraded by purified β-amylase, whereas other samples are not. The first sample represents about 40 per cent (by weight) of the total amylose in potato starch, and thus it follows that potato amylose is heterogeneous both in structure and in size. A large proportion is completely linear (and contains about 2 000 glucose units), and the remainder (which contains about 6 000 units) contains a small number of these anomalous linkages which, according to Manners *et al.* (1962), are 1,6-glucosidic inter-chain linkages and occur only in very small amount.

Amylopectin (B-fraction). Molecular weight determinations of amylopectin by means of osmotic pressure measurements indicate values of 50 000 to 1 000 000 (Meyer *et al.*, 1940). Larger values have also been reported, *e.g.*, Witnauer *et al.* (1952) have determined the molecular weight of potato amylopectin by the method of light scattering, and report an average value of 10 000 000 or more. Let us consider an amylopectin having an average molecular weight of 550 000; this corresponds to about 3 000 glucose units. The end-group assay by methylation shows the presence of one unit with four free hydroxyl groups per 24–30 glucose units; the same results are also obtained by the periodate method. Thus the 3 000 units are joined in such a manner as to give about 100 end units; it therefore follows that the chain must be *branched*. The problem is further complicated by the fact that Hirst (1940), after methylating amylopectin and hydrolysing the product, obtained, in addition to tri- and tetra-*O*-methyl-D-glucose, about 3 per cent of 2,3-di-*O*-methyl-D-glucose. This has been taken to mean that some glucose units are also joined by C-2 and C-6 atoms. Furthermore, in certain experiments, enzymic hydrolysis has given a small amount of 1,6 α-linked diglucose, isomaltose, §15a (Montgomery *et al.*, 1947, 1949). Wolfrom *et al.* (1955, 1956) have obtained evidence that there is also an α-D-1,3-bond in amylopectin; they isolated 0·1 per cent of the disaccharide nigerose (3-*O*-α-D-glucopyranosyl-D-glucopyranose). It therefore appears that the principal bond in amylopectin is α-D-1,4, and branching occurs through α-D-1,6- and 1,3-bonds.

The branching of the chains in amylopectin is supported by the following evidence:

(i) Amylopectin acetate does not form fibres; fibre formation is characteristic of *linear* molecules.

(ii) β-Amylase hydrolyses amylopectin to give only about 50 per cent of maltose. Thus there are 'blocked' points, and these will occur at the branch points.

(iii) Amylopectin solutions do not show an orientation of the molecules in the direction of flow in the concentric cylinder technique; the molecules are therefore not linear.

The detailed structure of amylopectin is still not settled. The general view appears to be that amylopectin is composed of three types of chain, A, B and C, each chain consisting of about 24 glucose units. A-chains are linked to B-chains (1,6 or 1,3) which are linked to other B-chains, one of which (the 'terminal' one) is linked to a single C-chain which is the only one that has a free reducing group. There are two different types of combination of these chains which explain reasonably well the properties of amylopectin: the laminated structure (I) (Haworth, 1937) and the randomly highly-branched structure (II) (Meyer, 1940).

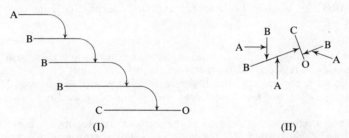

(I)   (II)

The action of β-amylase on amylopectin has been shown to degrade the 'exterior' parts of the B-chains and, when the enzyme is present in low concentration, the A-chains are degraded to within two or three glucose units of the branching point. When this partially degraded molecule is acted upon by R-enzyme (which splits 1,6-linkages), the A-residual chains are broken down to maltose and maltotriose, and the B-residual chains produce linear saccharides of higher molecular weight (then maltotriose). From the amount of maltose and maltotriose obtained in this way, it is possible to estimate the ratio of A:B chains. The results favour structure (II), and further evidence to support this is, *e.g.*, mathematical calculations which have shown that regular structure (I) is unlikely.

Products known as **dextrins** are obtained by degrading starch in various ways, *e.g.*, acid hydrolysis at low temperatures or at high temperatures. The dextrins formed under different conditions differ in structure. One reason is that at lower temperatures, dextrins are formed by recombination and reversion (§12).

§23. Some other polysaccharides

A number of other polysaccharides besides cellulose and starch also occur naturally, and some of these are described briefly below.

Glycogen. This is the principal reserve carbohydrate in animals. It is hydrolysed by β-amylase to maltose (~ 50 per cent), and molecular weight determinations by physical methods give values between 1 and 2×10^7. The molecular structure of glycogen appears to be similar to that of amylopectin; both polysaccharides have many features in common. One main difference is that the average chain-length in amylopectin is about 24 glucose units and in glycogen about 10–14.

Inulin. This is a fructosan, and occurs in dahlia tubers, dandelion roots, etc. Acid hydrolysis gives D-fructose, but if inulin is first methylated and then hydrolysed, 3,4,6-tri-O-methyl-D-fructose is the main product, thus indicating that inulin is composed of fructofuranose units. Small amounts of 1,3,4,6-tetra-O-methyl-D-fructose and 2,3,4,6-tetra-O-methyl-D-glucose are also obtained.

Mannans are polysaccharides which yield only mannose on hydrolysis; they are found in ivory nut, seaweeds, bakers' yeast, etc. Similarly, **galactans** yield only galactose on hydrolysis; they occur in seeds, wood, etc. There are also polysaccharides which contain pentose residues only, *viz.* **pentosans**, *e.g.*, **xylans** give D-xylose; **arabans** give L-arabinose. Some pentosans are composed of both xylose and arabinose, and other polysaccharides are composed of pentose and hexose units, *e.g.*, *xylo-glucans* (xylose and glucose), *arabo-galactans*, etc. In addition to these neutral polysaccharides, there are also the acid polysaccharides. These are gums and mucilages, and owe their acidity to the presence of uronic acids. Gums are substances which swell in water to form gels (or viscous solutions), *e.g.*, gum arabic and gum tragacanth; on hydrolysis, the former gives arabinose, galactose, rhamnose and glucuronic acid, and the latter xylose, L-fructose and galacturonic acid. Mucilages are polysaccharides which swell in water to form viscous solutions; on hydrolysis, they give galacturonic acid, arabinose, xylose, etc. The **hemi-celluloses** (which are widely distributed in the cell-wall of plants) also contain both uronic acids (glucuronic or galacturonic) and pentoses (xylose, arabinose).

Pectin. This occurs in plants, particularly fruit juices. Its main constituent is **pectic acid**, which is composed mainly of D-galacturonic acid residues and the methyl ester.

Alginic acid. This occurs in the free state and as the calcium salt in various seaweeds. Hydrolysis of alginic acid produces D-mannuronic acid and L-guluronic acid. Sodium alginate is used as a stabiliser in various foods, *e.g.*, ice cream.

Chitin. This is the polysaccharide that is found in the shells of crustaceans. Hydrolysis of chitin by acids produces acetic acid and D-glucosamine (chitosamine; 2-aminoglucose). Chitin is also hydrolysed by an enzyme (which occurs in the intestine of snails) to N-acetylglucosamine. X-ray analysis has shown that the structure of chitin is similar to that of cellulose (N-acetylglucosamine replaces glucose).

N-acetylglucosamine

N-Methyl-L-glucosamine is a component of streptomycin (see **18** §7).

Hyaluronic acid. This occurs in vitreous humour, etc., and is believed to act as a lubricant and shock absorbent in the joints of animals. Hyaluronic acid consists mainly of a chain of 1,4-linked β-D-glucuronic acid and 1,3-linked *N*-acetyl-β-D-glucosamine units.

—(4-acid-1)—(3-amine-1)—(4-acid-1)—(3-amine-1)—

Heparin. This is a powerful blood anticoagulant; it is composed of a D-glucuronic acid unit sulphated at C-2 or C-3 (*O*-sulphate) and C-6 (linked at C-4) linked to C-1 of D-glucosamine sulphated at *N* and at C-6.

Teichoic acids. A number of natural macromolecules are now known in which the repeating unit is a monosaccharide molecule attached to some other structural unit. In some cases, glycerol may be present instead of a monosaccharide. Most teichoic acids are polymers of ribitol phosphate (*ribitol teichoic acids*) or glycerol phosphate (*glycerol teichoic acids*); these have been isolated from the cells and walls of certain Gram-positive bacteria.

§23a. Photosynthesis of carbohydrates. Photosynthesis is the most important example of biosynthesis and represents the processes whereby plants containing the pigment chlorophyll absorb light energy and utilise it to convert atmospheric carbon dioxide, in the presence of water, to carbohydrates.

Photosynthesis has been shown to involve two separate types of reaction. The first involves a *photochemical* process in which light energy, absorbed by chlorophyll, is utilised to form 'activated' compounds. The second involves the reduction of carbon dioxide by the active molecules produced in the first process; the products are oxygen and carbohydrates (and some other compounds). Since this process can proceed in the presence or absence of light, it is referred to as the *dark reactions*; the first process is distinguished from this as the *light reactions*. Both the dark and light reactions require the presence of various enzymes. The overall equation for photosynthesis may be written as:

$$6CO_2 + 6H_2O \xrightarrow{\text{light}} 6(CH_2O) + 6O_2$$

Calvin *et al.*, using $^{14}CO_2$ as tracer, have worked out the pathway of the reduction of carbon dioxide in photosynthesis. The steps involved are as follows, each step requiring an enzyme (these have not been given in the equations). Also, all sugars have the D-configuration.

(i) D-Ribulose 1,5-diphosphate (I) accepts one molecule of carbon dioxide and the product is then split by water to give two molecules of 3-phospho-D-glyceric acid (II) [P = phosphate grouping, PO_3H_2, or an ionised form, $PO(OH)O^-$ and $PO(O^-)_2$; these ionised forms are most probably present].

(I)   (II)

(ii) (II) is reduced to D-glyceraldehyde 3-phosphate (III).

(II)   (III)

(iii) (III) is converted into D-glucose 6-phosphate (VII) *via* dihydroxyacetone phosphate (IV), D-fructose 1,6-diphosphate (V) and D-fructose 6-phosphate (VI).

(III)   (IV)   (V)   (VI)   (VII)

(**iv**) (VI) reacts with (III) to form D-xylulose 5-phosphate (VIII) and D-erythrose 4-phosphate (IX).

```
      CH₂OH                                   CH₂OH
      CO                                      CO
  HO——H         CHO                       HO——H         CHO
   H——OH   + H——OH   ⇌   HO——H      + H——OH
   H——OH        CH₂OP         H——OH      H——OH
      CH₂OP                                   CH₂OP        CH₂OP
      (VI)        (III)                       (VIII)        (IX)
```

(VIII) forms an equilibrium mixture with D-ribulose 5-phosphate (X) and D-ribose 5-phosphate (XI).

```
      CH₂OH           CH₂OH           CHO
      CO              CO           H——OH
  HO——H    ⇌   H——OH   ⇌   H——OH
   H——OH         H——OH         H——OH
      CH₂OP           CH₂OP         H——OH
      (VIII)           (X)            CH₂OP
                                       (XI)
```

(**v**) (IX) condenses with (IV) to give D-sedoheptulose 1,7-diphosphate (XII) and then D-sedo-heptulose 7-phosphate (XIII).

```
         CH₂OP
 (IV)    CO                    CH₂OP            CH₂OH
         CH₂OH                 CO               CO
                          HO——H           HO——H
          +          ⇌    H——OH   ⇌    H——OH
                          H——OH            H——OH
          CHO             H——OH            H——OH
 (IX)  H——OH                 CH₂OP            CH₂OP
        H——OH                (XII)            (XIII)
          CH₂OP
```

(XIII), together with (III), is also produced by an alternative path involving the condensation of (VI) with (IX).

```
                                         CH₂OH
      CH₂OH                              CO
      CO         CHO          HO——H           CHO
  HO——H   + H——OH   ⇌   H——OH + H——OH
   H——OH      H——OH          H——OH        CH₂OP
   H——OH        CH₂OP          H——OH
      CH₂OP                              CH₂OP
      (VI)        (IX)          (XIII)        (III)
```

(**vi**) The photosynthetic cycle is completed by reaction between (XIII) and (III) to give (VIII) and (XI).

$$
\begin{array}{cccc}
\text{CH}_2\text{OH} & & \text{CH}_2\text{OH} & \text{CHO} \\
\text{CO} & \text{CHO} & \text{CO} & \text{H—OH} \\
\text{HO—H} & \text{H—OH} & \text{HO—H} & \text{H—OH} \\
\text{H—OH} + & \text{H—OH} \rightleftharpoons & \text{H—OH} + & \text{H—OH} \\
\text{H—OH} & \text{CH}_2\text{OP} & \text{CH}_2\text{OP} & \text{CH}_2\text{OP} \\
\text{H—OH} & & & \\
\text{CH}_2\text{OP} & & & \\
\text{(XIII)} & \text{(III)} & \text{(VIII)} & \text{(XI)}
\end{array}
$$

(vii) Oligosaccharides and polysaccharides are produced from monosaccharide phosphate by the action of enzymes.

The biosynthesis of starch *in vitro* has been extensively studied in the presence of enzymes, but it is uncertain how important these pathways are *in vivo*. Enzymes catalyse both the synthesis and degradation of polysaccharides. The combination of two monosaccharide molecules may be written as:

$$\text{G—OR}^1 + \text{H—OR}^2 \rightleftharpoons \text{G—OR}^2 + \text{R}^1\text{—OH}$$

donor   acceptor

This is an example of the **glycosyl transfer reaction** or **transglycosylation**, in which a glycosyl residue is transferred from the *glycosyl donor* (G—OR^1) to a hydroxyl group of the *glycosyl acceptor* (R^2—OH). When the acceptor is of the type G$_n$—OH (*i.e.*, R^2 is an oligosaccharide or a polysaccharide), the reaction is a synthesis. If, on the other hand, the acceptor is water (R^2 = H), the reaction is a degradation (hydrolysis).

Many different enzymes are involved in the biosynthesis of starch *in vitro*, but synthetic amyloses have been obtained by the action of the enzyme phosphorylase on α-D-glucose 1-phosphate in the presence of a glucose oligosaccharide. Phosphorylase (from muscle, liver, potatoes, etc.) catalyses the reaction (the links formed are α-1 → 4):

$$1\text{—G—O—PO}_3^{2-} + \text{G}_n \rightleftharpoons \text{G}_{n+1} + \text{HOPO}_3^-$$

In these biosynthetic experiments, the acceptor molecule must be some 'polymer' of glucose, and hence is known as a **primer**. The function of the primer is to provide non-reducing terminal units for the chain-lengthening process. For the enzyme phosphorylase, the minimum value of n in the primer is 3.

The type of linkage formed between the donor and acceptor molecules depends on the nature of the enzyme, *e.g.*, phosphorylase is α-1 → 4, *Q*-enzyme is α-1 → 6. Thus, *e.g.*, when glycogen (α-1 → 4) is acted upon by the glycogen-branching enzyme, a chain of about seven glucose residues is removed from an α-1 → 4 position and transferred to an α-1 → 6 position. In this particular reaction, glycogen acts both as the donor and the acceptor.

Glycosides

§24. Introduction

Many glycosides are known, particularly those containing a phenolic group; they occur in most parts of plants (see also The Anthocyanins, Ch. 15). The simple glycosides are colourless, soluble in water and are optically active; they do not reduce Fehling's solution. On hydrolysis with inorganic acids, glycosides give a sugar and a hydroxylic compound, the aglycon (§3), which may be an alcohol or a phenol. Most glycosides are hydrolysed by emulsin; therefore they are β-glycosides. Actually, in the natural state, each glycoside is usually associated with an enzyme which occurs in different cells of the plant. Maceration of the plant thus produces hydrolysis of the glycoside by bringing the enzyme in contact with the glycoside. Glucose has been found to be the most common sugar component; when methylated and hydrolysed, most glycosides give 2,3,4,6-tetra-O-methyl-D-glucose. Thus most glucosides are β-D-glucopyranosides.

In addition to these O-glycosides, there are also C-, S- (see §30), and N-glycosides (see **16** §13c).

O-Glycosides (these contain the glycosyloxy group) are named systematically as aglycon glycoside, *e.g.*, salicin (§29) is *o*-hydroxymethylphenyl-β-D-glucopyranoside.

Synthesis of glycosides. The synthesis of a glycoside uses an **acetobromohexose** as the starting material; this compound is now named systematically as a tetra-O-acetyl-D-hexopyranosyl 1-bromide, *e.g.*, if the hexose is glucose, then the α-form will be tetra-O-acetyl-α-D-glucopyranosyl 1-bromide. The synthesis of *alkyl* glycosides has already been described; they are formed by direct reaction between a reducing sugar and lower alkanols in the presence of hydrogen chloride (see §3).

When glucose is treated with acetic anhydride at 0°C in the presence of zinc chloride, the product is 1,2,3,4,6-penta-O-acetyl-α-D-glucose (α-D-glucose penta-acetate). If, however, glucose is heated with acetic anhydride in the presence of sodium acetate, the product is 1,2,3,4,6-penta-O-acetyl-β-D-glucose. Furthermore, the β-isomer may be converted into the α- by heating with acetic anhydride at 110°C in the presence of zinc chloride. These penta-acetates are readily hydrolysed to

glucose by means of dilute aqueous sodium hydroxide, ethanolic ammonia at 0°C, or by methanol containing a small amount of sodium methoxide. When dissolved in glacial acetic acid saturated with hydrogen bromide, the glycosidic acetoxyl group of a hexose penta-acetate is replaced by bromine to give an α-acetobromohexose; the α-isomer is obtained whether the penta-acetate used is the α- or β-compound (Fischer, 1911). Thus a Walden inversion occurs with the β-compound (**3** §3).

Scheurer *et al.* (1954) have synthesised acetobromo sugars in good yield as follows. Bromine is added to a suspension of red phosphorus in glacial acetic acid, and to this solution (which now contains acetyl bromide) is added the sugar or acetylated sugar, the latter giving the better yields.

The bromine atom in these acetobromohexoses is very active. Thus it may be replaced by a hydroxyl group when the acetobromohexose is treated with silver carbonate in moist ether (Fischer *et al.*, 1909), or by an alkoxyl group when treated with an alcohol in the presence of silver carbonate

(Königs and Knorr, 1901). In either case, the α-acetobromohexose gives the β-glycoside. On the other hand, if mercuric acetate is used instead of silver carbonate, then the α-glycoside is obtained (Zemplen, 1929), but if mercuric cyanide is used, the product is the β-glycoside (Zemplen, 1930). Schroeder *et al.* (1966) have shown that the β-glycoside is also obtained when yellow mercuric oxide is used together with a small amount of mercuric bromide as catalyst. The α-glycoside is formed by the action of methanol containing methanesulphonic acid on β-D-glycopyranose 1-mesitoate (Helferich *et al.*, 1960, 1961), the mesitoate being first prepared by the action of silver mesitoate on the α-acetobromohexose (Micheel *et al.*, 1955). The foregoing reactions may thus be written (using the symbol $\multimap$ to represent a Walden inversion; see **3** §3).

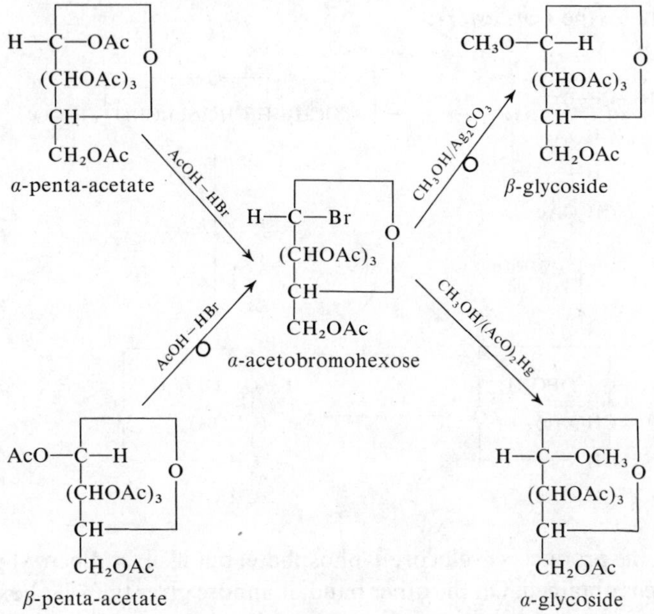

The above set of reactions may be illustrated with conformational formulae, *e.g.*, glucose penta-acetate ($ArCO_2H$ = mesitoic acid = 2,4,6-trimethylbenzoic acid):

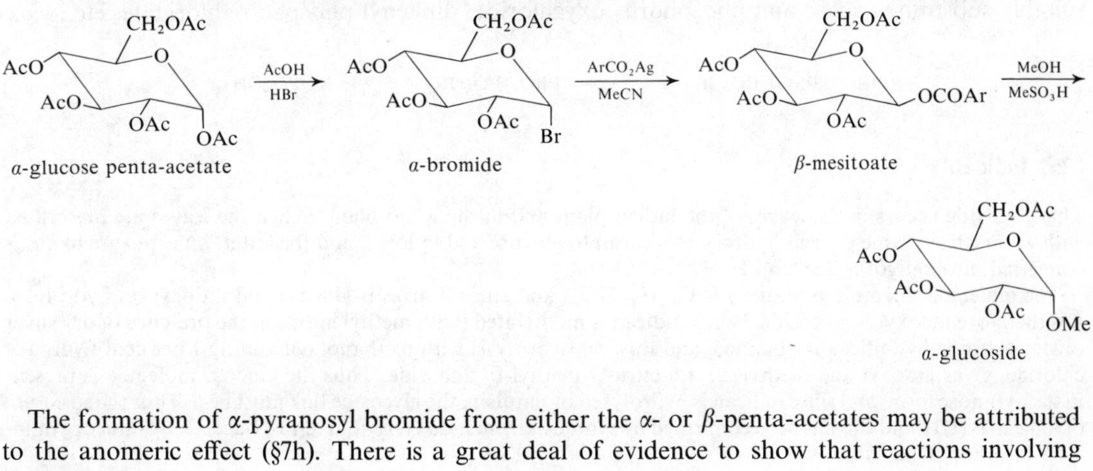

The formation of α-pyranosyl bromide from either the α- or β-penta-acetates may be attributed to the anomeric effect (§7h). There is a great deal of evidence to show that reactions involving pyranosyl halides proceed by the S_N1 mechanism. This is facilitated by the presence of metals such as silver or mercury (as their salts). The stereochemistry of these reactions is difficult to interpret; they may occur with predominant inversion or retention. Steric considerations, neighbouring group participation (when C-2 carries an appropriate group, *e.g.*, acetoxy), and the anomeric effect (when the incoming group is highly polar) all play a part in deciding the anomer preferred (α or β).

Aldose 1-phosphates are of fundamental importance in metabolic processes of all living organisms (see, *e.g.*, §23a). One method of preparation is by the action of silver phosphate on the acetobromo-hexose in benzene solution, followed by alkaline hydrolysis of the product, a tritetra-acetylphosphate. An alternative preparation is by the action of silver diphenyl phosphate on the acetobromohexose, followed by hydrogenolysis of the phenyl groups with H_2—PtO/Pt, and then by alkaline hydrolysis, *e.g.*, glucose 1-phosphate (the *Cori ester*):

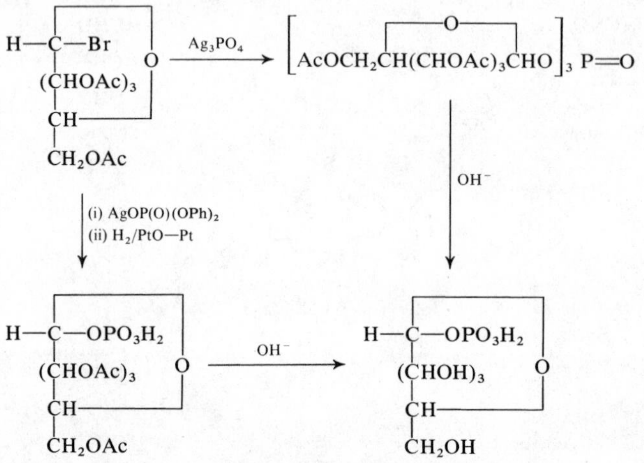

In the second method the product is α-glucose 1-phosphate, but if silver dibenzyl phosphate is used, β-glucose 1-phosphate is obtained. On the other hand, mannose gives the α 1-phosphate when either phosphorylating agent is used.

1-Phosphates can also be prepared by the action of anhydrous phosphoric acid on fully acetylated monosaccharides; hydrolysis occurs to give the sugar 1-phosphate.

Monophosphates other than the 1-derivative are usually best prepared by reaction between a suitably substituted sugar and phosphorus oxychloride, diphenyl phosphorochloridate, etc., *e.g.*,

$$\text{ROH} + (\text{PhO})_2\text{PO(Cl)} \xrightarrow{\text{C}_5\text{H}_5\text{N}} (\text{PhO})_2\text{PO(OR)} \xrightarrow{\text{H}_2/\text{Pt}} \text{ROPO(OH)}_2$$

§25. Indican

This glycoside occurs in the leaves of the indigo plant and in the woad plant. When the leaves are macerated with water, the enzyme present hydrolyses indican to glucose and indoxyl, and the latter, on exposure to air, is converted into indigotin (see Vol. I).

The molecular formula of indican is $C_{14}H_{17}NO_6$, and since it gives D-glucose and indoxyl on hydrolysis, it is therefore indoxyl D-glucoside. When indican is methylated (with methyl iodide in the presence of dry silver oxide), tetramethylindican is obtained, and this, on hydrolysis with methanol containing 1 per cent hydrogen chloride, gives indoxyl and methyl 2,3,4,6-tetra-*O*-methyl-D-glucoside. Thus the glucose molecule is present in the pyranose form, and since indican is hydrolysed by emulsin, the glycoside link must be β. Thus the structure of indican is (III), and this has been confirmed by synthesis from indoxyl (I) and tetra-*O*-acetyl-α-D-glucopyrano-syl 1-bromide (II) as follows:

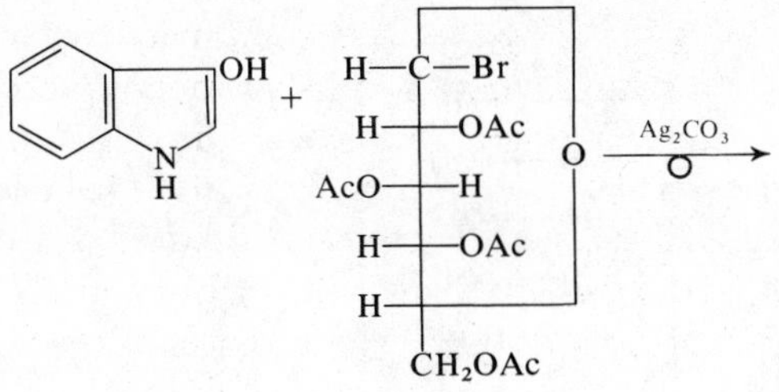

(I)   (II)

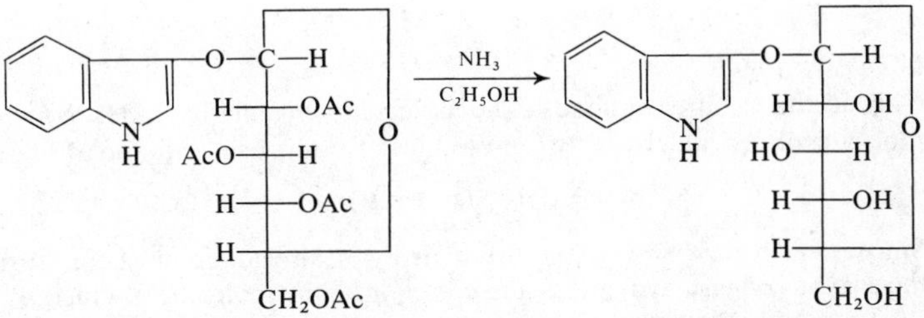

(III)

§26. Ruberythric acid

This occurs in the madder root, and on hydrolysis, it was originally believed to give one molecule of alizarin and two molecules of D-glucose. Jones and Robertson (1933), however, showed that two molecules of D-glucose were not present in the hydrosylate; a mixture of two sugars was actually present, D-glucose and D-xylose. Hence the molecular formula of ruberythric acid is $C_{25}H_{26}O_{13}$, and not, as was originally believed, $C_{26}H_{28}O_{14}$. Thus the hydrolysis is:

$$C_{25}H_{26}O_{13} + 2H_2O \longrightarrow C_6H_{12}O_6 + C_5H_{10}O_5 +$$

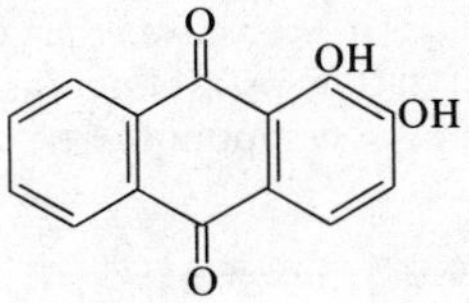

Jones and Robertson also showed that the two monosaccharide molecules were present in the form of the disaccharide **primeverose**. Now, this disaccharide is 6-*O*-β-D-xylopyranosyl-D-glucopyranose (Helferich, 1927),

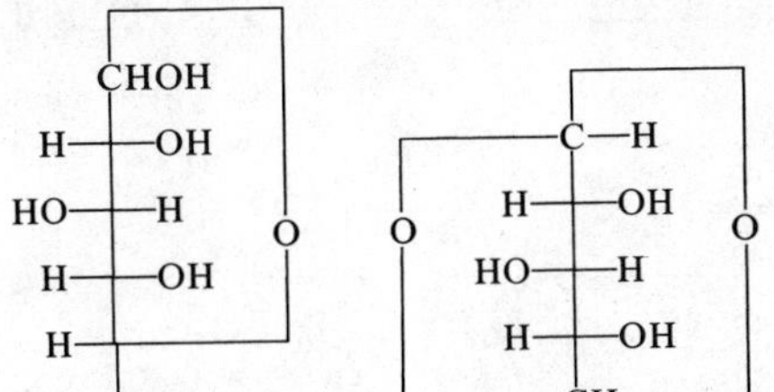

primeverose

and it therefore follows that alizarin is linked to the glucose half of the primeverose molecule. Further work has shown that the glucosidic link is β, and that it is the 2-hydroxyl group of alizarin that is involved. Thus the structure of ruberythric acid is:

§27. Amygdalin

This occurs in bitter almonds. The molecular formula is $C_{20}H_{27}NO_{11}$, and it is hydrolysed by acids to one molecule of benzaldehyde, two molecules of D-glucose, and one of hydrogen cyanide.

$$C_{20}H_{27}NO_{11} + 2H_2O \longrightarrow C_6H_5CHO + 2C_6H_{12}O_6 + HCN$$

Since emulsin also brings about this hydrolysis, amygdalin must contain a β-glycosidic link. On the other hand, the enzyme zymase hydrolyses amygdalin into one molecule of glucose and a glucoside of (+)-mandelonitrile (this compound is

$$C_{20}H_{27}NO_{11} + H_2O \longrightarrow C_6H_{12}O_6 + C_6H_5CH(CN)OC_6H_{11}O_5$$

identical with *prunasin*, a naturally occurring glucoside). Thus the aglycon of amygdalin is (+)-mandelonitrile, and the sugar is a disaccharide. Haworth *et al.* (1922, 1923) have shown that this disaccharide is gentiobiose (§19), and have synthesised amygdalin (in 1924) as follows. Gentiobiose (I) was converted into hepta-acetyl-bromogentiobiose (II) by means of acetic anhydride saturated with hydrogen bromide, and then (II) was condensed with racemic ethyl mandelate in the presence of silver oxide, whereby the β-glycoside (III) was obtained. Treatment of this with ethanolic ammonia hydrolysed the acetyl groups, and at the same time converted the ester group into the corresponding amide; thus the ($\pm$)-amido-glycoside (IV) was obtained. (IV) was then treated with acetic anhydride in pyridine solution, and the ($\pm$)-hepta-acetyl derivative of the amide (V) was then separated into its diastereoisomers by fractional crystallisation (the mandelic acid portion is + and −, the gentiobiose portion is +; hence the two forms present are + + and − +, *i.e.*, they are diastereoisomers). The (+)-form was then dehydrated with phosphorus pentoxide to give the (+)-nitrile (VI) and this, on de-acetylation with ethanolic ammonia, gave (+)-amygdalin, (VII), which was shown to be identical with the natural compound.

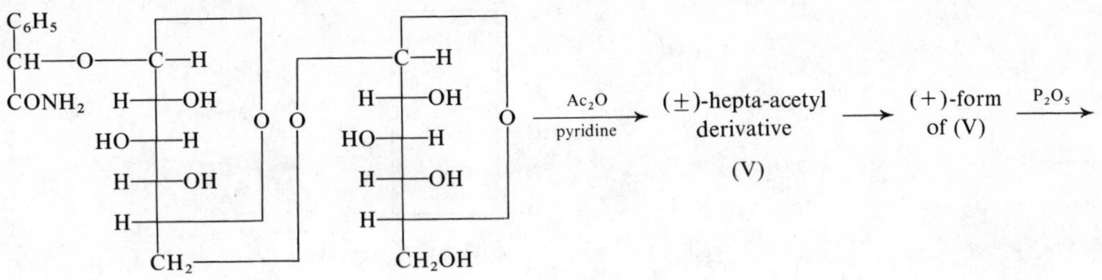

C_6H_5
CH—O—C—H   C—H
CONH₂ H—OH   H—OH
    HO—H   HO—H   O
    H—OH   H—OH
    H—   H—
    CH₂—   CH₂OH
        (IV)

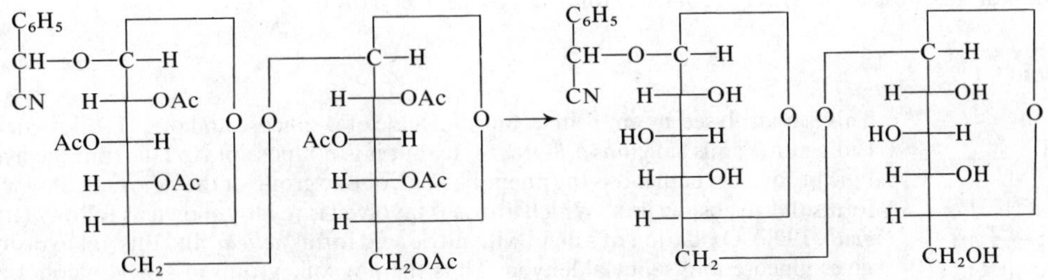

$\xrightarrow[\text{pyridine}]{Ac_2O}$ ($\pm$)-hepta-acetyl derivative (V) $\longrightarrow$ (+)-form of (V) $\xrightarrow{P_2O_5}$

C_6H_5
CH—O—C—H   C—H
CN   H—OAc   H—OAc
   AcO—H   AcO—H   O
   H—OAc   H—OAc
   H—   H—
   CH₂—   CH₂OAc
       (VI)

$\longrightarrow$

C_6H_5
CH—O—C—H   C—H
CN   H—OH   H—OH
   HO—H   HO—H   O
   H—OH   H—OH
   H—   H—
   CH₂—   CH₂OH
       (VII)

§28. Arbutin and methylarbutin

Arbutin is hydrolysed by emulsin to give one molecule of D-glucose and one of quinol; thus arbutin is a β-glucoside. When methylated (with methyl sulphate in the presence of sodium hydroxide), arbutin forms penta-methylarbutin, and this on hydrolysis with methanolic hydrogen chloride, gives methyl 2,3,4,6-tetra-O-methyl-D-glucoside and monomethylquinol (Macbeth *et al.*, 1923); structure (I) for arbutin accounts for all these facts.

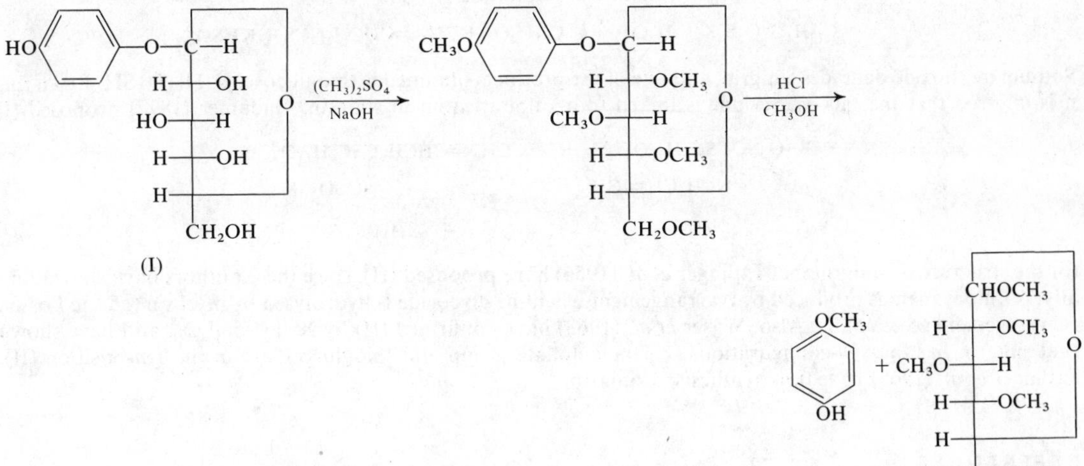

HO—⟨benzene⟩—O—C—H
            H—OH
        HO—H   O
            H—OH
            H—
            CH₂OH
     (I)

$\xrightarrow[\text{NaOH}]{(CH_3)_2SO_4}$

CH₃O—⟨benzene⟩—O—C—H
             H—OCH₃
         CH₃O—H   O
             H—OCH₃
             H—
             CH₂OCH₃

$\xrightarrow[CH_3OH]{HCl}$

⟨benzene, OCH₃, OH⟩ + CH₃O—

CHOCH₃
H—OCH₃
CH₃O—H   O
H—OCH₃
H—
CH₂OCH₃

Pentamethylarbutin has been synthesised by converting 2,3,4,6-tetra-O-methyl-D-glucose into tetra-O-methyl-α-D-glucopyranosyl 1-bromide, and condensing this with monomethylquinol; the product is identical with the methylated natural compound.

Methylarbutin. This is hydrolysed by emulsin to one molecule of D-glucose and one molecule of monomethyl-quinol; thus methylarbutin is a β-glucoside, and its structure is:

$$CH_3O-C_6H_4-O-\begin{array}{c} \text{C—H} \\ \text{H——OH} \\ \text{HO——H} \\ \text{H——OH} \\ \text{H——} \\ \text{CH}_2\text{OH} \end{array}$$

Methylarbutin has been synthesised by condensing tetra-O-acetyl-α-D-glucopyranosyl 1-bromide with mono-methylquinol in the presence of silver carbonate, followed by de-acetylation.

§29. Salicin

This is hydrolysed by emulsin to one molecule of D-glucose and one of salicyl alcohol (saligenin). Thus salicin is a β-glucoside, but it is not possible to tell from the hydrolytic products whether it is the phenolic or alcoholic group of the salicyl alcohol which forms the glycosidic link. Which group is involved is readily shown as follows (Irvine *et al.*, 1906). Oxidation of salicin with nitric acid forms *helicin*, and this, on hydrolysis, gives glucose and salicylaldehyde. Thus the phenolic group in salicyl alcohol must form the glucoside. Methylation of salicin produces pentamethylsalicin, and this, on hydrolysis, gives 2,3,4,6-tetra-O-methyl-D-glucose. Hence the glucose residue is in the pyranose form; the structure given for salicin fits the foregoing facts. This structure has been confirmed by condensing tetra-O-methyl-α-D-glucopyranosyl 1-bromide with salicyl alcohol, and then methylating the product. The pentamethylsalicin so obtained was identical with the methylated natural product (Irvine *et al.*, 1906).

§30. Sinigrin

This glycoside occurs in black mustard seed, and on hydrolysis with the enzyme myrosin, D-glucose, allyl isothiocyanate and potassium hydrogen sulphate are obtained.

$$C_{10}H_{16}NO_9S_2K + H_2O \longrightarrow C_6H_{12}O_6 + CH_2{=}CHCH_2NCS + KHSO_4$$

Sodium methoxide degrades sinigrin, and one of the products obtained is thioglucose, $C_6H_{11}O_5SH$. From this it is inferred that the glucose residue is linked to a sulphur atom in sinigrin. Gadamer (1897) proposed (I)

$$\underset{\underset{NCH_2CH=CH_2}{\shortparallel}}{K^+\bar{O}_3SOCSC_6H_{11}O_5} \qquad\qquad \underset{\underset{NOSO_3^-K^+}{\shortparallel}}{CH_2{=}CHCH_2CSC_6H_{11}O_5}$$

(I)   (II)

for the structure of sinigrin, but Ettlinger *et al.* (1956) have proposed (II), since these authors have shown that allyl isothiocyanate is produced by rearrangement when the glycoside is hydrolysed by myrosin (*cf.* the Lossen rearrangement; see Vol. I). Also, Waser *et al.* (1963) have confirmed (II) by X-ray analysis, and have shown that sinigrin has the *syn*-configuration, *i.e.*, the sulphate group and thioglucose are in the *syn*-position (II). Ettlinger *et al.* (1965) have now synthesised sinigrin.

REFERENCES

Handbook for Chemical Society Authors, Chemical Society (1960). Ch. 5. 'Nomenclature of Carbohydrates.'
ROSANOFF, 'On Fischer's Classification of Stereoisomers', *J. Am. chem. Soc.*, 1906, **28**, 114.
HUDSON, 'Emil Fischer's Discovery of the Configuration of Glucose', *J. chem. Educ.*, 1941, **18**, 353.
Advances in Carbohydrate Chemistry, Academic Press (1945–).
HAWORTH, *The Constitution of Sugars*, Arnold (1929).
PERCIVAL, *Structural Carbohydrate Chemistry*, Miller (2nd edn., 1962).
PIGMAN and GOEPP, *Chemistry of the Carbohydrates*, Academic Press (1957).

FLORKIN and STOTZ (eds.), *Comprehensive Biochemistry*, Elsevier. Vol. 5 (1963). 'Carbohydrates.'

DAVIDSON, *Carbohydrate Chemistry*, Holt, Rinehart and Winston (1967).

GUTHRIE and HONEYMAN, *An Introduction to the Chemistry of Carbohydrates*, Clarendon Press (1968, 3rd. edn.).

ASPINALL, *Polysaccharides*, Pergamon (1970).

Carbohydrate Chemistry, Chemical Society (1968–).

'Carbohydrate Research' (1965–).

BUDZIKIEWICZ, DJERASSI and WILLIAMS, *Structure Elucidation of Natural Products by Mass Spectrometry*, Holden-Day. Vol. II (1964). Ch. 27. 'Carbohydrates.'

CAPON, 'Mechanism in Carbohydrate Chemistry,' *Chem. Rev.*, 1969, **69**, 407.

Rodd's Chemistry of Carbon Compounds, Elsevier. Vol. 1, Part F (1967, 2nd edn.).

ELIEL, ALLINGER, ANGYAL, and MORRISON, *Conformational Analysis*, Interscience (1965). Ch. 6. 'Conformational Analysis in Carbohydrate Chemistry.'

MAYO (ed.), *Molecular Rearrangements*, Part II, Interscience (1964). Ch. 12. 'Rearrangements and Isomerisations in Carbohydrate Chemistry.'

NEWTH, 'Sugar Epoxides,' *Quart. Rev.*, 1959, **13**, 30.

FERRIER and OVEREND, 'Newer Aspects of the Stereochemistry of Carbohydrates,' *Quart. Rev.*, 1959, **13**, 265.

Progress in Stereochemistry, Butterworths. Vol. 4 (1969). Ch. 2. 'Configurational Analysis in Carbohydrate Chemistry.'

WOLFE et al., 'A Theoretical Study of the Edward-Lemieux Effect (The Anomeric Effect)', *J. chem. Soc. (B)*, 1971, 136.

REES and SCOTT, 'Polysaccharide Conformation. Part VI'. *J. chem. Soc. (B)*, 1971, 469.

BERNFELD (ed.), *Biogenesis of Natural Compounds*, Pergamon (1967, 2nd edn.). Ch. 6. 'The Biogenesis of Carbohydrates.'

GEISSMAN and GROUT, *Organic Chemistry of Secondary Plant Metabolism*, Freeman, Cooper and Co. (1969). Ch. 2. 'Primary Metabolic Processes.'

GEDDES, 'Starch Biosynthesis', *Quart. Rev.*, 1969, **23**, 57.

BOURNE and FINCH, 'Polysaccharides—Enzymic Synthesis and Degradation', *RIC Reviews*, Vol. 3, No. 1 (1970).

HOPKINSON, 'The Chemistry and Biochemistry of Phenolic Glycosides', *Quart. Rev.*, 1969, **23**, 98.

APSIMON (ed.), *The Total Synthesis of Natural Products*, Wiley-Interscience. Vol. 1 (1973). pp. 1–80. 'The Total Synthesis of Carbohydrates'.

8 Terpenoids

§1. Introduction

The terpenoids form a group of compounds the majority of which occur in the plant kingdom; a few terpenoids have been obtained from other sources. The simpler mono- and sesqui-terpenoids are the chief constituents of the essential oils; these are the volatile oils obtained from the sap and tissues of certain plants and trees. The essential oils have been used in perfumery from the earliest times. The di- and tri-terpenoids which are not steam volatile, are obtained from plant and tree gums and resins. The tetraterpenoids form a group of compounds known as the *carotenoids*, and it is usual to treat these as a separate group (see Ch. 9). Rubber is the most important polyterpenoid.

Most natural terpenoid hydrocarbons have the molecular formula $(C_5H_8)_n$, and the value of n is used as a basis for classification.

	Number of carbon atoms	Class
(i)	10	Monoterpenoids ($C_{10}H_{16}$)
(ii)	15	Sesquiterpenoids ($C_{15}H_{24}$)
(iii)	20	Diterpenoids ($C_{20}H_{32}$)
(iv)	25	Sesterterpenoids ($C_{25}H_{40}$)
(v)	30	Triterpenoids ($C_{30}H_{48}$)
(vi)	40	Tetraterpenoids (Carotenoids) ($C_{40}H_{64}$)
(vii)	>40	Polyterpenoids (C_5H_8)$_n$

The sesterterpenoids have been discovered recently, and so far only very few are known. In addition to the terpenoid hydrocarbons, there are the oxygenated derivatives of each class which also occur naturally, and these are mainly alcohols, aldehydes or ketones.

The group of compounds discussed in this chapter was originally classified as the 'terpenes', and although this name is still used, there is a tendency to use the more general name 'terpenoids'. This is due to the fact that since the suffix 'ene' signifies *unsaturated hydrocarbons*, the name 'terpene' is inappropriate to include compounds such as alcohols, aldehydes, ketones, etc. The term 'terpene' is restricted to the hydrocarbons $C_{10}H_{16}$.

The thermal decomposition of almost all terpenoids gives isoprene as one of the products, and this led to the suggestion that the skeleton structures of all naturally occurring terpenoids can be built up of isoprene units; this is known as the **isoprene rule**, and was first pointed out by Wallach

(1887). Thus the divisibility into isoprene units may be regarded as a necessary condition to be satisfied by the structure of any plant-synthesised terpenoid. Furthermore, Ingold (1925) pointed out that the isoprene units in natural terpenoids were joined 'head to tail' (the head being the branched end of isoprene). This divisibility into isoprene units, and their head to tail union, may conveniently be referred to as the **special isoprene rule**. It should be noted, however, that this rule, which has proved very useful, can only be used as a guiding principle and not as a fixed rule. Several exceptions occur, *e.g.*, lavandulol (§8a) and eremophilone (§28d); the carotenoids are joined tail to tail at their centre (see Ch. 9); there are also some terpenoids whose carbon content is not a multiple of five and those whose carbon content is a multiple of five but cannot be divided into isoprene units.

The carbon skeletons of open-chain monoterpenoids and sesquiterpenoids are:

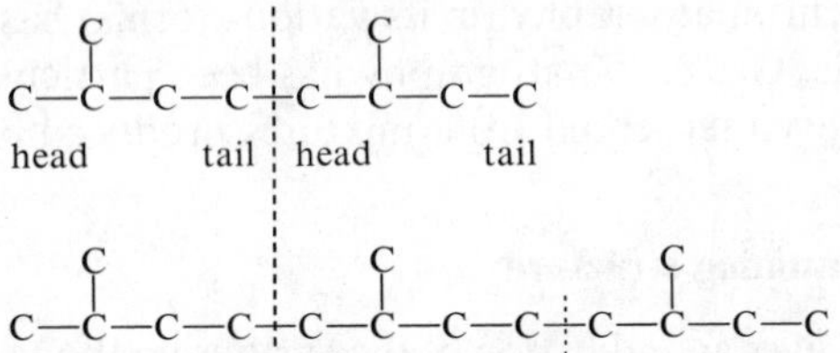

Monocyclic terpenoids contain a six-membered ring, and in this connection Ingold (1921) pointed out that a *gem*-dialkyl group tends to render the cyclohexane ring unstable. Hence, in closing the open chain to a cyclohexane ring, use of this '*gem*-dialkyl rule' limits the number of possible structures (but see, *e.g.*, abietic acid, §32). Thus the monoterpenoid open chain can give rise to only *one* possibility for a monocyclic monoterpenoid, *viz.*, the *p*-cymene structure. This is shown in the following structures, the acyclic structure being written in the conventional 'ring shape' (see §4).

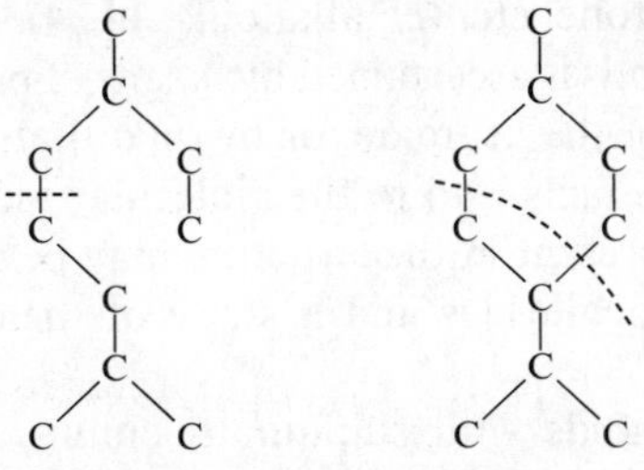

acyclic structure   *p*-cymene structure

Most natural monocyclic monoterpenoids are derivatives of *p*-cymene.

Bicyclic monoterpenoids contain a six-membered ring and a three-, four-, or five-membered ring. Ingold (1921) also pointed out that cyclopropane and cyclobutane rings require the introduction of a *gem*-dimethyl group to render them sufficiently stable to be capable of occurrence in nature. Thus closure of the 10C open chain gives three possible bicyclic structures; all three types are known.

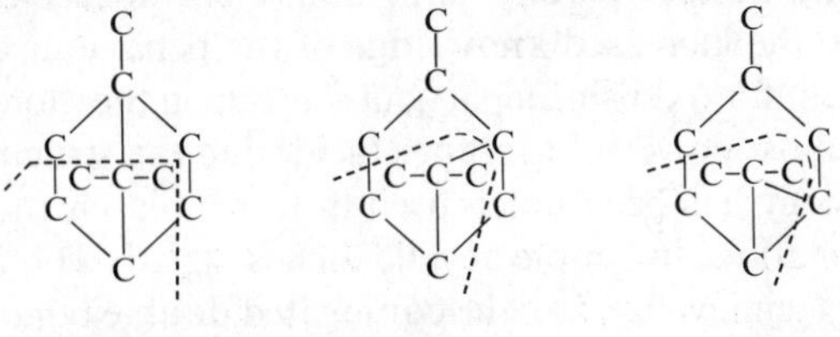

§2. Isolation of monoterpenoids and sesquiterpenoids

Plants containing essential oils usually have the greatest concentration at some particular time, *e.g.*, jasmine at sunset. In general, there are four methods of extraction of the terpenoids:

(i) expression; (ii) steam distillation; (iii) extraction by means of volatile solvents; (iv) adsorption in purified fats (*enfleurage*). Method (ii) is the one most widely used; the plant is macerated and then steam distilled. If the compound decomposes under these conditions, it may be extracted with light petrol at 50°C, and the solvent then removed by distillation under reduced pressure. Alternatively, the method of adsorption in fats is used. The fat is warmed to about 50°C, and then the flower petals are spread on the surface of the fat until the latter is saturated. The fat is now digested with ethanol, any fat that dissolves being removed by cooling to 20°C. The essential oils so obtained usually contain a number of terpenoids, and these are separated by fractional distillation. The terpenoid hydrocarbons distil first, and these are followed by the oxygenated derivatives. Distillation of the residue under reduced pressure gives the sesquiterpenoids, and these are separated by fractional distillation. More recently, chromatography (in its various forms) has been used both for isolation and separation of terpenoids. Gas chromatography has been particularly useful for isolating pure configurational forms of a given terpenoid from mixtures produced by synthesis.

§3. General methods of determining structure

The following brief account gives an indication of the various methods which have been particularly useful (especially oxidative degradation) in elucidating the structures of the terpenoids. Also included are the more modern methods (see the text for details).

(i) A pure specimen is obtained, and the molecular formula is ascertained by the usual methods, and also by means of mass spectrometry. If the terpenoid is optically active, its specific rotation is measured. Optical activity may be used as a means of distinguishing structures (see, *e.g.*, §12).

(ii) If oxygen is present in the molecule, its functional nature is ascertained, *i.e.*, whether it is present as hydroxyl, aldehyde, ketone, etc. (*cf.* alkaloids, **14** §4).

(iii) The presence of olefinic bonds is ascertained by means of bromine, and the number of double bonds is determined by analysis of the bromide, or by quantitative hydrogenation, or by titration with monoperphthalic acid. These facts lead to the molecular formula of the parent hydrocarbon, from which the number of rings present in the structure may be deduced.

(iv) The preparation of nitrosochlorides and a study of their behaviour (see also the nitroso compounds, Vol. I).

(v) Dehydrogenation of terpenoids with sulphur, selenium, platinum, or palladium, and an examination of the products thereby obtained (see also **10** §2vii).

(vi) Measurement of the refractive index leads to a value for the molecular refraction. From this may be deduced the nature of the carbon skeleton (see, in particular, sesquiterpenoids). Also, optical exaltation indicates the presence of double bonds in conjugation (*cf.* **1** §8).

(vii) Degradative oxidation. The usual reagents used for this purpose are ozone, acid, neutral, or alkaline permanganate, chromic acid and sodium hypobromite. Other reagents are osmium tetroxide, nitric acid, lead tetra-acetate, peroxy-acids, and N-bromosuccinimide for allylic bromination. Furthermore, owing to the increased knowledge of the behaviour of oxidising reagents, it is now possible to select a reagent for oxidising a particular group in the molecule. In general, degradative oxidation has been the most powerful tool for elucidating the structures of the terpenoids.

(viii) **Ultraviolet spectroscopy** has been much used in terpenoid chemistry, its main application being the detection of conjugation. In simple acyclic dienes, λ_{max} is 217–228 nm (ε 15 000–25 000). If the diene is heteroannular (semicyclic), *i.e.*, the conjugated double bonds are not in the same ring, λ_{max} is 230–240 nm (ε 1 300–20 000), and if the diene is homoannular, *i.e.*, both double bonds are in the same ring, λ_{max} is 256–265 nm (ε 2 500–10 000). If an α,β-unsaturated carbonyl system is present, the λ_{max} is 220–250 nm (ε 10 000–17 500), and there is also a weak band at λ_{max} 315–330 nm (ε 15–100).

The absorption maximum of a diene system is affected by substituents and Woodward (1942) found that the position of the absorption maximum depends on their number and type. As a result, Woodward developed a set of empirical rules (later modified by Fieser, 1948) for calculating λ_{max} from the molecular structure of the compound (see also 11 §4).

Polyenes

Homoannular dienes (basic value)	253 nm
Heteroannular (and acyclic) dienes (basic value)	214 nm
Increment for each C-substituent	5 nm
Increment for each exocyclic double bond	5 nm
Increment for each double bond that extends conjugation	30 nm
λ_{max} (of compound) =	Total

It should be noted that a C-substituent may be an alkyl group or a ring residue.

α,β-Unsaturated ketones

$$\underset{\delta}{C}=\underset{\gamma}{C}-\underset{\beta}{C}=\underset{\alpha}{C}-\overset{\overset{\displaystyle R}{|}}{C}=O$$

R is an alkyl group or a ring residue, and the *parent system* is $C=C-C(R)=O$.

Parent system (basic value)	215 nm
Increment for each C substituent:	
at α-C	10 nm
at β-C	12 nm
at γ- or δ-C	18 nm
Increment for each exocyclic double bond	5 nm
Increment for each double bond that extends conjugation	30 nm
λ_{max} (of compound) =	Total

The following examples illustrate the application of these rules (see also various individual terpenoids).

myrcene

λ_{max}:
Observed, 224 nm.
Calculated (for an acyclic diene with one C-substituent):
$214 + 5 = 219$ nm.

β-phellandrene

λ_{max}: Observed, 232 nm.
Calculated (for a heteroannular diene with two C-substituents and one exocyclic double bond):
$214 + 2 \times 5 + 5 = 229$ nm.

carvone

λ_{max}: Observed, 235 nm.

Calculated: Parent system	215 nm
C-substituent at α-C	10 nm
C-substituent at β-C	12 nm
λ_{max} =	237 nm

There is generally good agreement between the calculated and observed values, but notable exceptions are five-membered ring α,β-unsaturated ketones. These have a calculated λ_{max} about 10 nm longer than the observed value.

Allinger *et al.* (1965) have calculated λ_{max} for a number of unsaturated hydrocarbons, and have established a quantitative theoretical basis for Woodward's rules in these compounds.

In addition to their use for detecting conjugation, ultraviolet spectra may be used for detecting the presence of an isolated double bond (175–200 nm), and this is particularly valuable for tetra-substituted ethylenes, since this grouping cannot be ascertained with certainty in the infrared region. Also, α,β-unsaturated acids, esters, and lactones may often be recognised by their absorption maxima which occur in the region of 220 nm. Conjugated enes and ketones have absorption bands in about the same region, but they may, however, often be distinguished by treating them with a reducing agent, *e.g.*, lithium aluminium hydride. Since conjugated enes are usually unaffected, their spectra will remain unchanged, but the spectrum of the original conjugated ketone will now be very different (see also infrared spectroscopy below).

(ix) **Infrared spectroscopy** is also useful in terpenoid chemistry, and is very valuable for detecting the presence of a hydroxyl group ($\sim 3\,400$ cm^{-1}) or an oxo group (saturated: $1\,750$–$1\,700$ cm^{-1}; α,β-unsaturated: $1\,700$–$1\,660$ cm^{-1}; see also Table 1.2). Examination of Woodward values shows that heteroannular dienes and unsubstituted α,β-unsaturated ketones cannot be distinguished by means of their ultraviolet spectra, but usually can from their infrared spectra (see also above). Also, infrared spectroscopy is particularly useful for detecting the presence of the isopropenyl group, and may often distinguish between *cis*- and *trans*-isomers.

(x) **NMR spectroscopy** has been used to detect and identify double bonds, to determine the nature of end groups and also the number of rings present, and to ascertain the orientation of methyl groups in the molecule. In certain cases, definite structures have been assigned on the basis of NMR spectra.

(xi) **Mass spectrometry** is now being increasingly used as a means of elucidating the structure of terpenoids. Thus, it is possible to determine molecular weights, molecular formulae, the nature of various functional groups, and the relative positions of double bonds. Since even simple terpenoids give complicated fragmentation patterns, structural identification of an unknown terpenoid by means of mass spectrometry must be carried out with some caution. It is possible, however, to identify a terpenoid by comparison of its mass spectrum with the reference spectrum of an authentic specimen.

(xiii) **Optical rotation** methods have been successfully applied to the elucidation of the structure of terpenoids, and ORD studies have been used to assign absolute configurations (see Text).

(xiii) **X-ray analysis** is very useful, where applicable, for elucidating structure and stereochemistry of terpenoids.

(xiv) After the analytical evidence has led to a tentative structure (or structures), the final proof of structure depends on synthesis. In terpenoid chemistry, many of the syntheses are ambiguous, and in such cases analytical evidence is used in conjunction with the synthesis. Also, because of the introduction of stereoselective syntheses, it is now possible to prepare particular configurational forms of many terpenoids (see Text; see also **11** §9).

Monoterpenoids

The monoterpenoids may be subdivided into three groups: acyclic, monocyclic and bicyclic. This classification affords a convenient means of study of the monoterpenoids.

ACYCLIC MONOTERPENOIDS

§4. Myrcene, $C_{10}H_{16}$, b.p. 166–168°C

This is an acyclic monoterpenoid hydrocarbon (*i.e.*, is a terpene) which occurs in verbena and bay oils. Catalytic hydrogenation (platinum) converts myrcene into a decane, $C_{10}H_{22}$; thus myrcene contains three double bonds, and is an open-chain compound. Furthermore, since myrcene forms an adduct with maleic anhydride, two of the double bonds are conjugated (Diels *et al.*, 1929; see the Diels–Alder reaction, Vol. I). This conjugation is supported by the fact that myrcene shows optical exaltation (see also below). These facts, *i.e.*, that myrcene contains three double bonds, two of which are in conjugation, had been established by earlier investigators (*e.g.*, Semmler, 1901). Ozonolysis of myrcene produces acetone, formaldehyde and a ketodialdehyde, $C_5H_6O_3$, and the latter, on oxidation with chromic acid, gives succinic acid and carbon dioxide (Ruzicka *et al.*, 1924). These results can be explained by assigning structure (I) to myrcene. In terpenoid chemistry it has become customary to use conventional formulae rather than those of the type (I). In these conventional formulae only lines are used; carbon atoms are at the junctions of pairs of lines or at the end of a line, and unsaturation is indicated by double bonds (see Vol. I, Ch. 19). Inspection of (I) shows that the structure of myrcene is based on the 2,6-dimethyloctane skeleton. This would normally be drawn in a zig-zag fashion, but it is common practice in terpenoid chemistry to draw the carbon skeleton in a ring fashion (the 'open' cyclohexane ring), since this representation usually clearly shows the relationships between various classes of terpenoids. Even so, these 'ring' structures have been, and still are, written differently, *e.g.*, (II), (III), and (IV), but (IV) is now the one that is recommended.

(I)

(II)   (III)   (IV)

The systematic name of the compound is obtained by use of the rule for acyclic polyenes. Thus, myrcene is 7-methyl-3-methyleneocta-1,6-diene.

We can now represent the process of ozonolysis and oxidation of the ketoaldehyde as shown.

This structure for myrcene is supported by the fact that on hydration (under the influence of sulphuric acid), myrcene forms an alcohol which, on oxidation, gives citral. The structure of this compound is known (see §5), and its formation is in accord with the structure given to myrcene.

Myrcene has λ_{max} 224 (ε 14 600) nm (calc. value is $214 + 5 = 219$ nm) and, according to Sutherland *et al.* (1950), the absence of the band at 890 cm^{-1} shows the complete absence of the isopropenyl form (see also §5).

§4a. Ocimene, $C_{10}H_{16}$, **b.p. 81°/30 mm.** It occurs in the leaves of *Ocimum basilicum*. When catalytically hydrogenated, ocimene adds on three molecules of hydrogen to form a decane. Thus ocimene is an acyclic compound which contains three double bonds. Furthermore, since ocimene forms an adduct with maleic anhydride, two of the double bonds are conjugated. On ozonolysis, ocimene produces formaldehyde, methylglyoxal, laevulaldehyde, acetic and malonic acids, and acetone. All of these products are accounted for by structure (I) for ocimene (this has an isopropenyl end-group), and also by structure (II) (this has the isopropylidene end-group; Dupont *et al.*, 1938).

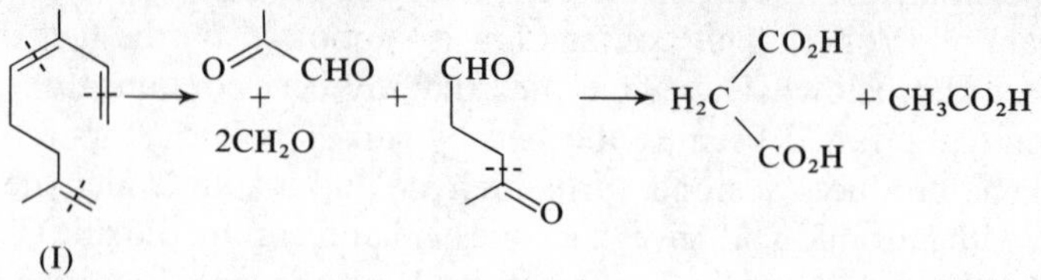

(I)

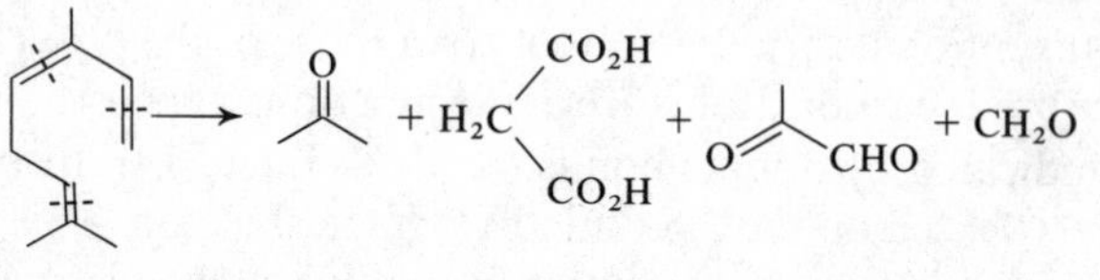

(II)

From the relative amounts of formaldehyde and acetone obtained, the authors believed that (II) was the major constituent in the mixture. More recent work has cast some doubt on these results (see also citral, §5). There is also evidence that ocimene is a mixture of geometrical isomers, α- and β-ocimene (structure II).

Ocimene is an unstable compound, so much so that it has not yet been obtained in a pure form. When heated, it readily isomerises to allo-ocimene (III), in which the three double bonds are conjugated (λ_{max} 275 nm). This structure has been confirmed by synthesis.

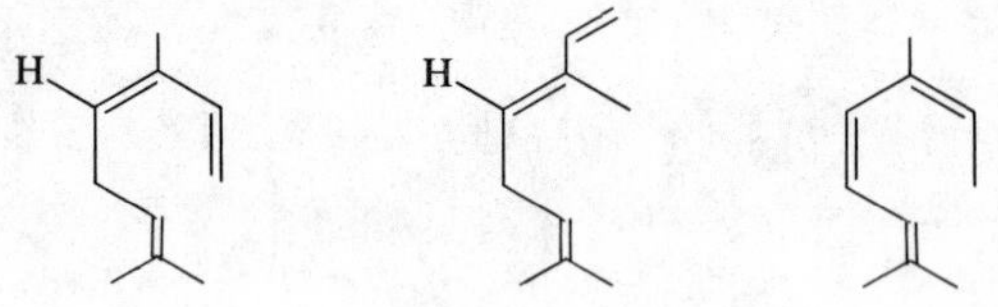

α-   β-   (III)

The λ_{max} of ocimene is 237 (ε 40 000) nm; this is 13 nm longer than that for myrcene, and indicates more substitution in the diene system; the calculated value is $214 + 5 + 5 = 224$ nm.

Mass spectrometry. Since isoprene is the building unit of the terpenoids, its mass spectrum is given here. The following include the peaks which are also usually observed in the spectra of terpenoids in general: 68 ($C_5H_8^+$, M^+), 67 ($C_5H_7^+$, *B.P.*), 53 ($C_4H_5^+$), 51 ($C_4H_3^+$), 41 ($C_3H_5^+$), 39 ($C_3H_3^+$), 29 ($C_2H_5^+$), 27 ($C_2H_3^+$). Paths that account for some of these are:

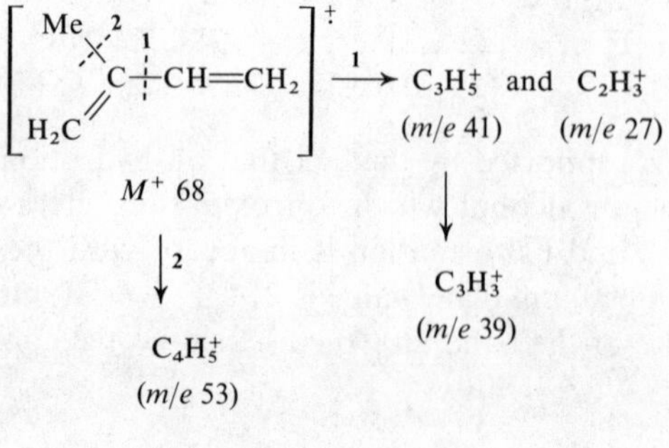

The mass spectra of myrcene and allo-ocimene have been examined. The former shows a weak molecular-ion peak (M^+ 136), whereas the latter shows a strong one (M^+ 136). This difference is attributed to the stability of the extended conjugated system in allo-ocimene. In myrcene, there are two allylic systems, and allylic fission at the bond common to both can therefore be expected to occur readily (1 §13a). This accounts for the extremely strong peak m/e 69 ($C_5H_9^+$) and the weak peak at m/e 67 ($C_5H_7^+$). The base peak for myrcene is m/e 41 ($C_3H_5^+$); its formation can only be explained by rearrangement. The base peak for allo-ocimene is m/e 121, corresponding to a loss of a methyl free radical (M-15 = 121). There are also peaks m/e 27 ($C_2H_3^+$) and m/e 91 ($C_7H_7^+$; tropylium ion) present in both spectra.

§5. Citral, $C_{10}H_{16}O$.

This is the most important member of the acyclic monoterpenoids, since the structures of most of the other compounds in this group are based on that of citral. Citral is widely distributed and occurs to an extent of 60–80 per cent in lemon grass oil. Citral is a liquid which has the smell of lemons.

Citral was shown to contain an oxo group, *e.g.*, it forms an oxime, etc. On heating with potassium hydrogen sulphate, citral forms *p*-cymene (II) (Semmler, 1891). This reaction was used by Semmler to determine the positions of the methyl and isopropyl groups in citral; Semmler realised that the citral molecule was acyclic, and gave it the skeleton structure (I) (two isoprene units joined head to

(I)   (II)

tail). Citral can be reduced by sodium amalgam to an alcohol, geraniol, $C_{10}H_{18}O$, and is oxidised by silver oxide to geranic acid, $C_{10}H_{16}O_2$; since there is no loss of carbon on oxidation to the acid, the oxo group in citral is therefore an aldehyde group (Semmler, 1890). Oxidation of citral with alkaline permanganate, followed by chromic acid, gives acetone, oxalic and laevulic acids (Tiemann and Semmler, 1895). Thus, if citral has structure (III), the formation of these oxidation products

(III)

may be accounted for. This structure is supported by the work of Verley (1897), who found that aqueous potassium carbonate converted citral into 6-methylhept-5-en-2-one (IV) and acetaldehyde. The formation of these products is readily explained by assuming (III) undergoes cleavage at the α,β-double bond; this cleavage by alkaline reagents is a general reaction of α,β-unsaturated oxo

(III)   (IV)

compounds (see Vol. I). Furthermore, methylheptenone itself is also oxidised to acetone and laevulic acid; this is again in accord with structure (III). The structure of citral was confirmed by the synthesis of methylheptenone (IV), the conversion of this into geranic ester (Barbier *et al.*, 1896), which was then converted into citral by heating a mixture of the calcium salts of geranic and formic acids (Tiemann, 1898).

A more recent synthesis of cital is that of Arens *et al.* (1948).

It should be noted that an *allylic rearrangement* occurs in both parts of this synthesis (see also §8). Ethoxyacetylenemagnesium bromide may conveniently be prepared from chloroacetaldehyde diethyl acetal as follows (Jones *et al.*, 1954):

$$ClCH_2CH(OC_2H_5)_2 \xrightarrow{NaNH_2} CH{\equiv}COC_2H_5 \xrightarrow{RMgBr} BrMgC{\equiv}COC_2H_5$$

Examination of the formula of citral shows that two geometrical isomers are possible. The functional group (aldehyde) is *trans* or *cis* with respect to the methylene group of the main chain. Both isomers occur in natural citral, *e.g.*, *two* semicarbazones are formed by citral; both forms of citral itself have also been obtained: **citral**-a (also known as *geranial*) has a b.p. 118–119°C/20 mm., and **citral**-b (also known as *neral*) has a b.p. 117–118°C/20 mm. The configurations of these two forms have been determined from a consideration of the ring closures of the corresponding alcohols (see

trans- (or *E*-) form;
citral-a; geranial

cis- (or *Z*-) form;
citral-b; neral

geraniol, §7). These assignments have been confirmed by the examination of the NMR spectra of citral-a and citral-b (in $CDCl_3$; Ohtsuru et al., 1967). Thus, for example, the τ-values of CH_2 (a) and CH_3 (b) are different due to the different magnetic shielding effects of the carbonyl double bond (in CHO).

citral-a

citral-b

	CH_2 (a)	CH_3 (b)
citral-a	τ 7·76	τ 7·84
citral-b	τ 7·42	τ 8·02

Ozonolysis was very much used by the classical workers in the determination of structures of terpenoids. In most cases, this method produced two types of products, one arising from the terminal *isopropylidene group*, $Me_2C=$ (to give acetone), and the other arising from the terminal *isopropenyl group*, $CH_2=CMe-$ (to give formaldehyde). Because of this, it was originally believed that many acyclic monoterpenoids were mixtures of both structures. However, infrared spectroscopic studies showed the presence of exclusively (or almost exclusively) the isopropylidene group (Barnard et al., 1950). In particular, a detailed study of the infrared spectrum of citronellol (§9a) showed a maximum at 890 cm^{-1}. This corresponds to some isopropenyl structure (the absorption region of $R_2C=CH_2$ is 895–885 cm^{-1}, whereas that of the isopropylidene structure, $R_2C=CHR$, is 850–790 cm^{-1}). Also, on the basis of the intensities of the bands, the authors calculated that there was about 2–3 per cent of isopropenyl form present. According to the authors, *during oxidative degradation*, partial rearrangement from the isopropylidene to the isopropenyl structure occurs, and so this method of determining fine structure is unreliable.

All recent work appears to support this and so the compounds are considered to have isopropylidene structures.

It might also be noted that the presence of the α,β-unsaturated carbonyl system is shown from the ultraviolet absorption spectrum of citral; λ_{max} is 238 (ε 13 500) nm, but this does not distinguish between the isopropylidene and isopropenyl forms.

§6. Ionones

When citral is condensed with acetone in the presence of barium hydroxide, ψ-ionone is formed and this, on heating with dilute sulphuric acid in the presence of glycerol, forms a mixture of α- and

ψ-ionone

β-ionone

α-ionone

β-ionones (Tiemann and Krüger, 1893). The proportion of α to β varies with the nature of the cyclising agent used, *e.g.*, with sulphuric acid, β-ionone is the main product; with phosphoric acid, α-ionone is the main product. Both ionones have been obtained from natural sources; the β-isomer is optically inactive, whereas the α-isomer can exist in optically active forms since it contains one chiral centre. Actually, the $(+)$-, $(-)$- and $(\pm)$-forms of α-ionone occur naturally. Very dilute ethanolic solutions of β-ionone have the odour of violets.

The structures of the ionones were established by a study of the oxidation products produced by potassium permanganate (Tiemann, 1898, 1900); β-ionone gave geronic acid, (I), 2,2-dimethyl-adipic acid, (II) and 2,2-dimethylsuccinic acid, (III). On the other hand, α-ionone gave a mixture of isogeronic acid, (IV), 3,3-dimethyladipic acid, (V) and 2,2-dimethylglutaric acid, (VI).

β-ionone   (I)   (II)   (III)

The structures of these two ionones is supported by the positions of the maxima of their ultra-violet spectra: α-, 228·5 (ε 14 300) nm; β-, 296 (ε 11 000) nm. The calculated value for the α-isomer

α-ionone   (IV)   (V)   (VI)

is $215 + 12 = 227$ nm, whereas that for the β-isomer (with extended conjugation) is (see §3vii):

$$215 + 30 + 18 + 2 \times 18 = 299 \text{ nm}$$

Theimer *et al.* (1962) have isolated γ-ionone (by vapour-phase chromatography) from the mixture

of ionones obtained above (this ionone corresponds to the γ-irone; see below).

The mass spectra of α- and β-ionone are interesting in that the base peak of the former is at m/e 136, whereas that of the latter is at m/e 177. The former molecular ion loses isobutene whereas the latter loses a methyl free radical (from the gem-dimethyl group), the loss of which occurs readily because the methyl group is in the allyl position (see structures).

(VII)   CH$_2$O +   (VIII)

irene   (IX)

The ionones are related to **irone**, $C_{14}H_{22}O$; this occurs in the oil obtained from the orris root. The structure of irone was established by Ruzicka *et al.* (1947), who showed that on ozonolysis, irone gives formaldehyde and 3,3,4-trimethylpimelic acid (VIII); also, reduction of irone with hydriodic acid and red phosphorus, followed by dehydrogenation with selenium, gives 1,2,6-trimethylnaphthalene, (IX). Ruzicka therefore proposed structure (VII) for irone. Ruzicka (1947) further showed that irone was a mixture of three isomers (VII is γ-irone). However, in view of what has been said about the isopropylidene–isopropenyl controversy, it appears possible that only γ-irone is the natural form.

α-irone   β-irone   γ-irone

λ_{max} (observed and calculated) for these three isomers are: α-, 229 nm (227); β-, 294·5 nm (299); γ-, 226·5 nm (227). Only the β-isomer has extended conjugation (*cf.* the ionones, above).

§7. Geraniol, $C_{10}H_{18}O$, b.p. 229–230°C/757 mm

This is found in many essential oils, particularly rose oil. Geraniol was shown to be a primary alcohol, *e.g.*, on oxidation it gives an aldehyde (citral-a); and since it forms a tetrabromide, geraniol therefore contains two double bonds. Reduction of citral produces geraniol, but at the same time some **nerol** is formed. The *structural* identity of geraniol and nerol is shown by the following facts. Both add on two molecules of hydrogen when hydrogenated catalytically; thus both contain two double bonds. Both give the same saturated alcohol, $C_{10}H_{22}O$. Also, on oxidation, geraniol and nerol give the same oxidation products which, at the same time, show the positions of the double bonds to be 2 and 7 (*cf.* citral, §5). Hence geraniol and nerol are geometrical isomers. Geraniol has been assigned the *trans* configuration and nerol the *cis* on the fact that cyclisation to α-terpineol (§11) by means of dilute sulphuric acid takes place about 9 times as fast with nerol as it does with geraniol; this faster rate with nerol is due to the proximity of the alcoholic group to the carbon (*) which is involved in the ring formation. Thus:

geraniol   α-terpineol   nerol
(*trans* or *E*)   (*cis* or *Z*)

These assignments have been supported by NMR studies on *trans*-methyl and *cis*-methyl geranates, which can be reduced to geraniol and nerol, respectively.

Most of the acyclic monoterpenoids undergo cyclisation to form six-membered rings. The usual product is a *p*-menthane derivative (4-isopropyl-1-methylcyclohexane), but a 1,1,3-trimethylcyclohexane derivative may be obtained when the oxo group (of the terpenoid) is blocked, *e.g.*, the formation of ionones (§6).

The mechanism for the hydration of geraniol and nerol to α-terpineol is believed to involve the formation of an intermediate allyl carbonium ion (see Vol. I).

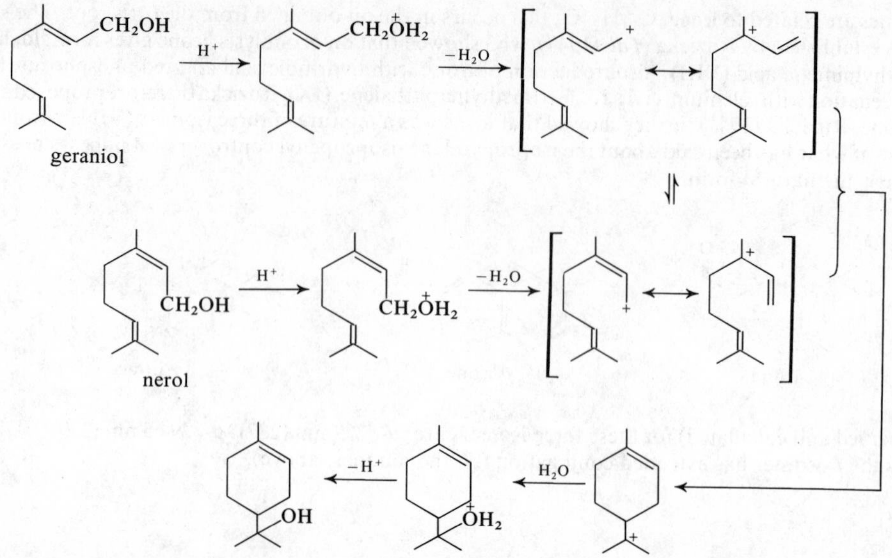

geraniol

nerol

Nerol occurs naturally in various essential oils, *e.g.*, oil of neroli, bergamot, etc.; its b.p. is 225–226°C.

The mass spectrum of geraniol shows that the main peaks can be divided into two groups, one which contains a hydrocarbon skeleton and the other the hydroxyl group. The base peak is m/e 69, which corresponds to $C_5H_9^+$, and can readily be accounted for by allylic fission (characteristic of alkenes; see 1 §13a; also note the absence of $CH_2=OH$, m/e 31; see 1 §13c).

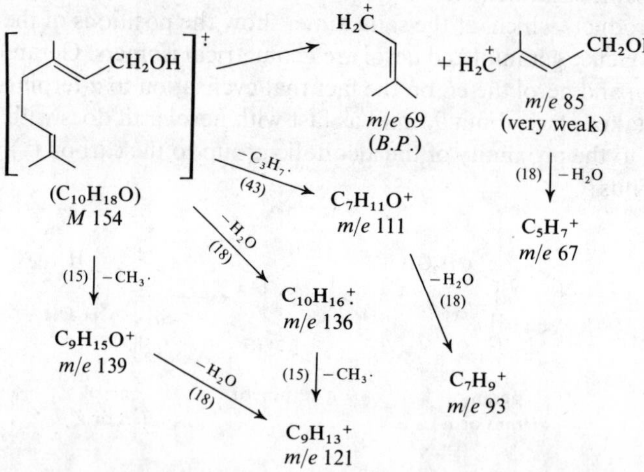

§8. Linalool, $C_{10}H_{18}O$, b.p. 198–199°C

This is an optically active compound; the (−)-form occurs in rose oil and the (+)-form in orange oil. It was shown to be a tertiary alcohol, and since it adds on two molecules of hydrogen on catalytic hydrogenation, it must contain two double bonds. When heated with acetic anhydride, linalool is converted into geranyl acetate; and the latter is converted into the former by heating with steam at 200°C under pressure. Also, linalool readily isomerises to geraniol under the influence of acids and, since the structure of geraniol is known, a possible

linalool   geraniol

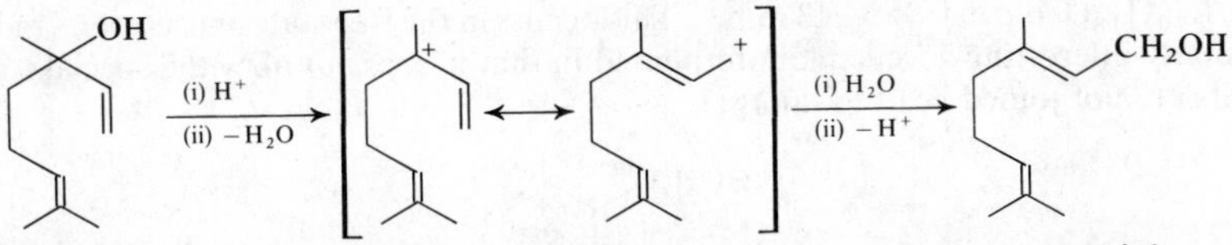

structure for linalool is obtained on the basis of an allylic rearrangement. Further support for this structure is obtained from the fact that oxidation of linalool with permanganate gives laevulic acid and acetone (Tiemann

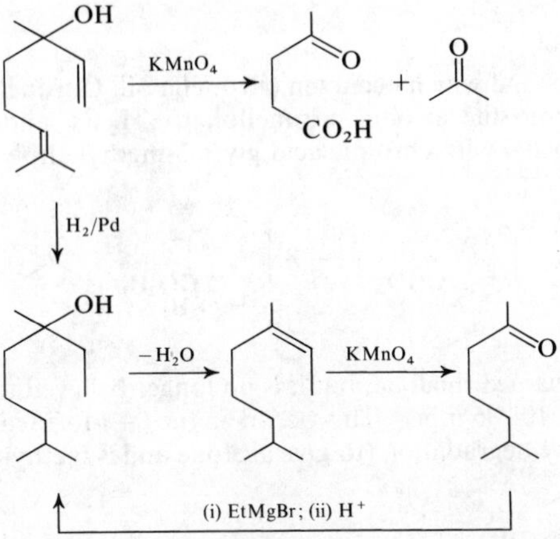

et al., 1895). The presence of a tertiary alcoholic group and its position are shown by dehydrating tetrahydro-linalool and then oxidising the alkene produced; methyl isohexyl ketone is formed (Barbier *et al.*, 1914). This structure has been confirmed by synthesis of linalool (Ruzicka *et al.*, 1919) who treated the sodium derivative of methylheptenone with acetylene, followed by partial reduction of the triple bond (*cf.* citral, §5).

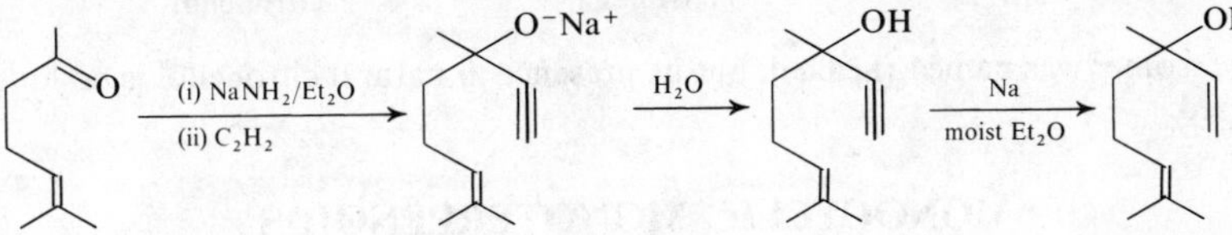

(±)-linalool

On the other hand, Normant (1955) has synthesised linalool in one step by the action of vinylmagnesium bromide on methylheptenone.

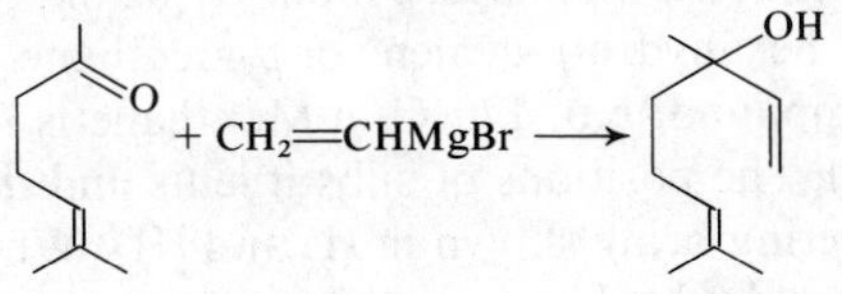

(±)-linalool

An interesting reaction of (−)-linalool is its stereoselective ring closure to partially active (+)-α-terpineol (as acetate) by acetic anhydride (Prelog *et al.*, 1957).

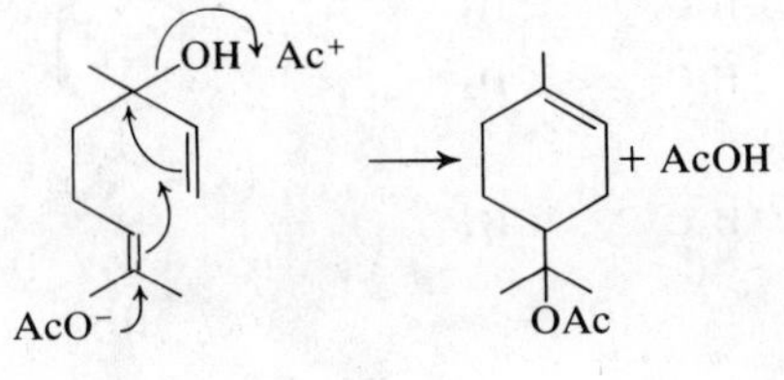

§8a. Lavandulol, $C_{10}H_{18}O$, b.p. 94–95°C/13 mm.   This occurs in the free state and as esters in French lavender oil. It is a particularly interesting acyclic monoterpenoid in that it does *not* obey the special isoprene rule, *i.e.*, two isoprene units are not joined head to tail (§1).

§9. Citronellal, $C_{10}H_{18}O$

This is an optically active compound which occurs in citronella oil. Citronellal is an aldehyde; reduction with sodium amalgam converts it into the alcohol citronellol, $C_{10}H_{20}O$, and oxidation gives citronellic acid, $C_{10}H_{18}O_2$. Oxidation of citronellal with chromic acid gives 3-methyladipic acid and acetone.

The isopropenyl isomer was named **rhodinal**, but it is no longer believed to be present in natural citronellal.

§9a. Citronellol, $C_{10}H_{20}O$, b.p. 103°/5 mm.   This occurs in the (−)-form in rose and geranium oils. Its structure was determined by oxidative degradation (to give acetone and 3-methyladipic acid), and by the following sequence of reactions:

citral   citronellal   citronellol

The isopropenyl isomer was named **rhodinol**, but its presence in natural citronellol is no longer accepted. It has been synthesised.

MONOCYCLIC MONOTERPENOIDS

§10. Nomenclature

For the purposes of nomenclature of the monocyclic monoterpenoids, the fully saturated compound *p*-methylisopropylcyclohexane, hexahydro-*p*-cymene or *p*-menthane, $C_{10}H_{20}$, is used as the parent substance; it is a synthetic compound, b.p. 170°C. *p*-Menthane is (I), and (II) is a conventional method of drawing formula (I). The positions of substituents and double bonds are indicated by numbers, the method of numbering being shown in (I) and (II). When a compound derived from *p*-menthane contains one or more double bonds, ambiguity may arise as to the position of a double

(I)   (II)

bond when this is indicated in the usual way by a number which locates the *first* carbon atom joined by the double bond. To prevent ambiguity, the *second* carbon atom joined to the double bond is also shown, but is placed in parentheses. The examples illustrate the method of nomenclature in

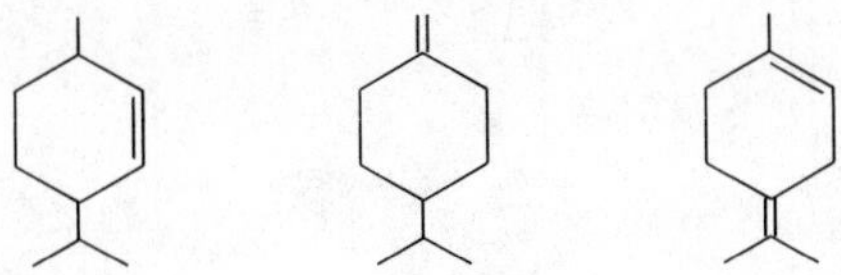

Δ^2-*p*-menthene;   *p*-menth-   *p*-mentha-
2-*p*-menthene;   1(7)-ene   1,4(8)-diene
p-menth-2-ene;
p-menthene-2.

the first example, all the types of methods of nomenclature have been given; in the second and third examples, only the nomenclature that will be used in this book is given.

§11. α-Terpineol.   This is an optically active monoterpenoid that occurs naturally in the (+)-, (−)- and (±)-forms; it is a solid, m.p. (of the racemic modification) 35°C. The molecular formula of α-terpineol is $C_{10}H_{18}O$, and the oxygen atom is present as a tertiary alcoholic group (as shown by the reactions of α-terpineol). Since α-terpineol adds on two bromine atoms, it therefore contains one double bond. Thus the parent (saturated) hydrocarbon of α-terpineol has the molecular formula $C_{10}H_{20}$. This corresponds to C_nH_{2n}, the general formula of the (monocyclic) cycloalkanes, and so it follows that α-terpineol is a monocyclic compound.

When heated with sulphuric acid, α-terpineol forms some *p*-cymene. Taking this in conjunction with the tentative proposal that α-terpineol is monocyclic, it is reasonable to infer that α-terpineol contains the *p*-cymene skeleton. Thus we may conclude that α-terpineol is probably *p*-menthane with one double bond and a tertiary alcoholic group. The positions of these functional groups were ascertained by Wallach (1893, 1895) by means of *graded* oxidation. The following chart gives the results of Wallach's work; only the carbon content is indicated to show the fate of these carbon atoms (the formulae are given in the text).

α-Terpineol $\xrightarrow[\text{KMnO}_4]{1\% \text{ alk.}}$ Trihydroxy compound $\xrightarrow{\text{CrO}_3}$ [Ketohydroxyacid] $\longrightarrow$ Keto-lactone $\xrightarrow[\text{KMnO}_4]{\substack{\text{warm} \\ \text{alk.}}}$
C_{10} C_{10} C_{10} C_{10}

(I)   (II)   (III)   (IV)

Terpenylic acid $\xrightarrow{\text{KMnO}_4}$ Terebic acid
C_8 C_7

(V)   (VI)
+
CH_3CO_2H

Oxidation of α-terpineol (I) with 1 per cent alkaline potassium permanganate hydroxylates the double bond to produce the trihydroxy compound (II), $C_{10}H_{20}O_3$. This, on oxidation with chromic acid (chromium trioxide in acetic acid), produces a compound with the molecular formula $C_{10}H_{16}O_3$ (IV). This compound was shown to contain a ketonic group, and that it was neutral, *e.g.*, it gave no reaction with sodium carbonate solution. When, however, (IV) was refluxed with excess of standard sodium hydroxide solution, and then back titrated, it was found that alkali had been consumed, the amount corresponding to the presence of one carboxyl group. Thus compound (IV) appears to be the *lactone* of a monocarboxylic acid. Furthermore, since it is the lactone that is isolated and not the hydroxy-acid, this *spontaneous* lactonisation may be interpreted as being produced from a γ-hydroxy-acid, *i.e.*, (IV) is a γ-lactone, and therefore (III) is a γ-hydroxy-acid. It is possible, however, for δ-hydroxy-acids to spontaneously lactonise, and so whether (IV) is a γ- or δ-lactone is uncertain at this stage of the evidence.

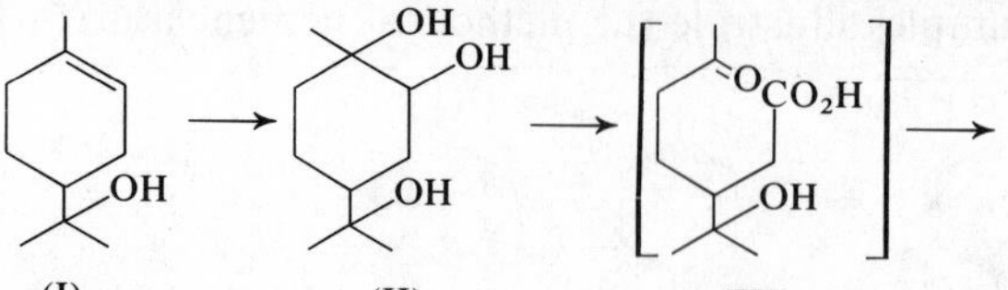

(I)   (II)   (III)

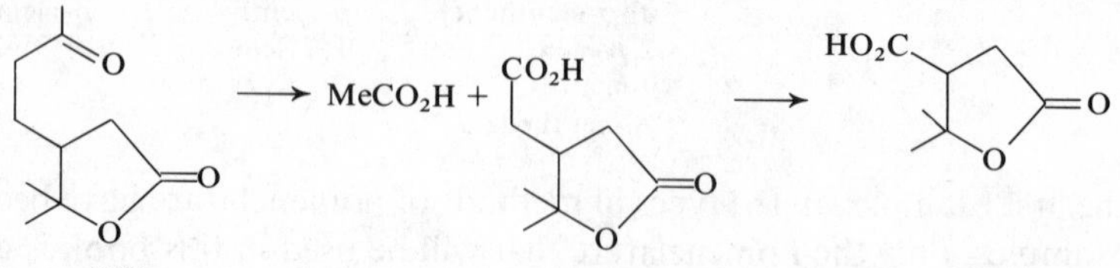

(IV)   (V)   (VI)

Now, since (IV) is formed from (II) by scission of the glycol bond, and since there is *no loss of carbon atoms* in the process, the double bond must therefore be in the ring in (I). On warming with alkaline permanganate, (IV) gave acetic acid and a compound $C_8H_{12}O_4$ (V). The formation of acetic acid suggests that (IV) is a *methyl ketone*, *i.e.*, a CH_3CO group is present. Thus (IV) is a methyl ketone and a lactone; it is known as homoterpenyl methyl ketone, and the structure assigned to it has been confirmed by synthesis (Simonsen *et al.*, 1932). A study of the properties of terpenylic acid (V) showed that it was the lactone of a monohydroxydicarboxylic acid. Further oxidation of terpenylic acid gives terebic acid, $C_7H_{10}O_4$ (VI), which is also the lactone of a monohydroxydicarboxylic acid.

The above reactions can be formulated as shown, *assuming* (I) (*p*-menth-1-en-8-ol) as the structure of α-terpineol. These reactions were formulated by Wallach, who adopted formula (I) which had been proposed by Wagner (1894). The structure of terpenylic (V) and terebic (VI) acids were established by synthesis, *e.g.*, those of Simonsen (1907).

Terebic acid, m.p. 175°C.

EAA

Terpenylic acid, m.p. 90°C.

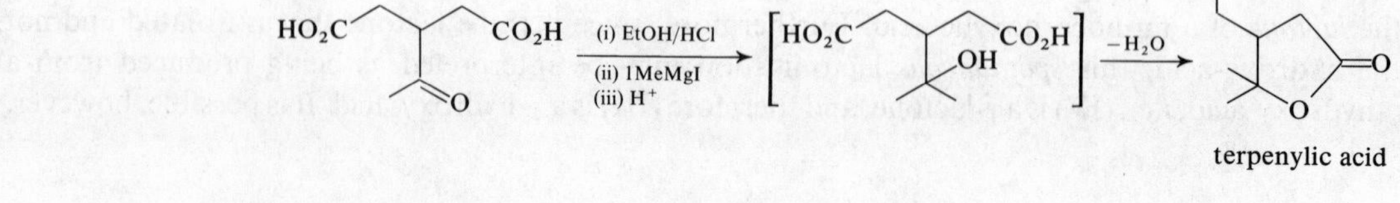

terpenylic acid

It is of interest to note here that Sandberg (1957) has prepared the β-acetotricarballylate in *one* step from acetoacetic ester and ethyl bromoacetate in the presence of sodium hydride (in benzene solution).

These syntheses strengthen the evidence for the structure assigned to α-terpineol. A synthesis of α-terpineol itself has been carried out by Perkin, junior (1904), and by Perkin, junior, with Meldrum and Fisher (1908). Only the second synthesis is given here; this starts with *p*-toluic acid.

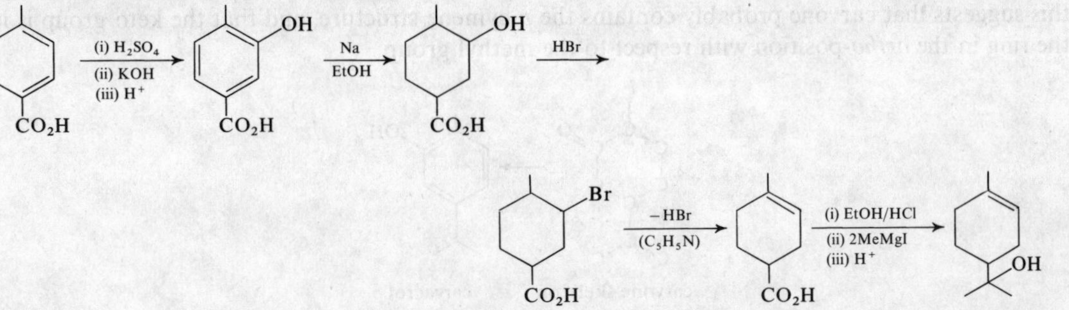

Compound (VII) was also resolved with strychnine, each enantiomer treated as shown above (esterified, etc.), and thereby resulted in the formation of (+)- and (−)-terpineol. It should be noted that in the above synthesis the removal of a molecule of hydrogen bromide from 3-bromo-4-methyl-cyclohexane-1-carboxylic acid to give (VII) is an ambiguous step; instead of (VII), compound (VIII)

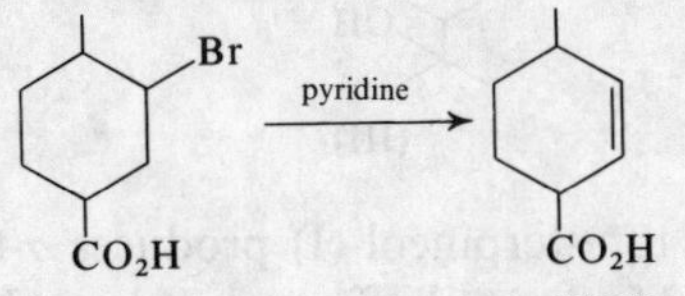

could have been formed. That (VII) and not (VIII) is formed rests on the analytical evidence for the position of this double bond; (VIII) cannot give the products of oxidation that are actually obtained from α-terpineol.

A much simpler synthesis of α-terpineol has been carried out by Alder and Vogt (1949); this makes use of the Diels–Alder reaction, using isoprene and methyl vinyl ketone as the starting materials (see also Vol. I).

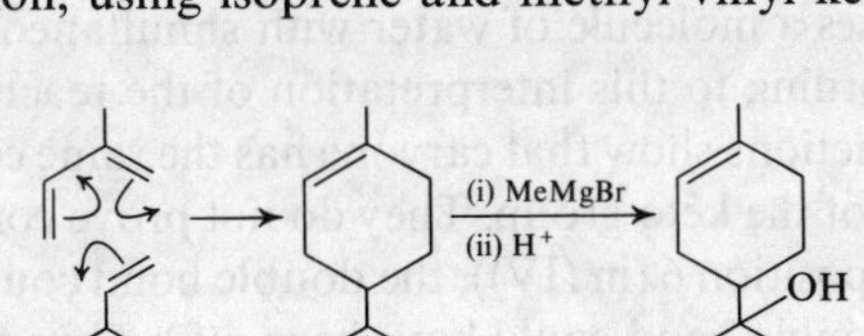

Two other terpineols are also known: β- and γ-terpineol; the latter occurs naturally.

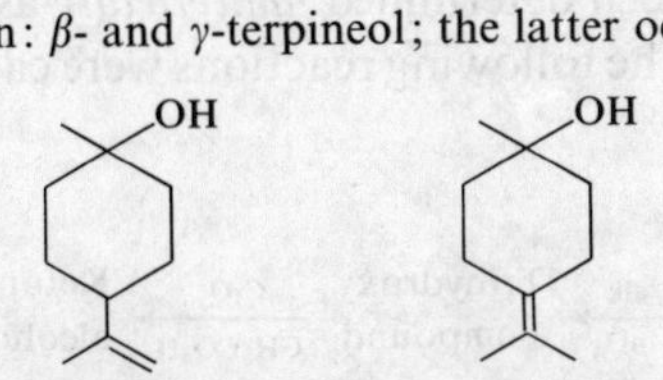

β-terpineol
m.p. 32-33°C

γ-terpineol
m.p. 68-70°C

§12. Carvone, $C_{10}H_{14}O$. b.p. 230°C/755 mm

This occurs in various essential oils, *e.g.*, spearmint and caraway oils, in optically active forms and also as the racemic modification.

Carvone behaves as a ketone and, since it adds on four bromine atoms, it therefore contains two double bonds. Thus the parent hydrocarbon is $C_{10}H_{20}$, and since this corresponds to the general formula C_nH_{2n}, carvone is monocyclic. When heated with phosphoric acid, carvone forms carvacrol; this suggests that carvone probably contains the *p*-cymene structure, and that the keto group is in the ring in the *ortho*-position with respect to the methyl group.

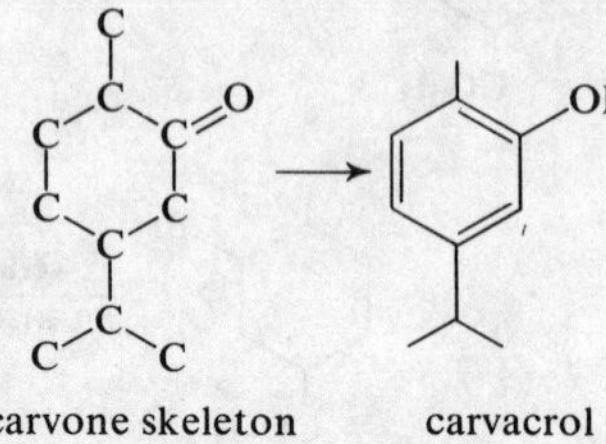

carvone skeleton   carvacrol

The structure of carvone is largely based on the fact that carvone may be prepared from α-terpineol as follows:

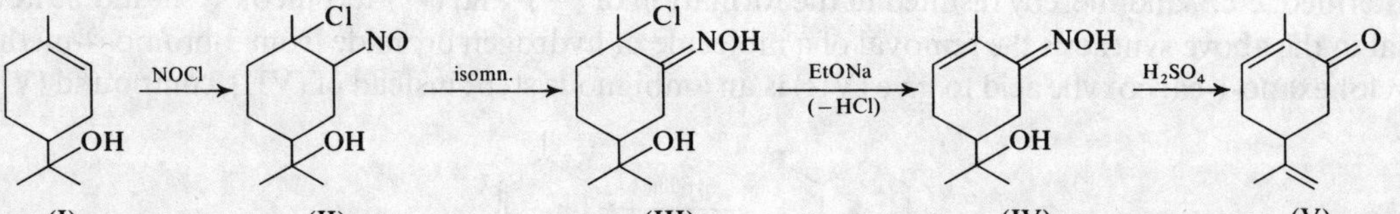

(I)   (II)   (III)   (IV)   (V)

The addition of nitrosyl chloride to α-terpineol (I) produces α-terpineol nitrosochloride (II), the addition occurring according to Markownikoff's rule (the chlorine is the negative part of the addendum; see Vol. I). This nitrosochloride rearranges spontaneously to the oximino compound (III) (see nitroso-compounds, Vol. I; it might be noted that this rearrangement proves the orientation of the addition of the nitrosyl chloride to the double bond; addition the other way could not give an oxime, since there is no hydrogen atom at position 1 in α-terpineol). Removal of a molecule of hydrogen chloride from (III) by means of sodium ethoxide produces (IV) and this, on warming with dilute sulphuric acid, loses a molecule of water with simultaneous hydrolysis of the oxime to form carvone (V). Thus, according to this interpretation of the reactions, carvone is *p*-menth-6,8-dien-2-one. Actually, these reactions show that carvone has the same carbon skeleton as α-terpineol, and also confirm the position of the keto group. They do not prove conclusively the positions of the two double bonds; instead of position 6 (in (IV)), the double bond could have been 1(7), and instead of position 8 (as in (V)), the double bond could have been 4(8). Thus the above reactions constitute an ambiguous synthesis of carvone (α-terpineol has already been synthesised). The exact positions of these two double bonds have been determined *analytically* as follows.

The double bond in the 8-position. The following reactions were carried out by Tiemann and Semmler (1895).

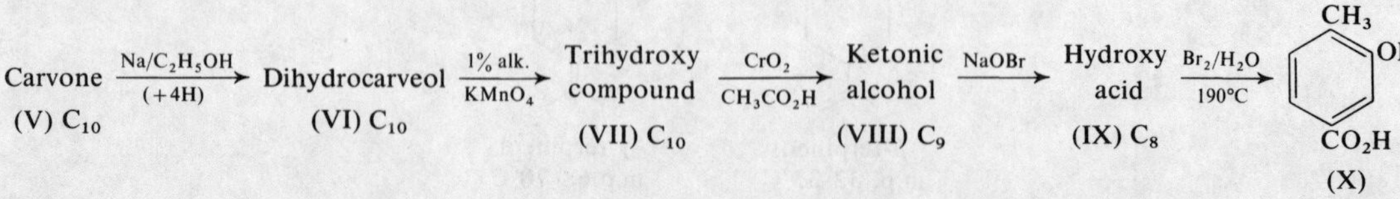

Carvone $\xrightarrow[(+4H)]{Na/C_2H_5OH}$ Dihydrocarveol $\xrightarrow[KMnO_4]{1\% \text{ alk.}}$ Trihydroxy compound $\xrightarrow[CH_3CO_2H]{CrO_2}$ Ketonic alcohol $\xrightarrow{NaOBr}$ Hydroxy acid $\xrightarrow[190°C]{Br_2/H_2O}$ (X)

(V) C_{10} (VI) C_{10} (VII) C_{10} (VIII) C_9 (IX) C_8

Reduction of carvone (V) with sodium and ethanol gives **dihydrocarveol**, $C_{10}H_{18}O$ (VI); this is a secondary alcohol and contains *one* double bond, *i.e.*, the keto group and *one* of the two double bonds in carvone have been reduced. Hydroxylation of the double bond in dihydrocarveol by means of 1 per cent alkaline permanganate produces the trihydroxy compound $C_{10}H_{20}O_3$ (VII). Oxidation of (VII) with chromic acid causes scission of the glycol bond to produce a compound $C_9H_{16}O_2$ (VIII); this was shown to contain a keto group and a hydroxyl (alcoholic) group. The action of sodium hypobromite on (VIII) caused the loss of one carbon atom to produce the compound $C_8H_{14}O_3$ (IX); this was shown to be a hydroxymonocarboxylic acid, and since *one* carbon is lost in its formation, its precursor (VIII) must therefore be a methyl ketone. Finally, dehydrogenation of (IX) by heating with bromine-water at 190°C under pressure produced *m*-hydroxy-*p*-toluic acid (X) (a *known* compound). Tiemann and Semmler explained these reactions on the assumption that one double bond in carvone is in the 8-position. Thus:

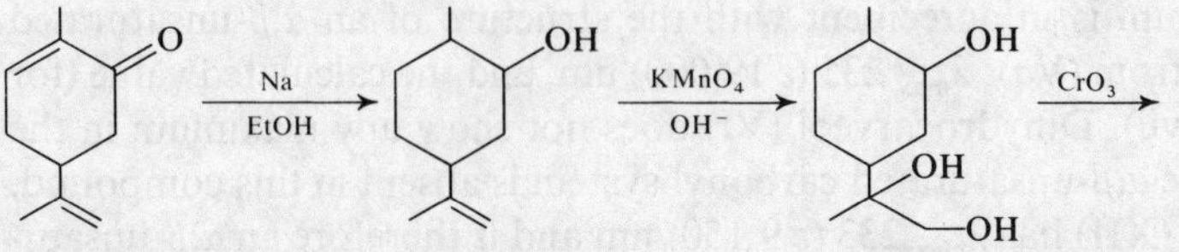

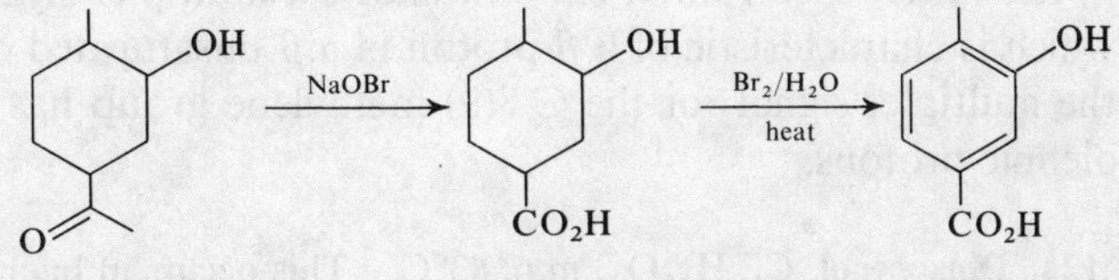

Had the double bond been in the 4(8)-position (structure (Va)), then compound (VIII), and consequently (X), could not have been obtained, since *three* carbon atoms would have been lost during the oxidation.

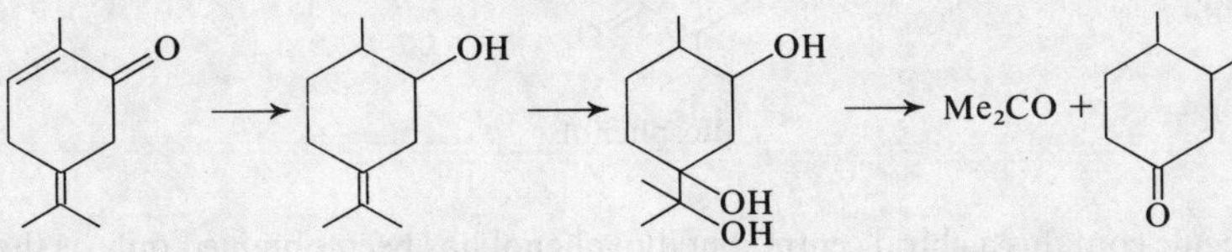

It might be noted in passing that (V) contains a chiral centre, whereas (Va) is symmetric and so cannot exhibit optical activity. Since carvone is known in optically active forms, structure (Va) must be rejected on these grounds.

The double bond in the 6-position. Carvone adds on one molecule of hydrogen bromide to form carvone hydrobromide, $C_{10}H_{15}OBr$ (XI), and this, on treatment with zinc dust and methanol, is converted into **carvotanacetone**, $C_{10}H_{16}O$ (XII), by replacement of the bromine atom by hydrogen. Thus the final result of these reactions is to saturate *one* of the two double bonds in carvone. Carvotanacetone, on oxidation with permanganate, gives isopropylsuccinic acid (XIII) and pyruvic acid (XIV) (Semmler, 1900). These products are obtainable only if the ring contains the double bond in the 6-position. Had the double bond been in the 1(7)-position, formic acid and not pyruvic acid would have been obtained. Further support for the 6-position is provided by the work of Simonsen *et al.* (1922), who obtained 3-isopropylglutaric acid and acetic acid on oxidation of carvotanacetone with permanganate.

(a) (V) →[HBr] (XI) →[Zn / MeOH] (XII) →[KMnO₄] (XIII) + (XIV)

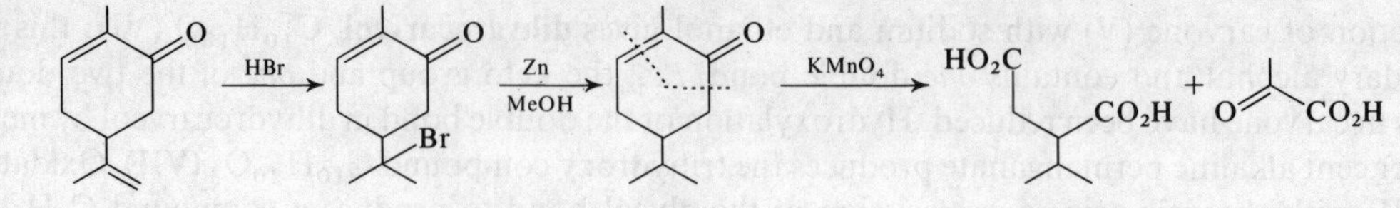

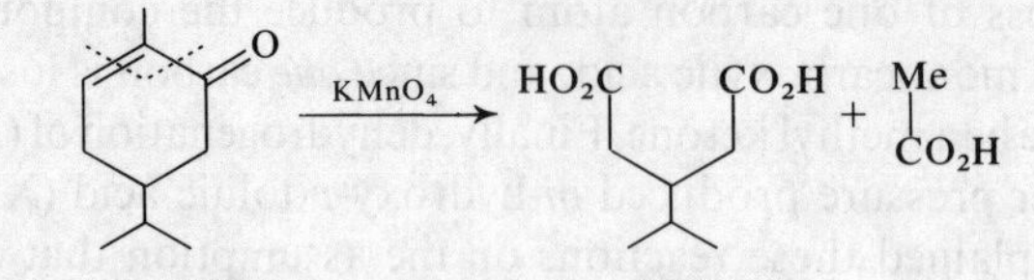

$$\text{(V)} \xrightarrow{\text{HBr}} \text{(XI)} \xrightarrow[\text{MeOH}]{\text{Zn}} \text{(XII)} \xrightarrow{\text{KMnO}_4} \text{(XIII)} + \text{(XIV)}$$

(b) (XII) →[KMnO₄] (XV)

$$\text{(XII)} \xrightarrow{\text{KMnO}_4} \text{(XV)}$$

The ultraviolet absorption spectrum is in agreement with the structure of an α,β-unsaturated ketone, but does not distinguish (V) from (Va); λ_{max} 235 (ε 19 000) nm, and the calculated value (for both (V) and (Va)) is 237 nm (see §3vii). Dihydrocarveol (VI) does not show any maximum in the region 220–250 nm, and therefore the α,β-unsaturated carbonyl system is absent in this compound. On the other hand, carvotanacetone (XII) has λ_{max} 233 (ε 9 150) nm and is therefore an α,β-unsaturated carbonyl compound.

The NMR spectrum of carvone shows a multiplet signal at τ 3·25 for the proton at C-6, a value which is characteristic of a β-proton in α,β-unsaturated carbonyl compounds. On the other hand, the multiplet signal for the C-8(9) methylene group has τ 4·78, which is in the normal range for olefinic protons.

§12a. **Diosphenol,** $C_{10}H_{16}O_2$, m.p. 83°C.   This occurs in buchu leaves. The enolic structure accounts for its acidic properties (soluble in alkali), the intense green colour it gives with ferric chloride, and its λ_{max} 274 nm (see

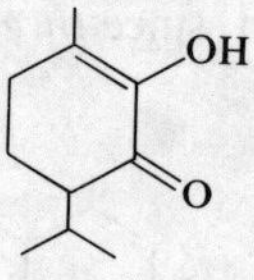

diosphenol

Table 1.5). The molecule contains a chiral centre, but diosphenol has been obtained only as the racemate. This could be due to either (or both) of the following mechanisms:

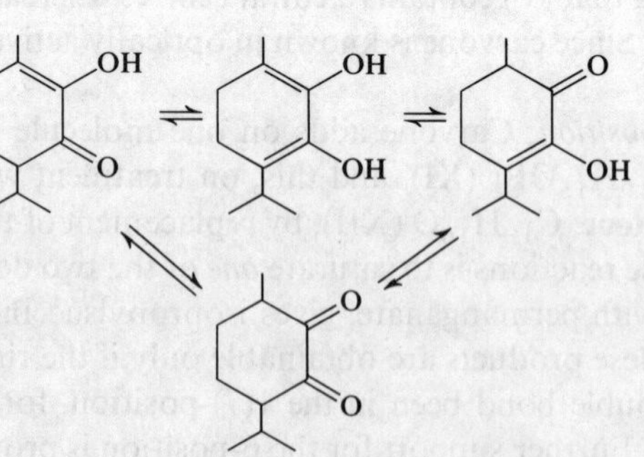

The structure given for diosphenol has been established by oxidative degradation and by synthesis.

(i)

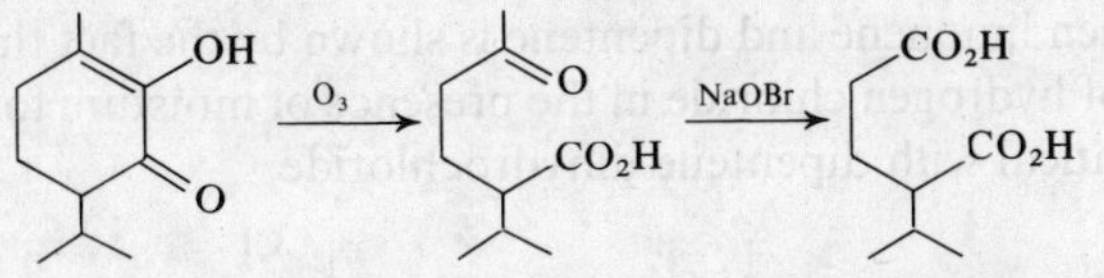

2-isopropyl-
glutaric acid

(ii)

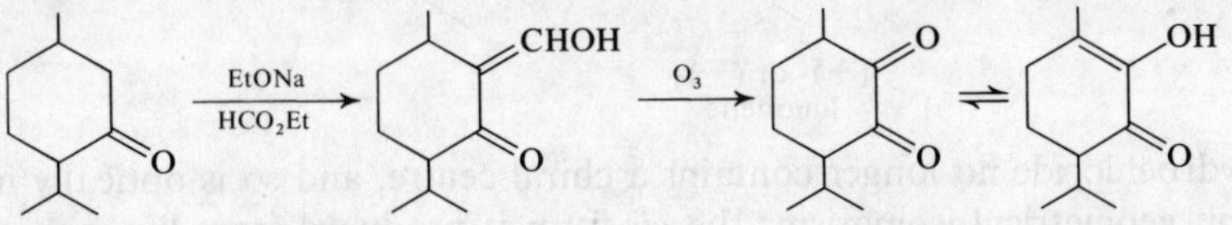

menthone

§13. Limonene, $C_{10}H_{16}$, b.p. 175·5–176·5°C

This is optically active; the (+)-form occurs in lemon and orange oils, the (−)-form in peppermint oil, and the (±)-form in turpentine oil. The racemic modification is also produced by racemisation of the optically active forms at about 250°C. The racemic modification is also known as **dipentene**; this name was given to the inactive form before its relation to the active form (limonene) was known.

Since limonene adds on four bromine atoms, it therefore contains two double bonds. (+)-Limonene may be prepared by dehydrating (+)-α-terpineol with potassium hydrogen sulphate, and limonene (or dipentene) may be converted into α-terpineol on shaking with dilute sulphuric acid.

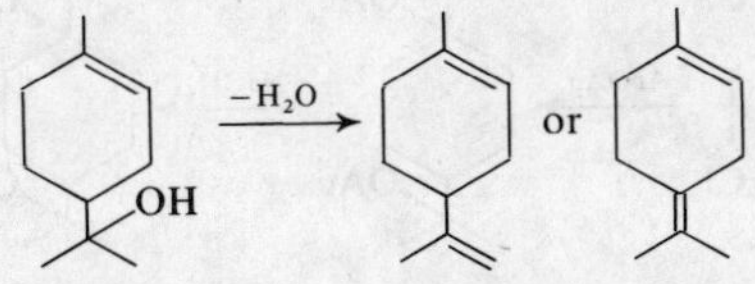

Thus the carbon skeleton and the position of one double bond in limonene are known. The position of the other double bond, however, remains uncertain from this preparation; (I) or (II) is possible. *Proof of position 8.* Structure (I) contains a chiral centre C-4, and hence can exhibit optical activity. (II) is symmetric and so cannot be optically active. Therefore (I) must be limonene.

Chemical proof for position 8 is afforded by the following reactions:

$$\text{Limonene} \xrightarrow{\text{NOCl}} \text{Limonene nitrosochloride} \xrightarrow[\text{EtOH}]{\text{KOH}} \text{carvoxime}$$
$$\text{(I)} \qquad\qquad\qquad \text{(III)} \qquad\qquad\qquad \text{(IV)}$$

Since the structure of carvoxime is known, it therefore follows that (I) must have one double bond in position 8; thus the above reactions may be written:

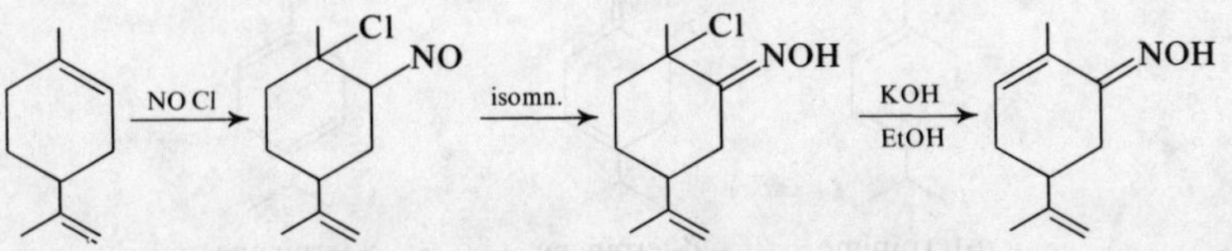

The connection between limonene and dipentene is shown by the fact that (+)- or (−)-limonene adds on two molecules of hydrogen chloride in the presence of moisture to form limonene dihydrochloride, and this is identical with dipentene dihydrochloride.

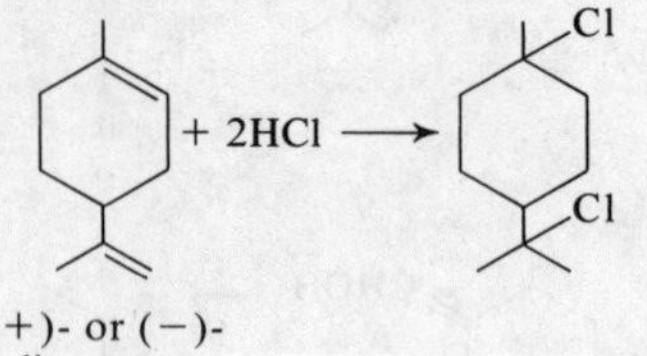

(+)- or (−)-
limonene

Limonene dihydrochloride no longer contains a chiral centre, and so is optically inactive. It can, however, exhibit geometrical isomerism; the *cis*-form is produced from limonene, and the *trans*-form from cineole (§14).

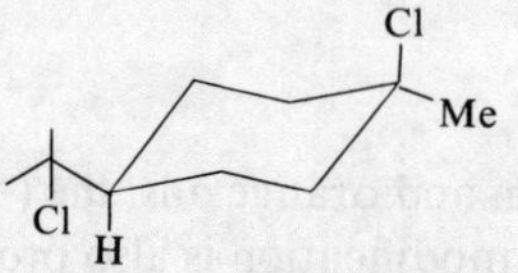

cis 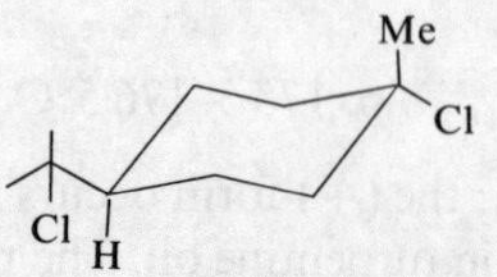   *trans*

Dipentene can be regenerated by heating the dihydrochloride with sodium acetate in acetic acid, or boiling with aniline. On the other hand, when limonene dihydrochloride is heated with silver acetate in acetic acid, and then hydrolysing the ester with sodium hydroxide, **1,8-terpin** is formed; the direct action of sodium hydroxide on the dihydrochloride regenerates dipentene.

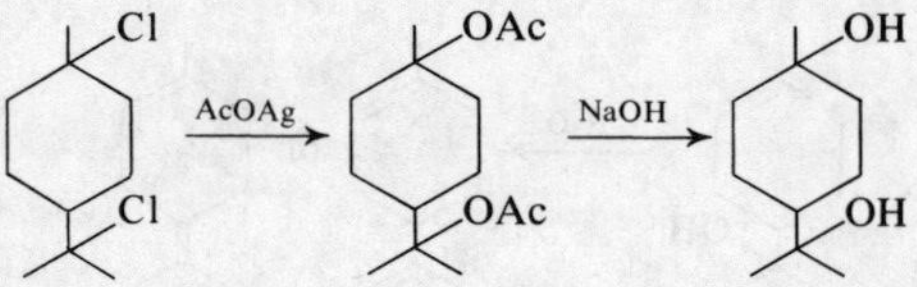

1,8-terpin

1,8-Terpin exists in two geometrical isomeric forms, corresponding to the *cis* and *trans* dipentene dihydrochlorides. *cis*-1,8-Terpin is the common form, m.p. 105°C, and readily combines with one molecule of water to form terpin hydrate. The *trans*-form, m.p. 158–159°C, does not form a hydrate (see also §14). 1,8-Terpin is not a natural product.

There is also a **1,4-terpin**; this was originally prepared by the action of dilute alkali on terpinene dihydrochloride.

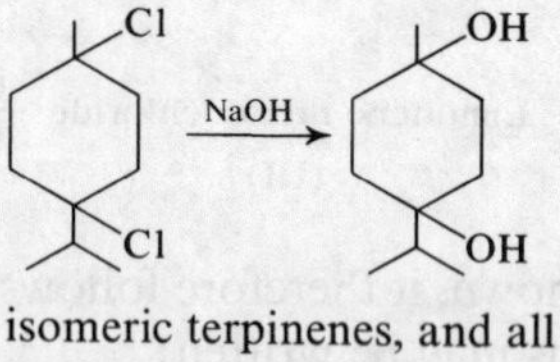

Terpinenes, $C_{10}H_{16}$. There are three isomeric terpinenes, and all give the same terpinene dihydrochloride with hydrogen chloride.

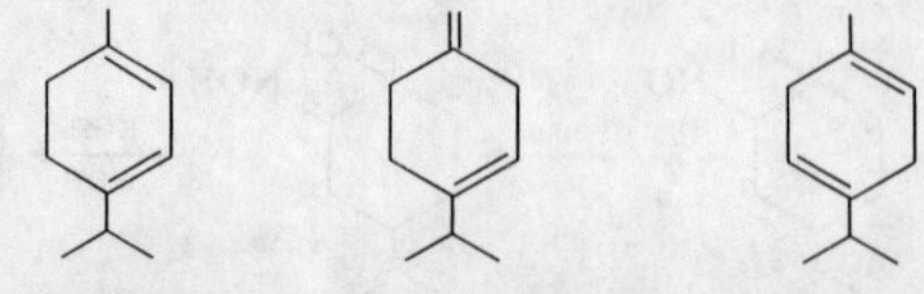

a-terpinene   *β*-terpinene   *γ*-terpinene
b.p. 180–182°C   b.p. 173–174°C   b.p. 69–73°C/20 mm

α- and γ-Terpinenes occur naturally, but it appears to be uncertain whether the β-isomer does. The structures of these compounds have been elucidated by means of oxidative degradation.

The λ_{max} of α-terpinene is 265 nm, and this is in fair agreement with the calculated value 273 (253 + 4 × 5). This homoannular conjugation is supported by the fact that α-terpinene forms a Diels–Alder adduct with maleic anhydride. Neither the β- nor the γ-isomer contains a conjugated system.

Terpinolene, $C_{10}H_{16}$, b.p. 67–68°C/10 mm. This occurs naturally. It is not optically active, and since it may be prepared by dehydrating α-terpineol with oxalic acid, its structure is known (it is II, the alternative formula offered for limonene). Terpinolene adds on two molecules of hydrogen chloride to form dipentene dihydrochloride.

(II)

Phellandrenes, $C_{10}H_{16}$. There are two phellandrenes, both of which are optically active, and all the enantiomers occur naturally. The structures of α- and β-phellandrene have been established by oxidative degradation,

α-phellandrene   β-phellandrene
b.p. 58–59°C/16 mm   b.p. 171–172°C

and are in agreement with the ultraviolet absorption maxima: α: obs., 263 (ε 2 500) nm; calc., 253 + 3 × 5 = 268 nm; β-: obs., 231 (ε 9 100) nm; calc., 214 + 2 × 5 + 5 = 229 nm.

§14. 1,8-Cineole, $C_{10}H_{18}O$, b.p. 174·4°C

This occurs in eucalyptus oils. It is isomeric with α-terpineol, but contains neither a hydroxyl group nor a double bond. The oxygen atom in cineole is inert, e.g., it is not attacked by sodium or by the usual reducing agents. This inertness suggests that the oxygen atom is of the ether type. Support for this is obtained from the fact that dehydration of cis-1,8-terpin gives 1,8-cineole; at the same time, this reaction suggests that the structure of cineole is (I).

(I)

Further support for this structure is afforded by a study of the products obtained by oxidation (Wallach et al., 1888, 1890, 1892). When oxidised with potassium permanganate, cineole forms cineolic acid (II) and this, on distillation with acetic anhydride, forms cineolic anhydride (III). When distilled at atmospheric pressure, cineolic anhydride forms 6-methylhept-5-en-2-one (IV), a known compound (§5). These reactions were interpreted by Wallach as follows:

(I)   (II)   (III)   (IV)

Further work on the structure of cineolic acid has confirmed the above sequence of reactions (Rupe, 1901,—).

It seems most probable that the 1,8-terpins have chair conformations, but when they form 1,8-cineole, the latter possesses the boat conformation; thus:

cis-terpin   1,8-cineole

There is also a **1,4-cineole**; this occurs naturally.

1,4-cineole
b.h. 172°C

Ascaridole, $C_{10}H_{16}O_2$, b.p. 96–97°C/8 mm.   The cineoles are oxides; ascaridole, however, is a peroxide, and it occurs naturally in, *e.g.*, chenopodium oil. When heated to 130–150°C, ascaridole decomposes with explosive violence. When reduced catalytically, ascaridole forms 1,4-terpin (Wallach, 1912), and this led to the suggestion that ascaridole is (V). This structure has been confirmed by further analytical work. Ascaridole has been synthesised by Ziegler *et al.* (1944) by the irradiation of α-terpinene in dilute solution in the presence of chlorophyll. Formation of cyclic peroxides by conjugated dienes is a general reaction, and although ultraviolet light often initiates the reaction, better results are achieved by carrying out the irradiation in the presence of *sensitisers*, *e.g.*, chlorophyll, dyes, etc. (see Vol. I, Ch. 31).

(V)

§15. Sylvestrene, $C_{10}H_{16}$, b.p. 175–178°C

m-cymene skeleton

This compound exists in (+)-, (−)- and (±)- forms; the racemic modification is also known as **carvestrene** (*cf.* limonene and dipentene, §13). The (+)-form of sylvestrene was first obtained from Swedish pine needle oil (Attenberg, 1877), and was shown to contain the *m*-cymene carbon skeleton (Baeyer *et al.*, 1898). Thus sylvestrene appeared to be the only monocyclic monoterpenoid which did not have the *p*-cymene structure and was obtainable from natural sources. Although the *m*-cymene structure can be divided into two isoprene units (Wallach's isoprene rule), these two units are not joined head to tail. Subsequent work, however, showed that sylvestrene does not occur in pine oil. In the extraction of sylvestrene, the pine oil is heated with hydrogen chloride to give dipentene dihydrochloride (I) and sylvestrene dihydrochloride (II). These two compounds were shown by Simonsen *et al.* (1923, 1925) to be produced by the action of hydrogen chloride on car-3-ene, *i.e.*, these workers showed conclusively that the terpene originally present in Swedish pine oil is car-3-ene. Sylvestrene may be obtained from its dihydrochloride by heating the latter with aniline; removal of hydrogen chloride from the ring can give rise to two possible positions for the ring double bond. Analytical work has shown that the side-chain is isopropenyl (and not isopropylidene), and that sylvestrene is a mixture of the two forms (III) and (IV). Furthermore, it has been shown that car-2-ene is also present in pine oil; both of these carenes are readily converted into sylvestrene, and so it appears that the precursor of sylvestrene (itself a mixture) is a mixture of the two carenes (see §21).

The enantiomers of sylvestrene have been synthesised (Perkin, junior, *et al.*, 1913), and it has also been shown

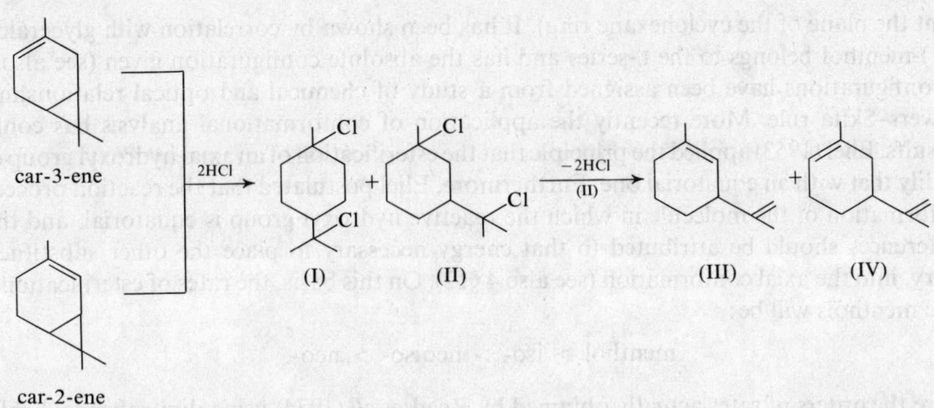

car-3-ene

car-2-ene

that an equimolecular mixture of the dihydrochlorides of (+)- and (−)-sylvestrene is identical with carvestrene dihydrochloride.

§16. Menthol and menthone

Menthol, $C_{10}H_{20}O$, is an optically active compound; only the (−)-form occurs naturally, *e.g.*, in peppermint oils. (−)-Menthol, m.p. 43°C, is a saturated compound, and the functional nature of the oxygen atom is alcoholic, as shown by its reactions, *e.g.*, menthol forms esters. Furthermore, since oxidation converts menthol into menthone, a *ketone*, the alcoholic group in menthol is therefore secondary. Also, since reduction with hydrogen iodide gives *p*-menthane, menthol most probably contains this carbon skeleton. Finally, since (+)-pulegone gives menthol on reduction, and since the structure of pulegone is known to be (I) (see §17), it therefore follows that menthol must be (II).

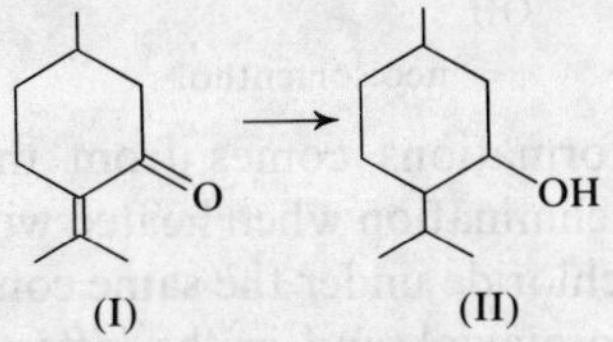

This structure for menthol has been confirmed by consideration of the oxidation products of menthone (see below), and also by the synthesis of menthol.

Examination of the menthol structure shows that three dissimilar chiral centres (1, 3 and 4) are present; thus eight optically active forms (four racemic modifications) are possible theoretically. All eight enantiomers are known and their configurations are as follows (the horizontal lines

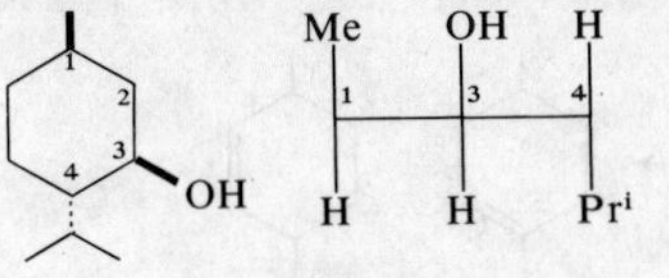

menthol

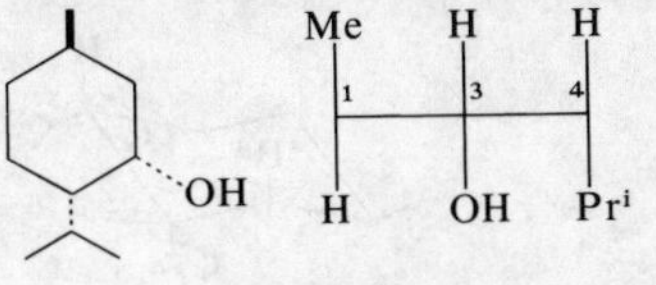

neomenthol

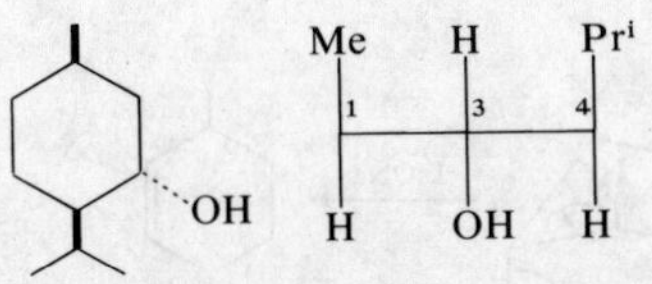

isomenthol

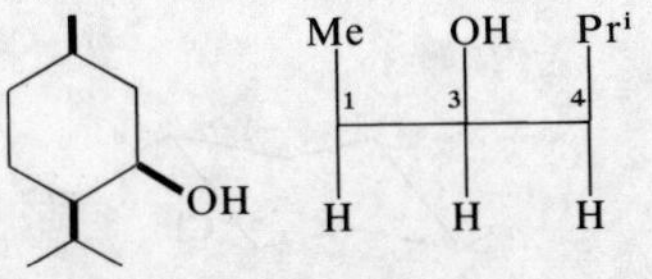

neoisomenthol

represent the plane of the cyclohexane ring). It has been shown by correlation with glyceraldehyde that ($-$)-menthol belongs to the L-series and has the absolute configuration given (see also §23e). These configurations have been assigned from a study of chemical and optical relationships and the Auwers–Skita rule. More recently the application of conformational analysis has confirmed these results. Eliel (1953) applied the principle that the esterification of an axial hydroxyl group occurs less readily that with an equatorial one. Furthermore, Eliel postulated that the reaction proceeds *via* the conformation of the molecule in which the reactive hydroxyl group is equatorial, and that the rate differences should be attributed to that energy necessary to place the other substituents, if necessary, into the axial conformation (see also 4 §12). On this basis, the rates of esterification of the isomeric menthols will be:

$$\text{menthol} > \text{iso-} > \text{neoiso-} > \text{neo-}.$$

These are the orders of rates actually obtained by Read *et al.* (1934) using dinitrobenzoyl chloride; the relative rates were: ($-$)-menthol, 16·5; ($+$)-isomenthol, 12·3; ($+$)-neoisomenthol, 3·1; ($+$)-neomenthol, 1·0. The following conformations have been assigned by Eliel from chemical studies, and are supported by Cole *et al.* (1956) from their infrared spectra and conformation studies.

menthol   isomenthol   neomenthol

or

neoisomenthol

Further support for these conformations comes from the following elimination reaction. Neomenthyl chloride undergoes E2 elimination when heated with ethanolic sodium ethoxide about 200 times faster than does menthyl chloride under the same conditions (Hückel *et al.*, 1940). In the former, the chlorine atom is therefore axial, and in the latter, equatorial. Furthermore, whereas neomenthyl chloride produces *two* menthenes (2- and 3-), menthyl chloride produces only menth-2-ene. In the former chloride, there are two available axial hydrogen atoms; but in the latter, if the ring changes to the other form, then the C1 and only one H are axial, and so menth-2-ene is the sole product (see also 4 §12).

On the basis that the larger of the two alkyl groups would be expected to be equatorial (*cf.* 4 §11a),

neomenthyl chloride   75%   25%

menthyl chloride

the accepted conformation of neoisomenthol has been the one with the equatorial isopropyl group. Armitage *et al.* (1964), however, have obtained evidence which suggests that the isopropyl group is axial. This has received support from mass spectra studies of the four menthols (Thomas *et al.*, 1966).

Menthone, $C_{10}H_{18}O$, b.p. 204°C/750 mm. (−)-Menthone occurs in peppermint oil, and it may readily be prepared by the oxidation of (−)-menthol with chromic acid. Menthone is a saturated compound which has the characteristic properties of a ketone. When heated with hydriodic acid and red phosphorus, menthone is reduced to *p*-menthane; thus this skeleton is present in menthone. Oxidation of menthone with potassium permanganate produces a compound $C_{10}H_{18}O_3$; this compound was shown to contain a keto-group and one carboxyl group, and is known as keto-menthylic acid (IV). Ketomenthylic acid itself is very readily oxidised by permanganate to 3-methyl-adipic acid (V) and some other acids (Arth, 1886; Manasse *et al.*, 1894). The foregoing oxidative reactions may be formulated as follows, on the *assumption* that (III) is the structure of menthone.

(III)   (IV)   (V)

This structure for menthone has been confirmed by synthesis, *e.g.*, Kötz and Schwarz (1907) obtained menthone by the distillation of the calcium salt of 2-isopropyl-5-methylpimelic acid, which was prepared as follows. 3-Methylcyclohexanone (VI) was condensed with ethyl oxalate in the presence of sodium, and the product (VII) then heated under reduced pressure; this gave the ethyl ester of 4-methylcyclohexan-2-one-1-carboxylic acid (VIII). (VIII), on treatment with sodium ethoxide followed by isopropyl iodide, gave (IX) and this, when boiled with ethanolic sodium ethoxide and the product then acidified, gave 2-isopropyl-5-methylpimelic acid (X) (note the acetoacetic ester fragment in (VIII)).

(VI)   (VII)   (VIII)

(IX)   (X)   (III)

Structure (III) contains two dissimilar chiral centres (1 and 4), and so four optically active forms (and two racemic modifications) are possible. All are known, and correspond to the menthones and isomenthones; these are geometrical isomers, each one existing as a pair of enantiomers. The configurations have been assigned on physical evidence; the *cis*-isomer has the higher refractive index and density (Auwers–Skita rule; see **4** §5j). The conformations which have been generally accepted are as shown.

These are based on the assumption that the isopropyl group is always almost completely equatorial, *i.e.*, the other chair form (with the axial isopropyl group) is present in very small amount (*cf.* the menthols, above). Djerassi *et al.* (1964), however, have examined the circular dichroism curves

trans-isomer
menthone

cis-isomer
isomenthone

(1 §9b) of these two menthones in different solvents, and at different temperatures in a given solvent. According to these authors, (−)-menthone is predominantly diequatorial at low temperature, but at high temperatures the diaxial form now makes a much larger contribution. On the other hand, the effect of temperature and solvent changes on the circular dichroism of (+)-isomenthone eliminates the possibility of the conformer with an equatorial isopropyl group making a large contribution to the conformer equilibrium. The authors have interpreted the ORD and circular dichroism curves as being most consistent with (+)-isomenthone existing as a mixture of the chair conformer with the axial isopropyl group and the twist-boat conformation (4 §11b).

(+)-isomenthone

Another point of interest is that menthone (*e,e*-form) would be expected to be more stable than isomenthone (*e,a,*-form). Willhalm *et al.* (1965) have examined the mass spectra of these two compounds and have shown that the molecular ion of the former is more stable than that of the latter (see also §23b).

§17. (±)-Pulegone, $C_{10}H_{16}O$, b.p. 221–222°C

This occurs in pennyroyal oils. Pulegone contains one double bond, and behaves as a ketone. On reduction, pulegone first gives menthone and this, on further reduction, gives menthol. When oxidised with permanganate, pulegone forms acetone and 3-methyladipic acid (Semmler, 1892); when boiled with aqueous ethanolic potassium hydroxide, acetone and 3-methylcyclohexanone are obtained (Wallach, 1896). These reactions show that pulegone is *p*-menth-4(8)-en-3-one.

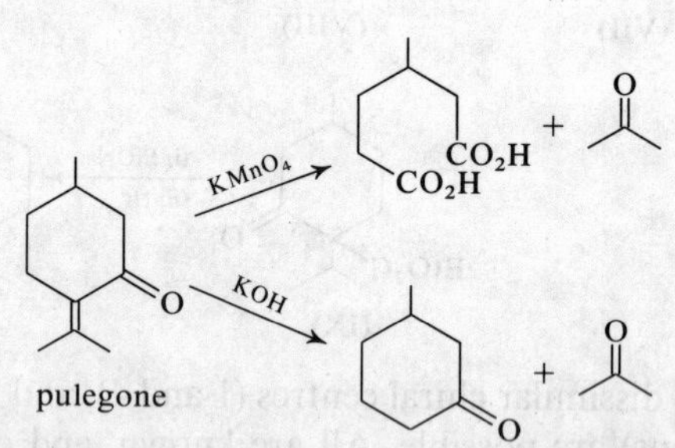

pulegone

This structure has been confirmed by synthesis, starting from 3-methylcyclohexanone (Black *et al.*, 1956: *cf.* menthone, §16).

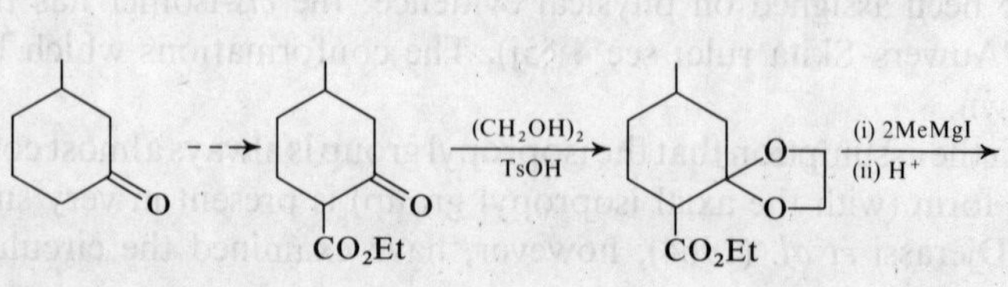

pulegone   isopulegone

Isopulegone can be isomerised to pulegone by alkaline reagents (Kon *et al.*, 1927), and Black *et al.* found that, on treating their mixture with sodium ethoxide, the resulting compound was pure pulegone.

The structure of pulegone is in agreement with the ultraviolet absorption maximum; obs., 252 (ε 5 130) nm, calc., $215 + 10 + 2 \times 12 = 249$ nm. Isopulegone has no conjugated system.

§18.   (−)-Piperitone, $C_{10}H_{16}O$, b.p. 232–233°C/768 mm

This occurs in eucalyptus oils, and is a valuable source of menthone and thymol. Piperitone contains one double bond, and behaves as a ketone. Piperitone, on catalytic hydrogenation (nickel), gives menthone in almost quantitative yield; on oxidation with ferric chloride, thymol is obtained (Smith *et al.*, 1920). These reactions show that piperitone is *p*-menthen-3-one, but do not show the position of the double bond. This had been

(I)   (II)   (III)   (IV)

shown by Schimmel (1910), who found that on oxidation with alkaline permanganate, piperitone gave 2-hydroxy-2-methyl-5-isopropyladipic acid (II), 4-acetyl-2-isopropylbutyric acid (III) and 2-isopropylglutaric acid (IV). These results can be explained only if piperitone is *p*-menth-1-en-3-one (I). This structure for piperitone has been confirmed by various syntheses (*e.g.*, Henecka, 1948; Birch *et al.*, 1949). Bergmann *et al.* (1959) have shown that piperitone is formed directly by the condensation of mesityl oxide with methyl vinyl ketone.

The structure given for piperitone is in agreement with the ultraviolet absorption spectrum: λ_{max} 235 (ε 15 000) nm; the calculated value is $215 + 2 \times 12 = 239$ nm.

§18a.   There are some monocyclic monoterpenoids which do not have the *p*-menthane skeleton. These are of two types:

(i) Those based on the 1,1,3-trimethylcyclohexane skeleton, *e.g.*, (see also ionones and irones, §6) [G = glucose]:

safranal   picrocrocin

Picrocrocin (the bitter principle of saffron) is hydrolysed by acid to **safranal**.

(ii) Those containing a five-membered ring system which is usually fused to a lactone ring. This group is known as the **cyclopentanoid monoterpenoids** or **iridoids**, *e.g.*,

anisomorphal   nepetalactone   iridodial

BICYCLIC MONOTERPENOIDS

§19. Introduction

The bicyclic monoterpenoids may be divided into three classes according to the size of the *second* ring, the first being a six-membered ring in each class.

Class I (6- + 3-membered ring)

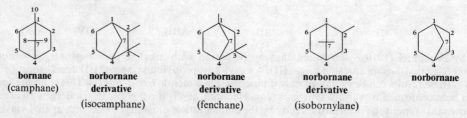

thujane   carane

Class II (6- + 4-membered ring)

or

pinane

Class III (6- + 5-membered ring)

bornane   norbornane   norbornane   norbornane   norbornane
(camphane)   derivative   derivative   derivative
                 (isocamphane)   (fenchane)   (isobornylane)

It is important to note that the two rings do not lie in one plane, but are almost perpendicular to each other (see, *e.g.*, §23b).

The names, including those given in parentheses, are still commonly used, but according to the IUPAC system of nomenclature, the names thujane, carane and pinane are retained, but the following changes are made: **bornane** for camphane, and the others shown above are to be named as derivatives of **norbornane**. Thus, isocamphane is 2,3,3-trimethylnorbornane; fenchane is 1,3,3-trimethylnorbornane; isobornylane is 2,7,7-trimethylnorbornane.

The thujane group

§20. A characteristic property of the thujane group is the ease of opening of the cyclopropane ring under acidic conditions. Proton addition usually occurs in accordance with Markownikoff's rule, *i.e.*, at position 1, to give the more stable cyclopentane tertiary carbonium ion, which then adds an anion or eliminates a proton to form a double bond.

(I)   (II)

α-**Thujene** (I) and (+)-**sabinene** (II) occur naturally, the (+)-form of α-thujene in turpentine oils, the (−)-form in eucalyptus oil, and (+)-sabinene in oil of savin. Their structures have been established by oxidative degradation. The ozonolysis of sabinene produces **sabina ketone** (III), which is isomerised by acid to the cyclohexenone (IV). In this case, the cyclopropane ring opens contrary to Markownikoff's rule. This may be explained by the nucleophilic oxygen atom being involved as shown.

(II)   (III)   (IV)

(−)-**Thujone** (V) and its geometrical isomer, (+)-**isothujone**, occur in oils of thuja, sage, etc. Since (−)-thujone has a lower density and lower refractive index than (+)-isothujone, then the former is probably the

(V)   (VI)   (VII)   (VIII)

trans-form (Auwers–Skita rule; 4 §5j). When thujone is dissolved in concentrated sulphuric acid, it rearranges to 'isothujone' (VI).

Thujyl alcohol (VII) occurs in wormseed oil as a mixture of stereoisomers, the stereochemistry of which has been elucidated by methods similar to those used for the menthols (§16). A mixture of stereoisomeric thujyl alcohols is also obtained by the reduction of thujone with sodium and ethanol.

Sabinol (VIII), an unsaturated alcohol, occurs in oil of savin.

Umbellulone (IX) is found in the leaves of the California laurel. Since it forms a hydroxylamino-oxime with hydroxylamine, this suggests that it is an α,β-unsaturated ketone. Furthermore, the ultraviolet spectrum of umbellulone shows two maxima, 220 nm (ε 5 000) and 265 nm (ε 2 900), and this suggests the presence of an α,β-unsaturated ketone cross-conjugated with a cyclopropane ring (the latter, in the position shown in (IX), behaves like a partial α,β-double bond; see carone, §21). The structure of umbellulone is confirmed by its oxidation by permanganate to umbellulonic acid (X) which, on distillation, gives the lactone (XI) and this, on further oxidation with permanganate, gives umbellularic acid (XII).

(IX)   (X)   (XI)   (XII)

The carane group

§21.   It appears that only two carane derivatives occur naturally:

car-3-ene   car-2-ene

Car-3-ene occurs in Swedish pine needle oil. It is a liquid, b.p. 170°C; when treated with hydrogen chloride it forms a mixture of sylvestrene dihydrochloride (see §15) and dipentene dihydrochloride (§13).

(+)-Car-2-ene, b.p. 165·5–167°C/707 mm, occurs in various essential oils. It forms sylvestrene dihydrochloride on treatment with hydrogen chloride (§15).

The NMR spectrum of car-2-ene shows different signals for the two gem-dimethyl groups of the bridge (which is roughly perpendicular to the plane of the six-membered ring which contains the double bond). The values are τ 9·23 and τ 8·97, and these two values are due to the fact that one of the methyl groups (τ 9·23) is closer to the double bond and is therefore shielded (with respect to the other methyl group; cf. α-pinene, §22a).

Carone, b.p. 99–100°C/15 mm, is a synthetic compound, and is of some importance because of its relationship to carane. It was first prepared by Baeyer et al. (1894) by the action of hydrogen bromide on dihydrocarvone, which was then treated with ethanolic potassium hydroxide, whereupon carone was obtained.

dihydrocarvone   carone   caronic acid

The structure of carone was established by Baeyer et al. (1896), who obtained caronic acid on oxidation of carone with permanganate. Baeyer suggested that caronic acid was a cyclopropane derivative, and this was confirmed by synthesis (Perkin, junior, and Thorpe, 1899), starting with ethyl β,β-dimethylacrylate and ethyl cyanoacetate (and using the Michael condensation).

An interesting point about carone is that its ultraviolet absorption spectrum shows similarities to that of α,β-unsaturated ketones; its λ_{max} is in the region 210–220 nm (cf. umbellulone, §20).

The pinane group

§22. Pinane. The parent compound of this group, it is a synthetic substance which may be prepared by the catalytic hydrogenation (nickel or platinum) of either α- or β-pinene. Pinane exists in two geometrical isomeric forms, cis and trans, and each of these exists as a pair of enantiomers.

α-pinene β-pinene

§22a. α-Pinene, b.p. 156°C. This is the most important member of the pinane class. It occurs in both the (+)- and (−)-forms in all turpentine oils.

The analytical evidence for the structure of α-pinene may conveniently be divided into two sections, each section leading independently to the structure, and the two taken together giving very powerful evidence for the structure assigned.

Method 1. The molecular formula of α-pinene is $C_{10}H_{16}$, and since α-pinene adds on two bromine atoms, one double bond is present in the molecule. Thus the parent hydrocarbon is $C_{10}H_{18}$, and since this corresponds to the general formula C_nH_{2n-2} the general formula of compounds containing *two* rings, it therefore follows that α-pinene is bicyclic (Wallach, 1887–1891). In the preparation of α-pinene nitrosochloride (by the action of nitrosyl chloride on α-pinene) the by-products which were formed were steam distilled, and the compound *pinol*, $C_{10}H_{16}O$, was thereby obtained. Pinol adds on one molecule of bromine to form pinol dibromide, and so pinol contains one double bond. Furthermore, the action of lead hydroxide on pinol dibromide converts the latter into pinol glycol, $C_{10}H_{16}O(OH)_2$, and this, on oxidation, gives terpenylic acid (Wallach *et al.*, 1889). Pinol (III) is also obtained by the action of sodium ethoxide on α-terpineol dibromide (II) (Wallach, 1893). Wagner (1894) showed that the oxidation of pinol with permanganate gives pinol glycol (IV), which is further oxidised to terpenylic acid (V). All these facts can be explained as follows, based on (I) being the structure of α-terpineol (see also §11).

Support for the structure given for pinol (III) is obtained from the fact that oxidation of *sobrerol* (pinol hydrate) produces a tetrahydric alcohol, *sobrerythritol*. Sobrerol itself is readily prepared by the action of hydrogen bromide on pinol, followed by sodium hydroxide. These reactions may thus be formulated:

pinol   pinol hydrobromide   sobrerol   sobrerythritol

(VI)

Thus, if the formula for α-pinene is (VI), then the formation of the above substances can be explained. This structure also accounts for other reactions of α-pinene, *e.g.*, its ready hydration to α-terpineol (see later).

Although the Wagner formula (VI) for α-pinene readily explains all the facts, there is no *direct* evidence for the existence of the cyclobutane ring. Such evidence was supplied by Baeyer (1896). This is described in method 2.

Method 2. As in *method 1*, α-pinene was shown to be bicyclic. When treated with ethanolic sulphuric acid, α-pinene is converted into α-terpineol (Flavitzky, 1879). Therefore α-pinene contains a six-membered ring and another ring (since it is bicyclic), the carbon skeleton of pinene being such as to give α-terpineol when this second ring opens. Since, in the formation of α-terpineol, one molecule of water is taken up and the hydroxyl group becomes attached to C-6, this suggests that the C-6 of α-terpineol is involved in forming the second ring in α-pinene. There are three possible points of union for this C-6, resulting in two three-membered and one four-membered ring (see (VII)); at the same time the position of the double bond in α-pinene is also shown by the conversion into α-terpineol (I).

(VII)   (I)   (VII*a*)

A point of interest here is that there are actually *four* possible points of union for C-8, the three shown in (VII) and the fourth being at the double bond to form a four-membered ring (VII*a*). This one, however, was rejected on the grounds of **Bredt's rule** (1924), which states that a double bond cannot be formed by a carbon atom occupying the bridge-head (of a bicyclic system). The explanation for this rule is that structures such as (VII*a*) have a large amount of strain.

This second ring was shown to be four-membered by Baeyer (1896), who carried out the following series of reactions.

$$\alpha\text{-Pinene} \xrightarrow[\text{KMnO}_4]{1\%\ \text{alk.}} \text{Pinene glycol} \xrightarrow[\text{KMnO}_4]{\text{warm alk.}} \text{Pinonic acid} \xrightarrow{\text{NaOBr}} \text{Pinic acid} + \text{CHBr}_3 \xrightarrow[\substack{\text{(ii) Ba(OH)}_2\\ \text{(iii) PbO}_2}]{\text{(i) Br}_2;} cis\text{-Norpinic acid}$$

(VI)C_{10} (VIII)C_{10} (IX)C_{10} (X)C_9 (XI)C_8

Pinene glycol, $C_{10}H_{16}(OH)_2$, is produced by hydroxylation of the double bond in α-pinene, and pinonic acid, $C_{10}H_{16}O_3$, is produced by scission of the glycol bond. At the same time, a small amount of pinoylformic acid was also formed (MeCO of (IX) is now $HO_2C—CO$). Pinonic acid was shown to be a saturated keto-monocarboxylic acid. The formation of pinic acid, $C_9H_{14}O_4$, and bromoform, indicates the presence of an acetyl group in pinonic acid. Pinic acid, which was shown to be a saturated dicarboxylic acid, on treatment with bromine, then barium hydroxide, and finally the product oxidised with lead dioxide, gives *cis*-norpinic acid, $C_8H_{12}O_4$. This was shown to be a saturated dicarboxylic acid, and so its formula may be written $C_6H_{10}(CO_2H)_2$. Furthermore, since α-pinene contains two methyl groups attached to a carbon atom in the second ring (see (VII)), and it is the *other* ring (the six-membered one containing the double bond) that has been opened by the above oxidation, then norpinic acid (with this second ring intact) contains these two methyl groups. Thus the formula for norpinic acid may be written $(CH_3)_2C_4H_4(CO_2H)_2$. Hence, if we regard the methyl and carboxyl groups as substituents, the parent (saturated) hydrocarbon (from which norpinic acid is derived) is C_4H_8. This corresponds to cyclobutane, and so norpinic acid is (probably) a dimethylcyclobutanedicarboxylic acid. On this basis, pinic acid could therefore be a cyclobutane derivative with one side-chain of $—CH_2CO_2H$.

(VI)   (VIII)   (IX)   (X)

bromopinic acid   hydroxypinic acid   (XI)

Baeyer therefore *assumed* that pinic and norpinic acids contained a cyclobutane ring, and so suggested structures (VI) to (XI) to account for the above reactions, accepting structure (VI) for α-pinene, the structure already proposed by Wagner (1894).

The synthesis of norpinic acid (to confirm the above reactions) proved to be a very difficult problem, and it was not carried out until 1929, when Kerr succeeded with the following ingenious method (apparently the presence of the *gem* dimethyl group prevents closure to form the cyclobutane ring).

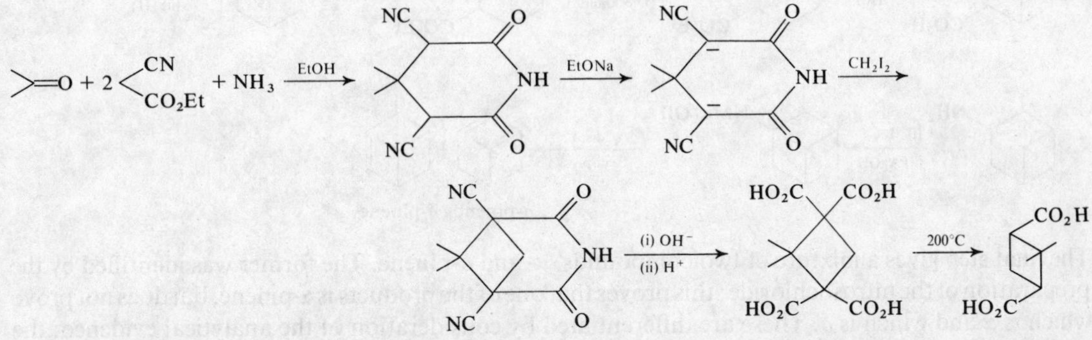

The norpinic acid obtained was the *trans*-isomer; this is readily converted into the *cis*-isomer (the isomer obtained from the oxidation of α-pinene) by heating the *trans* acid with acetic anhydride, whereupon the *cis* anhydride is formed and this, on hydrolysis, gives the *cis* acid (Simonsen *et al.*, 1929).

The total synthesis of α-pinene has now been carried out in the following way. Guha *et al.* (1937) synthesised pinic acid from norpinic acid, and Rao (1943) synthesised pinonic acid from synthetic pinic acid.

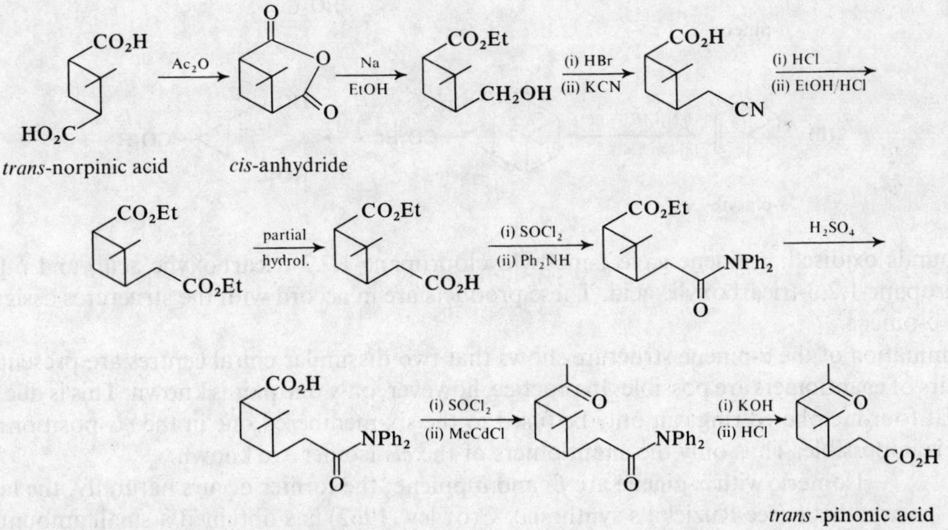

Ruzicka *et al.* (1920–1924) had already synthesised α-pinene starting from pinonic acid (obtained by the oxidation of α-pinene). Thus we now have a total synthesis of α-pinene. Ruzicka's synthesis makes use of the Darzens glycidic ester synthesis (see Vol. I); the steps are:

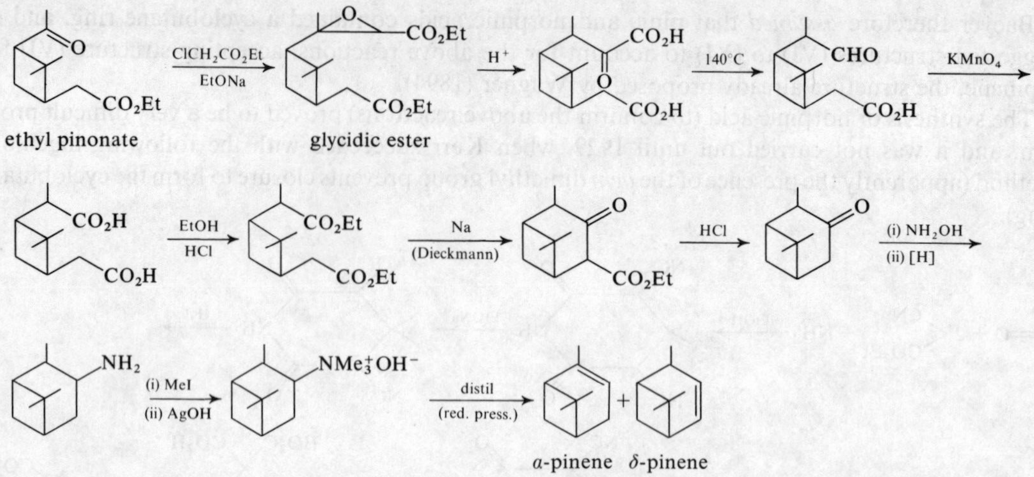

ethyl pinonate   glycidic ester

a-pinene   δ-pinene

The final step gives a mixture of two compounds, α- and δ-pinene. The former was identified by the preparation of the nitrosochloride; this proves that one of the products is α-pinene, but does not prove which is α and which is δ. These are differentiated by consideration of the analytical evidence; the following evidence also supports the structure given for α-pinene. This evidence is based on the fact that diazoacetic ester combines with compounds containing a double bond to form pyrazoline derivatives, and these, on heating alone or with copper powder, decompose to produce cyclopropane derivatives (see also 12 §2a). When the two pinenes were subjected to this treatment, and the resulting

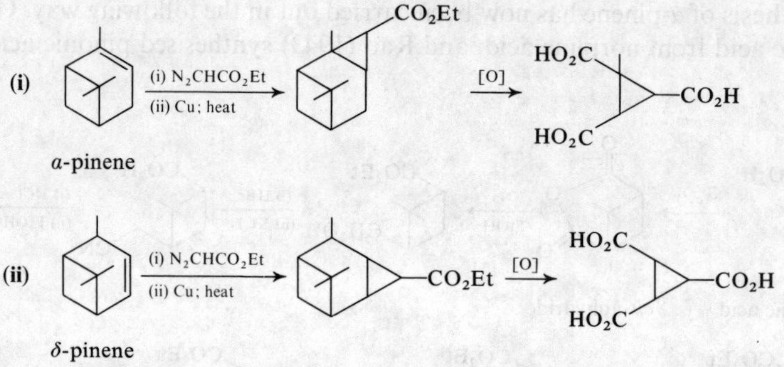

(i)
a-pinene

(ii)
δ-pinene

compounds oxidised, α-pinene gave 1-methylcyclopropane-1,2,3-tricarboxylic acid, and δ-pinene cyclopropane-1,2,3-tricarboxylic acid. These products are in accord with the structures assigned to α- and δ-pinene.

Examination of the α-pinene structure shows that two dissimilar chiral centres are present; thus two pairs of enantiomers are possible. In practice, however, only one pair is known. This is due to the fact that four-membered ring can only be fused to the six-membered one in the cis-position; trans fusion is impossible. Thus only the enantiomers of the cis-isomer are known.

β-pinene

Isomeric with α-pinene are β- and δ-pinene; the former occurs naturally, the latter is synthetic (see Ruzicka's synthesis). Crowley (1962) has obtained a small amount of β-pinene by irradiating a one per cent ethereal solution of myrcene (§4) with ultraviolet light. This is of some interest in connection with the biosynthesis of terpenoids (see §34).

Shoolery et al. (1958) have examined the NMR spectra of α- and β-pinene and found that the two gem-methyl groups have different τ-values: α-pinene, 8·73 and 9·15;

β-pinene, 8·77 and 9·28. The methyl group with the higher τ-value is the one closer to the double bond, and consequently is shielded by the π-electron cloud. The two isomers are distinguished by the fact that the spectrum of α-pinene shows the presence of *three* methyl groups (the third has a τ-value of 8·37), whereas the spectrum of β-pinene shows the presence of only *two* methyl groups.

The mass spectra of α- and β-pinene show peaks at m/e 27, 39, 41, and 53 (see isoprene, §4a). Both exhibit a molecular ion (M^+ 136) and both have a base peak at m/e 93 ($C_7H_9^+$). This could possibly arise as follows:

$$C_{10}H_{16}^+ \longrightarrow C_7H_9^+ + C_3H_7 \longrightarrow C_3H_5^+$$
$$(m/e\ 93)\ (43) \qquad\qquad (m/e\ 41)$$

There is also a peak at m/e 91 ($C_7H_7^+$).

α-Pinene undergoes molecular rearrangements, particularly under the influence of acids (see, *e.g.*, §23d).

When α-pinene, in the presence of air and moisture, is exposed to sunlight, it is converted into a mixture of **sobrerol** (§22a), **verbenol** and **verbenone**.

sobrerol   verbenol   verbenone

Verbenol and verbenone occur naturally, as do also (−)-**isopinocamphone** (see also §22a) and its corresponding alcohol (−)-**isopinocampheol**. Other naturally occurring oxygenated pinane derivatives are **myrtenol**, **myrtenal**, **pinocarveol** and **pinocarvone**.

isopinocamphone   isopinocampheol   myrtenol   myrtenal   pinocarveol   pinocarvone

The bornane (camphane)—norbornane (isocamphane) group

§23. Bornane (camphane), $C_{10}H_{18}$. This is a synthetic compound, and may be prepared from camphor, *e.g.*,

(i) By the reduction of camphor to a mixture of borneols (§23b), these then converted to the bornyl iodides which are finally reduced to bornane (Aschan, 1900).

bornane

(ii) Camphor may also be converted into bornane by means of the Wolff-Kishner reduction (see also Vol. I).

Bornane is a solid, m.p. 156°C; it is optically inactive.

§23a. Camphor. This occurs in nature in the camphor tree of Formosa and Japan. It is a solid, m.p. 180°C, and is optically active; the (+)- and (−)-forms occur naturally, and so does racemic camphor, which is the usual form of synthetic camphor (from α-pinene; see later).

A tremendous amount of work was done before the structure of camphor was successfully elucidated; in the following account only a small part of the work is described, but it is sufficient to justify the structure assigned to camphor.

The molecular formula of camphor is $C_{10}H_{16}O$, and the general reactions and molecular refraction of camphor show that it is saturated. The functional nature of the oxygen atom was shown to be oxo by the fact that camphor formed an oxime, etc., and that it was a keto group was deduced from the fact that oxidation of camphor gives a *dicarboxylic* acid containing 10 carbon atoms; a *mono-carboxylic* acid containing 10 carbon atoms cannot be obtained (this type of acid would be expected if camphor contained an *aldehyde* group). From the foregoing facts it can be seen that the parent hydrocarbon of camphor has the molecular formula $C_{10}H_{18}$; this corresponds to C_nH_{2n-2}, and so camphor is therefore bicyclic. Camphor contains a —CH_2CO— group, since it forms an oxime with nitrous acid (isoamyl nitrite and hydrogen chloride). Finally, distillation of camphor with zinc chloride or phosphorus pentoxide produces *p*-cymene.

Bredt (1893) was the first to assign the correct formula to camphor (over 30 have been proposed). Bredt based his formula on the above facts and also on the facts that (*a*) oxidation of camphor with nitric acid gives **camphoric acid**, $C_{10}H_{16}O_4$ (Malaguti, 1837); (*b*) oxidation of camphoric acid (or camphor) with nitric acid gives **camphoronic acid**, $C_9H_{14}O_6$ (Bredt, 1893).

Since camphoric acid contains the same number of carbon atoms as camphor, the keto group must be in one of the rings in camphor. Camphoric acid is a dicarboxylic acid, and its molecular refraction showed that it is saturated. Thus, in the formation of camphoric acid from camphor, the ring containing the keto group is opened, and consequently camphoric acid must be a monocyclic compound.

Camphoronic acid was shown to be a saturated tricarboxylic acid, and on distillation at atmospheric pressure, it gave isobutyric acid (II), trimethylsuccinic acid (III), carbon dioxide and carbon (and a small amount of some other products). Bredt (1893) therefore *suggested* that camphoronic acid is α,α,β-trimethyltricarballylic acid (I) since this structure would give the required decomposition products. In the following equations, the left-hand-side molecule is imagined to break up as shown; one molecule of carbon dioxide and two molecules of isobutyric acid are produced (but there is a shortage of two hydrogen atoms). The right-hand-side molecule breaks up to form one molecule of trimethylsuccinic acid, one molecule of carbon dioxide, one atom of carbon and *two atoms of hydrogen* which now make up the shortage of the left-hand-side molecule. Thus:

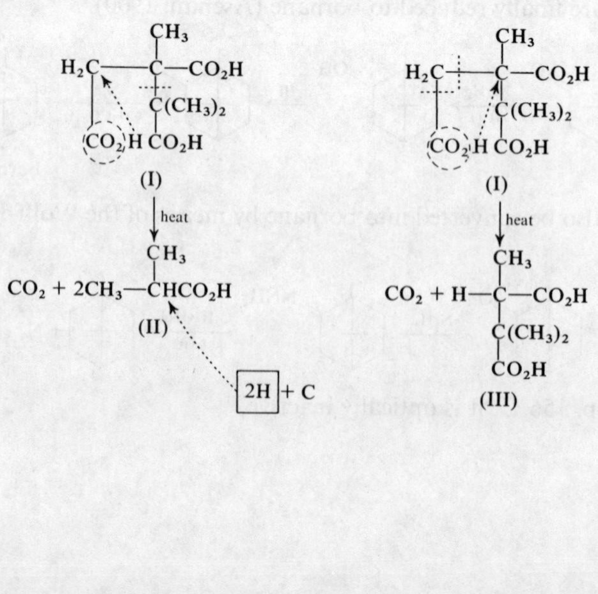

Hence, if camphoronic acid has structure (I), then camphoric acid (and camphor) must contain *three methyl groups*. On this basis, the formula of camphoric acid, $C_{10}H_{16}O_4$, can be written as $(CH_3)_3C_5H_5(CO_2H)_2$. The parent (saturated) hydrocarbon of this is C_5H_{10}, which corresponds to C_nH_{2n}, *i.e.*, camphoric acid is a cyclopentane derivative (this agrees with the previous evidence that camphoric acid is monocyclic). Thus the oxidation of camphoric acid to camphoronic acid may be written:

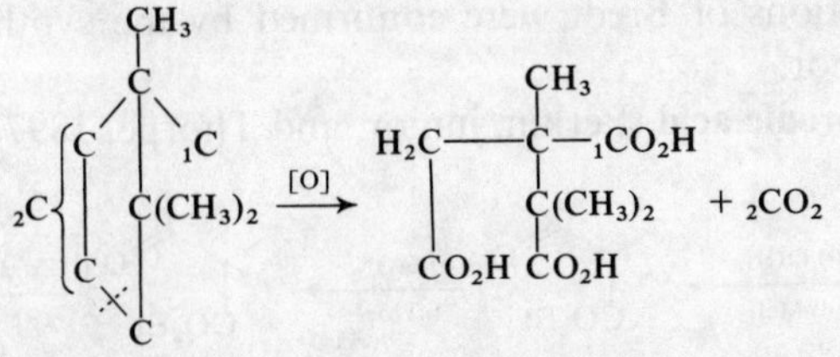

This skeleton, plus one carbon atom, arranged with two carboxyl groups, will therefore be the structure of camphoric acid. Now camphoric anhydride forms only one monobromo derivative (bromine and phosphorus); therefore there is only *one* α-hydrogen atom in camphoric acid. Thus the carbon atom of one carboxyl group must be $_1C$ (this is the only carbon atom joined to a tertiary carbon atom). Furthermore, $_1C$ must be the carbon of the keto or methylene group in camphor, since it is these two groups which produce the two carboxyl groups in camphoric acid. The problem is now to find the position of the other carboxyl group in camphoric acid. Its position must be such that when the cyclopentane ring is opened to give camphoronic acid, one carbon atom is readily lost. Using this as a working hypothesis, then there are only two reasonable structures for camphoric

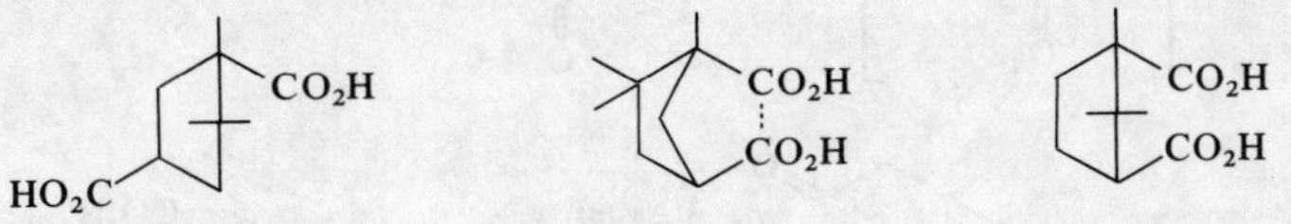

acid, (IV) and (V). (IV) may be rewritten as (IV*a*) and since the two carboxyl groups are produced from the —CH_2CO— group in camphor, the precursor of (IV*a*) (*i.e.*, camphor) will contain a six-membered ring with a *gem* dimethyl group. This structure cannot account for the conversion of camphor into *p*-cymene. On the other hand, (V) accounts for all the facts given in the foregoing discussion. Bredt therefore assumed that (V) was the structure of camphoric acid, and that (VI) was the structure of camphor, and proposed the following reactions to show the relationships between camphor, camphoric acid and camphoronic acid.

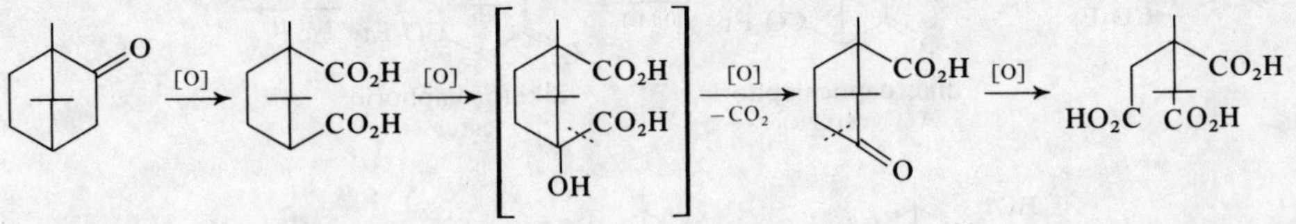

   Bredt, however, realised that if camphor had structure (VII), then all the foregoing facts would be equally satisfied, but he rejected (VII) in favour of (VI) for a number of reasons. One simple fact that may be used here for rejection of (VII) is that camphor gives carvacrol (VIII) when distilled with iodine. The formation of this compound can be expected from (VI) but not from (VII).

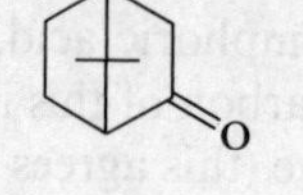

(VII) 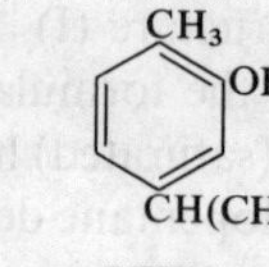   (VIII)

Formula (VI) for camphor was accepted with reserve at the time when Bredt proposed it (in 1893), but by 1903 all the deductions of Bredt were confirmed by the synthesis of camphoronic acid, camphoric acid and camphor.

Synthesis of (±)-camphoronic acid (Perkin, junior, and Thorpe, 1897).

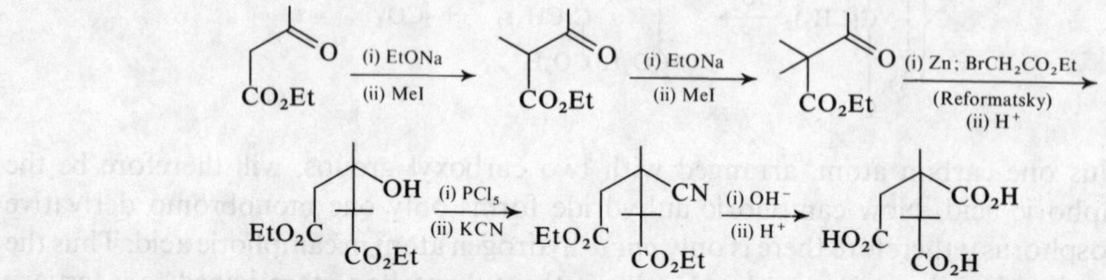

Synthesis of (±)-camphoric acid (Komppa, 1903). Komppa (1899) first synthesised 3,3-dimethyl-glutaric ester as follows, starting with mesityl oxide and ethyl malonate. The product obtained was

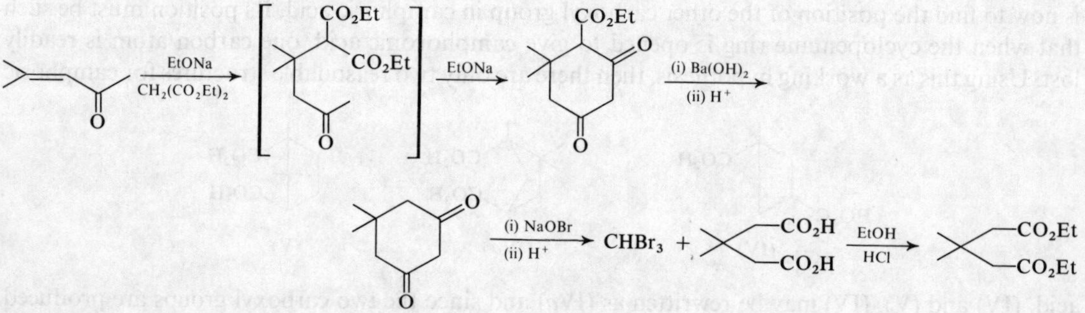

6,6-dimethylcyclohexane-2,4-dione-1-carboxylic ester (this is produced first by a Michael condensation, followed by a Dieckmann reaction). On hydrolysis, followed by oxidation with sodium hypobromite, 3,3-dimethylglutaric acid was obtained (cf. carone, §21).

Komppa (1903) then prepared camphoric acid as follows:

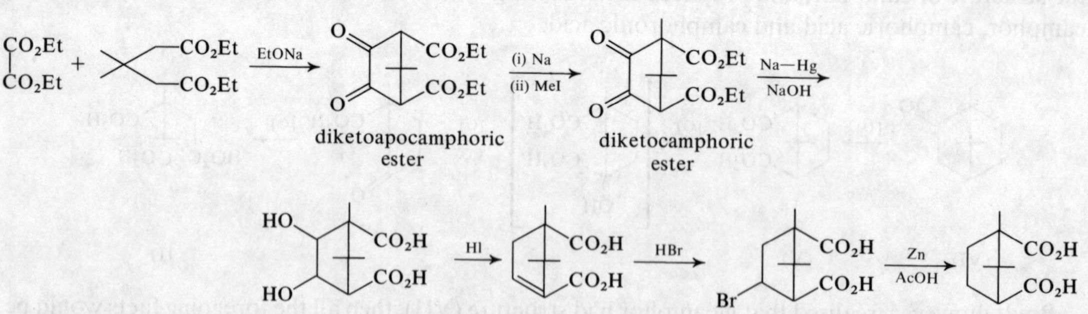

diketoapocamphoric
ester

diketocamphoric
ester

The structure given for camphoric acid can exist in two geometrical isomeric forms, *cis* and *trans*, neither of which has any elements of symmetry. Thus four optically active forms are possible; all are known, and correspond to the (+)- and (−)-forms of camphoric acid and isocamphoric acid. Since camphoric acid forms an anhydride, and isocamphoric acid does not, the former is the *cis*-isomer, and that latter the *trans*- (**4** §5i).

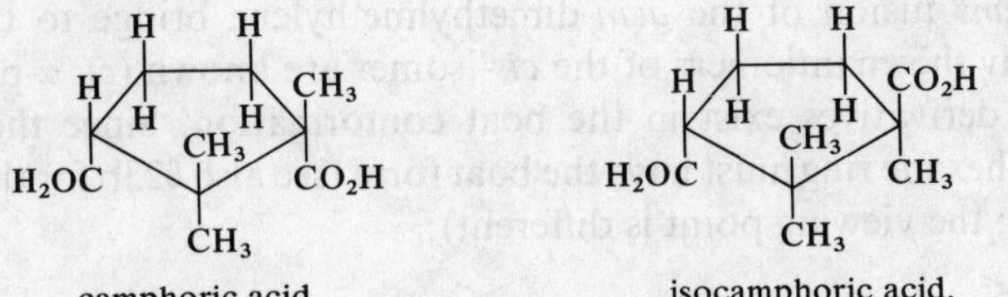

camphoric acid,
m.p. 187°C

isocamphoric acid,
m.p. 171-172°C

Synthesis of camphor (Haller, 1896). Haller started with camphoric acid prepared by the oxidation of camphor, but since the acid was synthesised later by Komppa, we now have a total synthesis of camphor.

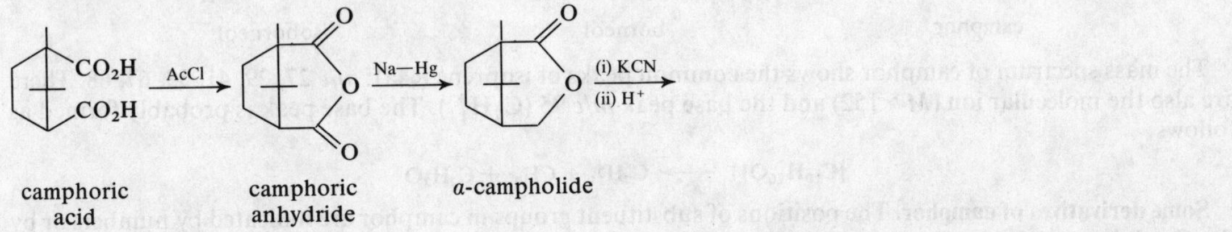

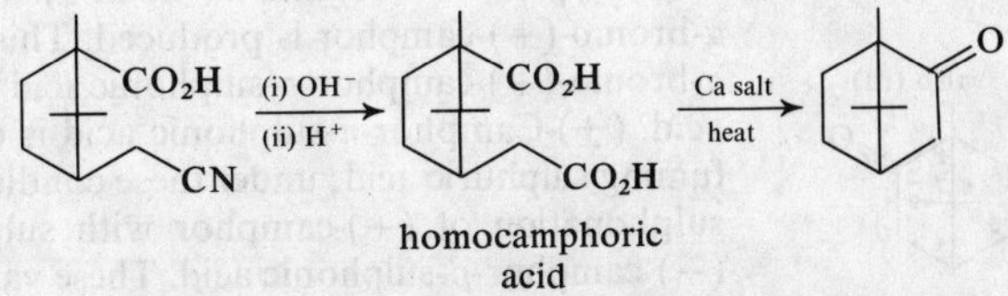

camphoric
acid

camphoric
anhydride

α-campholide

homocamphoric
acid

This is *not* an unambiguous synthesis, since the campholide obtained might have had the structure (IX) (this is actually β-campholide).

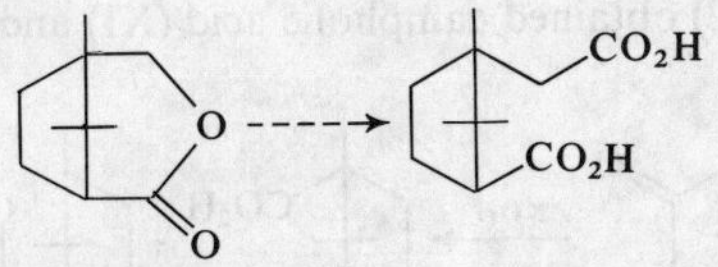

β-campholide
(IX)

(X)

In this case, homocamphoric acid would have had structure (X) and this would have given camphor with structure (VII) which, as we have seen, was rejected. Sauers (1959) has now oxidised camphor directly to the α-campholide by means of peracetic acid. It is also of interest to note that Otvös *et al.* (1960) have shown, using labelled —CH$_2$C*O$_2$H (^{14}C), that in the pyrolysis of the calcium salt of homocamphoric acid to camphor, it is the labelled carboxyl group that is lost.

Money *et al.* (1969) have now carried out a two-step synthesis of (±)-camphor from dihydro-carvone.

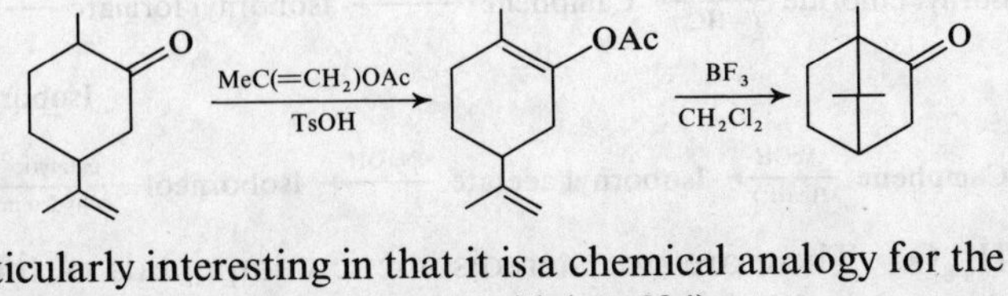

This synthesis is particularly interesting in that it is a chemical analogy for the biosynthetic conversion of a monocyclic into a bicyclic monoterpenoid (see §34).

Stereochemistry of camphor. Camphor has two dissimilar chiral centres (the same two as in camphoric acid), but only one pair of enantiomers is known. This is due to the fact that only the *cis*-form is possible; *trans* fusion of the *gem*-dimethylmethylene bridge to the cyclohexane ring is impossible. Thus only the enantiomers of the *cis*-isomer are known (*cf.* α-pinene, §22a).

Camphor and its derivatives exist in the boat conformation. Since the *gem*-dimethyl bridge must be *cis*, the cyclohexane ring must have the boat form (see also §23b for the usual way of drawing these conformations; the viewing point is different):

camphor   borneol   isoborneol

The mass spectrum of camphor shows the common peaks of isoprene (§4a): m/e 27, 29, 41, 53, 67, 68. There are also the molecular ion (M^+ 152) and the base peak m/e 95 ($C_7H_{11}^+$). The base peak is probably formed as follows:

$$[C_{10}H_{16}O]^{+} \longrightarrow C_7H_{11}^{+} + CH_3 \cdot + C_2H_2O$$

Some derivatives of camphor. The positions of substituent groups in camphor are indicated by numbers or by the Greek letters α (=3), β or ω (=10) and π (=8 or 9). When (+)-camphor is heated with bromine at 100°C, α-bromo-(+)-camphor is produced. This, on warming with sulphuric acid, is converted into α-bromo-(+)-camphor-π-sulphonic acid which on reduction, forms (+)-camphor-π-sulphonic acid. (±)-Camphor-π-sulphonic acid is obtained by the sulphonation of (+)-camphor with fuming sulphuric acid; under these conditions, (+)-camphor is racemised. On the other hand, sulphonation of (+)-camphor with sulphuric acid in acetic anhydride solution produces (+)-camphor-β-sulphonic acid. These various (+)-camphorsulphonic acids are very valuable reagents for resolving racemic bases (2 §10iv).

An interesting reaction of camphor is its fission when heated with potassium hydroxide. The general rule for alicyclic ketones is that fission occurs at the bond involving the least substituted carbon atom adjacent to the carbonyl group. Thus Guerbet (1912) obtained campholic acid (XI) and isocampholic acid (XII), the former being the major product.

(XI)   (XII)

Commercial preparation of camphor. Synthetic camphor is usually obtained as the racemic modification. The starting material is α-pinene, and the formation of camphor involves the Wagner–Meerwein rearrangements (see §23d), *e.g.*,

(i) α-Pinene $\xrightarrow[10°C]{\text{HCl gas}}$ Bornyl chloride $\xrightarrow[(-\text{HCl})]{\text{AcONa}}$ Camphene $\xrightarrow[H_2SO_4]{\text{AcOH}}$ Isobornyl acetate $\xrightarrow{\text{NaOH}}$

Isoborneol $\xrightarrow{\text{PhNO}_2}$ Camphor

(ii) α-Pinene $\xrightarrow[10°C]{\text{HCl gas}}$ Bornyl chloride $\xrightarrow[(-\text{HCl})]{\text{AcONa}}$ Camphene $\xrightarrow{\text{HCO}_2\text{H}}$ Isobornyl formate $\xrightarrow{\text{NaOH}}$

Isoborneol $\xrightarrow[\text{Ni; 200°C}]{O_2}$ Camphor

(iii) α-Pinene $\xrightarrow{\text{isomn.}}$ Camphene $\xrightarrow[(\text{rearr.})]{\text{AcOH}}$ Isobornyl acetate $\xrightarrow{\text{NaOH}}$ Isoborneol $\xrightarrow[\text{dehydrogn.}]{\text{catalytic}}$ Camphor

§23b. Borneols, $C_{10}H_{18}O$. There are two stereoisomeric compounds of the formula $C_{10}H_{18}O$; these correspond to **borneol** and **isoborneol**, and both are known in the (+)- and (−)-forms. The borneols occur widely distributed in essential oils, but it appears that the isoborneols have been isolated from only one essential oil. Borneol and isoborneol are secondary alcohols, and borneol has the *endo*-configuration in which the *gem*-dimethyl bridge is above the plane of the cyclohexane ring and the hydroxyl group is below the plane. Isoborneol has the *exo*-configuration in which the

borneol
m.p. 208·5

isoborneol
m.p. 217

bridge and the hydroxyl group are both above the plane of the cyclohexane ring (see also §23a). These configurations have been assigned mainly on the relative rates of reaction exhibited by the hydroxyl group. Borneol is more readily esterified than isoborneol, and the esters of borneol are more readily hydrolysed than those of isoborneol. Thus the hydroxyl group in borneol is less sterically

(II)   (I)   (III)

hindered than that in isoborneol. Further evidence which supports this is the work of Kwart *et al.* (1956). Bornyl dichloride (I), the structure of which has been established by Kwart (1953), is converted into bornyl chloride (II) by sodium amalgam and ethanol, and into bornane (III) by sodium and ethanol.

The stereochemistry of the borneols has also been solved by means of mass spectrometry. Since the structure of borneol and isoborneol are the same but differ in their stereochemistry, their mass

borneol
(*endo*)

isoborneol
(*exo*)

spectra would be expected to be similar. This has been shown to be the case in practice, *i.e.*, both have the same peaks, the only difference being the relative intensities of these peaks. The greatest difference is shown by the molecular ions, that of borneol being stronger than that of isoborneol. This may be attributed to the fact that the molecular ion of the former is the more stable one due to the smaller 1,3-steric interaction between OH and H in borneol than the 1,2-interaction between OH and Me in isoborneol.

Both borneol and isoborneol are produced when camphor is reduced, but the relative amounts of each are influenced by the nature of the reducing agent used, *e.g.*, electrolytic reduction gives mainly borneol, whereas catalytic hydrogenation (platinum) gives mainly isoborneol; isoborneol is also the main product when aluminium isopropoxide or lithium aluminium hydride is used as the reducing agent. The preferential formation of isoborneol is a case of steric approach control (see **4** §11b). Borneol is converted into a mixture of bornyl and isobornyl chlorides by the action of phosphorus pentachloride. Borneol and isoborneol are both dehydrated to camphene (§23c), but the dehydration occurs more readily with isoborneol than with borneol. Both alcohols are oxidised to camphor, but whereas borneol can be dehydrogenated to camphor by means of a copper catalyst, isoborneol cannot. Borneol, on fusion with potassium hydroxide, gives a mixture of campholic and isocampholic acids (Guerbet, 1909; see formulae XI and XII, §23a). Most secondary alcohols undergo fission under these conditions to give the same products obtained from the corresponding ketones.

§23c. Camphene and Born-2-ene (bornylene). Camphene, $C_{10}H_{16}$, m.p. 51–52°C, occurs naturally in the (+)-, (−)- and (±)-forms. It may be prepared by the removal of a molecule of hydrogen chloride from bornyl and isobornyl chlorides by means of sodium acetate, or by the dehydration of the borneols with potassium hydrogen sulphate. These methods of preparation suggest that camphene contains a double bond, and this is supported by the fact that camphene adds on one molecule of bromine or one molecule of hydrogen chloride. Oxidation of camphene with dilute nitric acid produces carboxyapocamphoric acid, $C_{10}H_{14}O_6$, and apocamphoric acid, $C_9H_{14}O_4$ (Marsh *et al.*, 1891). The formation of the former acid, which contains the same number of carbon atoms as camphene, implies that the double bond in camphene is in a ring; and the fact that carboxyapocamphoric acid is converted into apocamphoric acid when heated above its melting point

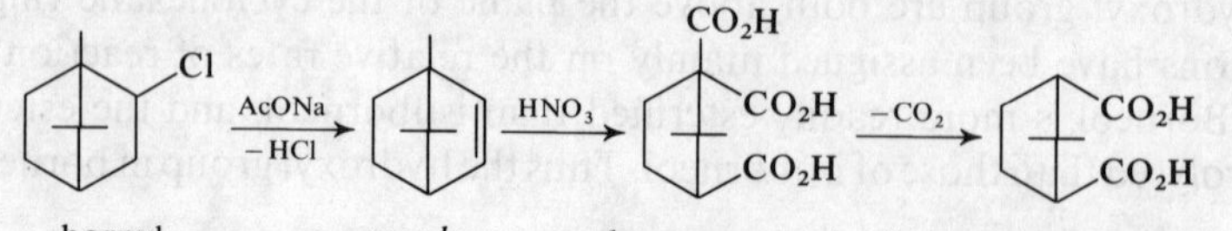

bornyl   *camphene*   carboxyapocamphoric   apocamphoric
chloride   (I)   acid   acid

implies that the former contains two carboxyl groups attached to the same carbon atom (*cf.* malonic ester syntheses). These facts were explained by giving camphene the formula shown (I). The structure of apocamphoric acid was later proved by synthesis (Komppa, 1901; *cf.* camphoric acid, §23a).

This structure for camphene, however, was opposed by Wagner. The oxidation of camphene with dilute permanganate gives camphene glycol, $C_{10}H_{16}(OH)_2$ [Wagner, 1890]. This glycol is saturated, and so camphene is a bicyclic compound (so, of course, is structure (I)). On further oxidation of camphene glycol, Wagner (1896, 1897) obtained camphenic acid, $C_{10}H_{16}O_4$ (a dibasic acid), and camphenylic acid, $C_{10}H_{16}O_3$ (a hydroxy-monobasic acid), which, on oxidation with lead dioxide, gave camphenilone, $C_9H_{14}O$ (a ketone). According to Wagner, it was difficult to explain the formation of these compounds if camphene had structure (I). Wagner (1899) therefore suggested that camphene is formed by a molecular rearrangement when the borneols or bornyl chlorides are converted into camphene, and proposed structure (II) for camphene (see also §23d).

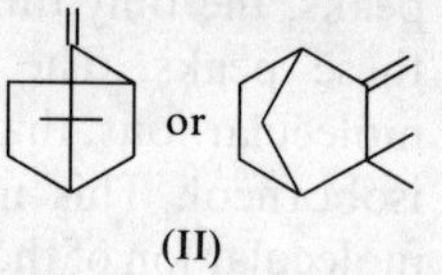

or

(II)

With this formula, the formation of camphene glycol, camphenylic acid and camphenilone could be explained as follows:

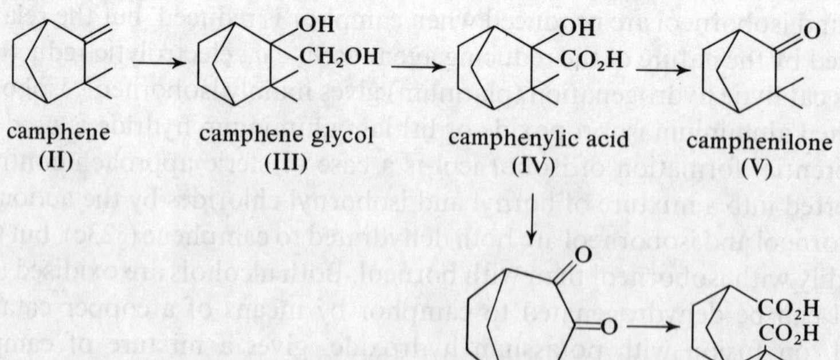

camphene   camphene glycol   camphenylic acid   camphenilone
(II)   (III)   (IV)   (V)

carbocamphenilone   camphenic acid
(VI)   (VII)

Although it was easy to explain the formation of (III), (IV) and (V), it was difficult to explain the formation of (VII). Various mechanisms have been proposed, one being *via* the formation of (IV). Mayo (1959), however, has suggested that camphene glycol (III) is oxidised to the aldehyde (IV*a*) and that this then undergoes the acyloin rearrangement to form (VII) *via* (VI).

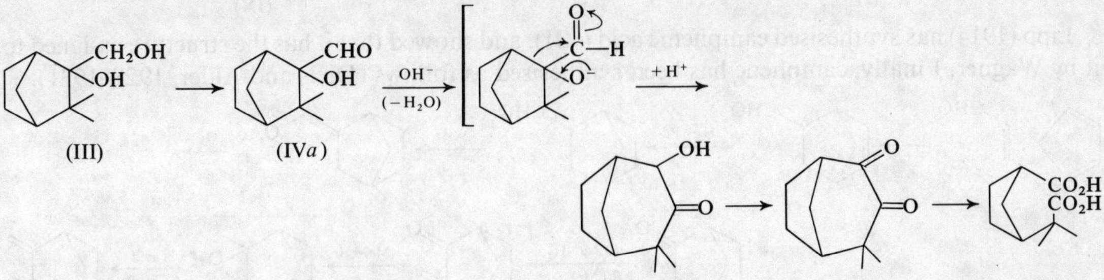

(III)   (IV*a*)

(VI)   (VII)

When camphene is oxidised with chromic acid (chromium trioxide in water or acetic acid), the product is camphor (Berlin *et al.*, 1945). The mechanism proposed involves the Wagner–Meerwein rearrangement (see §23d).

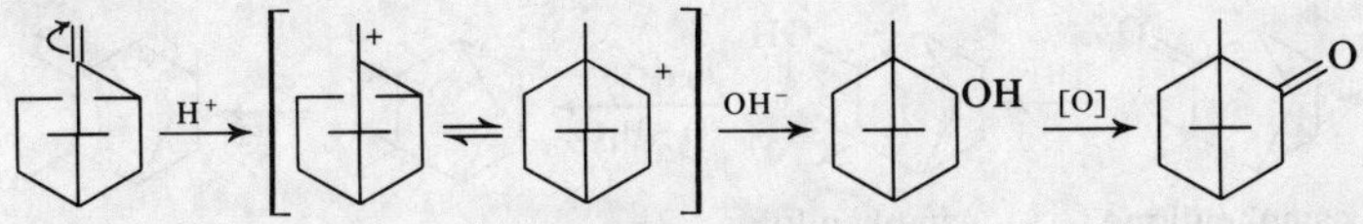

Structure (II) for camphene is supported by the fact that treatment of bornyl iodide with ethanolic potassium hydroxide at 170°C gives **born-2-ene (bornylene)**, $C_{10}H_{16}$ (m.p. 98°C), as well as camphene (Wagner *et al.*, 1899). Born-2-ene is readily oxidised by permanganate to camphoric acid; it therefore follows that born-2-ene has the structure (I), the structure originally assigned to camphene; no rearrangement occurs in the formation of born-2-ene.

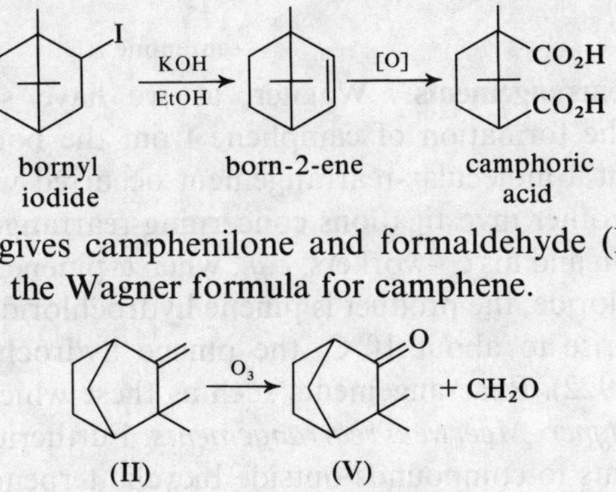

bornyl   born-2-ene   camphoric
iodide   acid

Ozonolysis of camphene gives camphenilone and formaldehyde (Harries *et al.*, 1910); these products are in keeping with the Wagner formula for camphene.

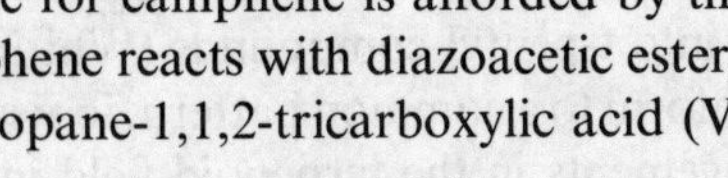

(II)   (V) $+ CH_2O$

Further support for this structure for camphene is afforded by the work of Buchner *et al.* (1913). These workers showed that camphene reacts with diazoacetic ester, and when the product is hydrolysed and then oxidised, cyclopropane-1,1,2-tricarboxylic acid (VIII) is produced. (VIII) is to be

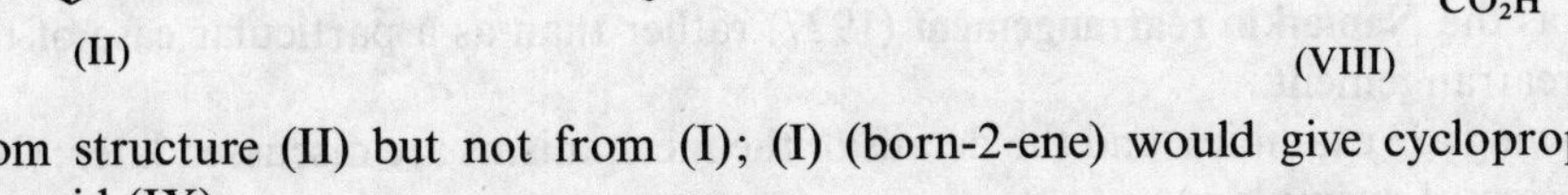

(II) $+ N_2CHCO_2Et \longrightarrow$ (i) hydrolysis (ii) oxidation   (VIII)

expected from structure (II) but not from (I); (I) (born-2-ene) would give cyclopropane-1,2,3-tricarboxylic acid (IX).

+ N$_2$CHCO$_2$Et → ⬡—CO$_2$Et $\xrightarrow[\text{(ii) oxidation}]{\text{(i) hydrolysis}}$

CO$_2$H
CO$_2$H
CO$_2$H

(I)   (IX)

Lipp (1914) has synthesised camphenic acid (VII), and showed that it has the structure assigned to it by Wagner. Finally, camphene has been synthesised as follows (Diels and Alder, 1928–1931).

CHO + CHO → CHO $\xrightarrow{\text{H}_2-\text{Pd}}$ CHO $\xrightarrow{\text{Ac}_2\text{O}}$ CHOAc $\xrightarrow{\text{O}_3}$

O $\xrightarrow[\text{(ii) MeI}]{\text{(i) NaNH}_2}$ O $\xrightarrow{\text{MeMgI}}$ OH $\xrightarrow[(-\text{H}_2\text{O})]{\text{acid}}$

(V)   (II)

Structurally related to camphene is the compound **santene**, C_9H_{14}, b.p. 142°C, which occurs in East Indian sandalwood oil. It is not a terpenoid and its interest lies in the fact that it is formed from camphene as follows

$\xrightarrow{\text{O}_3}$ O $\xrightarrow{\text{[H]}}$ OH $\xrightarrow[\text{(ii) } -\text{H}_2\text{O}]{\text{(i) H}^+}$ + → + → $\xrightarrow{-\text{H}^+}$

camphene   camphenilone   camphenilol   santene

(the Nametkin rearrangement is involved; see §23d). Santene, on oxidation with acid dichromate, undergoes a Nametkin rearrangement to give the ketone **santenone**.

$\xrightarrow{\text{[O]}}$ O

santenone

§23d. **Wagner–Meerwein rearrangements.** Wagner, as we have seen, proposed a molecular rearrangement to explain the formation of camphene from the borneols and bornyl chlorides. Wagner also recognised that a molecular rearrangement occurred when α-pinene was converted into bornyl chloride. Many other investigations concerning rearrangements in the terpenoid field were carried out by Meerwein and his co-workers, *e.g.*, when α-pinene is treated in ethereal solution at −20°C with hydrogen chloride, the product is pinene hydrochloride. This is unstable, and if the temperature is allowed to rise to about 10°C, the pinene hydrochloride rearranges to bornyl chloride (Meerwein *et al.*, 1922). Rearrangements such as these which occur with bicyclic mono-terpenoids are known as *Wagner–Meerwein rearrangements*. Furthermore, Meerwein extended the range of these rearrangements to compounds outside bicyclic terpenoids; these compounds were monocyclic (see also 4 §12). Finally, the range was extended to acyclic compounds, the classical example being that of neopentyl into t-pentyl compounds (Whitmore *et al.*, 1932–).

All of these rearrangements conform to a common pattern, ionisation to a carbonium ion followed by rearrangement. Most rearrangements in the terpenoid field involve a change in ring structure, and in a few cases the migration of a methyl group. All of these rearrangements are examples of the 1,2-shifts (Vol. I, Ch. 5). The rearrangements which involve migration of a methyl group are often referred to as the **Nametkin rearrangement** (1927) rather than as a particular case of the Wagner–Meerwein rearrangement.

The following are examples, and the details of the mechanisms are discussed later; (but see Vol. I for a discussion of example v).

(i) *The conversion of α-pinene hydrochloride into bornyl chloride.*

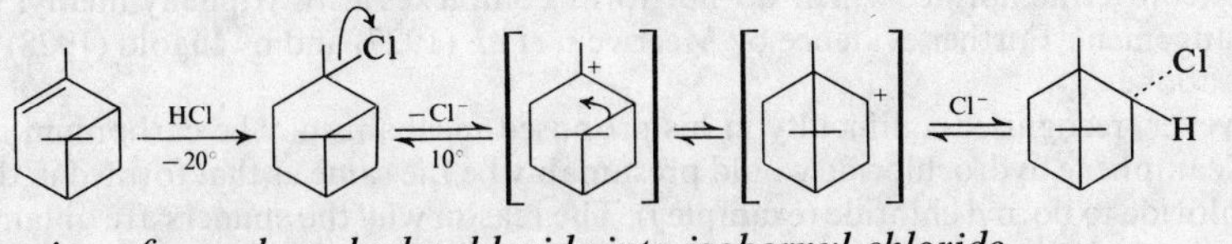

(ii) *The conversion of camphene hydrochloride into isobornyl chloride.*

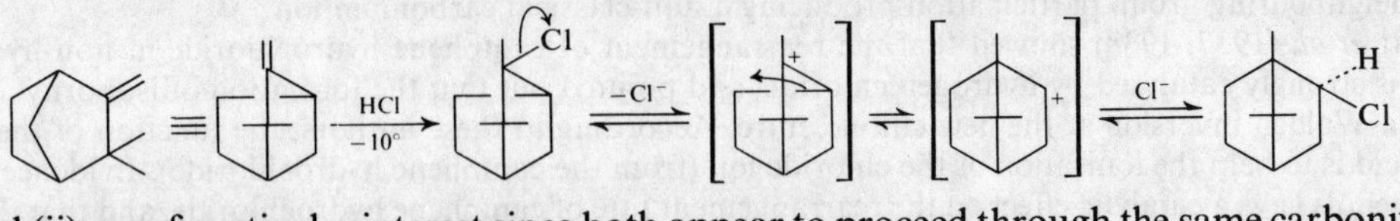

(i) and (ii) are of particular interest since both appear to proceed through the same carbonium ion. Why the epimers should be obtained is not certain (but see later).

(iii) *The dehydration of borneol to camphene* (*with acids*).

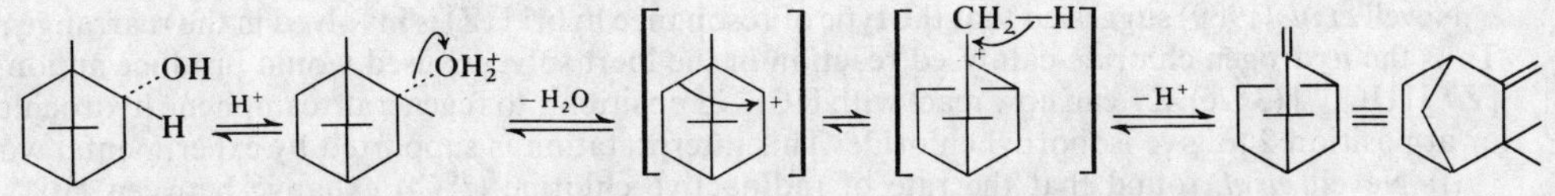

(iv) *The racemisation of camphene hydrochloride* (Nametkin rearrangement).

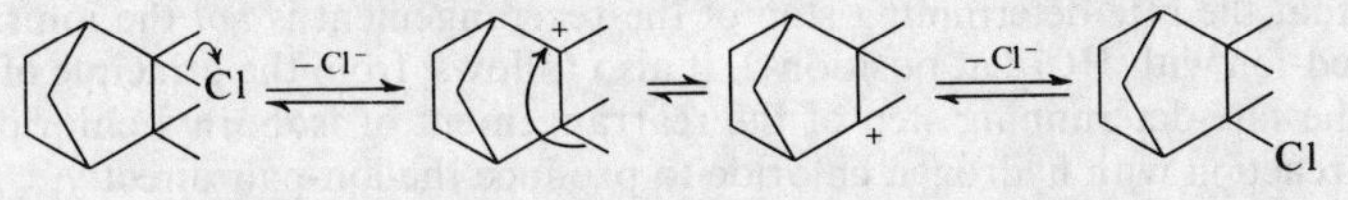

(v) *Rearrangements in the neopentyl system* (Nametkin rearrangement); *e.g.*, the action of hydrbromic acid on neopentyl alcohol to give t-pentyl bromide.

$$Me_3C-CH_2OH \xrightarrow{H^+} Me_3C-CH_2-\overset{+}{O}H_2^+ \xrightarrow{-H_2O} Me_2-\overset{Me}{\underset{}{C}}-\overset{+}{C}H_2 \longrightarrow Me_2\overset{+}{C}-CH_2Me \xrightarrow{Br^-} Me_2CBr-CH_2Me$$

Evidence for the intermediate formation of a carbonium ion in the Wagner–Meerwein rearrangement. Meerwein *et al.* (1922), in their detailed investigation of the reversible conversion of camphene hydrochloride into isobornyl chloride (example ii), concluded that the first step was isonisation, and this was then followed by rearrangement of the carbonium ion:

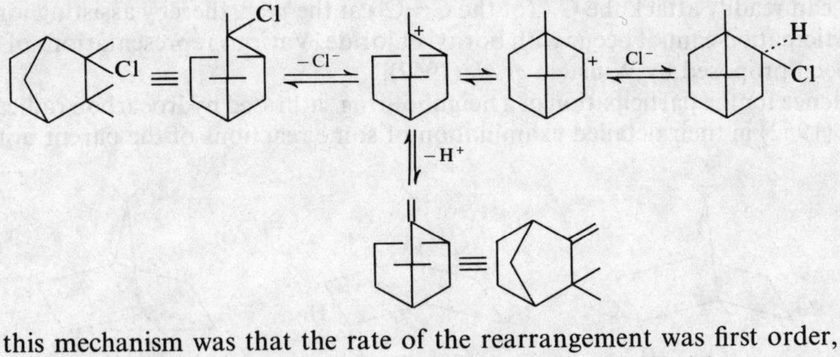

Their evidence for this mechanism was that the rate of the rearrangement was first order, and that the rate depended on the nature of the solvent, the rate being faster the greater the ionising power of the solvent. The order observed for some solvents was:

$$SO_2 > MeNO_2 > MeCN > PhOMe > PhBr > PhH > Et_2O$$

This dependence of rate on solvent was more clearly shown by also studying the solvolysis rates of triphenylmethyl chloride in the same solvents. It was found that the rate of the rearrangement of camphene hydrochloride was faster in those solvents in which triphenylmethyl chloride undergoes solvolysis more readily. Meerwein also found that the rearrangement was strongly catalysed by Lewis acids such as stannic chloride, ferric chloride, etc. All of these form complexes with triphenylmethyl chloride. Furthermore, halides such as phosphorus trichloride and silicon tetrachloride, which do not form complexes with triphenylmethyl chloride, did not catalyse the rearrangement. Further evidence by Meerwein *et al.* (1927) and by Ingold (1928) also supports the mechanism given above.

Meerwein, however, recognised a difficulty in his proposed mechanism. The carbonium ion formed in the rearrangement of camphene hydrochloride would presumably be the same as that formed in the rearrangement of pinene hydrochloride to bornyl chloride (example i). The reason why the epimers are obtained is not certain; one possibility is that the ions are *not* the same, and as we shall see later, the ions are not identical if we assume there is neighbouring group participation producing a non-classical carbonium ion.

Bartlett *et al.* (1937, 1938) showed that the rearrangement of camphene hydrochloride in non-hydroxylic solvents is strongly catalysed by hydrogen chloride, and pointed out that the formation of isobornyl chloride requires a Walden inversion at the new chiral centre. According to these authors, the function of the hydrochloric acid is to help the ionisation of the chloride ion (from the camphene hydrochloride). Evidence for this is that phenols have a catalytic effect on the rearrangement rate of camphene hydrochloride, and that the order of this catalytic activity of substituted phenols is the same as the order of the increase in acid strength of hydrogen chloride which phenols promote in dioxan as solvent. These catalytic effects were explained by Bartlett *et al.* (1941) as being due to hydrogen bonding between the phenolic hydroxyl group and the receding chloride ion.

(Z)

Nevell *et al.* (1939) suggested that the type of resonance hybrid (Z) is involved in the rearrangement. Thus the hydrogen chloride-catalysed reaction in the inert solvents used would produce an ion-pair $[Z^+][HCl_2^-]$ (**3** §2e). Z^+ can now react with HCl_2^- at position 1 to regenerate camphene hydrochloride or at position 2 to give isobornyl chloride. This interpretation is supported by experimental work.

(i) Nevell *et al.* found that the rate of radioactive chlorine (^{36}Cl) exhange between HCl* and camphene hydrochloride is 15 times faster than the rate of rearrangement to isobornyl chloride. It therefore follows that the rate-determining step of the rearrangement is *not* the ionisation step, but is the reaction of the bridged-ion with HCl_2^- at position 2. It also follows, from the principle of microscopic reversibility (Vol. I), that the rate-determining step of the rearrangement of isobornyl chloride back to camphene hydrochloride is the reaction with hydrogen chloride to produce the ion-pair directly.

(ii) On the basis of the bridged-ion being an intermediate in the rearrangement in inert solvents and also for solvolytic reactions of both camphene hydrochloride and isobornyl chloride, then both isomers should give the *same* products. Meerwein *et al.* (1922) found that methanolysis, in the cold, of camphene hydrochloride gave at first the t-methyl ether (attack at position 1) and this, on long standing, gave isobornyl methyl ether. Isobornyl chloride also gave isobornyl methyl ether, but in this case the reaction was slower. These results can be explained by the presence of the liberated hydrogen chloride which would make the methanolysis reversible.

(iii) The relative rates of solvolysis of cyclopentyl chloride, bornyl chloride and isobornyl chloride (in 80 per cent ethanol at 85°C) are respectively 9·4, 1·0 and 36 000 (Roberts *et al.*, 1949; Winstein *et al.*, 1952). This very large difference between the behaviour of bornyl and isobornyl chlorides is readily explained by neighbouring group participation. In isobornyl chloride the methylene group that forms the bridged ion is *trans* to the chloride ion ejected and so can readily attack the C^+ (of the C—Cl) at the rear, thereby assisting ionisation; this neighbouring group participation cannot occur with bornyl chloride. Various representations of this bridged-ion are possible; (I) has been proposed by Winstein *et al.* (1952).

Very strong evidence for the participation of a neighbouring saturated hydrocarbon radical has been obtained by Winstein *et al.* (1952) in their detailed examination of some reactions of the parent norbornyl systems.

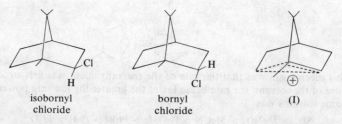

isobornyl
chloride

bornyl
chloride

(I)

These authors showed that the relative rates of acetolysis of the brosylates (*p*-bromobenzenesulphonates) of *exo/endo* norbornyl alcohols in acetic acid at 25°C are 350/1. The explanation offered for the large relative rate of the *exo*-isomer acetolysis was neighbouring group participation to form the non-classical carbonium ion (I*a*). As the OBs⁻ ion is leaving from the front, the neighbouring group (group C_6) can attack from the rear

exo-norbornyl alcohol　　　　　　　*endo*-norbornyl alcohol

to form the bridged-ion. This sequence is not possible as such for the *endo*-compound, and so the latter reacts far more slowly. Further support for the formation of (I*a*) is as follows. This ion has a plane of symmetry (see I*b*) and hence is optically inactive. It has been shown that solvolysis of *exo*-norbornyl brosylate in aqueous acetone, ethanol or acetic acid gives only *exo*-products, but in these products the carbon atoms have become

$-OBs^-$

(I*a*)　　　　　　(I*b*)

'shuffled' (see below). Winstein *et al.* (1952) also showed that acetolysis of optically active *exo*-norbornyl brosylate gave racemic *exo*-norbornyl acetate. Attack must be from the back of the CH_2 bridge and so this results in the *exo*-product; also, since positions 1 and 2 are equivalent, equal amounts of the enantiomers (*i.e.*, racemate) will be produced.

When *endo*-norbornyl brosylate undergoes acetolysis, ionisation of the OBs^- group leaves the *endo*-norbornyl carbonium ion. This is probably originally the classical carbonium ion, but it then rearranges to the

more stable *exo*-bridged-ion. The formation of the latter is shown by the fact that acetolysis of the optically active *endo*-brosylate produces racemic *exo*-acetate.

The structure of the bridged carbonium ion, however, appears to be more complicated than that shown by formula (I*a*). Examination of (I*b*) shows the equivalence of positions 1 and 2, and of positions 3 and 7. Thus labelling the brosylate with ^{14}C at positions 2 and 3 should give products equally labelled at positions 1, 2, 3 and 7. Roberts *et al.* (1954) carried out the acetolysis of this labelled *exo*-brosylate, and the tracer atom was found at 1, 2, 3 and 7, but positions 5 and 6 also contained labelled carbon (15 per cent of the total radioactivity).

6,2 hydride shift　　　　　　　　　　　　3,2 hydride shift

These results can be explained on the basis that there is also a hydride shift from position 6 to position 2. Thus positions 1, 2 and 6 become shuffled to a certain extent and there is also the same amount of interchange among positions 3, 5 and 7. This raises the question as to whether some ions have both carbon and hydrogen bridging. Winstein (1955) has pointed out that the 'extra' carbon shuffling (to positions 5 and 6) depends on the nucleophilic activity of the solvent, and is zero for very reactive solvents in which the life of the carbonium ion is short. This suggests that the hydrogen shift competes with the solvent attack and so occurs *after* the formation of the purely carbon bridged-ion.

Although the mechanisms described above appeared to explain much of the experimental data, nevertheless they did not explain all, and at present there are two extreme views under consideration: the intermediate formation of bridged ions and that of classical carbonium ions. The main evidence for the non-classical

C-bridging

or

H-bridging

carbonium ion theory, as we have seen, has been the stereoselective *exo*-attack by solvent and the phenomenon of anchimeric assistance. The latter factor has presented much difficulty, since its method of measurement has often been somewhat arbitrary (see **3** §6). Comparisons for the norbornyl compounds have been made with cyclohexyl derivatives rather than with the more rapidly solvolysing cyclopentyl derivatives. Winstein *et al.* (1958) obtained the following relative rates of solvolysis of the tosylates in acetic acid at 25°C.

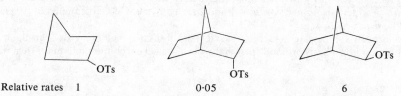

Relative rates   1   0·05   6

These rates are a more valid comparison, and it can be seen that the differences are too small to assume, with confidence, that anchimeric assistance is operating.

Camphene hydrochloride (II) undergoes ethanolysis 13 600 times faster than t-butyl chloride, but only 206 times faster than 1-chloro-1-methylcyclopentane, (III) (*cf.* bornyl chlorides and cyclopentyl chloride, above). On the other hand, a more significant result is that *exo*-2-chloro-2-methylnorbornane (IV) undergoes ethanolysis only 5·4 times faster than 1-chloro-1-methylcyclopentane (III). It can be seen that for these tertiary chlorides,

(II)   (III)   (IV)

the bicyclic compounds solvolyse at rates which are comparable to the appropriately methylated monocyclic models (Brown *et al.*, 1963). Also, the relatively high solvolysis rate of (II) can be explained by steric acceleration, and does not require the postulation of an intermediate non-classical ion.

Now let us consider the 'scrambling' experiments of Roberts described above. More recent work has shown that alkyl carbonium ions undergo internal rearrangements extremely rapidly, and this rapidity leads to the conclusion that scrambling of carbon atoms prior to solvolysis can no longer be accepted as evidence for the equivalence of carbon atoms in carbonium ion structures (*i.e.*, evidence for hybrid structures). Thus Roberts' work with labelled norbornyl compounds can no longer be regarded as definite evidence for the mechanism involving a non-classical carbonium ion (I*b*).

As we have seen, one of the early bits of evidence in support of the formation of (I*b*) was the complete racemisation that occurred in the solvolysis of *exo*-norbornyl brosylate. Here again, more recent work has shown that this is now always the case, *e.g.*, Corey *et al.* (1963) found that the deamination of *exo*- and *endo*-norbornylamine in acetic acid gave predominantly *exo*-norbornyl acetate with 15 per cent retention of optical activity (*cf.* **3** §6e). These results can be explained in terms of the classical carbonium ion (V). The amount of retention then depends on the *competition* between (i) internal rearrangement leading to racemisation, and

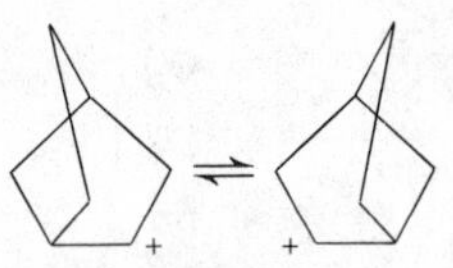

(V)

(ii) attack by solvent leading irreversibly to the acetate. It is possible, however, that the classical and non-classical ions are both present. On the other hand, Schleyer *et al.* (1963), using NMR spectroscopy, have shown that the dianisylnorbornyl cation exists in rapid equilibrium between two identical structures (VI) rather than the single hybrid structure (VII). In this case the carbonium ion is different from the simple norbornyl ion; in (VI) the positive charge can be partially neutralised by resonance with the aromatic nucleus, Ar; this is not possible in (V).

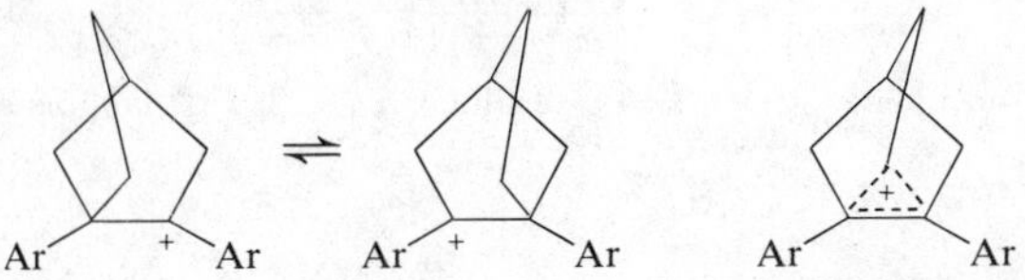

(VI)   (VII)

Evidence of a different nature has also been obtained to try to decide between the two extremes. It is well known that ionisation is accompanied by a net decrease in volume. This is due to the large forces exerted by the ions on the surrounding molecules, and a typical decrease is 20 cm^3/mole. Inspection of the classical and non-classical ions shows that in the latter the charge is more diffuse. Consequently, the formation of the non-classical ion would be expected to be accompanied by a smaller volume change than the formation of the classical ion (*cf.* **3** §2e). Noble *et al.* (1965) measured the effect of pressure on the hydrolysis rates of *exo*- and *endo*-norbornyl, and cyclopentyl brosylates; (if a volume change occurs, the rate will therefore depend on the pressure). The authors have interpreted their results as being consistent with the view that the *exo*-compound is hydrolysed through the non-classical ion.

Trahanovsky (1965) has calculated the energy contents of different shapes for the norbornyl cation and found that the geometry of the most stable form corresponds to (I*a*). The ion is symmetrical; carbon atoms 1, 2 and 6 are trigonally hybridised, and this form contains less energy than the classical ion. On the other hand, Goering *et al.* (1965) have determined the activation energies for the solvolysis (in acetic acid) of *exo*- and *endo*-norbornyl derivatives and found that E for the *exo* was lower than E for the *endo* by about 18·41 kJ mol^{-1}. this is evidence for the non-classical ion (delocalisation lowers the energy of the *exo*-transition state). Presumably, the classical ion is formed with the *endo*-compound.

It can be seen from the foregoing account that the problem is not yet settled.

Examples of the Nametkin rearrangement are camphenilol into santene (§23c), the racemisation of camphene hydrochloride (see example (iv) above), and the racemisation of camphene the mechanism of which may be formulated as follows:

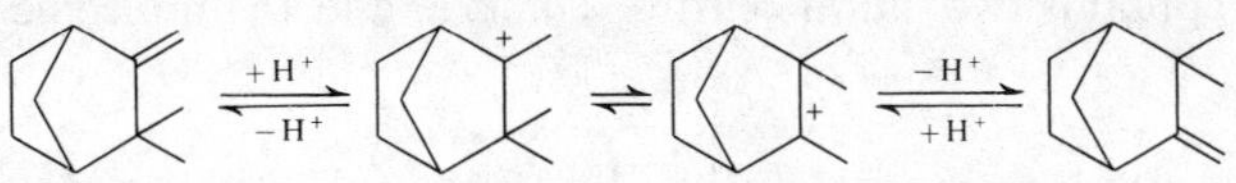

§23e. Correlation of configurations of terpenoids.
This has been made possible by the work of Fredga on quasi-racemic compounds (see **2** §9a). This author has established the following configurations:

CHO	CO$_2$H	CO$_2$H	CO$_2$H
HO—C—H	CH$_3$—C—H	(CH$_3$)$_2$CH—C—H	(CH$_3$)$_2$CH—C—H
CH$_2$OH	CH$_2$CO$_2$H	CH$_2$CO$_2$H	CH$_2$CH$_2$CO$_2$H
L-glyceraldehyde	L(−)-methyl-succinic acid	L(−)-isopropylsuccinic acid	L(+)-2-isopropylglutaric acid

By means of these configurations, combined with various interrelations obtained by oxidative degradations and by molecular rearrangements, it has been possible to correlate the configurations of many mono- and bicyclic terpenoids with L-glyceraldehyde (see also §28); *e.g.*,

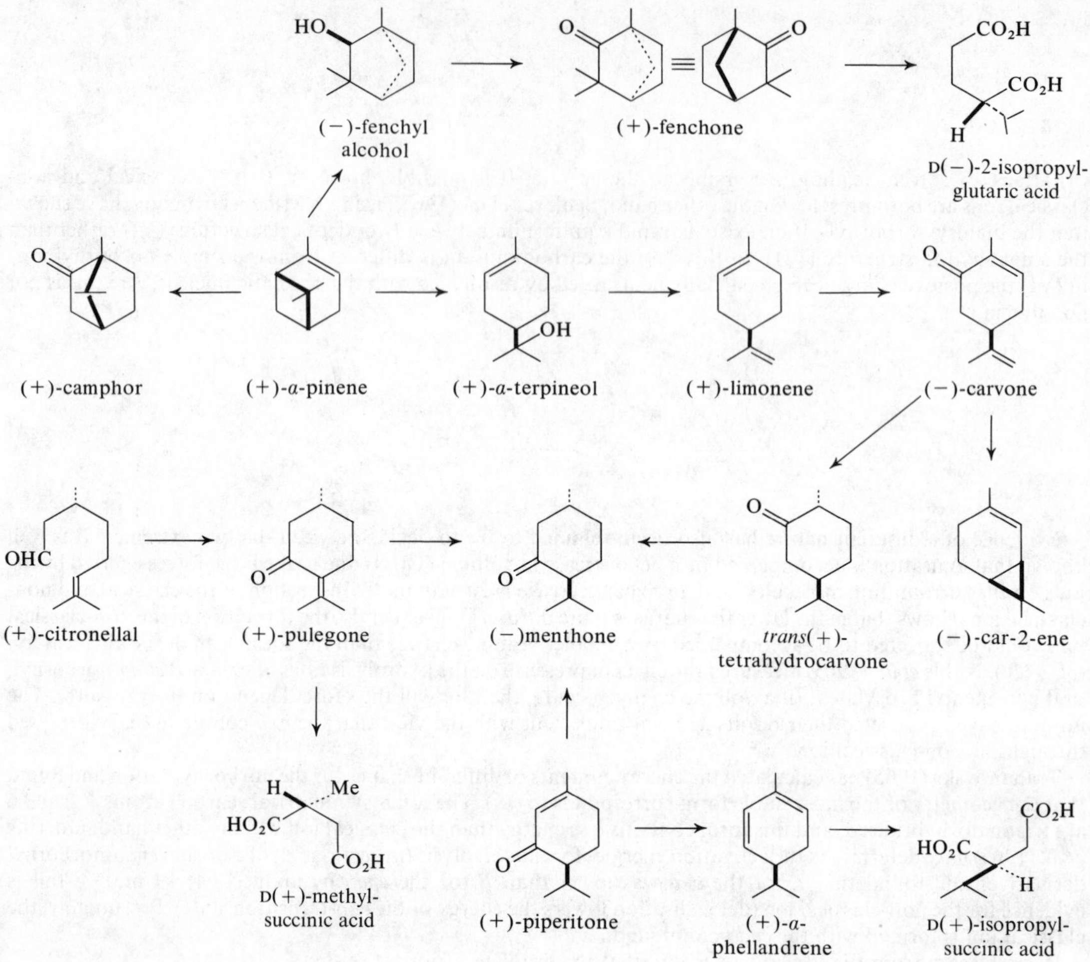

(−)-fenchyl
alcohol

(+)-fenchone

D(−)-2-isopropyl-
glutaric acid

(+)-camphor

(+)-*a*-pinene

(+)-*a*-terpineol

(+)-limonene

(−)-carvone

(+)-citronellal

(+)-pulegone

(−)menthone

trans(+)-
tetrahydrocarvone

(−)-car-2-ene

D(+)-methyl-
succinic acid

(+)-piperitone

(+)-*a*-
phellandrene

D(+)-isopropyl-
succinic acid

The specification of configuration of a chiral centre in acyclic and monocyclic compounds has been described in **2** §5d. The scheme for a bicyclic terpenoid may be illustrated with (−)-car-3-ene as the example. This contains two chiral centres, 1 and 6, and the molecule can be dissected into

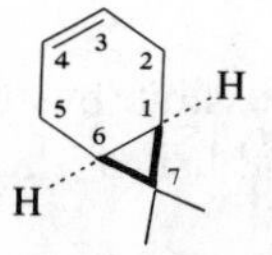

(−)-car-3-ene

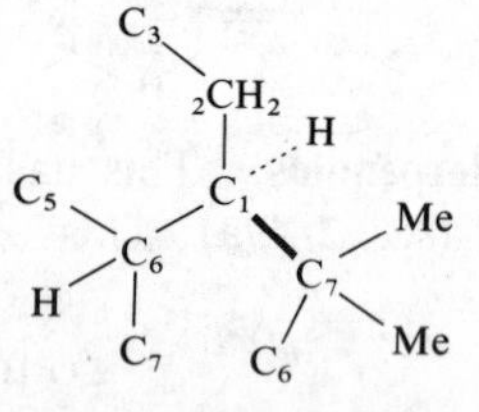

(I)

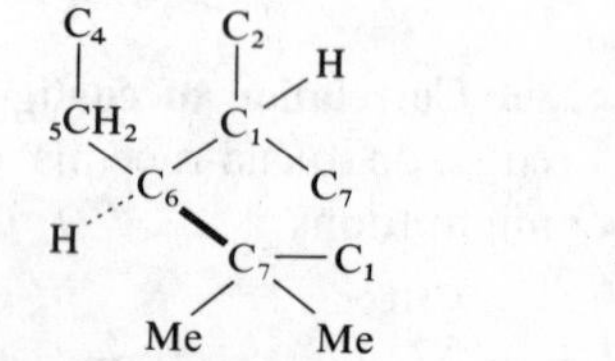

(II)

fragments (I) and (II) in order that the nature of the groups attached to each chiral centre may be seen more readily. Since the order of priority of alkyl groups is tertiary > secondary > primary (**2** §5d), the group sequence in (I) is C_7 (CCC) = a, C_6 (CCH) = b, C_2 (CHH) = c, and H = d; and in (II), C_7 (CCC) = a, C_1 (CCH) = b, C_5 (CHH) = c, and H = d. Thus (I) has the (R)-configuration and (II) has the (S)-configuration, and hence this carene is (1R,6S)-car-3-ene.

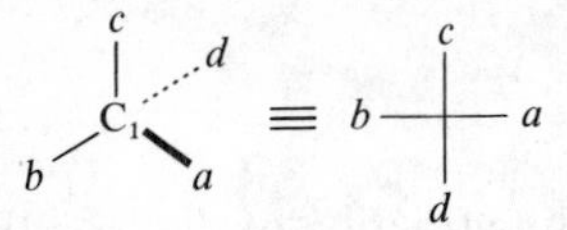

(I) (R) 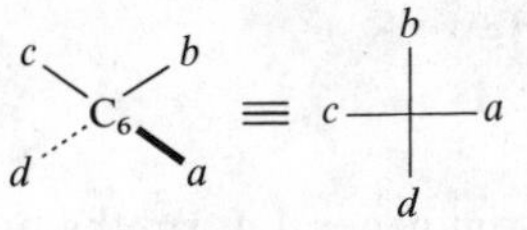   (II) (S)

The norbornane (fenchane) group

§24. The most important natural terpenoid of this group is **fenchone**; this occurs in oil of fennel. It is a liquid, b.p. 192–193°C, and is optically active, both enantiomers occurring naturally.

The molecular formula of fenchone is $C_{10}H_{16}O$, and the compound behaves as a ketone. When fenchone (I) is reduced with sodium and ethanol, fenchyl alcohol, $C_{10}H_{18}O$ (II), is produced, and this, on dehydration under the influence of acids, gives α-fenchene, $C_{10}H_{16}$ (III). On oxidation with permanganate, α-fenchone gives the hydroxy-acid (IV). This, on treatment with lead dioxide, is converted into α-fenchocamphorone, $C_9H_{14}O$ (IV), which, on oxidation with nitric acid, forms apocamphoric acid (V), a compound of known structure. This work was carried out by Wallach *et al.* (1890–1898), but it was Semmler (1905) who was the first to assign the correct structure to fenchone; the foregoing reactions may be formulated:

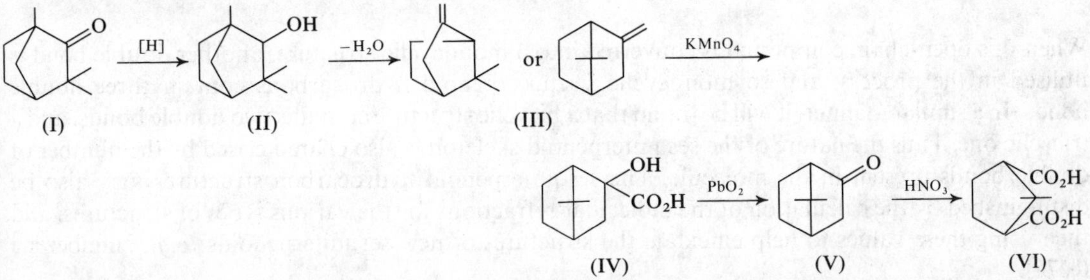

(I) [H] → (II) $-H_2O$ → (III) or KMnO₄ →

(IV) PbO₂ → (V) HNO₃ → (VI)

It should be noted that the dehydration of fenchyl alcohol (II) to α-fenchene (III) occurs *via* a Wagner–Meerwein rearrangement; the mechanism for this reaction may thus be written (*cf.* §23d):

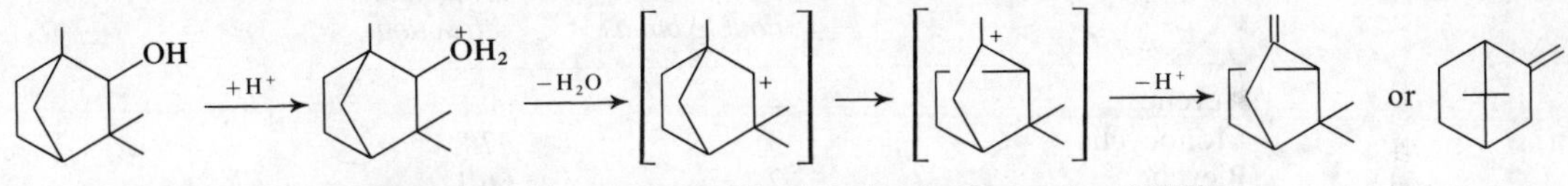

$+H^+$ $-H_2O$ $-H^+$ or

The structure of fenchone has been confirmed by synthesis (Ruzicka, 1917).

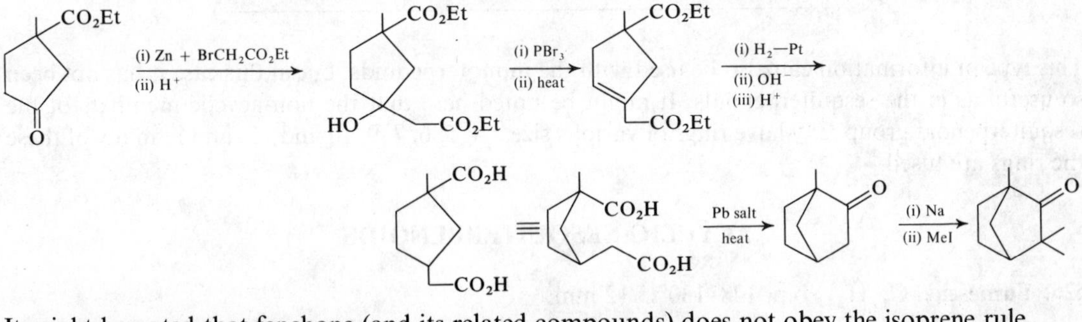

(i) Zn + BrCH₂CO₂Et
(ii) H⁺

(i) PBr₃
(ii) heat

(i) H₂—Pt
(ii) OH⁻
(iii) H⁺

Pb salt
heat

(i) Na
(ii) MeI

It might be noted that fenchone (and its related compounds) does not obey the isoprene rule.

α-Fenchyl alcohol (II) occurs naturally, and in addition to being prepared by the reduction of fenchone (as shown above), may be prepared by the hydration (with rearrangement) of α- and β-pinene.

Sesquiterpenoids

§25. Introduction

The sesquiterpenoids, in general, form the higher boiling fraction of the essential oils; this provides their chief source. Wallach (1887) was the first to suggest that the sesquiterpenoid structure is built up of three isoprene units; this has been shown to be the case for the majority of the known sesquiterpenoids, but there are some exceptions.

The sesquiterpenoids are classified into four groups according to the number of rings present in the structure. If we use the *isoprene rule*, then when three isoprene units are linked (head to tail) to form an acyclic sesquiterpenoid hydrocarbon, the latter will contain *four* double bonds. Each isoprene unit contains *two* double bonds, but one disappears for each pair that is connected:

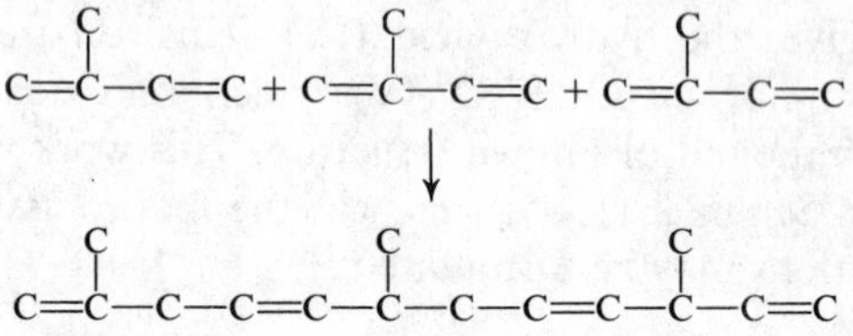

$$C{=}\overset{\overset{\text{C}}{|}}{C}{-}C{=}C \ + \ C{=}\overset{\overset{\text{C}}{|}}{C}{-}C{=}C \ + \ C{=}\overset{\overset{\text{C}}{|}}{C}{-}C{=}C$$

$$\downarrow$$

$$C{=}\overset{\overset{\text{C}}{|}}{C}{-}C{-}C{=}C{-}\overset{\overset{\text{C}}{|}}{C}{-}C{-}C{=}C{-}\overset{\overset{\text{C}}{|}}{C}{-}C{=}C$$

When this open-chain compound is converted into a monocyclic structure, another double bond is utilised in the process, and so monocyclic sesquiterpenoid hydrocarbons contain three double bonds. In a similar manner, it will be found that a bicyclic structure contains two double bonds, and a tricyclic one. Thus the nature of the sesquiterpenoid skeleton is also characterised by the number of double bonds present in the molecule. The sesquiterpenoid hydrocarbon structures may also be distinguished by the calculation of the molecular refractions for the various types of structures, and then using these values to help elucidate the structures of new sesquiterpenoids; *e.g.*, zingiberene (§27a).

Class of sesquiterpenoids	Number of double bonds	Molecular refraction
Acyclic	4	69.5
Monocyclic	3	67.8
Bicyclic	2	66.1
Tricyclic	1	64.4

This type of information can also be used with the monoterpenoids, but in this case it has not been so useful as in the sesquiterpenoids. It might be noted here that the non-acyclic members of the sesquiterpenoid group may have rings of various sizes: 4, 5, 6, 7, 9, 10 and 11; and in many of these the rings are fused.

ACYCLIC SESQUITERPENOIDS

§26. Farnesene, $C_{15}H_{24}$, b.p. 128–130°C/12 mm.

This is obtained by the dehydration of farnesol with potassium hydrogen sulphate (Harries *et al.*, 1913). This compound is the α-isomer, and it has now been shown that the β-isomer occurs naturally (in oil of hops), and Sorm *et al.* (1949, 1950) have assigned it the structure shown. β-Farnesene is also obtained by the dehydration of nerolidol.

α-farnesene   β-farnesene

§26a. Farnesol, $C_{15}H_{26}O$, b.p. 120°C/0·3 mm.   This occurs in the oil of ambrette seeds, etc. Its structure was elucidated by Kerschbaum (1913) as follows. When oxidised with chromic acid, farnesol (I) is converted into farnesal (II), $C_{15}H_{24}O$, a compound which behaves as an aldehyde. Thus farnesol is a primary alcohol. Conversion of farnesal into its oxime, followed by dehydration with acetic anhydride, produces a cyanide (III) which, on hydrolysis with alkali, forms farnesenic acid (IV), $C_{15}H_{24}O_2$, and a ketone, $C_{13}H_{22}O$ (V). This ketone was then found to be dihydro-*pseudo*-ionone (geranylacetone). In the formation of this ketone, two carbon atoms are removed from its precursor. This reaction is characteristic of α,β-unsaturated carbonyl compounds, and so it is inferred that the precursor, farnesenic acid (or its nitrile), is an α,β-unsaturated compound. Thus the foregoing facts may be formulated as follows, on the basis of the known structure of geranylacetone.

This structure for farnesol has been confirmed by its synthesis from synthetic nerolidol (Ruzicka, 1923; see §26b).

nerolidol   farnesol

A recent synthesis of farnesol has been carried out by Corey *et al.* (1967) [see juvenile hormone, §26d, for further details].

trans-geranyl-
acetone

A number of geometrical isomers of farnesol have now been prepared (Naves *et al.*, 1958; Cornforth *et al.*, 1960; Bates *et al.*, 1963; see also **9** §6b). The prefixes *cis* and *trans* are used to denote the positions of methylene groups (in the main chain) with respect to each other for each double bond (in the chain), and at the end of the chain the position of the functional group with respect to the methylene group of the chain (o and x denote each pair).

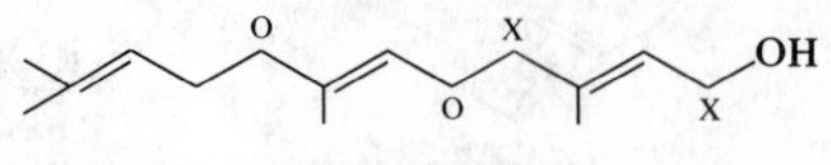

trans-trans

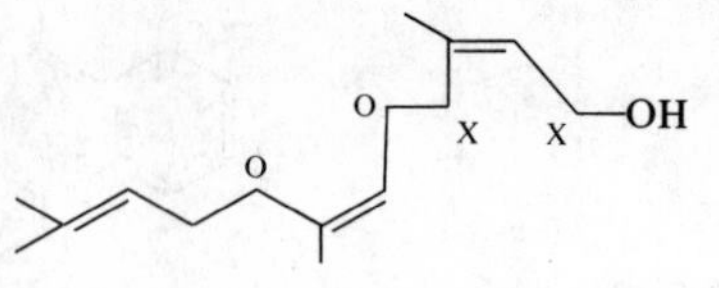

cis-cis

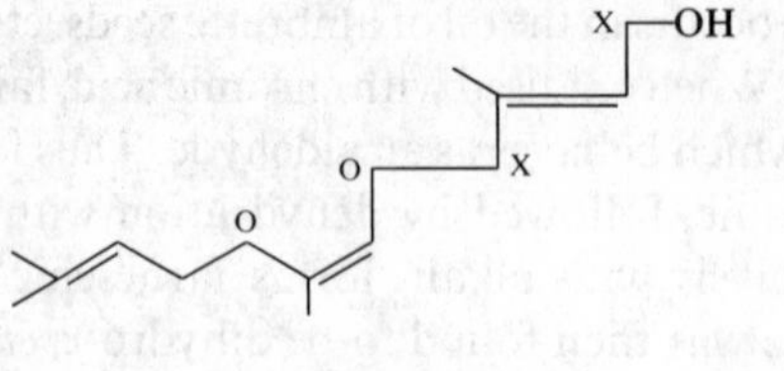

trans-cis

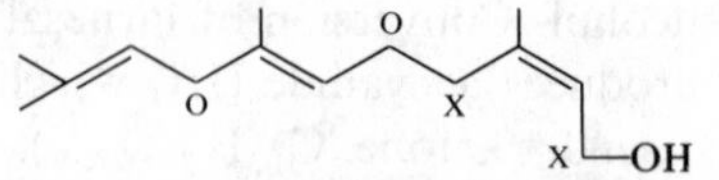

cis-trans

§**26b. Nerolidol,** $C_{15}H_{26}O$, b.p. 125–127°C/4·5 mm. This occurs in the oil of neroli, etc., in the (+)-form. Nerolidol is isomeric with farnesol, and Ruzicka (1923) showed that the relationship between the two is the same as that between linalool and geraniol (see §8) and confirmed the structure of nerolidol by synthesis.

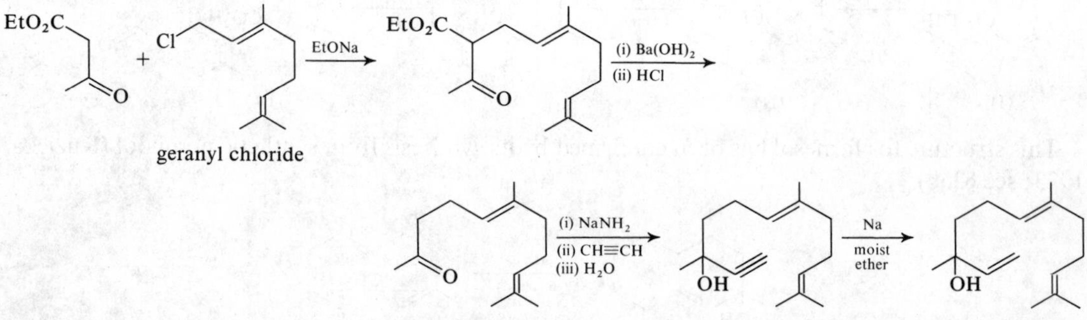

geranyl chloride

geranylacetone

(+)-nerolidol

Julia *et al.* (1959, 1960) have synthesised *trans*-nerolidol by a method in which isoprene units can be repetitively introduced by reaction between a Grignard reagent and cyclopropyl methyl ketone. The carbinol produced, on treatment with hydrobromic acid, undergoes rearrangement:

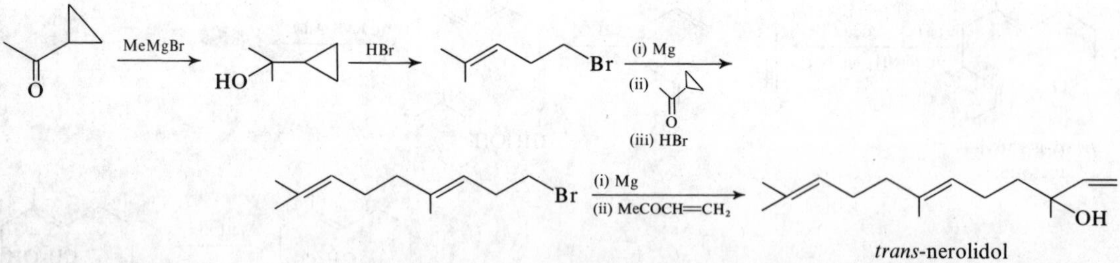

trans-nerolidol

This nerolidol is a major constituent of some naturally occurring oils, and under the influence of acid produces a mixture of *trans-trans*- and *cis-trans*-farnesol (by the allylic rearrangement).

§**26c. (−)-Ngaione.**   This occurs in the leaves of a New Zealand tree, and its enantiomer, (+)-**ipo-meamarone** (*cis*-form), has been isolated from black-rotted sweet potatoes. These compounds are referred to as **furano-sesquiterpenoids**, and examination of the carbon skeleton will show that ngaione is composed of three isoprene units joined head to tail.

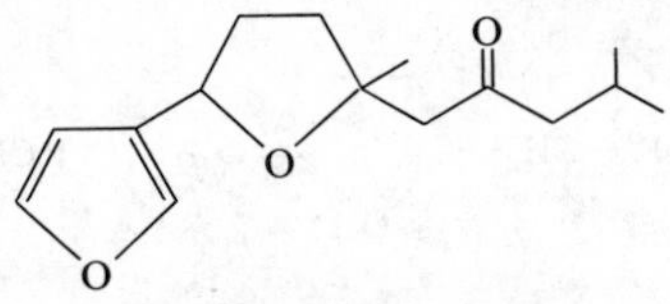

ngaione

Freelingyne, m.p. 164°C, is also a furano-sesquiterpenoid; it occurs in the wood-oil of *Eremophila freelingii*. A structure has been assigned by Massy-Westropp *et al.* (1966). Freelingyne is the first acetylenic terpenoid to be discovered, and it was isolated by chromatography on silica gel. Its

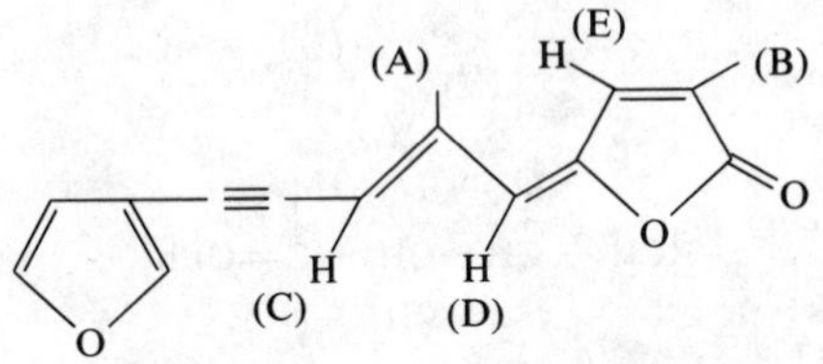

(I)

infrared spectrum (CHCl$_3$) showed the presence of a conjugated disubstituted acetylene (2 190 cm^{-1}) and an α,β-unsaturated lactone (1 755 cm^{-1}; see Table 1.6). Also present were bands typical of a furan (1 504, 1 164 and 874 cm^{-1}). Examination of the ultraviolet spectrum (EtOH) showed the presence of extended conjugation (λ_{max} 365 nm, ε 45 000). The structure (I) assigned was based mainly on the authors' interpretation of the NMR spectrum (60 MHz; CDCl$_3$). The elemental analysis and integration of the NMR spectrum were in agreement with the molecular formula C$_{15}$H$_{12}$O$_3$. The NMR spectrum showed the presence of two methyl groups attached to double bonds (τ 7·97 and 7·67), two olefinic protons (τ 4·38 and 4·41), one strongly deshielded olefinic proton (τ 2·98), and three furan-ring protons (τ 3·53, 2·62 and 2·35; see Table 1.9). These protons give a total of twelve, which is in agreement with the proposed molecular formula. A detailed analysis of the NMR spectrum (τ and J values) established the 3-position of the methyl group (B; τ 7·97, d) and identified proton (E; τ 2·94, q; long range coupling). The methyl group (A; τ 7·67, d) was coupled only to proton (C). The small value for J_{DE} (0·4 Hz) suggested the stereo-chemical arrangement shown (the alternative arrangement about the double bond would have been expected to give $J_{DE} \sim 0·7$ Hz). However, because of the small difference, the authors pointed out that the stereochemistry is not certain.

The position and substitution pattern of the lactone was confirmed by the following degradations.

$$C_{15}H_{12}O_3 \xrightarrow[\text{Pd—C}]{H_2} C_{15}H_{26}O_3 \xrightarrow[\text{(ii) H}^+]{\text{(i) 2PhMgBr}} C_{27}H_{38}O_3 \xrightarrow[\text{in PhH}]{I_2} C_{27}H_{36}O_2 \xrightarrow{\text{Li/NH}_3} C_{27}H_{38}O_2 \xrightarrow[\text{C}_5\text{H}_5\text{N}]{\text{CrO}_3} C_{27}H_{36}O_2$$

(I)   (II)   (III)   (IV)   (V)   (VI)

The infrared spectrum (film) of (II) showed the presence of a carbonyl band at 1 770 cm^{-1}; this is characteristic of a saturated γ-lactone (see Table 1.6). Hence, in (II), all the carbon-carbon multiple bonds in (I) have been hydrogenated (seven moles of hydrogen have been added). Thus (II) has the structure shown. (III) is therefore a diol (see Vol. I) and produces the tetrahydrofuran (IV) on mild oxidation. (IV) is a cyclic benzylic ether, and is split by lithium in ammonia to give the alcohol (V) which, on oxidation, gives the ketone (VI). The NMR spectrum of (VI) showed the presence of four protons adjacent to the carbonyl group (τ 7·95 and 7·77).

Acetylation of diol (III) with acetic anhydride gave the corresponding diacetate, C$_{31}$H$_{42}$O$_5$ which, on heating with *p*-toluenesulphonic acid in acetic acid solution, gave the unsaturated mono-acetate ((VII); C$_{29}$H$_{38}$O$_3$). The ultraviolet spectrum (EtOH) of (VII) had λ_{max} 242 nm (ε 27 000) which was consistent with loss of acetic acid from the benzylic end (conjugation with Ph). Also, the

$(CH_2)_3CHMe$— (structure R, tetrahydrofuran ring)

R

R—CH_2— (lactone ring with =O)

(II)

RCH_2—$\overset{OH}{\underset{|}{CH}}$—$CH_2$—$\overset{Me}{\underset{|}{CH}}$—$C(OH)Ph_2$

(III)

RCH_2— (tetrahydrofuran ring with Me, two Ph)

(IV)

RCH_2—$\overset{OH}{\underset{|}{CH}}$—$CH_2$—$\overset{Me}{\underset{|}{CH}}$—$CHPh_2$

(V)

RCH_2COCH_2—$\overset{Me}{\underset{|}{CH}}$—$CHPh_2$

(VI)

RCH_2—$\overset{OAc}{\underset{|}{CH}}$—$CH_2$—$\overset{Me}{\underset{|}{C}}$=$CPh_2$

(VII)

NMR spectrum of (VII) showed the presence of one methyl group attached to the double bond (τ 8·2).

§26d. Juvenile hormone (JH).   This hormone prevents the metamorphosis of immature insects by maintaining the juvenile (or larval) character of the growing insect. Juvenile hormone was isolated in pure form from the giant silk-worm moth *Hyalophora cecropia* by Röller *et al.* (1965), who used molecular distillation at 60–90°C (2 × 10^{-5} mm), TLC, and finally GSC. These workers, together with Trost (1967) then elucidated the structure of JH using 300 μg(!) of the compound.

Catalytic hydrogenation (20 μg) of JH (I) with Pd—C gave product (II). Mass spectrometry of (II) showed the presence of a molecular ion at M^+ 284, which corresponds to the molecular formula $C_{18}H_{36}O_2$. The most abundant ions in this mass spectrum were $M - 31$ and m/e 74 and 101. Loss of 31 mass units indicates the presence of an OMe group (31) in (II). The ion m/e 74 indicates the

(structures I, II, III depicted)

(I)

(II)

(III)

group CH_2=$C(OH)OMe$, which arises from the methyl ester of an aliphatic acid containing the group —CH_2CO_2Me and a γ-hydrogen atom (McLafferty rearrangement). Finally, the ion m/e 101 corresponds to the group —$CHMeCH_2CO_2Me$, *i.e.*, the chain contains a methyl group at C-3 (see **1** §13h; see also Table 1.11). Also present in the mass spectrum of (II) were the relatively highly abundant ions at m/e 143, 185, and 153 (185 − 32). These indicate the presence of an ethyl or dimethyl branch at C-7, *e.g.*, fission between C-7 and C-6 (a point of high branching in the chain) can give the ion m/e 143 ($C_8H_{15}O_2$) and between C-8 and C-7 the ion m/e 185 ($C_{11}H_{21}O_2$).

The mass spectrum of JH (I) contained the molecular ion M^+ 294, which corresponds to the formula $C_{18}H_{30}O_3$. Also present were the ions at $M - 18$, $M - 31$, and $M - 32$. These results led to the conclusion that JH had three double bonds and/or rings, and an oxygen atom that is easily eliminated.

When JH (30 μg) was catalytically hydrogenated with Pd—C poisoned with triethylamine, several products were obtained with molecular ions at M^+ 296 (dihydro-JH) and 298 (tetrahydro-JH). In both of these all the oxygen atoms had been retained.

When JH (15 μg) was subjected to oxidative degradation by osmium tetroxide followed by periodic acid, one product (identified by gas chromatography) was laevulaldehyde (III). Another product in the gas chromatogram corresponded to a homologue of laevulaldehyde.

The NMR spectrum of JH (I; 200 μg) contained the following signals (the assignments are also given): τ 9·04 (t, 6H), CH$_3$-7″ and CH$_3$-13; 8·84 (s, 3H), CH$_3$-11′; 8·78–8·30 (m, 4H), CH$_2$-9 and CH$_2$-12; 8·20–7·70 (b), CH$_2$-4, CH$_2$-5, CH$_2$-7′, and CH$_2$-8; 7·88 (d, J 0·8 Hz, 11H), CH$_2$ groups 4, 5, 7′, 8, and CH$_3$-3′; 7·54 (t, 1H), epoxide CH-10; 6·41 (s, 3H), CH$_3$-1; 5·04 (m, 1H), vinyl CH-6; 4·54 (bs, 1H), vinyl CH-2. Since the multiplicities are different, these vinyl protons are situated at different double bonds (see also **1** §12e).

On the basis of the foregoing data, JH was assigned structure (I), *i.e.*, methyl 10-epoxy-7-ethyl-3,11-dimethyltrideca-2,6-dienoate. Hence, JH may be regarded as an acyclic sesquiterpenoid-type of compound (*cf.* methyl farnesenate with additional methyl groups at C-7 (7″) and C-12 (13); see §26a). It was also deduced from the coupling constant $J_{3', 2}$ (0·8 Hz) and the τ-value of the protons at C-3′ that the double bond at 2,3 had the *trans*-configuration. It was also deduced that the other double bond at 6,7 also had the *trans*-configuration.

Structure (I) can exist in sixteen stereoisomeric forms, corresponding to ($\pm$)-pairs of eight geometrical isomers. The natural compound has been shown to be 2,3-*trans*, 6,7-*trans*, 10,11-*cis*. Also, the absolute configuration has been shown, by synthesis, to be (10R, 11S) [Faulkner *et al.*, 1971; Johnson *et al.*, 1971]. Nakanishi *et al.* (1971) have also deduced this configuration from an examination of the circular dichroism of the derived glycol of JH.

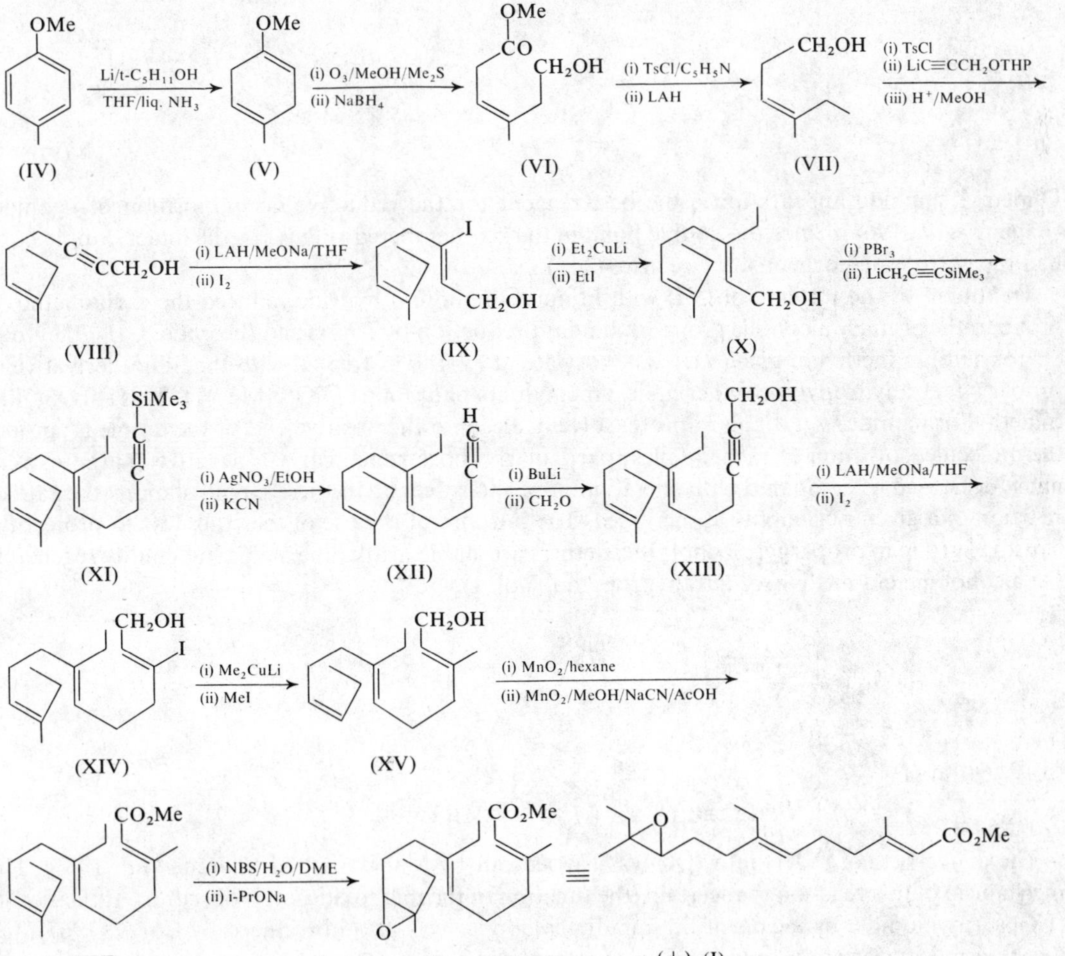

(IV)   (V)   (VI)   (VII)

(VIII)   (IX)   (X)

(XI)   (XII)   (XIII)

(XIV)   (XV)

(XVI)   ($\pm$)-(I)

Many stereospecific total syntheses of JH have been carried out; here, we shall describe that due to Corey *et al.* (1968). The basic problem is the stereospecific (or stereoselective) formation of tri-substituted double bonds. Corey's approach made use of double bonds in a cyclic system (*cis*-double bonds) and additions to acetylenic bonds. A number of new synthetic processes were also introduced. The product was (±)-JH, and most of the intermediate products were examined for identity by means of NMR, i.r., and mass spectroscopy, and for purity by means of chromatography.

p-Methoxytoluene (IV) was converted into the diene (V) by an improved Birch reduction (4 §5l). One possible mechanism for the conversion of (V) to (VI) is as follows. The presence of the methoxyl group activates the double bond towards electrophilic reagents (one resonating structure of ozone is $\overset{+}{O}—O—\bar{O}$; see Vol. I):

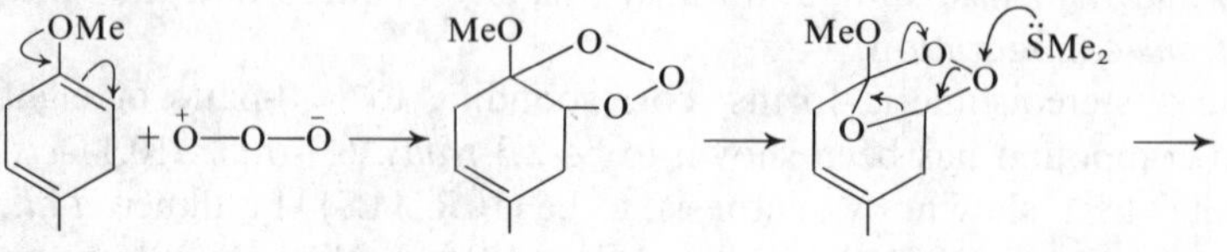

Dimethyl sulphide appears to be the best reagent for the reductive decomposition of ozonides (Pappas *et al.*, 1966). Since the double bond in the six-membered ring is *cis*, the intact double bond had the correct stereochemistry (see also 4 §13).

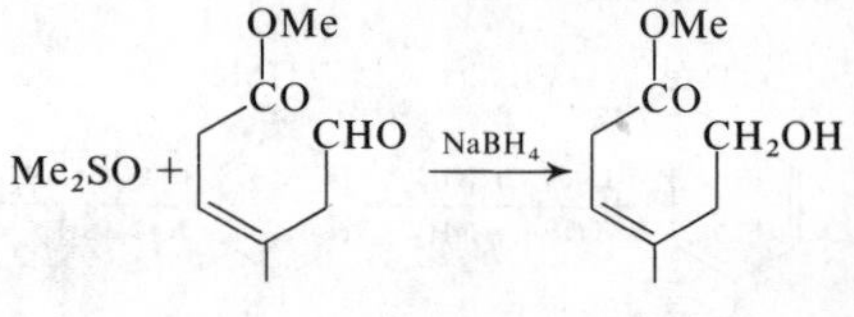

Treatment of the tosylate of (VI) with lithium aluminium hydride reduced the carbomethoxy-group to the primary alcoholic group (a standard reduction by LAH) and the initial CH_2OH group (as tosylate) to methyl to give (VII). The tosylate of (VII) was treated with the lithio derivative of propargyl tetrahydropyranol ether in hexamethylphosphoramide $[PO(NMe_2)_3]$. This solvent, like dimethylformamide, is a dipolar aprotic solvent. Because the positive end of the dipole is 'inside' the molecule, solvation of nucleophiles (particularly those which carry a negative charge) is very much decreased as compared with solvation in protic solvents. In these circumstances, the rate of reaction of a given nucleophile is increased. The purpose of the use of the ether was to protect the hydroxyl group in propargyl alcohol; these ethers are stable in alkaline media but readily regenerate the alcohol in acid media (see tetrahydropyran, Vol. I).

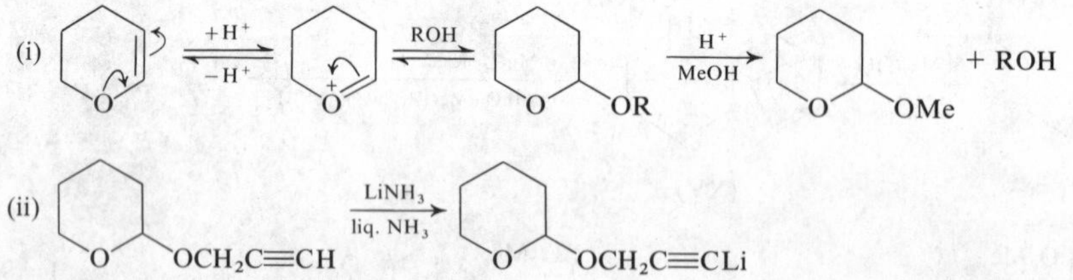

The conversion of (VIII) into (IX) was carried out by a new method (Corey *et al.*, 1967). The mechanism of this reaction is uncertain (the function of the methoxide ion is obscure). Alkylation of (IX), a vinyl iodide, by means of lithium diethylcopper was also introduced by Corey (1967); the mechanism is uncertain. Corey (1968) also introduced a new method for the preparation of 1,5-di-unsaturated systems. (X) was converted into the bromide which, on treatment with lithio-1-trimethylsilylprop-1-yne, gave (XI).

$$-CH_2Br \xrightarrow{LiCH_2C\equiv CSiMe_3} -CH_2CH_2C\equiv CSiMe_3 \xrightarrow{Ag^+} -CH_2CH_2C\equiv C-SiMe_3 \quad HOEt \longrightarrow$$
$$Ag^+$$

$$-CH_2CH_2C\equiv CAg + Me_3SiOH + H^+$$

Acetylenes form π-complexes with the silver ion and this results in an electron-withdrawing effect on the $C-SiMe_3$ bond and consequently the protecting silyl group is readily removed by the nucleophilic ethanol (see Vol. I). The resulting silver acetylide is decomposed by potassium cyanide to form the pure acetylene (see Vol. I). Lithiation of (XII) followed by treatment with paraformaldehyde gave (XIII). Conversion of (XIII) to (XV) was carried by reactions already described. Oxidation of (XV), an allylic alcohol, with oxidising agents to give the acid, would also have resulted in attack at the double bonds. Manganese dioxide oxidises allylic alcohols to α,β-unsaturated aldehydes (see Vol. I), and the subsequent method of conversion to the ester was introduced by Corey (1968).

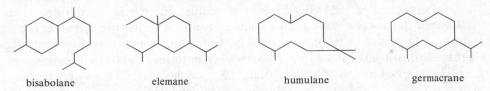

$$RCH{=}CHCH_2OH \xrightarrow{MnO_2} RCH{=}CHCHO \xrightarrow{HCN} RCH{=}CHCH(OH)CN \xrightarrow{MnO_2} RCH{=}CHC{-}CN \longrightarrow$$
$$MeOH$$

$$RCH{=}CHCO_2Me + HCN$$

Treatment of (XVI) with N-bromosuccinimide in aqueous dimethoxyethane resulted in the addition of HOBr to form the bromohydrin which then gave the epoxide with sodium propoxide. The reason for the selective 10,11-epoxidation (52 per cent) is not certain.

MONOCYCLIC SESQUITERPENOIDS

Four different types of skeletons of the monocyclic sesquiterpenoids are known.

      bisabolane   elemane   humulane   germacrane

Bisabolane group

§27. Bisabolene, $C_{15}H_{24}$, b.p. 133–134°C/12 mm.   This occurs in the oil of myrrh and other essential oils. The structure of bisabolene was determined by Ruzicka *et al.* (1925). Bisabolene adds on three molecules of hydrogen chloride to form bisabolene trihydrochloride, and this regenerates bisabolene when heated with sodium acetate in acetic acid solution. Thus bisabolene contains three double bonds and is therefore monocyclic (see §25). Nerolidol may be dehydrated to a mixture of α- and β-farnesenes (*cf.* §26). This mixture, on treatment with formic acid, forms a monocyclic sesquiterpenoid (or possibly a mixture) which combines with hydrogen chloride to form bisabolene trihydrochloride. Removal of these three molecules of hydrogen chloride (by means of sodium acetate in acetic acid) produces bisabolene; thus bisabolene could be (I), (II) or (III), since all three would give the *same* bisabolene trihydrochloride.

    Ruzicka *et al.* (1929) showed that synthetic and natural bisabolene consisted mainly of the γ-isomer (III), since on ozonolysis of bisabolene, the products were acetone, laevulic acid and a

nerolidol $-H_2O$ α-farnesene   +   β-farnesene   (i) HCO_2H (ii) HCl $-3HCl$

(I)
α-bisabolene

(II)
β-bisabolene

(III)
γ-bisabolene

small amount of succinic acid. These products are readily accounted for by (III); and this structure has been confirmed by synthesis (Ruzicka *et al.*, 1932). β-Bisabolene, however, has now been found to occur naturally (Herout *et al.*, 1961, 1962), and has been synthesised by Manjarrez *et al.* (1966) *via* the Wittig reaction (see Vol. I).

COCl + BrMg⟶ $Ph_3PMe^+Br^-$ n-BuLi ⟶

(±)-β-bisabolene

§27a. **Zingiberene,** $C_{15}H_{24}$, b.p. 134°C/14 mm.   This occurs in the (−)-form in ginger oil. It forms a dihydrochloride with hydrogen chloride, and thus apparently contains two double bonds. The molecular refraction, however, indicates the presence of three double bonds and, if this be the case, zingiberene is monocyclic (see §25). The presence of these three double bonds is conclusively shown by the fact that catalytic hydrogenation (platinum) converts zingiberene into hexahydrozingiberene, $C_{15}H_{30}$. Zingiberene can be reduced by means of sodium and ethanol to dihydrozingiberene, $C_{15}H_{26}$; this indicates that two of the double bonds are probably conjugated (Semmler *et al.*, 1913). Further evidence for this conjugation is afforded by the fact that zingiberene shows optical exaltation, whereas dihydrozingiberene does not. Also, zingiberene forms an adduct with maleic anhydride, and has λ_{max} 260 (ε 2 700) nm. The calculated value of λ_{max} on the basis of a homoannular conjugated diene system is 253 + $\cdots$, whereas the value for a heteroannular system is 214 + $\cdots$. The conjugated system is therefore almost certainly the former (see §3viii).

Ozonolysis of zingiberene gives acetone, laevulic acid and succinic acid (Ruzicka *et al.*, 1929). Since these products are also obtained from bisabolene (§27), it appears probable that zingiberene and bisabolene have the same carbon skeleton. Oxidation of dihydrozingiberene (I) with permanganate gives a keto-dicarboxylic acid, $C_{12}H_{20}O_5$ (II), which, on oxidation with sodium hypobromite, forms a tricarboxylic acid, $C_{11}H_{18}O_6$ (III). Thus (II) must contain a methyl ketone group (CH₃CO—), and so, if (I) be assumed as the structure of dihydrozingiberene, the foregoing oxidation reactions may be formulated:

(I)   (II)   (III)

The position of the conjugated system was shown as follows (Eschenmoser *et al.*, 1950). Zingiberene forms an adduct with methyl acetylenedicarboxylate, and this adduct (which was not isolated), on pyrolysis, gives 1,6-dimethylocta-3,6-diene and methyl 4-methylphthalate. These reactions can be explained on the assumption that zingiberene has the structure shown below.

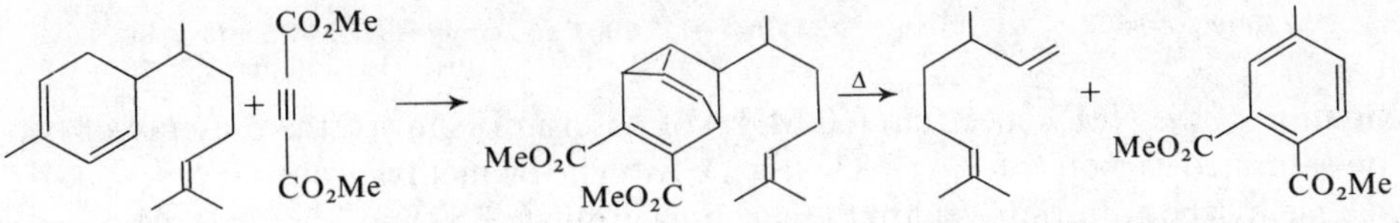

The structure of zingiberene has been confirmed by synthesis (Bhattacharya *et al.*, 1950).

Zingiberene contains two chiral centres. The acyclic chiral centre has been stereochemically related to that in ($+$)-citronellal, and the cyclic chiral centre to that in ($-$)-α-phellandrene (see §23e). Hence ($-$)-zingiberene has the absolute configuration (IV).

Other monocyclic sesquiterpenoids of the bisabolane group are **lanceol** (V) and **perezone** ((VI); this is the first sesquiterpenoid quinone discovered).

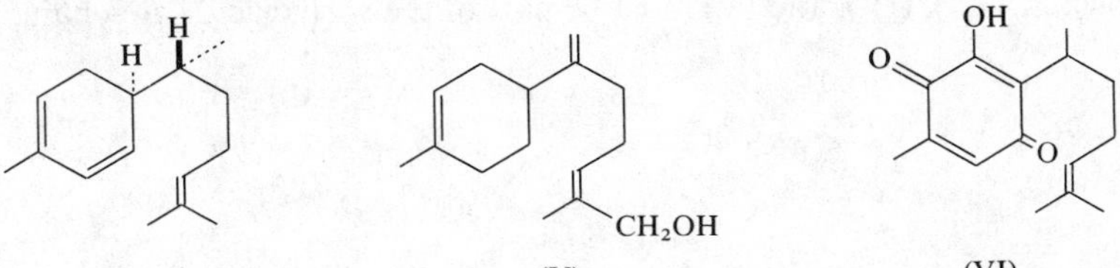

(IV)   (V)   (VI)

Elemane group

§27b. Elemol.   This is a tertiary alcohol that occurs in oil of elemi.

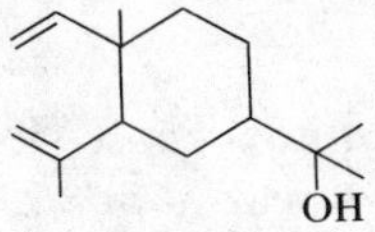

elemol

Abscisin II is a plant hormone which occurs in young cotton fruit and has been shown to be identical with **dormin**, the dormancy-inducing substance from sycamore leaves. A structure has been proposed for abscisin II by Ohkuma *et al.* (1965). Since these workers had only nine milligrams(!), their investigations were confined to elemental analysis and spectroscopic studies.

Elemental analysis, together with mass spectral data ($M^+ = 264$), led these workers to propose the molecular formula $C_{15}H_{20}O_4$. This corresponds to C, 68·16; H, 7·63 per cent. The actual values found were C, 68·76; H, 7·9 per cent (the differences are greater than those *usually* accepted).

The infrared spectrum (KBr pellet) of abscisin II showed the presence of an alcoholic hydroxyl group and a carboxyl group. The presence of the latter was confirmed by the fact that abscisin II was soluble in aqueous sodium carbonate. There were also bands present at 1 650, 1 674, 1 623, and 1 600 cm^{-1}. These were interpreted as being consistent with an α,β-unsaturated carbonyl system and also characteristic of sorbic acid. Also, a strong band at 978 cm^{-1} which was present is characteristic of a *trans*-disubstituted alkene.

On the basis of these assumptions, it was found that the addition of the ultraviolet absorption curves (MeOH) of isophorone (I) and *cis,trans*-3-methylsorbic acid (II) gave a composite spectrum having λ_{max} 244 nm (ε 24 800), which was in good agreement with the observed ultraviolet spectrum of abscisin II.

Abscisin II

(I)
236 nm (ε 2600)

(II)
255 nm (ε 17600)

composite: 244 nm (ε 24800)
observed: 246 nm (ε 25200)

Examination of the NMR spectrum (60 MHz) of abscisin II showed the presence of two methyl groups on saturated carbon (τ 8·9, s; 8·83, s; $\equiv$I), two vinylic methyl groups (τ 8·9, s; $\equiv$II; 7·90, s; $\equiv$I), and a methylene group adjacent to the carbonyl group (τ 7·59 and 7·53; $\equiv$I). Also present were four vinyl protons (τ 4·21, s; $\equiv$II; 4·02, s; $\equiv$I; 3·83, d; $\equiv$II; 2·39, d; $\equiv$II). Furthermore, the τ values of the two singlet vinyl protons are consistent with a position α or γ (but not β or δ) with respect to a carbonyl group, and the J value of the doublets (each 16 Hz) is typical for *trans*-olefinic protons (see Table 1.9). The equivalence of corresponding groups in abscisin II and (I) and (II) were obtained from the NMR spectra of all three.

The authors then proposed, on the basis of these data, that the following fragments must be present in abscisin II. (III), (IV), and (V) must be part of the sorbic acid side-chain, but (IX) or (X)

(III)   (IV)   (V)   (VI)   (VII)

(VIII)   (IX)   (X)   (IXa)

are possible from the NMR data. The authors chose (IX) in preference to (X) because the mass spectrum of abscissin (II) showed a strong peak at m/e 208 ($M - 56$). This is readily explained by the loss of isobutene (C_4H_8 = mass 56) from (IX), but not from (X) (see (IXa)). Fragments (III)–(V) can be added to (IX) in two different ways to give (XI) and (XII), both of which satisfy the NMR splitting pattern observed for abscisin II. Since (XI) can be divided into three isoprene units joined

(XI)
abscisin II

(XII)

head to tail whereas (XII) cannot, the authors chose (XI) as the more likely structure of abscisin II (see the isoprene rule, §1).

Finally, the *cis-trans* configuration of the sorbic acid side-chain was decided from a comparison of the NMR spectra of abscisin II with those of *cis,trans*- and *trans,trans*-sorbic acid.

Humulane and germacrane groups

§27c.   These groups are characterised by the presence of medium rings (8–11) and their tendency to undergo transannular reactions (see **4** §14). These groups of compounds are also referred to as the **macrocyclic sesquiterpenoids**.

Humulene, $C_{15}H_{24}$, b.p. 264°C, occurs in oil of hops and is now known to be identical with α-caryophyllene (the name given in the earlier literature to a constituent of oil of cloves; see also §28e). On catalytic hydrogenation, humulene gave humulane (hexahydrohumulene), $C_{15}H_{30}$; it therefore contains three olefinic double bonds and is monocyclic. On ozonolysis, purified humulene gave only laevulic acid and 2,2-dimethylsuccinic acid. Partial hydrogenation of humulene produced tetrahydrohumulene which, on ozonolysis, gave the dicarboxylic acid $C_{15}H_{28}O_4$. Also, the ozonolysis of dihydrohumulene produced 2,2-dimethylsuccinic acid and 3,3-dimethyl-adipic acid and a C_{15} keto-acid. The ultraviolet spectrum of humulene showed the absence of conjugation of the double bonds, and the infrared spectrum showed the presence of the RCH=CHR group (band at 975 cm^{-1}). Structure (I) for humulene satisfies all the facts. The nature of the skeleton has been confirmed by the synthesis of 1,1,4,8-tetramethylcyclo-undecane, which was shown to be identical with humulane (by comparison of the infrared spectra). Dev (1960), from his NMR studies, proposed that the double bonds had the all-*trans*-configuration and this, as well as the complete structure, has been shown by X-ray analysis of the silver nitrate adduct (Sim *et al.*, 1966).

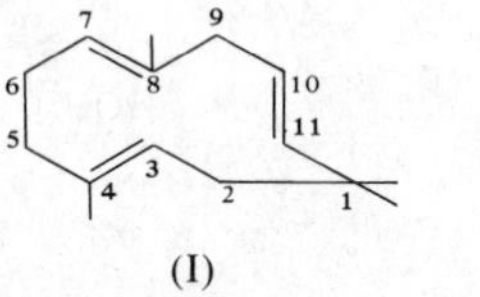

(I)

Germacrone (II) is a ten-membered ring compound and contains the basic skeleton in the **germacranolides**. These include a large number of lactones (and other compounds), of which pyrethrosin is the most well known.

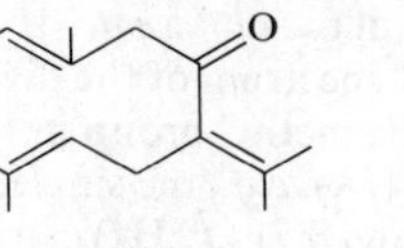

(II)

Pyrethrosin, $C_{17}H_{22}O_5$, m.p. 198–200°C, is the bitter constituent of African pyrethrum flowers. It contains two double bonds and a lactone ring (see also santonin, §28c). The infrared spectrum showed the absence of a hydroxyl group, and this was confirmed by the failure to incorporate deuterium when dissolved in deuterium oxide. This led to the suggestion that an ether oxygen was present. This left four oxygen atoms to be accounted for; two were assigned to the lactone and the remaining two to an acetoxy-group. The ultraviolet spectrum showed the presence of one double bond conjugated with the keto-group of the lactone, and ozonolysis produced formaldehyde as one of the products (Barton *et al.*, 1957). These workers proposed several structures but later (1960), based largely on the rearrangement of pyrethrosin to cyclopyrethrosin acetate (IV) when treated

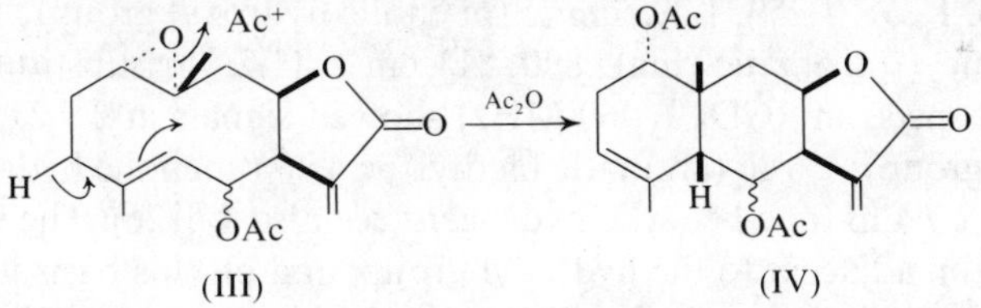

(III)   (IV)

with acetic anhydride and toluene-*p*-sulphonic acid, proposed (III) as the structure of pyrethrosin. The structure of (IV), the key compound, was elucidated by degradative work. Some stereochemical details in (III) and (IV) are not certain.

Aristolactone, which occurs in *Aristolachia reticulata*, was originally given structure (V) (Steele *et al.*, 1959). This was later revised to (VI) on the basis of NMR studies (Martin-Smith *et al.*, 1963). Because of certain

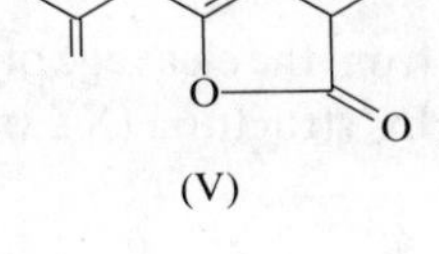

(V) 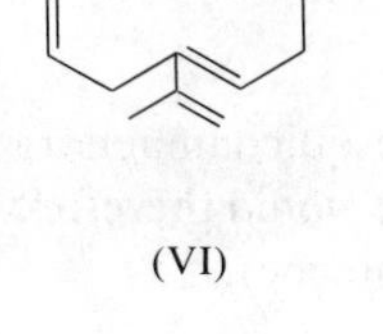   (VI) 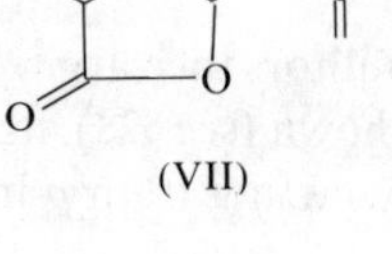   (VII)

unsatisfactory features of this structure, Martin-Smith *et al.* (1964) reinvestigated the structure of aristolactone and now proposed (VII). These workers showed that aristolactone is an α,β-unsaturated lactone, in accordance with the τ3·27 absorption in the NMR spectrum (this was incorrectly assigned in the earlier work). This structure (VII) has been assigned despite the apparent anomalies in the ultraviolet and infrared spectra of the parent compound and its derivatives. The work that led to the proposal of this structure was based on the examination of the products of ozonolysis, hydrogenation, behaviour with various reagents, and spectral studies. Biogenetic considerations have also been invoked to justify structure (VII).

Arctiopicrin was originally given structure (VIII) (Suchý *et al.*, 1957, 1959). However, Suchý *et al.* (1964) reinvestigated the structure of this compound because some chemical aspects were unsatisfactory and also

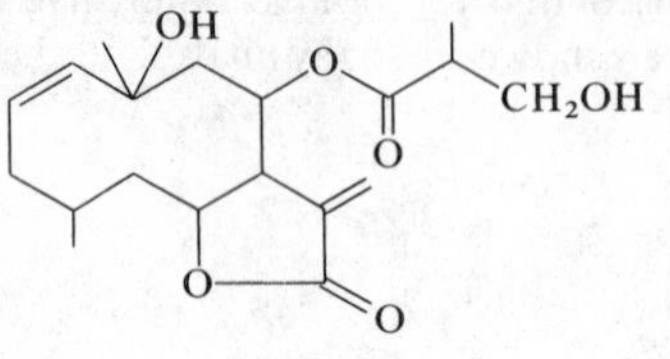

(VIII) 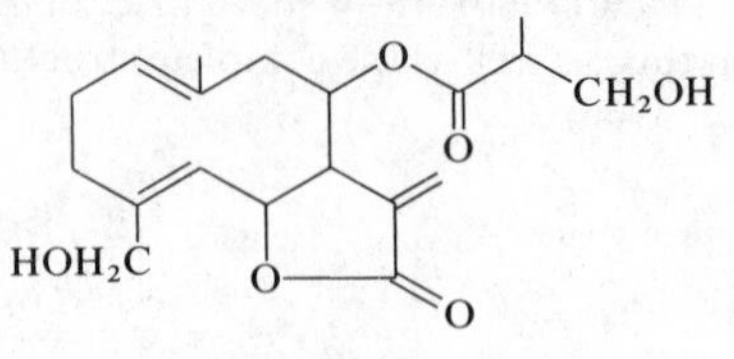   (IX)

because of some biogenetic considerations. This has led to the proposal of structure (IX). Examination of the NMR spectrum (CDCl₃, 60 MHz) of arctiopicrin definitely showed that (VIII) was incorrect. According to these workers, the spectrum showed the presence of two *different* CH₂OH groups, and this was confirmed by the shift of the signals to lower field when the NMR spectrum of the diacetate of hexahydroarctiopicrin was examined. A sharp doublet (τ 8·82) was assigned to the methyl group in the β-hydroxyisobutyryl side-chain.

Further NMR data were consistent with (IX), *e.g.*, the singlet signal τ 8·52 can be assigned to a methyl group in =CMe—, and a pair of doublets, τ 4·11 and 3·71 (*J* 2Hz) can be assigned to the exocyclic methylene protons.

Chemical evidence also supported structure (IX), *e.g.*, ozonolysis (O₃; H₂O₂) of arctiopicrin gave succinic acid, together with a trace of laevulic acid.

Sesquichamaenol is a phenolic sesquiterpenoid which has been isolated from the Benihi tree by Takase *et al.* (1970), who elucidated its structure by spectroscopic methods and a total synthesis.

The molecular formula of sesquichamaenol (X) was shown to be $C_{15}H_{22}O_2$ (M^+ 234). Its ultraviolet spectrum had λ_{max} (MeOH) 283 nm (ε 2 818) and λ_{max} (MeOH—NaOH) 290 nm (ε 2 512), indicating the presence of a phenolic chromophore (see Table 1.5). The infrared spectrum (KBr disc) showed bands at 3 430, 1 265, 1 259, 1 205 cm⁻¹ (phenolic hydroxyl group); 1 695 cm⁻¹ (carbonyl group); 1 613, 1 513 cm⁻¹ (aromatic ring); 890, 811 cm⁻¹ (1,2,4-trisubstituted benzene; see also Table 1.6). The NMR spectrum (CDCl₃; 60 MHz) showed signals at τ 9·27, d; 9·00, d (isopropyl group); τ 7·97 (acetyl group); τ 6·76 (aromatic methyl); τ 4·70 (phenolic hydroxyl); τ 3·5–3·0 (three aromatic hydrogens); τ 7·4 m (one benzylic hydrogen; see also **1** §12e). The signal at τ 3·36, d was assigned to a ring proton adjacent to the hydroxyl group, and on this basis it was inferred that the hydroxyl group must be *ortho* to a substituent group (the benzene ring is 1,2,4-trisubstituted; see

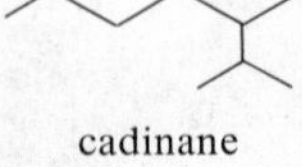

cadinane 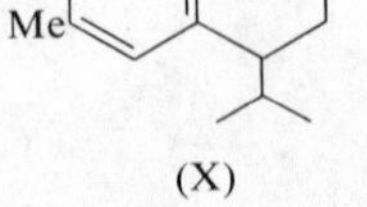   (X)

above). The authors then argued that if sesquichamaenol originates from the cleavage of the cadinane structure as shown (see §28), its structure would therefore be (X). This structure, (X), was confirmed by synthesis (starting from *p*-methoxytoluene).

(X)

BICYCLIC SESQUITERPENOIDS

The cadinane group

§28. α-Cadinene, $C_{15}H_{24}$, **b.p. 134–136°C/11 mm.** This occurs in the $(-)$-form in oil of cubebs, etc. Catalytic hydrogenation converts cadinene into tetrahydrocadinene, $C_{15}H_{28}$. Thus cadinene contains two double bonds and is bicyclic. On dehydrogenation with sulphur, cadinene forms cadalene, $C_{15}H_{18}$ (Ruzicka *et al.*, 1921). Cadalene does not add on bromine, and forms a picrate. This led to the belief that cadalene was an aromatic compound, and its structure was deduced as follows. Ruzicka assumed that the relationship of farnesol (§26a) to cadinene was analogous to that of geraniol (§7) to dipentene (§13). Furthermore, since dipentene gives *p*-cymene when dehydrogenated with sulphur, then cadalene should be, if the analogy is correct, 1,6-dimethyl-4-isopropylnaphthalene; thus:

geraniol   dipentene   *p*-cymene

farnesol   cadinene skeleton   cadalene

1,6-Dimethyl-4-isopropylnaphthalene was synthesised by Ruzicka *et al.* (1922), and was found to be identical with cadalene.

Thus cadinene has the carbon skeleton assumed. The only remaining problem is to ascertain the positions of the two double bonds in cadinene. Since the molecular refraction shows no optical exaltation, the two double bonds are not conjugated (**1** §8); this is supported by the fact that cadinene is not reduced by sodium and amyl alcohol, and also does not show strong absorption in the ultra-violet region. Ozonolysis of cadinene produces a compound containing the *same* number of carbon atoms as cadinene. The two double bonds are therefore in ring systems, but they cannot be in the *same* ring, since in this case carbon would have been lost on ozonolysis. Ruzicka *et al.* (1924) were thus led to suggest (I) (*α or β*) for the structure of cadinene, basing it on the relationship of cadinene to copaene, which had been given structure (II) by Semmler (1914). (I) was proposed mainly on the fact that copaene adds two molecules of hydrogen chloride to form copaene dihydrochloride, which is *identical* with cadinene dihydrochloride (both the *α* and *β* structures of (I) would give the *same* dihydrochloride as (II)). Structure (I) (*α* or *β*) was accepted for cadinene until 1942, when Campbell

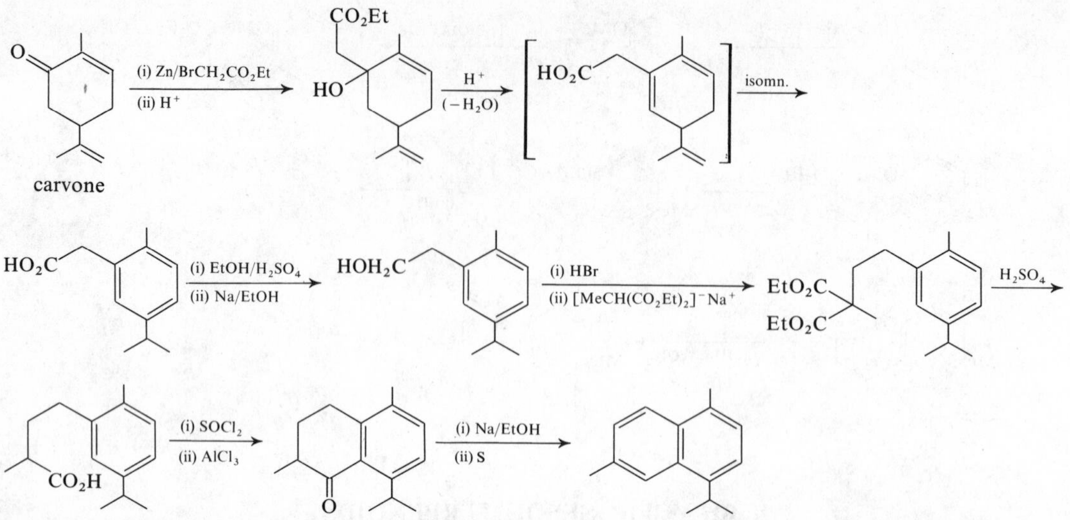

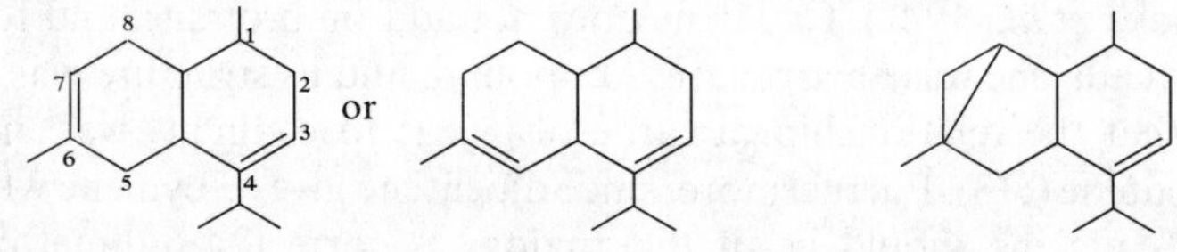

and Soffer reinvestigated the problem. These authors converted cadinene into its monoxide and dioxide by means of perbenzoic acid, treated these oxides with excess of methylmagnesium chloride, and then dehydrogenated the product with selenium. By this means, Campbell and Soffer obtained a monomethylcadalene from cadinene monoxide, and a dimethylcadalene from cadinene dioxide. Now the introduction of a methyl group *via* the oxide takes place according to the following scheme:

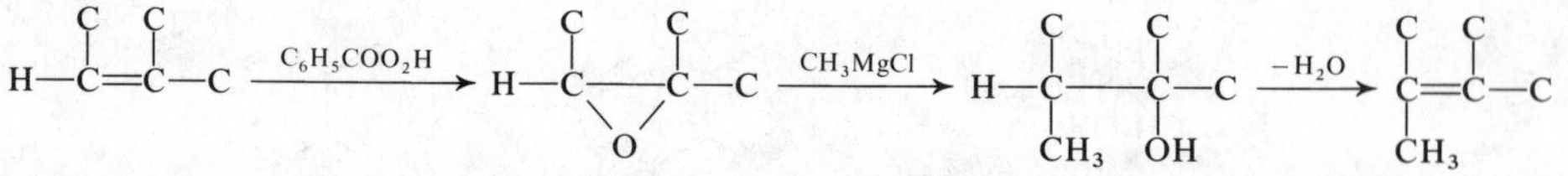

Thus the positions of the additional methyl groups show the positions of the double bonds in cadinene. The Ruzicka formula for cadinene would give dimethylcadalene (III) (from the *α* isomer) or (IV) (from the *β*), and the monomethylcadalenes would be (V) (from *α* or *β*), (VI) (from *α*) and (VII) (from *β*). Campbell and Soffer oxidised their dimethylcadalene, first with chromic acid and then with nitric acid, and thereby obtained pyromellitic acid (benzene-1,2,4,5-tetracarboxylic acid), (VIII). The formation of (VIII) therefore rules out (III) as the structure of dimethylcadalene, but (IV), with the two methyl groups at positions 6 and 7 in ring B, could give (VIII). Therefore the double bond in cadinene in ring B is 6,7. From this it follows that (VI) is also eliminated. If the double bond in ring A is as in structure (I), then dimethylcadalene is (IV) and monomethylcadalene is (V) or (VII). Campbell and Soffer synthesised (IV) and (VII), and found that each was different from the methylcadalenes they had obtained from cadinene. Thus (IV) and (VII) are incorrect; consequently

(III)   (IV)   (V)

(VI)   (VII)   (VIII)

the double bond in ring A cannot be 3,4. The only other dimethylcadalene which could give (VIII) on oxidation is (IX). This was synthesised, and was found to be identical with the dimethylcadalene from cadinene. Cadinene must therefore be (X), and the introduction of one or two methyl groups may thus be formulated as follows:

(IX)   (X)   (XI)

(X) could give two monoxides (oxidation of ring A or B), and one of these (ring B oxidised) would give (VII). This, as pointed out above, was different from the monomethylcadalene actually obtained. Therefore, if (X) is the structure of cadinene, the monomethylcadalene obtained from cadinene must be (XI). (XI) was synthesised, and was found to be identical with the compound obtained from cadinene. Thus (X) is the structure of α-cadinene.

The absolute configurations of the cadinenes (and cadinols) have now been established (Motl *et al.*, 1958; Soffer *et al.*, 1958). X-ray analysis of (−)-cadinene dihydrobromide showed that the two rings have the *trans*-decalin structure and that the isopropyl group is *cis* with respect to the hydrogen atom at the nearer ring junction. Also, ozonolysis of (−)-cadinene, followed by oxidation with nitric acid in the presence of vanadium pentoxide, gave D(+)-isopropylsuccinic acid (XII). Thus the absolute configuration of the ring carbon atom attached to the isopropyl group is established (*cf.* §23e).

(X)   (XII)

Because of the new structure assigned to cadinene, it has therefore been necessary to revise the structure of copaene. Briggs and Taylor (1947) proposed (XIII), but this has been criticised by Birch (1951). Mayo (1958) proposed alternative structures, but later (1963, 1965) came to the conclusion, from chemical evidence and NMR spectroscopic studies, that (XIV) fitted the facts best. Dev *et al.*

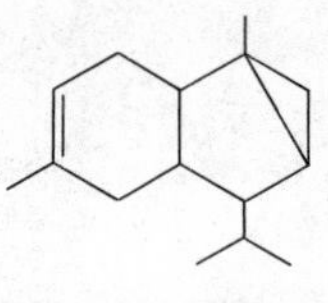

(XIII) 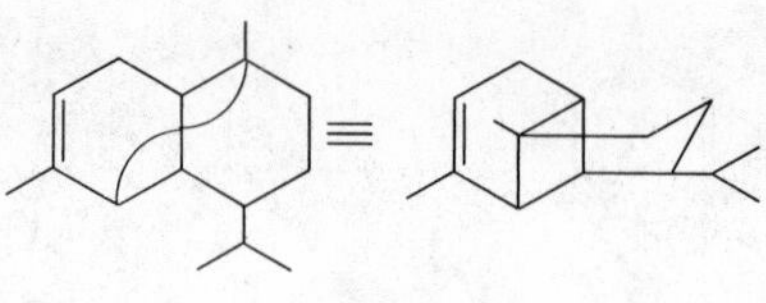   (XIV)

(1965) also proposed (XIV) on the basis of chemical work and infrared and NMR spectroscopic studies.

The two tertiary alcohols, **α-cadinol** and **δ-cadinol** occur together in various essential oils.

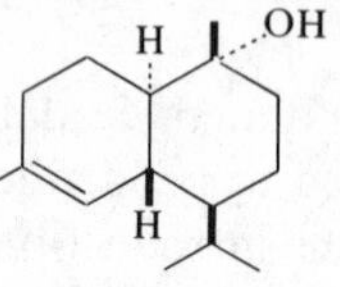

a-cadinol 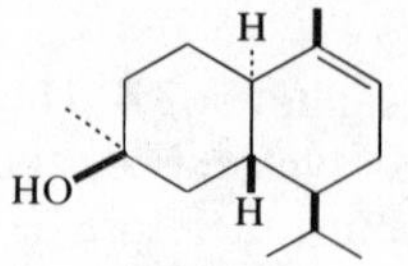   δ-cadinol

The eudesmane group

§28a. Selinenes, $C_{15}H_{24}$. Selinene occurs in celery oil; when treated with hydrogen chloride, it forms a dihydrochloride which, when warmed with aniline, is converted into the compound $C_{15}H_{24}$. This is isomeric with selinene, and the natural compound was called β-selinene and the synthetic isomer α-selinene (Semmler et al., 1912). Semmler showed that the catalytic hydrogenation of the two selinenes gives the same tetrahydro-selinene, $C_{15}H_{28}$. Thus they each contain two double bonds, and are bicyclic. Ozonolysis of β-selinene produces a diketone (I) with the loss of two carbon atoms, and oxidation of (I) with sodium hypobromite gives a tricarboxylic acid (II), with the loss of one carbon atom. From this it follows that (I) contains a CH_3CO— group. Ozonolysis of α-selinene gives a diketo-monocarboxylic acid (III) with loss of one carbon atom, and (III), on oxidation with sodium hypobromite, loses two carbon atoms to form (II). Thus (III) contains *two* CH_3CO— groups (Semmler et al., 1912). Ruzicka et al. (1922) distilled β-selinene with sulphur, and thereby obtained eudalene (see §28b for the evidence for the structure of this compound). If we use the isoprene rule, all the foregoing facts are explained by giving the selinenes the following structures (Ruzicka et al., 1922). The relationship of the selinenes to eudesmol (§28b) confirms the nature of the carbon skeleton given to the selinenes.

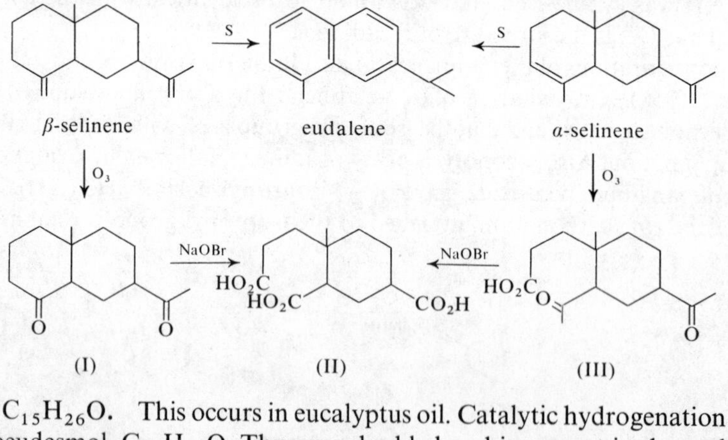

β-selinene   eudalene a-selinene

(I)   (II)   (III)

§28b. Eudesmol, $C_{15}H_{26}O$. This occurs in eucalyptus oil. Catalytic hydrogenation converts eudesmol into dihydroeudesmol, $C_{15}H_{28}O$. Thus one double bond is present in the molecule, and since eudesmol behaves as a tertiary alcohol, the parent hydrocarbon is $C_{15}H_{28} \equiv C_nH_{2n-2}$; eudesmol is therefore bicyclic. When dehydrogenated with sulphur, eudesmol forms eudalene, $C_{14}H_{16}$, and methanethiol (Ruzicka et al., 1922). Eudalene behaved as an aromatic compound (cf. cadalene, §28), and its structure was deduced as follows. Since eudalene was a naphthalene derivative, and since it contained one carbon atom less than cadalene, it was thought to be an apocadalene, *i.e.*, cadalene minus one methyl group. Thus eudalene is either 1-methyl-4-isopropylnaphthalene (II*a*) or 7-methyl-1-isopropylnaphthalene (I*a*). To test this hypothesis, Ruzicka oxidised cadalene with chromic acid, and thereby obtained a naphthoic acid, $C_{15}H_{16}O_2$, which must be (I) or (II).

Distillation of this acid with soda-lime gives a methylisopropylnaphthalene which must be (I*a*) or (II*a*). (II*a*) was synthesised from carvone (the synthesis is the same as for cadalene except that ethyl malonate is used instead of ethyl methylmalonate; see §28). The synthetic compound (II*a*) was found to be different from the hydrocarbon obtained by the distillation of the naphthoic acid from cadalene. Thus the apocadalene obtained must be (I*a*), *i.e.*, 7-methyl-1-isopropylnaphthalene.

Ruzicka then found that eudalene was not identical with either (I*a*) or (II*a*). On oxidation, however, eudalene gives the same naphthalenedicarboxylic acid as that which is obtained by the oxidation of (I*a*). This is only possible if in eudalene the two side-chains in (I*a*) are interchanged, *i.e.*, eudalene is 1-methyl-7-isopropylnaphthalene; thus:

This structure for eudalene was proved by synthesis (Ruzicka *et al.*, 1922).

To develop the sesquiterpenoid carbon skeleton from that of eudalene, it is necessary to introduce one carbon atom in such a position that it is eliminated as methanethiol during the sulphur dehydrogenation (see above). If we use the *isoprene rule* with the units joined head to tail, then there is only one possible structure that fits the requirements, *viz.*, (III) (*cf.* §1).

(III)

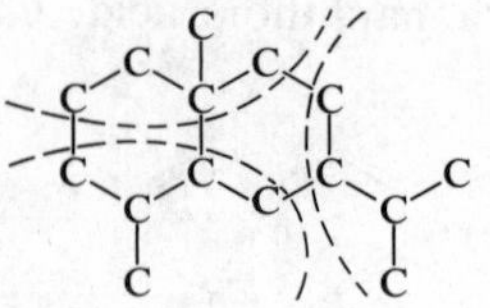

Now β-selinene combines with hydrogen chloride to form selinene dihydrochloride, which is also obtained by the action of hydrogen chloride on eudesmol (Ruzicka *et al.*, 1927, 1931). Since eudesmol contains one double bond and a tertiary alcohol group, it follows that the double bond must be in the side-chain, and the hydroxyl group in the ring, or *vice versa*, *i.e.*, (IV), (V) or (VI) is the structure of eudesmol.

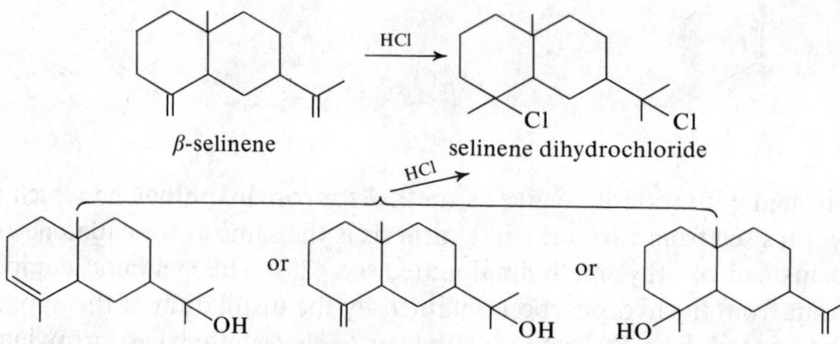

β-selinene selinene dihydrochloride

(IV) or (V) or (VI)

Hydrogenation of eudesmol forms dihydroeudesmol (VII) and this, on treatment with hydrogen chloride followed by boiling with aniline (to remove a molecule of hydrogen chloride), gives dihydroeudesmene (VIII) and (VIIIa). (VIII), on ozonolysis, forms 3-acetyl-5,9-dimethyldecalin (IX) and (VIIIa) forms 5,9-dimethyldecal-3-one (IXa). These results are explained if (IV) or (V) is the structure of eudesmol, but not by (VI). Thus the hydroxyl group is in the isopropyl side-chain.

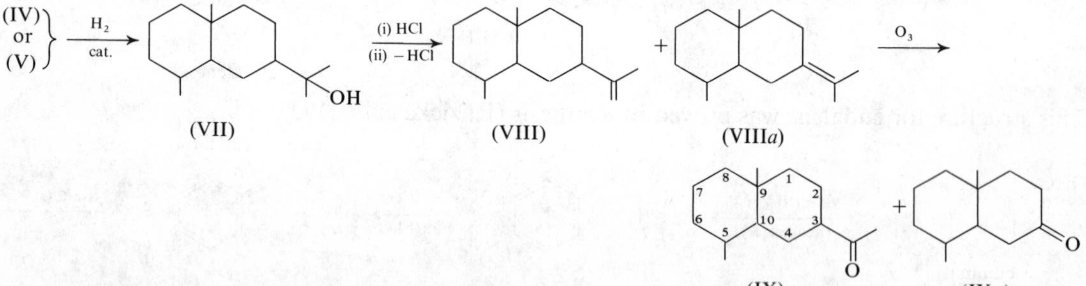

(VII) (VIII) (VIIIa)

(IX) (IXa)

The final problem was to ascertain the position of the double bond in eudesmol, *i.e.*, Is the structure (IV) or (V)? Ozonolysis of eudesmol showed that eudesmol is a mixture of (IV) (α-eudesmol) and (V) (β-eudesmol), since *two* products are obtained: a hydroxyketo-acid (X), with no loss of carbon, and a hydroxyketone (XI), with the loss of one carbon atom (but *cf.* §5). The two isomers are also clearly distinguished from each other by their infrared absorption spectra. The β-isomer shows a strong band at 889 cm^{-1}; this is characteristic of the alkene $R_2C=CH_2$ (895–885 cm^{-1}). The α-isomer does not show this band.

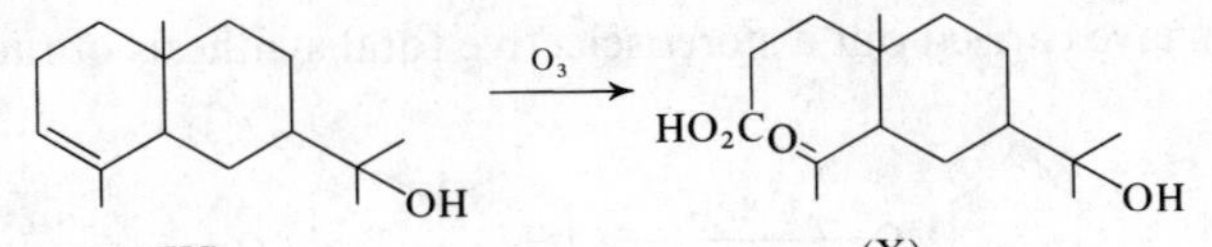

(IV)
α-eudesmol

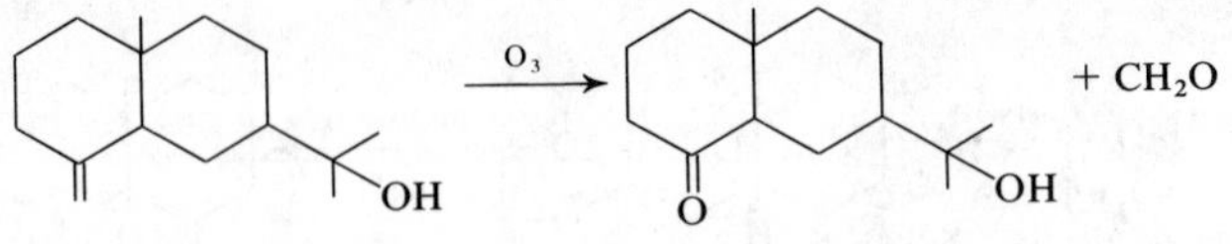

(X)

(V)
β-eudesmol

(XI)

+ CH₂O

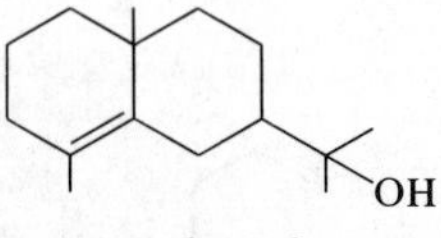

γ-eudesmol

The proportions of these two isomers vary with the source, and McQuillin *et al.* (1956) have succeeded in separating them (*via* their 3,5-dinitrobenzoates), and at the same time have characterised a third, synthetic γ-isomer.

As described above, the position of the angular methyl group was determined on the basis of the isoprene rule. Since there are exceptions to this rule, it is therefore desirable to confirm its position by other means. This has been done chemically as follows. Ketone (IX*a*) was converted into its dibenzylidene derivative (XII) and this, on ozonlysis, gave the dicarboxylic acid (XIII). However, there is always the possibility that the dicarboxylic acid produced had structure (XIV). This was therefore also prepared as shown in the Chart.

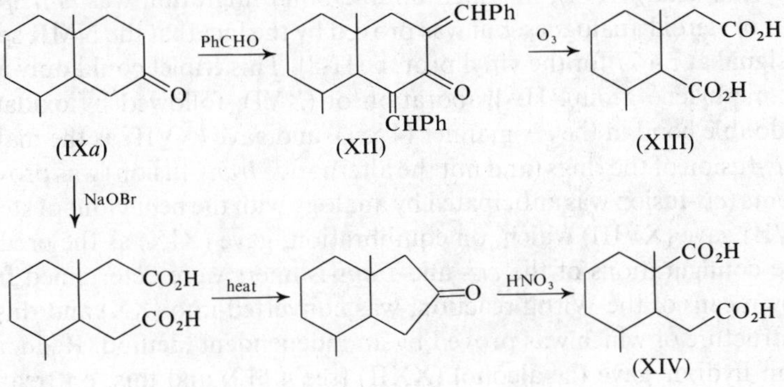

(IX*a*)

(XII)

(XIII)

(XIV)

Since only the dicarboxylic acid prepared from the dibenzylidene derivative could be epimerised by boiling in concentrated acid, this indicates that one carboxyl group must be joined to an asymmetric carbon atom attached to a hydrogen atom. Hence this dicarboxylic acid is (XIII) and so confirms the position of the angular methyl group.

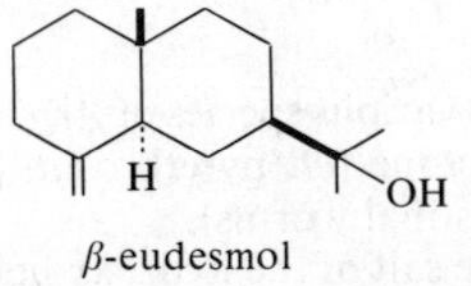

β-eudesmol

Stereochemical considerations have shown that β-eudesmol has the *trans*-decalin configuration and that the angular methyl group and the isopropyl group are on the same side (see also the synthesis described below).

Marshall *et al.* (1965) have carried out a stereoselective total synthesis of racemic β-eudesmol as follows.

The conversion of (XV) into (XVI), by the use of *prescribed conditions*, resulted in the formation of the dioxolan (ethylene ketal) (XVI), in which double-bond migration was *anticipated* by analogy with the behaviour of steroid analogues, but was proved by the fact that the NMR spectrum of (XVI) showed a triplet signal at τ 4·77 for the vinyl proton (H-8). This triplet could only arise by coupling with an adjacent methylene group. Hydroboration of (XVI), followed by oxidation, resulted in hydration of the double bond in the *cis*-manner (**4** §51), and gave (XVII) as the major product. The addition to give *cis*-fusion of the rings (and not the alternative *trans*-fusion) was proved by a separate series of experiments (*cis*-fusion was anticipated by analogy with the behaviour of steroid analogues). Oxidation of (XVII) gave (XVIII) which, on equilibration, gave (XIX) as the predominant isomer (65 per cent). The configurations of the *cis*- and *trans*-isomers were determined from their NMR spectra. (XIX), by means of the Wittig reaction, was converted into (XX) and this, on hydrolysis, gave (XXI), the structure of which was proved by an independent method. Reduction of (XXI) by lithium aluminium hydride gave the alcohol (XXII) (see **4** §12) and this, on treatment with tosyl chloride, gave the tosyl ester (no inversion) and this with potassium cyanide, gave the inverted cyanide (XXIII) (see **3** §3). Hydrolysis of this cyanide now gave the corresponding acid *with inversion* (at the carbon atom attached to the carboxyl group). The stereochemistry of this acid was proved by an independent method. Finally, this acid was converted into ($\pm$)-β-eudesmol as shown. The identity of the natural and the synthetic racemic compound was established by means of their infrared spectra, etc.

§28c. Santonin, $C_{15}H_{18}O_3$.   This occurs in various species of *Artemesia* (found in Asia). It possesses the eudesmane skeleton but is a sesquiterpenoid lactone (*cf.* pyrethrosin, §27c). It is widely used in medicine as an anthelmintic (it has the power to expel intestinal worms).

Santonin (I) dissolves in alkali to form the salt of the hydroxy-acid, **santoninic acid** (II). Hence santonin is a lactone and its infrared spectrum showed it to be a γ-lactone. Santonin contains two double bonds (shown by catalytic hydrogenation) and behaves like an α,β-unsaturated ketone, the presence of this grouping being confirmed by its ultraviolet absorption spectrum (λ_{max} 236 nm, ε 11 200). When distilled with zinc dust, santonin gives 1,4-dimethylnaphthalene, propene and a small amount of 1,4-dimethyl-2-naphthol. These products suggest the presence of the naphthalene skeleton. Reduction of santonin oxime produces the amine, **santon-amine** (III) which, with nitrous acid, gives **hyposantonin** (IV). These reactions may be formulated as shown if we accept the structure of santonin as (I).

Inspection of the structure of hyposantonin (IV) shows that deamination is accompanied with rearrangement. It was because santonin undergoes facile rearrangements that its structure proved such a difficult problem. Hence it is not surprising that many incorrect structures were proposed for santonin (*cf.* camphor, §23a).

The structure of hyposantonin was elucidated as follows. Oxidation with permanganate gives 3,6-dimethyl-phthalic acid (V), and when heated with ethanolic hydrochloric acid, hyposantonin gives a mixture of two isomeric acids, **dihydrosantinic acid** (VI), which, on heating with barium hydroxide, give the hydrocarbon (VII). Hyposantonin (or VI) on oxidation with iodine in acetic acid gives **santinic acid** (VIII) which, on heating with barium hydroxide, also gives (VII).

Other reactions carried on santonin (I) were the reduction (HI/P) to **santonous acid** (IX), catalytic reduction to tetrahydrosantonin (X) and to hexahydrosantonin (XI). (X), by means of the Clemmensen reduction, gave **deoxytetrahydrosantonin** (XII) and this, on distillation with selenium, gave 7-ethyl-1-methylnaphthalene (XIII), which was also obtained from (XI) by similar treatment. Also, on treatment with cold fuming hydrochloric acid, santonin underwent rearrangement to give **desmotroposantonin** (XIV).

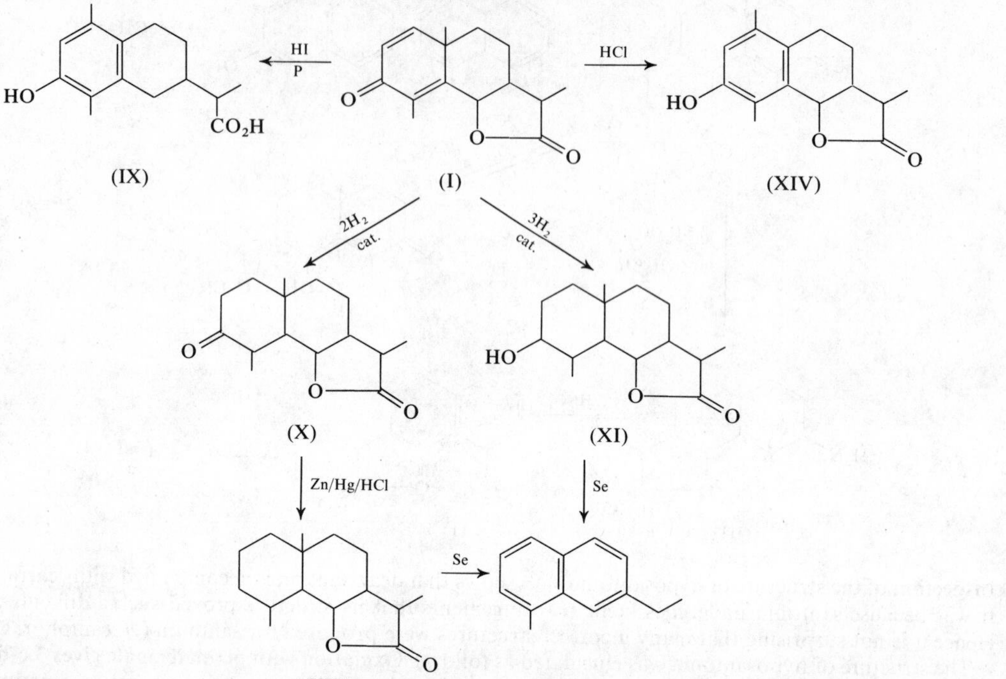

(IX)   (I)   (XIV)

(X)   (XI)

(XII)   (XIII)

Another set of reactions carried out was the oxidation of santonin with permanganate to give (XV).

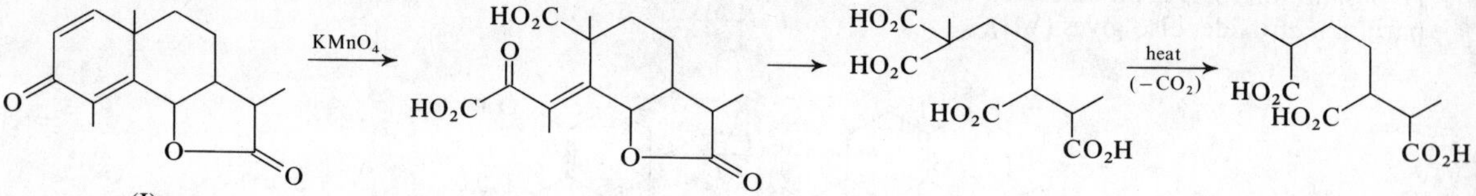

(I)   (XV)

All the early structures proposed for santonin (I) placed the two methyl groups in the same ring as the keto-group. In this case, santonin would be a tautomer of a phenol. Santonin, however, has no phenolic properties. Clemo *et al.* (1929, 1930), who carried out most of the foregoing reactions, were the first to propose the correct structure. They argued that if santonin is a sesquiterpenoid, then it could be assumed that it obeyed the isoprene rule (*cf.* eudesmol, §28b). They confirmed this argument by the synthesis of santonous acid (IX) and showed the position of the angular methyl group by the synthesis of (XV). They also established the position of the ether-oxygen atom in the lactone ring by the synthesis of desmotroposantonin (XIV). The structure of santonin has been confirmed by synthesis (see below).

The rearrangement of santonamine (III) into hyposantonin can now be explained on the basis of a 1,2-shift as follows:

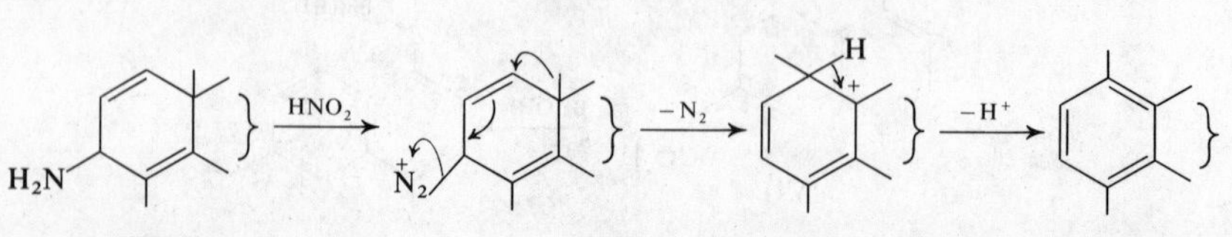

(III)   (IV)

The conversion of santonin into desmotroposantonin (XIV) can be explained in a similar way.

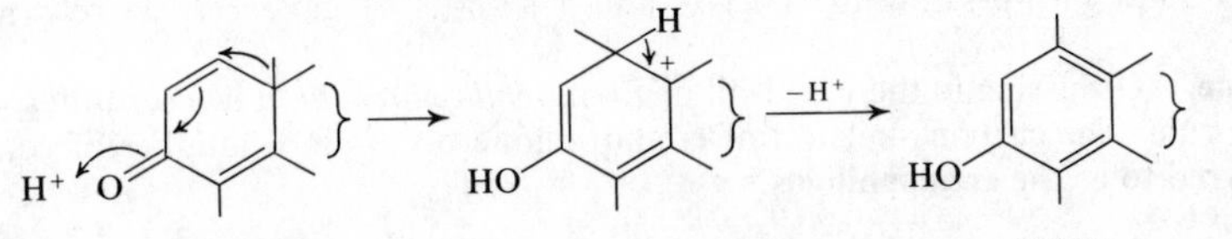

(I)   (XIV)

Santonin undergoes many unusual transformations. Here we shall discuss only the conversion of santonin into **santonic acid** (XVI) by prolonged heating with barium hydroxide solution. Woodward *et al.* (1948) proposed the following mechanism, which involves an internal Michael condensation.

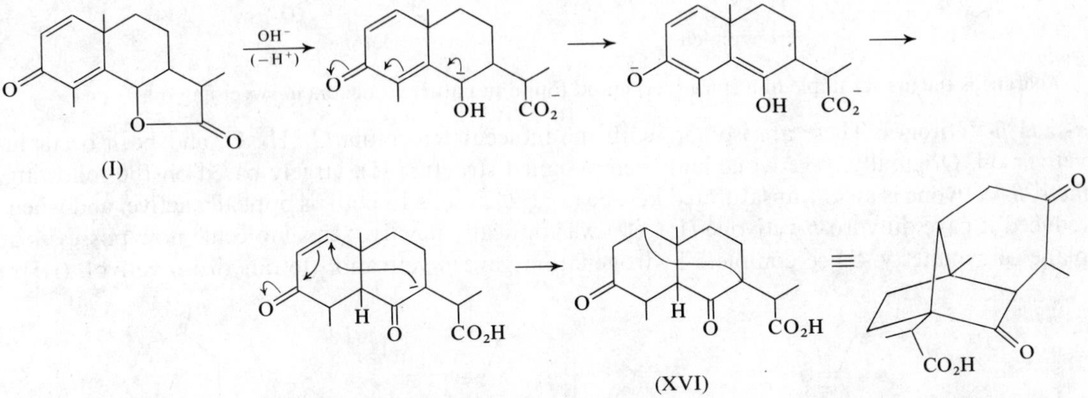

(I)

(XVI)

The stereochemistry of santonin has been the subject of extensive investigation, and its absolute configuration is as shown. This is α-santonin; β-santonin, which also occurs naturally, is the C-11 epimer.

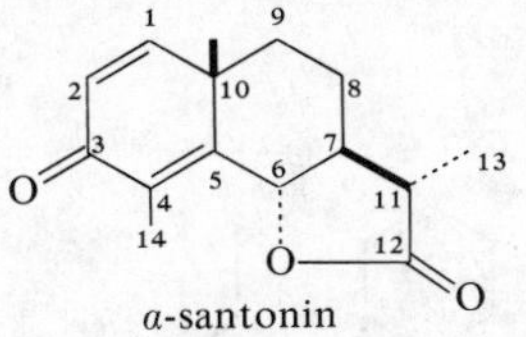

a-santonin

Randall *et al.* (1972) have shown that the ^{13}C chemical shifts in α- and β-santonin provide a simple method of determining the stereochemistry of the lactone ring fusion and also the configuration of the methyl group at C-11.

Natural α- and β-santonin have been synthesised, *e.g.*, (Abe *et al.*, 1956).

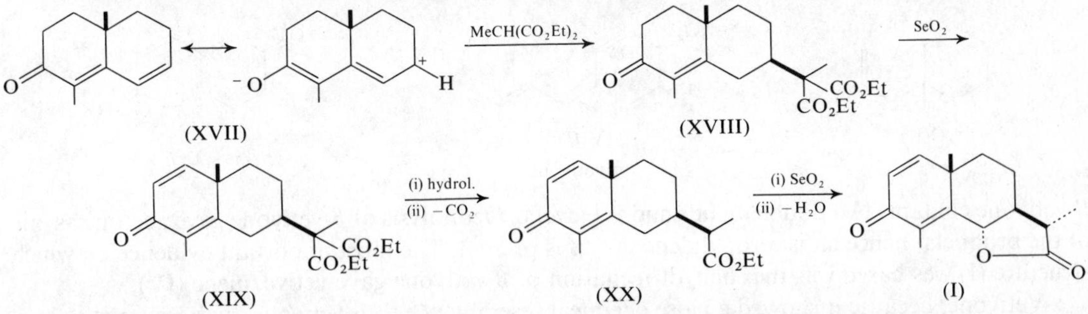

(XVII)   (XVIII)

(XIX)   (XX)   (I)

The Michael addition is stereospecific, the malonic ester group taking the more stable equatorial position in (XVIII). Decarboxylation to give (XX) results in the formation of two racemic acids (XX; α and β). These were separated; the α-acid led to (±)-α-santonin and the β-acid to (±)-β-santonin on oxidation and lactonisation. Since the lactone ring is fused *trans* (*e,e*; see above stereochemical formula), the selenium dioxide oxidation results in the formation of an equatorial hydroxyl group. Resolution of (±)-(XX) [α and β] *via* the brucine salts, followed by the same treatment as before, gave the following products: $(-)$-α- and $(-)$-β-(XX) gave respectively $(+)$-α- and $(+)$-β-santonin; $(+)$-α- and $(+)$-β-(XX) gave respectively natural $(-)$-α- and $(-)$-β-santonin.

§28d. Eremophilone.   Occurring in the wood-oil of *Eremophila mitchelli*, it is a sesquiterpenoid that does not obey the isoprene rule. The carbon skeleton of eremophilone occurs in a number of compounds which are consequently referred to as the **eremophiloids**.

eremophilone   acorone

Acorone is the first example of a spiran terpenoid found in nature; it occurs in sweet flag oil.

α- and β-Vetivones. These are isomers with the molecular formula $C_{15}H_{22}O$, and both occur in vetiver oil. Originally, β-vetivone had been assigned structure (I), largely based on the following facts. β-Vetivone is an α,β-unsaturated ketone (λ_{max} 242 nm, ε 15 600), is optically active, and when reduced it gave dihydro-β-vetivone (II). (II) was optically inactive; this molecule now possesses a plane of symmetry. Since complete hydrogenation gave β-vetivanol (tetrahydro-β-vetivol, (III)),

(I)   (II)   (III)

(IV)   (V)   (VI)

(VII)   (VIII)   (IX)
                          a-vetivone

β-vetivone contains two double bonds and is bicyclic. Ozonolysis of β-vetivone gave acetone as one of the products; hence an isopropylidene group is present. The most important evidence on which structure (I) was based was that dehydrogenation of β-vetivone gave vetivazulene (IV).

α-Vetivone, because it showed a close chemical resemblance to β-vetivone, was assumed to be a stereoisomer of the β-compound. However, de Mayo *et al.* (1967) found that the NMR spectrum of β-vetivone is in accord with its assigned structure (I) but that of α-vetivone is not. This is because of the *absence* of a signal which can be attributed to a vinylic methyl group and the *presence* of a singlet (τ 9·03) which is consistent with the presence of a methyl group attached to a saturated carbon atom.

De Mayo *et al.* now converted eremophilone (V) into the enol acetate (in which reaction migration of the double bond to the isopropylidene position occurred), oxidised the acetate with sodium dichromate to (VI) which, on isomerisation with base, gave (VII). On the other hand, acetylation of α-vetivone (VIII) also gave an enol acetate, but when this was oxidised with sodium dichromate, (IX) was obtained. Air oxidation of (VIII) in the presence of base gave the enantiomer of (VII).

It therefore follows that the reported dehydrogenation of β-vetivone to vetivazulene (IV) is misleading. De Mayo *et al.* dehydrogenated β-vetivanol (III) (in which the possibility of rearrangement is restricted compared to β-vetivone itself) and obtained vetivazulene ((IV); 8 per cent). α-Vetivanol gave no vetivazulene at all. Thus α-vetivone is an eremophiloid.

Structure (VIII) for α-vetivone (*Isonootkatone*) has been confirmed by a stereospecific synthesis (Marshall *et al.*, 1967).

The Michael reaction was anticipated to result in the formation of the *cis*-bicyclic product (NMR spectral data were consistent with *cis*; *cf.* the synthesis of santonin, §28c). Also note the migration of the double bond in the formation of the dioxolan and in its hydrolysis (see also the synthesis of β-eudesmol, §28b).

Now let us consider the structure of β-vetivone. Although de Mayo *et al.* believed that the NMR spectrum of β-vetivone was in accord with the original proposed structure (I) (see above), Marshall *et al.* (1967), after carrying out extensive synthetic and degradative work, disproved structure (I)

(XI)

and proposed (XI); a spiran structure (*cf.* acorone, above). This has been confirmed by the total synthesis of (±)-β-vetivone (Marshall *et al.*, 1968).

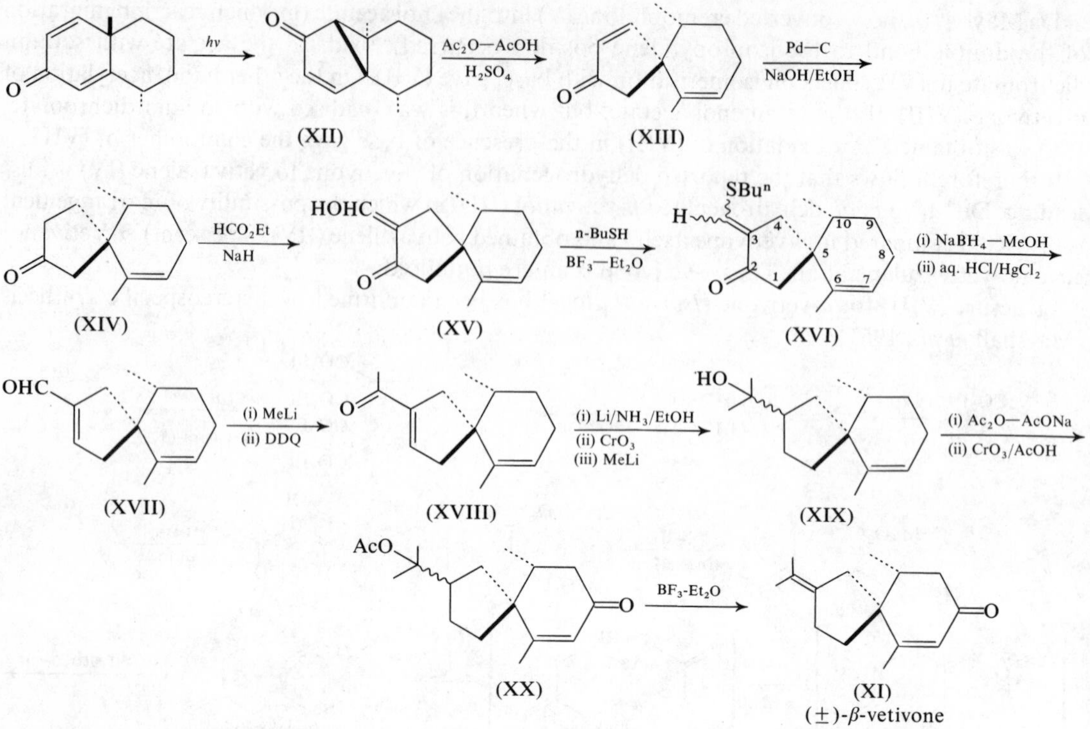

(XII)   (XIII)

(XIV)   (XV)   (XVI)

(XVII)   (XVIII)   (XIX)

(XX)   (XI)
(±)-β-vetivone

The starting material (XII) was a known compound. The conversion of (XIII) into (XIV) is an example of selective hydrogenation. The configuration of (XVI) is uncertain; it may be the other geometrical isomer, or a mixture of the two, but since the conversion of (XVI) into (XVIII) (DDQ is 2,3-dichloro-5,6-dicyanobenzoquinone; see Vol. I) results in only one possible product, this uncertainty makes no difference in the final stages. However, the important point is whether in (XV) and (XVI) the group introduced is in position 1 or 3. Examination of the infrared and NMR spectra of (XVI) led to assignment to position 3 as shown. This was anticipated for steric reasons and confirmed by the fact that the methylene side-chain proton gave a triplet signal (long-range coupling with C-4 protons).

§28e. Caryophyllene, b.p. 130°C/14 mm.   This occurs in oil of cloves together with its geometrical isomer, isocaryophyllene. As will be shown below, it is a macrocyclic sesquiterpenoid (§27c). Originally, it was believed that there were three isomers, α-, β- and γ-caryophyllene. However, the α-isomer has now been shown to be identical with humulene (§27c); the β-isomer is referred to as caryophyllene and the γ-isomer is isocaryophyllene.

The molecular formula of caryophyllene is $C_{15}H_{24}$ and, on catalytic hydrogenation, tetrahydrocaryophyllene, $C_{15}H_{28}$, is formed. Hence caryophyllene is a bicyclic compound and contains two double bonds. Ozonolysis followed by oxidation with nitric acid converted caryophyllene into a mixture of two dicarboxylic acids, caryophyllenic acid (I), $C_9H_{14}O_4$, and norcaryophyllenic acid (II), $C_8H_{12}O_4$. (II), on bromination, dehydrobromination, and ozonolysis, gave 2,2-dimethyl-4-ketoglutaric acid (III). This suggests that (II) is a

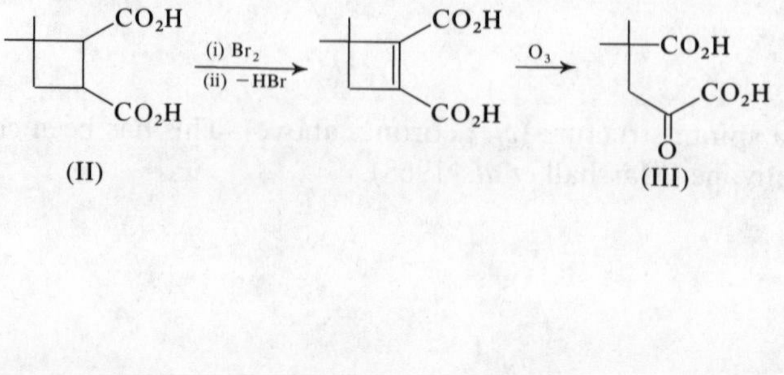

(II)   (III)

cyclobutane derivative, and so the reactions may be written as shown. The structure of (II) was confirmed by synthesis. It therefore follows that caryophyllenic acid must be (I) or (Ia), since it can be degraded to (II). Synthesis of these two dicarboxylic acids showed that caryophyllenic acid is (I).

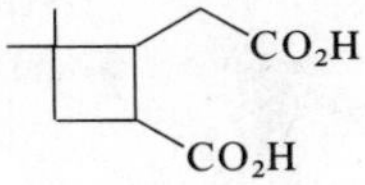

(I)   (Ia)

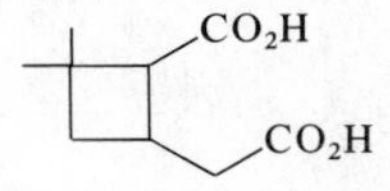

The problem now was to elucidate the size of the other ring in caryophyllene. Ozonolysis of caryophyllene gave formaldehyde, a monoketo-acid (IV), $C_{11}H_{18}O_3$, and a diketo-acid (V), $C_{14}H_{22}O_4$. Since both keto-acids gave the haloform reaction, both contain an acetyl group. Thus, caryophyllene contains the group —CMe=CH— and an exocyclic methylene group (formaldehyde formation). Both (IV) and (V) were oxidised by nitric acid to (I) and (II) and hence (IV) and (V) contain the dimethylcyclobutane system. Further work

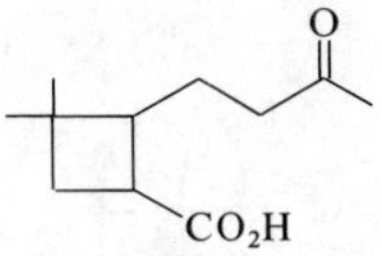

(IV) 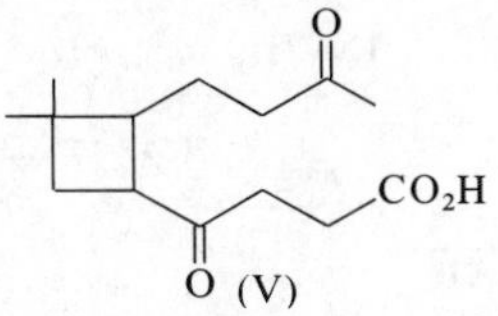   (V)

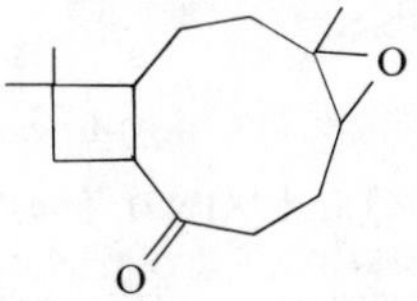

(VI) 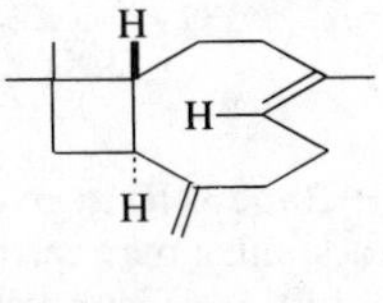   (VII)   (VIII)
          caryophyllene   isocaryophyllene

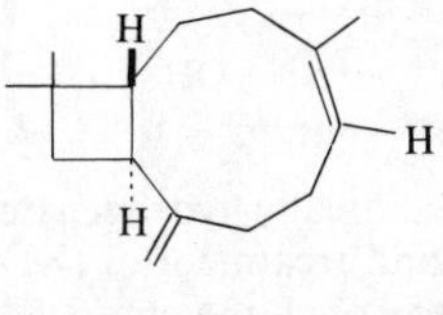

showed that (IV) had the structure shown. Oxidation of caryophyllene with hydrogen peroxide produced a mono-epoxide which, on oxidation with permanganate, gave a keto-epoxide (VI) by removal of the exocyclic methylene carbon atom. Sorm *et al.* (1950) studied the infrared spectra of this keto-epoxide and related compounds, and from the observation of the unusual position of the carbonyl band suggested that a nine-membered ring was present. On this evidence and that obtained by other workers, structure (VI) was assigned to the keto-epoxide and (VII) to caryophyllene. It therefore follows that (V) is the structure of the diketo-acid (see above).

Evidence obtained chemically and by X-ray analysis shows that the ring fusion is *trans* and that the endocyclic double bond also has the *trans* configuration. Isocaryophyllene (VIII) is the isomer in which the endocyclic double bond has the *cis* configuration.

(±)-Caryophyllene and (±)-isocaryophyllene have now been synthesised by Corey *et al.* (1964). These workers first proved that both isomers contained the same ring fusion (*trans*). Pure caryophyllene was converted into the secondary-tertiary diol, this oxidised (only the secondary alcoholic group) and the resulting ketone subjected to the Wolff-Kishner reduction to give isocaryophyllene.

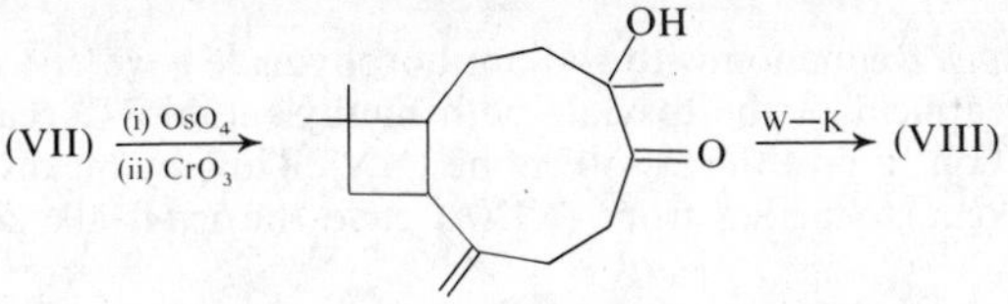

$$(VII) \xrightarrow[\text{(ii) } CrO_3]{\text{(i) } OsO_4} \qquad \xrightarrow{W-K} (VIII)$$

The syntheses were then carried out as shown.

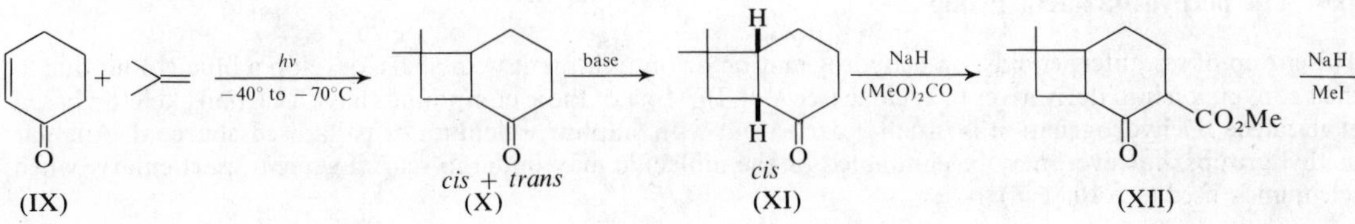

(IX)   *cis + trans*   *cis*   (XII)
          (X)   (XI)

(XIII)   (XIV)   (XV)

(XVI)   (XVII)   (XVIII)

(XIX) R¹ = H, R² = OH   (XX)   (VIII)
(XIXa) R¹ = OH, R² = H   (±)-isocaryophyllene

(XVIII) was catalytically hydrogenated (H_2—Raney Ni) to give (XIX) and (XIXa). These were separated by chromatography and treatment of (XIXa) in a similar manner (as described) gave (±)-caryophyllene (VII).

The first point to note is the photochemical addition of isobutene to (IX) to give (X), which was a mixture of *cis*- and *trans*-isomers, and the conversion of the unstable *trans*-isomer into the stable *cis*-isomer (XI). The NMR spectrum of (XI) was consistent with this structure and stereochemistry. The NMR analysis of (XII) showed it was a mixture of stereoisomers. These were not separated, and so (XIV) was also a mixture of stereoisomers. A point of interest to note is that the conversion of (XVI) into (XVII) (a Dieckmann type of reaction) could be effected only by methylsulphinylcarbanion. (XVI) was also a mixture of stereoisomers, whereas the NMR spectrum of (XVIII) showed it to be a pure stereoisomer, but its stereochemistry is not given by these reactions. This, however, does not affect the final result. The essential requirement is the stereochemistry of the internal elimination reaction to give a *cis*- or *trans*-double bond. Corey *et al.* argued that if it be assumed that the internal elimination is concerted (*i.e.*, E2) and that the stereoelectronically coplanar mode of elimination operates, the configuration of the alkene formed will be controlled by the relative orientation of the angular methyl group and the vicinal leaving group, the tosyloxy group. When these groups are *cis* (as in XIXa), the

resulting alkene should be *trans*. Reduction with sodium borohydride gave one stereoisomer only, *viz.* (XIX; Me and sec—OH *trans*). Treatment of the tosylate with methylsulphinylcarbanion isomerised the *cis*-ring fusion to *trans*, with elimination to give the *cis*-alkenone (XX). This, by means of the Wittig reaction, gave (±)-isocaryophyllene (*cis*-alkene). Starting from (XIXa) gave the *trans*-alkenone, which gave (±)-caryophyllene (*trans*-alkene).

§29. The perhydroazulene group

This group of sesquiterpenoids, on dehydrogenation or on treatment with acids, develop a blue colour due to their conversion into derivatives of azulene (see Vol. I). Most of these compounds have a carbon skeleton based **guaiazulene**. Dehydrogenation is usually carried out with sulphur, selenium or palladised charcoal. Angular methyl groups, however, may be eliminated or the molecule may undergo rearrangement, particularly when selenium is used (see **10** §2vii).

Guaiol, $C_{15}H_{26}O$, m.p. 93°C, occurs in guaiacum wood oil. It was shown to be a tertiary alcohol and to contain one ethylenic double bond. When dehydrogenated with sulphur, guaiol gives guaiazulene (II). The degradations shown in the Chart suggest (I) as the structure of guaiol.

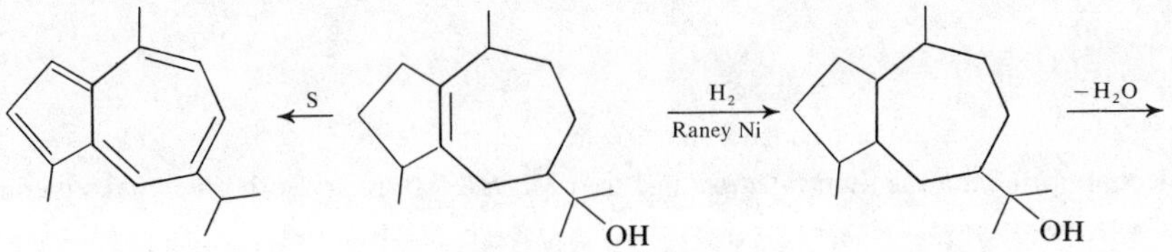

(II)   (I)   (III)
                        guaiol   dihydroguaiol

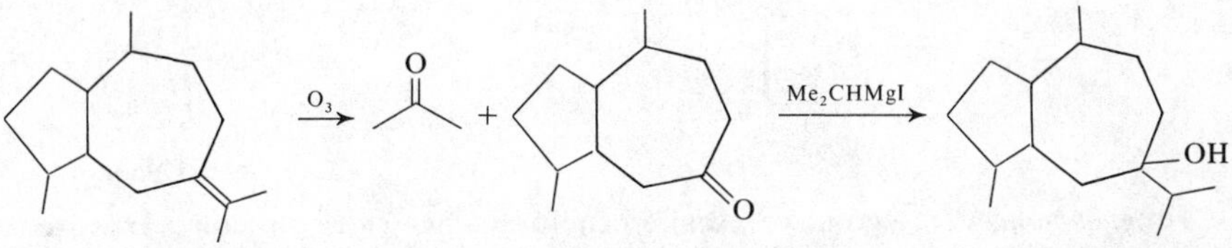

(IV)

The properties of (IV) were entirely different from those of (III), and therefore the position of the hydroxyl group in guaiol must be as shown in (I).

The position of the double bond in guaiol was elucidated from the series of reactions shown. The diketone (V) undergoes an internal aldol condensation (*via* the carbanion) to give (VI), which finally leads to cadalene (VII).

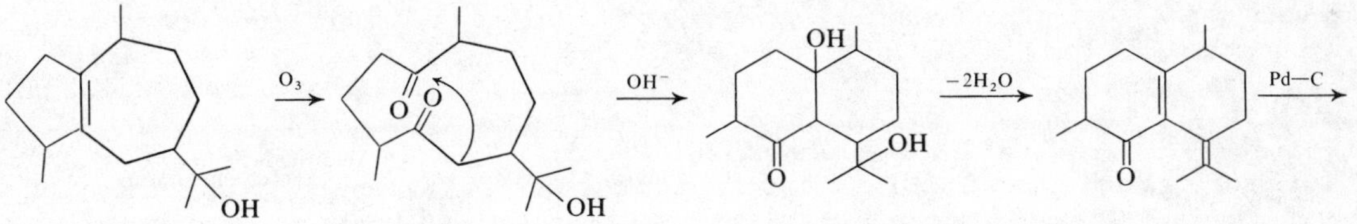

(I)   (V)   (VI)

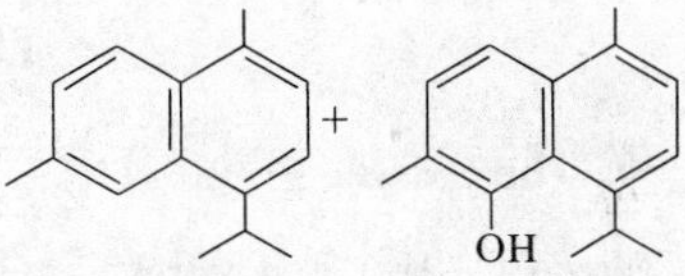

(VII)

Minato (1961) has shown from ORD studies that guaiol has the absolute configuration shown. A stereo-selective synthesis of guaiol has now been carried out (Marshall *et al.*, 1971). Buchanan *et al.* (1971) have also synthesised guaiol.

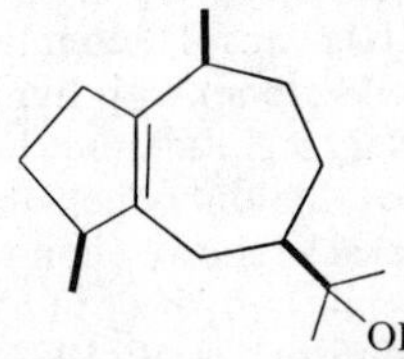

Aromadendrene is the principal sesquiterpenoid hydrocarbon in eucalyptus oils. It was shown to contain one double bond, to be tricyclic, and its skeleton was elucidated by the fact that on dehydrogenation it gave guaiazulene. This information, together with that obtained from oxidative degradation, led to the proposal of the structure shown. The absolute configuration of aromadendrene has been elucidated from ORD studies, and this and the structure have been confirmed by synthesis.

aromadendrene

Kessoglycol and **kessyl alcohol** both occur as their *acetates* in Japanese valerian root. Both give guaiazulene on dehydrogenation.

kessoglycol   kessyl alcohol

The *guaianolides* are a group of sesquiterpenoid lactones whose structures are based on that of guaiol but, on dehydrogenation, usually give chamazulene, *e.g.*,

matricin   carpesia lactone   chamazulene

TRICYCLIC SESQUITERPENOIDS

§30. The cedrene group

Cedrene, $C_{15}H_{24}$, and **cedrol**, $C_{15}H_{26}O$.   Both of these occur in cedar wood oil. Cedrol, on dehydration, gives cedrene, and since cedrol is a saturated tertiary alcohol, cedrene contains one double bond and is tricyclic. Oxidative degradation of cedrene led to the elucidation of its structure. We shall here describe some of the evidence and for our purpose use the structure of cedrene (I) as reference in order to explain the course of the various stages. Oxidation of cedrene (I) with permanganate gave three products, one of which was the keto-acid (II). Since there was no loss of carbon, the double bond in (I) must be in a ring. Oxidation of (II) with hypobromite gave cedrenedicarboxylic acid (III). Thus (II) contains a methyl ketone group. Ozonolysis of (I) followed by oxidation of the product (a methyl ketone) with hypobromite gave norcedrenedicarboxylic acid (IV). Since (II) gave a dibromo-derivative (H.V.Z. method) and (IV) gave only the monobromo-derivative, the former contains two α-hydrogen atoms and the latter only one. Hence (IV) contains a tertiary carboxyl group. The infrared spectrum of the cyclic anhydride of (IV) showed bands at 1 796 and 1 765 cm^{-1}. These are characteristic of a glutaric anhydride and not of a succinic anhydride (1 852 and 1 776 cm^{-1}), and so the ring containing the double bond is therefore six-membered (Stork *et al.*, 1953).

The dimethyl ester of (IV) was treated as shown and resulted in (V), the infrared spectrum of which showed it was a glutaric anhydride (*cf.* above). Hence, the second ring that has now been opened is five-membered.

(V) was converted into its corresponding dicarboxylic acid and a double bond introduced as before (from IV) to give (VI) and this was treated as shown to give (VII), which was identified by synthesis (Plattner *et al.*, 1953). Thus, the third ring in cedrene is five-membered.

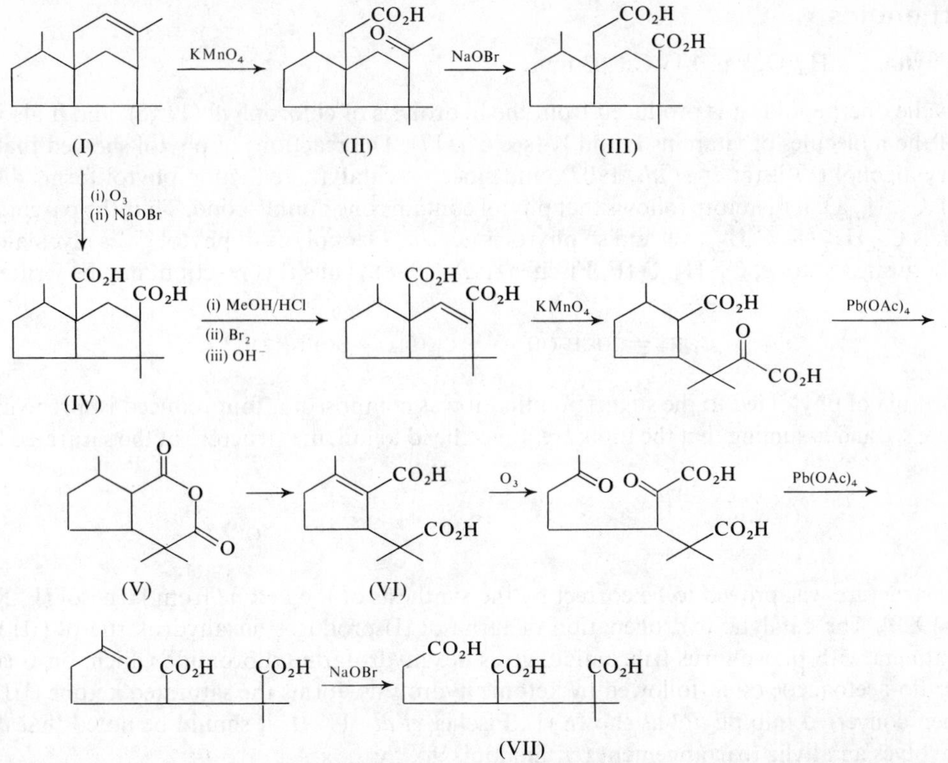

The configuration of cedrene (and cedrol) was deduced mainly from the course of the reactions discussed above, *e.g.*, the formation of the anhydride (V) indicates that in the parent acid the carboxyl group and the dimethylacetic acid residue are *cis*. The structures and absolute configurations of cedrene and cedrol have now been confirmed by a stereospecific total synthesis of cedrol (Stork *et al.*, 1961).

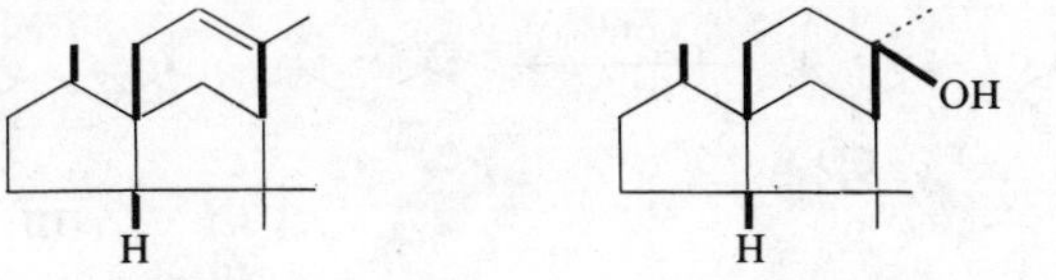

cedrene

cedrol

The longifolene group

§30a. Longifolene, $C_{15}H_{24}$.   This occurs in the oleoresins of *Pinus longifolia* (and other species of pine). Its structure was established by the X-ray analysis of its hydrochloride (Moffett *et al.*, 1953). Inspection of the

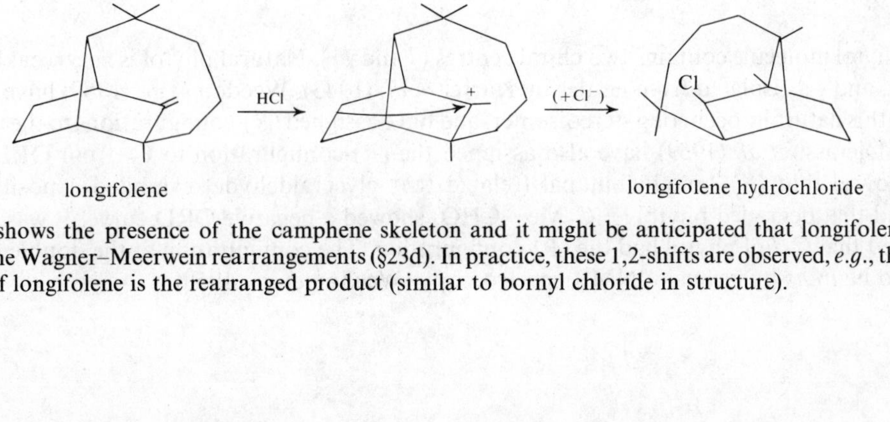

longifolene

longifolene hydrochloride

structure shows the presence of the camphene skeleton and it might be anticipated that longifolene would undergo the Wagner–Meerwein rearrangements (§23d). In practice, these 1,2-shifts are observed, *e.g.*, the hydrochloride of longifolene is the rearranged product (similar to bornyl chloride in structure).

Diterpenoids

§31. Phytol, $C_{20}H_{40}O$, b.p. 145°C/0·03 mm.

An acyclic diterpenoid; it is produced from the hydrolysis of chlorophyll (**19** §6), and it also forms part of the molecules of vitamins E and K (see Ch. 17). The reactions of phytol showed that it is a primary alcohol (Willstätter *et al.*, 1907), and since on catalytic reduction phytol forms dihydro-phytol, $C_{20}H_{42}O$, it therefore follows that phytol contains one double bond. Thus the parent hydro-carbon is $C_{20}H_{42}$ ($\equiv C_nH_{2n+2}$), and so phytol is acyclic. Ozonolysis of phytol gives glycolaldehyde and a saturated ketone, $C_{18}H_{36}O$ (F. Fischer *et al.*, 1928). Thus this reaction may be written:

$$C_{18}H_{36}{=}CHCH_2OH \xrightarrow{O_3} C_{18}H_{36}O + OCHCH_2OH$$

The formula of phytol led to the suggestion that it was composed of four reduced isoprene units. If this were so, and assuming that the units are joined head to tail, the structure of the saturated ketone would be:

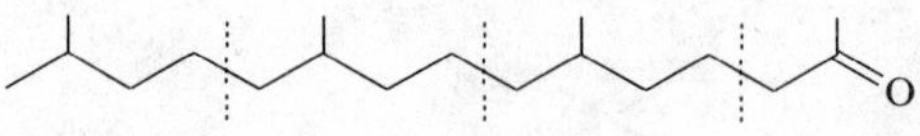

This structure was proved to be correct by the synthesis of the ketone from farnesol (F. Fischer *et al.*, 1928). The catalytic hydrogenation of farnesol (I) produces hexahydrofarnesol (II) which, on treatment with phosphorus tribromide, gives hexahydrofarnesyl bromide which, on treatment with sodio-acetoacetic ester, followed by ketonic hydrolysis, forms the saturated ketone (III). This was then converted into phytol as shown (F. Fischer *et al.*, 1929); it should be noted that the last step involves an allylic rearrangement (*cf.* linalool, §8).

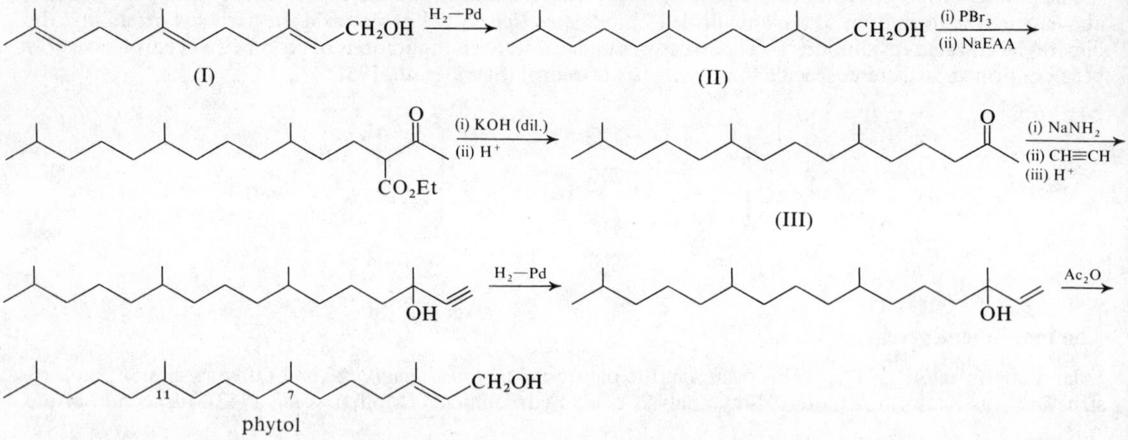

The phytol molecule contains two chiral centres (7 and 11). Natural phytol is very weakly dextro-rotatory, and was isolated from nettles by Karrer *et al.* (1943). Weedon *et al.* (1959) have now syn-thesised this naturally occurring stereoisomer, and have assigned (*R*)-configurations to the two chiral centres. Djerassi *et al.* (1959) have also assigned the (*R*)-configuration to C_7 from ORD studies. They showed that (*S*)-2-methylbutanal (related to L-glyceraldehyde) exhibited a positive ORD curve and that degraded phytol ($-C_7Me-CHO$) showed a negative ORD curve. It was therefore concluded that C-7 of phytol had the (*R*)-configuration. The configuration at the double bond was shown to be *trans* by means of NMR spectroscopy (Weedon *et al.*, 1959).

Vitamin A_1 is a monocyclic diterpenoid (see **9** §7).

Cembrene occurs naturally and is a member of the group of macrocyclic diterpenoids. It contains a fourteen-membered ring (Dauben *et al.*, 1965).

cembrene

Resin acids

§32. When incisions are made in the bark of pine trees, an oleoresin is exuded. When this is steam-distilled, the volatile fraction consists of turpentine and the residue is known as rosin (or colophony). Turpentine consists mainly of pinene (§22a), whereas rosin is a complex mixture of acids, most of which have the formula $C_{19}H_{29}CO_2H$. A small number of these acids are bicyclic, *e.g.*,

agathic acid
(agathenedicarboxylic acid)

labdanolic acid

cativic acid

The most important resin acid is abietic acid. It does not, apparently, occur naturally, but is formed from labile precursors during the collection, storage and steam-distillation of the oleoresin.

Abietic acid, $C_{20}H_{30}O_2$, m.p. 172–175°C, is a tricyclic diterpenoid. For our purpose it is useful to have the structure of abietic acid as a reference, and then describe the evidence that led to this structure.

abietic acid

The general reactions of abietic acid showed that it was a monocarboxylic acid. On dehydrogenation with sulphur, abietic acid gives retene (Vesterberg, 1903); better yields of retene are obtained by dehydrogenating with selenium (Diels *et al.*, 1927), or with palladised charcoal (Ruzicka *et al.*, 1933). Retene, $C_{18}H_{18}$, m.p. 99°C, was shown by oxidative degradation to be 1-methyl-7-isopropyl-phenanthrene (Bucher, 1910). Oxidation of retene (I) gave retenequinone (II) which, on oxidation with alkaline permanganate, gave the key intermediate (II) and this, on oxidation with dichromate, gave (IV). (IV), when heated with concentrated aqueous potassium hydroxide, gave (V).

The conversion of (II) into (III) involves a benzilic acid rearrangement (see Vol. I). Since (V) formed a cyclic anhydride and (IV) did not, one carboxyl group in (IV) must be *ortho* to the centre ring. This carboxyl group is derived from an alkyl group in retene and so one alkyl group must be at position 1 (in the phenanthrene nucleus; see (I)). Since (III) is formed from (II) by loss of *one* carbon atom only, this suggests that the carboxyl group is derived from a methyl group (at position 1). On heating, (IV) gave fluorenone and (V) gave biphenyl. Hence the carbon skeletons of (IV) and (V) are established.

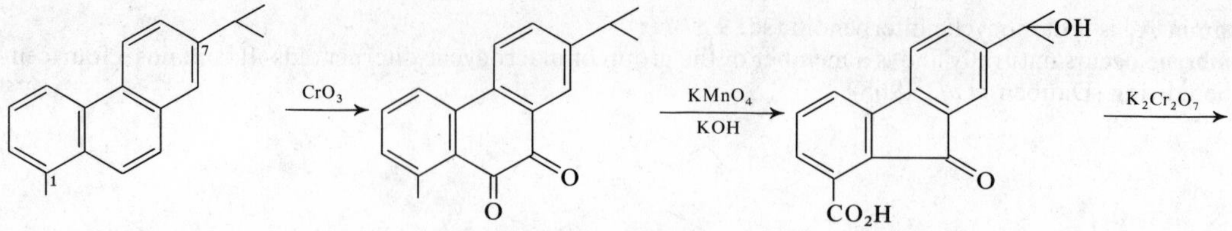

The problem now was to locate the position of the isopropyl group in retene (I). This was solved by fusing (III) with potassium hydroxide. The product was shown to be 4-isopropylbiphenyl by oxidation to biphenyl-4-carboxylic acid. Hence retene contains an isopropyl group at position 7.

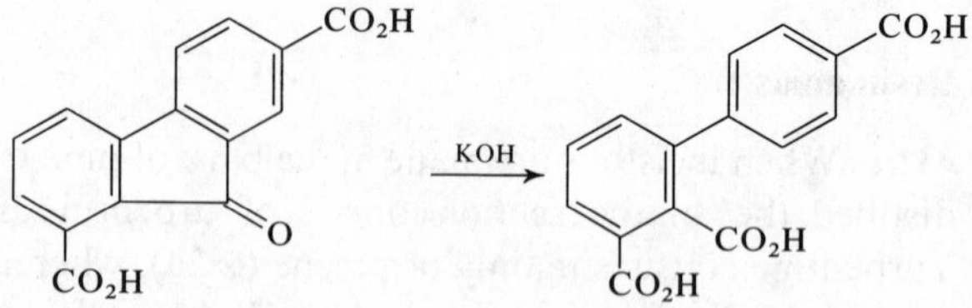

Structure (I) for retene has been confirmed by synthesis, *e.g.*, that of Haworth *et al.* (1932) [see also **10** §2(vi b)].

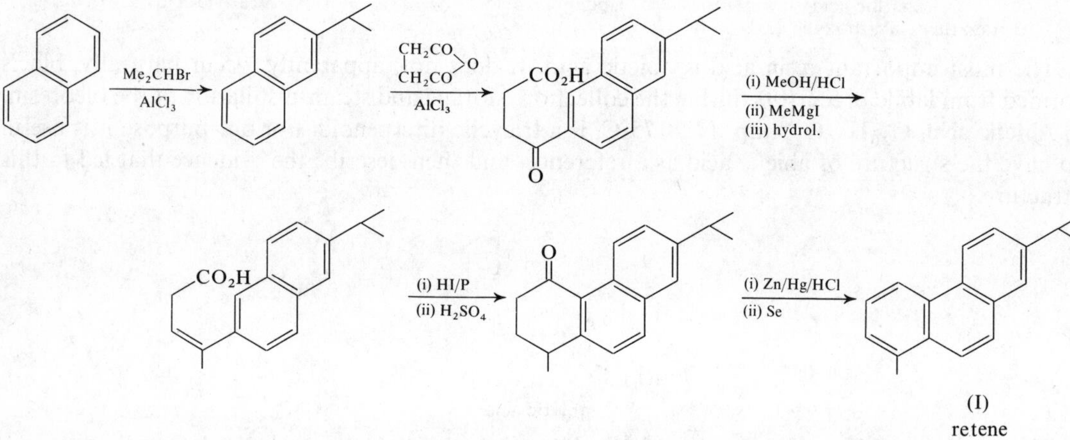

Since two carbon atoms were lost from abietic acid (C_{20}) to form retene (C_{18}), we have:

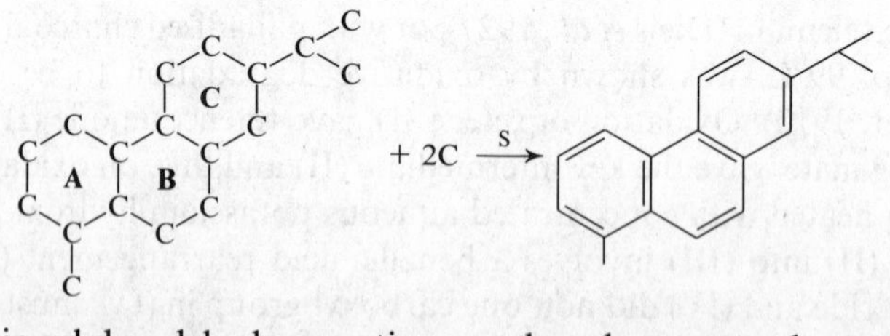

Now it is known that in sulphur dehydrogenations, carboxyl groups and *angular* methyl groups can be eliminated (see **10** §2vii). It is therefore possible that the two carbon atoms lost may have been originally the carboxyl group (in abietic acid) and an angular methyl group.

Abietic acid is very difficult to esterify, and since this is characteristic of a carboxyl group attached to a tertiary carbon atom, it suggests that abietic acid contains a carboxyl group in this state. This is supported by the fact that abietic acid evolves carbon monoxide when warmed with concentrated sulphuric acid; this reaction is also characteristic of a carboxyl group attached to a tertiary carbon atom.

Catalytic hydrogenation of abietic acid gives tetrahydroabietic acid, $C_{20}H_{34}O_2$. Thus abietic acid contains two double bonds; also, since the parent hydrocarbon is $C_{19}H_{34}$ (regarding the carboxyl group as a substituent group), abietic acid is tricyclic (parent corresponds to C_nH_{2n-4}), which agrees with the evidence already given.

Oxidation of abietic acid with potassium permanganate gives a mixture of products among which are two tricarboxylic acids, $C_{11}H_{16}O_6$ (VI), and $C_{12}H_{18}O_6$ (VII) [Ruzicka *et al.*, 1925, 1931]. (VI) on dehydrogenation with selenium, forms *m*-xylene, and (VII) forms hemimellitene (1,2,3-trimethylbenzene) [Ruzicka *et al.*, 1931]. In both cases there is a loss of three carbon atoms, and if we assume that these were the three carboxyl groups, then two methyl groups in (VI) and (VII) must be in the *meta*-position. Furthermore, since (VI) and (VII) each contain the methyl group originally present in abietic acid (position 4), acids (VI) and (VII) must contain ring A of abietic acid. This suggests, therefore that there is an angular methyl group at position 10, since it can be expected to be eliminated from this position in sulphur dehydrogenations of abietic acid (this 10-methyl group is *meta* to the 4-methyl group). Vocke (1932) showed that acid (VI) evolves two molecules of carbon dioxide when warmed with concentrated sulphuric acid; this indicates that (VI) contains two carboxyl groups attached to tertiary carbon atoms. These results can be explained by *assuming* that one carboxyl group in (VI) is that in abietic acid, and since in both cases this carboxyl group is attached to a tertiary carbon atom, the most likely position of this group is 4 (in abietic acid). Accepting these assumptions, the oxidation of abietic acid may be formulated as follows, also assuming (VIII) as the carbon skeleton of abietic acid. Vocke subjected (VI) to oxidative degradation,

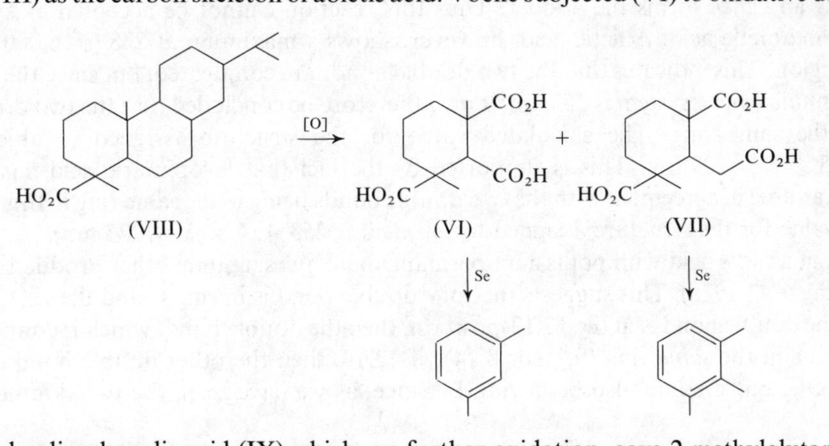

and obtained a dicarboxylic acid (IX) which, on further oxidation, gave 2-methylglutaric acid (X). Vocke assumed that (VI) had the structure shown, and formulated the reactions as below, *assuming* structure (IX) as the best way of explaining the results.

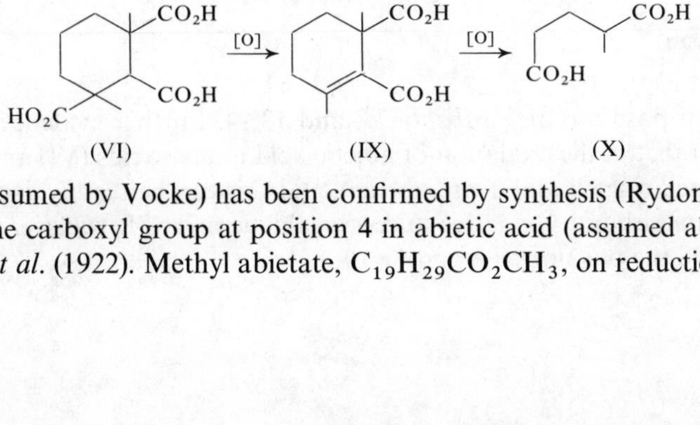

Structure (IX) (assumed by Vocke) has been confirmed by synthesis (Rydon, 1937).

The position of the carboxyl group at position 4 in abietic acid (assumed above) has been confirmed by Ruzicka *et al.* (1922). Methyl abietate, $C_{19}H_{29}CO_2CH_3$, on reduction with sodium and ethanol, forms abietinol, $C_{19}H_{29}CH_2OH$, which, on treatment with phosphorus pentachloride, loses a molecule of water to form 'methylabietin', $C_{20}H_{30}$. This, on distillation with sulphur, forms homoretene, $C_{19}H_{20}$. Homoretene contains one CH_2 group more than retene, and on oxidation with alkaline potassium ferricyanide, gives phenanthrene-1,7-dicarboxylic acid, the identical product obtained from the oxidation of retene under similar conditions (Ruzicka *et al.*, 1932). These results can only be explained by assuming that homoretene has an ethyl group at position 1 (instead of the methyl group in retene), *i.e.*, homoretene is 1-ethyl-7-isopropylphenanthrene. This has been confirmed by synthesis (Haworth *et al.*, 1932; ethylmagnesium iodide was used instead of methylmagnesium iodide in the synthesis of retene). The formation of an ethyl group in homoretene can be explained by assuming that abietinol undergoes a Wagner–Meerwein rearrangement on dehydration (see §23d). Thus:

methyl abietate   abietinol   "methylabietin"   homoretene

It has already been pointed out that abietic acid has two double bonds. Since abietic acid forms an adduct with maleic anhydride *at above* 100°C, it was assumed that the two double bonds are conjugated (Ruzicka *et al.*, 1932). It was later shown, however, that levopimaric acid also forms the same adduct *at room temperature*. It thus appears that abietic acid isomerises to levopimaric acid at above 100°C, and *then* forms the adduct. Thus this reaction cannot be accepted as evidence for conjugation in abietic acid. Abietic acid, however, shows a maximum at 238 (ε 16 000) nm in the ultraviolet region. This indicates that the two double bonds are conjugated, but since the basic value for a homoannular diene system is 253 nm, it may therefore be concluded that the two double bonds are not in the same ring. The calculated value for the structure assigned to abietic acid is $214 + 4 \times 5 + 5 = 239$ nm. This is supported by the fact that levopimaric acid has λ_{max} 272·5 (ε 7 000) nm, a value in agreement with the two double bonds being in the same ring in this compound (calculated value for the structure assigned to this acid is $253 + 4 \times 5 = 273$ nm).

Oxidation of abietic acid with potassium permanganate gives, among other products, isobutyric acid (Ruzicka *et al.*, 1925). This suggests that one double bond is in ring C and the 12,13- or 13,14-position. If the double bond is in the 12,13-position, then the double bond, which is conjugated with it, must also be in the *same* ring (9,11 or 8,14); if 13,14, then the other double bond could be in the same ring C, but it could also be in ring B. Since, as we have seen, the two double bonds are

12,13   13,14

in different rings, their positions are *probably* 7,8 and 13,14. Further evidence for these positions is afforded by the fact that in the oxidation of abietic acid to give acids (VI) and (VII) (see above), *in which ring A is intact*, rings B and C are opened, and this can be readily explained only if rings B and C each have a double bond. Oxidative studies on abietic acid by Ruzicka *et al.* (1938–1941) have conclusively confirmed the positions 7,8 and 13,14.

The stereochemistry of abietic acid has been elucidated and has the absolute configuration shown. Since the tricarboxylic acid (VI) is optically inactive, it must possess a plane of symmetry. This is possible only if the *meta*-carboxyl groups are *cis* with respect to each other. Barton *et al.* (1948)

abietic acid

deduced from the study of the dissociation constants of this acid that the centre carboxyl group was *trans* to the other two. Their argument was based on the observation that the difference between pK_1 and pK_2 of cycloalkane-1,2-dicarboxylic acids is greater for the *cis*- than for the *trans*-acid. Hence rings **A** and **B** are fused in a *trans* manner. This is true only if inversion does not occur in the formation of (VI); this was confirmed by other work.

The remaining chiral centre is C-9. Since abietic acid is readily formed from other related acids by acid catalysis which involves double bond migration (see below), it was argued that if the C_{10}-methyl group and the C_9-hydrogen are *trans*, this would be the more stable form and so this is the configuration present in abietic acid (Barton, 1949). Klyne (1953) supported this on the basis of his molecular rotation studies and also deduced the absolute configuration shown in the formula of abietic acid.

The stereochemistry of abietic acid has been confirmed by Stork *et al.* (1956), who have carried out a stereospecific synthesis of ($\pm$)-dehydroabietic acid (XVII). This is shown in the sequence (XI) to (XVII). β-Tetralone (XI) was methylated (MeI) *via* the pyrrolidine enamine (see Vol. I) to give (XII)

(XI)   (XII)   (XIII)

(XIV)   (XV)

(XVI)   (XVII)

and this, on condensation with ethyl vinyl ketone, gave (XIII). Alkylation of (XIII) with ethyl bromo-acetate produced (XIV) in which, because of the steric effect of the angular methyl group in (XIII), the acetic ester residue was introduced on the less hindered side of the molecule. (XIV) was converted into its thioketal by ethanedithiol and this, on hydrolysis with alkali, gave (XV) which, on con-version into its methyl ester followed by Raney nickel desulphurisation, hydrolysis, and hydrogena-tion with Pd—C in acetic acid, gave (XVI). The two rings in the tetralin fragment in (XVI) are *trans*-fused because addition of hydrogen occurs on the face opposite to the two *cis*-methyl groups. Application of the Barbier–Wieland degradation (**11** §3) gave ($\pm$)-dehydroabietic acid (XVII). Since this may be prepared from abietic acid and *vice versa*, the stereochemistry of abietic acid is determined.

As mentioned above, abietic acid is apparently produced by the isomerisation of a number of labile precursors present in the oleoresin. These labile precursors are referred to as the primary resin acids, and the two principal ones are **levopimaric acid** and **neoabietic acid**. Both acids are readily isomerised to abietic acid in the presence of acid or by heat, and levopimaric and abietic acids form the same adduct with maleic anhydride (see above). Since levopimaric acid has λ_{max} 272·5 nm, this shows that this acid is a homoannular diene (§3viii). We can therefore formulate the Diels–Alder reaction as shown (using as our basis the given structures):

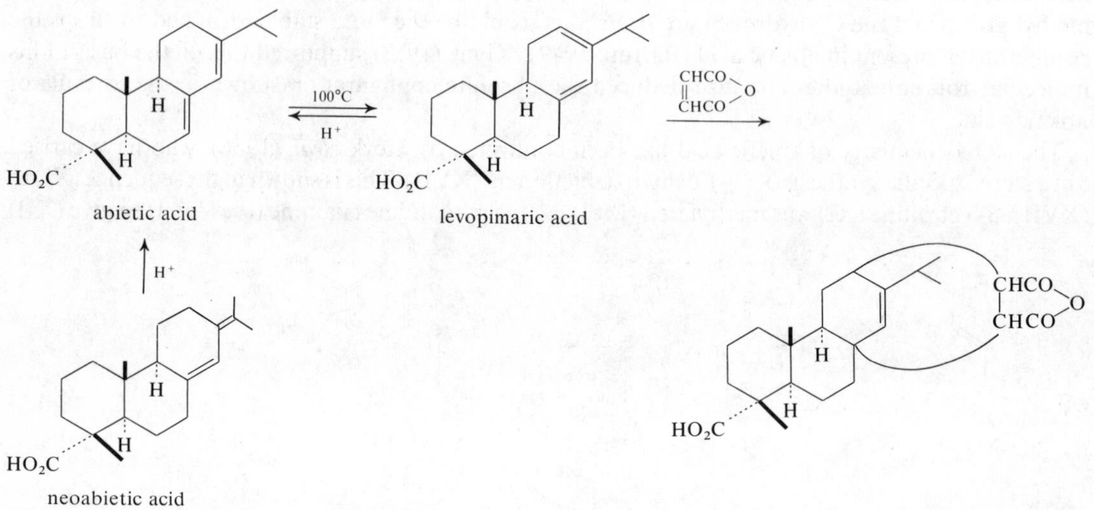

abietic acid   levopimaric acid

neoabietic acid

Another acid, **palustric acid**, has been isolated (by chromatography) from pine rosin; this also isomerises to abietic acid. There are also other resin acids which have been isolated but are not primary resin acids, *i.e.*, do not isomerise to abietic acid (see above); *e.g.*, **pimaric acid** and **isopimaric acid**.

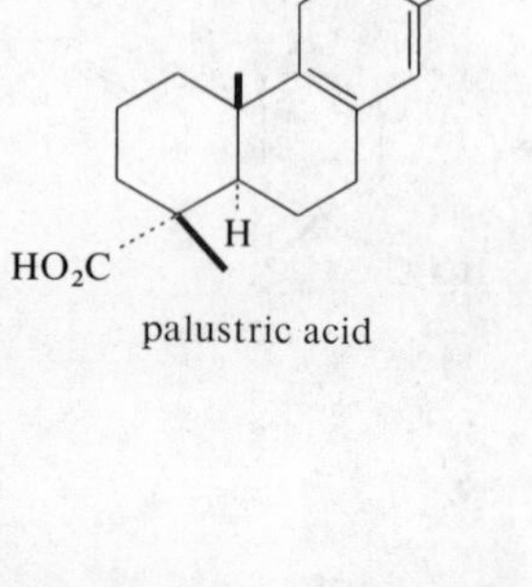

palustric acid 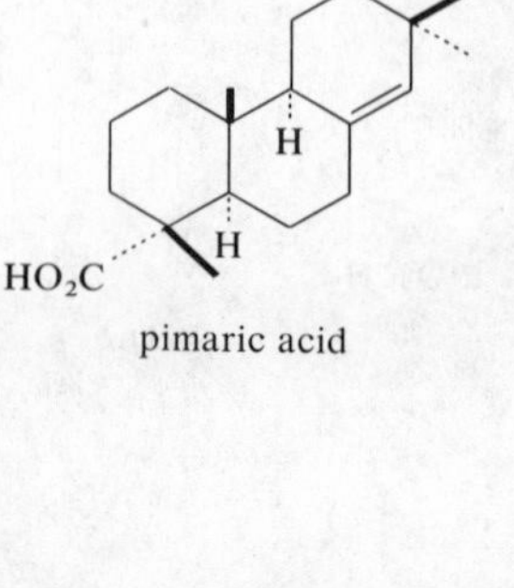   pimaric acid 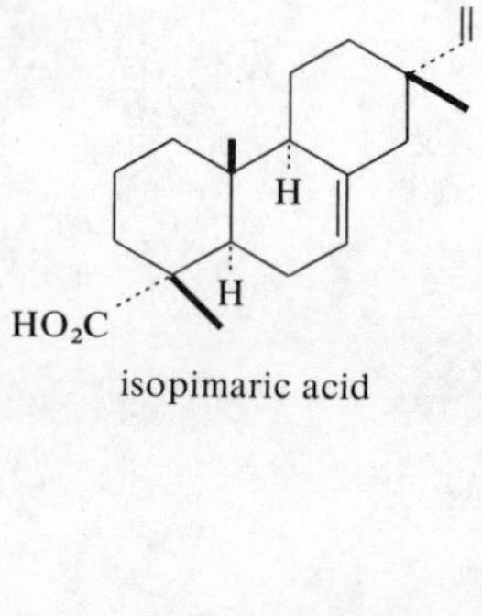   isopimaric acid

Many other tricyclic diterpenoids are known, *e.g.*, (note that the acid does not obey the isoprene rule):

ferruginol   vinhaticoic acid

Tetracyclic diterpenoids

§32a. Most of the members of this group are based on the carbon skeleton of **phyllocladene** (*cf.* with cedrene, §30), *e.g.*,

phyllocladene   isophyllocladene

kaurene   cafestol

Phyllocladene and kaurene are stereoisomers, and the latter is important in that it is a biosynthetic intermediate in the formation of gibberellic acid (see below).

    Gibberellins are a group of tetracyclic compounds which occur in the culture fluid of the fungus *Gibberella fujikuroi*. It is now believed, however, that they are widely distributed in higher plants and behave as a plant hormone, *i.e.*, they control and regulate the growth of plants.

    Gibberellic acid, m.p. 233–235°C, is the most important member and has been produced in greater quantities than any other gibberellin. The gibberellins have been named as gibberellin A_1, A_2, ... as they have been isolated. Gibberellic acid is also known as gibberellin A_3.

    Here we shall discuss some of the evidence that led to the elucidation of the structure of gibberellic acid. Its molecular formula was shown to be $C_{19}H_{22}O_6$ (hence it is not a true diterpenoid; it is *derived* from this group; see kaurene above and also §34). Microhydrogenation showed the presence of two ethylenic double bonds, and since acetylation gave a diacetate two hydroxyl groups were present. Because the monoacetate was easily prepared but not the diacetate, it was assumed that a tertiary alcoholic group was present. Also, since the reduction products of gibberellic acid could be oxidised to a ketone, the other alcoholic group was secondary. The presence of one carboxyl group was shown by the formation of a monomethyl ester. This left two unaccounted oxygen atoms. When gibberellic acid was treated with excess of alkali, two equivalents were consumed. This suggested the presence of a lactone ring, and this was confirmed and shown to be a γ-lactone by the presence of a band near 1 780 cm^{-1} in the infrared spectrum. The double bond equivalent (see **1** §12e) of gibberellic acid is $19 + 1 - 22/2 = 9$. Since there are two ethylenic double bonds and two carbonyl double bonds, this leaves $9 - 4 = 5$ rings. One of these is the lactone ring; hence gibberellic acid contains four carbocyclic rings. The system of numbering the fully saturated tetracyclic system, known as **gibbane**, is as shown.

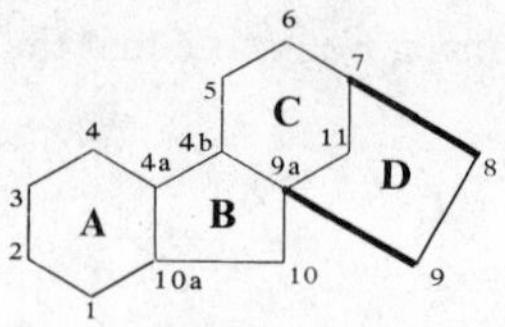

gibbane

The 8,9-bridge (above the plane) is said to be β, and atoms or groups below the plane are named α (see **11** §4b for a discussion of the conventions).

Acid hydrolysis of gibberellic acid (I) gave two products, gibberic acid (II) and allogibberic acid (III). Using structure (I) as reference for gibberellic acid, we can formulate this hydrolysis as:

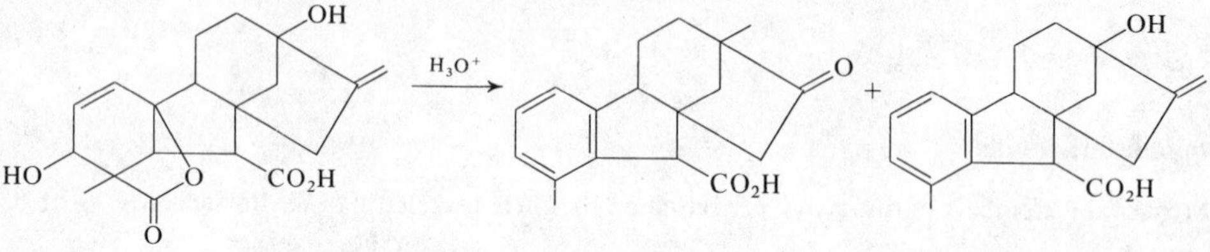

Both (II) and (III) gave gibberene, $C_{15}H_{14}$, (IV), on selenium dehydrogenation. This was deduced to be a fluorene derivative from its ultraviolet spectrum, and shown to be 1,7-dimethylfluorene by oxidative degradation and by synthesis.

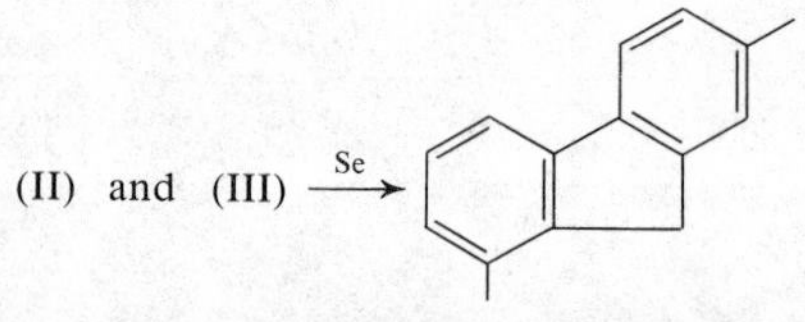

Hence it is reasonable to assume that all three compounds (I–III) contain the carbon skeleton of (IV).

Examination of gibberic acid (II) by the usual chemical methods showed it contained a carbonyl (formation of an oxime) and a carboxyl group (formation of an ester). The infrared spectrum of (II) showed a band at $1\,741\ cm^{-1}$, which is characteristic of a keto-group in cyclopentanone, and the ultraviolet spectrum showed the presence of a benzene ring (λ_{max} 265, 274 nm).

The following degradations (V–VIII) showed the presence of the hexahydrofluorene nucleus in gibberic acid (II).

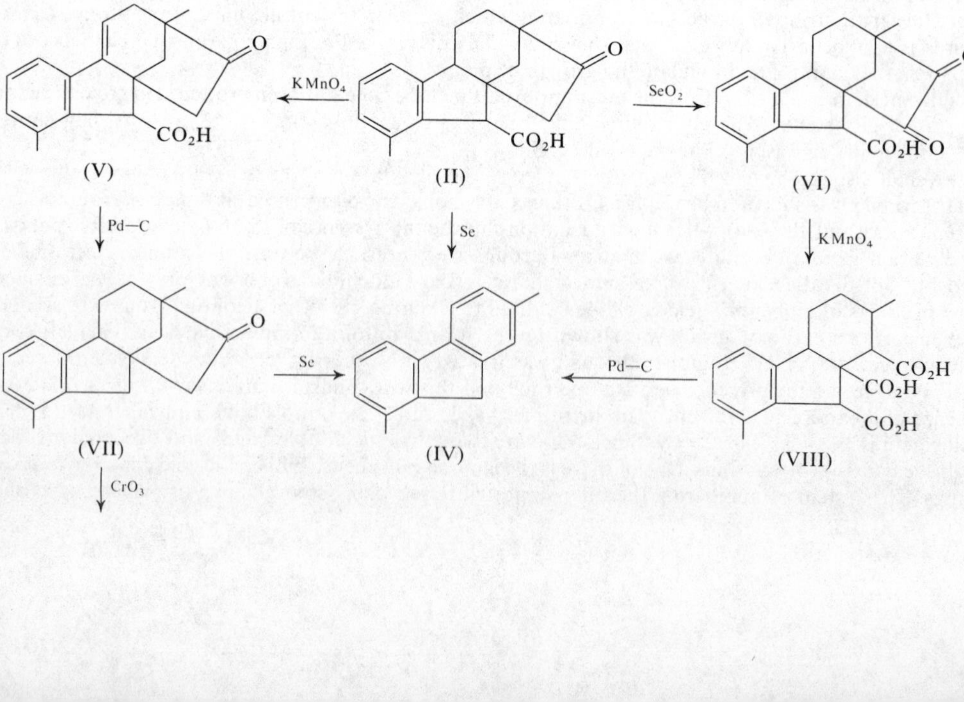

(IX)   (X)   (XI)

(XII)

The substitution pattern of the cyclopentanone ring fragment was deduced from the fact that the ultraviolet spectrum of the α-diketone (VI) showed that no enolisable hydrogen was present. The position of the carboxyl group was established by dehydrogenation of the methyl ester of (VI) to 1,7-dimethylfluorene-9-carboxylate, the structure of which was proved by synthesis.

The position of the —CH₂CO— bridge was established by the conversion of gibberone (VII) into the spiro-compound (IX) and this into (X) and (XI). (IX) was also converted (*via* oxime, Beckmann rearrangement, hydrolysis, and methylation) into a mixture of two diastereoisomers (XII), the structures of which have been confirmed by synthesis. Hence the —CH₂CO— bridge must be in the position given in (II). The structures of gibberone (VII) and gibberic acid (II) have been confirmed by total syntheses (Loewenthal *et al.*, 1960, 1962).

Some of the degradations carried out to establish the structure of allogibberic acid (III) are (XIII)–(XV). This acid contained a benzene ring (λ_{max} 266, 274 nm; *cf.* gibberic acid above) and an exocyclic methylene group (shown by ozonolysis to give formaldehyde and XIII). Since the methyl ester of allogibberic acid could be

(III)   (XIII)

(XIV)   (XV)

isomerised to methyl gibberate by acid, the position of the carboxyl group is the same in both acids. The third oxygen atom in allogibberic acid was shown to be hydroxylic (ν_{max} 3 460 cm^{-1}) and was assumed to be tertiary because of the difficulty of acetylation and the failure to oxidise dihydroallogibberic acid to a ketone (*cf.* gibberellic acid, above). (XIV) was shown to be a ketodicarboxylic acid in which the carbonyl group was in a cyclohexane ring. Conversion of (XIV) into (XV), the structure of which was proved by synthesis, established the position of the carbonyl group. All of these facts support (III) as the structure of allogibberic acid.

Since methyl gibberellate is isomerised by acid to methyl gibberate, the carboxyl group is in the same position in (I), (II) and (III). Also, ozonolysis of methyl gibberellate followed by oxidation, gave a keto-acid which could be converted into the dimethyl ester of (XIV). Hence, gibberellic acid and allogibberic acid differ only in the

Me ester of (I)   Me$_2$ ester of (XIV)

nature of ring A, which must undergo aromatisation in the former to give the latter. Ring A in gibberellic acid therefore contains one ethylenic double bond, a secondary hydroxyl group, a methyl group, and a γ-lactone ring. The position of the hydroxyl group was established by the fact that the selenium dehydrogenation of two ketones derived from gibberellin A$_1$ (see XIX) gave 1-methylfluoren-2-ol and 1,7-dimethylfluoren-2-ol, *i.e.*, the hydroxyl group is *vicinal* to the methyl group in ring A. Also, since oxidation of methyl gibberellate with manganese dioxide gave an α,β-unsaturated ketone (XVI; λ$_{max}$ 228 nm), the position of the double bond is established. The position of the lactone ring was deduced as being allylic because (i) catalytic reduction converted methyl gibberellate into the acid (XVII) in very high yield, and (ii) the formation of a heteroannular diene, gibberellenic acid (XVIII; λ$_{max}$ 253 nm; see §3viii), from gibberellic acid in aqueous solution. Structure (I) fits the facts and is supported by NMR studies (Sheppard, 1960).

Me ester of (I)   (XVI)

(XVII)   (XVIII)

The stereochemistry of gibberellic acid has been based largely on the work described. Thus, the dimethyl ester of (XIV), on hydrolysis, gave (XIV) and its C-9 epimer. Both of these, on heating with acetic anhydride, were converted into the *same* cyclic anhydride, hydrolysis of which gave only (XIV). Hence the substituents at 9 and 8a must be *cis* (*cf.* **4** §5a), and therefore the C-10 carboxyl group and the 8,9-bridge (gibbane numbering) must be *cis* in allogibberic acid. Now, the catalytic hydrogenation of dehydroallogibberic acid (XX) would be expected to occur at the less-hindered side of the molecule (see **4** §5l), *i.e.*, the hydrogen atom at C-4b will be on the side *opposite* to the C-10 carboxyl group and the 8,9-bridge. Also, since this reduction generated the original stereochemistry at C-4b, rings B/C must therefore be *trans*-fused in allogibberic acid. Furthermore, because gibberellic acid differs from allogibberic acid only in ring A (see above), this led to the proposal that the B/C fusion in the former acid is *trans*. However, the examination of the CD curves of ketone (XXI)—derived from (XIX)—showed that the configuration of the C-4b hydrogen was β, *i.e.*, the rings B/C are *cis*-fused. Thus, this is the configuration in gibberellic acid. It therefore follows that in the conversion of gibberellic acid (I) into allogibberic acid (III), C-4b is epimerised.

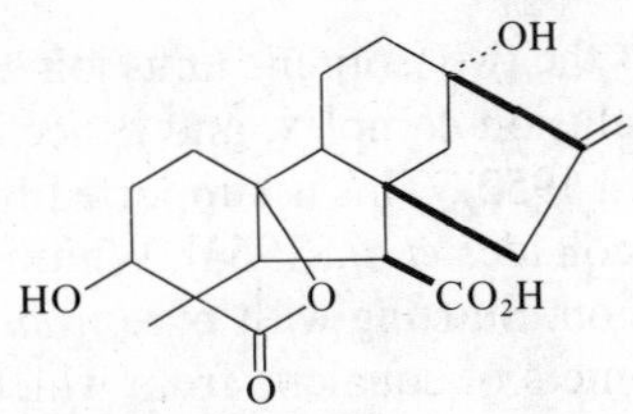

(XIX) 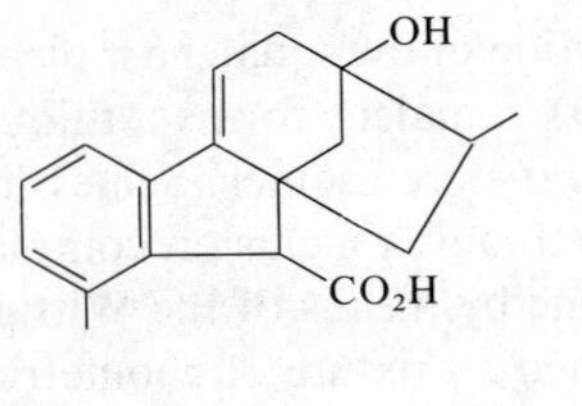   (XX) 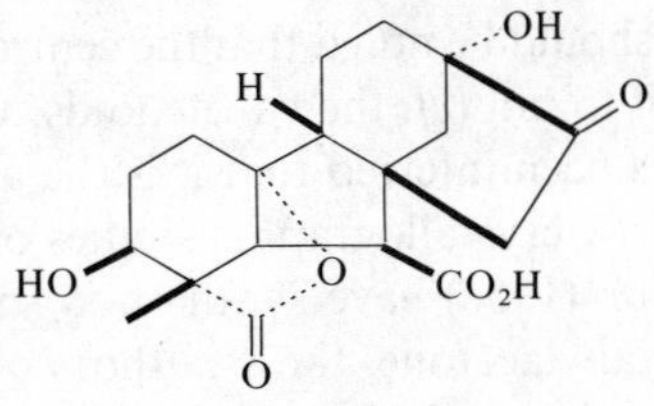   (XXI)

Since gibberellin A_1 (XIX) readily undergoes base-catalysed isomerisation at the C-2 hydroxyl group, this suggests that the C-2 hydroxyl group is axial in (XIX) and is therefore quasi-axial in gibberellic acid (unstable axial → stable equatorial).

The chemical behaviour of (XVII) led to the suggestion that the lactone ring in gibberellic acid had the β-configuration. However, the X-ray analysis of methyl bromogibberellate showed that the lactone ring had an α-configuration (McCapra *et al.*, 1962). On the basis of the evidence presented, the absolute stereochemistry of gibberellic acid is that shown in (I*a*).

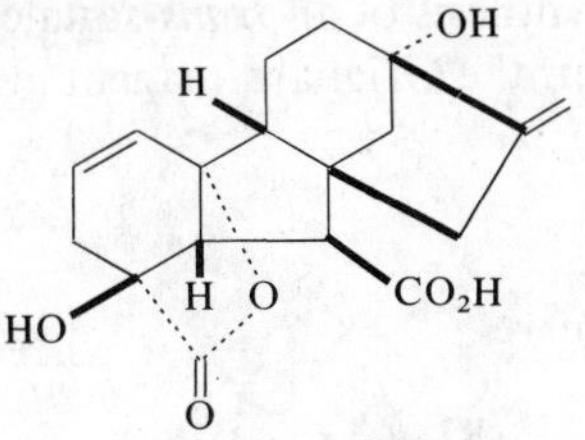

(I*a*)
gibberellic acid

Many diterpenoid alkaloids are also known, and so are many pentacyclic diterpenoids.

Triterpenoids

§33. Squalene, $C_{30}H_{50}$, b.p. 240–242°C/4 mm

It has been isolated from the liver oils of sharks. Other sources are olive oil and several other vegetable oils. Squalene has also been detected in leaves. Catalytic hydrogenation (nickel) converts squalene into perhydrosqualene, $C_{30}H_{62}$; therefore squalene has six double bonds, and is acyclic. Ozonolysis of squalene gives, among other products, laevulic acid; this suggests that the group (I) is present in squalene. Since squalene cannot be reduced by sodium and amyl alcohol, there are no conjugated double bonds present in the molecule. Perhydrosqualene was found to be identical with the product obtained by subjecting hexahydrofarnesyl bromide to the Wurtz reaction. This led Karrer *et al.* (1931) to synthesise squalene (II) from farnesyl bromide by a Wurtz reaction.

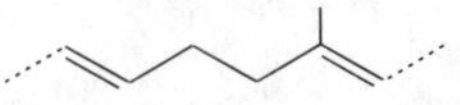

(I)

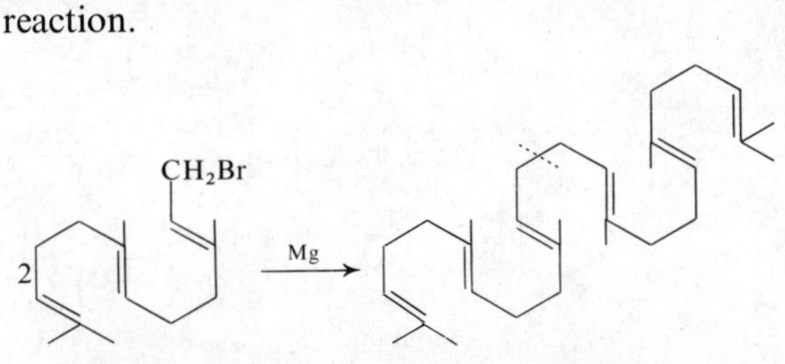

(II)
squalene (all-*trans*)

It should be noted that the centre portion of the squalene molecule has the two isoprene units joined tail to tail (*cf.* the carotenoids, Ch. 9). Squalene forms a thiourea inclusion complex, and hence it has been inferred that it is the all-*trans*-stereoisomer (Schiessler *et al.*, 1952). This is supported by X-ray crystallographic studies of the thiourea inclusion complex (Nicolaides *et al.*, 1954). Whiting *et al.* (1958) have synthesised squalene by means of the Wittig reaction. Starting with pure *trans*-geranylacetone, these authors obtained a mixture of geometrical isomers of squalene from which they isolated 12·5 per cent pure all-*trans*-squalene *via* the thiourea complex (see also §26a). This isomer was identical with natural squalene.

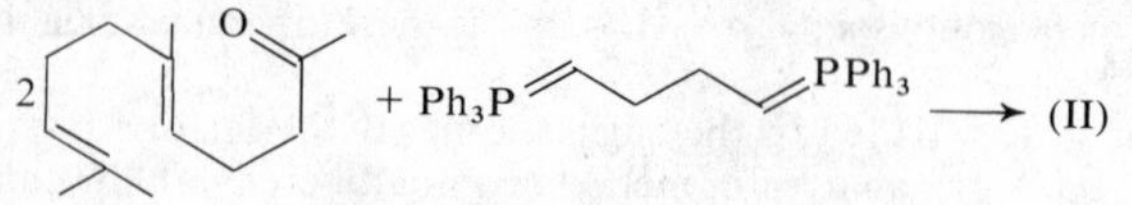

On the other hand, Cornforth *et al.* (1959), using a general stereoselective synthesis of alkenes, have carried out a highly stereoselective synthesis of all-*trans*-squalene. The alkene-synthesis is based on the principle of asymmetric induction; the Grignard reagent attacks the ketone, an α-chloroketone, from the less hindered side (see 3 §7):

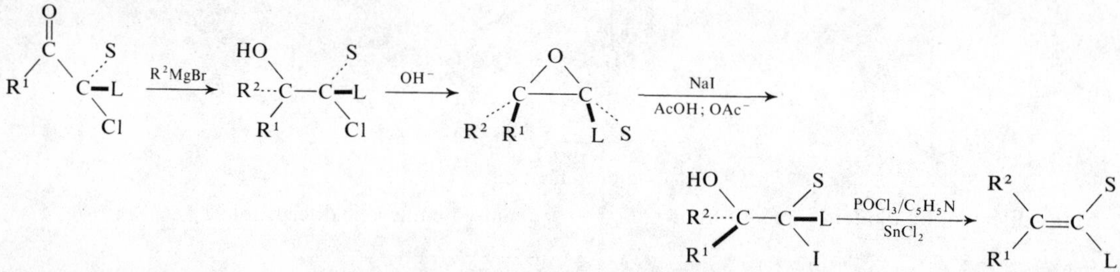

The assignment of the configuration of the alkene is based on the observation that the α-chloro-ketone is most reactive in the conformation shown, even though this conformation may be present in low concentration (*cf.* 4 §5m). This synthesis gave an 18–20 per cent yield of all-*trans*-squalene.

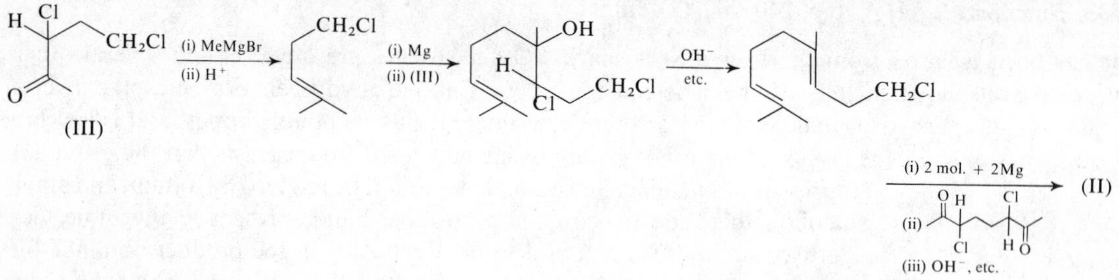

§33a. **Ambrein.**   This is a *tricyclic triterpenoid* alcohol that has been isolated from ambergris (a secretion of the sperm whole).

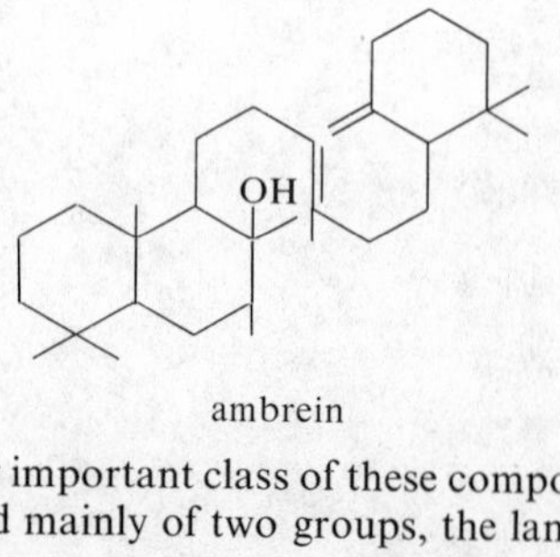

ambrein

§33b. **Tetracyclic triterpenoids.**   A very important class of these compounds is that which contains the steroid carbon skeleton. This class is comprised mainly of two groups, the lanosterol and the euphol group.

lanosterol   euphol

§33c. Pentacyclic triterpenoids. These are comprised of various subgroups, *e.g.*, oleanane (β-amyrin) group, ursane (α-amyrin) group, lupane (lupeol) group, etc.

β-amyrin   α-amyrin

lupeol

Biosynthesis of terpenoids.

§34. As more and more natural products were synthesised in the laboratory, so grew the interest in how these compounds are synthesised in the living organism (both animal and plant). The general approach to biosynthesis has been to break up the structure into units from which the compound could plausibly be derived. These units must, however, be known, or can be expected, to be available in the organism. Furthermore, this does not means that the units chosen must necessarily be involved in the building-up of the compound. The general principle is that although a particular unit may itself be involved, it is also possible that its 'equivalent' may act as a substitute, *i.e.*, any compound that can readily give rise to this unit (by means of various reactions such as reduction, oxidation, etc.) may be the actual compound involved in the biosynthesis; *e.g.*, the equivalent of formaldehyde could be formic acid, and that of acetone acetoacetic acid. One other point about the choice of units or their equivalents is to attempt to find some relationships between the various groups of natural products so that the units chosen are *common* precursors.

When the units have been chosen, the next problem is to consider the types of reactions whereby the natural products are synthesised in the organism. The general principle is to use reactions which have been developed in the laboratory. The difficulty here is that some types of laboratory reactions require conditions that cannot operate in the organism, *e.g.*, carboxylation and decarboxylation are known biological processes, but when carried out in the laboratory, these reactions normally require elevated temperatures. Deamination is also a known biological process, but in the laboratory this reaction is usually carried out under conditions (of pH) which would be lethal to the living organism. These differences between laboratory syntheses and biosyntheses are due to the action of enzymes in the latter. Chemical syntheses (these do not involve the use of enzymes) must therefore, from the point of biosynthetic studies, be carried out under conditions of pH and temperatures comparable with those operating in plants. Chemical syntheses performed in this way (with the suitable units) are said to be carried out under *physiological conditions* (which involve a pH of about 7 in aqueous media and ordinary temperatures).

Another term used in connection with the study of the synthesis of natural products in the living organism is **biogenesis**. This term appears to have several meanings. One is that biogenesis and biosynthesis are synonymous. Another, on the other hand, makes a distinction between the two. In this case, biogenesis is a *collection of hypotheses* which have been proposed to describe the syntheses of natural products in the living organism. Thus biogenesis describes *hypothetical* transformations, whereas biosynthesis describes the *actual* pathways whereby natural products are synthesised in the living organism. Furthermore, biogenesis is often an *overall picture* and does not necessarily state individual steps which are involved in the syntheses.

Reactions which are commonly postulated in biosynthesis are oxidation, hydrogenation, dehydrogenation, dehydration, esterification, hydrolysis, carboxylation, decarboxylation, amination, deamination, isomerisation, condensation and polymerisation. It might be noted here that the choice of units and type of reaction are usually dependent on each other. Furthermore, other reactions which are known to occur in biological syntheses are *O*- and *N*-methylation or acylation. These may be described as *extra-skeletal processes*, and can occur at any suitable stage in the postulated biosynthesis. Another extra-skeletal process is *C*-methylation, but this is much rarer than those mentioned above.

Probably the most satisfactory method of elucidating biosynthetic pathways is the use of isotopic labelling. The labels used in terpenoid biosynthesis are: ^{2}H (D), ^{3}H (T), ^{13}C, ^{14}C, ^{18}O, and ^{32}P. These have generally been used separately but sometimes they have been used in combination. The general approach has been the incorporation of the isotopic label indiscriminately at first and then with increasing specificity, into a precursor or suspected precursor of the natural product under investigation. Then the labelled compounds are introduced into an enzyme-containing system, which may be the whole living organism, or preparations of its tissues, or 'synthetic' enzyme systems. Finally, the labelled product is isolated after a period of incubation.

Now let us apply these principles to the biosynthesis of terpenoids. As we have seen, according to the special isoprene rule, terpenoids are built up of isoprene units joined head to tail (§1). Assuming then that the isoprene unit is the basic unit, the problem is: How is it formed, and how do these units join to form the various types of terpenoids? At present it is believed that the fundamental units used in the cell in syntheses are water, carbon dioxide, formic acid (as 'active formate'), and acetic acid (as 'active acetate'). These 'active' compounds are acyl derivatives of coenzyme A. This coenzyme is a complex thiol derivative (see later) and is usually written as CoA—SH, but CoA is also in common usage. Thus, acetylcoenzyme A may be represented as CH_3CO—SCoA or CH_3CO—CoA. This compound is 'energy-rich' (see **13** §15). Now the biosynthesis of cholesterol (**11** §13) from acetic acid labelled with ^{14}C in the methyl group (C_m) and in the carboxyl group (C_c) has led to the suggestion that the carbon atoms in the isoprene unit are distributed as shown in (**A**).

This distribution is in agreement with a scheme in which senecioic acid (3-methylbut-2-enoic acid) is formed first, and this pathway was supported by the isolation of this acid from natural sources. Further support for the formation of this carbon skeleton was given by the fact that labelled isovaleric acid (**B**) gives rise to cholesterol in which the isopropyl group and the carboxyl group have been incorporated.

$$C_m \diagdown_{C_c - C_m - C_c} \diagup^{C_m} \qquad\qquad {}^{13}CH_3 \diagdown_{CHCH_2{}^{14}CO_2H} \diagup^{{}^{13}CH_3}$$

(A)   (B)

Tavormina *et al.* (1956), however, have shown that the lactone of mevalonic acid (β-hydroxy-β-methyl-δ-valerolactone) is converted almost completely into cholesterol by rat liver, and is a much better precursor than senecioic acid. Further work has now shown that the five-carbon precursors mentioned above are first degraded to acetate, which is then built up into mevalonic acid. The structure of mevalonic acid has been proved by synthesis (Tschesche *et al.*, 1960) and the absolute configuration of this acid has been shown to be (R) (Eberle *et al.*, 1960).

The conversion of acetate into mevalonic acid is believed to proceed as follows (NADPH is nicotinamide-adenine dinucleotide phosphate; see **13** §15).

$$2CH_3CO_2H + 2CoA—SH \longrightarrow 2H_2O + 2CH_3CO—SCoA \rightleftharpoons CoA—SH + \underset{S—CoA}{\overset{O\quad O}{\diagdown\diagup}} \xrightarrow{CH_3CO—SCoA}$$

(R)-HMG   mevaldic acid   (R)-MVA

Hydroxymethylglutarate (HMG) is reduced stepwise (*via* mevaldic acid) to mevalonic acid (MVA). This is believed to be the most important route to HMG, but it can be formed by other processes (see **15** §16).

The biosynthesis of terpenoids can be subdivided into three definite steps: (i) the formation of a biological isopentane unit from acetate; (ii) the condensation of this unit to form acyclic terpenoids; (iii) the conversion of acyclic into cyclic terpenoids.

Since mevalonic acid contains six carbon atoms, one must be lost to form the isopentane unit. By starting with labelled MVA (2-^{14}C), it has been shown that it is the carboxyl group in MVA which is lost. The steps involved in this transformation are believed to be as shown (ADP is adenosine diphosphate and ATP is adenosine triphosphate; see also **13** §15).

MVA   (I)   (II)   (III)

Phosphorylation of MVA first produces MVA 5-phosphate (I) (P = PO_3H_2; see also **7** §23a), and this is followed by a second phosphorylation to give MVA 5-pyrophosphate (II) (PP = $P_2O_6H_3$). (II) now loses a molecule of water to form 3-methylbut-3-enyl (isopentenyl) pyrophosphate (III). The details of this conversion are uncertain, but there is reason to believe it might be (note the *trans* elimination):

(II) $\xrightarrow{\text{ATP} \quad \text{ADP}}$ (III) + CO_2 + HOP

Evidence for this comes from the fact that one mole of ATP is converted into one mole of ADP, and one mole of inorganic phosphate is produced. However, the 3-phosphate has not yet been isolated. Thus, the biogenetic isoprene unit is 3-methylbut-3-enyl pyrophosphate, but its participation in the biosynthesis of terpenoids involves its equilibration, in the presence of the appropriate enzyme, with 3-methylbut-2-enyl (β,β-dimethylallyl) pyrophosphate (IV). This isomerisation is stereospecific,

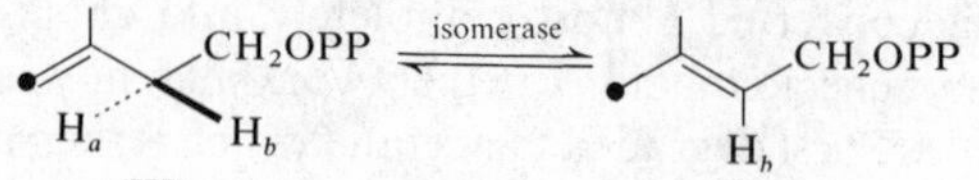

H_a being the proton that is eliminated. Also, the newly formed Me group is *trans* to the CH_2OPP group.

On the basis of the biosynthetic studies carried out, another isoprene rule (in addition to the isoprene and special isoprene rules, §1) has been formulated. This is known as the *biogenetic isoprene rule*, and states that members of the isopentane group should be derivable from simple hypothetical precursors such as geraniol, farnesol and squalene. The biogenetic isoprene rule also includes compounds that originated from regular isoprenoid precursors which, by rearrangement or degradation, give products that no longer obey the isoprene rule, *e.g.*, gibberellins (§32a).

We shall now consider the biosynthesis of the various classes of terpenoids.

The monoterpenoids

All the experimental evidence supports the view that units (III) and (IV) combine to form geranyl pyrophosphate (*trans* isomer), (III) acting as the nucleophilic reagent and (IV) as the electrophilic reagent (to give head to tail union). The steps involved are not yet clear (an enzyme may be involved as an intermediate complex). The reaction is therefore shown in its simplest form:

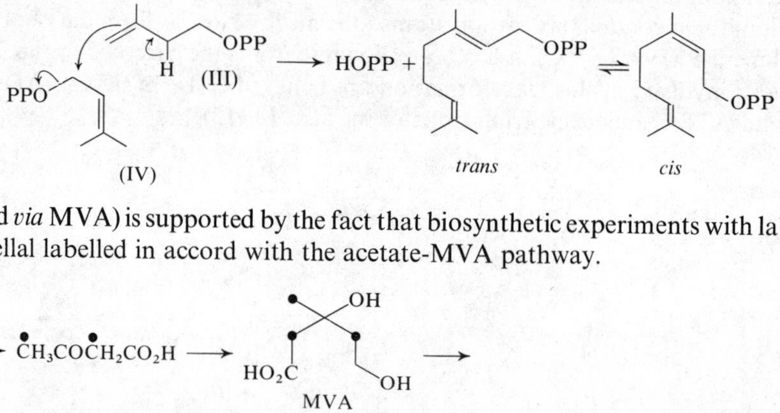

This route (and *via* MVA) is supported by the fact that biosynthetic experiments with labelled acetate lead to citronellal labelled in accord with the acetate-MVA pathway.

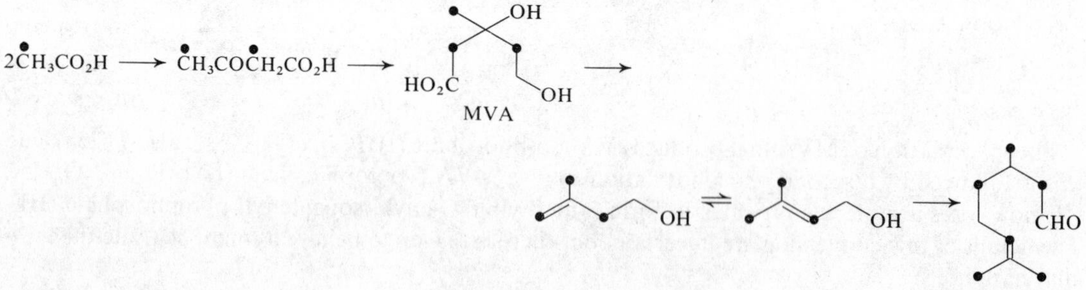

Geranyl pyrophosphate now serves as the precursor for the monocyclic monoterpenoids *via* the *cis*-isomer (nerol). The mechanisms involved in ring-closure are not certain, but a favoured one is *via* ionic intermediates (see the acid-catalysed cyclisation of geraniol into α-terpineol, §7); *e.g.*,

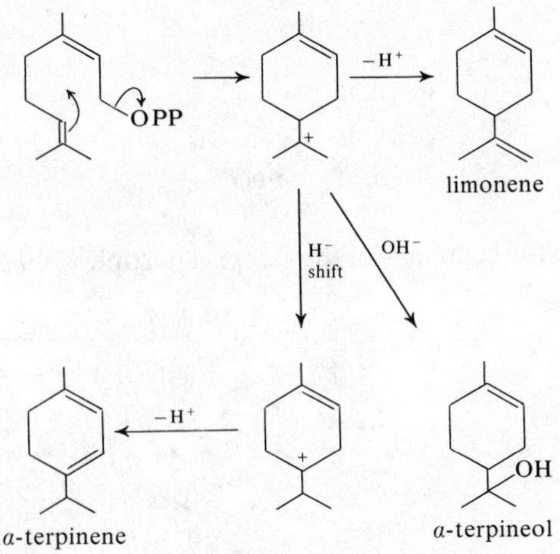

limonene

−H⁺

H⁻ shift

OH⁻

α-terpinene   −H⁺   α-terpineol

It is then reasonable to extend these arguments to the formation of bicyclic monoterpenoids, *e.g.*, (see also camphor, §23a).

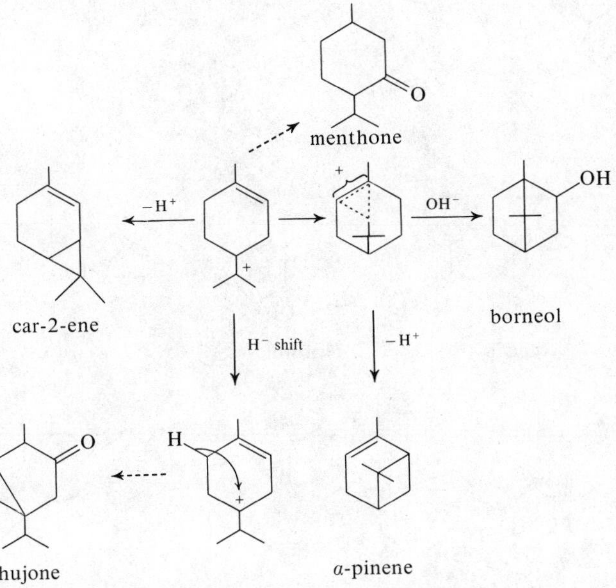

menthone

−H⁺

car-2-ene

OH⁻

borneol

H⁻ shift   −H⁺

thujone   α-pinene

There is, however, some evidence obtained from biosynthetic experiments that is not in accord with the labelling of the products based on the mechanisms given.

The sesquiterpenoids

The arguments developed for the monoterpenoids can now be applied to the sesquiterpenoids, but in the latter the key compound is farnesyl pyrophosphate. Geranyl pyrophosphate contains the 3-methylbut-2-enyl structure and hence it can be anticipated that this can react with the nucleophilic 3-methylbut-3-enyl pyrophosphate to extend the chain by a five-carbon unit. This would give the *trans*-isomer and then, just as for the cyclic monoterpenoids, farnesyl pyrophosphate can undergo cyclisation *via* carbonium ions to form cyclic sesquiterpenoids. However, it appears that the course of the cyclisation depends on the geometry of the farnesyl pyrophosphate, *e.g.* (note the non-classical ion intermediates):

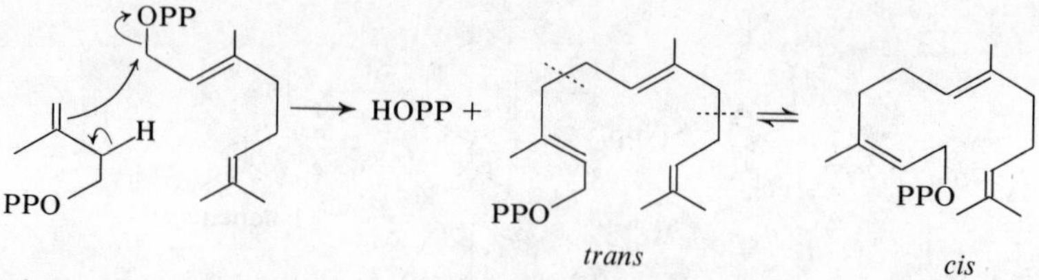

(i)

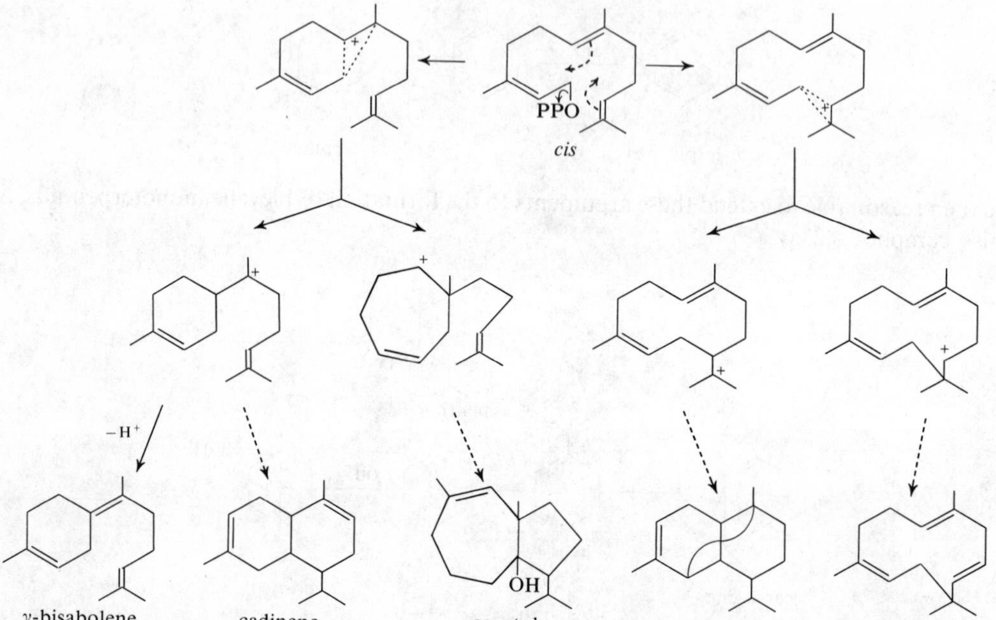

γ-bisabolene   cadinene   carotol   copaene   humulene

(ii)

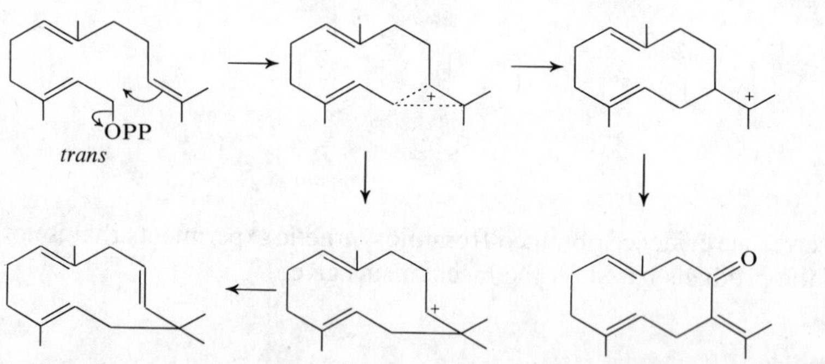

humulene   germacrone

The diterpenoids

The key compound for this group is geranylgeranyl pyrophosphate, formed by the addition of an isopentyl unit to farnesyl pyrophosphate (*cf.* sesquiterpenoids, above). Thus, for example, cembrene may be postulated as being formed as follows:

cembrene

The biosynthesis of bicyclic and polycyclic diterpenoids proceeds by mechanisms similar to those of the steroids (see **11** §13).

The triterpenoids

The key compound is squalene but its biosynthesis is still the subject of much discussion. Formally, it may be regarded as being formed by the linkage of two farnesyl pyrophosphate residues joined tail to tail. This reaction may be represented as:

Just how this linkage is formed and what intermediates are involved are still uncertain.

The cyclisation of squalene is discussed in **11** §13.

Polyterpenes

§35. Rubber

Rubber (*caoutchouc*) is obtained from latex, which is an emulsion of rubber particles in water that is obtained from the inner bark of many types of trees which grow in the tropics and sub-tropics. When the bark of the rubber tree is cut, latex slowly exudes from the cut. Addition of acetic acid coagulates the rubber, which is then separated from the liquor and either pressed into blocks or rolled into sheets, and finally dried in a current of warm air, or smoked.

Crude latex rubber contains, in addition to the actual rubber hydrocarbons (90–95 per cent), proteins, sugars, fatty acids and resins, the amounts of these substances depending on the source. Crude rubber is soft and sticky, becoming more so as the temperature rises. It has a low tensile strength and its elasticity is exhibited only over a narrow range of temperature. When treated with solvents such as benzene, ether, light petrol, a large part of the crude rubber dissolves; the rest swells but does not dissolve. This insoluble fraction apparently contains almost all of the protein impurity. On the other hand, rubber is insoluble in acetone, methanol, etc. When unstretched, rubber is amorphous; stetching or prolonged cooling causes rubber to crystallise.

Structure of rubber.   The destructive distillation of rubber gives isoprene as one of the main products; this led to the suggestion that rubber is a polymer of isoprene, and therefore to the molecular formula $(C_5H_8)_n$. This molecular formula has been confirmed by the analysis of pure rubber. Crude rubber may be purified by fractional precipitation from benzene solution by the addition of acetone. This fractional precipitation, however, produces molecules of different sizes, as shown by the determination of the molecular weights of the various fractions by osmotic pressure, viscosity and ultracentrifuge measurements; molecular weights of the order of 300 000 have been obtained.

The halogens and the halogen acids readily add on to rubber, *e.g.*, bromine gives an addition product of formula $(C_5H_8Br_2)_n$, and the hydrogen chloride the addition product $(C_5H_9Cl)_n$. Pure rubber has been hydrogenated to the fully saturated hydrocarbon $(C_5H_{10})_n$—this is known as *hydrorubber*—by heating with hydrogen in the presence of platinum as catalyst (Pummerer *et al.*, 1922). Rubber also forms an ozonide of formula $(C_5H_8O_3)_n$. All these addition reactions clearly indicate that rubber is an unsaturated compound, and the formulae of the addition products show that there is one double bond for each isoprene unit present.

Ozonolysis of rubber produces laevulaldehyde and its peroxide, laevulic acid and small amounts of carbon dioxide, formic acid and succinic acid (Harries, 1905–1912). Pummerer (1931) showed that the laevulic derivatives comprised about 90 per cent of the products formed by the ozonolysis. This observation led to the suggestion that rubber is composed of isoprene units joined head to tail. Thus, if rubber has the following structure, the formation of the products of ozonolysis can be explained:

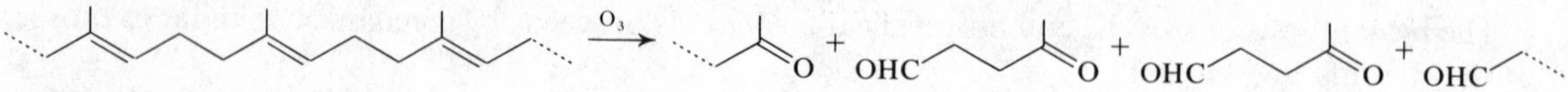

Some of the laevulaldehyde is further oxidised to laevulic and succinic acids.

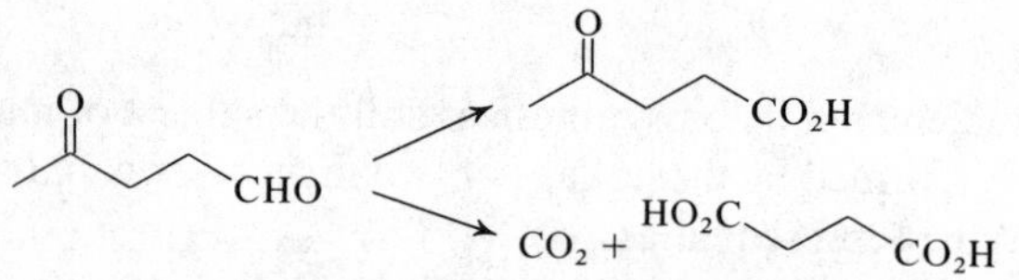

Gutta-percha.   (Also obtained from the bark of various trees.) It is isomeric with rubber; their structures are the same, as shown by the methods of analysis that were used for rubber. X-ray diffraction studies (Bunn, 1942)

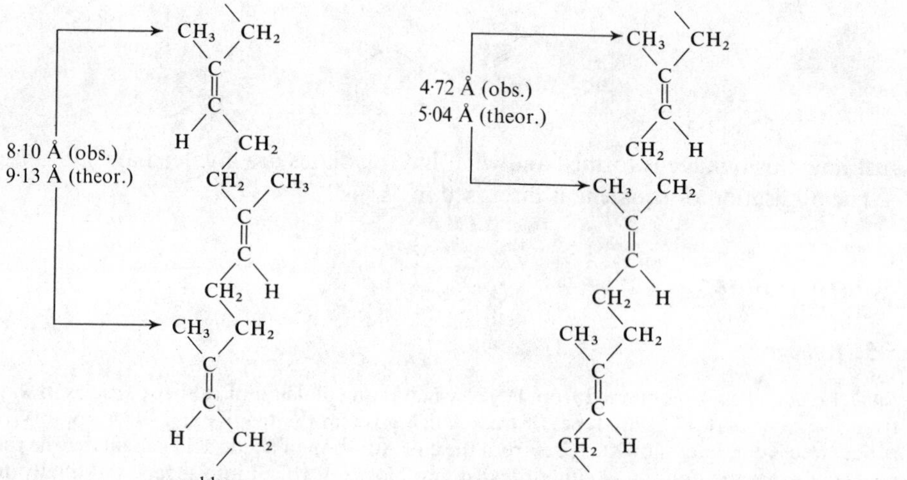

have shown that rubber is composed of long chains built up of isoprene units arranged in the *cis*-form, whereas gutta-percha is the *trans*-form. Gutta-percha is hard and has a very low elasticity.

In rubber, the chain repeat unit is 8·10 Å, whereas in gutta-percha it is 4·72 Å. Both of these values are shorter than the theoretical values of the repeat distances (9·13 Å and 5·04 Å respectively) calculated from models. The reasons for these discrepancies are not clear, but for gutta-percha it has been explained by assuming that the isoprene units are not coplanar. The infrared absorption spectrum of rubber has bands which are in keeping with the structure that has been proposed. Also, the *linear* shape of the molecule is indicated by viscosity measurements of rubber solutions. Schulz *et al.* have examined cyclohexane solutions of rubber by light-scattering methods, and obtained a value of 1 300 000 for the molecular weight. Their other work also supports the linear nature of the chain.

The biosynthesis of natural rubber occurs by the indefinite linking of the five-carbon units discussed in §34, but each added unit must assume the *cis*-configuration. Just how this takes place is still to be solved.

§35a. Vulcanisation of rubber. When crude rubber is heated with a few per cent of sulphur, the rubber becomes *vulcanised*. Vulcanised rubber is less sticky than crude rubber, and is not so soluble and does not swell so much in organic solvents. Furthermore, vulcanised rubber has greater tensile strength and elasticity than crude rubber.

The mechanism of vulcanisation is still not clear. Vulcanised rubber is not so unsaturated as rubber itself, and it appears that intermolecular cross-links are formed which may be of two types:

$$
\begin{array}{ccccc}
-CH_2-CMe=CH-CH- & & -CH_2-CMe=CH-CH_2- & & -CH_2-CHMe-CH-CH_2- \\
\quad\quad\quad\quad\quad | & \xleftarrow{\ S\ } & & \xrightarrow{\ S\ } & \quad\quad\quad\quad\quad\quad | \\
\quad\quad\quad\quad\quad S & & & & \quad\quad\quad\quad\quad\quad S \\
\quad\quad\quad\quad\quad | & & & & \quad\quad\quad\quad\quad\quad | \\
-CH_2-CMe=CH-CH- & & -CH_2-CMe=CH-CH_2- & & -CH_2-CHMe-CH-CH_2-
\end{array}
$$

Attack at the saturated carbon atom can be attributed to the fact that this atom is in the allylic position. It is also possible that *both* types of cross-linkage occur along the pair of chains.

Vulcanisation may be accelerated and carried out at lower temperatures in the presence of certain organic compounds. These compounds are consequently known as *accelerators*, and all of them contain nitrogen or sulphur, or both, *e.g.*,

$NH=C\begin{array}{c}NHC_6H_5\\ \\NHC_6H_5\end{array}$	$(CH_3)_2N\overset{\underset{\|\|}{S}}{C}S\overset{\underset{\|\|}{S}}{C}N(CH_3)_2$	$(CH_3)_2N\overset{\underset{\|\|}{S}}{C}SZnS\overset{\underset{\|\|}{S}}{C}N(CH_3)_2$	benzothiazole-SH structure
diphenylguanidine	tetramethylthiuram disulphide	zinc dimethyldithiocarbamate	mercaptobenzothiazole

Mercaptobenzothiazole is the most widely used accelerator. Many inorganic compounds can also act as accelerators, *e.g.*, zinc oxide. Organic accelerators are promoted by these inorganic compounds, and current practice is to vulcanise rubber with, *e.g.*, mercaptobenzothiazole in the presence of zinc oxide.

The actual properties of vulcanised rubber depend on the amount of sulphur used, the best physical properties apparently being achieved by using about 3 per cent sulphur, 5 per cent zinc oxide and about 1 per cent of the accelerator. When 30–50 per cent sulphur is used, the product is *ebonite*.

The elasticity of rubber is believed to be due to the existence of rubber as long-chain molecules which are highly 'kinked' in the normal state. When subjected to a stretching force, these chains 'unkink', and return to their normal condition when the force is removed.

§35b. Synthetic rubbers. There are many synthetic rubbers in use, each type possessing certain desirable properties. A great deal of work has been done on the synthesis of *natural* rubber, but the difficulty has been to obtain the isoprene units in the all-*cis*-configuration. This has now been achieved by means of the Ziegler–Natta catalysts, *e.g.*, a triethylaluminium–titanium chloride complex to which has been added finely divided lithium (see Vol. I). The product obtained in this way is identical with natural rubber.

Buna rubbers. Under the influence of sodium, butadiene polymerises to a substance which has been used as a rubber substitute under the name of *Buna* (see Vol. I). *Buna N* is a synthetic rubber which is produced by the copolymerisation of butadiene and vinyl cyanide. *Buna S* or *Perbunan* is a copolymer of butadiene and styrene.

Butyl rubber. Copolymerisation of isobutene with a small amount of isoprene produces a polyisobutene known as *Butyl rubber*.

Neoprene. When passed into a solution of cuprous chloride in ammonium chloride, acetylene dimerises to vinylacetylene. This dimer can add on one molecule of hydrogen chloride to form *Chloroprene* (2-chlorobuta-1,3-diene), the addition taking place in accordance with Markownikoff's rule (see also Vol. I).

$$2CH\equiv CH \longrightarrow CH_2=CH-C\equiv CH \xrightarrow{HCl} CH_2=CH-CCl=CH_2$$

Chloropene readily polymerises to a rubber-like substance known as *Neoprene*. Actually, the nature of the polychloroprene depends on the conditions of the polymerisation.

REFERENCES

The Terpenes, Cambridge University Press (2nd edn.). Sir John Simonsen and Owen. Vol. I (1947); Vol. II (1949). Sir John Simonsen and Barton. Vol. III (1952). Sir John Simonsen and Ross. Vol. IV (1957); Vol. V (1957).

MAYO, Vol. I. *Mono-* and *Sesquiterpenoids*. Vol. II. *The Higher Terpenoids*. Interscience (1959).

PINDER, *The Chemistry of the Terpenes*, Chapman and Hall (1960).

FLORKIN and STOTZ, *Comprehensive Biochemistry*, Elsevier. Vol. 9 (1963). Part B. 'Isoprenoid Compounds.'

RUZICKA, 'History of the Isoprene Rule', *Proc. chem. Soc.*, 1959, 341.

Rodd's Chemistry of Carbon Compounds, Elsevier (2nd edn.). Vol. IIB (1968); Vol. IIC (1969).

TEMPLETON, *An Introduction to the Chemistry of the Terpenoids and Steroids*, Butterworths (1969).

Terpenoids and Steroids, Specialist Periodical Reports. The Chemical Society, Vol. 1 (1971).

MAYO (ed.), *Molecular Rearrangements*, Interscience (1964). Part I. Ch. 3. 'Carbonium Ion Rearrangements in Bridged Bicyclic Systems.' Part II. Ch. 13. 'Terpenoid Rearrangements.'

BUDZIKIEWIEZ, DJERASSI and WILLIAMS, *Structure Elucidation of Natural Products by Mass Spectrometry*, Holden-Day. Vol. II (1964). Chs. 23, 24. 'Terpenoids.'

MASSEY-WESTROPP, REYNOLDS, and SPOTSWOOD, 'Freelingyne, An Acetylenic Sesquiterpenoid', *Tetrahedron Letters*, 1966, 1939.

COREY *et al.*, 'Stereospecific Total Synthesis of the *dl*-C$_{18}$ Cecropia Juvenile Hormone', *J. Am. chem. Soc.*, 1968, **90**, 5618.

BERKOFF, 'The Chemistry and Biochemistry of Insect Hormones', *Quart. Rev.*, 1969, **23**, 372.

TROST, 'The Juvenile Hormone of Hyalophora Cecropia', *Accounts chem. Res.*, 1970, **3**, 120.

OHKUMA, ADDICOTT, SMITH, and THIESSEN, 'The Structure of Abscisin II', *Tetrahedron Letters*, 1965, 2529.

BARTON, BOCKMAN, and DE MAYO, 'Sesquiterpenoids. Part XII. Further Investigations on the Chemistry of Pyrethrosin', *J. chem. Soc.*, 1960, 2263.

MARTIN-SMITH *et al.*, 'Revised Structure of Aristolactone', *Tetrahedron Letters*, 1964, 2391.

SUCHÝ *et al.*, 'The Constitution of Arctiopicrin', *Tetrahedron Letters*, 1964, 3907.

MARSHALL and PIKE, 'Stereoselective Total Synthesis of Racemic β-Eudesmol', *Tetrahedron Letters*, 1965, 3107.

ENDO and DE MAYO, 'α-Vetivone', *Chem. Comm.*, 1967, 89.

MARSHALL, FAUBL, and WARNE, JUN., 'The Total Synthesis of Racemic Isonootkatone (α-Vetivone)', *Chem. Comm.*, 1967, 753.

MARSHALL and JOHNSON, 'The Total Synthesis of (±)-β-Vetivone', *Chem. Comm.*, 1968, 391.

COREY, MITRA, and UDA, 'Total Synthesis of d,l-Caryophyllene and d,l-Isocaryophyllene', *J. Am. chem. Soc.*, 1964, **86**, 485.

STORK and CLARKE, JR., 'Cedrol: Stereochemistry and Total Synthesis', *J. Am. chem. Soc.*, 1961, **83**, 3114.

STORK and SCHULENBERG, 'The Total Synthesis of d,l-Dehydroabietic acid', *J. Am. chem. Soc.*, 1956, **78**, 250.

APSIMON (ed.), *The Total Synthesis of Natural Products*, Wiley-Interscience. Vol. 2 (1973). pp. 1–640. 'The Synthesis of Monoterpenes, Sesquiterpenes, Triterpenes'.

BERNFELD (ed.), *Biogenesis of Natural Compounds*, Pergamon (1967), 2nd edn.). Ch. 14, 'The Biogenesis of Terpenes in Plants'. Ch. 16, 'Rubber Biosynthesis'.

GEISSMAN and GROUT, *Organic Chemistry of Secondary Plant Metabolism*, Freeman, Cooper and Co. (1969). Chs. 8–13. 'Terpenoids.'

MULHEIRN and RAMM, 'The Biosynthesis of Sterols', *Chem. Soc. Rev.*, 1972, **1**, 259.

9 Carotenoids

§1. Introduction

The carotenoids are yellow or red pigments which are widely distributed in plants and animals. Chlorophyll is always associated with the carotenoids carotene and lutein; the carotenoids acts as photosensitisers in conjunction with chlorophyll. When chlorophyll is absent, *e.g.*, in fungi, then the carotenoids are mainly responsible for colour. Carotenoids are also known as lipochromes or chromolipids because they are fat-soluble pigments. They give a deep blue colour with concentrated sulphuric acid and with a chloroform solution of antimony trichloride (the Carr-Price reaction); this Carr–Price reaction is the basis of one method of the quantitative estimation of carotenoids. Some carotenoids are hydrocarbons; these are known as the *carotenes*. Other carotenoids are oxygenated derivatives of the carotenes; these are the *xanthophylls*. There are also the *xanthophyll esters* which are the natural esters of hydroxy-carotenoids. Finally, there are some natural polyenes which contain fewer than 40 carbon atoms but are structurally related to the carotenoids. These are generally classified as the 'apocarotenoids' and contain aldehyde or carboxyl groups, *e.g.*, bixin, crocetin (these are carotenoid acids). When the loss of carbon atoms occurs at one end of the C_{40}

chain, this is shown by a numeral which follows the prefix 'apo' and indicates the last carbon atom remaining from the parent carotenoid, *e.g.*, β-apo-12′-carotenal (see §3 for numbering).

Carotenoids may also be classified on the basis of their partition between the two immiscible solvents 90 per cent aqueous methanol and light petrol. Hydrocarbons, xanthophyll esters, and carotenoids which contain an ether group or one oxo group appear in the upper (light petrol) phase; these are **epiphasic carotenoids**. Those carotenoids which contain two or more hydroxyl groups appear in the lower (aqueous methanol) phase; these are the **hypophasic carotenoids**. Carotenoids which contain one hydroxyl group, two oxo groups or a carboxyl group are distributed between both phases.

Chemically, the carotenoids are polyenes, and almost all the carotenoid hydrocarbons have the molecular formula $C_{40}H_{56}$. Also, since the carbon skeleton of these compounds has a polyisoprene structure, they may be regarded as tetraterpenes (*cf.* **8** §1).

In most of the carotenoids, the central portion of the molecule is composed of a long conjugated chain comprised of four isoprene units, the centre two of which are joined tail to tail. The ends of the chain may be two open-chain structures, or one open-chain structure and one ring, or two rings. The colour of the carotenoids is attributed to the extended conjugation of the central chain (see Vol. I). X-ray analysis has shown that in the majority of natural carotenoids, the double bonds are in the all-*trans*-position; a few natural carotenoids are *cis-trans*. Thus, if we represent the ends of the chain by R (where R may be an open-chain structure or a ring system), all-*trans*-carotenes may be written:

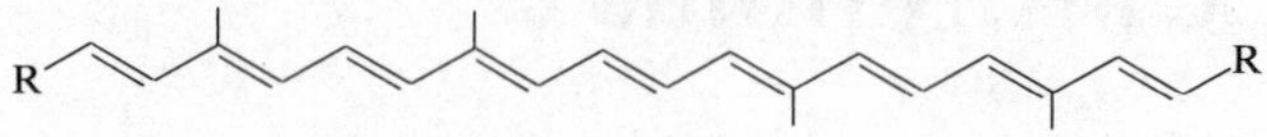

The earlier method of separating carotenoids used adsorption chromatography (see §2), but now both paper and thin-layer chromatography are used for the separation and analysis of carotenoids (Jensen, 1963; Stahl *et al.*, 1963).

Characterisation of carotenoids by means of their melting points is unreliable, since this physical constant depends on the rate of heating. The best way of characterising carotenoids is by their visible, infrared and NMR spectra. However, it is important to note that the visible maxima depend very much on the nature of the solvent, *e.g.* (principal absorption band):

Compound	Solvent	
	Light petroleum	Chloroform
α-carotene	444 nm	454 nm
β-carotene	451	466
γ-carotene	462	475
lycopene	475·5	480

The empirical rules developed for the ultraviolet absorption spectra in terpenoid (and steroid) chemistry (see **8** §3viii) cannot be applied to carotenoids; the rules are satisfactory only for polyenes up to 3 or 4 double bonds in conjugation.

Geometrical isomerism of the carotenes.   It has already been pointed out above that the majority of natural carotenoids are all-*trans*-isomers, but a few are *cis-trans*-isomers. Theoretically, a very large number of geometrical isomers are possible, but isomerisation has been found to produce relatively few of them. Thus, lycopene, with 11 double bonds, can theoretically exist in 1 056 geometrical isomeric forms; about 40 have been prepared so far. An interesting point in this connection is that Pauling (1939) pointed out that steric hindrance in the *cis*-configuration (I) is very small, but that this is not the case in the *cis*-configuration (II). In keeping with this is the fact that isomerisation of

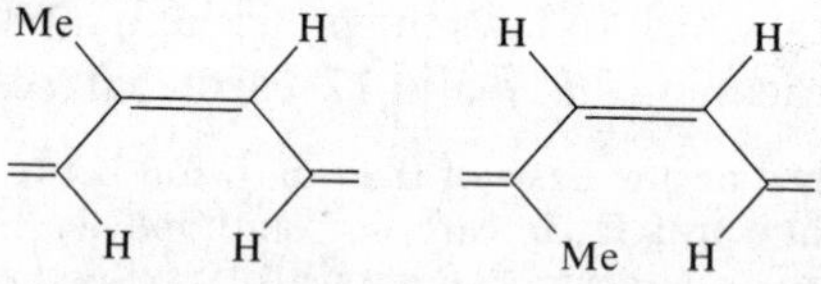

(I)   (II)

all-*trans*-isomers apparently never produces isomers with configuration (II). If (II) is excluded from lycopene isomers, then the number with configuration (I) is now 72. However, some isomers containing configuration (II) have been prepared by synthesis.

The general methods of effecting stereomutation of carotenoids is to heat them in solution, irradiate solutions with light of wavelength corresponding to the principal absorption band, or irradiation of solutions containing a catalytic amount of iodine. The last method appears to be the best.

There is still another problem in connection with the geometry of all-*trans*-isomers. There are two extreme planar conformations when the end-group is a β-ionone ring, the *s-cis* and the *s-trans*, i.e., *cis* and *trans* about the 6,7-*single* bond (see buta-diene, Vol. I). Between these extremes are those confor-mations in which the ring and chain are not coplanar. Ultraviolet and NMR spectroscopy have shown that the conformations are not planar, but X-ray analysis, how-ever, of some all-*trans*-carotenoids has shown that their conformations (in the crystalline state) are close to the *s-cis*.

s-cis   *s-trans*

The non-planarity has been ascribed to steric effects (between the ring methyl groups and hydrogen at position 7); this prevents complete conjugation of the ring double bond with the unsaturated side-chain. Thus, e.g., this accounts for λ_{max} of β-carotene (two β-ionone rings) being shorter than that of γ-carotene (one acyclic end) and lycopene (two acyclic ends).

Since the overall length of the all-*trans*-isomer is greater than that of any *cis*-isomer, the former would be expected to absorb at a longer wavelength. This is the case in practice. Furthermore, the spectra of *cis*-isomers often show a 'cis-peak', i.e., a peak that is *absent* in the all-*trans*-isomer. The all-*trans*-form of a carotenoid is usually the most stable one, i.e., more stable than any *cis*-form; it also usually has the highest melting point and lowest solubility.

Infrared spectroscopy, apart from being used to characterised carotenoids, is very useful as an analytical tool. The presence of common functional groups may readily be ascertained: hydroxyl (unbonded, $3\,670$–$3\,580$ cm^{-1}); carbonyl group (acyclic aldehyde, $1\,740$–$1\,720$ cm^{-1}; acyclic ketone, $1\,725$–$1\,700$ cm^{-1}; α,β-unsaturated carbonyl compounds, $1\,705$–$1\,660$ cm^{-1}). The presence of *trans* double bonds is shown by the appearance of a band at ~ 960 cm^{-1}, and *cis* double bonds by a band at ~ 730 cm^{-1}.

NMR spectroscopy, as a means of elucidating carotenoid structures, was introduced by Weedon et al. (1959). The examination of many carotenoids of known structure has shown that methyl groups give rise to a singlet peak and that their τ-values depend on the position of the methyl group in the molecule, e.g.,

$\sim 8{\cdot}41$ (*trans*--Me)

$\sim 8{\cdot}35$
(*cis*-Me)   H

in-chain methyl   end-of-chain methyl   τ 7·87–7·95
τ 7·95–8·15   τ 8·31–8·44

Also, since aldehydic protons have a τ-value of 0·45–0·60, it is therefore possible to distinguish between aldehydes and ketones.

Mass spectrometry has been applied to the elucidation of structures of carotenoids. It has been particularly useful for accurate molecular weight determinations (and hence molecular formulae) and the detection and estimation (of the number) of hydroxyl groups. Two characteristic peaks $(M - 106)$ and $(M - 92)$ arise from acyclic and cyclic 'ended' chains, and are due to the loss of toluene (92) or *m*-xylene (106) from the *central* conjugated system of the molecule, e.g. (see also §3):

(i)

M^+ $M - 106$ (106)

(ii)

M^+ $M - 92$ (92)

Also, a characteristic peak arises from an acyclic ($M - 69$) or a cyclic end ($M - 56$).

(iii)

M^+ $M - 69$ (69)

(iv)

M^+ $M - 56$ (56)

Hence, the presence of these 'ends' can be identified in the molecule. Keto- and epoxy-carotenoids also show recognisable molecular ions and this class of pigments can therefore be identified.

§2. Carotenes

Carotene was first isolated by Wackenroder (1831) from carrots (this was the origin of the name *carotin*, which was later changed to *carotene*). The molecular formula of carotene, however, was not determined until 1907, when Willstätter showed it was $C_{40}H_{56}$. Carotene was shown to be unsaturated, and when treated with a *small* amount of iodine, it forms a crystalline di-iodide, $C_{40}H_{56}I_2$. Kuhn (1929) separated this di-iodide into two fractions by means of fractional crystallisation. Treatment of each fraction with thiosulphate regenerated the corresponding carotenes, which were designated α- and β-carotene. Kuhn *et al.* (1933) then found that chromatography gives a much better separation of the carotenes themselves, and in this way isolated a third isomer, which they designated γ-carotene.

α-Carotene, violet crystals, m.p. 187–187·5°C; optically active (dextrorotatory).
β-Carotene, red crystals, m.p. 183°C; optically inactive.
γ-Carotene, dark red crystals, m.p. 152–154°C; optically inactive.

It appears that all three carotenes occur together in nature, but their relative proportions vary with the source, *e.g.*, carrots contain 15 per cent α, 85 per cent β and 0·1 per cent γ. Carotenes are obtained commercially by chromatography, two of the best sources being carrots and alfalfa.

Many carotenoids (including the carotenes) are unstable to air, heat, or to acids and alkalis.

§3. β-Carotene, $C_{40}H_{56}$

When catalytically hydrogenated (platinum), β-carotene forms perhydro-β-carotene, $C_{40}H_{78}$. Thus β-carotene contains eleven double bonds, and since the formula of perhydro-β-carotene corresponds to the general formula C_nH_{2n-2}, it follows that the compound contains two rings.

When exposed to air, β-carotene develops the odour of violets. Since this odour is characteristic of β-ionone, it was thought that this residue is present in β-carotene (see **8** §6). This was confirmed by the fact that the oxidation of a benzene solution of β-carotene with cold aqueous potassium permanganate gives β-ionone. Now β-ionone (I), on ozonolysis, gives, among other things, geronic acid (II) (Karrer *et al.*, 1929).

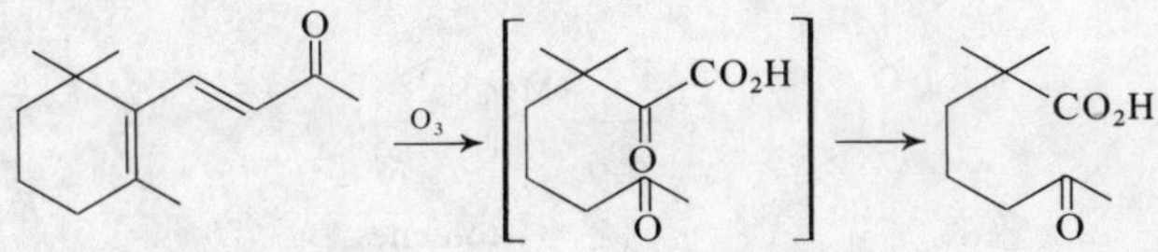

β-Carotene, on ozonolysis, gives geronic acid in an amount that corresponds to the presence of two β-ionone residues (Karrer *et al.*, 1930). Thus a tentative structure for β-carotene is:

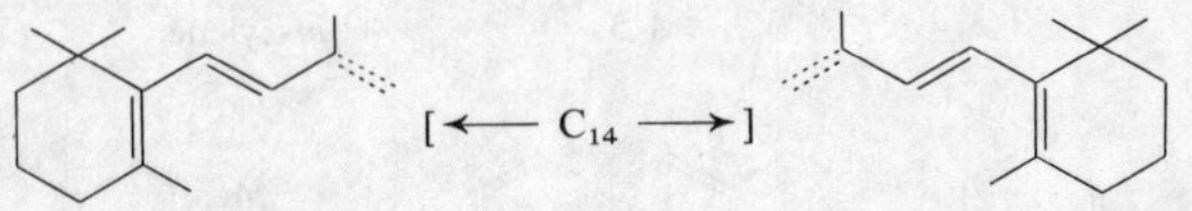

Since the colour of β-carotene is due to extended conjugation (§1), the C_{14} portion of the molecule will be conjugated. The presence of conjugation in this central portion is confirmed by the fact that β-carotene forms an adduct with five molecules of maleic anhydride (Nakamiya, 1936).

Geronic acid, on oxidation with cold aqueous potassium permanganate, forms a mixture of acetic acid, dimethylglutaric (III), 2,2-dimethylsuccinic (IV) and dimethylmalonic acids (V).

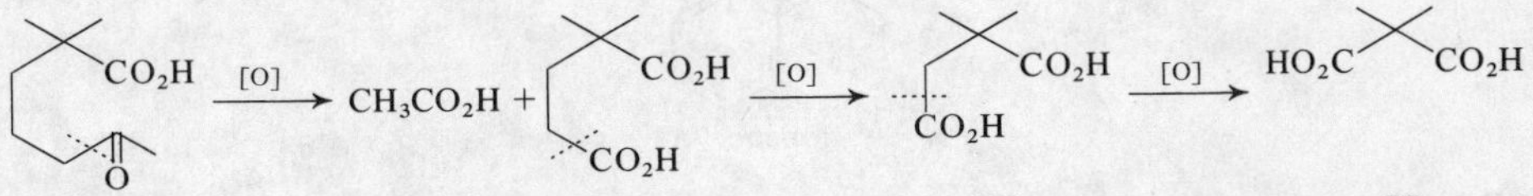

Oxidation of β-carotene in benzene solution with cold aqueous permanganate gives a mixture of β-ionone, (III), (IV), (V), and acetic acid, the amount of acetic acid being more than can be accounted for by the presence of two β-ionone residues. Thus there must be some methyl side-chains in the central C_{14} portion of the molecule. Since it is essential to know the exact number of these methyl side-chains, this led to the development of the **Kuhn–Roth methyl side-chain determination** (1931). The first method used was to oxidise the carotenoid with alkaline permanganate, but later chromic acid (chromium trioxide in sulphuric acid) was found to be more reliable, the methyl group in the fragment $-C(CH_3)=$ being always oxidised to acetic acid. It was found that alkaline permanganate only oxidises the fragment $=C(CH_3)-CH=$ to acetic acid, and fragments such as $=C(CH_3)-CH_2-$ are incompletely oxidised to acetic acid, or not attacked at all (Karrer *et al.*, 1930). Since a molecule ending in an isopropylidene group also gives acetic acid on oxidation with chromic acid, this end group is determined by ozonolysis, the acetone so formed being estimated volumetrically. Application of the Kuhn–Roth methyl side-chain determination to β-carotene gave ~ 5.4 molecules of acetic acid, thus indicating that there are four $-C(CH_3)=$ groups in the *chain* (since two molecules are produced, one from the $-CMe=$ group in each ionone ring; the *gem*-dimethyl groups do not appear to give any acetic acid under these conditions). The positions of two of these have already been tentatively placed in the two end β-ionone residues (see tentative structure above), and so the problem is now to find the positions of the remaining two. This was done as follows. Distillation of carotenoids under normal conditions brings about decomposition with the formation of aromatic compounds. Thus the distillation of β-carotene produces toluene, *m*-xylene and 2,6-dimethylnaphthalene (Kuhn *et al.*, 1933). The formation of these compounds may be explained by the cyclisation of fragments of the polyene chain, without the β-ionone rings being involved. The following types of chain fragments would give the desired aromatic products:

(a)

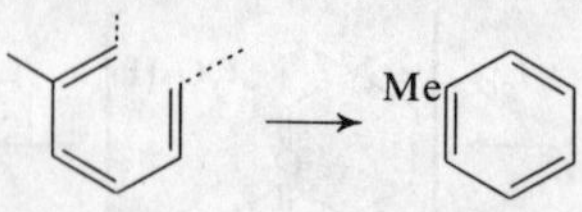

toluene

(b)   or

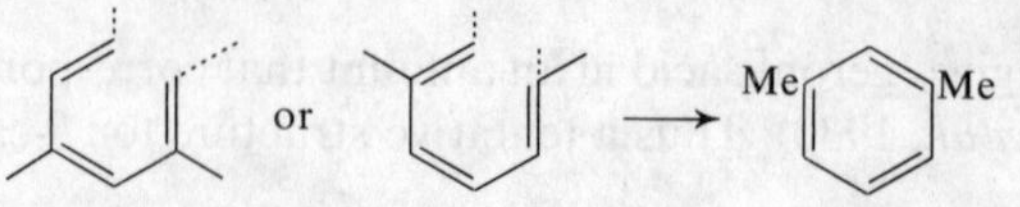

1,3   1,5   m-xylene

(c)   or

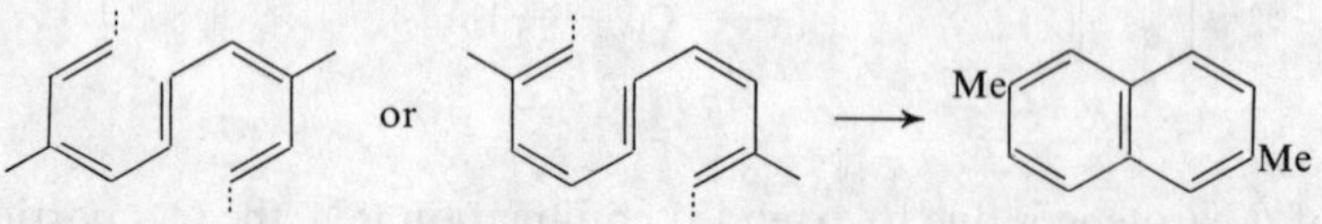

1,6   1,8   2,6-dimethylnaphthalene

By the use of the more recent methods of chromatography (TLC), it has now been shown that the main product of heating β-carotene *in vacuo* is **ionene**.

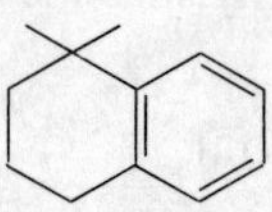

ionene

The following *symmetrical* structure for β-carotene would satisfy the requirements of (a), (b) and (c); the tail to tail union of the two isoprene units at the centre should be noted.

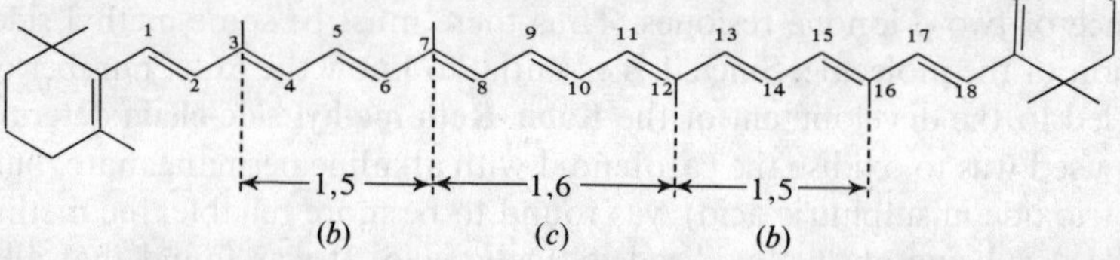

$\longmapsto$ 1,5 $\longrightarrow$|$\longleftarrow$ 1,6 $\longrightarrow$|$\longleftarrow$ 1,5 $\longrightarrow$|

(b)   (c)   (b)

This use of pyrolytic degradations is of limited value since, apart from the poor yields of identifiable products, the possibility of rearrangements at these elevated temperatures cannot be excluded. However, this symmetrical formula for β-carotene has been confirmed by the following oxidation experiments (Kuhn *et al.*, 1932–1935). When β-carotene is oxidised *rapidly* with potassium dichromate, dihydroxy-β-carotene (VI) is obtained and this, on oxidation with lead tetra-acetate, gives semi-β-carotenone (VII), a diketone. Since both (VI) and (VII) contain the *same* number of carbon atoms as β-carotene, it follows that the *double bond in one of the β-ionone rings* has been oxidised; otherwise there would have been chain scission had the chain been oxidised. Oxidation of semi-β-carotenone with chromium trioxide produces β-carotenone (VIII), a tetraketone which also has the same number of carbon atoms as β-carotene. Thus, in this compound, the *other* β-ionone ring is opened. Now only *one* dihydroxy-β-carotene and *one* semi-β-carotenone are obtained, and this can be explained only by assuming a symmetrical structure for β-carotene. Hence the oxidations may be formulated:

β-carotene   (VI)

(VII)   (VIII)

This structure for β-carotene has been confirmed by synthesis. The first total synthesis was carried out by Karrer *et al.* (1950) (the yield was poor). The acetylenic carbinol (IX) was treated with ethyl-magnesium bromide and the product then treated as shown.

Catalytic hydrogenation results in *cis*-addition (11,12; 11′,12′), but the removal of water and migration of double bonds resulted in the all-*trans*-compound.

(IX) has been prepared by Isler (1949) by treating β-ionone with propargyl bromide in the presence of zinc (*cf.* the Reformatsky reaction):

(IX)

The most convenient way of preparing the diketone (oct-4-ene-2,7-dione) (X) starts with but-1-yn-3-ol (Inhoffen *et al.*, 1951):

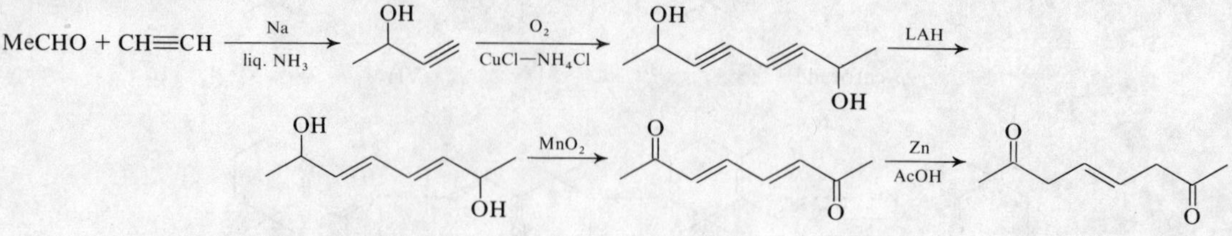

An important point to note in this synthesis is that lithium aluminium hydride will reduce a triple bond to a double bond when the former is adjacent to a propargylic hydroxyl group (*trans*-alkene).

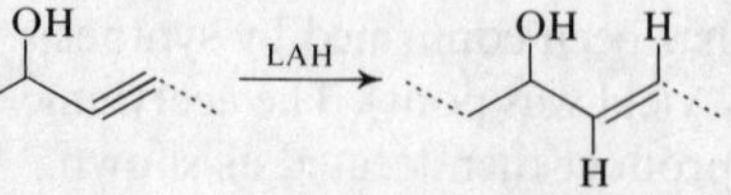

It is worthwhile at this point to consider the general aspects of carotene syntheses. All syntheses have used the union of a bifunctional unit, which forms the central part of the carotene molecule, with two molecules (identical as for, *e.g.*, β-carotene, or not identical as for, *e.g.*, α-carotene). The various methods have been divided into four groups according to the carbon content of the three units used in the synthesis: $C_{19} + C_2 + C_{19}$; $C_{16} + C_8 + C_{16}$; $C_{14} + C_{12} + C_{14}$; $C_{10} + C_{20} + C_{10}$. The second group ($C_{16} + C_8 + C_{16}$) has been used in the above synthesis of β-carotene.

β-Carotene has also been synthesised by the combination ($C_{19} + C_2 + C_{19}$) by Inhoffen *et al.* (1950) [$R_\beta = \beta$-ionone ring; see also (XIV), below]:

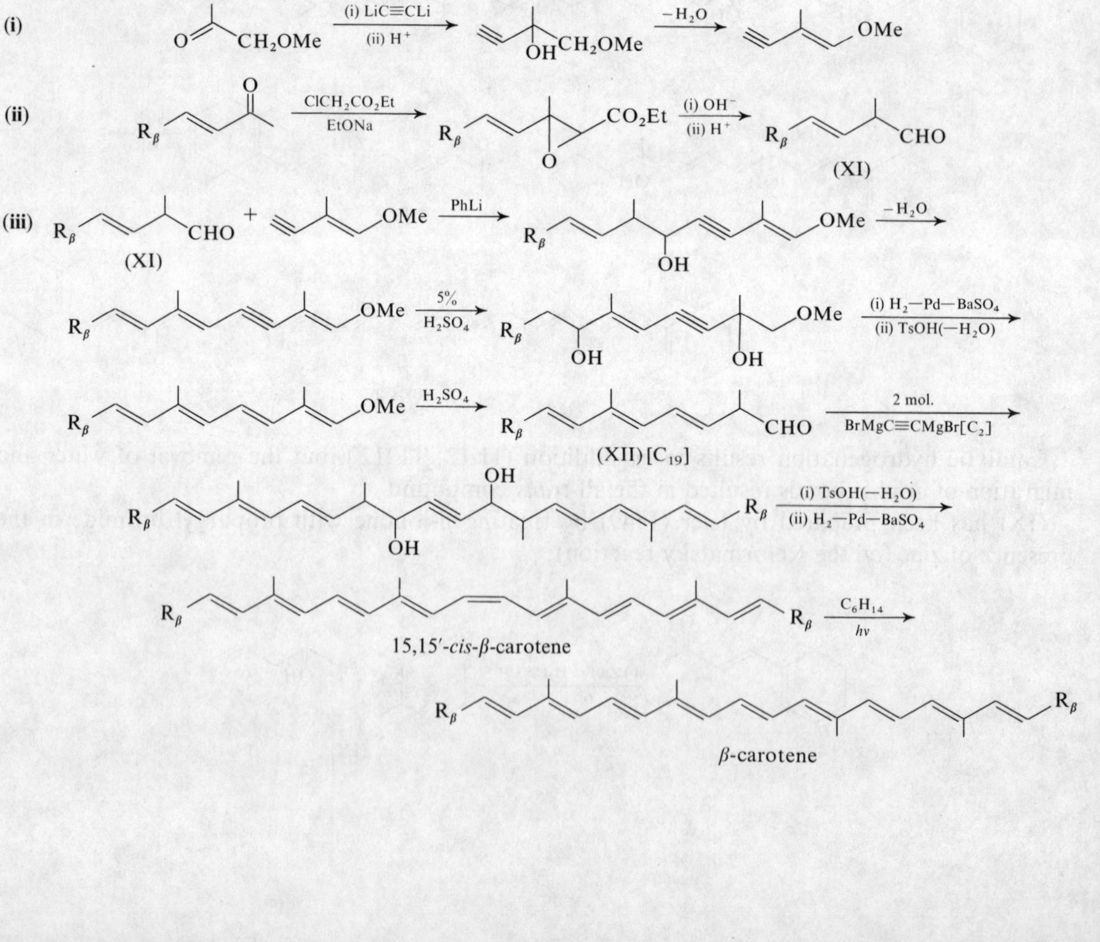

(i)

(ii)

(iii)

15,15'-*cis*-β-carotene

β-carotene

An example of the synthesis of β-carotene by the third group ($C_{14} + C_{12} + C_{14}$) is that of Isler *et al.* (1957). This was the first synthesis of β-carotene that gave a high yield.

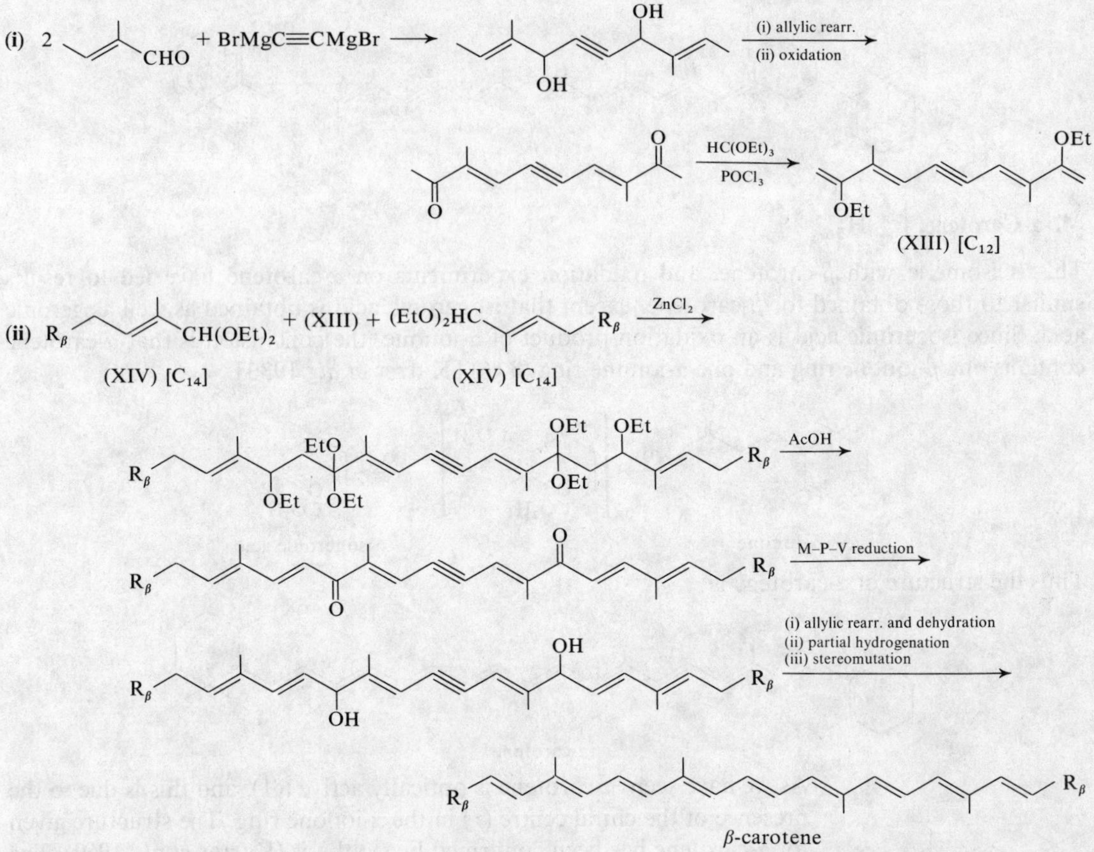

(i) reaction scheme:

2 (3-methylbut-2-enal, CHO) + BrMgC≡CMgBr →
→ (i) allylic rearr. (ii) oxidation →

HC(OEt)$_3$ / POCl$_3$ →

(XIII) [C$_{12}$]

(ii) R_β CH(OEt)$_2$ (XIV) [C$_{14}$] + (XIII) + (EtO)$_2$HC R_β (XIV) [C$_{14}$] → ZnCl$_2$ →

AcOH →

M–P–V reduction →

(i) allylic rearr. and dehydration
(ii) partial hydrogenation
(iii) stereomutation →

β-carotene

The use of the Lindlar catalyst for carrying out partial hydrogenation of the triple bond should be noted (see §7). (XIV) was prepared from β-ionone by means of the Darzens glycidic ester reaction (see also Vol. I) (see also (XI), above).

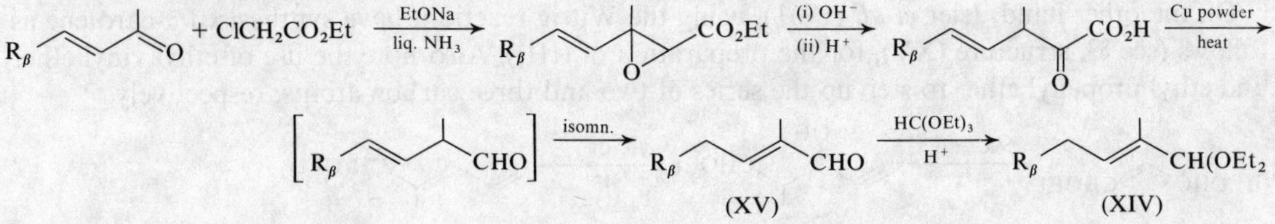

R_β ...O + ClCH$_2$CO$_2$Et —EtONa, liq. NH$_3$→ R_β ...CO$_2$Et (epoxide) —(i) OH⁻ (ii) H⁺→ R_β ...CO$_2$H —Cu powder, heat→

[R_β ...CHO] —isomn.→ R_β ...CHO (XV) —HC(OEt)$_3$ / H⁺→ R_β ...CH(OEt)$_2$ (XIV)

A very interesting synthesis of β-carotene is that of Isler *et al.* (1962). The starting material is vitamin A, and one step involves the Wittig reaction. If we write Vitamin A$_1$ as RCH_2OH (see §7), then the synthesis may be formulated as follows:

(i) $RCH_2OH \longrightarrow RCH{=}PPh_3 \xrightarrow{O_2} RCHO + Ph_3PO$

(ii) $RCHO + RCH{=}PPh_3 \longrightarrow RCH{=}CHR + Ph_3PO$ (28%)

β-carotene

The conventional numbering of the β-carotene molecule is as shown. If the carotenoid is unsymmetrical, the plain numerals are used for the half of the molecule containing the β-ionone end-group. Also, if only one end-group is cyclic, this end is given the plain numerals.

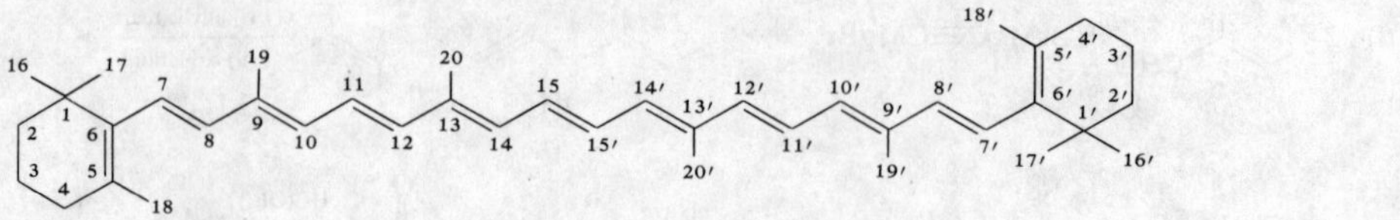

§4. α-Carotene, $C_{40}H_{56}$

This is isomeric with β-carotene, and oxidation experiments on α-carotene have led to results similar to those obtained for β-carotene, except that isogeronic acid is obtained as well as geronic acid. Since isogeronic acid is an oxidation product of α-ionone, the conclusion is that α-carotene contains one β-ionone ring and one α-ionone ring (**8** §6) [Karrer *et al.*, 1933].

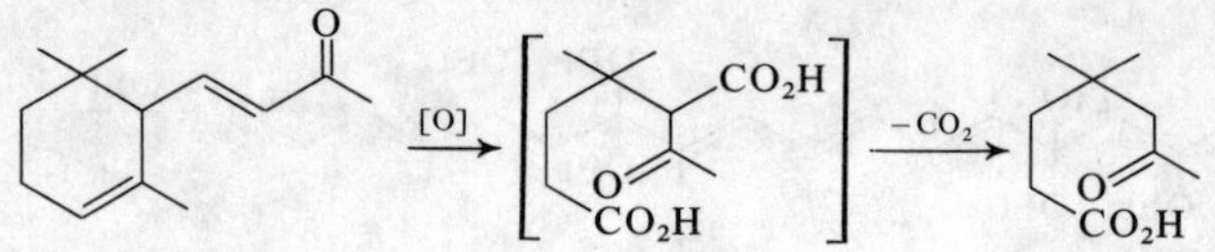

α-ionone isogeronic acid

Thus the structure of α-carotene is:

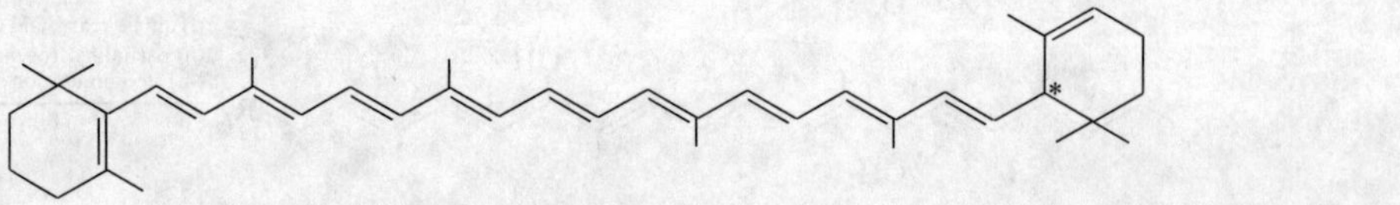

α-carotene

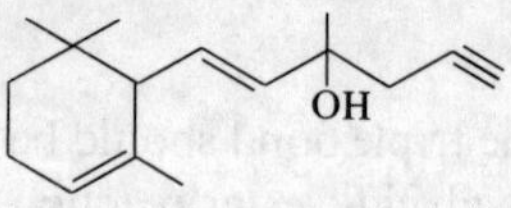

(I)

As we have seen, α-carotene is optically active (§1), and this is due to the presence of the chiral centre (*) in the α-ionone ring. The structure given for α-carotene has been confirmed by synthesis (Karrer *et al.*, 1950). The method is the same as that described for β-carotene, except that *one* molecule of the acetylenic alcohol (structure (IX), §3) is used together with one molecule of the corresponding α-ionone derivative (I) [$C_{16} + C_8 + C_{16}$ combination].

On the other hand, Isler *et al.* (1961), using the Wittig reaction, have synthesised α-carotene as follows (see §3, structure (XV), for the preparation of (III)). Also note the use of ethyl vinyl ether and ethyl propenyl ether to step up the series of two and three carbon atoms, respectively.

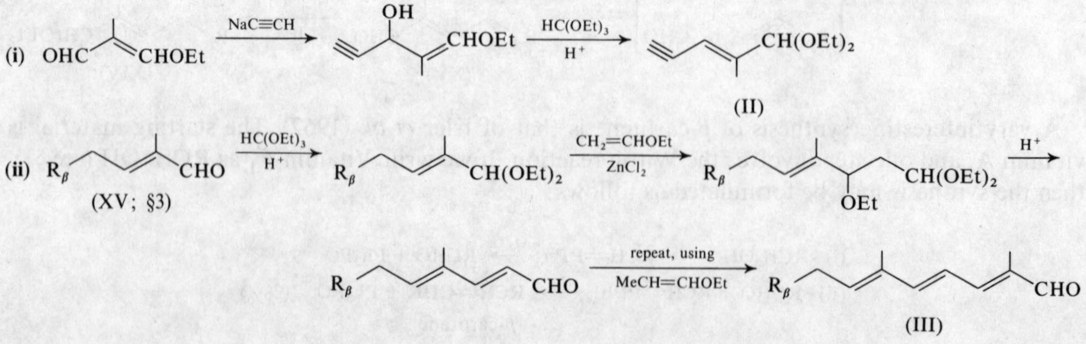

(iii) (II) + (III) $\xrightarrow[\text{liq. NH}_3]{\text{LiNH}_2}$ R$_\beta$ [structure] OH CH(OEt)$_2$ $\xrightarrow{\text{H}^+}$

R$_\beta$ [structure] CHO

(IV)

(iv) R$_\alpha$ [structure] O $\xrightarrow[\text{(ii) H}_2-\text{Lindlar cat.}]{\text{(i) LiC}\equiv\text{CH}}$ R$_\alpha$ [structure] OH $\xrightarrow{\text{Ph}_3\text{P}\cdot\text{HBr}}$

α-ionone

R$_\alpha$ [structure] CH$_2\overset{+}{\text{P}}$Ph$_3$Br$^-$ $\xrightarrow{\text{PhLi}}$ R$_\alpha$ [structure] PPh$_3$

(V)

(v) (IV) + (V) $\longrightarrow$ R$_\beta$ [structure] R$_\alpha$ $\xrightarrow[\text{and isomn.}]{\text{partial hydrogn.}}$

R$_\beta$ [structure] R$_\alpha$

It is interesting to note that α-carotene has been converted into the β-isomer by heating the α-compound with ethanolic sodium ethoxide and benzene at 100–110°C for some time (Karrer *et al.*, 1947); this is an example of *three carbon prototropy*.

§5. Lycopene, C$_{40}$H$_{56}$, m.p. 173°C

This is a carotenoid that is the red tomato pigment. Since the structure of γ-carotene depends on that of lycopene, the latter will be discussed here, and the former in the next section.

On catalytic hydrogenation (platinum), lycopene is converted into perhydrolycopene, C$_{40}$H$_{82}$. Therefore lycopene has thirteen double bonds, and is an acyclic compound (Karrer *et al.*, 1928).

[structure]

acetone : laevulic acid

←methylheptenone→

Ozonolysis of lycopene gives, among other products, acetone and laevulic acid; this suggests that lycopene contains the terminal residue shown. This is supported by the fact that controlled oxidation of lycopene with chromic acid produces 6-methylhept-5-en-2-one (*cf.* **8** §5). Quantitative oxidation experiments (ozonolysis) indicate that this grouping occurs at each end of the molecule (Karrer *et al.*, 1929, 1931). Also, the quantitative oxidation of lycopene with chromic acid gives eight molecules of acetic acid per molecule of lycopene, thereby suggesting that there are six —C(CH$_3$)= groups present in the chain (*cf.* §3). Controlled oxidation of lycopene with chromic acid gives one molecule of methylheptenone and one molecule of lycopenal, C$_{32}$H$_{42}$O, and the latter may be further oxidised with chromic acid to another molecule of methylheptenone and one molecule of a dialdehyde, C$_{24}$H$_{28}$O$_2$ (Kuhn *et al.*, 1932). Thus this dialdehyde constitutes the central part of the chain, and the two molecules of methylheptenone must have been produced by the oxidation of each end of the chain in lycopene. The dialdehyde may be converted into the corresponding dioxime, and this, on dehydration to the dicyanide, followed by hydrolysis, forms the dicarboxylic acid C$_{24}$H$_{28}$O$_4$, which is identical with norbixin (§9). Hence the dialdehyde must be bixindial, and so it may be inferred that the structure of lycopene is the symmetrical one shown since it accounts for all the above facts.

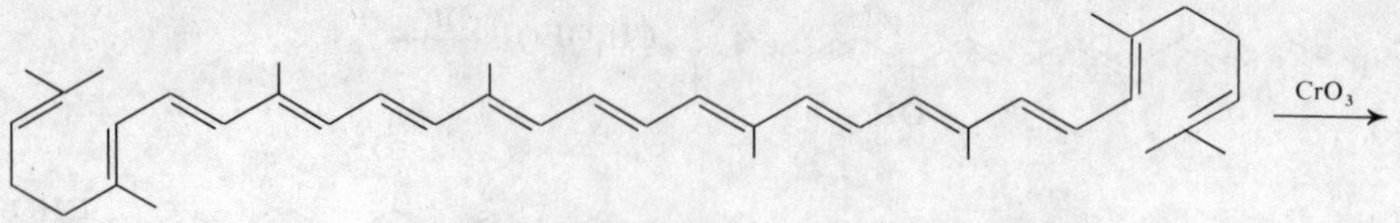

lycopene

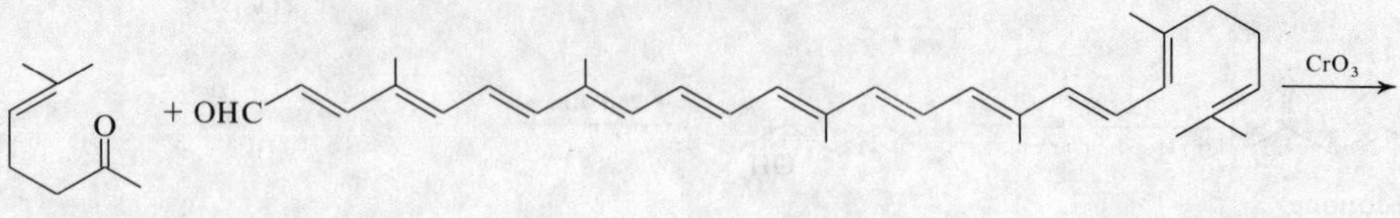

methyl-
heptenone

lycopenal

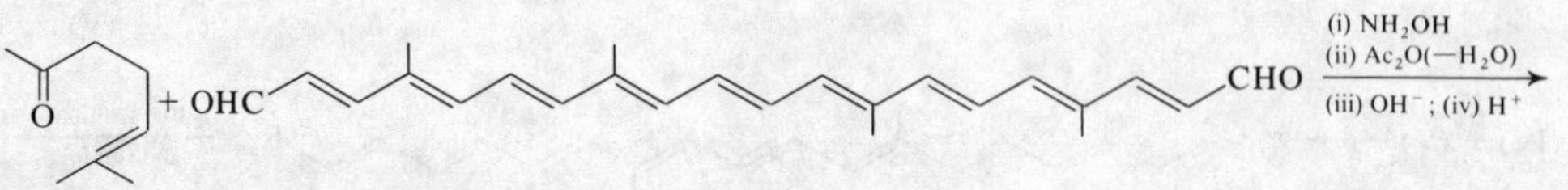

methyl-
heptenone

bixindial

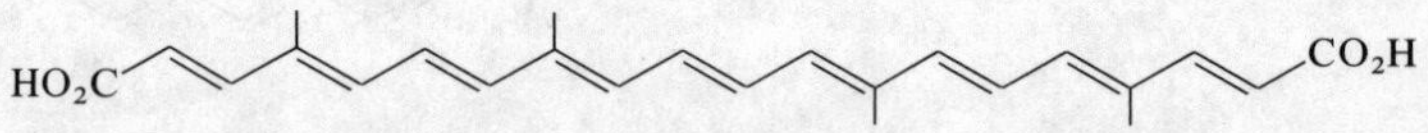

(i) NH₂OH
(ii) Ac₂O(—H₂O)
(iii) OH⁻ ; (iv) H⁺

norbixin

It should be noted that, just as in terpenoid chemistry, it is often convenient to draw acyclic structures as 'rings' to show the structural relationships between acyclic and cyclic end-groups.

The structure assigned to lycopene has been confirmed by synthesis (Karrer *et al.*, 1950). Instead of the acetylenic carbinol (IX) in §3, two molecules of (I) were used ($C_{16} + C_8 + C_{16}$ combination).

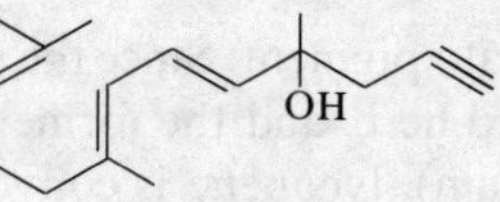

(I)

Weedon *et al.* (1965) have also synthesised lycopene by means of the Wittig reaction:

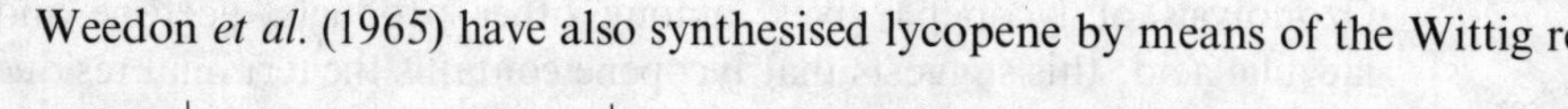

(III)   (II)   (III)

$\left(R = \right)$

(II) has been synthesised by Buchta *et al.* (1960) as follows.

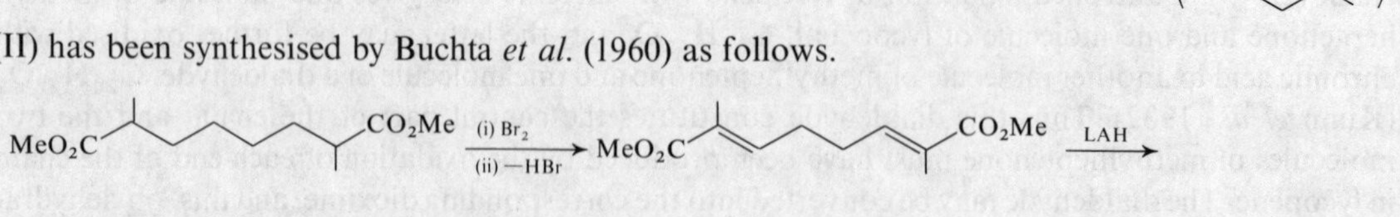

(i) Br₂
(ii) —HBr

LAH

MnO₂

(II)

It should be noted that the oxidation step is unusual in that dehydrogenation to the conjugated all-*trans*-dialdehyde occurs simultaneously with oxidation of the terminal alcoholic group.

(III) has been prepared in a similar manner to compound (V) in §4, but ψ-ionine (8 §6) is used instead of α-ionone.

A number of poly-*cis*-lycopenes have been isolated from natural sources.

§6. γ-Carotene, $C_{40}H_{56}$

Catalytic hydrogenation converts γ-carotene into perhydro-γ-carotene, $C_{40}H_{80}$. Thus there are twelve double bonds present, and the compound contains one ring. Ozonolysis of γ-carotene gives, among other products, acetone, laevulic acid and geronic acid. The formation of acetone and laevulic acid indicates the structural relationship of γ-carotene to lycopene, and the formation of geronic acid indicates the presence of a β-ionone ring (Kuhn *et al.*, 1933). On this evidence, and also on the fact that the growth-promoting response in rats was found to be half that of β-carotene, Kuhn suggested that γ-carotene consists of half a molecule of β-carotene joined to half a molecule of lycopene; thus:

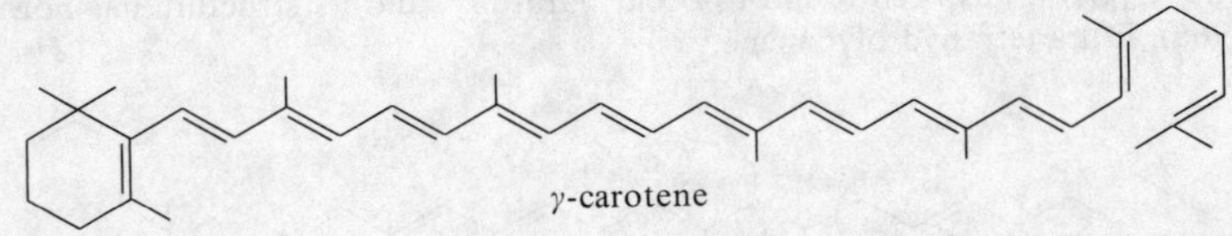

γ-carotene

This structure for γ-carotene is supported by the fact that the absorption maximum of γ-carotene in the visible region lies between that of β-carotene and that of lycopene. Final proof for this structure has been obtained by the synthesis of γ-carotene (Karrer *et al.*, 1953), who used the combination $(C_{16} + C_8 + C_{16})$ [see also §3, compound (IX) and (X)].

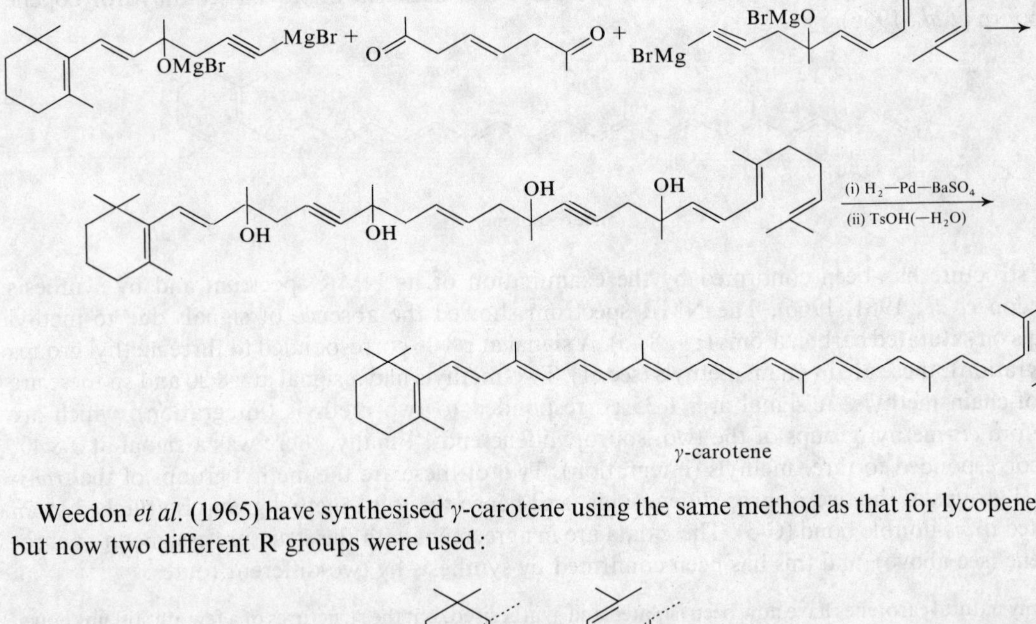

γ-carotene

Weedon *et al.* (1965) have synthesised γ-carotene using the same method as that for lycopene (§5), but now two different R groups were used:

and

§6a.   Other carotenes have been isolated from natural sources, *e.g.*, δ-carotene and ε-carotene. The former is the α-ionone analogue of γ-carotene, and the latter is the α-ionone analogue of α-carotene. Both contain chiral centres and both have been synthesised, as racemic modifications, by Weedon *et al.* (1965), using the Wittig reaction.

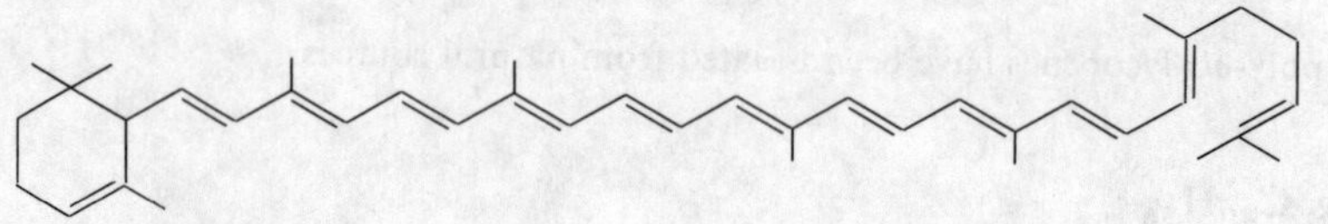

δ-carotene

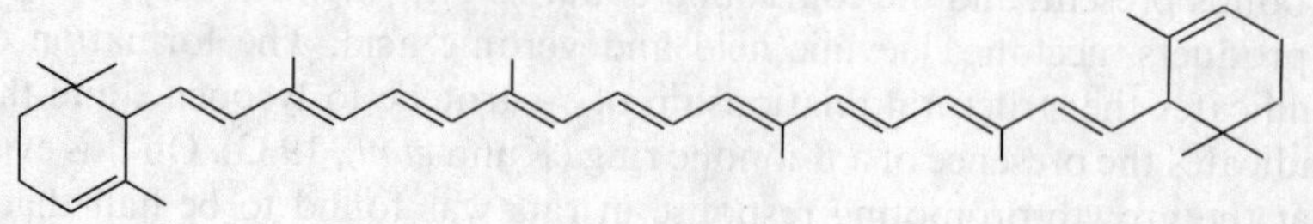

ε-carotene

ζ (zeta)-Carotene, $C_{40}H_{60}$, has been found to occur naturally, and its structure has now been elucidated (Weedon *et al.*, 1966). It is a tetrahydrolycopene.

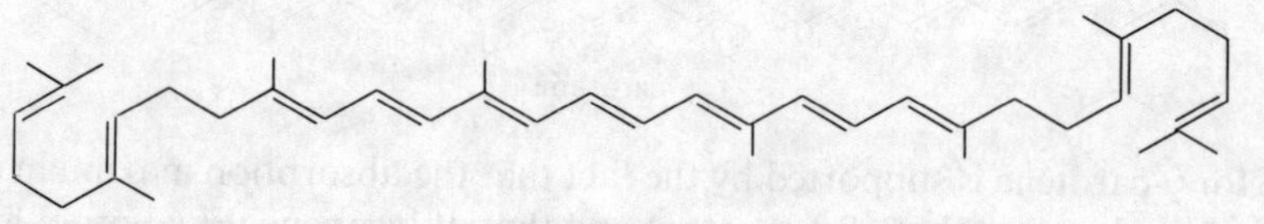

ζ-carotene

Neurosporene, $C_{40}H_{58}$, m.p. 124°C, has been isolated from the fungus *Neurospora crassa*, and on the basis of analytical and degradative studies has been shown to be 7,8-dihydrolycopene (Rabourn *et al.*, 1956).

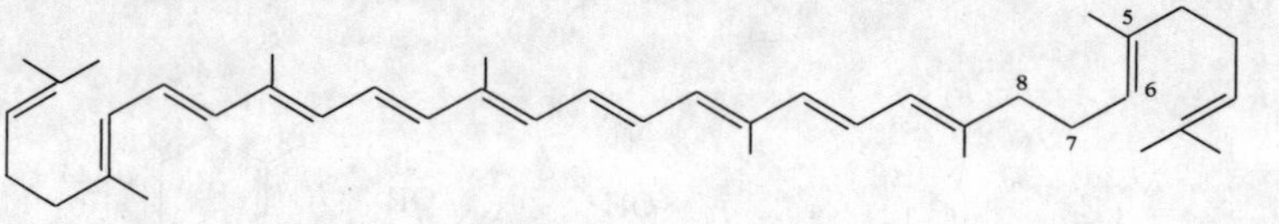

neurosporene

This structure has been confirmed by the examination of its NMR spectrum and by synthesis (Weedon *et al.*, 1961, 1966). The NMR spectrum showed the absence of signals due to methyl groups on saturated carbon atoms ($\tau \sim 8.75$). A signal at $\tau\ 8.06$ corresponded to three methyl groups (integration); these are in-chain methyls (see §1). Two methyls had a signal at $\tau\ 8.20$ and so these are end-of-chain methyls. A signal at $\tau\ 8.35$ corresponded to two methyls (integration), which are therefore *cis*-methyl groups of the two isopropylidene ends. Finally, there was a signal at $\tau\ 8.40$; this corresponded to three methyls (integration). Two of these are the methyl groups of the *trans*-methyl groups of the two isopropylidene ends, and hence the third methyl group is attached to an isolated *trans*-double bond (C-5). These data are in agreement with the structure assigned to neurosporene (see above), and this has been confirmed by synthesis by two different routes.

Many natural carotenes have now been isolated and synthesised, but the structures of a few are still unknown. Of particular interest are the three isomeric hydrocarbons, $C_{40}H_{48}$, which have been isolated from a sea sponge: isorenieratene, renieratene and renierapurpurin. These contain 'benzenoid ends'.

isorenieratene: $R^1 = R^3$; $R^2 = R^3$
renieratene: $R^1 = R^3$; $R^2 = R^4$
renierapurpurin: $R^1 = R^4$; $R^2 = R^4$

§7. Vitamin A, $C_{20}H_{30}O$

Vitamin A (**Retinol, Axerophthol**) is also usually referred to as vitamin A_1 since a second compound, known as vitamin A_2, has been isolated. These vitamins are diterpenoids; they are usually classified as belonging to the apocarotenoid group (see §1).

Vitamin A_1 influences growth in animals, and also apparently increases resistance to disease. Night blindness is due to vitamin A_1 deficiency in the human diet, and a prolonged deficiency leads to xerophthalmia (hardening of the cornea, etc.). Vitamin A_1 occurs free and as esters in fats, in fish livers and in blood. It was originally isolated as a viscous yellow oil, but later it was obtained as a crystalline solid, m.p. 63–64°C (Baxter *et al.*, 1940). Vitamin A_1 is estimated by the blue colour reaction it gives with a solution of antimony trichloride in chloroform (the Carr–Price reaction; *cf.* §1); it is also estimated by light absorption (λ_{max} 325 (ε 51 000) nm).

The IUPAC name of vitamin A (A_1) is **retinol**; that of the corresponding aldehyde is **retinal** (retinene, retinene$_1$); and that of the corresponding acid is **retinoic acid**. The traditional names are still widely used.

Carotenoids are converted into vitamin A_1 in the intestinal mucosa, and feeding experiments showed that the potency of α- and γ-carotenes is half that of β-carotene. This provitamin nature of β-carotene led to the suggestion that vitamin A_1 is half the molecule of β-carotene (see also §3).

The biological conversion of β-carotene into vitamin A_1 is still not certain. There is evidence that one molecule of β-carotene undergoes central fission to give two molecules of vitamin A_1. This, however, does not appear to be the only path of breakdown. There is also evidence that indicates a stepwise oxidative degradation which starts at one end of the molecule and results in the formation of *one* molecule of vitamin A_1.

On catalytic hydrogenation, vitamin A_1 is converted into perhydrovitamin A_1, $C_{20}H_{40}O$; thus vitamin A_1 contains five double bonds. Since vitamin A_1 forms an ester with *p*-nitrobenzoic acid (this ester is not crystallisable), it follows that vitamin A_1 contains a hydroxyl group. Hence the parent hydrocarbon of vitamin A_1 is $C_{20}H_{40}$, and consequently the molecule contains one ring. Ozonolysis of vitamin A_1 produces one molecule of geronic acid (§3) per molecule of vitamin A_1, and so there must be one β-ionone nucleus present (Karrer, 1931, 1932). Oxidation of vitamin A_1 with permanganate produces acetic acid; this suggests that there are some $—C(CH_3)=$ groups in the chain. All of the foregoing facts are in keeping with the suggestion that vitamin A_1 is half the β-carotene structure. When heated with an ethanolic solution of hydrogen chloride, vitamin A_1 is converted into some compound (II) which, on dehydrogenation with selenium forms 1,6-dimethyl-naphthalene (III) (Heilbron *et al.*, 1932). Heilbron *assumed* (I) as the structure of vitamin A_1, and explained the course of the reaction as follows:

(I)   (II)   (III)

Perhydrovitamin A_1 has been synthesised from β-ionone (Karrer, 1933), and was shown to be identical with the compound obtained by reducing vitamin A_1; thus there is evidence to support the structure assigned to vitamin A_1. Final proof of structure must rest with a synthesis of vitamin A_1 itself, and this has now been accomplished by several groups of workers. The following synthesis is that of Isler *et al.* (1947). This starts with methyl vinyl ketone to produce compound (IV), one stage of the reactions involving an allylic rearrangement (*cf.* **8** §8). Also note the formation of the *cis*-product. The preparation of (V) has been described in §3 (see structure XV).

Preparation of (IV)

Combination of (IV) and (V)

In the hydrogenation of (VI) to (VII), barium sulphate is used to act as a poison to the catalyst to prevent hydrogenation of the *double* bonds. Partial acetylation of (VII) (primary alcoholic groups are more readily acetylated than secondary) protects the terminal alcoholic group from an allylic rearrangement in the conversion of (VIII) to (IX). It should also be noted that dehydration with iodine is accompanied by isomerisation to the all-*trans* configuration.

The crude vitamin A_1 obtained in the above synthesis was purified *via* its ester with anthraquinone-2-carboxylic acid, and was thereby obtained in a crystalline form which was shown to be identical with natural vitamin A_1.

Lindlar (1952) has shown that triple bonds may be partially hydrogenated in the presence of a Pd—$CaCO_3$ catalyst that has been partially inactivated by treatment with lead acetate; better results are obtained by the addition of quinoline. Thus the hydrogenation of (VI) gives (VII) in 86 per cent yield when the Lindlar catalyst is used.

Another method of synthesising vitamin A_1 is due to van Dorp *et al.* (1949), who prepared retinal$_1$ (X), which was then reduced by means of lithium aluminium hydride to vitamin A_1; β-ionone and ethyl γ-bromocrotonate were the starting materials.

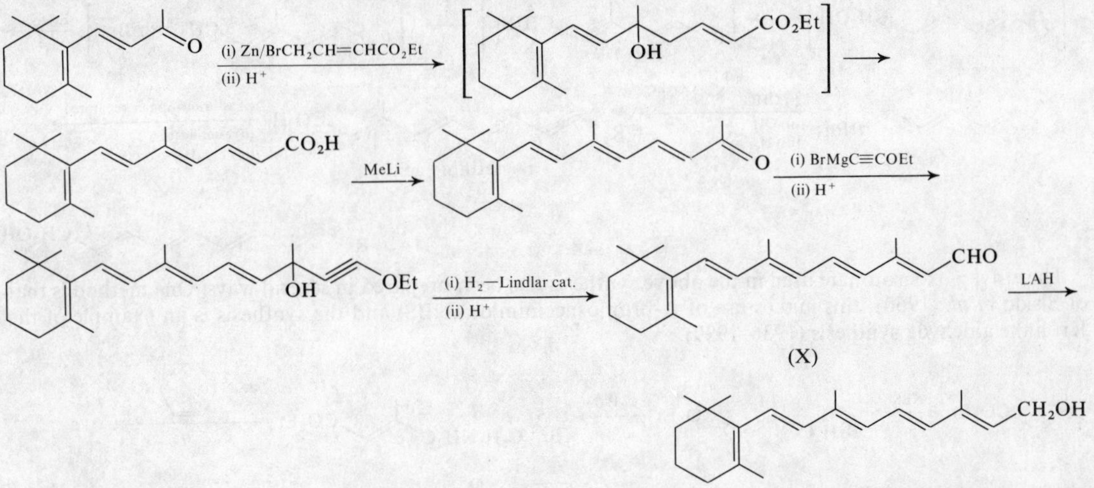

(X)

vitamin A_1 (retinol)

Attenburrow *et al.* (1952) have also synthesised vitamin A_1 starting from 2-methylcyclohexanone.

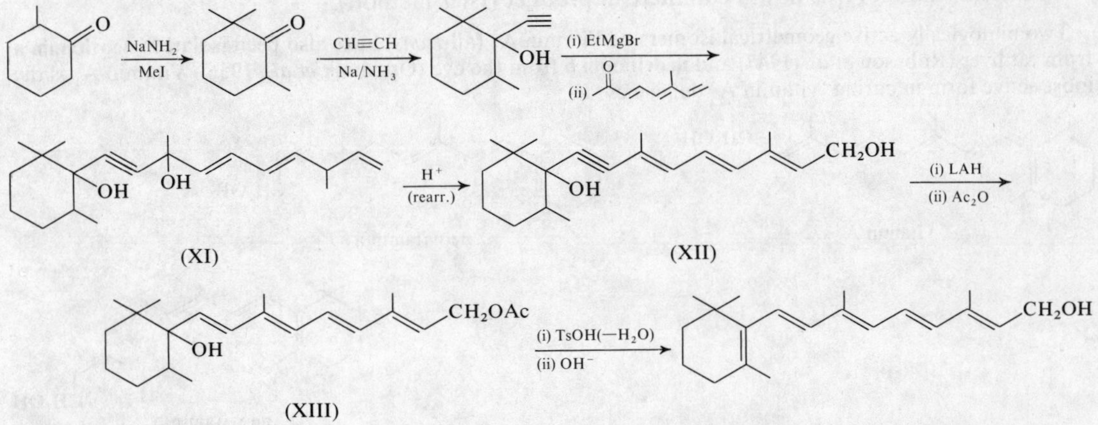

(XI)   (XII)

(XIII)

Acid causes rearrangement of (XI) to (XII) in which all multiple bonds are in complete conjugation, and the reduction of (XII) to (XIII) by lithium aluminium hydride is possible because of the presence of the propargylic hydroxyl grouping (§3).

The unsaturated ketone used in the third stage (given in the Chart) was prepared as follows:

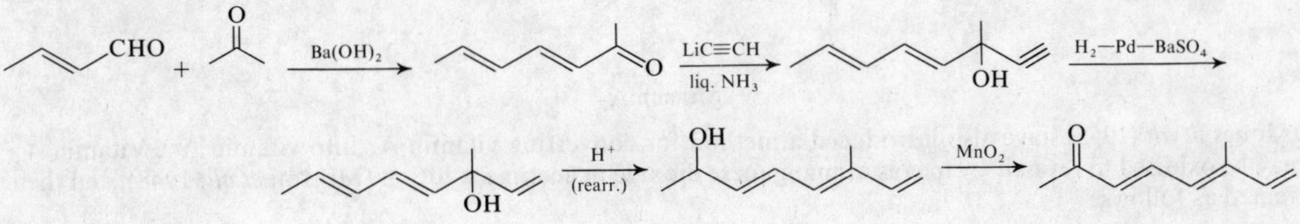

Pommer *et al.* (1958, 1959) have synthesised vitamin A_1 *via* a Wittig reaction ($R_\beta = \beta$-ionone ring; also *cf.* §4, structure (V)).

$$R_\beta \xrightarrow[\text{(ii) CH} \equiv \text{CH}]{\text{(i) Na—liq. NH}_3} \quad R_\beta \underset{\text{OH}}{} \xrightarrow[\text{quinoline}]{\text{H}_2\text{—Pd}} \quad R_\beta \underset{\text{OH}}{} \xrightarrow[\substack{\text{EtOH} \\ \text{(allylic rearr.)}}]{\text{Ph}_3\text{P. HBr}}$$

$$\left[R_\beta \underset{}{} \text{CH}_2\text{OH} \right] \longrightarrow \left[R_\beta \underset{}{} \text{CH}_2\text{Br} \right] \longrightarrow \left[R_\beta \underset{}{} \text{CH}_2\overset{+}{\text{P}}\text{Ph}_3\text{Br}^- \right] \xrightarrow{\text{EtONa}}$$

$$R_\beta \underset{}{} \text{PPh}_3 \xrightarrow[\substack{\text{(ii) OH}^- \\ \text{(iii) H}^+}]{\text{(i) OHC} \diagup \text{CO}_2\text{Et}} \quad R_\beta \underset{}{} \text{CO}_2\text{H} \xrightarrow[\substack{\text{(ii) esterification} \\ \text{(iii) LiAlH}_4}]{\text{(i) all-}\textit{trans}\text{-isomer separated}}$$

retinoic acid

$$R_\beta \underset{}{} \text{CH}_2\text{OH}$$

The ethyl γ-oxocrotonate used in the above synthesis has been prepared in several ways. One method is that of Sisido *et al.* (1960); this makes use of *N*-bromosuccinimide (NBS) and the synthesis is an example of the Kröhnke aldehyde synthesis (1936–1939).

$$\underset{}{}\text{CO}_2\text{Et} \xrightarrow{\text{NBS}} \text{BrH}_2\text{C}\underset{}{}\text{CO}_2\text{Et} \xrightarrow{\text{C}_5\text{H}_5\text{N}} \text{Br}^- \text{ C}_5\text{H}_5\overset{+}{\text{N}}\text{H}_2\text{C}\underset{}{}\text{CO}_2\text{Et} \xrightarrow{} $$

$$\text{Me}_2\text{N}\underset{}{}\overset{\text{O}^-}{\underset{}{\overset{+}{\text{N}}}}\text{CH}\underset{}{}\text{CO}_2\text{Et} \xrightarrow{\text{H}_3\text{O}^+} \text{OHC}\underset{}{}\text{CO}_2\text{Et}$$

Synthetic vitamin A_1 is now a commercial product (Isler method).

Two biologically active geometrical isomers of Vitamin A_1 (all-*trans*) have also been isolated: **neovitamin a** from rat liver (Robeson *et al.*, 1947) and **neovitamin b** from the eye (Oroshnik *et al.*, 1956). Vitamin A_1 is the most active form in curing 'vitamin A' deficiency.

vitamin A_1

neovitamin a

neovitamin b

Vitamin A_2. A second vitamin A, vitamin A_2, has been isolated from natural sources, and has been synthesised by Jones *et al.* (1951, 1952); it is dehydrovitamin A_1 (3,4-dehydroretinol). Vitamin A_2 has two absorption maxima in the ultraviolet region: 287 (ε 22 000) and 351 (ε 41 000) nm.

vitamin A_2

Jones *et al.* (1955) have also introduced a method for converting vitamin A_1 into vitamin A_2. Vitamin A_1 may be oxidised to retinal$_1$ by means of manganese dioxide in acetone solution (Morton *et al.*, 1948), and then treated as follows:

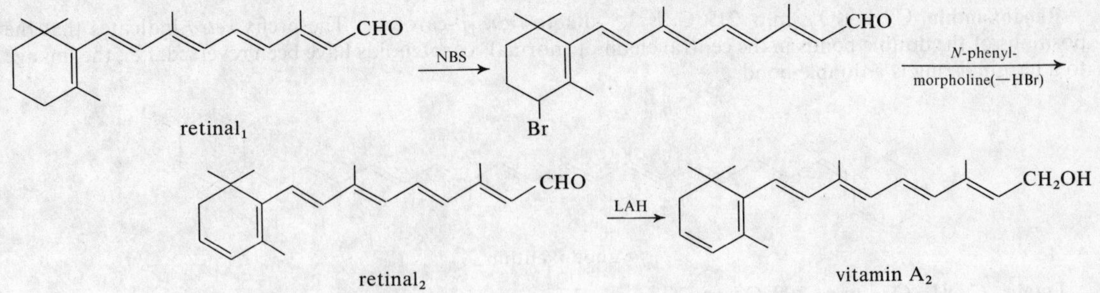

Vitamin A_2, m.p. 63–65°C, is the all-*trans*-isomer and this (and several other geometrical isomers) has been synthesised by Isler *et al.* (1962).

§7a. Vision. Two types of light receptor exist in the retina of the eye: rods (for vision in dim light) and cones (for vision in bright light and for colour vision). A chromoprotein (see **13** §7) rhodopsin (or visual purple), which is a highly photosensitive protein complex with retinal$_1$, accumulates in the rods in the dark, and when the retina is illuminated the rhodopsin is bleached. Bleaching occurs by rhodopsin undergoing a series of changes, one part of the sequence involving the isomerisation of retinal$_1$ into all-*trans*-retinal$_1$. It is the latter form which is produced together with the protein opsin in the dissociation of rhodopsin.

Experimental work has shown that the 11-*cis* form of retinal$_1$ (see neovitamin b, above) is the geometrical isomer of rhodopsin and is isomerised to the all-*trans* form when bleaching occurs. Since the 11-*cis* isomer is the only one which can combine with opsin, once the all-*trans* form is produced, recombination is not possible. Complex-formation to regenerate rhodopsin, however, occurs after a time in the dark, due to the action of an enzyme which catalyses the isomerisation of the *trans*- into the *cis*-retinal$_1$.

Vitamin A_1 is the source of all-*trans*-retinal$_1$ and hence its deficiency results in night blindness. The rhodopsin cycle may be represented as shown (no enzymes are given).

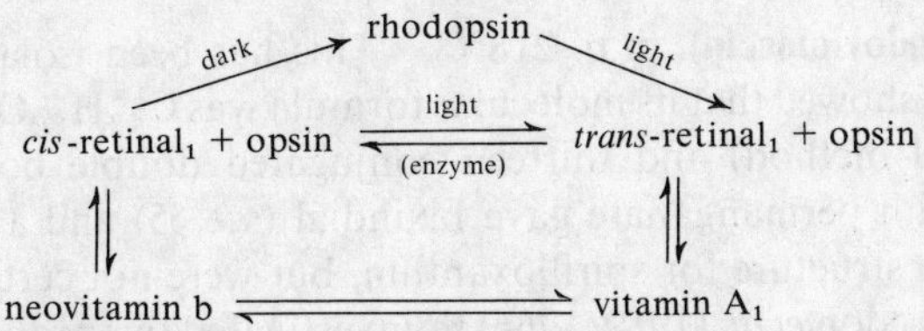

An interesting point about this problem of vision is that 11-*cis*-retinal$_1$ is sterically hindered (see §1). There would also appear to be some connection with the fact that this isomer, a 'bent' molecule, can form a complex with opsin, whereas the all-*trans* isomer, a 'straight' molecule, cannot.

§8. Xanthophylls

These are naturally occurring carotenoids which contain an oxygen function. Many have been synthesised.

Cryptoxanthin, $C_{40}H_{56}O$, m.p. 169°C, is 3-hydroxy-β-carotene; it has pro-vitamin-A activity. **Rubixanthin**, $C_{40}H_{56}O$, m.p. 160°C, is 3-hydroxy-γ-carotene, and **lycoxanthin**, $C_{40}H_{56}O$, m.p. 168°C, is 3-hydroxylycopene.

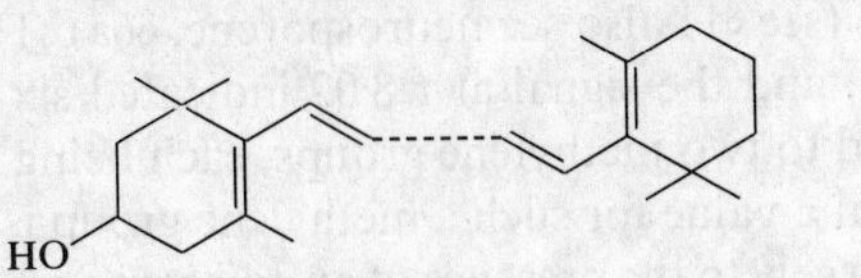

cryptoxanthin

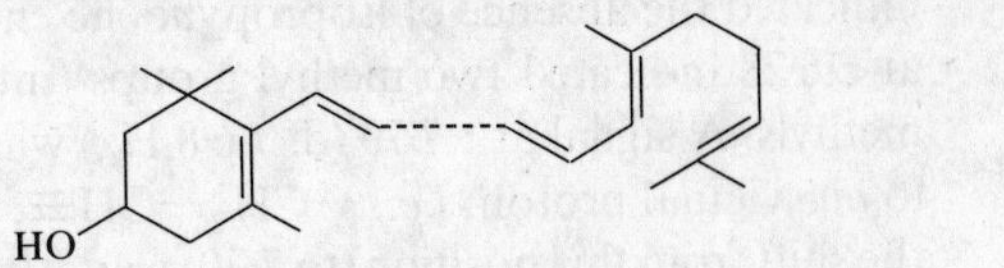

rubixanthin

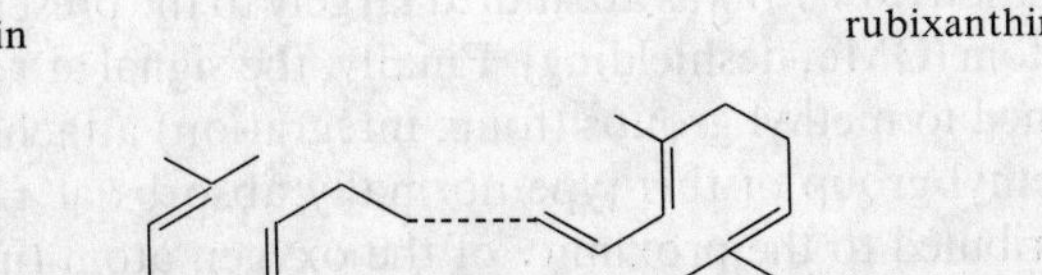

lycoxanthin

Rhodoxanthin, $C_{40}H_{52}O_2$, m.p. 219°C, is 3,3'-diketo-*retro*-β-carotene. The prefix *retro* indicates that the positions of the double bonds in the central chain of 'normal' carotenoids have been reversed, *i.e.*, the linkage to a terminal ring is a double bond.

rhodoxanthin

Lutein, $C_{40}H_{56}O_2$, m.p. 193°C, was formerly known as xanthophyll; it is 3,3'-dihydroxy-α-carotene. **Zeaxanthin,** m.p. 205°C, and **lycophyll,** m.p. 179°C, are the corresponding 3,3'-dihydroxy derivatives of β-carotene and lycopene, respectively.

lutein

zeaxanthin

lycophyll

§8a. Spirilloxanthin (rhodoviolascin), m.p. 218°C.   This has been isolated from various sources. Karrer *et al.* (1935–1940) showed that its molecular formula was $C_{42}H_{60}O_2$ and that it contained two methoxyl groups (Zeisel method) and thirteen conjugated double bonds (hydrogenation; u.v. spectrum). Oxidation with permanganate gave bixindial (see §5) and a higher dialdehyde. These workers then proposed a structure for spirilloxanthin, but were not certain of the positions of the two methoxyl groups. Weedon *et al.* (1959, 1966) re-investigated this problem and assigned structure (I). They examined the NMR spectrum in the τ 9·5–6·5 region. The absence of signals τ 8·35 and 8·41

(I)
spirilloxanthin

indicated the absence of isopropylidene end-groups (see §1; also see neurosporene, §6a). The signal at τ 6·78 indicated two methyl groups (integration) and the signal at τ 8·02 indicated six in-chain methyls. A signal at τ 7·70 (d, *J* 6·8 Hz) was assigned to two methylene groups, each being adjacent to *one* vicinal proton, *i.e.*, —CH₂—CH≡. The usual τ-value for such a methylene group is 8·3–8·7; the shift from this position (to 7·70) was attributed largely to the presence of an adjacent carbon atom carrying an oxygen atom (OMe; deshielding). Finally, the signal at τ 8·83, because it was exceptionally sharp, was assigned to methyl groups (four; integration) attached to saturated carbon atoms. However, since a methyl group of this type normally absorbs at τ 9·10–9·15, the downfield shift (deshielding) was attributed to the proximity of the oxygen atom (in OMe). These data led to the proposal of the structure given for spirilloxanthin (I). This structure has also been inferred from chemical evidence (Jensen, 1959), and has been confirmed by synthesis (Surmatis *et al.*, 1963).

Methylheptenone was converted into the phosphorane (II) and this was condensed with crocetindial (III).

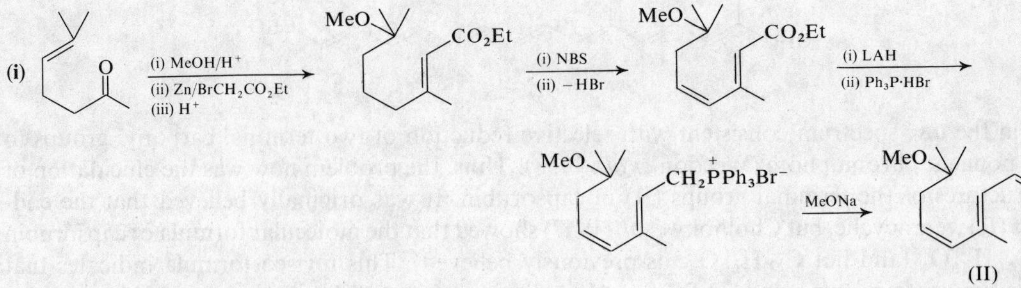

(i)

(i) MeOH/H⁺ → (i) MeOH/H⁺
(ii) Zn/BrCH₂CO₂Et
(iii) H⁺

MeO ... CO₂Et

(i) NBS
(ii) –HBr

MeO ... CO₂Et

(i) LAH
(ii) Ph₃P·HBr

MeO ... CH₂PPh₃Br⁻   MeONa→   MeO ... PPh₃

(II)

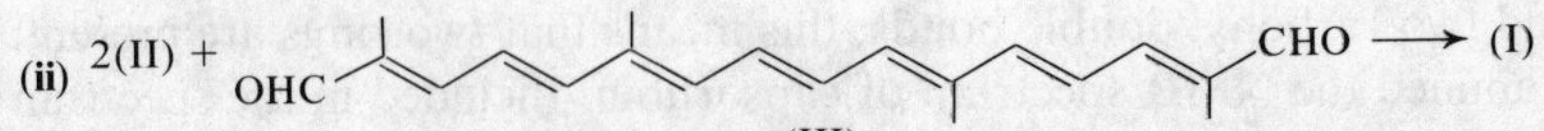

(ii)   2(II) +   OHC ... CHO → (I)

(III)

Crocetindial (III) has been prepared as follows (Isler *et al*., 1959; see also §4).

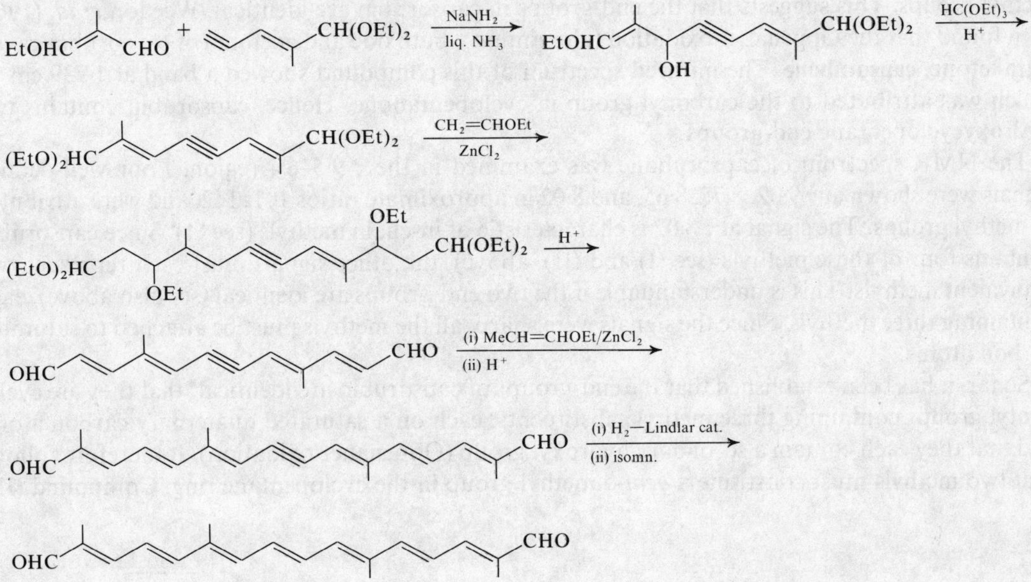

EtOHC / CHO + ≡ ... CH(OEt)₂   NaNH₂ / liq. NH₃→   EtOHC ... CH(OEt)₂
                                                         OH

HC(OEt)₃ / H⁺

(EtO)₂HC ... CH(OEt)₂   CH₂=CHOEt / ZnCl₂→

(EtO)₂HC ... CH(OEt)₂   H⁺→
       OEt   OEt

OHC ... CHO   (i) MeCH=CHOEt/ZnCl₂ / (ii) H⁺→

OHC ... CHO   (i) H₂—Lindlar cat. / (ii) isomn.→

OHC ... CHO

(III)

§8b. Capsorubin, m.p. 218°C.   This occurs in red peppers. The early work showed that capsorubin contained four oxygen atoms, two of which were present in hydroxyl groups. The results of micro-hydrogenation and the similarity of the visible spectrum of capsorubin with those of β-carotene (§3) and bixindial (§5) suggested that the two remaining oxygen atoms were ketonic. This led to the proposal that capsorubin had the partial structure (I).

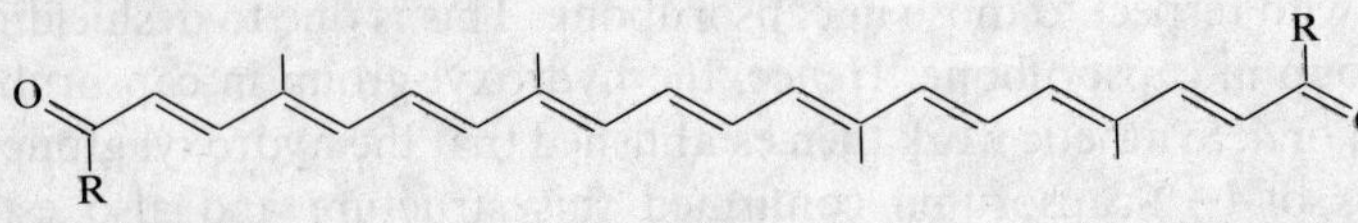

R—CO ... CO—R

(I)

This was supported by the fact that on heating with aqueous alkali, capsorubin gave crocetindial (II) (this is the reversal of the aldol condensation). Further support was afforded by the observation that the infrared spectrum of capsorubin showed a band which was also present in the spectra of authentic compounds of the type (I). Also, the reduction of capsorubin with potassium borohydride produced

(II)

shifts in the u.v. spectrum consistent with selective reduction of two terminal carbonyl groups to give a nonaene chromophore (Weedon *et al.*, 1958). Thus, the problem now was the elucidation of the structures of the terminal groups (R) in capsorubin. It was originally believed that the end-groups (R) were acyclic, but Cholnoky *et al.* (1957) showed that the molecular formula of capsorubin was $C_{40}H_{56}O_4$ (and not $C_{40}H_{60}O_4$, as previously believed). This revised formula indicates that capsorubin contains two rings: D.B.E. $= 41 - 28 = 13$ (see **1** §12e). Since capsorubin contains nine olefinic double bonds and two carbonyl double bonds, this means that two rings are present. Weedon *et al.* (1960) now examined the NMR spectrum of capsorubin. Included in the spectrum were three sharp singlets at τ 9·16, 8·80, and 8·63. These were attributed to methyl groups on saturated quaternary carbon atoms in the end-groups (R). Each signal had an intensity corresponding to two methyl groups. This suggests that the end-groups in capsorubin are identical. Weedon *et al.* (1961) then found that the Oppenauer oxidation (aluminium t-butoxide and acetone) of capsorubin gave a tetraketone, **capsorubone**. The infrared spectrum of this compound showed a band at 1 739 cm^{-1}, which was attributed to the carbonyl group in cyclopentanone. Hence, capsorubin contains two hydroxycyclopentane end-groups.

The NMR spectrum of capsorubone was examined in the τ 9·5–6·4 region. Four well-defined signals were shown at τ 9·02, 8·77, 8·65, and 8·02 in approximate ratios 1:1:1:2, and were attributed to methyl groups. The signal at τ 8·02 is characteristic of in-chain methyls (see §1). Since capsorubin contains four of these methyls (see (I) and (II), above), the other signals must each represent two equivalent methyls. This is understandable if the two end-groups are identical (see also above), each containing three methyls. Since the signals were sharp, all the methyls must be attached to saturated carbon atoms.

So far, it has been established that the end-groups of capsorubin are identical; that they are cyclopentyl groups containing three methyl substituents, each on a saturated quaternary carbon atom; and that they each contain a secondary hydroxyl group (Oppenauer oxidation). It therefore follows that two methyls must constitute a *gem*-dimethyl group in the cyclopentane ring. Compound (III)

(III)

was synthesised and examination of its NMR spectrum showed that the τ values of the methyls were upfield (0·12–0·16) with respect to those in capsorubone. This is due to deshielding by the presence of the carbonyl group in capsorubone. Hence, the hydroxyl group in capsorubin was tentatively placed at position 3 or 4. Synthetic work then established that the hydroxyl group was at position 4. Complete synthesis of ($\pm$)-capsorubin confirmed this structure and also established that the hydroxyl group at position 4 and the keto group at position 6 were *trans* (as previously suggested from infrared and NMR data). The structure (and absolute stereochemistry) of capsorubin is (IV) [Weedon *et al.*, 1962].

(IV)

capsorubin

The relative configurations of the 4-OH and 1-Me were established independently as follows. The (±)-form of (V) was synthesised and, on reduction, gave (VI)-(±)-*trans* and (VII)-(±)-*cis*. These were separated and differentiated by the fact that only (VII) formed a lactone. Each of these ((VI)

(V) (±)-acids

(VI)
(±)-*trans*

(VII)
(±)-*cis*

and (VII); $CO_2H \rightarrow COMe$) was condensed with crocetindial, and it was shown that it was (VII) that gave a product identical with natural capsorubin. Also, the absolute configuration of C-1 has been established by correlation with that of C-1 of (+)-camphor (**8** §23e).

§8c. **Capsanthin**, m.p. 175–176°C. This occurs in red peppers together with capsorubin but in far greater amount. The structure of capsanthin was actually elucidated alongside that of capsorubin (Weedon *et al.*, 1958, 1962). The early work showed that when heated with aqueous alkali capsanthin

(I)
β-citraurin

gave β-citraurin (I), a known compound. It was also found, from ultraviolet spectroscopic studies, that capsanthin contained a decaenone chromophore, and Cholnoky *et al.* (1957) showed that the molecular formula of capsanthin was $C_{40}H_{56}O_3$. Thus, capsanthin contains two rings (*cf.* capsorubin, above). The Oppenauer oxidation of capsanthin gave **capsanthone**, a hydroxydiketone, the infrared spectrum of which indicated the presence of a cyclopentanone ring and a hydroxyl group (Weedon *et al.*, 1960). The NMR spectrum of capsanthone was examined and some of the signals observed were the same as those for capsorubin, but only half the intensity of the latter. Thus, both compounds have a common end-group. This, as we have seen, is the 4-hydroxy-1,2,2-trimethyl-cyclopentyl residue (see capsorubin, §8b). The NMR spectrum of capsanthin showed methyl signals at τ 9·02, 8·95, *8·77, 8·65*, 8·3, and *8·02* in the approximate ratios 1 : 2 : 1 : 1 : 1 : 4 (the italicised values are the same as those shown by capsorubin). However, the signals at τ 8·95 and 8·3 are characteristic of methyls in cyclohexene rings in, *e.g.*, zeaxanthin, §8). This is in agreement with the formation of (I) from capsanthin. Hence, from the data given, it follows that the structure of capsanthin is (II). A point to note is the failure of the Oppenauer oxidation to convert the secondary hydroxyl group in the cyclohexene end-group into the ketonic group.

(II)

capsanthin

§8d. **Fucoxanthin,** m.p. 166–167°C.   The characteristic carotenoid of brown algae and diatoms; it appears to be the most abundant xanthophyll in nature. Weedon *et al.* (1964), from mass spectrometry, established the molecular formula as $C_{42}H_{58}O_6$, and the presence of two hydroxyl groups and one acetoxy-group (these groups had also been shown to be present by Jensen, 1961). Since fucoxanthin formed only a monoacetate, this suggested that one hydroxyl group was tertiary. On reduction with lithium aluminium hydride, fucoxanthin gave a mixture of 'fucoxanthols', the u.v. spectrum of which indicated the presence of a conjugated octaene. Potassium permanganate oxidation of fucoxanthin gave dimethylmalonic acid and 2,2-dimethylsuccinic acid. Thus, fucoxanthin contains the grouping (I) and this was confirmed by examination of the i.r. spectrum, which also indicated the presence of an allenic grouping.

(I)   (II)   (III)

Partial oxidation of fucoxanthin with zinc permanganate gave four aldehydes. Structure (II) was assigned to one of these (based on molecular formula and u.v. spectrum); (III) was a known compound. The other two aldehydes had molecular formulae $C_{25}H_{34}O_4$ (τ 0·55) and $C_{27}H_{36}O_4$ (τ 0·45; d, J 7·5 Hz). These formulae were obtained by mass spectrometry. The C_{25}- and C_{27}-aldehydes were shown to be a pentaenealdehyde and a hexaenealdehyde, respectively, by examination of their u.v. spectra before and after lithium aluminium hydride reduction (*cf.* capsorubin, §8b). In addition to these aldehydes, there was also a mixture of 'allenic aldehydes', which were classified as such because their i.r. spectrum exhibited bands in the region normally associated with allenes (see also above). Further oxidation of the C_{25}- and C_{27}-aldehydes gave (II) and (III), respectively. On the other hand, complete oxidation of the C_{27}-aldehyde and the mixture of 'allenic aldehydes' gave 2,2-dimethylsuccinic acid; the former also gave dimethylmalonic acid.

The NMR spectra of fucoxanthin and the C_{27}-aldehyde showed a number of common signals, *e.g.*, τ 6·32 and 7·40; J 18 Hz, which were attributed to a methylene group adjacent to an oxo group. It was also found that the C_{27}-aldehyde formed a monoacetate, and condensed with the geranyl Wittig reagent (*cf.* §5) to give a conjugated octaenone (as shown by the u.v. spectra before and after hydride reduction).

(IV)

(V)

On the basis of this work, Weedon *et al.* proposed (IV) as the structure of the C_{27}-aldehyde (and the C_{25}-aldehyde as its lower vinylogue). They also tentatively formulated fucoxanthin as (V). This was confirmed by later work of Weedon *et al.* (1966). The mixture of 'allenic aldehydes' (see above) was separated (chromatography) into (VI), (VII), and (VIII). All of these exhibited spectral properties (u.v., visible, i.r., NMR) in keeping with the structures assigned.

$$R =$$

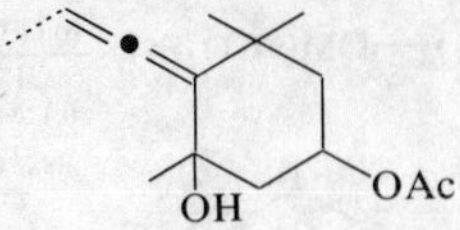

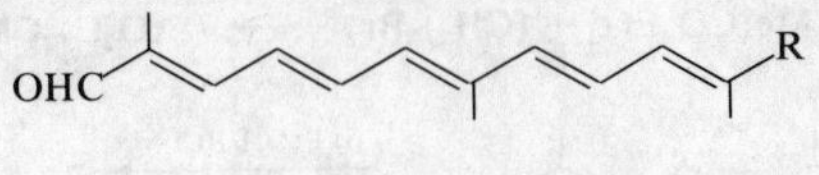

$$(VI) \ C_{27}H_{36}O_4$$

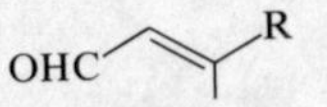

$$(VII) \ C_{17}H_{24}O_4 \qquad\qquad (VIII) \ C_{15}H_{22}O_4$$

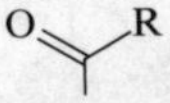

§9. Carotenoid acids (apocarotenoids)

These are compounds which do not contain 40 carbon atoms (see §1).

§9a. Bixin, $C_{25}H_{30}O_4$.   Natural bixin is a brown solid, m.p. 198°C, and is the *cis-trans*-form; it is readily converted into the more stable all-*trans*-form, m.p. 216–217°C, by iodine in benzene solution.

When boiled with potassium hydroxide solution, bixin produces one molecule of methanol and a dipotassium salt which, on acidification, gives the dibasic acid **norbixin**, $C_{24}H_{28}O_4$. Thus bixin is a monomethyl ester, and can be esterified to give methylbixin.

On catalytic hydrogenation, bixin is converted into perhydrobixin, $C_{25}H_{48}O_4$; thus there are 9 double bonds present in the molecule (Liebermann *et al.*, 1915). Perhydrobixin, on hydrolysis, forms perhydronorbixin. Oxidation of bixin with permanganate produces four molecules of acetic acid (Kuhn *et al.*, 1929); hence there are four —C(CH$_3$)= groups in the chain. Furthermore, since the parent hydrocarbon of perhydronorbixin, $C_{24}H_{46}O_4$, is $C_{22}H_{46}$ (the two carboxyl groups are regarded as substituents), the molecule is acyclic.

The thermal decomposition of bixin produces toluene, *m*-xylene, *m*-toluic acid and the methyl ester of this acid (Kuhn *et al.*, 1932). Hence the following assumptions may be made regarding the nature of the chain (*cf. β*-carotene, §3).

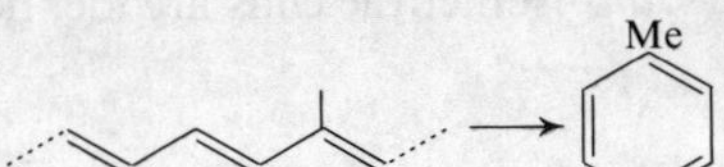

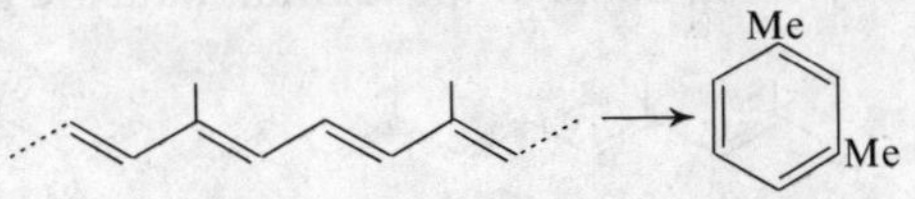

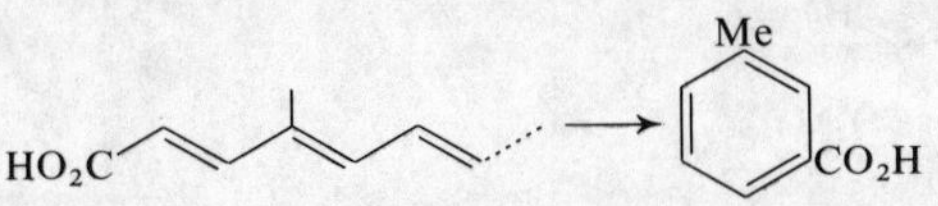

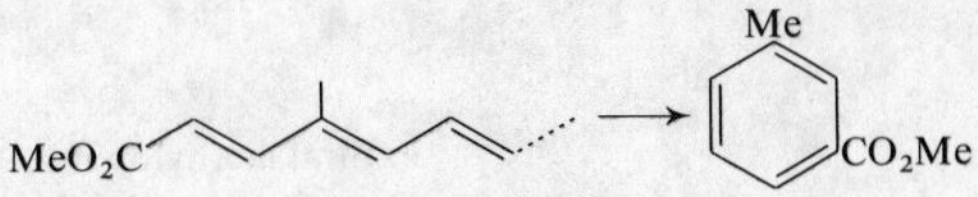

The foregoing facts may be explained by assuming the following structure for bixin (Kuhn *et al.*, 1932):

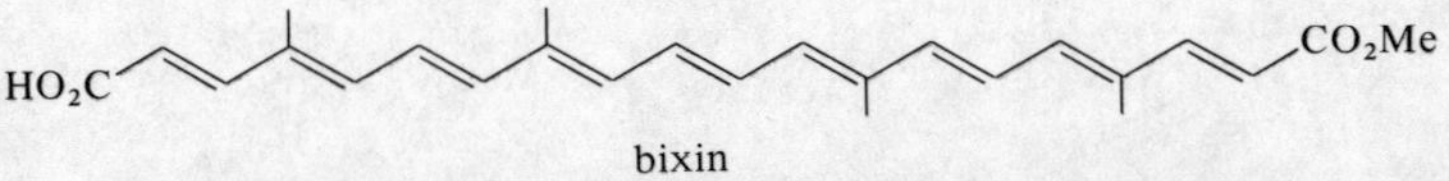

bixin

This structure is in agreement with the nature of the products of ozonolysis of methylbixin (*i.e.*, bixin methyl ester). These are methyl 4-oxopent-2-enoate (I), methylglyoxal (II) and compound (III) which, on oxidation, gives methyl *trans-β*-muconate (IV).

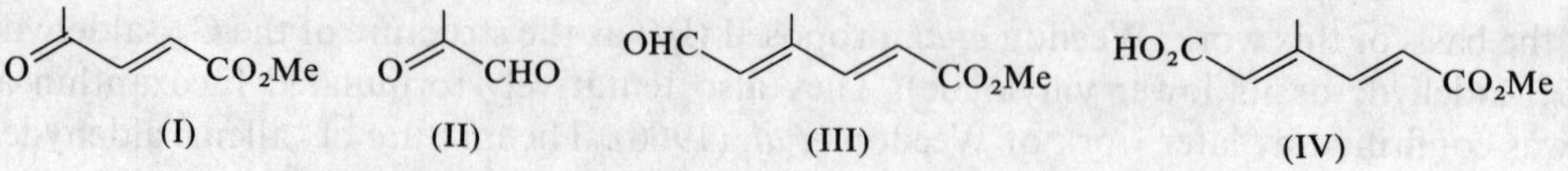

(I)   (II)   (III)   (IV)

Further support comes from the fact that perhydronorbixin has been synthesised, and shown to be identical with the compound obtained from the reduction of bixin (Karrer *et al.*, 1933).

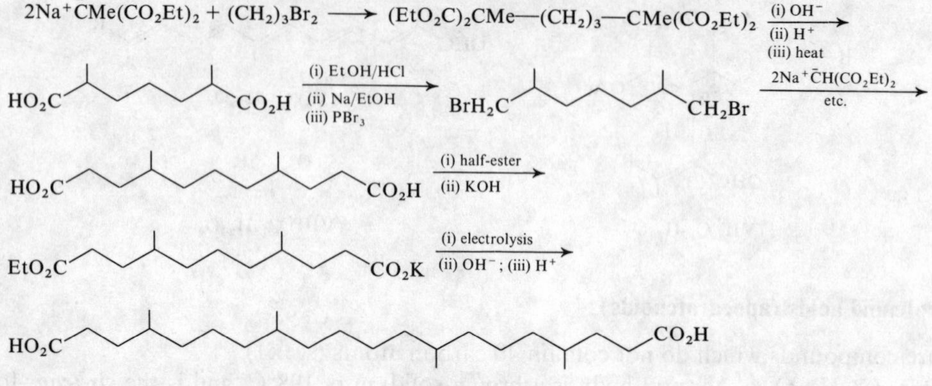

$$2Na^+\bar{C}Me(CO_2Et)_2 + (CH_2)_3Br_2 \longrightarrow (EtO_2C)_2CMe\!-\!(CH_2)_3\!-\!CMe(CO_2Et)_2 \xrightarrow[\text{(iii) heat}]{\text{(i) OH}^-\ \text{(ii) H}^+}$$

HO_2C ⋯ CO_2H $\xrightarrow[\text{(iii) PBr}_3]{\text{(i) EtOH/HCl} \ \text{(ii) Na/EtOH}}$ BrH_2C ⋯ CH_2Br $\xrightarrow[\text{etc.}]{2Na^+\bar{C}H(CO_2Et)_2}$

HO_2C ⋯ CO_2H $\xrightarrow[\text{(ii) KOH}]{\text{(i) half-ester}}$

EtO_2C ⋯ CO_2K $\xrightarrow[\text{(ii) OH}^-; \text{(iii) H}^+]{\text{(i) electrolysis}}$

HO_2C ⋯ CO_2H

perhydronorbixin

Still further proof is the synthesis of all-*trans* methylbixin (Buchta *et al.*, 1959, 1960).

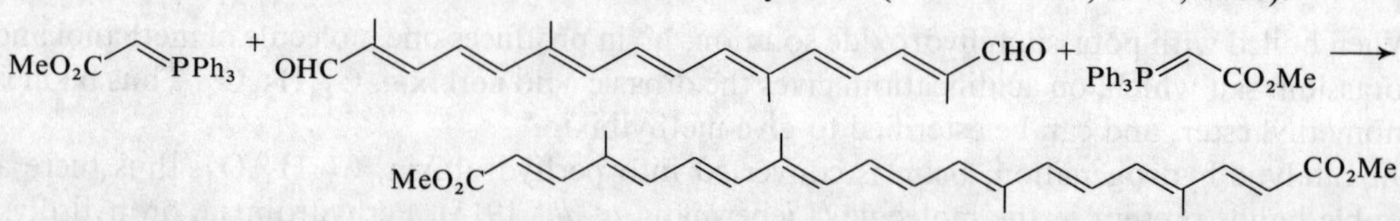

MeO_2C—PPh_3^+ OHC ⋯ CHO + Ph_3P—CO_2Me $\longrightarrow$

MeO_2C ⋯ CO_2Me

It has been known for some time, based on infrared, ultraviolet, and visible absorption spectroscopy, that bixin had a *cis*-configuration about one of its double bonds. Also, the ultraviolet data excluded the possibility that the *cis*-isomer was one of the hindered type (see structure (II) §1). Hence, the *cis*-isomerism cannot be at the 6,7 or the 14,15 double bond (see structure of bixin, above). Furthermore, the central double bond (10,11) was eliminated by synthesis. One suggestion was that the 2,3-double bond was involved, and the other suggestion was that it was the 4,5. Weedon *et al.* (1960) have settled the problem by the examination of the NMR spectra of natural and all-*trans* methylbixin. Some of the relevant data are given here. In the all-*trans* isomer the ends are identical

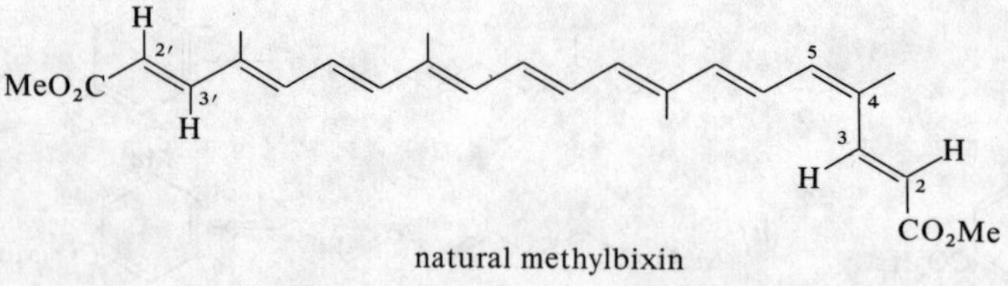

natural methylbixin

| H-2 | τ 4·12d | H-2′ | τ 4·12d |
| H-3 | τ 2·07d | H-3′ | τ 2·63d |

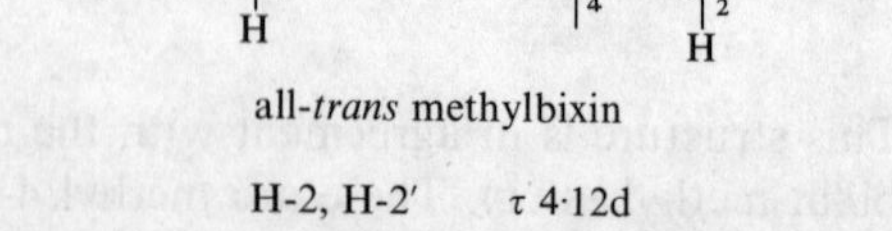

all-*trans* methylbixin

| H-2, H-2′ | τ 4·12d |
| H-3, H-3′ | τ 2·61d |

and so only one signal is given by H-2 and H-2′, and one signal by H-3 and H-3′ (note that the α-proton absorbs upfield with respect to the β-proton in α,β-unsaturated oxo compounds). Since four signals were observed for the end protons in natural methylbixin, these ends must be different. However, the J values $J_{2,3}$ and $J_{2′,3′}$ were the same (15·8 Hz). This indicates that the configurations about the end double bonds (2,3 and 2′,3′) are unaffected (*trans*). As pointed out above, 6,7- (14,15-) and 10,11-double bonds have been excluded. This leaves the 4,5- and the 8,9-double bond as possibilities. If *cis*-isomerism occurred at the 8,9-double bond, it is then difficult to explain the large change in τ value for H-3. It therefore follows that the difference between the natural and all-*trans* methylbixin is at the 4,5-double bond. However, since bixin is unsymmetrical at its ends, the isomerism could therefore be at the 16,17-double bond (instead of 4,5). This uncertainty was settled

by the examination of the NMR spectrum of *cis*-apo-1-norbixinal methyl ester, obtained by oxidation of natural bixin. The spectrum showed doublets at τ 4·08 and τ 2·04. Hence, the isomerism occurs at the 4,5-double bond at the ester end in bixin, *i.e.*, bixin is

bixin

§9b. Crocetin, $C_{20}H_{24}O_4$. This occurs in saffron as the digentiobioside, *crocin*. The structure of crocetin was elucidated by Karrer *et al.* (1928) and Kuhn *et al.* (1931). Crocetin behaves as a dicarboxylic acid and has seven double bonds (as shown by catalytic hydrogenation to perhydrocrocetin, $C_{20}H_{38}O_4$). On oxidation with chromic acid, crocetin gives 3–4 molecules of acetic acid per molecule of crocetin; thus there are 3–4 methyl side-chains. The structure of crocetin was finally shown by the degradation of perhydronorbixin, $C_{24}H_{46}O_4$, by means of the following method:

$$RCH_2CO_2H \xrightarrow{Br_2-P} RCHBrCO_2H \xrightarrow{hydrolysis} RCHOHCO_2H \xrightarrow{CH_2N_2} RCHOHCO_2CH_3 \xrightarrow{CH_3MgI}$$

$$RCHOHC(OH)(CH_3)_2 \xrightarrow{(CH_3CO_2)_4Pb} RCHO \xrightarrow{[O]} RCO_2H$$

This set of reactions was performed *twice* on perhydronorbixin, thereby resulting in the loss of four carbon atoms (two from each end); the product so obtained was perhydrocrocetin, $C_{20}H_{38}O_4$. On these results, crocetin is therefore:

crocetin

This structure is supported by the fact that the removal of two carbon atoms from perhydrocrocetin by the above technique (one carbon atom is lost from each end) resulted in the formation of a *diketone*. The formation of this compound shows the presence of an α-methyl group at each end of the molecule. The structure of crocetin is further supported by the synthesis of perhydrocrocetin, and by the synthesis of crocetin diesters by Isler *et al.* (1957). It appears, however, that part of the crocetin in crocin is present in the form of the 2,3-*cis* isomer. The evidence for this has been obtained from a study of the NMR spectrum of the dimethyl ester (Weedon *et al.*, 1960; *cf.* bixin, §9a). This *cis*-form is readily converted into the all-*trans* form by iodine. The *trans*-crocetin dimethyl ester has also been synthesised by the Wittig reaction between the dialdehyde (I) and two molecules of the phosphorane (Buchta *et al.*, 1959, 1960) [see §5, structure (II), for the preparation of (I)].

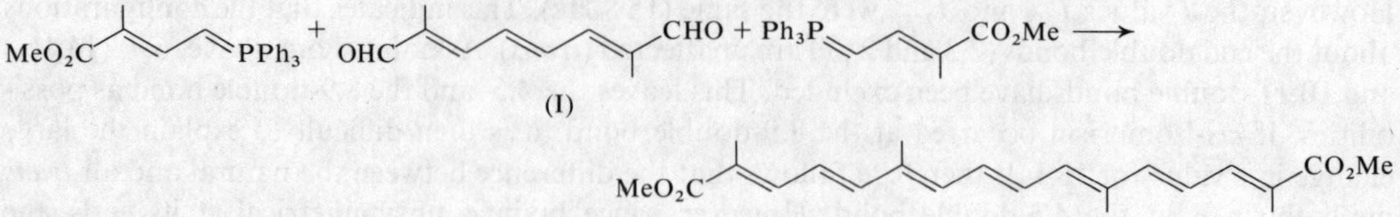

$$MeO_2C \diagup PPh_3 \;+\; OHC \diagup CHO \;+\; Ph_3P \diagup CO_2Me \longrightarrow$$

(I)

$$MeO_2C \diagup\diagup\diagup\diagup CO_2Me$$

§10. Biosynthesis of carotenoids

Biosynthetic studies of the carotenoids have been carried out, and the pathways are those for the terpenoids (**8** §34). Thus Braithwaite *et al.* (1957) and Grob (1957) have shown that labelled mevalonic acid is incorporated into β-carotene. Scheuer *et al.* (1959) have also shown that this acid is incorporated into lycopene. Furthermore, Modi *et al.* (1961) have isolated mevalonic acid from carrots and Goodwin *et al.* (1967) have shown that labelled mevalonic acid is incorporated into phytoene. The actual sequence is: isopentyl pyrophosphate (IPP; 5 carbon atoms) → geranyl pyrophosphate (10C) $\xrightarrow{\text{IPP}}$ farnesyl pyrophosphate (15C) $\xrightarrow{\text{IPP}}$ geranylgeranyl pyrophosphate (20C) $\xrightarrow{\text{2 mols}}$ phytoene (40C) → carotenoids.

Various geometrical isomers of phytoene have been isolated from natural sources, *e.g.*, the main isomer

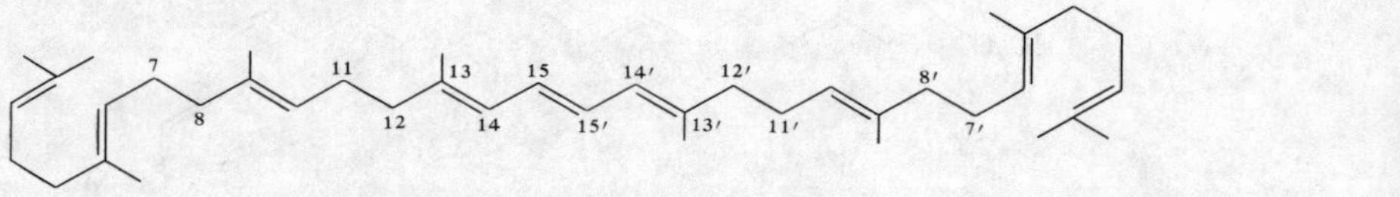

phytoene (all-*trans* isomer)

from carrot oil has the *trans* configuration about all unconjugated non-terminal double bonds, and a *cis* configuration about the central (15,15′) double bond (*cf.* §3). On the other hand, the main isomer from diphenylamine-inhibited cultures of *Flavobacterium dehydrogenases* is the all-*trans* isomer (Weedon *et al.*, 1966–1972).

There is now a great deal of evidence to show that the route to lycopene is (the 'extra' double bonds are shown in parentheses):

phytoene $\xrightarrow{-2H}$ phytofluene (11, 12) $\xrightarrow{-2H}$ ζ-carotene (11,12; 11′,12′) $\xrightarrow{-2H}$

neurosporene (7,8; 11,12; 11′,12′) $\xrightarrow{-2H}$ lycopene (7,8; 11,12; 11′,12′; 7′,8′)

This is known as the **Porter–Lincoln pathway** (1950). All of these compounds occur naturally. In the laboratory it is easy to dehydrogenate phytoene by means of *N*-bromosuccinimide, and chromatographic separation of the products has shown the presence of the series of carotenes given above (phytoene → lycopene). On the other hand, the mechanism of biological dehydrogenation is still uncertain. It appears that at least in some cases (atmospheric) oxygen must be present. A point of interest is that the dehydrogenation occurs successively and alternately from the 'middle' of the chain.

Lycopene can then undergo terminal cyclisation to give the carotenes (*cf.* **8** §34). Xanthophylls are probably produced by oxygenation of the carotenes.

REFERENCES

BENTLEY, *The Natural Pigments*, Interscience (1960).
Rodd's Chemistry of Carbon Compounds, Elsevier (2nd edn.). Vol. IIB (1968). Ch. 7. 'The Carotenoid Group.'
BERNFELD (ed.). *Biogenesis of Natural Compounds*, Pergamon (2nd edn., 1967). Ch. 10. 'The Biosynthesis of Carotenoids and Vitamin A.'
GOODWIN (ed.), *Chemistry and Biochemistry of Plant Pigments*, Academic Press (1965).
WEEDON *et al.*, 'Stereochemistry of Capsorubin and Synthesis of its Optically Inactive Epimers,' *Proc. chem. Soc.*, 1962, 215 (and References therein).
WEEDON *et al.*, 'Fucoxanthin and Related Pigments', *Chem. Comm.*, 1966, 515.

WEEDON *et al.*, 'Mass Spectrometry of Carotenoid Epoxides and Furanoid Oxides', *Chem. Comm.*, 1966, 852.
WEEDON *et al.*, 'Carotenoids and Related Compounds. Part XV. The Structure and Synthesis of Phytoene, Phytofluene, ζ-Carotene, and Neurosporene', *J. chem. Soc.* (*C*), 1966, 2154.
WEEDON *et al.*, 'Mass Spectrometry of Carotenoid Ketones', *Chem. Comm.*, 1969, 415.
WEEDON *et al.*, 'Synthesis of Zeaxanthin, β-Cryptoxanthin, and Zeinoxanthin', *J. chem. Soc.* (*C*), 1971, 404.

10 Polycyclic aromatic hydrocarbons

§1. Introduction

Naphthalene, anthracene, phenanthrene, fluorene, etc., have been described in Volume I. All these compounds occur in coal-tar, but also present are many polynuclear hydrocarbons containing four or more rings, and others of this type have been synthesised.

Various ways of writing polynuclear systems have been used, *e.g.*, pyrene and perylene:

pyrene   perylene

Also, the numbering of polynuclear hydrocarbons has undergone a number of changes.

According to the IUPAC rules, when the polynuclear aromatic hydrocarbon contains five or more fused benzene rings in a linear arrangement, the name ends in 'acene'. The number of rings is then indicated by the appropriate prefix chosen from the prefixes used for designating the alkanes, *e.g.*, penta (5), hexa (6), hepta (7), etc. (see Vol. I, Ch. 3).

Many non-linear polycyclic aromatic hydrocarbons have accepted trivial names (see Text). More complex hydrocarbons are then named as derivatives of the 'trivial parent' which has the largest number of rings possible. The attached components are indicated by prefixes derived from the aromatic system, *e.g.*, benz(o) for benzene; naphth(o) for naphthalene, etc. For the purpose of numbering, the structure is written with the greatest number of rings in a horizontal position and a maximum number of rings above and to the right of the horizontal row. If two or more ways of writing the structure satisfy these requirements, the one chosen is that which has as few rings as possible to the left and below the horizontal row. Numbering is then carried out in a clockwise direction, starting with the uppermost ring to the right and omitting atoms at ring junctions. These ring-junction atoms are designated by adding roman letters 'a', 'b', etc. to the number of the position immediately preceding. These atoms follow the highest number, the clockwise sequence always being taken wherever possible. When there is a choice, however, the ring-junction atoms follow the lowest possible numbers. Also, carbon atoms which carry an *indicated hydrogen atom* are numbered as low as possible.

Points of attachment of the arene 'substituents' are indicated by numbers or by italicised letters. This lettering is applied to the *peripheral* sides of the *parent* compound and begins with *a* for the side 1,2, *b* for 2,3, etc. Isomers are distinguished by prefixing the letter (which is as early in the alphabet as possible) with numbers indicating the positions of fusion of the other component. The order of these numbers conforms to the direction of lettering of the parent compound. Numbers and letters are enclosed in square brackets and immediately follow the prefix designating the 'substituent'.

The following illustrate the rules (some earlier names are given in parentheses). There are, however, some recommended exceptions, such as anthracene and phenanthrene.

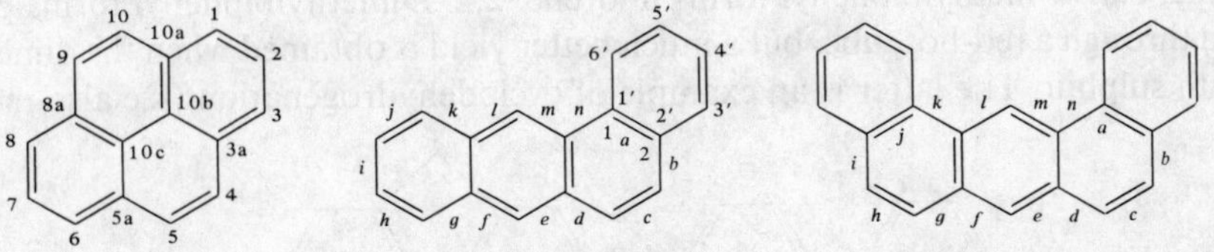

pyrene

benz[*a*]anthracene
(1,2-benzanthracene)

dibenz[*a*, *j*]anthracene
(1,2:7,8-dibenzanthracene)

Polynuclear hydrocarbons may be classified as *ortho*-fused and as *ortho*- and *peri*-fused, *e.g.*, the benzanthracenes shown above are *ortho*-fused, and pyrene is *ortho*- and *peri*-fused.

§2. General methods of preparation of polynuclear hydrocarbons

Before dealing with a number of individual hydrocarbons, it is instructive to review some of the general methods whereby these polynuclear hydrocarbons may be prepared (see also Vol. I, Ch. 29).

(i) **Fittig reaction**, *e.g.*, anthracene and phenanthrene may be prepared by the action of sodium on *o*-bromobenzyl bromide.

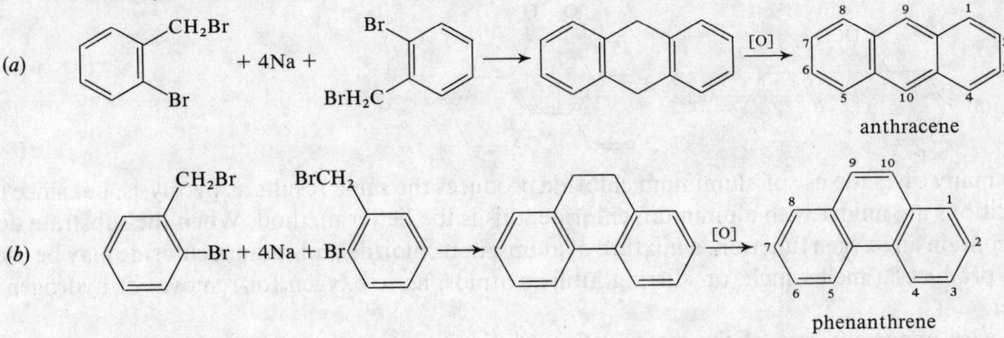

anthracene

phenanthrene

(ii) **Ullman biaryl synthesis.** This method results in the formation of isolated polynuclear compounds, *e.g.*, heating iodobenzene with copper powder in a sealed tube produces biphenyl.

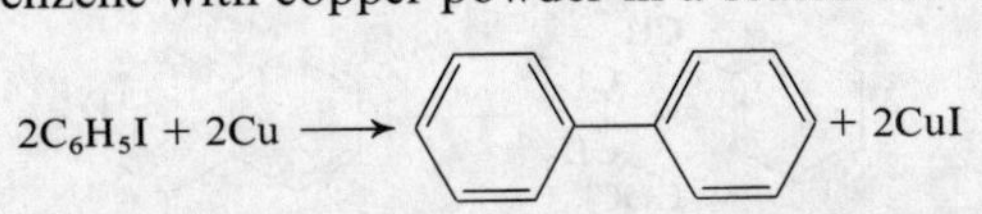

$$2C_6H_5I + 2Cu \longrightarrow \text{(biphenyl)} + 2CuI$$

Compounds of the isolated system type can, under suitable conditions, be converted into condensed polynuclear compounds (see method (iii)). In certain cases, the Ullmann synthesis leads to condensed systems (see §5c).

Aryl chlorides and bromides do not usually react unless there is a −I group *ortho* and/or *para* to the halogen atom, *e.g.*, *o*-chloronitrobenzene gives 2,2′-dinitrobiphenyl.

Dimethylformamide is a good solvent for this synthesis (higher yields are obtained).

The mechanism of the Ullman biaryl synthesis is still uncertain; both a free-radical and an ionic mechanism have been proposed.

(iii) Many compounds of the isolated system type can be converted into condensed systems by strong heating, *e.g.*, *o*-methylbiphenyl forms fluorene. 2,2′-Dimethylbiphenyl forms phenanthrene when passed through a red-hot tube, but a much better yield is obtained when the dimethylbiphenyl is heated with sulphur. The latter is an example of cyclodehydrogenation (see also method (vii)).

Pyrolysis as a method of dehydrogenation and cyclodehydrogenation is drastic. Its use is avoided where other methods are applicable (see below).

(iv) **Friedel–Crafts reaction.** Condensed polynuclear compounds may be prepared *via* an external or an internal Friedel–Crafts reaction. An example of the former is the preparation of anthracene from benzyl chloride; an example of the latter is the preparation of phenanthraquinone from benzil.

In many cases the use of aluminium chloride produces the same results as pyrolysis, but since the conditions are milder with aluminium chloride, this is the better method. When the substrate does not contain an oxygen function, a mixture of aluminium chloride and sodium chloride may be used. This produces a melt which, on stirring, utilises atmospheric oxygen for removal of hydrogen as water.

A very important case of the internal Friedel–Crafts reaction is that in which ring closure is effected on acid chlorides, *e.g.*, the conversion of γ-phenylbutyryl chloride to α-tetralone.

This type of ring closure may be effected by the action of concentrated sulphuric acid or, better still, polyphosphoric acid (PPA), on the carboxylic acid itself, *e.g.*,

9-Alkylanthracenes may be prepared from *o*-benzoylbenzoic acid *via* anthrone (note the use of HF for ring-closure).

(*va*) **Elbs reaction.** In this method, polynuclear hydrocarbons are produced from a diaryl ketone containing a methyl group in the *o*-position to the keto group. The reaction is usually carried out by heating the ketone under reflux or at 400–450°C until water is no longer evolved, *e.g.*, *o*-methyl-benzophenone forms anthracene.

(*vb*) Anthracene may also be synthesised by a Diels–Alder reaction involving 1,4-naphtha-quinone and butadiene (see also §3b).

Zinc-dust distillation has been a common method of removing oxygen from various types of oxygenated polynuclear hydrocarbons (see Text).

(vi) **Phenanthrene syntheses.** The phenanthrene nucleus is particularly important in steroid chemistry, and so a number of methods for synthesising phenanthrene are dealt with in some detail.

(*a*) **Pschorr synthesis** (1896). This method offers a means of preparing phenanthrene and sub-stituted phenanthrenes with the substituents in known positions. Phenanthrene may be prepared as follows, starting with *o*-nitrobenzaldehyde and sodium β-phenylacetate.

Although substituted phenanthrenes with substituents in known positions may be prepared in those cases where isomerism in the cyclised product is possible, it is usual to obtain both isomers, e.g.,

Since ring-closure is effected between two rings, these rings must be in the *cis*-position, e.g., *cis-o*-aminostilbene gives phenanthrene, but the *trans* isomer does not.

The Pschorr synthesis is really an example of intramolecular phenylation, and the decomposition can be effected in several ways. The method described above is the catalysed (copper) decomposition and is believed to proceed *via* a free-radical mechanism. Decomposition can also be effected in the absence of copper, in which case the mechanism is believed to be of the nucleophilic unimolecular type. On the other hand, decomposition can be carried out in *alkaline* solution and in this case it is a free-radical mechanism that operates.

Kessar *et al.* (1969) have prepared phenanthrenes from cinnamic acids *via* what they believe to be benzyne intermediates (see Vol. I), e.g.,

(b) **Haworth synthesis** (1932). Naphthalene is condensed with succinic anhydride in the presence of aluminium chloride in nitrobenzene solution. Two naphthoylpropionic acids are obtained, and these may be readily separated. It should be noted that no anthracene is formed; ring-closure occurs only in the 1- or 2-position of naphthalene, but not in the 3-position.

The Haworth synthesis is very useful for preparing alkylphenanthrenes with the alkyl group in position 1 (from (I)) or position 4 (from (II)); *e.g.*,

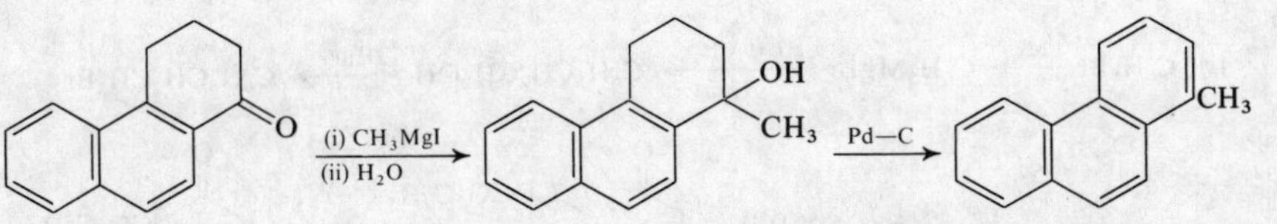

$$\text{(I)} \quad \xrightarrow[\text{(ii) } H_2O]{\text{(i) } CH_3MgI} \quad \xrightarrow{Pd-C}$$

(I)

By using methylsuccinic anhydride instead of succinic anhydride, a methyl group can be introduced into the 2- or 3-position; in this case the condensation occurs at the less hindered keto group, *i.e.*, at the one which is farther removed from the methyl substituent.

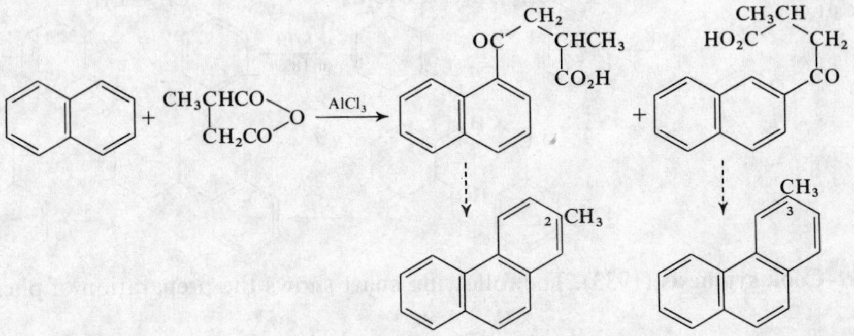

$$+ \; CH_3CHCO\!\!-\!\!O, \; CH_2CO \quad \xrightarrow{AlCl_3}$$

α-Bromoketone derivatives of naphthalene may be used in the malonic ester synthesis to prepare alkylphenanthrenes, *e.g.*,

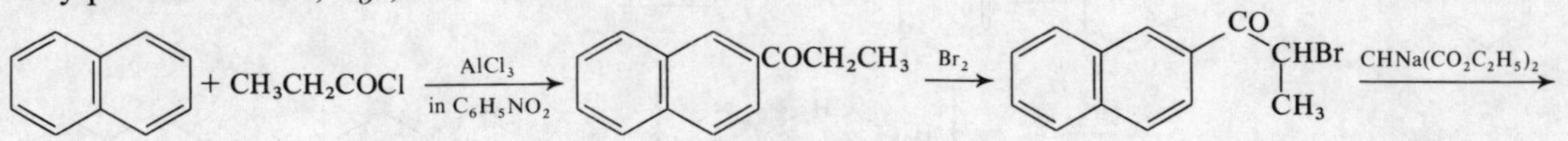

$$+ \; CH_3CH_2COCl \xrightarrow[\text{in } C_6H_5NO_2]{AlCl_3} \quad COCH_2CH_3 \xrightarrow{Br_2} \quad CO\;CHBr\;CH_3 \xrightarrow{CHNa(CO_2C_2H_5)_2}$$

main product

$$CO\;CHCH_3\;CH(CO_2C_2H_5)_2 \xrightarrow[\substack{\text{(ii) HCl} \\ \text{(iii) heat}}]{\text{(i) KOH}}$$

(*c*) **Stobbe condensation** (1893). This method has been improved by Johnson (1944), and has been used to prepare phenanthrene derivatives; *e.g.*,

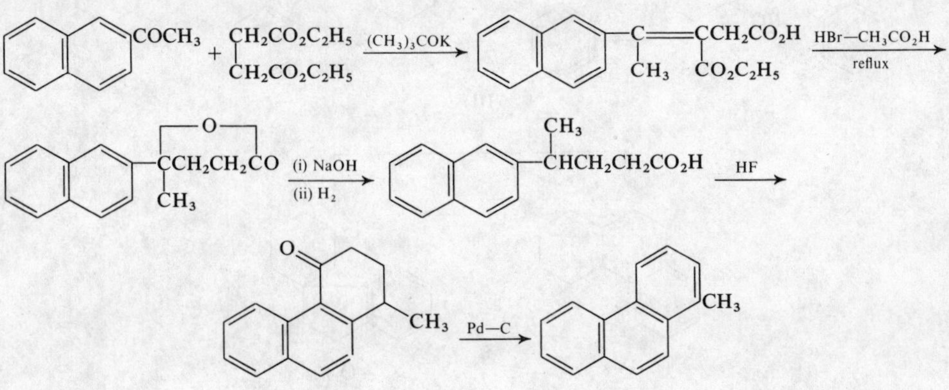

$$COCH_3 + \substack{CH_2CO_2C_2H_5 \\ CH_2CO_2C_2H_5} \xrightarrow{(CH_3)_3COK} \quad C\!=\!CCH_2CO_2H, CH_3 \; CO_2C_2H_5 \xrightarrow[\text{reflux}]{HBr-CH_3CO_2H}$$

$$CCH_2CH_2CO, CH_3 \xrightarrow[\text{(ii) } H_2]{\text{(i) NaOH}} \quad CHCH_2CH_2CO_2H, CH_3 \xrightarrow{HF}$$

$$\xrightarrow{Pd-C}$$

(d) **Bardhan–Sengupta synthesis** (1932). In this synthesis the starting materials are 2-phenylethyl bromide and ethyl cyclohexane-2-carboxylate; these may be prepared as follows:

(i) $C_6H_5Br \xrightarrow{Mg} C_6H_5MgBr \xrightarrow{\overset{O}{\overset{/\backslash}{CH_2CH_2}}} C_6H_5CH_2CH_2OH \xrightarrow{HBr} C_6H_5CH_2CH_2Br$

(ii) 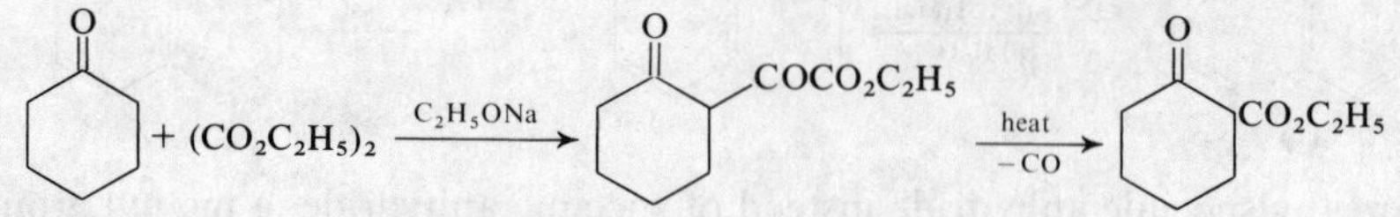 $+ (CO_2C_2H_5)_2 \xrightarrow{C_2H_5ONa}$ $\xrightarrow[-CO]{heat}$

These two compounds are then treated as shown:

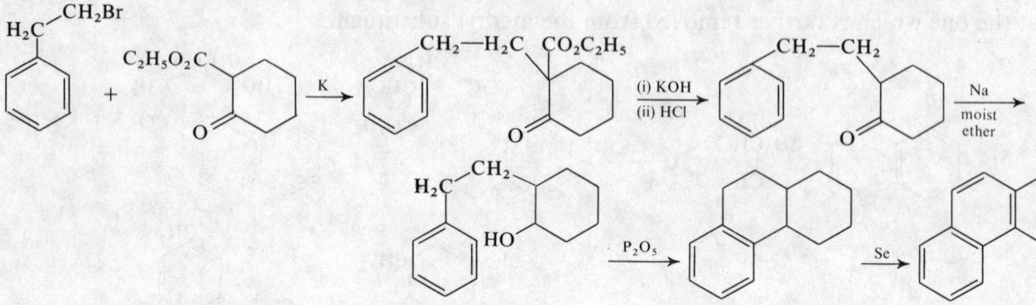

(e) **Bogert–Cook synthesis** (1933). The following chart shows the preparation of phenanthrene.

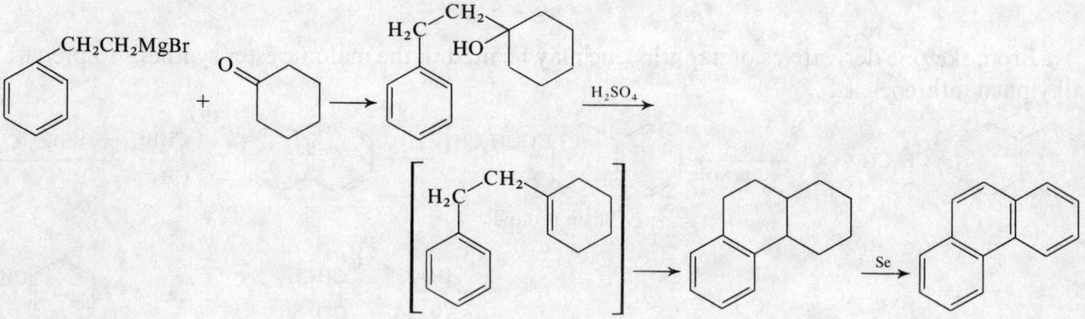

It might be noted here that the Bardhan–Sengupta and Bogert–Cook methods both proceed *via* the formation of (III) which then gives a mixture of octahydrophenanthrene (IV) and the spiran (V).

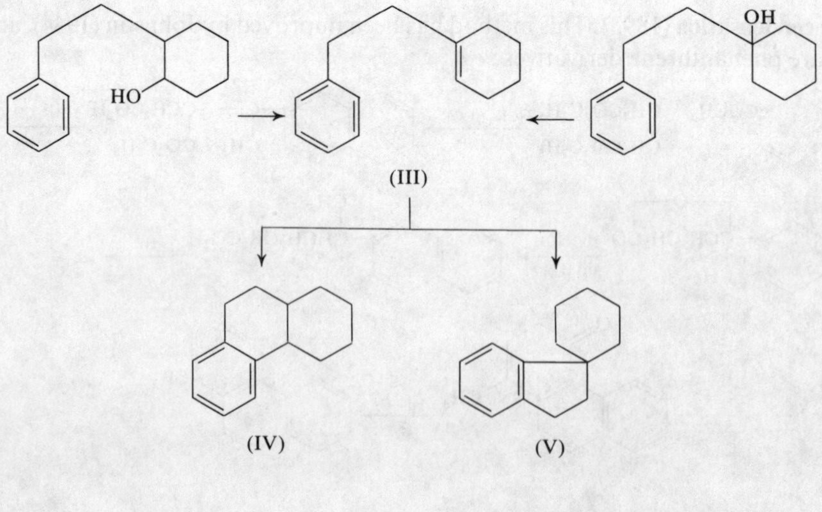

(III)

(IV)   (V)

(*f*) Bacon *et al.* (1956) have prepared substituted phenanthrenes from biphenyl-2,2′-dialdehydes as follows:

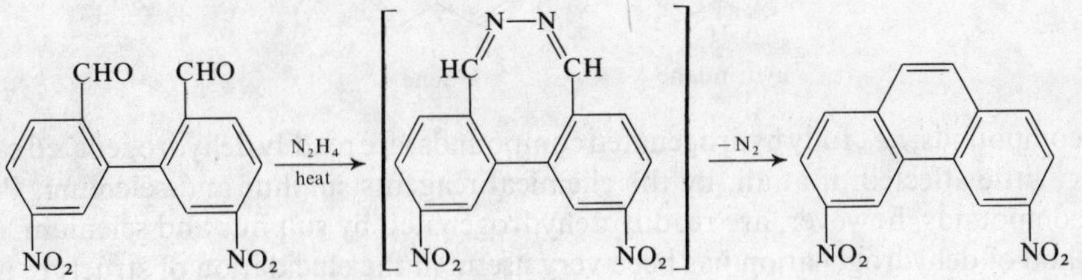

Bradsher *et al.* (1956) have shown that 2-phenylbenzyl cyanides are cyclised to 9-phenanthryl-amines with concentrated sulphuric acid.

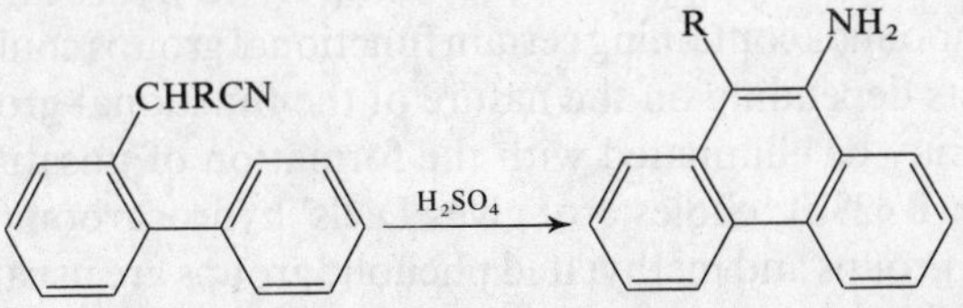

(*g*) Stilbene (*cis* and *trans*) is converted into phenanthrene on irradiation.

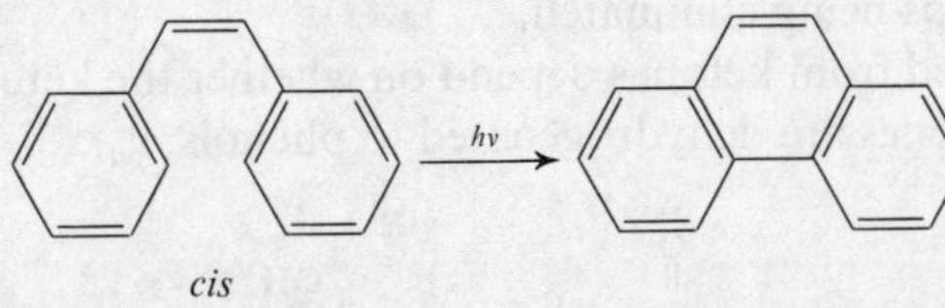

Substituted stilbenes are also readily converted into substituted phenanthrenes (Mallory *et al.*, 1964).

(vii) **Dehydrogenation of hydroaromatic compounds with sulphur, selenium, palladised or platinised charcoal.** This method is mainly confined to the dehydrogenation of six-membered rings, but five-membered rings may sometimes be dehydrogenated when they are fused to a six-membered ring. The general methods are as follows:

(*a*) Heating the compound with the calculated amount of sulphur at 200–220°C; hydrogen is eliminated as hydrogen sulphide (Vesterberg, 1903).

(*b*) Heating the compound with the calculated amount of selenium at 250–280°C; hydrogen is eliminated as hydrogen selenide (Diels, 1927). Since selenium is a milder dehydrogenating reagent than sulphur, *i.e.*, fewer side reactions occur, it is better to use selenium.

(*c*) Heating the compound with palladium- or platinum-charcoal up to about 300°C, or passing the vapour of the compound over the catalyst heated at 180–350°C; hydrogen is eliminated cata-lytically. Simple examples of catalytic dehydrogenation are:

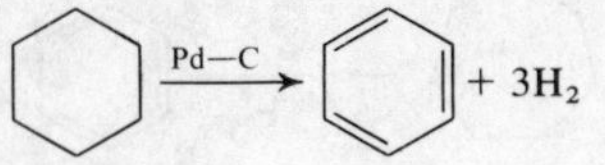

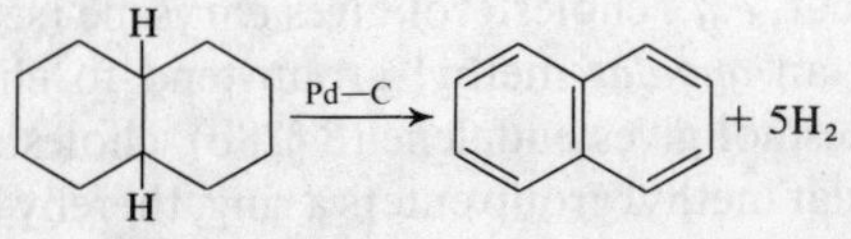

cyclohexane

decalin

hydrindane   indene

Perhydro-compounds, *i.e.*, fully hydrogenated compounds, are readily dehydrogenated catalytically, but are very little affected, if at all, by the chemical reagents sulphur and selenium. Partially unsaturated compounds, however, are readily dehydrogenated by sulphur and selenium.

The method of dehydrogenation has been very useful in the elucidation of structure in terpenoid and steroid chemistry; specific examples are described in these two chapters. The following is an account of some of the general problems involved in dehydrogenation.

Originally, dehydrogenation was applied almost entirely to hydrocarbons, but subsequently it was found that many compounds containing certain functional groups could also be dehydrogenated, the nature of the products depending on the nature of the functional group.

(i) Alcoholic groups may be eliminated with the formation of unsaturated hydrocarbons, *e.g.*, eudesmol gives eudalene (**8** §28b); cholesterol gives Diels' hydrocarbon (**11** §1).

(ii) Phenolic hydroxyl groups and methylated phenolic groups are usually unaffected by dehydrogenation with sulphur. With selenium, these groups may or may not be eliminated, but the higher the temperature at which the dehydrogenation is carried out (particularly above 300°C), the greater the likelihood of these groups being eliminated.

(iii) The products obtained from ketones depend on whether the keto group is in a ring or in an open chain. Thus cyclic ketones are dehydrogenated to phenols, *e.g.*,

When the keto group is in a side-chain, then it is often unaffected.

(iv) Carboxyl (or carboalkoxyl) groups are eliminated when attached to a tertiary carbon atom, *e.g.*, abietic acid gives retene (**8** §32). If, however, the carboxyl group is attached to a primary or secondary carbon atom, it is usually unaffected when the dehydrogenation is carried out with sulphur or palladium-charcoal. On the other hand, the carboxyl group is usually eliminated (decarboxylation) when selenium is used, but in some cases it is converted into a methyl group (see, *e.g.*, vitamin D, **11** §11).

(v) In a number of cases, dehydrogenation is accompanied by a rearrangement of the carbon skeleton, this tending to occur at higher temperatures and when the heating is prolonged.

(*a*) Ring contraction may occur, *e.g.*,

cycloheptane

(*b*) Ring expansion may occur, *e.g.*, cholesterol gives chrysene (see **11** §1).

(*c*) Compounds containing an *angular* methyl group tend to eliminate this methyl group as CH_3SH or CH_3SeH, *e.g.*, eudesmol gives eudalene (**8** §28b), cholesterol gives Diels' hydrocarbon (**11** §1). In some cases, the angular methyl group enters a ring, thereby bringing about ring expansion [*cf*. (*b*) above]. On the other hand, a normal substituent methyl group may migrate to another position, *e.g.*, 5,6,7,8-tetrahydro-1,5-dimethylphenanthrene gives 1,8-dimethylphenanthrene on dehydrogenation with selenium.

(*d*) Side-chains larger than methyl may remain intact, or be eliminated or be degraded, *e.g.*,

cholesterol   Diels' hydrocarbon

(*e*) Dehydrogenation may produce new rings (*cf.* method (iii)); *e.g.*,

LINEAR *ORTHO*-FUSED POLYNUCLEAR HYDROCARBONS

§3. Naphthacene, $C_{18}H_{12}$

An orange solid, m.p. 357°C, it occurs in coal-tar, and has been synthesised as follows (Fieser, 1931).

phthalic anydride   tetralin

When oxidised with fuming nitric acid, naphthacene forms naphthacenequinone (I), m.p. 294°C. (I), on treatment with phenylmagnesium bromide followed by dilute acid, gives (II) which is formed by 1,4-addition (*cf.* α,β-unsaturated carbonyl compounds; see Vol. I).

(I)   (II)

The antibiotics known as the 'tetracyclines' contain the naphthacene skeleton (see **18** §7a).

§3a. Rubrene (5,6,11,12-tetraphenylnaphthacene).   This may be prepared by heating 3-chloro-1,3,3-triphenyl-prop-1-yne alone, or better, with quinoline at 120°C *in vacuo* (Dufraisse *et al.*, 1935).

Rubrene is an orange-red solid, m.p. 334°C. Its solution in benzene has a yellow fluorescence, but when this solution is shaken with air in sunlight, the fluorescence slowly disappears, and a white solid can now be isolated. This is rubrene peroxide, and when heated to 100–140°C in a high vacuum, it emits yellow-green light and evolves oxygen, reforming rubrene.

Rubrene peroxide is actually a derivative of 5,12-dihydronaphthacene, and so the molecule is not flat but folded about the O–O axis (the carbon atoms at 5 and 12 are tetrahedrally hybridised).

§3b.   Three linear benzene derivatives of naphthacene have been prepared, *viz.*, **pentacene** (a deep violet-blue solid) and **hexacene** (a deep-green solid) [Clar, 1930, 1939], and **heptacene** (a very deep-green solid) [Bailey *et al.*, 1953].

pentacene   hexacene

heptacene

Bailey *et al.* (1953) have synthesised pentacene, hexacene and heptacene by a similar method (*via* a Diels–Alder reaction). Let us consider pentacene first. 1,2-Dimethylenecyclohexane (I) was condensed with *p*-benzoquinone (II) in boiling dioxan solution to give the diketo compound (III).

This was then converted into the dithioketal (IV) which, on heating with Raney nickel, gave (V) and this, on dehydrogenation with palladised charcoal, gave pentacene (30 per cent).

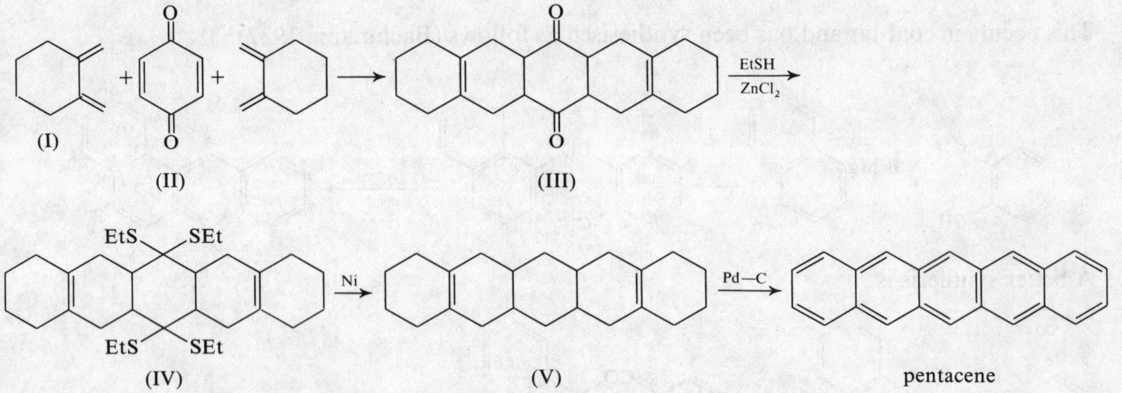

(I)   (II)   (III)

(IV)   (V)   pentacene

Hexacene and heptacene require 2,3-dimethylenedecalin (VI) as a starting material, which was prepared from (I) *via* the maleic anhydride adduct as shown.

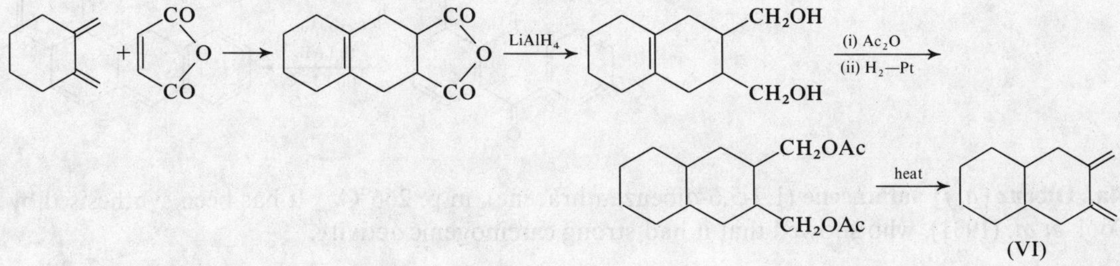

Heptacene was then synthesised from two molecules of (VI) and one molecule of *p*-benzoquinone, etc., and hexacene from one molecule of (I) and one molecule of (VI), etc.

Hexacene has also been synthesised by (*a*) Lang *et al.* (1963) and by (*b*) Stacey *et al.* (1971).

(*a*)

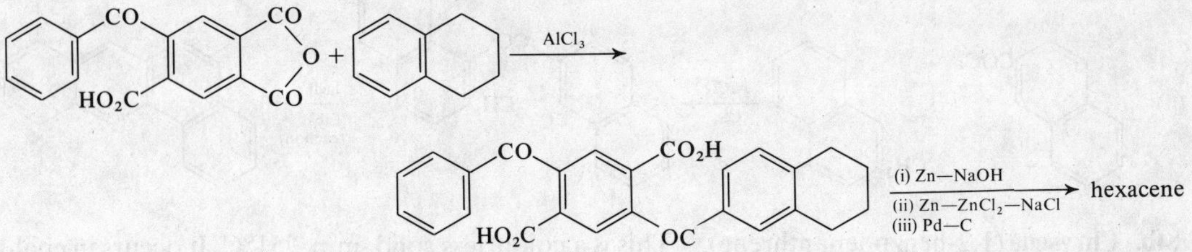

(*b*)

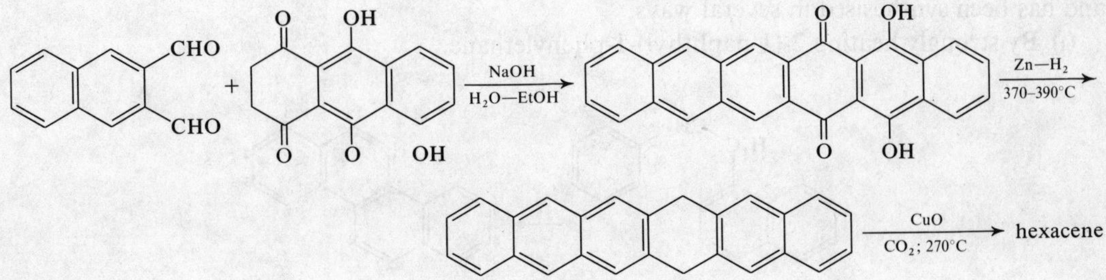

NON-LINEAR *ORTHO*-FUSED POLYNUCLEAR HYDROCARBONS

§4. Benz[*a*]anthracene (1,2-benzanthracene), m.p. 160°C

This occurs in coal-tar and has been synthesised as follows (Bachmann, 1937).

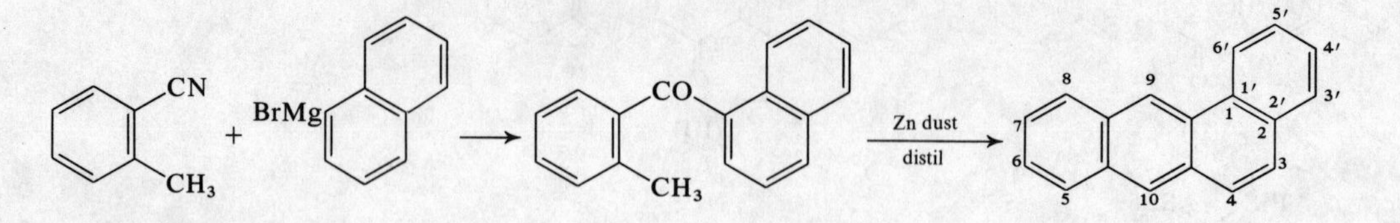

A better synthesis is:

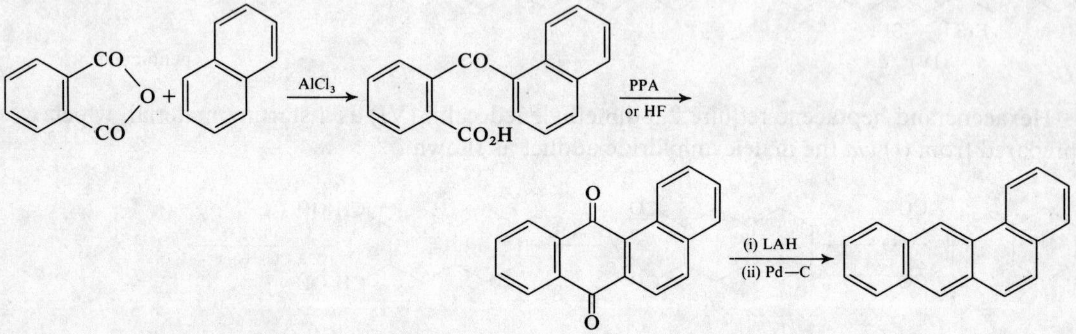

§4a. Dibenz [*a, j*] anthracene (1,2-5,6-dibenzanthracene), m.p. 266°C.   It has been synthesised by Cook *et al.* (1931), who showed that it had strong carcinogenic activity.

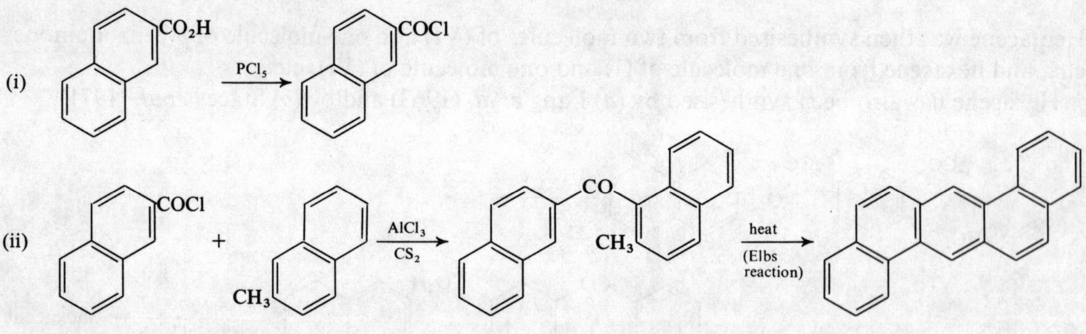

(i)

(ii)

§4b. Chrysene (1,2-benzphenanthrene).   This is a colourless solid, m.p. 251°C. It occurs in coal-tar, and has been synthesised in several ways:

(i) By strongly heating 2-(1-naphthyl)-1-phenylethane.

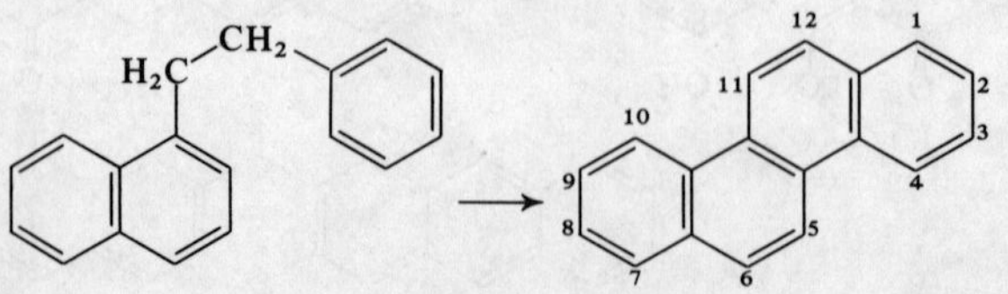

(ii) By a Bogert–Cook synthesis (cf. §2vie).

(iii) By a Pschorr synthesis [cf. §2via].

(iv) Phillips (1956) has prepared chrysene from naphthalene and the lactone of trans-2-hydroxy-cyclohexaneacetic acid:

(v) Chrysene has also been synthesised via a Diels–Alder reaction (Davies et al., 1957), using 1-vinylnaphthalene.

(I)

(II)

The intermediate quinone (I) is oxidised by excess of benzoquinone (see Vol. I) and chrysene-1,4-quinone (II) is reduced to chrysene.

(vi) The irradiation of 1,6-diphenylhexa-1,3,5-triene produces chrysene (Fonken, 1962).

Chrysene is produced by the pyrolysis of indene, and also by the dehydrogenation of steroids with selenium.

The most reactive position of chrysene to electrophilic attack is position 6 (12); this corresponds to position 9 in phenanthrene (see Vol. I).

§4c. **Picene** (1,2-7,8-dibenzphenanthrene), m.p. 366–367°C. This is obtained when cholesterol or cholic acid is dehydrogenated with selenium. It has been synthesised by heating 1-methylnaphthalene with sulphur at 300°C (see also §4a).

Phillips (1953) has synthesised picene by condensing 9,10-dihydrophenanthrene with succinic ester chloride, and proceeding as shown.

It might also be noted that some 1,2-6,7-dibenzphenanthrene was also produced.

Picene has also been prepared by the photocyclisation of 1,2-distyrylbenzene (Dietz *et al.*, 1968).

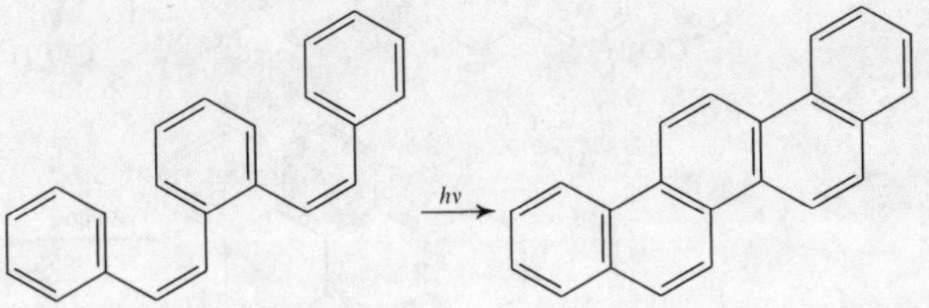

ORTHO- AND PERI-FUSED POLYNUCLEAR HYDROCARBONS

§5. Pyrene

Pyrene is a colourless solid, m.p. 156°C. It occurs in coal-tar, and has been synthesised from biphenyl-2,2'-diacetyl chloride as follows:

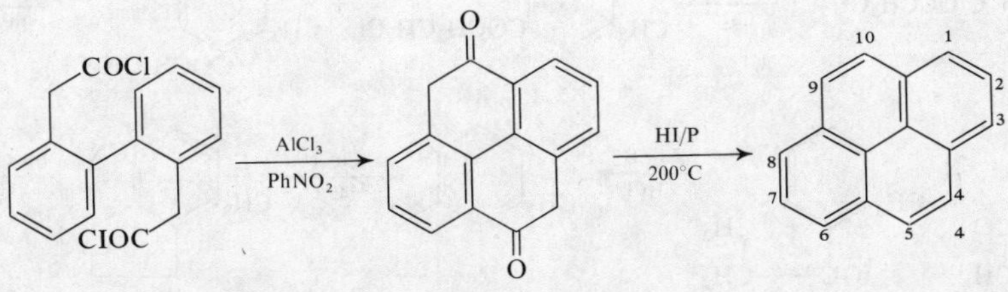

Buchta *et al.* (1958) have synthesised pyrene using an internal Stobbe reaction [§2vi*e*] (see also §5d):

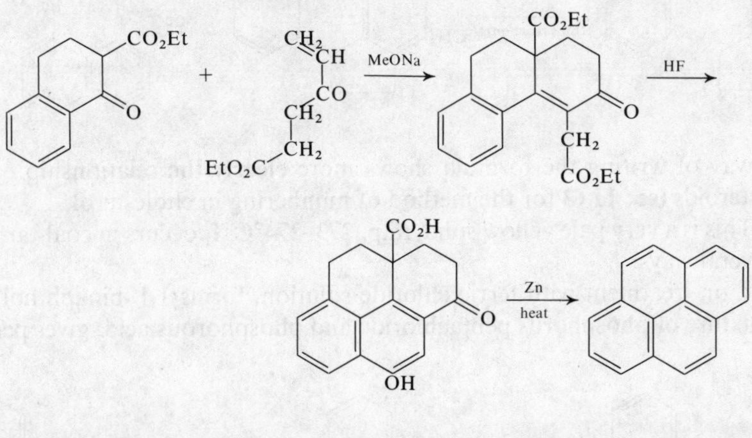

Bacon *et al.* (1956) have synthesised pyrene by reaction between biphenyl-2,2',6,6'-tetra-aldehyde and hydrazine (see §2vi*f*).

Pyrene is most reactive in the 1 (6)-position towards electrophilic reagents (*cf.* chrysene, §4b).

§5a. 1,2-Benzpyrene (3,4-benzpyrene).   This is a pale yellow solid, m.p. 179°C, which is very strongly carcinogenic. It occurs in coal-tar and has been synthesised from pyrene.

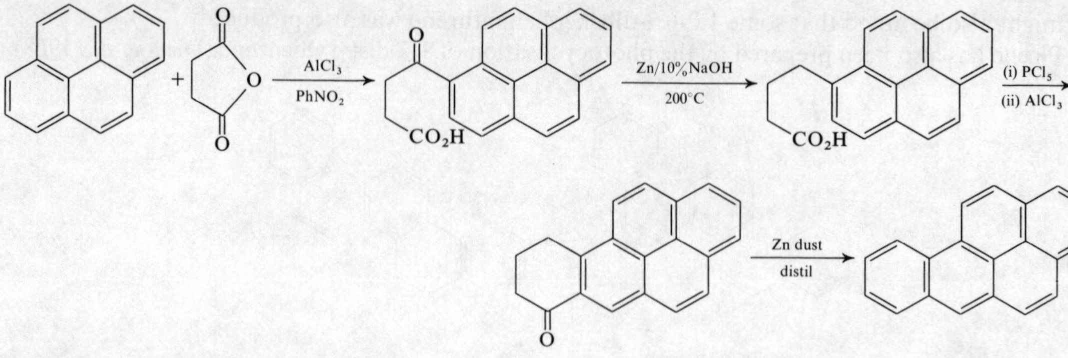

The most reactive position in this compound is 1 (*cf.* 9 of anthracene or phenanthrene).

§5b. 20-Methylcholanthrene.   This is a pale yellow solid, m.p. 180°C. A steroid derivative, it has been prepared by the degradation of, *e.g.*, cholesterol (see 11 §3iii). Cook (1934) showed that methylcholanthrene has powerful carcinogenic properties, and Fieser *et al.* (1935) synthesised it in the following way:

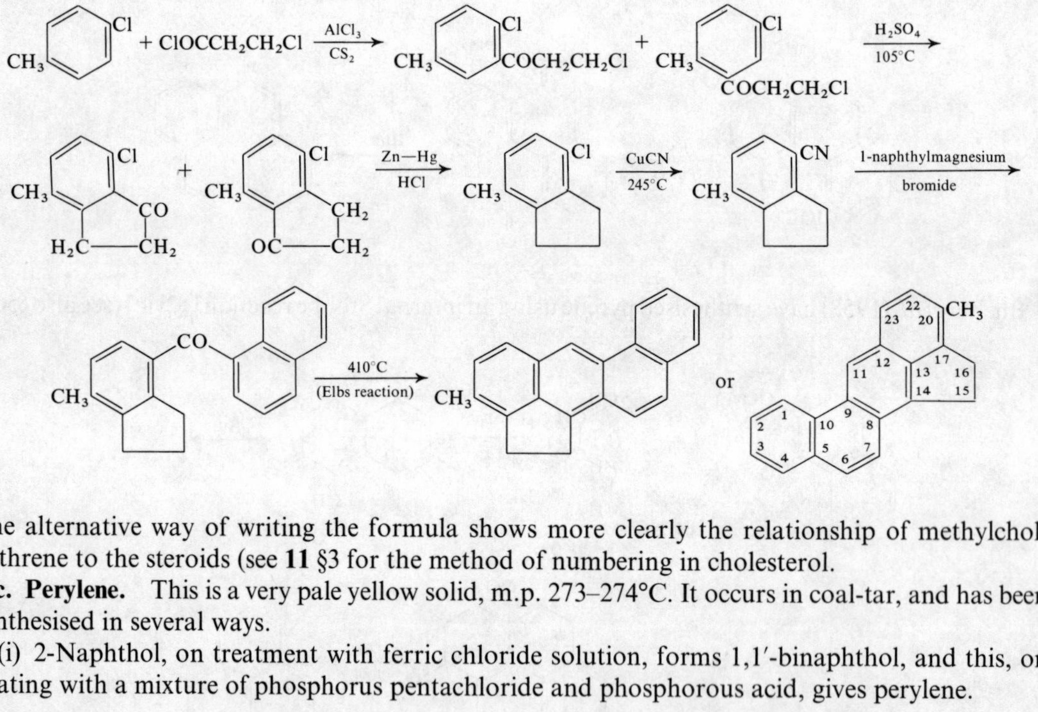

The alternative way of writing the formula shows more clearly the relationship of methylcholanthrene to the steroids (see 11 §3 for the method of numbering in cholesterol).

§5c. Perylene.   This is a very pale yellow solid, m.p. 273–274°C. It occurs in coal-tar, and has been synthesised in several ways.

(i) 2-Naphthol, on treatment with ferric chloride solution, forms 1,1′-binaphthol, and this, on heating with a mixture of phosphorus pentachloride and phosphorous acid, gives perylene.

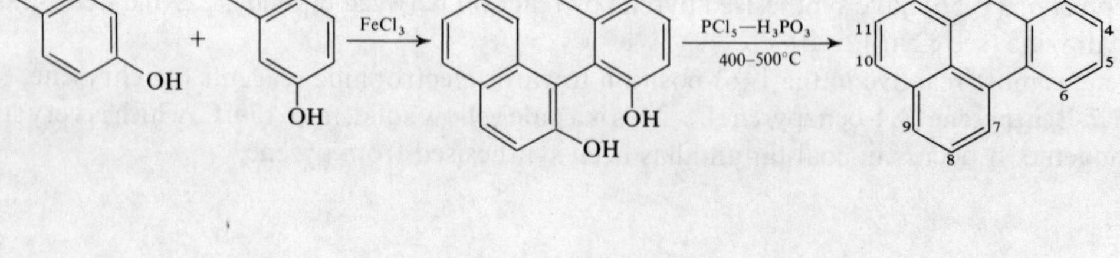

(ii) Perylene may also be prepared by heating 1,8-di-iodonaphthalene with copper powder (*i.e.*, by an Ullmann synthesis; *cf.* §2ii), or by heating 1,1′-binaphthyl with hydrogen fluoride under pressure.

Perylene is most reactive in the 3-position towards electrophilic reagents.

§5d. **Coronene**, m.p. 430°C.   This is a yellow solid with a blue fluorescence in benzene solution; it has been found in coal-gas (Lindsay *et al.*, 1956). It was synthesised by Scholl *et al.* (1932), starting from *m*-xylene and anthraquinone-1,5-dicarbonyl chloride, the latter behaving in the tautomeric form shown in the chart.

Newman (1940) has also synthesised coronene, starting from 7-methyltetralone, and proceeding as follows:

Baker *et al.* (1951, 1952) have synthesised coronene by a shorter method as follows (NBS = *N*-bromosuccinimide):

It might be noted here that starting with *m*-xylene gives pyrene (§5).

The simplest and most efficient synthesis of coronene appears to be that of Clar *et al.* (1957). The starting material is perylene (§5c), and this is treated with (i) maleic anhydride and chloranil, and followed by (ii) heating with soda-lime; these processes are then repeated (*cf.* §5f).

All positions in coronene are equivalent.

§5e. Hexabenzcoronene, m.p. > 700°C.   This has been prepared in several ways, *e.g.*, by heating hexaphenylbenzene with a mixture of aluminium chloride and sodium chloride (Martin *et al.*, 1958).

§5f. Circumanthracene (dark red solid).   This has been prepared *via* a Diels–Alder reaction between diperinaphthylanthracene and maleic anhydride (I). The adduct was oxidised with chloranil (II) and the product was then heated with soda-lime at 400°C to give circumanthracene (III) and dinaphthoperopyrene (IV). (IV) is formed without ring-closures that occur in (III). In fact, milder conditions of decarboxylation (copper powder in quinoline) gave only (IV).

(IV)   (III)

§6

Many polynuclear hydrocarbons and their derivatives exhibit **molecular overcrowding**; this has been discussed in **5** §3a.

SPECTRAL PROPERTIES OF POLYNUCLEAR HYDROCARBONS

The **infrared absorption regions** of polynuclear hydrocarbons include many of those characteristic of the benzene compounds (see Table 1.6). The C—H (str.) absorption region is 3 080–3 030 cm^{-1} (w), and the bands for C=C (in-plane vibration) are 1 625–1 600 cm^{-1} (v), 1 590–1 575 cm^{-1} (v), and 1 525–1 474 cm^{-1} (v). In addition, there is the region 1 000–650 cm^{-1}, in which several strong bands may appear (C—H out-of-plane def.), *e.g.*, phenanthrene, anthracene, naphthacene and pentacene all show a strong band at ~750 cm^{-1}. This is due to *four* adjacent hydrogens (terminal benzene rings). On the other hand, the last three also show a strong band at ~900 cm^{-1}, which is due to *para*-hydrogen atoms. Phenanthrene differs from the others in that it shows a band at ~830 cm^{-1}, which is due to *two* adjacent hydrogen atoms.

Infrared spectra can be used to detect the presence of various functional groups, but have not yet been fully worked out for assigning orientation.

Ultraviolet and visible absorption spectra are very useful in the examination of polynuclear hydrocarbons, since they are characteristic of the hydrocarbon and its derivatives. The spectra of most aromatic compounds show three absorption bands (see also **1** §12a), *e.g.*,

Table 10.1

Hydrocarbon	λ_{max} (ε) nm	λ_{max} (ε) nm	λ_{max} (ε) nm
Benzene	184 (60 000)	204 (7 500)	254 (210)
Naphthalene	220 (100 000)	275 (5 700)	312 (250)
Phenanthrene	252 (50 000)	293 (16 000)	330 (250)
Anthracene	253 (200 000)	375 (8 000)	—
Naphthacene	278 (200 000)	474 (13 000)	—
Pentacene	310 (270 000)	580 (15 000)	—

It can be seen from Table 10.1 that it is relatively easy to identify *unsubstituted* hydrocarbons. When substituents are present, the bands are usually shifted to longer wavelengths, but the pattern is usually characteristic of the substituent group and its position in the nucleus. Thus ultraviolet-visible spectroscopy is particularly useful for polycyclic systems and, when used in conjunction with 'model compounds', is a very powerful tool for elucidating structures.

It can also be seen from the colours of the 'acenes' that as the number of rings increases the colour deepens. This is in keeping with increased conjugation in the system.

NMR spectroscopy of benzene and its derivatives has been discussed in **1** §12e. As we have seen, τ-values of aromatic protons lie between 1·0 and 3·0 due to the shielding effect of the ring current (outside the ring). Theoretical considerations have shown that in polycyclic aromatic hydrocarbons each ring has its *own* ring current. This accounts for the fact that protons in these compounds also absorb in the same region as benzene. The actual τ-value, however, depends on the position of the proton in the polycyclic system. Thus, a proton in ring A which is nearer another fused benzene ring, ring B, will experience some deshielding due to ring B, and consequently its signal will appear down-field with respect to other protons in ring A which are further from ring B. However, although π-ring currents appear to be the dominant factor in contributing to chemical shifts, other contributing factors also operate. When the latter contributions become increasingly larger, deviations from the general rule given above become greater. One important contributing factor (other than the π-ring currents) is overcrowding of hydrogen atoms leading to deviations from coplanarity of the polycyclic system.

Mass spectrometry of benzene and its derivatives has been discussed in **1** §13a. Polycyclic aromatic hydrocarbons, however, generally show relatively few fragment ions, and the most abundant ion is usually the molecular ion (M) or the $(M-1)$ ion (loss of one hydrogen atom). The molecular ion is almost always the base peak, and a common ion is $[M-26]^+$ due to loss of acetylene. This ion has been used to detect the presence of polycyclic structures (Reed, 1960).

§7. Carcinogenic properties

Many polynuclear hydrocarbons are carcinogenic, *i.e.*, produce tumours (cancer), *e.g.*, benzpyrene (§5a), methylcholanthrene (§5b). Tests are made on experimental animals (usually mice or rabbits) by application of a solution of the compound in benzene or acetone to the skin at regular intervals. A great deal of work has been carried out to elucidate the relationship between carcinogenic activity and structure. Methylcholanthrene appears to be the most potent carcinogen (in experimental animals) and it also appears that the 1,2-benzanthracene structure (§4) is the type of carbon skeleton responsible, particularly when it carries a methyl group at the 10-position, and even more so when there are methyl groups at the 9,10-positions.

Many carcinogens are non-polynuclear hydrocarbons, *e.g.*, carbon tetrachloride, urethan, etc.

QUINONOID PIGMENTS

§8

A very large number of these pigments occur naturally and are widely distributed. They may be conveniently classified as benzoquinonoid, naphthaquinonoid and anthraquinonoid pigments. There are also pigments which are quinones of polynuclear hydrocarbons, but in these the two keto-groups of the quinone system are *not* in the *same* ring. Some examples of the various pigments are: **perezone** (I) [orange pigment from certain plants], **juglone** (II) [yellow pigment from walnut shells], **kermesic acid** (III) [red pigment from the insect Kermococcus ilicis], **hypericin** (IV) [the dark red pigment from St. John's wort and other plants of the genus *Hypericum*].

(I)   (II)   (III)   (IV)

§8a. Lapachol, m.p. 140°C. This is described here to illustrate some of the earlier methods used to elucidate the structures of quinonoid pigments. Preliminary investigations showed that its molecular formula was $C_{15}H_{14}O_3$ and that it contained a quinonoid system and an acidic hydroxyl group. Since lapachol gave naphthalene when distilled with zinc dust, it is therefore a naphthaquinone derivative. At the same time, isobutene was formed in this reaction; this indicates the presence of a side-chain. Since oxidation of lapachol (alkaline hydrogen peroxide) gave acetone, the side-chain therefore contains an isopropylidene end-group.

Oxidation with nitric acid converted lapachol into phthalic acid, and so it follows that the naphthalene nucleus has one unsubstituted ring. Reductive acetylation (Zn—Ac$_2$O) of lapachol gave a triacetate which was converted back again into lapachol by atmospheric oxygen (quinol → quinone). Hydrogenation of lapachol (PtO—H$_2$) also gave a saturated trihydroxyphenol (Hooker, 1936). A structure for lapachol which fits these facts (all substituents in one ring) is (I). This is supported by the fact that the condensation of 2-hydroxy-1,4-naphthaquinone (II) with isovaleraldehyde (III) gave isolapachol (IV). This is isomeric with lapachol and on reduction followed by oxidation (to regenerate the quinone) gave dihydrolapachol (V), which was identical with the reduction product of lapachol.

Structure (I) for lapachol has been confirmed by synthesis by Fieser (1927), who condensed the silver salt of (II) with 2-methylbut-2-enyl bromide (note the *C*-alkylation; see also Vol. I).

A more recent synthesis of lapachol is that of Pettit *et al.* (1971); note the use of succinyl peroxide.

Zn—Ac₂O, Et₃N

heat in xylene; I₂

hydroxyhydrolapachol (I)

(i) NaOH
(ii) H⁺

(I)

§8b. 7-Acetylemodin. Cameron *et al.* (1970) isolated a group of seven polyhydroxyanthraquinones from the insect *Eriococcus coraceus*. These pigments occur in the living insect as glycosides, from which the aglycons may be obtained by hydrolysis with acid. We shall here discuss the structure of one of these aglycons, 7-acetylemodin (II). Its molecular formula was shown to be $C_{17}H_{12}O_6$ (elemental analysis and mass spectrum). The aglycon emodin (I), a *known* compound, was also isolated, but had been previously isolated from a related species of insect.

(I)   (II)   (III)

The u.v. spectrum of (II) was similar to that of emodin (I), and the presence of an acetyl group in (II) was indicated by a band at $1\,685\ \mathrm{cm}^{-1}$ in its i.r. spectrum. The presence of this acetyl group was also supported by the appearance of a three-proton singlet τ 7·30 in the NMR spectrum, the remainder of which was consistent with structure (II). When (II) was treated with alkaline hypoiodite (haloform reaction) and followed by di-thionite reduction to remove an introduced nuclear iodo-substituent, endocrocin (III) was produced. Hence, the structure of 7-acetylemodin is established (as (II)).

§8c. Many spinochrome pigments have been isolated from sea urchins. The major spinochrome in the species *Diadema antillarum* is the common 6-ethyl-2,3,7-trihydroxynaphthazarin (I). This nomenclature is based on the parent compound naphthazarin, the systematic name of which is 5,8-dihydroxy-1,4-naphthaquinone.

(I) was first isolated (chromatography) by Millot (1957), who also observed a minor component which he did not identify. Thomson *et al.* (1971) isolated this component and elucidated its structure. It was soluble in aqueous sodium hydrogen carbonate, had a typical naphtha-1,4-quinone u.v.—visible spectrum with a multi-band centred at 489 nm, a strong C—H (stretching) band at $2\,955\ \mathrm{cm}^{-1}$ in the i.r. spectrum, and a molecular weight of 280 (mass spectrum). The NMR spectrum indicated the presence of an ethyl group, and included two

(I)   (II)   (III)

singlets at *ca.* τ 5·8 (ratio 2:1) which were attributed to methoxy-groups. The authors thought that some of these data were contradictory and so carried out a very careful separation by TLC and showed that the 'compound' was a mixture of two components.

The NMR and mass spectra of these two pigments showed that they were monomethyl derivatives of (I), which was obtained when each pigment was demethylated (HBr). Careful methylation of (I) by diazomethane produced (II); only the most acidic hydroxyl group (3) is methylated. (II) was found to be identical with the major pigment of the *D. antillarum* mixture. On the other hand, when the trimethyl ether of (I) was partially demethylated, (II) was obtained together with a larger amount of the isomeric 2-methyl ether (III), which was shown to be identical with the minor pigment of the mixture. The NMR spectra of (II) and (III) were now examined, and it was found that the signals of the methoxy-groups appeared at τ 5·80 for (II) and at τ 5·87 for (III) [*cf.* the signals of the mixture, above]. The empirically calculated values are τ 5·77 and 5·86, respectively.

REFERENCES

Handbook for Chemical Society Authors, Chemical Society. Special Publication, No. 14 (1960), pp. 63–74.
RODD (ed.), *Chemistry of Carbon Compounds, Elsevier.* Vol. IIIB (1956). Chs. XX, XXI, XXII.
CLAR, *Polycyclic Hydrocarbons*, Academic Press. Vols. I and II (1964).
Organic Reactions, Wiley. Vol. I (1952), Ch. 6. 'The Elbs Reaction.' Vol. VI (1951), Ch. 1. 'The Stobbe Condensation.' Vol. IX (1957), Ch. 7. 'The Pschorr Synthesis and Related Diazonium Ring Closure Reactions.'
TROTTER, 'Crystal-Structure Studies of Aromatic Hydrocarbons', *Roy. Inst. Chem.* Lecture Series (1964), No. 2.
FANTA, 'The Ullmann Synthesis of Biaryls', *Chem. Rev.*, 1964, **64**, 613.
BLACKBURN and TIMMONS, 'The Photocyclisation of Stilbene Analogues', *Quart. Rev.*, 1969, **23**, 482.
TAYLOR (ed.), *Advances in Organic Chemistry: Methods and Results.* Vol. 8 (1972). 'The Application of of Proton Magnetic Resonance Spectroscopy to Structure Identification in Polycyclic Aromatic Molecules', p. 317.
BENTLEY, *The Natural Pigments*, Interscience (1960). Ch. 11. 'Quinonoid Pigments.'
MATHIESON and THOMPSON, 'Naturally Occurring Quinones. Part XVIII', *J. chem. Soc.* (C), 1971, 153.

11 Steroids

§1. Introduction

The steroids form a group of structurally related compounds which are widely distributed in animals and plants. Included in the steroids are the sterols (from which the name *steroid* is derived), vitamin D, the bile acids, a number of sex hormones, the adrenal cortex hormones, some carcinogenic hydrocarbons, certain sapogenins, etc. The structures of the steroids are based on the 1,2-cyclopentenophenanthrene skeleton (Rosenheim and King, 1932; Wieland and Dane, 1932). All the steroids give, among other products, Diels' hydrocarbon on dehydrogenation with selenium at 360°C (Diels, 1927). In fact, a steroid could be defined as any compound which gives Diels' hydrocarbon when distilled with selenium. When the distillation with selenium is carried out at 420°C, the steroids give mainly chrysene (**10** §4b) and a small amount of picene (**10** §4c).

1,2-cyclopentenophenanthrene

In the earlier work, the various steroids were designated by trivial names, but the tendency now is to discard these in favour of systematic names, which may be applied when the structure is known (see §7).

Diels' hydrocarbon is a solid, m.p. 126–127°C. Its molecular formula is $C_{18}H_{16}$, and the results of oxidation experiments, X-ray crystal analysis and absorption spectrum measurements showed that the hydrocarbon is probably 3′-methyl-1,2-cyclopentenophenanthrene. This structure was definitely established by synthesis, *e.g.*, that of Harper, Kon and Ruzicka (1934), who used the Bogert–Cook method [**10** §2vi], starting from 2-(1-naphthyl)-ethylmagnesium bromide and 2,5-dimethylcyclopentanone.

Diels' hydrocarbon

Sterols

§2

Sterols occur in animal and plant oils and fats. They are crystalline compounds, and contain an alcoholic group; they occur free or as esters of the higher fatty acids, and are isolated from the unsaponifiable portion of oils and fats. Cholesterol, 5α-cholestan-3β-ol (cholestanol) and 5β-cholestan-3β-ol (coprostanol) are the animal sterols; ergosterol and stigmasterol are the principal plant sterols. The sterols that are obtained from animal sources are often referred to as the *zoosterols*, and those obtained from plant sources as the *phytosterols*. A third group of sterols, which are obtained from yeast and fungi, are referred to as the *mycosterols*. This classification, however, is not rigid, since some sterols are obtained from more than one of these groups.

§3. **Cholesterol**, $C_{27}H_{46}O$, m.p. 149°C.

This is the sterol of the higher animals, occurring free or as fatty esters in all animal cells, particularly in the brain and spinal cord. Cholesterol was first isolated from human gallstones (these consist almost entirely of cholesterol). The main sources of cholesterol are the fish-liver oils, and the brain and spinal cord of cattle. Lanoline, the fat from wool, is a mixture of cholesteryl palmitate, stearate and oleate.

Cholesterol is a white crystalline solid which is optically active, ($[\alpha]_D$ 39°). Cholesterol (and other sterols) gives many colour reactions, *e.g.*,

(i) *The Salkowski reaction* (1908). When concentrated sulphuric acid is added to a solution of cholesterol in chloroform, a red colour is produced in the chloroform layer.

(ii) *The Liebermann–Burchard reaction* (1885, 1890). A greenish colour is developed when a solution of cholesterol in chloroform is treated with concentrated sulphuric acid and acetic anhydride.

When an ethanolic solution of cholesterol is treated with an ethanolic solution of digitonin (a saponin; see §32), a large white precipitate of cholesterol digitonide is formed. This is a molecular complex containing one molecule of cholesterol and one of digitonin, from which the components may be recovered by dissolving the complex in pyridine (which brings about complete dissociation) and then adding ether (the cholesterol remains in solution and the digitonin is precipitated). An alternative method is to dissolve the digitonide in dimethyl sulphoxide and heat on a steam bath. Dissociation occurs, and on cooling only the sterol is precipitated (Issidorides *et al.*, 1962). Digitonide formation is used for the estimation of cholesterol. An interesting point in this connection is that 3β-hydroxysteroids usually form complexes with digitonin, whereas the corresponding 3α-compounds do not (see §5 for the meaning of α and β).

The structure of cholesterol was elucidated only after a tremendous amount of work was done, particularly by Wieland, Windaus and their coworkers (1903–1932). Only a very bare outline is given here, and in order to appreciate the evidence that is going to be described, it is necessary to have the established structure of cholesterol at the beginning of our discussion. (I) is the structure of

(I)

cholesterol, and shows the method of numbering. The molecule consists of a *side-chain* and a *nucleus* which is composed of four rings; these rings are usually designated A, B, C and D (or (I), (II), (III) and (IV)), beginning from the six-membered ring on the left (see also (iii) below). It should be noted that the nucleus contains two angular methyl groups, one at C-10 and the other at C-13.

(i) **Structure of the ring system.** Under this heading we shall deal with the nature of the ring system present in cholesterol; the problem of the angular methyl groups is dealt with later [see (iv)].

The usual tests for functional groups showed that cholesterol contains one double bond and one hydroxyl group. Now let us consider the following set of reactions.

$$\text{Cholesterol} \xrightarrow{\text{H}_2-\text{Pt}} \text{Cholestanol} \xrightarrow{\text{CrO}_3} \text{Cholestanone} \xrightarrow[\text{HCl}]{\text{Zn}-\text{Hg}} \text{Cholestane}$$
$$\text{C}_{27}\text{H}_{46}\text{O (I)} \qquad \text{C}_{27}\text{H}_{48}\text{O (II)} \qquad \text{C}_{27}\text{H}_{46}\text{O (III)} \qquad \text{C}_{27}\text{H}_{48} \text{ (IV)}$$

The conversion of cholesterol into cholestanol (II) shows the presence of one double bond in (I) and the oxidation of (II) to the ketone cholestanone (III) shows that cholesterol is a secondary alcohol. Cholestane (IV) is a saturated hydrocarbon, and corresponds to the general formula C_nH_{2n-6}, and consequently is tetracyclic; thus cholesterol is tetracyclic. [D.B.E. of cholestane is $27 + 1 - 48/2 = 4$.]

When cholesterol is distilled with selenium at 360°C, Diels' hydrocarbon is obtained (see §1). The formation of this compound could be explained by assuming that this nucleus is present in cholesterol. The yield of this hydrocarbon, however, is always poor, and other products are always formed at the same time, particularly chrysene (see §1). Thus, on the basis of this dehydrogenation, the presence of the cyclopentenophenanthrene nucleus must be accepted with reserve. Rosenheim and King (1932) thought that chrysene was the normal product of the selenium dehydrogenation, and so proposed (on this basis and also on some information obtained from X-ray analysis work of Bernal, 1932; see §5) that the steroids contained the chrysene skeleton. Within a few months, however, Rosenheim and King (1932) modified this suggestion, as did also Wieland and Dane (1932). These two groups of workers proposed that the cyclopentenophenanthrene nucleus is the one present in cholesterol (*i.e.*, in steroids in general). This structure fits far better all the evidence that has been obtained from a detailed investigation of the oxidation products of the sterols and bile acids, and has now been confirmed by the synthesis of cholesterol (see §9).

(*a*) The nature of the *nucleus* in sterols and bile acids was shown to be the same, since 5β-cholanic acid (cholanic acid) or 5α-cholanic acid (allocholanic acid) is one of the oxidation products (see §5).

(*b*) The oxidation of the bile acids led to the formation of products in which various rings were opened. The examination of these products showed that the positions of the hydroxyl groups were limited mainly to three positions 3, 7 and 12, and further work showed that the hydroxyl groups behaved differently towards a given reagent (see also §5).

(c) The rings in the steroid nucleus were opened to give a dicarboxylic acid and the relative positions of the two carboxyl groups with respect to each other were determined by the application of **Blanc's rule**: On heating with acetic anhydride, 1,5-dicarboxylic acids form cyclic anhydrides, and 1,6-dicarboxylic acids form cyclopentanones with elimination of carbon dioxide (see also Vol. I).

Ring A. Cholesterol and the cholic acids were converted into the dicarboxylic acid (A) which gave a cyclopentanone, and so ring A is six-membered (R is the appropriate side-chain).

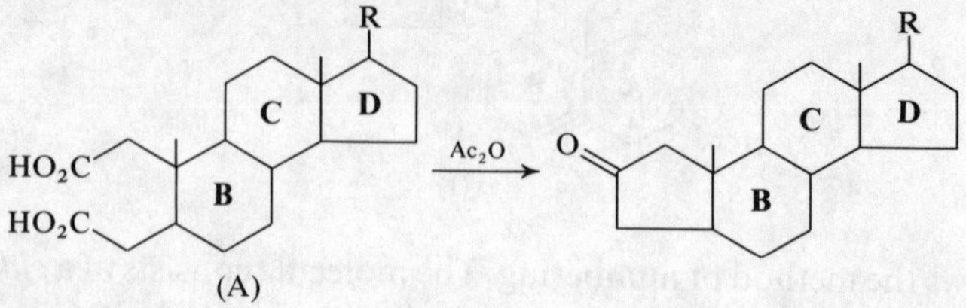

(A)

Ring B. Cholesterol was converted into the tricarboxylic acid (B) which gave the cyclopentanone derivative shown. Hence ring B is six-membered.

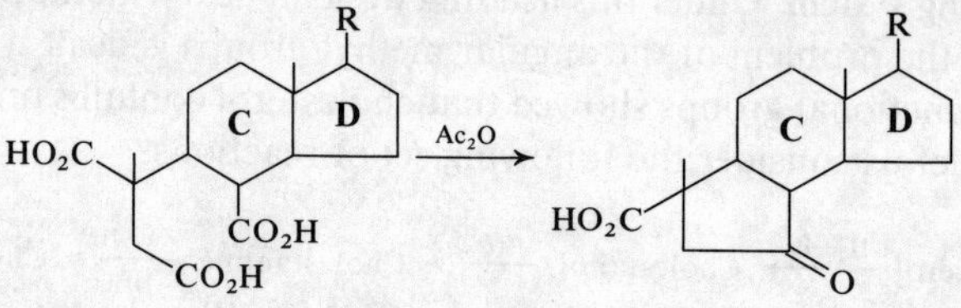

(B)

Ring C. Deoxycholic acid was converted into a dicarboxylic acid which gave a cyclic anhydride. It was therefore assumed that ring C was five-membered, and this led Windaus and Wieland (1928) to propose the following formula for cholesterol, and the uncertain point (at that time) was the nature of the two extra carbon atoms. These were *assumed* to be present as an ethyl group at position 10, but Wieland *et al.* (1930) finally proved that there was no ethyl group at this position. These two 'homeless' carbon atoms were not placed until Rosenheim and King first proposed that steroids contained the chrysene nucleus and then proposed the cyclopentenophenanthrene nucleus (see above). Bernal (1932) also showed, from the X-ray analysis of cholesterol, ergosterol, etc., that the molecule was thin, whereas the above structure for the steroid nucleus would be rather thick.

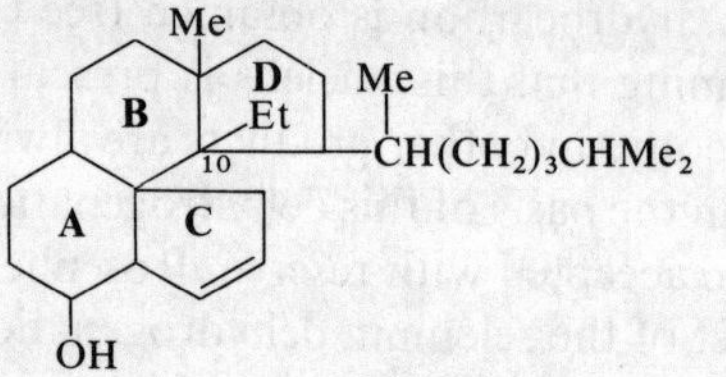

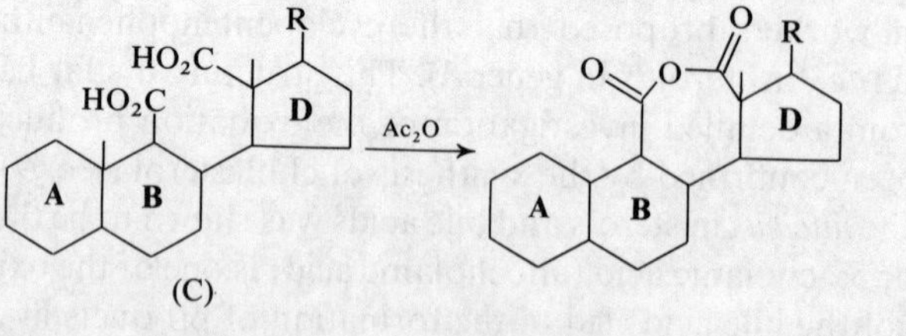

(C)

If we use the correct structure of cholesterol, the cyclisation reaction results in the formation of a *seven-membered cyclic anhydride*. Thus, in this case (and in some others), the Blanc rule fails and leads to erroneous conclusions.

Ring D. 5β-Cholestane (Coprostane) was converted into etiobilianic acid (see (iii), below), and this gave a cyclic anhydride. Hence ring D is five-membered.

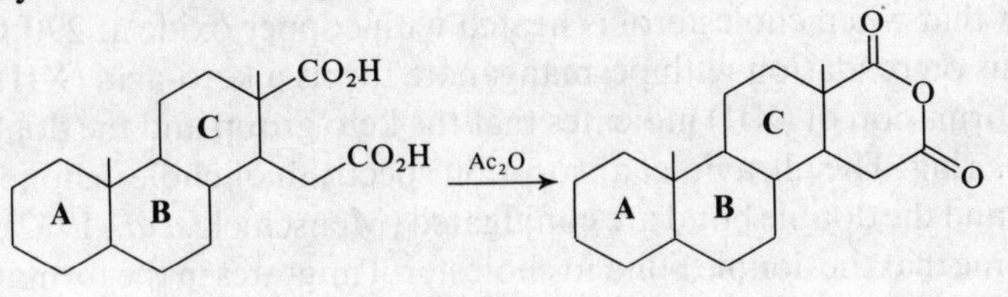

(D)

(ii) **Positions of the hydroxyl group and double bond.** Let us consider the following reactions:

$$\text{Cholestanone} \xrightarrow{\text{HNO}_3} \underset{\text{C}_{27}\text{H}_{46}\text{O}_4 \ (\text{V})}{\text{Dicarboxylic acid}} \xrightarrow{300°\text{C}} \underset{\text{C}_{26}\text{H}_{44}\text{O} \ (\text{VI})}{\text{Ketone}}$$
$$\underset{\text{C}_{27}\text{H}_{46}\text{O} \ (\text{III})}{}$$

Since the dicarboxylic acid (V) contains the same number of carbon atoms as the ketone (III) from which it is derived, the keto group in (III) must therefore be in a ring. Also, since pyrolysis of the dicarboxylic acid (V) produces a ketone with the loss of one carbon atom, it therefore follows from Blanc's rule that (V) is either a 1,6- or 1,7-dicarboxylic acid. Now we have seen that the nucleus contains three six-membered rings and one five-membered ring. Thus the dicarboxylic acid (V) must be obtained by the opening of ring A, B or C, and consequently it follows that the hydroxyl group in cholesterol (which was converted into the keto group in cholestanone; see (i) above) is in ring A, B or C.

Actually *two* isomeric dicarboxylic acids are obtained when cholestanone is oxidised. The formation of these two acids indicates that the keto group in cholestanone is flanked on either side by a methylene group, *i.e.*, the grouping —CH$_2$COCH$_2$—is present in cholestanone. Examination of the reference structure (I) of cholesterol shows that such an arrangement is possible only if the hydroxyl group is in ring A.

Now let us consider the further set of reactions:

$$\underset{\text{C}_{27}\text{H}_{46}\text{O} \ (\text{I})}{\text{Cholesterol}} \xrightarrow[\text{CH}_3\text{CO}_2\text{H}]{\text{H}_2\text{O}_2} \underset{\text{C}_{27}\text{H}_{48}\text{O}_3 \ (\text{VII})}{\text{Cholestanetriol}} \xrightarrow{\text{CrO}_3} \underset{\text{C}_{27}\text{H}_{44}\text{O}_3 \ (\text{VIII})}{\text{Hydroxycholestanedione}} \xrightarrow[\text{(ii) Zn—CH}_3\text{CO}_2\text{H}]{\text{(i) } -\text{H}_2\text{O}}$$

$$\underset{\text{C}_{27}\text{H}_{44}\text{O}_2 \ (\text{IX})}{\text{Cholestanedione}} \xrightarrow{\text{CrO}_2} \underset{\text{C}_{27}\text{H}_{44}\text{O}_8 \ (\text{X})}{\text{Tetracarboxylic acid}}$$

In the conversion of (I) into (VII), the double bond in (I) is hydroxylated. Since only two of the three hydroxyl groups in (VII) are oxidised to produce (VIII), these two groups are secondary alcoholic groups (one of these being the secondary alcoholic group in cholesterol), and the third, being resistant to oxidation, is probably a tertiary alcoholic group. Dehydration of (VIII) (by heating *in vacuo*) and subsequent reduction of the double bond forms (IX), and this, on oxidation, gives a tetracarboxylic acid *without loss of carbon atoms*. Thus the two keto groups in (IX) must be in *different* rings; had they been in the *same* ring, then carbon would have been lost and (X) not obtained. It therefore follows that the hydroxyl group and double bond in cholesterol must be in *different* rings. Furthermore, since (IX) forms a pyridazine derivative with hydrazine, (IX) is a γ-diketone. Since we have already tentatively placed the hydroxyl group in ring A, the above reactions can be readily explained if we place the hydroxyl group at position 3, and the double bond between 5 and 6. In the following equations only rings A and B are drawn; this is an accepted convention of focusing attention on any part of the steroid molecule that is under consideration (also note that full lines represent groups lying above the plane, and broken lines groups lying below the plane; see also §5). Noller

(1939) has shown that the pyridazine derivative is a polymer, and so the interpretation that (IX) is a γ-diketone is rendered uncertain. Supporting evidence, however, for the above interpretation is afforded by the fact that when cholesterol is heated with copper oxide at 290°C, cholestenone (XI) is produced, and this on oxidation with permanganate forms a keto-acid (XII) with the loss of one carbon atom. The formation of (XII) indicates that the keto group and the double bond in cholestenone are in the *same* ring. The ultraviolet absorption spectrum of cholestenone, λ_{max} 240 nm, shows that the keto group and the double bond are conjugated (Menschick *et al.*, 1932). These results can be explained if we assume that the double bond in cholesterol migrates in the formation of cholestenone, the simplest explanation being that the hydroxyl group is in position 3 and the double bond between 5 and 6, *position 5 being common to both rings A and B*. Thus:

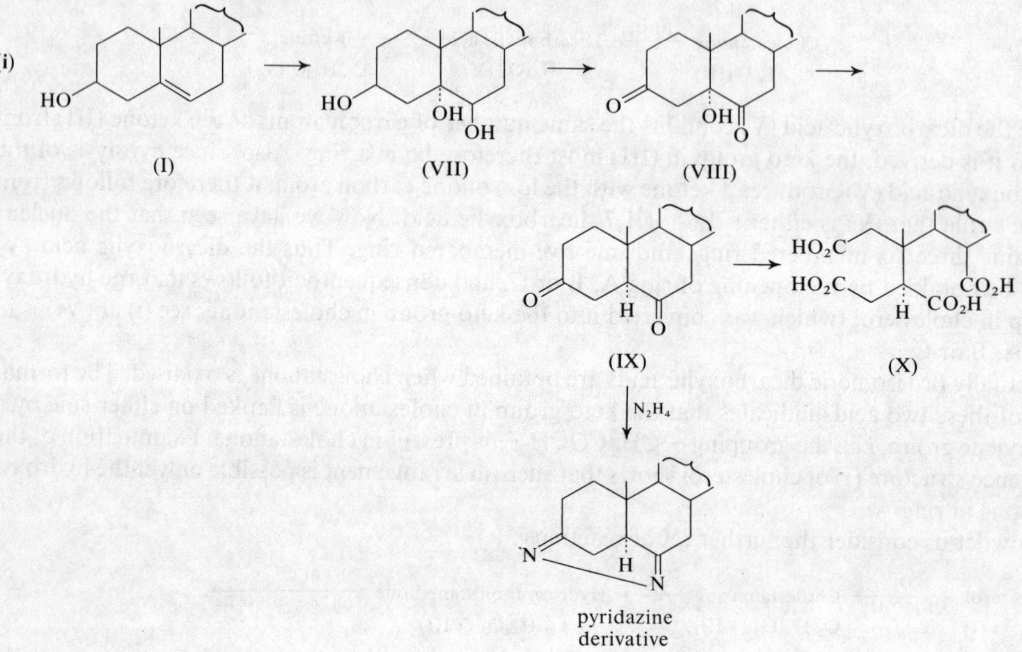

(i)

(I)   (VII)   (VIII)

(IX)   (X)

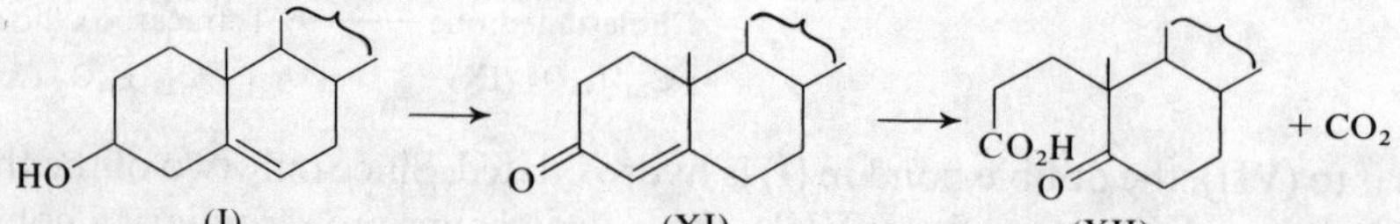

N_2H_4

pyridazine
derivative

(ii)

(I)   (XI)   (XII)   + CO₂

The position of the hydroxyl group at position 3 is definitely proved by the experiments of Kon *et al.* (1937, 1939). These authors reduced cholesterol (I) to cholestanol (II), oxidised this to cholestanone (III), treated this with methylmagnesium iodide and dehydrogenated the product, a tertiary alcohol (XIII), to 3′,7-dimethylcyclopentenophenanthrene (XIV) by means of selenium. The structure of (XIV) was proved by synthesis, and so the reactions may be formulated as follows, with the hydroxyl at position 3.

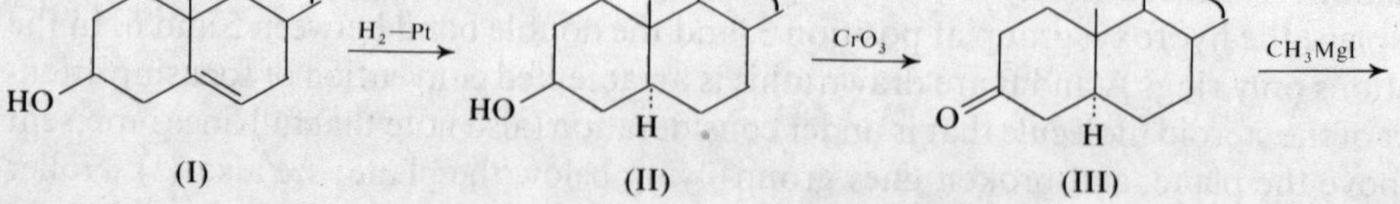

(I) H_2–Pt   (II)   CrO₃   (III)   CH₃MgI

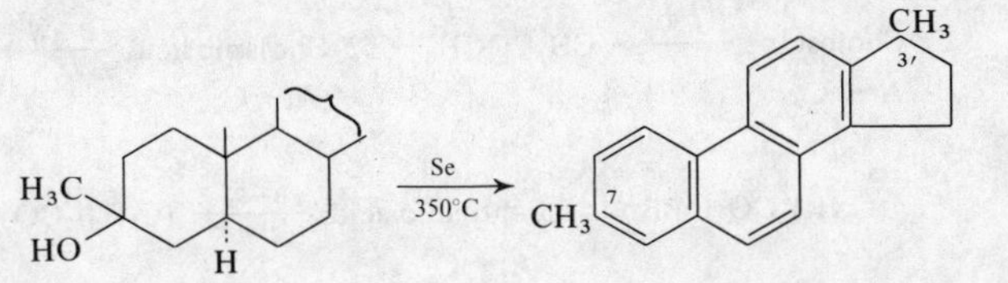

(XIII)   (XIV)

The stereochemistry of the various reactions given above is discussed in §§5 and 8.

(iii) **Nature and position of the side-chain.** Acetylation of cholesterol produces cholesteryl acetate and this, on oxidation with chromium trioxide, forms a steam-volatile ketone and the acetate of a hydroxyketone (which is not steam volatile). The ketone was shown to be isohexyl methyl ketone, $CH_3CO(CH_2)_3CH(CH_3)_2$. Thus this ketone is the side-chain of cholesterol, the point of attachment of the side-chain being at the carbon of the keto group. These results do not show where the side-chain is attached to the nucleus of cholesterol, but if we accept that the position is at 17, then we may formulate the reactions as follows:

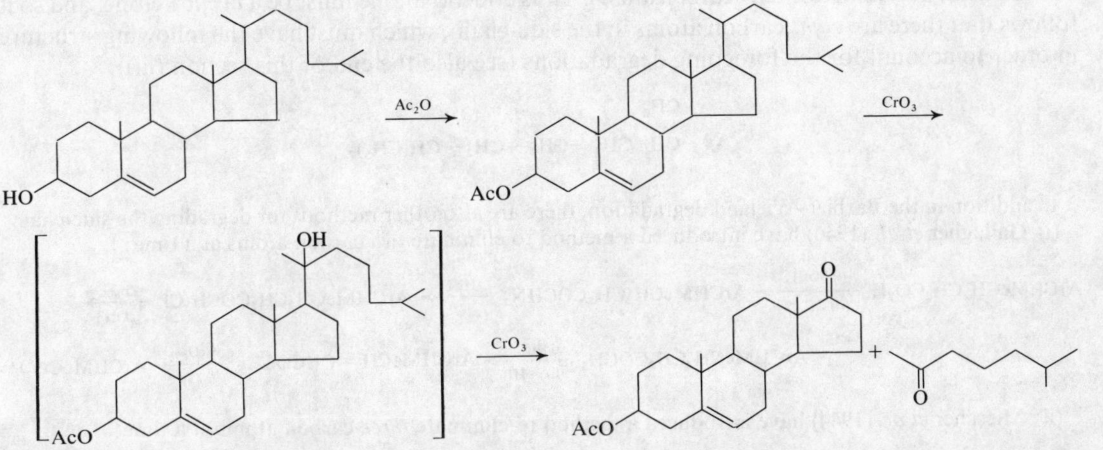

The nature of the side-chain has also been shown by the application of the Barbier–Wieland degradation. Since this method also leads to evidence that shows *which ring* of the nucleus is attached to the side-chain, we shall consider the problem of the nature of the side-chain again.

The Barbier–Wieland degradation offers a means of 'stepping down' an acid one carbon atom at a time as follows:

$$RCH_2CO_2H \xrightarrow[HCl]{CH_3OH} RCH_2CO_2CH_3 \xrightarrow{2C_6H_5MgBr} RCH_2C(OH)(C_6H_5)_2 \xrightarrow{-H_2O} RCH{=}C(C_6H_5)_2 \xrightarrow{CrO_3}$$
$$RCO_2H + (C_6H_5)_2CO$$

Methylmagnesium bromide may be used instead of phenylmagnesium bromide, and the alcohol so obtained may be directly oxidised:

$$RCH_2C(OH)(CH_3)_2 \xrightarrow{CrO_3} RCO_2H + (CH_3)_2CO$$

In the following account, only phenylmagnesium bromide will be used to demonstrate the application of the method to the steroids.

Cholesterol was first converted into 5β-cholestane (coprostane). If we represent the nucleus of 5β-cholestane as Ar, and the side-chain as C_n, then we may formulate the degradation of 5β-cholestane as follows (B–W represents a Barbier–Wieland degradation):

$$5\beta\text{-Cholestane} \xrightarrow{\text{CrO}_3} CH_3COCH_3 + 5\beta\text{-Cholanic acid} \xrightarrow{\text{B—W}} (C_6H_5)_2CO + \text{Nor-}5\beta\text{-cholanic acid} \xrightarrow{\text{B—W}}$$
$$\text{Ar—C}_n \qquad\qquad\qquad\qquad\qquad \text{Ar—C}_{n-3} \qquad\qquad\qquad\qquad \text{Ar—C}_{n-4}$$

$$(C_6H_5)_2CO + \text{Bisnor-}5\beta\text{-cholanic acid} \xrightarrow{\text{B—W}} (C_6H_5)_2CO + \text{Etiocholyl methyl ketone} \xrightarrow{\text{CrO}_3} 5\beta\text{-Etianic acid}$$
$$\text{Ar—C}_{n-5} \qquad\qquad\qquad\qquad\qquad \text{Ar—C}_{n-6} \qquad\qquad\qquad\qquad \text{Ar—C}_{n-7}$$

The formation of acetone from 5β-cholestane indicates that the side-chain terminates in an iso-propyl group. The conversion of bisnor-5β-cholanic acid into a ketone shows that there is an alkyl group on the α-carbon atom in the former compound. Furthermore, since the ketone is oxidised to 5β-etianic acid (formerly known as aetiocholanic acid) with the loss of one carbon atom, the ketone must be a methyl ketone, and so the alkyl group on the α-carbon atom in bisnor-5β-cholanic acid is a methyl group.

Now the carboxyl group in etianic acid is directly attached to the nucleus; this is shown by the following fact. When etianic acid is subjected to one more Barbier–Wieland degradation, a ketone, etiocholanone, is obtained and this, on oxidation with nitric acid, gives a dicarboxylic acid, etio-bilianic acid, *without loss of any carbon atoms*. Thus etiocholanone must be a *cyclic* ketone, and so it follows that there are *eight* carbon atoms in the side-chain, which must have the following structure in order to account for the foregoing degradations (see also the end of this section (iii)):

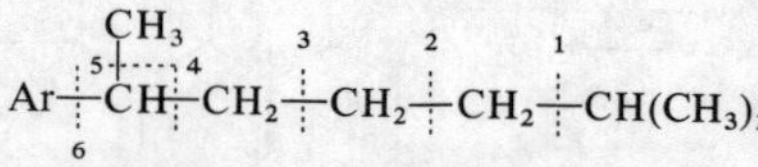

$$\underset{6}{\overset{\overset{\displaystyle CH_3}{\underset{5\,\cdots\,4}{|}}}{\text{Ar} \overset{}{|} \text{CH}}\,\text{CH}_2 \overset{3}{|} \text{CH}_2 \overset{2}{|} \text{CH}_2 \overset{1}{|} \text{CH}(CH_3)_2}$$

In addition to the Barbier–Wieland degradation, there are also other methods for degrading the side-chain:
(i) Gallagher *et al.* (1946) have introduced a method to eliminate *two* carbon atoms at a time:

$$ArCHMeCH_2CH_2CO_2H \xrightarrow[\text{(ii) CH}_2\text{N}_2]{\text{(i) SOCl}_2} ArCHMeCH_2CH_2COCHN_2 \xrightarrow{\text{HCl}} ArCHMeCH_2CH_2COCH_2Cl \xrightarrow[\text{AcOH}]{\text{Zn}}$$

$$ArCHMeCH_2CH_2COCH_3 \xrightarrow[\text{(ii) } -\text{HBr}]{\text{(i) Br}_2} ArCHMeCH=CHCOCH_3 \xrightarrow{\text{CrO}_3} ArCHMeCO_2H$$

(ii) Miescher *et al.* (1944) have introduced a method to eliminate *three* carbon atoms at a time:

$$ArCHMeCH_2CH_2CO_2Me \xrightarrow{\text{2PhMgBr}} ArCHMeCH_2CH_2C(OH)Ph_2 \xrightarrow{-\text{H}_2\text{O}} ArCHMeCH_2CH=CPh_2 \xrightarrow[\text{succinimide}]{N\text{-bromo-}}$$

$$ArCHMeCHBrCH=CPh_2 \xrightarrow{-\text{HBr}} ArCMe=CHCH=CPh_2 \xrightarrow{\text{CrO}_3} ArCOMe$$

(iii) Jones *et al.* (1958) have carried out the fission of a steroid side-chain with an acid catalyst and have then subjected the volatile products to chromatography. This method has been used with as little as 30 mg of material.

The problem now is: Where is the position of this side-chain? This is partly answered by the following observation. The dicarboxylic acid, etiobilianic acid, forms an anhydride when heated with acetic anhydride. Thus the ketone (etiocholanone) is probably a five-membered ring ketone (in accordance with Blanc's rule), and therefore the side-chain is attached to the five-membered ring D. The actual point of attachment to this ring, however, is not shown by this work. The formation of Diels' hydrocarbon (§1) from cholesterol suggests that the side-chain is at position 17, since selenium dehydrogenations may degrade a side-chain to a methyl group (see **10** §2vii). Position 17 is also supported by evidence obtained from X-ray photographs and surface film measurements. Finally, the following chemical evidence may be cited to show that the position of the side-chain is 17. As we have seen above, 5β-cholanic acid may be obtained by the oxidation of 5β-cholestane. 5β-Cholanic acid may also be obtained by the oxidation of deoxycholic acid (a bile acid; see §14) followed by a Clemmensen reduction. Thus the side-chains in cholesterol and deoxycholic acid are in the same position. Now deoxycholic acid can also be converted into 12-keto-5β-cholanic acid which, on heating to 320°C, loses water and carbon dioxide to form dehydronorcholene (Wieland *et al.*, 1930). This, when distilled with selenium, forms 20-methylcholanthrene, the structure of which is indicated by its oxidation to 5,6-dimethyl-1,2-benzanthraquinone which, in turn, gives on further oxidation, anthraquinone-1,2,5,6-tetracarboxylic acid (Cook, 1933). Finally, the structure of 20-methyl-cholanthrene has been confirmed by synthesis (see **10** §5b). The foregoing facts can be explained only if the side-chain in cholesterol is in position 17; thus:

12-keto-5β-cholanic acid   dehydronorcholene   20-methylcholanthrene

5,6-dimethyl-1,2-benzanthraquinone   anthraquinone-1,2,5,6-tetracarboxylic acid

It should be noted that the isolation of methylcholanthrene affords additional evidence for the presence of the cyclopentenophenanthrene nucleus in cholesterol.

Thus, now that we know the nature and position of the side-chain, we can formulate the conversion of 5β-cholestane into etiobilianic acid as follows:

5β-cholestane CH_3COCH_3 +   5β-cholanic acid   nor-5β-cholanic acid

bisnor-5β-cholanic acid   etiocholyl methyl ketone   etianic acid   etiocholanone   etiobilianic acid

A point of interest in this connection is that when the anhydride of etiobilianic acid is distilled with selenium, 1,2-dimethylphenanthrene is obtained (Butenandt *et al.*, 1933). This also provides proof for the presence of the phenanthrene nucleus in cholesterol, and also evidence for the position of the C-13 angular methyl group (see (iv)).

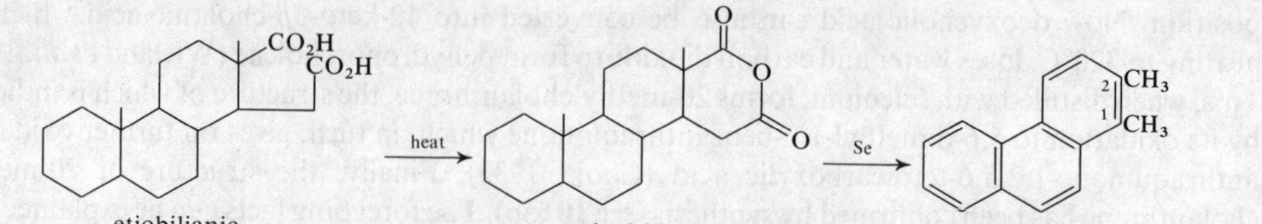

etiobilianic acid (XV) — anhydride — 1,2-dimethylphenanthrene (XVI)

(iv) **Positions of the two angular methyl groups.** The cyclopentenophenanthrene nucleus of cholesterol accounts for seventeen carbon atoms, and the side-chain for eight. Thus twenty-five carbon atoms in all have been accounted for, but since the molecular formula of cholesterol is $C_{27}H_{46}O$, two more carbon atoms must be fitted into the structure. These two carbon atoms have been shown to be angular methyl groups.

In elucidating the positions of the hydroxyl group and double bond, one of the compounds obtained was the keto-acid (XII). This compound, when subjected to the Clemmensen reduction and followed by two Barbier–Wieland degradations, gives an acid which is very difficult to esterify, and evolves carbon monoxide when warmed with concentrated sulphuric acid (Tschesche, 1932). Since these reactions are characteristic of an acid containing a carboxyl group attached to a tertiary carbon atom (*cf.* abietic acid, **8** §32), the side-chain in (XII) must be of the type

$$C-\overset{C}{\underset{C}{\overset{|}{\underset{|}{C_{\gamma}}}}}-C_{\beta}-C_{\alpha}-CO_2H \xrightarrow{2B-W} C-\overset{C}{\underset{C}{\overset{|}{\underset{|}{C_{\gamma}}}}}-CO_2H$$

Thus there must be an alkyl group at position 10 in (XII). This could be an ethyl group (as originally believed by Windaus and Wieland) or a methyl group, provided that in the latter case the second 'missing' carbon atom can be accounted for. As we shall see later, there is also a methyl group at position 13, and so the alkyl group at position 10 must be a methyl group. On this basis, the degradation of (XII) may be formulated:

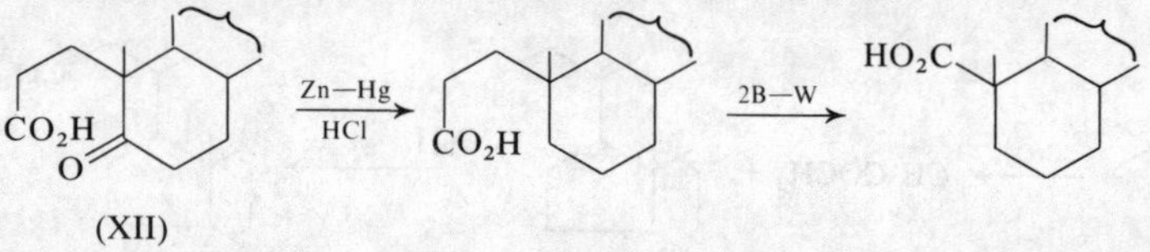

(XII)

The position of the other angular methyl group is indicated by the following evidence. When cholesterol is distilled with selenium, chrysene is obtained as well as Diels' hydrocarbon (see §1). How, then, is the former produced if the latter is the ring skeleton of cholesterol? One possible explanation is that there is an angular methyl group at position 13, and on selenium dehydrogenation, this methyl group enters the five-membered ring D to form a six-membered ring; thus:

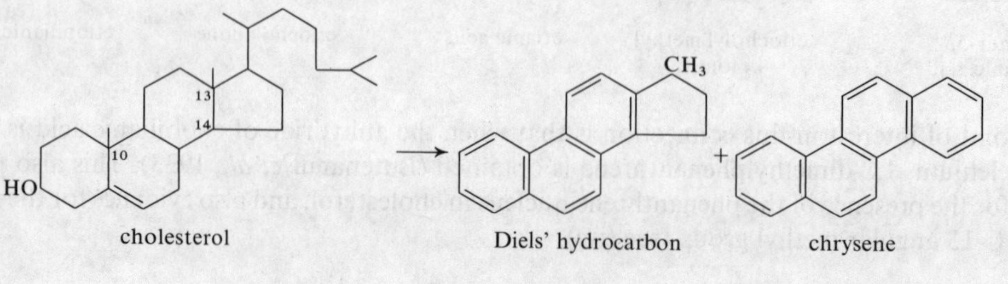

cholesterol — Diels' hydrocarbon — chrysene

This evidence, however, is not conclusive, since ring expansion could have taken place had the angular methyl group been at position 14. Further support for the positions of the two angular methyl groups is given by the following degradative experiments (Wieland *et al.*, 1924, 1928, 1933):

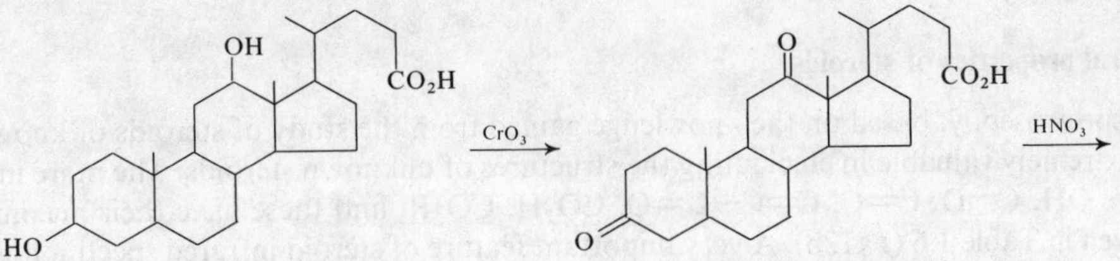

deoxycholic acid

$\xrightarrow{CrO_3}$

dehydrodeoxycholic acid

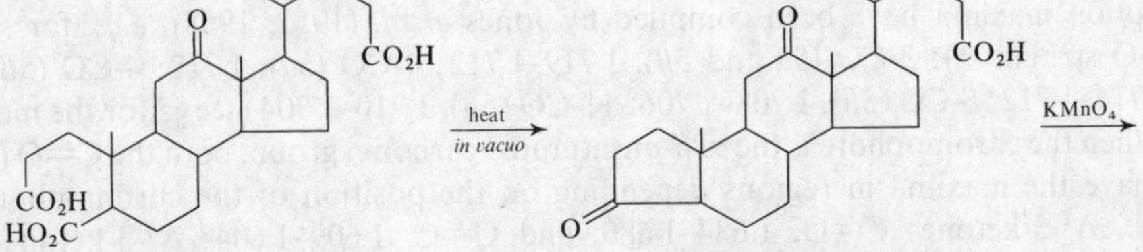

$\xrightarrow{HNO_3}$

deoxybilianic acid

$\xrightarrow[\text{in vacuo}]{\text{heat}}$

pyrodeoxybilianic acid

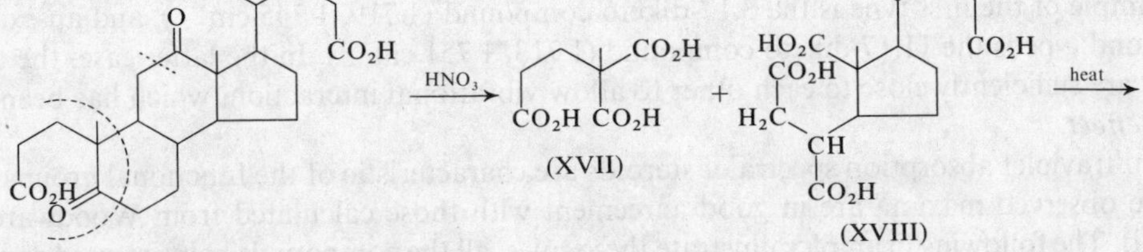

$\xrightarrow{KMnO_4}$

diketo-dicarboxylic acid

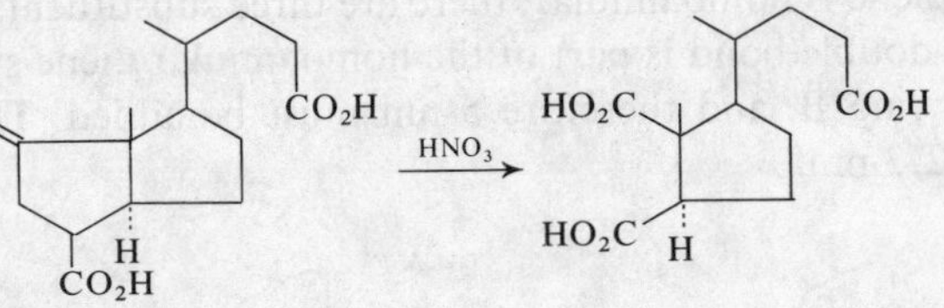

$\xrightarrow{HNO_3}$

(XVII)

$+$

(XVIII)

$\xrightarrow{\text{heat}}$

(XIX)

$\xrightarrow{HNO_3}$

(XX)

(XVII) was shown to be butane-2,2,4-tricarboxylic acid; thus there is a methyl group at position 10. (XVIII) was shown to be a tetracarboxylic acid containing a cyclopentane ring with a side-chain

$$-CH(CH_3)CH_2CH_2CO_2H.$$

Thus this compound is derived from ring D. (XX) was also shown to be a tricarboxylic acid containing a cyclopentane ring. Furthermore, one carboxyl group in (XX) was shown to be attached to a tertiary carbon atom, and so it follows that there is a methyl group at 13 or 14. (XX) was then shown to have the *trans* configuration, *i.e.*, the two carboxyl groups are *trans*. Thus its precursor (XIX) must have its two rings in the *trans* configuration (the methyl group and hydrogen atom at the junction of the rings are thus *trans*). Theoretical considerations of the strain involved in the *cis*- and *trans*-forms of (XIX) suggest that the *cis*-form of (XIX) would have been obtained had the methyl group been at position 14. Thus the position of this angular methyl group appears (from this evidence) to be at 13, and this is supported by the fact that etiobilianic acid ((XV), section (iii)) gives 1,2-dimethylphenanthrene (XVI) on dehydrogenation with selenium. Had the angular methyl group been at position 14, 1-methylphenanthrene would most likely have been obtained.

§4. Spectral properties of steroids

Infrared spectroscopy, based on the knowledge gained from the study of steroids of known structures, is extremely valuable in elucidating the structures of unknown steroids. The more important groups are OH, C=O, C=C, C=C—C=O, CO_2H, CO_2R, and these have their maxima in the ranges given in Table 1.6 (1 §12b). A very important feature of steroid infrared spectra, however, is the dependence of the absorption maximum of the keto group on its position in the nucleus, and also, in some cases, according to whether the hydrogen atom at a ring junction is α or β.

The absorption maxima have been compiled by Jones *et al.* (1952, 1958), *e.g.*, for saturated ketones (C=O str. cm^{-1}): 3-CO (5α and 5β), 1 719–1 712; 4-CO (5α), 1 712; 4-CO (5β), 1 713; 6-CO (5α), 1 714–1 712; 6-CO (5β), 1 708–1 706; 11-CO (5β), 1 710–1 704 (see §5 for the meaning of 5α and 5β). When the chromophore is the α, β-unsaturated carbonyl group, both the C=O (str.) and C=C (str.) have the maxima in regions depending on the position of the chromophore in the molecule, *e.g.*, Δ^1-3-ketone: C=O, 1 684–1 680, and C=C, 1 609–1 604; Δ^4-3-ketone: C=O, 1 681–1 677, and C=C, 1 619–1 615. It was also found that if the nucleus contained two keto groups, each showed its own maximum (or one very close to it) in some cases, but was different in other cases. An example of the first type is the 3,17-diketo compound (1 719, 1 745 cm^{-1}), and an example of the second type is the 11,17-diketo compound (1 713, 1 751 cm^{-1}). In the latter case, the two keto groups are sufficiently close to each other to allow vibrational interaction, which has been called a *vicinal effect*.

The ultraviolet absorption spectra of steroids are characteristic of the functional groups present, and the observed maxima are in good agreement with those calculated from Woodward's rules (8 §3viii). The following examples illustrate these rules, all the compounds being steroid derivatives; only the part of the molecule concerned is shown.

In example (I), the diene is homoannular, there are three substituents, and there is one exocyclic double bond. The 4,5-double bond is part of the homoannular diene system in ring A, but is exocyclic with respect to ring B, and therefore 5 nm must be added. Thus the calculated value is $253 + 3 \times 5 + 5 = 273$ nm.

	(I)	(II)	(III)
obs.	275 nm	275 nm	235 nm
calc.	273 nm	273 nm	234 nm

	(IV)	(V)	(VI)
obs.	355 nm	241 nm	230 nm
calc.	343 nm	244 nm	227 nm

COMe

	(VII)	(VIII)	(IX)	(X)
obs.	244 nm	244 nm	284 nm	239 nm
calc.	244 nm	242 nm	280 nm	237 nm

In example (IV) the basic diene system has been taken to be the homoannular one in ring B. There are then two double bonds extending this conjugation, and the double bond in ring A is exocyclic to ring B. Thus the calculated value is $253 + 2 \times 30 + 5 \times 5 + 5 = 353$ nm.

The rules apply to three double bonds in conjugation, but may break down for four, and definitely cannot be applied to five or more double bonds in conjugation (cf. carotenoids, **9** §1). In compound (VII) there is crossed conjugation (see Vol. I). In such cases the calculation is made for the linear system which gives the *higher* value for λ_{max}. Thus, the linear system using the 1,2-double bond gives 227 nm (this is equivalent to (VI)), but for the system with the 4,5-double bond, the value is 244 nm (this is equivalent to (V)). Hence the calculated value is taken as 244 nm.

The foregoing discussion has dealt with conjugated systems and as far as *isolated* double bonds are concerned, u.v. spectroscopy is useful in detecting double bonds of the type $R_2C=CR_2$ (170–210 nm). On the other hand, the position of an isolated double bond can be investigated on a micro-scale by treating the compound with osmium tetroxide to give a cyclic osmic ester, which is reduced by lithium aluminium hydride to the 1,2-diol and this is then oxidised (with fission) by lead tetra-acetate. Examination of the oxo products gives the position of the ethylenic double bond. Ruthenium tetroxide may also be used; this results in direct oxidative fission of the double bond (see also Vol. I).

NMR spectroscopy has been used in structural studies of steroids, but complete analysis of such complex molecules is extremely difficult. Shoolery *et al.* (1958) have examined 48 steroids and observed certain regularities. Steroids appear to have a finger print region which is characteristic of the CH and CH_2 protons in the *nucleus*. Also, the proton in the group $=CH—$ has a definite τ-value, and so this group can usually be reaily detected, and the number of these groups present can be estimated from the area of the proton peak (see **1** §12e). Furthermore, from the table compiled from spectra of known compounds) it may be possible to determine the position of a double bond in an unknown steroid.

Shoolery also found that the protons of the angular methyl groups at C-10 and C-13 have their own characteristic chemical shifts, the actual shift depending on the presence of various functional groups such as $C=C$, $C=O$. Thus a 3-keto group causes a shift of 0·15 p.p.m. in the C_{19}-methyl line, but has no effect on the position of the C_{18}-methyl line. Hence it may be possible to deduce both the nature and position of a functional group in the molecule. It was also found that the methyl protons of an acetoxyl group has a characteristic τ-value depending on its position in the nucleus. In this way, it is possible to determine the position of a hydroxyl group in the molecule (see also §4a).

All the above methods of spectroscopy have also been used in conformational analysis of steroids (see §5).

Molecular rotations may be used to help elucidate steroid structures, and more recently, optical rotatory dispersion has become very useful for locating the position of a keto group in the steroid nucleus (see §5).

Mass spectrometry is very useful for structural analysis of steroids. The subject is too lengthy to discuss here, but some idea of the approach is as follows. Steroids usually give an abundant molecular ion and so it is easy to determine the molecular weight and molecular formula. Four common peaks usually observed are: (a) $[M - R]^+$, where R is the side-chain; (b) $[M - (R + 42)]^+$, where mass 42 is C_3H_6; (c) $[M - 15]^+$, due to loss of an angular methyl group; (d) $[M - (R + 42 + 15)]^+$. Because of this general fragmentation pattern, it is possible to detect the presence of a steroid nucleus.

Steroid alcohols usually show the presence of a peak at m/e $[M - 18]^+$ due to the loss of water, and a peak at $[M - (18 + 15)]^+$ due to loss of both water and an angular methyl group. On the other hand, the fragmentation pattern of ketones depends on the position of the keto group, and it appears that the positive charge always resides with the oxygen-containing fragment. However, it has been found that ethylene ketals are particularly useful for the purpose of directing fragmentation in a predictable manner. Since the 3-hydroxyl group and 3-keto group are very common in steroids, the cracking pattern of 3-ethylene ketals has been worked out. Three ions that have been observed in greatest amount from the steroid shown are (XI), (XII) and (XIII).

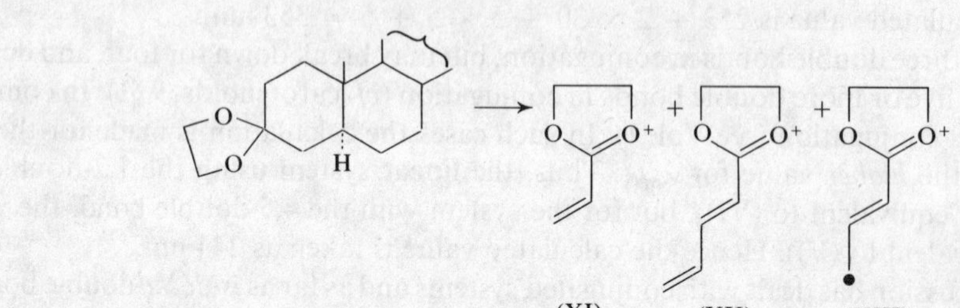

In a steroid with a 3-keto group and a 5,6-double bond, fragment (XI) shows an intense peak and the peaks of (XII) and (XIII) are extremely weak. On the other hand, if the steroid contains a 7-keto group, the predominant peak is (XII).

It can thus be seen that it is possible to locate a 3- or 7-keto group and a 5,6-double bond in an unknown steroid. However, there are some complications, since a 17-ethylene ketal also gives (XI).

Another interesting application of mass spectrometry is the location of an ethylenic double bond in a steroid molecule. The double bond is first converted into the epoxide which, on treatment with dimethylamine, forms the dimethylamino-alcohol. This, on electron impact, is split into fragments, and the m/e value of the nitrogen-containing fragment indicates the position of the double bond, e.g., (see also §8):

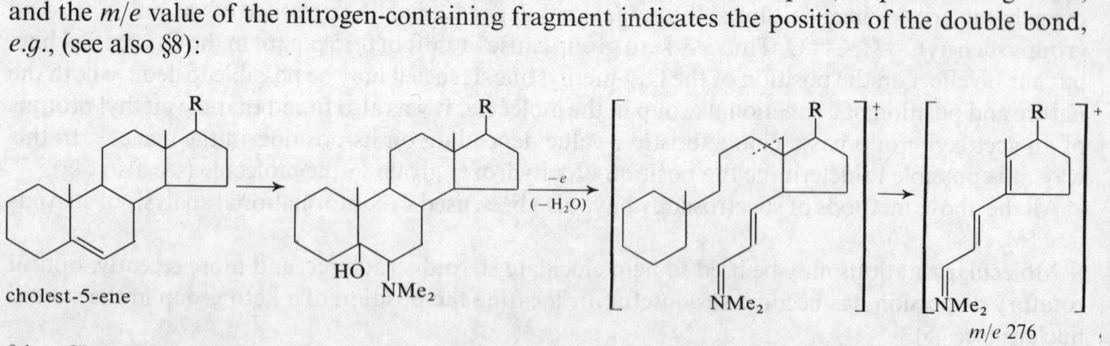

§4a. Chromatography. This was originally used in the form of column chromatography (on alumina) as a means of separating mixtures of steroids. Paper chromatography, however, is a better means of separation, and because of the large amount of work done, it is now possible to identify natural steroids (see **1** §15). TLC is also useful for this purpose.

§5. Stereochemistry of the steroids

If we examine the fully saturated sterol, we find that there are eight dissimilar chiral centres in the nucleus (3, 5, 8, 9, 10, 13, 14 and 17). Thus there are $2^8 = 256$ optical isomers possible. If we also include the chiral centre in the side-chain (20), then there are 512 optical isomers possible.

The stereoisomerism of the steroids is conveniently classified into two types, one dealing with the way in which the rings are fused together, and the other with the configurations of substituent groups, particularly those at C-3 and C-17.

Configuration of the nucleus.   There are six chiral centres in the nucleus (5, 8, 9, 10, 13 and 14), and therefore there are $2^6 = 64$ optically active forms theoretically possible. In practice, however, many of these cannot exist because of steric limitations.

A great deal of the evidence for the stereochemistry of the nucleus was obtained from oxidative degradation experiments. Thus, Windaus (1926) prepared the four isomeric acids: lithobilianic (I), allolithobilianic (II), isolithobilianic (III), and alloisolithobilianic acid (IV); in all of these, R = CHMe(CH$_2$)$_2$CO$_2$H (see also §16). When each of these was heated, (I) and (II) gave the *same* product, pyrolithobilianic acid (V); (III) gave pyroisolithobilianic acid (VI); and (IV) gave pyro-alloisolithobilianic acid (VII). Also the Clemmensen reduction of *both* (V) and (VI) gave the *same*

product, deoxypyroacid (VIII). It therefore follows that (V) has the *cis*-configuration, since cyclisation will be expected to occur readily when the two carboxyl groups are in the *cis*-position. Since (II) *does* give (V), inversion at C-5 must have occurred. This inversion takes place *via* the enol form involving the adjacent carbonyl group in (V) or possibly by the carboxyl group before cyclisation. Evidence to support this is that *cis*-hydrindanones are more stable than the corresponding *trans*-isomers, *i.e.*, the former are the thermodynamically controlled products. On the other hand, in (VI) and (VII), the carbonyl group is no longer adjacent to the hydrogen at C-5 and so inversion *via* the enol form is not possible. Hence, because (III) and (IV) each form a cyclised product, their geometry is not differentiated by this reaction. However, since (V) and (VI) both give the same product on reduction, (VI) is therefore the *cis*-isomer.

Lithobilianic acid (I) and isolithobilianic acid (III) can be prepared from the natural bile acid, lithocholic acid (see §16), and so all have the same *cis*-A/B fusion. Finally, because these acids may also be prepared from 5β-cholestane (coprostane), this compound also has *cis*-A/B fusion. Both types of fusion (*cis* and *trans*) occur in natural steroids.

The fusion of rings B and C was shown to be *trans* by X-ray analysis (Bernal *et al.*, 1932). The steroid molecule is long and thin, *i.e.*, the molecule is essentially *flat*. This is possible only if rings B and C are fused together in a *trans* manner; rings A/B and C/D could be *cis* or *trans*. Only *trans*-B/C fusion occurs in natural steroids.

Chemical evidence was obtained by Wieland *et al.* (1933) to show that rings C/D have *trans*-fusion in sterols and bile acids, *e.g.*, degradation of deoxycholic acid (IX) [see also §16] gave (X) which did not readily form an anhydride. The anhydride (XI), however, was obtained on heating *in vacuo* and after hydrolysis formed (XII), which was different from (X). Thus the anhydride (XI) and the acid (XII) must have the *cis*-configuration, and so rings C and D have the *trans*-configuration in deoxycholic acid (IX). *trans*-C/D Fusion occurs in most steroids (including the bile acids) except the cardiac glycosides and toad poisons, in which the fusion is *cis* (see §30).

(IX)   (X)   (XI)   (XII)

X-ray analysis has shown that the hydrogen atom at C-9 is *trans* to the methyl group at C-10 (Bernal *et al.*, 1940), and this has been supported by chemical evidence which has also established that the methyl groups at C-10 and C-13 are *cis*. Chemical evidence and the X-ray analysis of cholesteryl iodide have shown that the side-chain and the two angular methyl groups are *cis* (Crowfoot *et al.*, 1945).

The use of NMR spectroscopy in steroid chemistry has been discussed in §4. Williamson *et al.* (1966) have now shown that the angular methyl groups couple with certain protons on the steroid nucleus; coupling occurs between H_x and H_y in the group shown. Thus the C_{19}-methyl group, if

freely rotating, can couple with an axial hydrogen at C-1, C-5 and C-9 in the steroid if rings A and B are fused in the *trans*-position (see also §5). If A/B is *cis*, then only one axial hydrogen (at position 9) can couple in this manner. The authors found that the peak width (of the angular methyl groups) at half-height for the *trans*-fused isomer is always larger than that for the *cis*-fused isomer. It is therefore possible to assign the stereochemistry of the A/B junction in both types of compounds.

Configurations of substituent groups.   The configuration of the side-chain at C-17 has already been mentioned above. The only other configuration that we shall discuss here is that of the hydroxyl group at C-3. *By convention*, the hydroxyl at C-3 in **cholestanol** (and cholesterol) is taken as being **above** the plane of the ring, *i.e.*, the hydroxyl group is taken as being in the *cis* position with respect to the methyl group at C-10. This configuration occurs in all *natural* sterols, and gives rise to the

β-series, the prefix β always indicating that the substituent group lies *above* the plane of the molecule. When the hydroxyl group lies **below** the plane, the compounds are said to belong to the **α-series**. This series has also been called the **epi-series**, the prefix 'epi' indicating the epimer due to the inversion of the configuration of C-3. Because of this, many compounds were named as epi-compounds, *e.g.*, epicholesterol, epiandrosterone, etc. Also, when a compound differed from a natural steroid in the configuration of any chiral centre other than C-5, it has been called the iso-compound (see also §7).

X-ray analysis studies have shown that the hydroxyl group in cholesterol is above the plane of the molecule, *i.e.*, it is *cis* to the methyl group at C-10.

This β-configuration has also been proved chemically by Shoppee (1948) as follows:

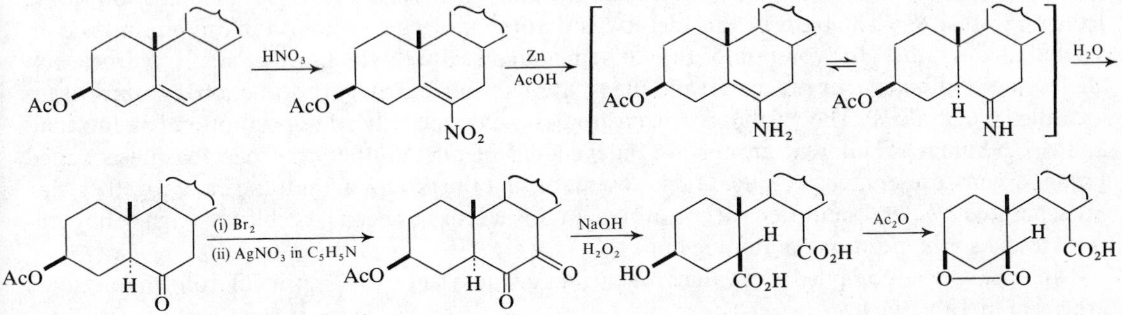

The formation of the γ-lactone, as the final product, is only possible if both the hydroxyl and carboxyl groups have the same orientation, *i.e.*, are *cis* with respect to each other. Since other work showed that the reduced product is a 5α-cholestane derivative, the carboxyl group involved in lactone formation must have the β-configuration, and consequently the 3-hydroxyl group must also be β. Further evidence to support this is that Shoppee *et al.* (1954–58) also prepared the corresponding 5β-diacid, and showed it did not form the γ-lactone.

§6. Absolute configurations of steroids

So far, we have discussed the relative configurations of chiral centres in the steroids which, *by convention*, have been drawn as, *e.g.*, for 5α-cholestan-3β-ol (cholestanol).

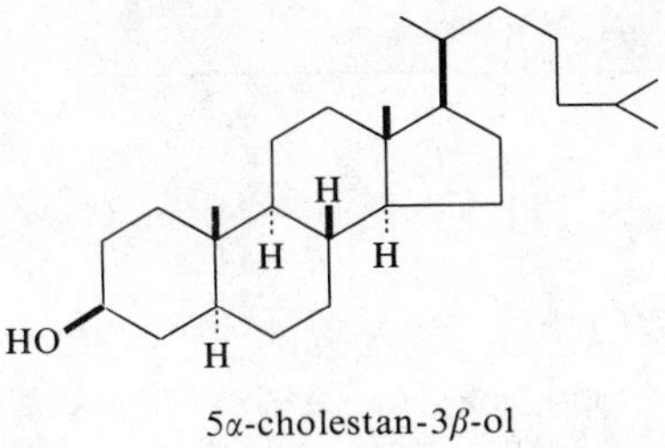

5α-cholestan-3β-ol 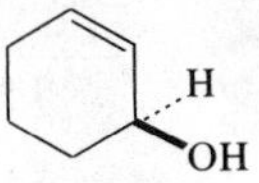   (I) 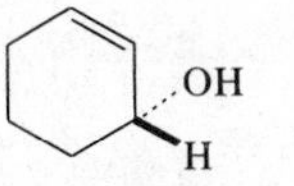   (II)

Mills (1952) has correlated the configurations of steroids with glyceraldehyde. This author collected the molecular optical rotations of a number of pairs of epimeric cyclohex-2-enols and their esters, and on the assumption that the configurations given (in the literature) were correct, Mills showed that the alcohol represented as (I) is more laevorotatory than its epimer (II), irrespective of the positions of alkyl groups in these allylic terpenoid alcohols (these compounds had already been correlated with glyceraldehyde by the work of Fredga; **8** §23e). The differences in rotation are large, and are increased on esterification. Mills then applied this rule to seven known pairs of epimeric, allylic steroid alcohols, and found that the differences were those which may be predicted on the basis that the conventional steroid formulae represent the absolute configurations. Thus the configuration of the 3β-hydroxyl group in cholesterol corresponds to that of D(+)-glyceraldehyde.

These stereochemical relationships of steroids to D(+)-glyceraldehyde have now been proved by the degradation of cholesterol to derivatives of (+)-citronellal (**8** §23e), in which the only chiral centre is the C-20 of the steroid (Cornforth *et al.*, 1954; Riniker *et al.*, 1954). Thus the arbitrary choice of placing the angular methyl groups above the plane in the cholesterol nucleus (*i.e.*, the β-configuration) has proved to be the absolute configuration. Furthermore, since the configuration of the 3-hydroxyl group in cholesterol is β, this configuration is also the absolute one.

Barton (1944–) has also applied the method of optical rotations to steroid chemistry, and has called his treatment the Method of Molecular Rotation Differences (this is a modification of the Rule of Shift, **1** §9). The basis of this method is that the molecular rotation of any steroid is considered as the sum of the rotation of the fundamental structure (which is the parent hydrocarbon cholestane, androstane, or pregnane) and the rotations contributed by the functional groups (these are called the Δ values). The Δ value of a given group is a characteristic of its position and orientation, and the Δ values of different groups are independent of one another provided that unsaturated groups are not present, *i.e.*, conjugation is absent, or that the groups are not too close together, *i.e.*, are separated by 3 or 4 saturated carbon atoms. In this way it has been possible to assign configurations and also the positions of double bonds.

Tables have been compiled of Δ values for various groups; some values (for chloroform solutions) are given in Table 11.1.

Table 11.1

Substituent position	α OH	β OH	CO	C=C
			5α-series	
1	+35	−17	+339	
3	+5	−2	+71	
6	+55	−50	−113	
2,3				+152
3,4				+123
5,6				−298
			5β-series	
3	+30	+1	+37	
6	−100	+7	−262	
2,3				−24
3,4				−44
5,6				−298

$[M]_D$ 5α-Cholestane, +91;   5β-Cholestane, +97
          5α-Androstane, +5;   5β-Androstane, +11
          5α-Pregnane, +52;   5β-Pregnane, +58

EXAMPLES

Cholestanol (5α-Cholestan-3β-ol): calculated value = 91 + 1 = 92; observed values is 93.

Cholest-2-ene: The action of quinoline on cholestanyl chloride produces cholest-2-ene. The structure of this was proved by chemical methods (Mauthner, 1909), the alternative compound, cholest-3-ene being ruled out.

2-ene   3-ene

If we consider these two possible structures from the point of view of their molecular rotations, we may be in a position to decide (with a certain amount of confidence) the structure of the product. The observed $[M]_D$ of the product is 248°, and the calculated value for the 2-ene is $91 + 152 = 243°$, and that for the 3-ene is $91 + 123 = 214°$. Thus the compound is most likely the 2-ene. Actually, when Mauthner did his work the 3-ene was unknown, but when it was discovered later its $[M]_D$ was found to be 211°.

A more recent method of conformational analysis of steroids makes use of optical rotatory dispersion curves. As pointed out in **1** §9a, ORD curves have been examined mainly for compounds containing a keto group, and the application of this method to the study of keto steroids by Djerassi *et al.* (1956 onwards) has proved highly successful in elucidating configurations. The examination of a large number of saturated keto steroids has shown that the sign, wavelengths of the peak and trough, and amplitude of the ORD curve depend on the position of the keto group in the nucleus. Furthermore, for a given position of the keto group, differences arise in the ORD curve according as the fusion of rings A and B is *cis* or *trans*. Table 11.2 gives some ORD data.

Table 11.2

Ketone	λ nm		Sign of curve and molr amplitude
	Peak	Trough	
5α-Cholestan-3-one	307	267	+65
5β-Cholestan-3-one	307	265	−27
5α-Cholestan-4-one	307	267	−94
5β-Cholestan-4-one	300	278	+3
5α-Cholestan-6-one	307	270	−78
5β-Cholestan-6-one	308	270	−77
5α-Cholestan-7-one	305	275	−26

It can thus be seen that if the position of the keto group in the steroid is known, the sign and amplitude of the ORD curve will permit a decision to be made about the nature of the configuration of the ring junction. This is illustrated by the following example (Rapala *et al.*, 1958). 17α-Ethinyl-19-nortestosterone (III) [17α-ethynyl-19-norandrost-4-en-17β-ol; the prefix 'nor' indicates the absence of the methyl group] on catalytic reduction (ruthenium oxide) followed by oxidation with N-bromoacetamide, gave predominantly 17α-ethyl-19-nor-5α-androstan-17β-ol-3-one (IV) together with a small amount of the corresponding 5β-isomer (V). Configurations were assigned on the following evidence. The two possible products will differ only in the nature of the fusion of rings A and B. Compound (IV) gave an ORD curve that corresponded to the *trans* A/B 3-keto steroids, whereas the curve of (V) was very closely similar to that of 5β-androstan-17β-ol-3-one (a known compound, and used as the model; see also §19). Thus A/B is *cis* in (V).

If a steroid contains two keto groups, then if they are sufficiently far apart to prevent any interaction between them (*i.e.*, there is no vicinal effect), the ORD curve is approximately the sum of the two corresponding monoketo compounds.

An interesting use of steric interactions has been made by Djerassi *et al.* (1959) in differentiating

(III)   (IV)   (V)

between 2- and 3-keto steroids. Measurement of the rotation at the peak of the ORD curve of the
ketone in methanol solution is carried out first and then repeated after addition of acid. It was
observed that there was a reduction in rotation in the latter case. Thus, cholestan-3-one showed a
65 per cent reduction, whereas cholest-2-one showed only a 10 per cent reduction. The explanation
offered is that a ketal is formed in acid solution, and since there is now an axial group at 2 or 3,

3-keto   2-keto   hemi-ketal   ketal

1,3-interactions operate. An axial substituent at C-2 (resulting from ketal formation) will experience
1,3-interactions, particularly with the axial group at C-10, whereas an axial substituent at C-3 will
experience 1,3-interactions with hydrogen atoms only (see also §5). Hence steric interactions are
much greater at C-2 and consequently ketal formation will be more depressed than for the C-3
position. Support for this explanation comes from the fact that increase in size of the alkyl group
in the alcohol (as solvent) leads to a decrease in ketal formation. Furthermore, Djerassi found that
when an alkyl group is in the α-position with respect to the keto group, the decrease in rotation due
to ketal formation is less than when the alkyl group is absent. Hence, in addition to differentiating
between 2- and 3-keto steroids, ketal formation may be used to detect the presence of an α-alkyl
group.

ORD data can also be used to determine relative and absolute configurations in steroids. One
way is to compare the ORD curve of the compound of unknown configuration with curves of
analogous compounds whose absolute stereochemistry has been established. Since model compounds have the structural features of the unknown compound, the structure of the latter must be
known.

An alternative way of using ORD data makes use of the **Octant Rule** (Moffitt *et al.*, 1961). This is a
generalisation and is essentially qualitative, and relates the sign of the ORD curve with the configuration or conformation of a keto steroid. The rule is applied as follows. The region of the keto group
is divided into eight octants by three mutually perpendicular planes. To illustrate how this is done,
let us take cyclohexanone as our example. The C=O double bond is made the *x*-axis, with the origin
at the mid-point of the bond. Through this point are drawn the *y*- and *z*-axes (see Fig. 11.1). The
observer then views the molecule along the *x*-axis from the positive side, *i.e.*, from the side nearer
the oxygen atom. The three planes, *xy*, *xz* and *yz*, divide the region of the keto group into octants.
Projection of the molecule on a *yz*-plane situated somewhere along the −*x*-axis, *i.e.*, at a distance
remote from the observer, is also shown in Fig. 11.1. This projection contains the four *back* octants,
and in similar fashion, the four *front* octants may be obtained.

It is also useful to consider the projection when cyclohexanone is drawn in the conventional way,
with the C=O at the bottom. This is shown in Fig. 11.2(*a*), and at the same time the projections of the
axial and equatorial bonds are also shown. The sign for each octant is given in Fig. 11.2(*b*). These

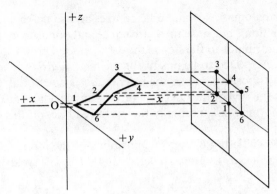

Fig. 11.1

signs are obtained from the sign of the product of the co-ordinates of any given atom, *e.g.*, atom 3 has co-ordinates -x, -y, +z; the product is +xyz. Since it is unusual for substituents to lie in front of the oxygen atom, the front octants are generally unoccupied.

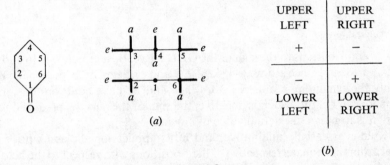

Fig. 11.2

The **Octant Rule** states that atoms lying in the back upper left and back lower right octants make positive contributions, atoms in the back lower left and back upper right octants make negative contributions, and atoms lying in any of the three planes make no contribution; these last named atoms have at least one co-ordinate equal to zero. It is also important to note that hydrogen atoms are ignored, *i.e.*, their contributions are insignificant, and that equatorial substituents on either α-carbon atom (with respect to the keto group), because they lie on the y-axis, also make no contribution (Fig. 11.2*a*). We can therefore also formulate the Octant Rule as follows: **The contribution of an atom to the sign of the ORD curve is the sign of the product of its co-ordinates.**

Since cyclohexanone does not contain a chiral centre, let us now consider 3-methylcyclohexanone, which has a chiral centre at C-3. Two possible orientations are equatorial and axial methyl, and to apply the Octant Rule, the two forms are drawn with the carbonyl bond horizontal. If we line these up with the cyclohexanone molecule shown in Fig. 11.2(*a*), then the *e*-methyl group will fall into the back upper left octant (positive), whereas the *a*-methyl group will fall into the back upper right

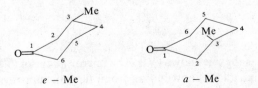

e − Me a − Me

octant (negative). Carbon atoms 1, 2, 4 and 6 lie on axes and so make no contribution, but atoms
3 and 5 do make contributions, but since these are equal and opposite in sign, the net contribution
is zero. Thus the only contributor to the sign is the 3-(5-) methyl group, and consequently the sign
of the ORD curve will be expected to be positive if the methyl group is equatorial and negative if
axial. The observed sign is positive and so the orientation is equatorial. It can be seen from this
example that if we know the sign of the ORD curve, we can elucidate the conformation. However,
since the equatorial conformation is normally the preferred one, on this basis we can predict the
sign of the ORD curve.

Now let us consider 5α-cholestan-6-one. The positions of the atoms in the back octants are as
shown (each ring being projected as a rectangle; *cf.* Fig. 11.2*a*). If we *assume* that all *ring* carbon

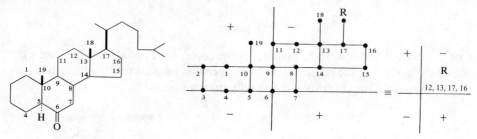

5α-cholestan-6-one

atoms make *equal* contributions to the sign of the ORD curve, then atoms 2, 1, 10 and 19 cancel out
atoms 8, 14, 15 and 18, and since atoms 3, 4, 5, 6, 7, 9 and 11 lie on axes, they make zero contributions. Thus, only the remaining atoms, 12, 13, 17, 16 and R make contributions, and since they
all lie in the upper right octant, which is negative, the sign of the curve is predicted to be negative.
The observed sign is negative, the actual value of *a* being −78.

The Octant Rule is essentially qualitative, and in its application the assumption made is that
contributions of atoms are equal irrespective of their positions with respect to the keto group. Some
cases, however, have been found where these assumptions do not apply, the result being that the
wrong sign may be predicted. It appears that, in general, the further an atom is from the keto group,
the smaller is its contribution to the sign of the ORD curve.

An example of the application of the Octant Rule to the determination of absolute configuration
is (+)-*trans*-10-methyldecal-2-one (VI). This application is possible because its conformation is
known. The diagram for the back octants will be as shown (*cf.* Fig. 11.2*a*). Atoms 1, 2, 3, 5 and 10,
and the methyl-carbon atom lie on axes, and so their contribution is zero. Since all the other atoms,
6, 7, 8 and 9 lie in the upper left octant, all make a positive contribution to the sign of the curve,
which is therefore predicted to be positive. Djerassi *et al.* (1957) observed a positive effect, and so

(VI)

the absolute configuration is the one shown (VI). The mirror image of (VI) is (VI*a*), and application
of the Octant Rule shows that all the contributing atoms lie in the upper right octant. The sign of the

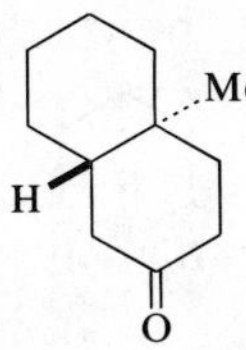

(VI)   (VIa)

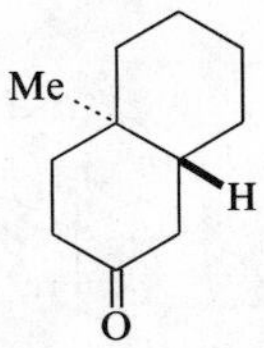

curve for (VIa) is therefore negative. As pointed out in **1** §9a, the ORD curves of enantiomers are mirror images of each other.

§7. Nomenclature of steroids

Steroids are numbered as shown in formula (I) [see also §3]. When some of the carbon atoms in (I) are missing, the numbering of the remainder remains unchanged. Solid lines (preferably thickened)

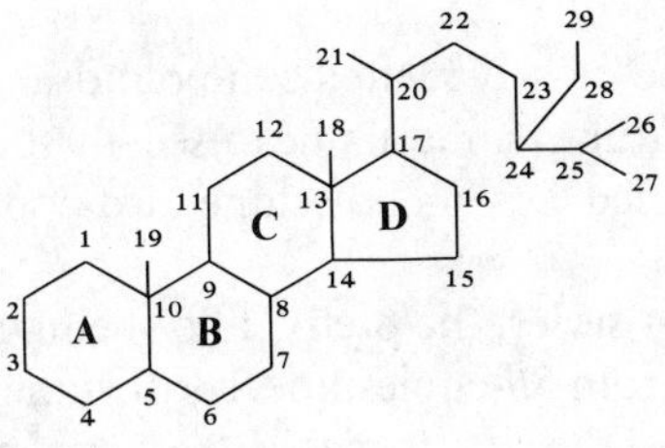

(I)

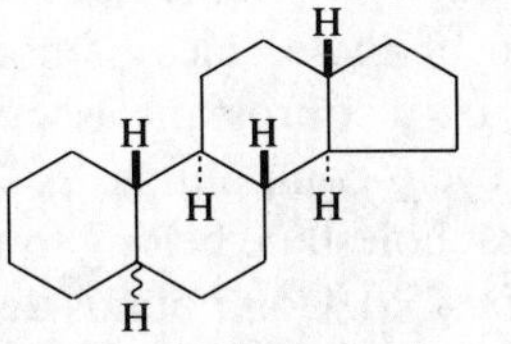

5(α or β)-gonane
(II)

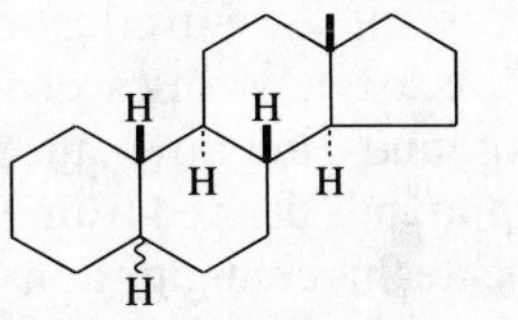

5(α or β)-oestrane
(estrane) (III)

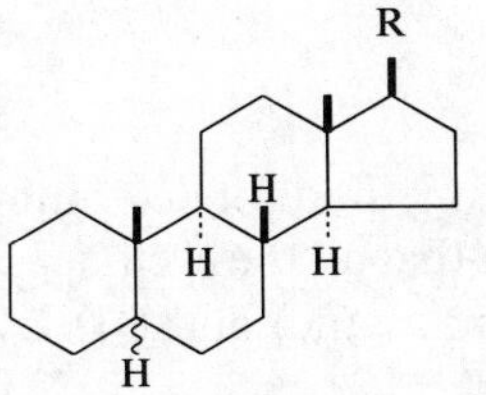

(IV)

R = H; 5(α or β)-androstane
R = Et; 5(α or β)-pregnane
R = —CHMe(CH₂)₂Me; 5(α or β)-cholane
R = —CHMe(CH₂)₃CHMe₂;5(α or β)-cholestane

denote groups above the plane of the nucleus (β-configuration), and dotted or broken lines denote groups below the plane (α-configuration). If the configuration of the substituent is unknown, its bond to the nucleus is drawn as a wavy line and this is indicated by ζ (xi) in the name. Wherever possible, the name of the steroid should specify stereochemical configuration. Formulae (II)–(IV) represent the more important parent hydrocarbons.

When a methylene group is missing from the side-chain, this is indicated by the prefix 'nor' preceded by the number of the carbon atom which has disappeared. When a ring has been contracted or enlarged, this is indicated by prefixes 'nor' and 'homo' respectively, preceded by a small capital letter indicating the ring affected. The prefix 'nor' is also used to indicate the loss of an angular methyl group, and in this case is preceded by the number designating that methyl group: 18-nor and 19-nor (see also §26). When ring-fission has occurred with addition of a hydrogen atom to each new terminal group, this is indicated by the numbers showing the position of the bond broken, followed by the prefix 'seco'. The prefix 'cyclo', preceded by the numbers of the positions concerned, is used to indicate a three-membered ring. Some examples of these rules are:

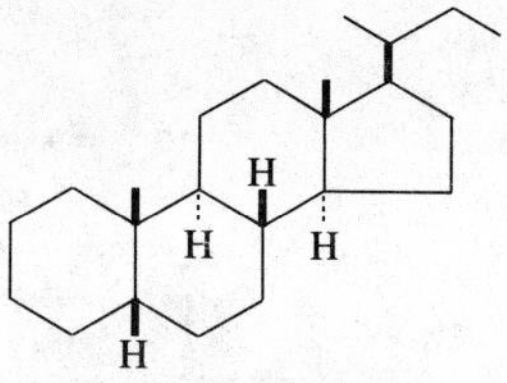

23-nor-5β-cholane 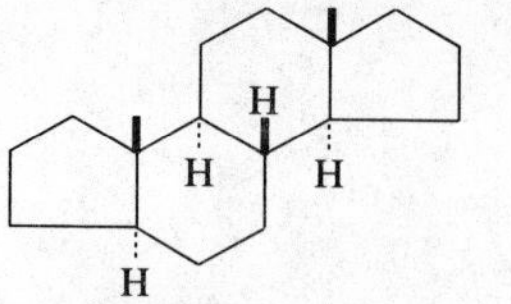   A-nor-5α-androstane 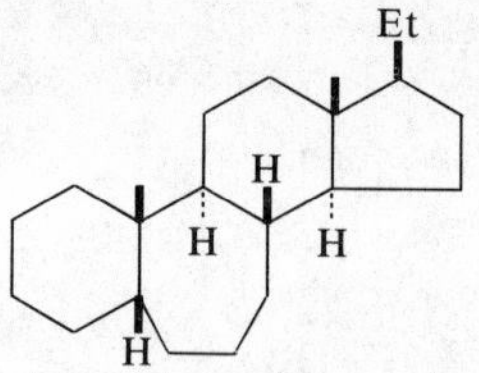   B-homo-5β-pregnane 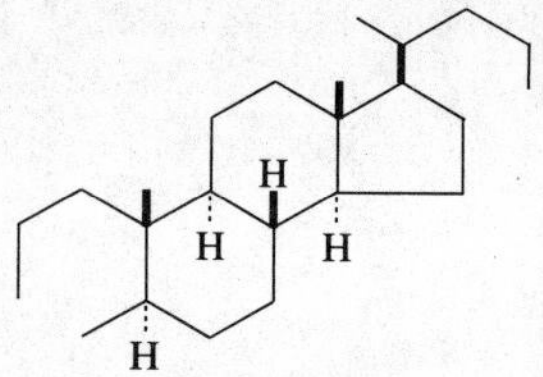   3,4-seco-5α-cholane

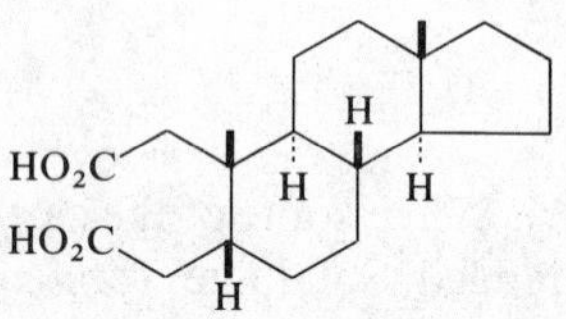

2,3-seco-5β-androstane-2,3-dioic acid   3α,5α-cyclocholestane

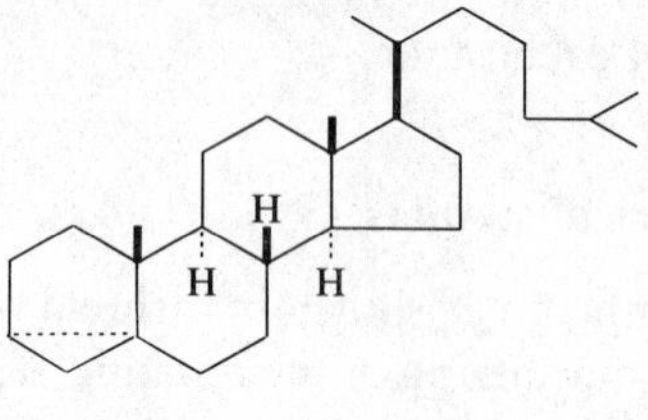

Trivial names have been retained for steroid hormones and closely related compounds (see Text).

Because of the introduction of these rules of nomenclature, some names used in the earlier literature are now discarded, *e.g.*, coprostane is now named as 5β-cholestane; iso-compounds (i-compounds) are now called cyclo-compounds.

Compounds derived from 5α-cholestane belong to the **allo-series**, the prefix 'allo' being reserved to indicate this configuration (*i.e.*, 5α). Compounds derived from 5β-cholestane (coprostane) belong to the **normal-series**. It is not customary to prefix compounds of the latter series by the word 'normal', *e.g.*, cholanic acid can be derived from 5β-cholestane (coprostane). Although this scheme has been discarded, many of the compounds named as allo-compounds have retained this prefix.

§8. Some reactions of steroids

Since the course and rate of reactions depend on conformation, methods of determining conformation will be discussed first. All the evidence obtained has shown that all the cyclohexane rings in the steroid nucleus are chair forms; thus (I) is 5α-cholestane (cholestane) and (II) is 5β-cholestane (coprostane).

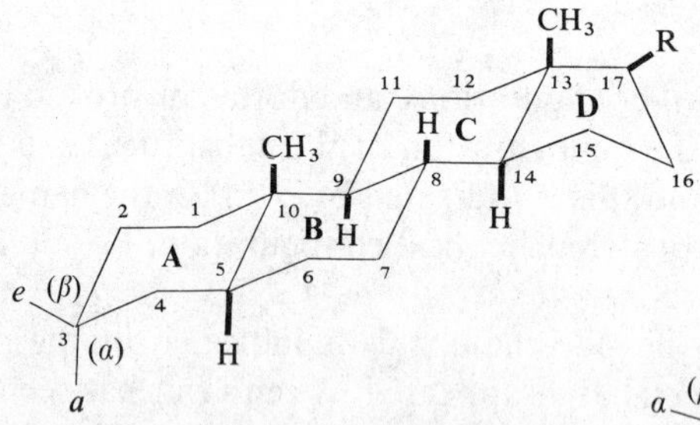

5α-cholestane
(I)

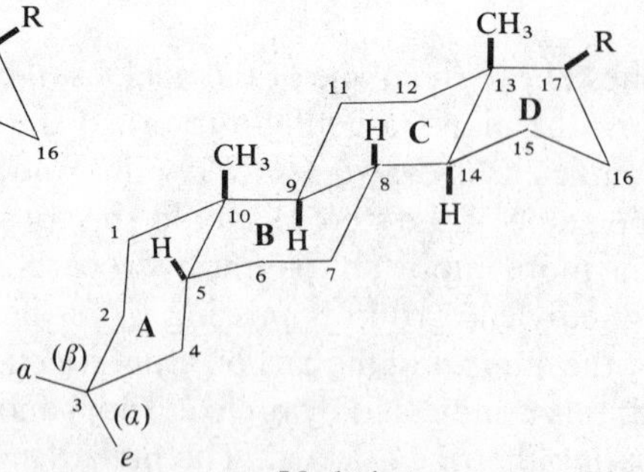

5β-cholestane
(II)

As we have seen, groups lying above the plane of the steroid nucleus have the β-configuration, and those lying below the α-configuration. Another way of describing this is that a bond is β if it projects above the plane and is α if it projects below the plane. We can therefore write the planar formulae of steroids as (III) and (IV) which show the relationship between the α and β designation and the axial and equatorial positions. It should also be noted that an α-substituent is *trans* to the angular methyl groups and a β-substituent is *cis*.

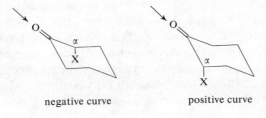

Infrared and ultraviolet spectra have been used in conformational analysis of steroids. It has already been mentioned in **4** §11 that the infrared absorption maximum of a particular substituent in cyclohexane depends on its orientation. In this way it has been possible to determine the orientations of various groups in steroids.

Jones *et al.* (1952) have found that the presence of an α-halogen atom in cyclohexanone increases the stretching frequency of the keto group by about 33 cm^{-1} when the halogen is equatorial, and has very little effect when it is axial. This effect also applies to keto steroids. On the other hand, the effect of an α-halogen atom on the ultraviolet absorption maximum is different. An axial halogen shifts the keto absorption to a longer wavelength (bathochromic shift) and an equatorial halogen to a shorter wavelength (hypsochromic shift). At the same time, the intensity of absorption is increased for either orientation. Shifts also occur for other α-substituents, *e.g.*, (Cookson *et al.*, 1954, 1955):

α-*Substituent*	*Shift* (nm)	
	e	*a*
Cl	−7	+22
Br	−5	+28
OH	−12	+17

Since α-*e*-halogen has comparatively little effect on the ultraviolet absorption maximum of a keto group, it can be expected that the ORD curves of the ketone and its α-*e*-halogen derivative will be very similar. This has been found to be the case in practice. On the other hand, the large effect of an α-*a*-halogen on the absorption maximum can be expected to have some considerable effect on the ORD curve. It has been found that the amplitude is increased and that the sign of the curve is inverted. On the basis of these experimental results, Djerassi *et al.* (1957, 1960) proposed the **Axial Haloketone Rule**, which may be stated as follows: When a halogen atom is introduced into either α-position of a cyclohexanone then, if the orientation is equatorial, there will be no change in sign of the ORD curve of the halogen-free ketone, but if the orientation is axial, the sign of the curve may be affected. The sign of the curve may be predicted by viewing the α-halogenocyclohexanone along the O=C axis (as shown by the arrow). If the halogen is on the left of the observer, there will be a negative curve, but if it is on the right, there will be a positive curve.

The Axial Haloketone Rule may be used in the following ways:

(*a*) Halogenation of the cyclohexanone is carried out; the resulting compound will be the α-product. If there are two α-positions that may be substituted, then it is necessary to first locate the actual position by chemical methods. If the ORD curve shows reversal of sign, the halogen is axial. If there is no change in sign, the halogen could be either axial or equatorial. In this case, differentiation may be made by examination of the infrared and ultraviolet spectra.

(*b*) If the configuration and conformation of the cyclohexanone are known, and after halogenation the orientation of the halogen atom is determined (by i.r. and u.v. spectroscopy) and found to be axial, then its position (α or α') may be located from the sign of the ORD curve of the halogeno-ketone. If the halogen is equatorial, its position cannot be located by use of the rule. However, it may be possible to introduce *two* halogen atoms into the α-position. In this case, one halogen atom must be axial, and so the rule may be applied.

(*c*) If the conformation and the position of the α-axial halogen are known, then the absolute configuration can be assigned by application of the rule.

(*d*) If the configuration and the position of the α-axial halogen are known, then the conformation of the ring may be assigned by use of the rule. A very interesting example is the bromination of 2α-methylcholestan-3-one. The product was shown to be 2-bromo-2-methylcholestan-3-one, and the examination of the infrared and ultraviolet spectra by Sondheimer *et al.* (1958) indicated that the bromine is axial, *i.e.*, the product is 2β-bromo-2α-methylcholestan-3-one (V). This is in keeping with the observation that the kinetically controlled product in halogenation of a ketone usually gives the axial isomer. Application of the rule to (V) predicts a positive curve, but Djerassi *et al.* (1959, 1960) found the halogeno-ketone exhibited a negative curve. If the conformation were (VI), *i.e.*, *e*-Br:*a*-Me, the compound would have a positive curve (*i.e.*, no change). However, this is not in

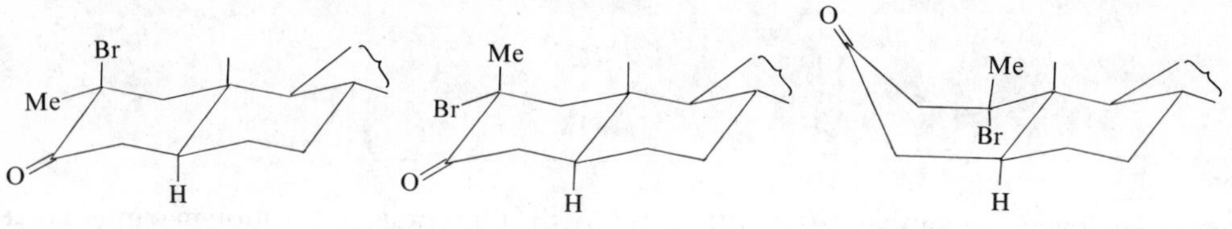

(V)   (VI)   (VII)

accord with the spectroscopic data (that the bromine is axial). Djerassi therefore proposed the boat conformation (VII) in which there is no longer the 1,3-interaction between the Br and C_{10}-Me as in (V), or between the two methyl groups in (VI).

NMR spectroscopy is used to determine the conformation of the hydroxyl group in steroids. Shoolery *et al.* (1958) have found that the chemical shift of the hydrogen in >CH of the >CHOH group (*not* the H of the OH group) depends on the position of the group in the nucleus and on whether the group is axial or equatorial. Tables have been compiled from a study of known compounds, and so it is possible to determine the position and orientation of a hydroxyl group in unknown compounds. On the other hand, Williamson *et al.* (1961) have used the magnitude of the coupling constant for conformational analysis, this application depending on the fact that the coupling constant depends on the dihedral angle between the coupled protons. The authors studied acetates of hydroxy-3-keto steroids, *e.g.*, it was shown that in the acetate of 2α-hydroxy-5α-cholestan-3-one (AcO group is equatorial), ring A was a slightly deformed chair, whereas in the corresponding 2β-hydroxy-compound (AcO group axial), ring A was in the boat form.

Mass spectrometry is also being used in conformational analysis of steroids. Consider andro-sterone and epiandrosterone (see §18). 1,3-Interaction between the 5α-hydrogen (axial) and the axial OH in androsterone is absent in epiandrosterone (*e*-OH), and consequently the molecular ion of the former compound is less stable than that of the latter. Thus, the abundance ratio of the former

androsterone
(*a*-H; *a*-OH)

epiandrosterone
(*a*-H; *e*-OH)

ion will be less than that of the latter, and so the two epimers may be distinguished and identified.

We shall now discuss some reactions of steroids and relate their mechanisms to the conformational features of the molecule (see also **4** §12).

Saturated steroids. Since equatorial groups are normally more stable than axial, when a (poly-cyclic) secondary alcohol is equilibrated with alkali, it is the equatorial isomer that predominates in the product. Furthermore, because of the rigidity of the system (which prevents interconversion of chair forms), the stable configurations of hydroxyl groups at different positions in the cholestane series will be as shown in (III) and (IV).

The following are examples of equilibration (using sodium ethoxide at 180°C (see also **4** §11b)): In the earlier literature, (IX) was known as epicholestanol, (X) as coprostanol, and (XI) as epicopro-stanol.

5α-cholestan-3β-ol (*e*)   5β-cholestan-3β-ol (*a*)
(VIII)   (X)

10% ⇅ 90%   10% ⇅ 90%

5α-cholestan-3α-ol (*a*)   5β-cholestan-3α-ol (*e*)
(IX)   (XI)

Equatorial hydroxyl and carboxyl groups are esterified more rapidly than the corresponding axial groups. Similarly, hydrolysis of equatorial esters and acyloxy groups is more rapid than for the corresponding axial isomers. In the acetates of (VIII) and (XI), the acetoxy groups are equatorial, whereas in the acetates of (IX) and (X) these groups are axial and therefore subject to 1,3-inter-actions. Hence the former pair are hydrolysed more rapidly than the latter pair. In 3β,6β-diacetoxy-5α-cholestane (XII), the former group is equatorial and the latter axial. When this compound is hydrolysed under controlled conditions, the product is 3β-hydroxy-6β-acetoxy-5α-cholestane (Petrow *et al.*, 1939). Apart from the normal 1,3-interactions, the 6β-acetoxyl group is also hindered by the 10β-methyl group. Thus selective hydrolysis can be performed on suitable derivatives, and in the same way selective acylation (acetic anhydride in pyridine-benzene solution) occurs preferentially at an equatorial hydroxyl group rather than at an axial one. A very useful selective acylating reagent

(XII)   (XIII)   (XIV)

is ethyl chloroformate (*cathyl chloride*) in pyridine solution, *e.g.*, cholestane-3β,5α,6β-triol undergoes cathylation to form the 3β-monocathylate (XIII), almost quantitatively (Fieser *et al.*, 1952). On the other hand, the corresponding 3β,5α,6α-triol forms the 3β,6α-dicathylate (XIV) under the same conditions.

Although the above principles are generally valid, there are exceptions, and so there is some possibility of wrong interpretation. Henbest *et al.* (1957) showed that the alkaline hydrolysis of 3α-acetoxycholestan-5α-ol proceeds faster than that of the corresponding 3β-isomer. The reason for this being opposite to the usual rate order is uncertain, but Bruice *et al.* (1962) have obtained some evidence to show that the reaction may possibly proceed as follows for the 3α-compound. Hydrogen bonding at the oxygen atom of the carbonyl group is possible for the 3α-isomer because both substituents are axial. This intramolecular hydrogen bonding causes the oxygen atom of the

carbonyl group to acquire a small positive charge and so facilitates attack at the carbon atom by the hydroxide ion, thereby increasing the rate of hydrolysis. On the other hand, this intramolecular hydrogen bonding cannot occur in the 3β-isomer, in which the 3-hydroxyl group is equatorial (see formula (III), above).

Secondary axial alcohols are more rapidly oxidised by chromic acid (or hypobromous acid) than secondary equatorial alcohols. Schreiber *et al.* (1955) have shown that the more hindered the alcohol, the faster is the oxidation (with chromic acid). This is readily understandable on the basis that the rate-determining step is attack at the C—H bond in the secondary alcohol:

(i) $\quad Cr_2O_7^{2-} + H_2O \rightleftharpoons 2HCrO_4^-$ (ii) $\quad >CHOH + HCrO_4^- + 2H^+ \rightleftharpoons >CH—O—CrO_3H_2^+ + H_2O$

(iii) $\quad >C\underset{H_2O{\uparrow} H}{\overset{\frown}{—}}O—CrO_3H_2^+ \xrightarrow{\text{slow}} >C{=}O + H_3O^+ + H_2CrO_3$

N-Bromosuccinimide (NBS) and *N*-bromoacetamide (NBA), in aqueous acetone or aqueous dioxan, generally selectively oxidise axial alcohols, and so are useful reagents in steroid chemistry.

It appears, however, that the greater accessibility of the equatorial hydrogen (for axial hydroxyl) does not explain all the facts. As we have seen, when the hydroxyl group is axial, the 1,3-interactions are greater than when the hydroxyl group is equatorial. When oxidation to the ketone occurs, the strain is now relieved, much more so than for the corresponding equatorial isomer. This would also hold for the two transition states, and so the activation energy for the axial isomer would be expected to be lower than that of the equatorial isomer. Hence, the greater the steric strain (due to 1,3-interactions), the faster will be the rate of oxidation. By using this argument, it is possible to estimate relative strain at different positions. Let us consider the two pairs of epimers, 5α-cholestan-2α- and 2β-ol, and 5α-cholestan-3α- and 3β-ol. Examination of the formulae shows that in the 2β-ol, the 2*a*-OH will experience a very strong 1,3-interaction with the 10*a*-Me group and a less strong one with the 4*a*-H. On the other hand in the 3α-ol, the 3*a*-OH experiences the two less strong 1,3-interactions with the 2*a*-H and the 5*a*-H. Thus the strain in the 2β-ol will be greater than that in the 3α-ol. Furthermore, since the *e*-OH in the 2α- and 3β-ols experiences very weak 1,2-interactions with hydrogen atoms only, the strain in these two compounds can be expected to be the same, and smaller than that in the 3α-ol. Thus the expected order of strain would be $2\beta >> 3\alpha > 2\alpha = 3\beta$. The actual relative rates of oxidation are (Schreiber *et al.*, 1955): 2β, 20; 3α, 3·0; 2α, 1·3; 3β, 1·0.

2α-ol   2β-ol   3α-ol   3β-ol

If we apply this method to all the possible 5α-cholestane secondary alcohols, it will be seen that the 11β-hydroxyl group (axial) would experience the greatest strain of all, since this is the only one with two 1a-OH, 3a-Me interactions. It is this variation in steric strain of functional groups in the steroid nucleus that permits selective reactions to be carried with such success (see text). Also, Grimmer (1960) has developed an analytical method for determining the position and orientation of hydroxyl groups in the steroid nucleus, based on their different rates of oxidation by chromium trioxide.

Steroid secondary alcohols may also be converted into ketones by means of the Oppenauer oxidation. Since this involves a cyclic transition state (see Vol. I), the reaction is very sensitive to steric effects. Thus, a 3-hydroxyl group is readily oxidised but an 11-hydroxyl group is not. Hence, when both are present (3,11-diol), the 3-hydroxyl group can be selectively oxidised.

Many steroid alcohols react with phosphorus pentachloride and phosphorus tribromide to give the halogeno-compound with inversion (S_N2; see **3** §3). In certain cases, however, there may be complete or predominant retention of configuration. This is the case with 2α- and 6α-hydroxy-steroids, and is believed to be due to steric factors arising from the angular CH_3-19 group (see also later).

In the same way, halogen may be replaced by the acetoxy-group with inversion (by means of potassium acetate). Similarly, tosylates undergo various nucleophilic substitutions with inversion, but in this case elimination also occurs, the amount depending on the nature of the nucleophile and the conditions.

Unsaturated steroids. Allylic alcohols are more readily oxidised than the corresponding saturated alcohols, and the equatorial isomer is oxidised more rapidly than the axial isomer. Manganese dioxide is usually used for the selective oxidation of allylic alcohols (see also Vol. I). Selenium dioxide in acetic acid oxidises cholesterol to cholest-5-ene-3β,4β-diol (see Vol. I).

Replacement of the hydroxyl group in cholesterol by halogen by means of phosphorus penta-chloride, phosphorus tribromide, etc., results in *retention* of configuration at C-3 in the cholesteryl halide. The mechanism is S_N1 and involves the π-electrons of the homoallylic double bond (see elimination reactions, below).

The stereochemisty of addition reactions to a double bond is determined by the nature of the reagent, *i.e.*, whether the addition is normally *cis* or *trans* (**4** §5l), and on the position of the double bond in the nucleus. Since angular methyl groups at C-10 and C-13 in natural steroids have the β-configuration, this generally causes attack at the double bond from the less hindered α-face for *cis*-addition. On the other hand, for those addenda which normally give *trans*-addition, *e.g.*, X_2, HX, the first step is usually the formation of a bridged-ion on the α-face, followed by attack at the β-face. With unsymmetrical addenda, Y—Z, the bridged-ion is formed from the more positive part of the addendum (electrophilic reaction), and consequently this part of the addendum usually has the α-configuration in the *trans*-diaxial product (there are exceptions). Furthermore, when the bridged-ion contains a secondary and a tertiary carbon atom, it is attacked by the anion at the secondary carbon atom. Since tertiary carbon atoms are those at ring junctions, secondary carbon atoms are further removed from the angular methyl groups and so attack at the secondary positions involves less steric repulsion than at the tertiary. This leads to the anti-Markownikoff addition (there are exceptions).

Some examples that illustrate these principles are the conversion of cholesterol (cholest-5-en-3β-ol) into cholestane-3β,5α,6β-triol (XV) by hydrogen peroxide or *via* the epoxide, or into cholestane-3β,5α,6α-triol (XVI) by potassium permanganate or osmium tetroxide (see also **4** §51). Similarly the addition of bromine to cholesterol gives (XVII), and the addition of hydrogen bromide

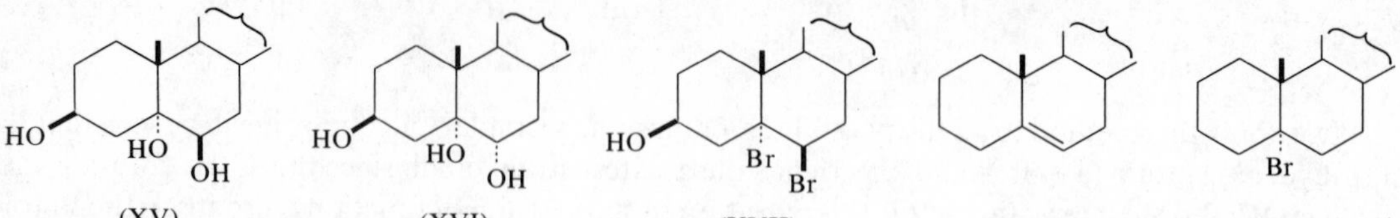

| (XV) | (XVI) | (XVII) | (XVIII) | (XIX) |

to cholest-5-ene (XVIII) gives (XIX). (XIX) is the Markownikoff product and its formation could be explained by assuming the reaction proceeds through the more stable classical tertiary carbonium ion by addition of a proton.

Epoxides are readily converted into 1,2-diaxial compounds by acids, *e.g.*, hydrogen bromide, to give the *trans*-diaxial compound (*cf.* above). Epoxides may also be reduced catalytically or by lithium aluminium hydride into axial alcohols (there are exceptions).

As we have seen above, the addition of bromine to cholesterol produces the *trans*-product, *i.e.*, the 5α,6β-dibromo compound (XVII). When a chloroform solution of this dibromide is allowed to stand for several weeks, the result is an equilibrium mixture of the 5α,6β- and 5β,6α-dibromo forms,

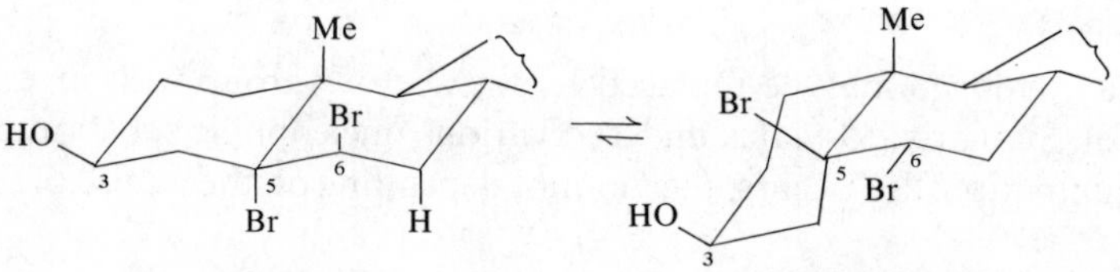

| (XVII) | (XVIIa) |
| *trans*-diaxial | *trans*-diequatorial |

with the latter predominating. The stability of the *trans*-diaxial form is decreased by 1,3-interactions (particularly with the 10-methyl group), but this form cannot change into the more stable *trans*-diequatorial one by interconversion because of the rigidity of the ring system. Since the change does occur, it is believed that bromine ionises and recombines with a Walden inversion occurring. It therefore follows that the *trans*-diaxial form is the kinetically controlled product, whereas the *trans*-diequatorial form is the thermodynamically controlled product.

In the bromination of 3-keto steroids, the position entered by the bromine atom depends on the configuration at C-5. 5α-Cholestan-3-one (cholestan-3-one) gives the 2-bromo derivative, whereas 5β-cholestan-3-one (coprostan-3-one) gives the 4-bromo derivative. These results may be explained

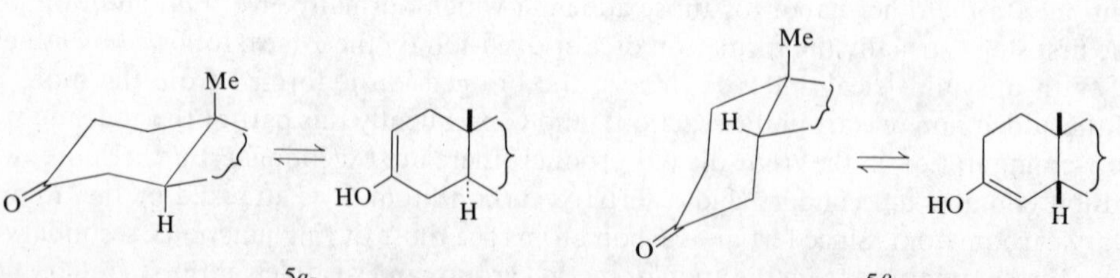

| 5α- | 5β- |

on the basis that bromination proceeds *via* the enol form. Dreiding (1954) has shown that the 5α-ketone enolises to the 2-ene, whereas the 5β-ketone enolises to the 3-ene. Thus, bromination occurs at 2 in the 5α-compound, and at 4 in the 5β-. In both isomers, the bromine atom has been shown to be equatorial, but there is some evidence to show that the axial form is produced first (kinetically controlled product), and then this changes to the equatorial form (thermodynamically controlled product; Corey *et al.*, 1954, 1956). The enol form exists in the half-chair conformation, and addition across the double bond produces the diaxial product (*cf.* **4** §13). The direction of enolisation of the 3-ketone is governed by the strain produced in the enol.

Now let us consider the addition of hydrogen to a double bond in an unsaturated steroid. As we have seen (**4** §5l), hydroboronation results in *cis*-addition to give the di-α-product. Oxidation of the intermediate borane almost always results in the formation of α-alcohols of which the predominant product is usually that in which the hydroxyl group is further removed from the angular methyl groups.

The problem of catalytic reduction of unsaturated steroids is complicated by the fact that the steric course of the addition depends on the nature of functional groups present and on the conditions (see also **4** §5l). The catalytic hydrogenation (platinum) of cholesterol produces only

5α-cholestan-3β-ol (cholestanol). On the other hand, oxidation of 5α-cholestan-3β-ol with chromium trixodie in acetic acid gives 5α-cholestan-3-one and this, on catalytic reduction in neutral solution, gives mainly 5α-cholestan-3β-ol, whereas catalytic reduction in acid solution gives mainly 5α-cholestan-3α-ol (epicholestanol). The corresponding C-5 epimers, 5β-cholestan-3β-ol (coprostanol) and 5β-cholestan-3α-ol (epicoprostanol) may be prepared from cholesterol as follows, the first step being the conversion of cholesterol into cholest-4-en-3-one by means of the Oppenauer oxidation (aluminium t-butoxide in acetone; see also Vol. 1).

A detailed study of the catalytic reduction of the decalones has shown that in an acid medium the product is usually the *cis*-compound, whereas in a neutral or alkaline medium the product is usually the *trans*-compound (von Auwers, 1920; Skita, 1920). This principle, which is known as the *Auwers–Skita rule of catalytic hydrogenation*, was used by Ruzicka (1934) to determine the configurations of the above 'stanols'. The configurations assigned have been supported by measurement of the rates of hydrolysis of the acetates of the various 'stanols' (Ruzicka *et al.*, 1938). The acetates of 5α-cholestan-3β-ol and 5β-cholestan-3α-ol are hydrolysed much faster than those of 5α-cholestan-3α-ol and 5β-cholestan-3β-ol (see above).

A point of interest in connection with the Auwers–Skita rule is that this generalisation does not allow for the possibility of isomerisation. Schuetz *et al.* (1962) have shown that in the hydrogenation of the three xylenes the yield of the *trans*-isomer increased with temperature.

Now let us consider the configuration at C-5. The results of experiments on the catalytic hydrogenation of substituted cyclohexanones and substituted phenols have led to the generalisation that the initial addition is *cis*, and occurs on the more accessible side of the double bond (Peppiatt *et al.*, 1955; Wicker, 1956). In accordance with this generalisation, it has been found that when saturated steroids of the A/B-*cis*- and the A/B-*trans*- series are produced by catalytic hydrogenation of 3α-substituted Δ^5-steroids, then the larger the size of the 3α-substituent, the larger is the proportion of the A/B-*cis*-steroid; in some cases, this *cis*-steroid is apparently formed exclusively (Shoppee *et al.*, 1955).

Elimination reactions. Bimolecular ionic elimination reactions occur readily when the two groups (which are eliminated) are *trans*-diaxial, and less readily when *trans*-diequatorial or *cis*-axial, equatorial. This may be illustrated with cholesterol dibromide discussed above (see (XVII) and (XVIIa), above). Both the $5\alpha,6\beta$- (*trans*-diaxial) and the $5\beta,6\alpha$- (*trans*-diequatorial) forms are debrominated by sodium iodide in acetone solution to cholesterol, but the former reacts much faster than the latter. The ease of diaxial elimination is also illustrated by the work of Barton *et al.* (1956) with the epimeric 3-methyl-5α-cholestanols.

The 3α-ol gave the 2-ene on treatment with phosphoryl chloride-pyridine, whereas the 3β-ol gave the 3-methylene derivative under the same conditions. These reactions occur by the E2 mechanism, but when each 3-ol is treated with perchloric acid in acetic acid, both form the 2-ene by the E1 mechanism. The formation of only the 2-ene also shows this cycloalkene is more stable than the 3-ene.

Another reaction that shows the ease of diaxial elimination (E2) is the Hofmann degradation with the 3-trimethylammonium-5α-cholestanes; the 3α-compound gave the 2-ene, but no unsaturated products were obtained from the 3β-compound (McKenna *et al.*, 1958):

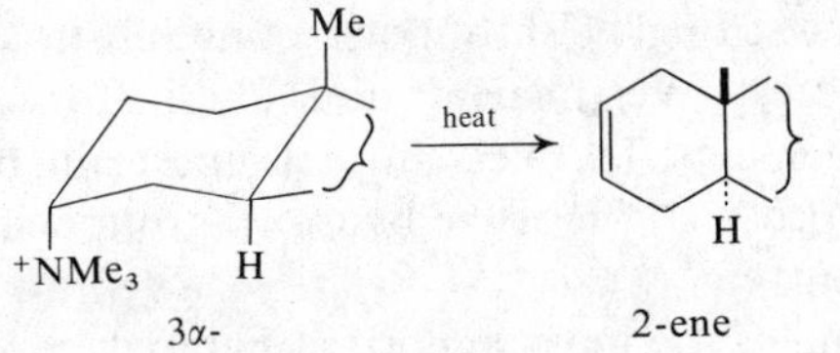

Me

heat →

$^+NMe_3$ H

3α-

2-ene

An interesting reaction is the action of potassium acetate on the tosyl derivative of cholesterol in aqueous acetone to form 6β-acetoxy-3α,5α-cyclocholestane (Wallis, 1937). Only the 3β-tosylate undergoes this reaction; the 3α-tosylate forms the 3-acetate. In the 3β-compound, the stereo-electronic requirements are satisfied (2 §4a), but this is not the case for the 3α-isomer.

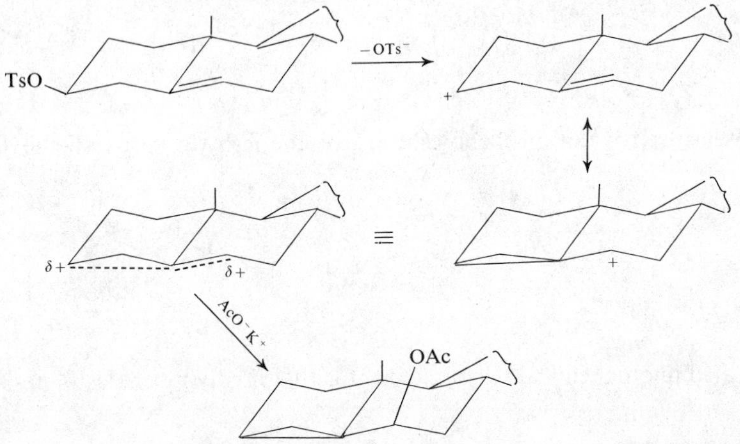

TsO $-OTs^-$ →

+

⥮

δ+   ≡   +

δ+

AcO·K·

OAc

The above type of rearrangement involves the group C=CCH$_2$CHOH (parent alcohol). This group has been designated as *homoallylic alcohol* (Winstein *et al.*, 1954), and the rearrangement involved as the 3,5-cyclosteroid (*i-steroid*) *rearrangement* (*cf.* the allylic rearrangement).

This rearrangement proceeds by an S$_N$1 mechanism and when the 3-substituent has the β-configu-ration then, because of neighbouring group participation, *attack at position 3* will occur with reten-tion of configuration. This mechanism explains why cholesterol (3β-OH) is converted into cholesteryl halides (3β-X) [see unsaturated steroids, above].

Other examples of cyclosteroids are also known, *e.g.*, the conversion of 7β-tosyloxy-5α-cholestan-4-one into 5α,7α-cyclocholestan-4-one by means of a base.

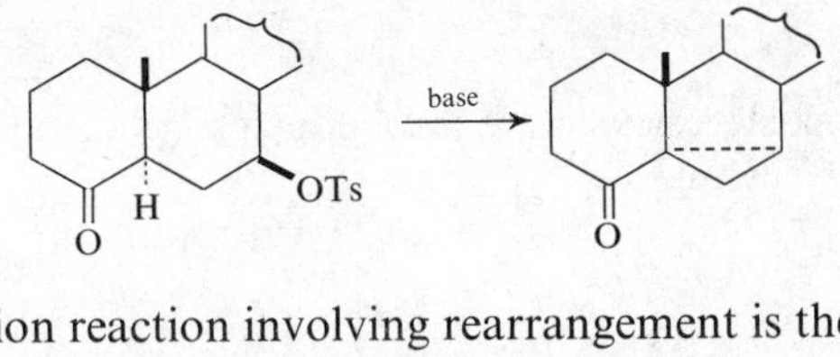

O   H   OTs   base →   O

Another type of elimination reaction involving rearrangement is the **Westphalen rearrangement**. This occurs with 5α-hydroxysteroids under the influence of acids, *e.g.*,

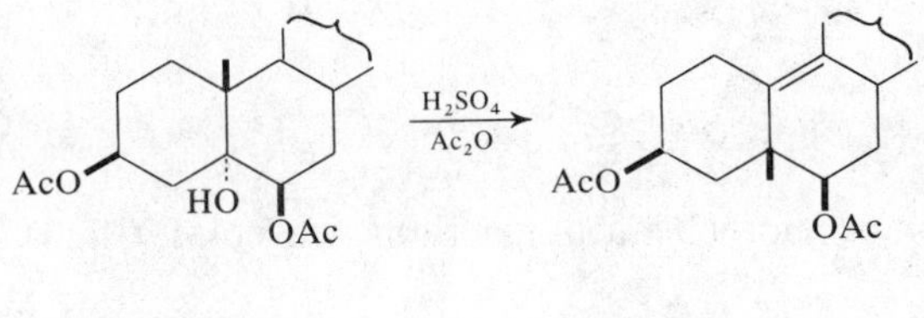

AcO   HO   OAc $\xrightarrow[Ac_2O]{H_2SO_4}$ AcO   OAc

It appears that the presence of a strongly electron-attracting substituent in the 6β-position is neces-sary. The product is the acetate of 'Westphalen's diol' and its formation is an example of a class known as 'backbone' rearrangements. The mechanism is uncertain, but it appears to be established that it is not simply a case of protonation of the hydroxyl group with subsequent loss of water to form the tertiary carbonium ion, etc.

Photochemical reactions. One of the most important photochemical reactions of steroids is the conversion of ergosterol into vitamin D (see §11a). Some other examples are:

(*a*) The conversion of oestrone (§20) into lumi-oestrone (the 13α-epimer).

(*b*) The photosensitised oxidation of cholesterol gives the 5α-hydroperoxy-6-ene (the double bond has migrated).

(*c*) A complicated photochemical rearrangement is that involving cholest-4-en-3-one.

(*d*) Photochemical reactions have supplied a method of carrying out substitutions at the angular methyl groups and to their removal under mild conditions (*cf.* selenium dehydrogenations), *e.g.*,

(ii) The conversion of corticosterone acetate into aldosterone acetate (see also §28).

For a general discussion of photochemical reactions, see Vol. I, Ch. 31.

§9. Synthesis of cholesterol

Before describing the synthesis of cholesterol, we shall discuss the problem of the synthesis of complex molecules in general. Many examples of these syntheses have already been described (see Ch. 8, Terpenoids. Ch. 9, Carotenoids). Two difficulties of the classical chemists were the isolation of pure compounds from natural sources and the separation of isomers (usually geometrical and optical) formed in the various steps of a synthesis. Modern methods of separation, particularly chromatography, have overcome these problems. Also, recent syntheses have been more successful and more elegant due to the increased knowledge of reaction mechanisms and to the introduction of selective reagents.

An interesting development in the presentation of recent syntheses is the *discussion* of the reasons that led to the adoption of the sequence of steps for carrying out the synthesis. Classical chemists obviously also had their reasons for carrying out their syntheses in a particular way, but these are not often described or are only briefly mentioned in their publications.

A characteristic feature of recent syntheses is the use of control elements. These may be divided into two types: **regiospecific** or **regioselective control elements**, and **stereospecific** or **stereoselective control elements**. The terms 'specific' and 'selective' are used in the sense described in **4** §5k. Regiospecific control elements are groups which have been deliberately introduced to cause reactions to occur at a specific site in a molecule and, if necessary, can be readily removed without affecting the rest of the molecule. Stereospecific control elements are those which cause a reaction to proceed in such manner that the product has one particular type of geometry rather than another. Control elements were used by the classical chemists, but many more of these elements have now been introduced. Some examples of their application have already been described, *e.g.*, regiospecific: protecting groups, activating of a methylene group by an adjacent oxo group; stereospecific: asymmetric synthesis (more correctly this is an example of stereoselectivity), stereochemical control by steric effects, addition and elimination reactions.

A simple molecule may be described as one which is small and whose total synthesis requires a relatively small number of steps. Very often, such a synthesis may be readily achieved by 'working backwards'. On the other hand, a complex molecule may be described as a large molecule whose total synthesis requires a large number of steps. Furthermore, the synthesis of a complex molecule usually involves problems of stereochemistry. It is important to note, however, that success in achieving a synthesis, be it of a simple or a complex molecule, ultimately depends on a very good knowledge of organic reactions and their application.

Some points that may be noted for the general approach to the synthesis of complex molecules are (see the appropriate reading references):

(i) The recognition of structural units within the molecule which can be formed and/or assembled by known chemical methods. Starting materials should be readily accessible. The first objective is assisted by examination of the molecule (to be synthesised) for any type of symmetry. Recognition of symmetry will lead to a shorter route. Structural units within a molecule are termed 'synthons', and their recognition may suggest routes for the synthesis. Furthermore, recognition of a relationship of the molecule to some other *known* compound may permit the use of a complicated synthon if the known compound is readily available.

(ii) The necessicity of obtaining the best yields of the products is of paramount importance, and to achieve this may require the use of control elements.

(iii) The relative positions of chiral centres (when present) may give information on the type of control elements required to give the desired configurations.

(iv) The presence of reactive functional groups which can give rise to neighbouring group participation may suggest steps that lead to a desired intermediate, *e.g.*, by temporary cyclisation and so controlling the stereochemical course of the reaction.

We shall now discuss the synthesis of cholesterol and consider it in the light of the above discussion. Basically, the synthesis of steroids involves the construction of the steroid nucleus in the form of the required conformation. The early methods started with ring A or rings A/B, and the other rings were then built up as follows: A → AB → ABC → ABCD. However, as the number of selective reagents increased, different starting points and different orders of fusion were developed, e.g., (i) AB → ABCD; (ii) AC → ABC → ABCD; (iii) AD → ABCD; (iv) BC → BCD → ABCD; (v) CD → ACD → ABCD; (vi) CD → BCD → ABCD.

Two groups of workers, viz., Robinson et al. (1951) and Woodward et al. (1951), have synthesised cholesterol. One of the outstanding difficulties in the synthesis of steroids is the stereochemical problem. The cholesterol nucleus contains eight chiral centres and so 256 optical isomers are possible (see also §4 for further details). Thus every step in the synthesis which produced a new chiral centre had to result in the formation of some (the more the better) of the desired stereoisomer, and at the same time resolution of racemic modifications also had to be practicable. Another difficulty was attacking a particular point in the molecule without affecting the other parts. This problem led to the development of specific reagents. The following is an outline of the Woodward synthesis. Some steps are not stereospecific or even stereoselective. Later syntheses of various steroids are superior in this respect (see, e.g., aldosterone, §28b). The synthesis of cholesterol described here is of the type: C → CD → BCD → ABCD.

4-Methoxy-2,5-toluquinone (I) was prepared from 2-methoxy-p-cresol as follows:

(I) was condensed with butadiene (Diels–Alder reaction) to give (II). This has the cis configuration and was isomerised (quantitatively) to the trans-isomer (III) by dissolving in aqueous alkali, adding a seed crystal of the trans-isomer and then acidifying. Isomerisation occurs via the enolate to give the more stable trans-isomer (see also §5; configuration of the nucleus). (III), on reduction with lithium aluminium hydride, gave (IV). (IV) is a vinyl ether of a glycol which, on treatment with aqueous acid, undergoes hydrolysis (demethylation) to give a β-hydroxyketone which is readily dehydrated to (V) in acid solution. Conversion of (V) to (VI) by removal of the hydroxyl group was carried out by a new technique: (V) was acetylated and the product, the ketol acetate, was heated with zinc in acetic anhydride to give (VI) [reduction with metal and acid usually reduces α,β-unsaturated bonds in ketones]. (VI), on treatment with ethyl formate in the presence of sodium methoxide, gave the hydroxymethylene ketone (VII) [Claisen condensation]. When this was treated with ethyl vinyl ketone in the presence of potassium t-butoxide, (VIII) was formed (Michael condensation). The object of the double bond in the ketone ring in (VI) is to prevent formylation occurring on that side of the keto group, and the purpose of the formyl group is to produce an active methylene group (this is now flanked on both sides by carbonyl groups). The necessity for this 'activation' lies in the fact that ethyl vinyl ketone tends to self-condense, and consequently decrease the yield of (VIII). Both operations are examples of the introduction of regiospecific control elements. (VIII) was now cyclised quantitatively by means of potassium hydroxide in aqueous dioxan to the single product (IX). This is the desired compound; the other possible isomer ((IX) with the two hydrogens cis instead of trans as shown) is not formed since the cis-isomer is less stable than the trans due to greater steric interactions in the former, i.e., the cyclisation is stereospecific (steric effect control). Also, the cyclisation occurs by an intramolecular aldol condensation followed by dehydration. (IX) was then treated with osmium tetroxide to give two *cis*-glycols of structure (X) [one is *cis* with respect to the angular methyl group and the other is *trans*]. Glycol formation occurs readily at the isolated double bond (the other two double bonds are conjugated and so have less double bond character than an isolated double bond; the reaction with osmium tetroxide is very sensitive to this change). These glycols were separated and the desired isomer (the one insoluble in benzene) was treated with acetone in the presence of anhydrous copper sulphate to give the isopropylidene derivative (XI). This, on catalytic reduction (H_2—Pd/SrCO$_3$) gave (XII) which was condensed with ethyl formate in the presence of sodium methoxide to give (XIII), and this was then converted into (XIV) by means of methylaniline. The purpose of this treatment was to block undesired condensation reactions on this side of the keto group (at this position 3); this is another example of a regiospecific control element. When (XIV) was condensed with vinyl cyanide (cyanoethylation) and the product hydrolysed with alkali, the product was a mixture of two keto acids. These were separated and the stereoisomer (XV) [methyl group in front and propionic acid group behind the plane of the rings] was converted into the enol lactone (XVI) which, on treatment with methylmagnesium bromide, gave (XVII), and this, on ring closure by means of alkali, gave (XVIII). When this was oxidised with periodic acid in aqueous dioxan, the dialdehyde (XIX) was obtained (*via* hydrolysis of the diol), and this, when heated in benzene solution in the presence of a small amount of piperidine acetate, gave (XX) [and a small amount of an isomer]. This cyclisation occurs by an intramolecular aldol condensation under the influence of the base, piperidine acetate. Since either aldehyde group can be involved in the condensation, two products are possible. In (XIX), the upper methylene group is *cis* to the hydrogen atom at C-14, whereas the lower methylene group is *cis* to the 18-methyl group. Hence, the upper methylene group experiences less steric hindrance than the lower one and consequently it is the former that loses a proton to form the carbanion. Therefore (XX) is the predominant isomer. (XX) was oxidised to the corresponding acid which was then converted into the methyl ester (XXI) with diazomethane. (XXI), a racemate, was resolved by reduction of the keto group with sodium borohydride to the hydroxy esters [($\pm$)-3α- and ($\pm$)-3β-]. The ($+$)-form of the 3β-alcohol was preferentially precipitated by digitonin, and this stereoisomer was now oxidised (Oppenauer oxidation) to give the desired stereoisomer ($+$)-(XXI). This was catalytically reduced (H_2—Pt) to (XXII), which was then oxidised to (XXIII) which was now a mixture of stereoisomers (from the mixture of (XXII); H at 17 behind and in front). These were separated, reduced (sodium borohydride), and hydrolysed. The β-isomer, (XXIV), was converted into the methyl ketone by first acetylating, then treating with thionyl chloride and finally with dimethylcadmium. This acetylated hydroxyketone, (XXV), on treatment with isohexylmagnesium bromide, gave (XXVI). This was a mixture of isomers (a new chiral centre has been introduced at position 20). (XXVI), on dehydration, gave one product, (XXVII), and this, on catalytic hydrogenation (H_2—Pt), gave a mixture of 5α-cholestanyl acetates (the chiral C-20 has been re-introduced). These acetates were separated and the desired isomer, on hydrolysis, gave 5α-cholestan-3β-ol, (XXVIII), which was identical with natural cholestanol. The conversion of cholestanol into cholesterol (XXXIII) is then carried out by a series of reactions introduced by various workers. Bromination of (XXIX) in acetic acid in the presence of hydrogen bromide (as catalyst) gives the 2α-bromo-derivative ((XXX); see §8). (XXX), on treatment with pyridine, gives (XXXI). The mechanism of this elimination is uncertain. A possibility is that because the *equatorial* bromine is difficult to remove by the E2 mechanism, a 1,4-elimination occurs by removal of a proton

(XXX) (XXXI)

from position 4 by the base (the methylene group in this position is activated by the adjacent oxo group; *cf.* however, the bromination of acetone).

Heating (XXXI) with acetyl chloride in the presence of acetic anhydride gives the enol acetate (XXXII) which, on reduction with lithium aluminium hydride followed by acidification, gives cholesterol (XXXIII). The mechanism of this reaction is uncertain.

Possibly the electron-attracting effect of the acetoxy-group activates the 3,4-double bond to hydride transfer from the lithium aluminium hydride.

(XIV) $\xrightarrow{\text{(i) CH}_2\text{=CHCN}}$ (XV) $\xrightarrow[\text{CH}_3\text{CO}_2\text{Na}]{(\text{CH}_3\text{CO})_2\text{O}}$

(XVI) $\xrightarrow{\text{CH}_3\text{MgBr}}$ (XVII) $\xrightarrow{\text{NaOH}}$

(XVIII) $\xrightarrow{\text{HIO}_4}$ (XIX) $\xrightarrow[\text{dioxan}]{\text{boil in}}$

(XX) $\xrightarrow[\text{(ii) CH}_2\text{N}_2]{\text{(i) K}_2\text{Cr}_2\text{O}_7}$ (XXI) $\xrightarrow[\text{(ii) H}_2\text{—Pt}]{\text{(i) (+)-form}}$

(XXII) $\xrightarrow{\text{CrO}_3}$ (XXIII) $\xrightarrow[\text{(ii) hydrolysis}]{\text{(i) NaBH}_4}$

(XXIV) $\xrightarrow[\substack{\text{(ii) SOCl}_2 \\ \text{(iii) Cd(CH}_3)_2}]{\text{(i) (CH}_3\text{CO})_2\text{O}}$ (XXV) $\xrightarrow{(\text{CH}_3)_2\text{CH(CH}_2)_3\text{MgBr}}$

(XXVI) → heat (−H₂O) → (XXVII) → (i) H₂—Pt (ii) NaOH →

(XXVIII) cholestanol → Na₂Cr₂O₇ / H₂SO₄ → (XXIX) → Br₂/HBr →

(XXX) → pyridine → (XXXI) → CH₃COCl (CH₃CO)₂O →

(XXXII) → (i) LiAlH₄ (ii) HCl → (XXXIII) cholesterol

An important point to note is that this total synthesis has involved a very large number of steps, and in most cases of this type the overall yield is very small. It may vary from about 4 to about 0·0005 per cent, depending on the number of steps involved. Thus, these syntheses cannot be expected to be a commercial source of these compounds. However, once a total synthesis has been accomplished, other syntheses of the compound may be carried out by starting from any particular intermediate prepared in the sequence. Such a compound may actually occur naturally or be a degradation product of the desired final product. In many cases, the starting material may be a natural compound that can be efficiently converted into the desired product. In such cases, the synthesis of the desired product is referred to as a **partial synthesis**. In general, most complex molecules have been prepared by partial syntheses before total syntheses have been achieved. Partial syntheses can be commercially important, but complete confirmation of structure is always necessary, and this is usually achieved by total synthesis.

A more recent total synthesis of ($\pm$)-cholesterol has been carried out by Johnson *et al.* (1966) using the hydrochrysene approach (see appropriate reading reference; see also §28b).

§10. Ergosterol, $C_{28}H_{44}O$, m.p. 165°C, $[\alpha]_D$-135°, λ_{max} 282 nm

This occurs in yeast. Ergosterol forms esters, *e.g.*, an acetate with acetic anhydride; thus there is a hydroxyl group present in ergosterol. Catalytic hydrogenation (platinum) of ergosterol produces ergostanol, $C_{28}H_{50}O$; hence there are three double bonds in ergosterol. When ergostanol is acetylated and the product then oxidised, the acetate of 3β-hydroxynor-5α-cholanic acid, (I) is obtained (Fernholz *et al.*, 1934). The identity of (I) is established by the fact that 5α-cholestanyl 3β-acetate (II) [a compound of known structure], gives, on oxidation, the acetate of 3β-hydroxy-5α-cholanic acid (III) and this, after one Barbier–Wieland degradation (§3iii), gives (I); thus:

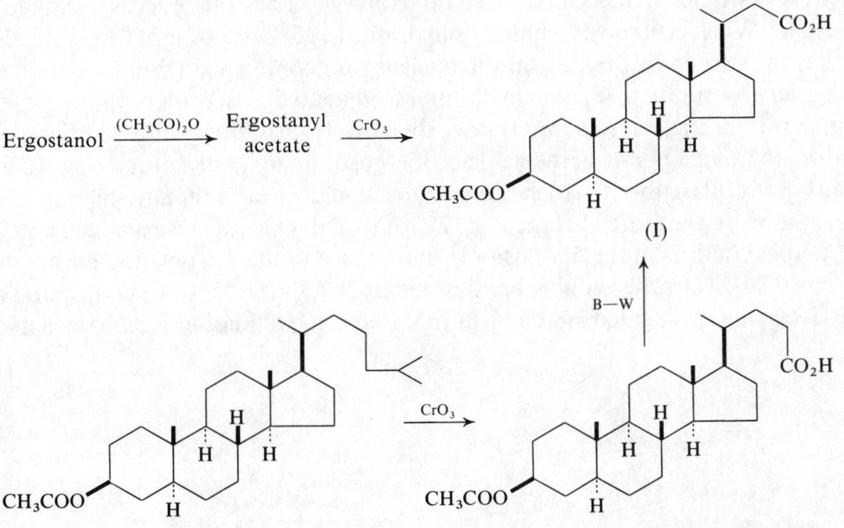

Thus ergostanol and 5α-cholestan-3β-ol have identical nuclei, the same position of the hydroxyl group and the same position of the side-chain. The only difference must be the *nature* of the side-chain, and hence it follows that ergosterol contains one more carbon atom in its side-chain than cholesterol (the former compound is $C_{28}H_{44}O$ and the latter $C_{27}H_{46}O$). Ozonolysis of ergosterol gives, among other products, methylisopropylacetaldehyde (IV). This can be accounted for if the side-chain of ergosterol is as shown in (V) (Windaus *et al.*, 1932). Also, since the infrared spectrum of ergosterol showed a band at $\sim$970 cm^{-1}, the 22,23-double bond has the *trans*-configuration (see Table 1.6).

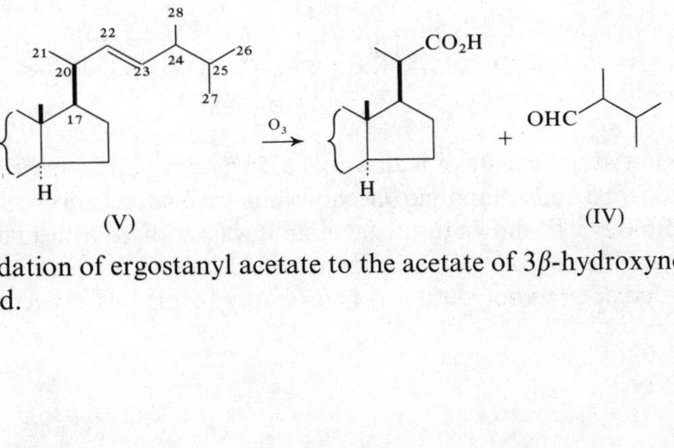

On this basis, the oxidation of ergostanyl acetate to the acetate of 3β-hydroxynor-5α-cholanic acid (I) is readily explained.

We have now accounted for all the structural features of ergosterol except the positions of the three double bonds. The position of one of these is actually shown in the above account; it is C_{22}—C_{23}. The side-chain must contain only *one* double bond, since if more than one were present, more than

ergostanyl acetate

(I)

one fragment (IV) would have been removed on ozonlysis. Thus the other two double bonds must be in the nucleus. When heated with maleic anhydride at 135°C, ergosterol forms an adduct, and so it follows that the two double bonds (in the nucleus) are conjugated (Windaus *et al.*, 1931). Now ergosterol has an absorption maximum at 282 nm. Conjugated *acyclic* dienes absorb in the region of 220–250 nm, but if the diene is in a *ring system*, then the absorption is shifted to the region 260–290 nm. Thus the two double bonds in the nucleus of ergosterol are in *one* of the rings (Dimroth *et al.*, 1936). When ergosterol is subjected to the Oppenauer oxidation (aluminium t-butoxide and acetone), the product is an α,β-unsaturated ketone (λ_{max} 235 nm). This can only be explained by assuming that one of the double bonds is in the 5,6-position, and moves to the 4,5-position during the oxidation (*cf.* cholesterol, §3ii). The other double bond is therefore 7,8 in order to be conjugated with the one that is 5,6. Hence the conjugated system is in ring B and the oxidation is explained as follows:

ergosterol

This is supported by the oxidation of ergosterol with perbenzoic acid to give the monobenzoate of a triol. This, on catalytic hydrogenation followed by hydrolysis, gave a saturated triol which underwent fission when treated with lead tetra-acetate. Hence, two hydroxyl groups must be in the vicinal position and also, since the diol formed only a diacetate, one hydroxyl group is therefore tertiary. These results are readily explained on the basis that one double bond is in the 5,6-position.

An interesting point about this triol is that it is a 5α,6α-derivative, whereas it might have been expected to have been the 5α,6β-compound (*cf.* cholestanetriol, §8; reactions of unsaturated steroids). That it was the *cis*-5,6-diol was shown by the fact that it was oxidised by lead tetra-acetate extremely rapidly when compared to the rate of oxidation of cholestanetriol, which is a *trans*-5,6-diol. With ergosterol, the 5,6-epoxide (α-configuration) is probably formed as expected, but because of the

7,8-double bond which is allylic with C-6, this epoxide is readily opened by benzoic acid (from the per-acid) to give the 6-benzoate with *retention* at this position, *i.e.*, the *cis*-1,2-glycol.

§11. Vitamin D

This vitamin is the antirachitic vitamin; it is essential for bone formation, its function being the control of calcium and phosphorus metabolism.

Steenbock *et al.* (1924) showed that when various food were irradiated with ultraviolet light, they acquired antirachitic properties. This was then followed by the discovery that the active compound was in the unsaponifiable fraction (the sterol fraction). At first, it was believed that the precursor of the active compound was cholesterol, but subsequently the precursor was shown to be some 'impurity' that was in the cholesterol fraction (*e.g.*, by Heilbron *et al.*, 1926). The ultraviolet absorption spectrum of this 'impure cholesterol' indicated the presence of a small amount of some substance that was more unsaturated than cholesterol. This led to the suggestion that ergosterol was the provitamin D in the 'impure cholesterol', and the investigation of the effect of ultraviolet light on ergosterol resulted in the isolation from the irradiated product of a compound which had very strong antirachitic properties. This compound was named **calciferol** by the Medical Research Council (1931), and **vitamin D_1** by Windaus (1931). This potent crystalline compound, however, was subsequently shown to be a molecular compound of calciferol and lumisterol (one molecule of each). Windaus (1932) therefore renamed the pure potent compound as **vitamin D_2**, but the M.R.C. retained the original name calciferol. The *Chemical Society* (1951) has proposed the name **ergocalciferol** for this pure compound.

A detailed study of the irradiation of ergosterol with ultraviolet light (~ 280 nm) has led to the proposal that the series of changes is as follows ($R = C_9H_{17}$):

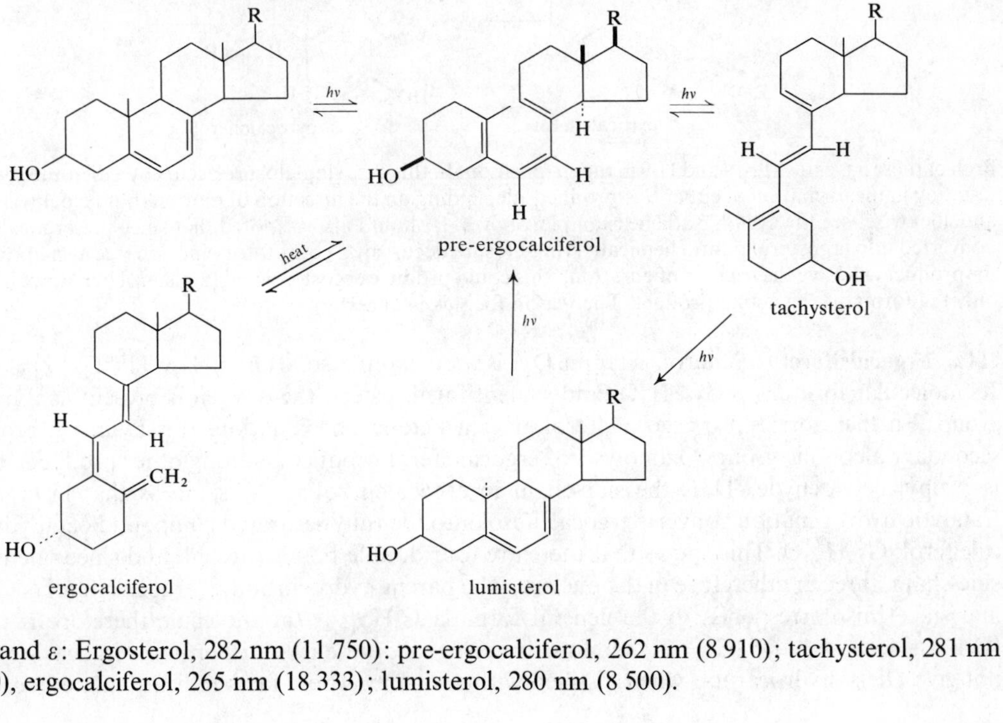

pre-ergocalciferol

tachysterol

ergocalciferol

lumisterol

λ_{max} and ε: Ergosterol, 282 nm (11 750): pre-ergocalciferol, 262 nm (8 910); tachysterol, 281 nm (24 550), ergocalciferol, 265 nm (18 333); lumisterol, 280 nm (8 500).

The course of these changes can now be explained in terms of the *Woodward–Hoffmann selection rules* for electrocyclic reactions (see Vol. I, Ch. 31). The primary reaction is the opening of the 1,3-diene ring B in ergosterol to give an equilibrium mixture with the acyclic triene, pre-ergocalciferol. Under the influence of light, this occurs by a conrotatory motion, whereas by means of heat the ring-opening occurs by a disrotatory motion, *e.g.*, the opening of *trans*-5,6-dimethylcyclohexa-1,3-diene to give octa-2,4,6-triene.

Me H H Me   Me H   Me H Me H
trans, cis, trans   H Me   *trans, cis, trans*

hv; con. / con.   heat; dis. / dis.

Thus, ergosterol undergoes photochemical ring-opening and by a conrotatory motion to give pre-ergocalciferol, in which the centre double bond 6,7 is *cis*. When this is irradiated, isomerisation about the 6,7-double bond (to *trans*) now occurs to give tachysterol. When this is further irradiated, ring-closure occurs to give lumisterol in which Me-19 and H-9 are still *trans*, but now Me-19 has the α-configuration and H-9 the β. This is believed to occur as follows. The *trans*-6,7-double bond acquires a large amount of single-bond character and this permits rotation so that carbon atoms 9 and 10 can reform the σ-bond (only the conjugated system has been drawn).

When *heated*, pre-ergocalciferol forms an equilibrium mixture with ergocalciferol. Further heating of either of these two compounds results in the formation of a mixture of pyrocalciferol and isopyrocalciferol.

HO   pyrocalciferol   HO   isopyrocalciferol

Both of these have the Me-19 and H-9 in the *cis*-position. In this case ring-closure occurs by a disrotatory motion, resulting in the formation of either '*cis*-product', depending on the direction of motion (both clockwise or both anticlockwise; see the cyclohexadiene example, above). It should also be noted that since pre-ergocalciferol is converted into ergosterol photochemically, ring-closure occurs by a conrotatory motion (see also above). Thus the product will have the *trans*-configuration. This could produce ergosterol and lumisterol but, as we have seen, only the former is the actual product. The reason for this is uncertain.

§11a. **Ergocalciferol** (calciferol, vitamin D_2) is a crystalline solid, m.p. 115–117°C, $[\alpha]_D + 130°$. Its molecular formula is $C_{28}H_{44}O$, and since it forms esters, the oxygen is present as a hydroxyl group. Furthermore, since ergocalciferol gives a ketone on oxidation, this hydroxyl group is a secondary alcoholic group. Ozonolysis of ergocalciferol produces, among other products, methyl-isopropylacetaldehyde. Thus the side-chain in ergocalciferol is the same as that in ergosterol. Catalytic hydrogenation converts ergocalciferol into the fully saturated compound octahydroergo-calciferol, $C_{28}H_{52}O$. This shows that there are four double bonds present, and since one is in the side-chain, three are therefore in the nucleus. The parent hydrocarbon of ergocalciferol is $C_{28}H_{52}$, and since this corresponds to the general formula C_nH_{2n-4}, the molecule therefore is *tricyclic* (D.B.E. $= 28 + 1 - 52/2 = 3$; therefore three rings are present). Furthermore, ergocalciferol does not give Diels' hydrocarbon when distilled with selenium. These facts indicate that ergocalciferol does not contain the four-ring system of ergosterol. The problem is therefore to ascertain which of the rings in ergosterol has been opened in the formation of ergocalciferol. The following reactions of ergocalciferol are readily explained on the assumption that its structure is (I). The absorption spectrum of the semicarbazone of (II) ($C_{21}H_{34}O$) was shown to be characteristic of α,β-unsaturated aldehydes (λ_{max} 275 nm). The absence of the hydroxyl group and the carbon content of (II) indicate the *absence* of ring A. These facts suggest that in ergocalciferol 'ring B' is open between C-9 and C-10, and that (II) arises by scission of the molecule at a double bond in position 5,6, and can be an α,β-unsaturated aldehyde only if there is a double bond at 7,8 (these double bonds are also present in ergosterol). The isolation of the ketone (III) ($C_{19}H_{32}O$) confirms the presence of the double bond at 7,8 (Heilbron *et al.*, 1935).

The isolation of formaldehyde (IV) shows the presence of an exocyclic methylene group, and the presence of this group at C-10 is in keeping with the opening of ring B at 9,10. The formation of (V) ($C_{13}H_{20}O_3$), a keto-acid, suggests that ring B is open at 9,10, and that there are two double bonds at 7,8 and 22,23. The position of the latter double bond is confirmed by the isolation of methyliso-propylacetaldehyde (VI) [Heilbron *et al.*, 1936].

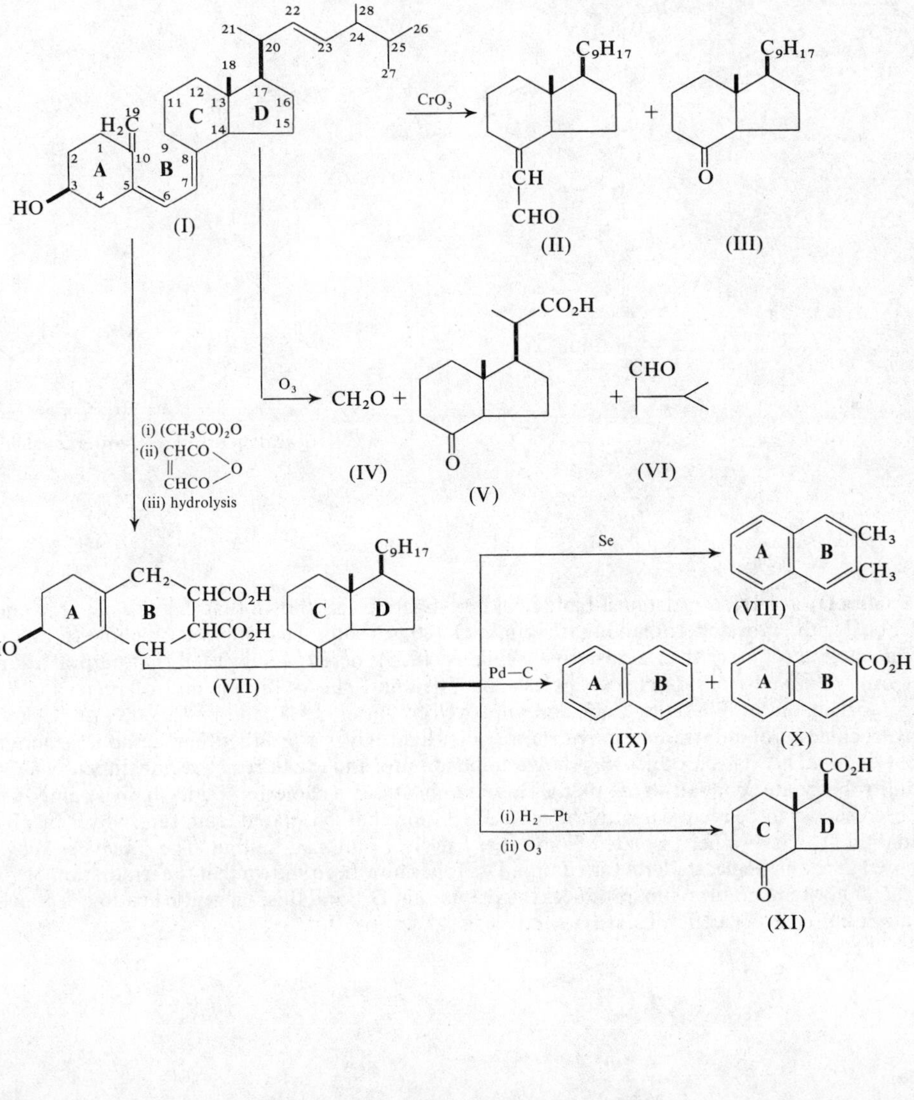

Structure (I) for ergocalciferol is also supported by the formation of (VII), the structure of which is shown by the products (VIII), (IX), (X) and (XI) [Windaus *et al.*, 1936]. The production of 2,3-dimethylnaphthalene (VIII) is in keeping with the fact that carboxyl groups sometimes give rise to methyl groups on selenium dehydrogenation (*cf.* **10** §2vii). Similarly, the formation of naphthalene (IX) and naphthalene-2-carboxylic acid (X) shows the presence of rings A and 'B' in (VII). Catalytic reduction of (VII) [to reduce the double bond in the *side-chain* only], followed by ozonolysis, gives (XI). Thus the formation of these compounds (VIII)–(XI) establishes the structure of (VII) and shows that the double bonds are at 5,6, 10,19 and 7,8.

The presence of the two double bonds 5,6 and 7,8 gives rise to the possibility of various geometrical isomeric forms for ergocalciferol. Ultraviolet spectroscopic studies (Braude *et al.*, 1955) and other work (§6) have led to the conclusion that ergocalciferol has the configuration shown in the chart in §11. This is further supported by Crowfoot *et al.* (1957), who examined the 4-iodo-3-nitrobenzoate by X-ray analysis.

Lythgoe *et al.* (1958) have carried out a partial synthesis of ergocalciferol from the aldehyde (II) as follows (R = C$_9$H$_{17}$):

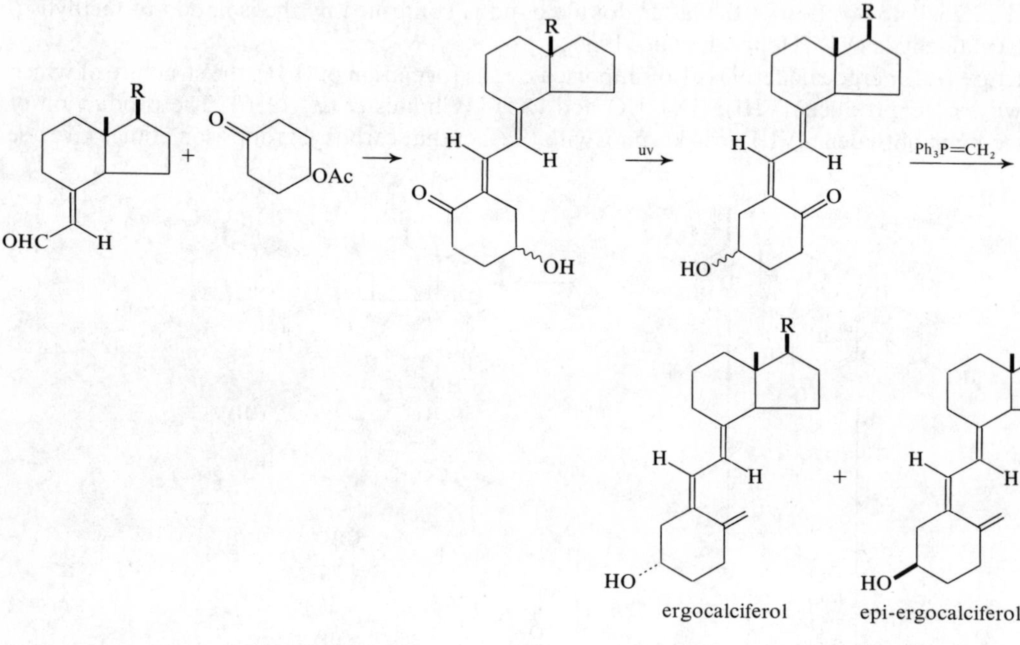

ergocalciferol   epi-ergocalciferol

§11b. Vitamins D$_3$ and D$_4$. A detailed biological investigation has shown that the vitamin D in cod-liver oil is not identical with ergocalciferol, and that vitamin D activity could be conferred on cholesterol, or on some impurity in cholesterol other than ergosterol. Windaus (1935) therefore suggested that natural vitamin D (in cod-liver oil) is derived from 7-dehydrocholesterol. The chart shows the method of preparing 7-dehydrocholesterol (originated by Windaus, 1935, and improved by Buser, 1947, and by Fieser *et al.*, 1950).

7-Dehydrocholesterol, on irradiation with ultraviolet light, gives a product that is about as active as ergocalciferol (vitamin D$_2$). This product was shown to be impure, and the pure active constituent was isolated as the 3,5-dinitrobenzoate (Windaus *et al.*, 1936). This vitamin D with a cholesterol side-chain is named **vitamin D$_3$**, and has been shown to be identical with the natural vitamin that is isolated from tunny-liver oil (Brockman, 1937). Vitamin D$_3$ has also been isolated from other fish-liver oils, *e.g.*, halibut. The *Chemical Society* (1951) has proposed the name **cholecalciferol** for vitamin D$_3$. It has now been shown that the irradiation of 7-dehydrocholesterol (at low temperature) first produces the previtamin D$_3$, and this, on gentle heating, is converted into the vitamin itself (*cf.* ergocalciferol, §11a).

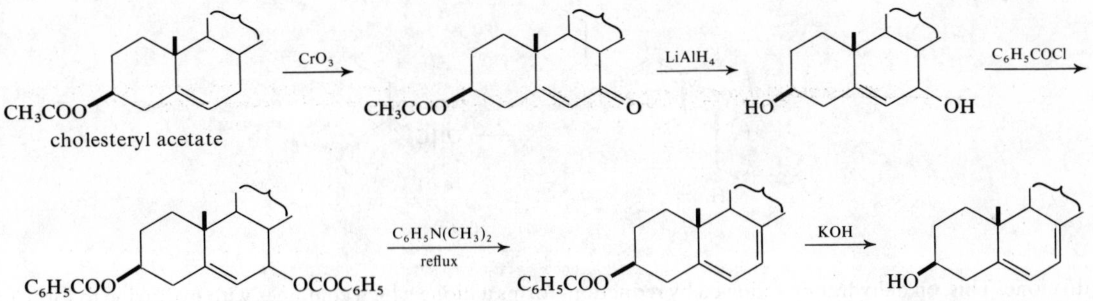

cholesteryl acetate

7-dehydrocholesterol

Irradiation of 22,23-dihydroergosterol gives a compound with antirachitic properties (Windaus *et al.*, 1937); this is known as **vitamin D$_4$**.

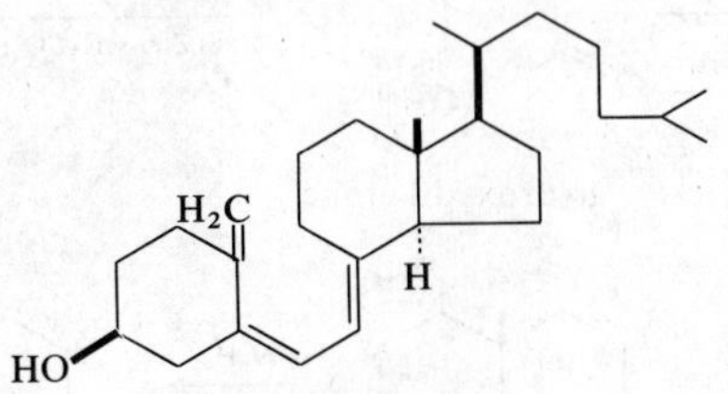

vitamin D$_3$
5,6-*cis*-cholecalciferol
m.p. 84–85°C, $[\alpha]_D$ +85°

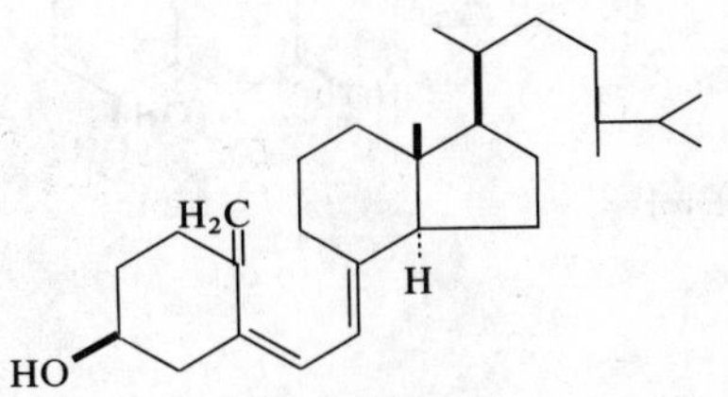

vitamin D$_4$
22,23-dihydro-5,6-*cis*-ergocalciferol
m.p. 107°C, $[\alpha]_D$ +89°

Several other vitamins of this group are also known: D$_5$, D$_6$ and D$_7$.

§12. Stigmasterol, C$_{29}$H$_{48}$O, m.p. 170°C, $[\alpha]_D$ −40°

This is best obtained from soya bean oil. Since stigmasterol forms an acetate, etc., a hydroxyl group is therefore present. Stigmasterol also forms a tetrabromide; thus it contains two double bonds. Hydrogenation of stigmasterol produces stigmastanol, C$_{29}$H$_{52}$O, and since the acetate of this gives the acetate of 3β-hydroxynor-5α-cholanic acid on oxidation with chromium trioxide, it follows that stigmastanol differs from 5α-cholestan-3β-ol only in the *nature* of the side-chain (Fernholz *et al.*, 1934; *cf.* ergosterol, §10). Ozonolysis of stigmasterol gives, among other products, ethylisopropylacetaldehyde (Guiteras, 1933). This suggests that the side-chain is as shown in (I), with a double bond at 22,23.

Thus the final problem is to ascertain the position of the second double bond in stigmasterol. This has been

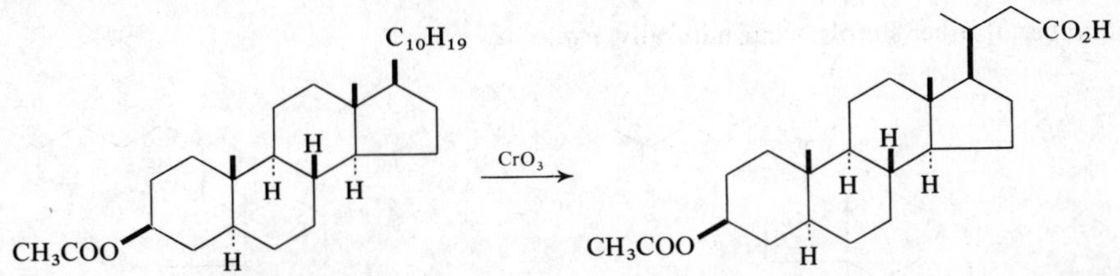

stigmastanyl acetate

acetate of 3α-hydroxynor-5α-cholanic acid

shown to be 5,6 by the method used for cholesterol (Fernholz, 1934). Stigmasterol, on hydroxylation with hydrogen peroxide in acetic acid, gives a triol which, on oxidation with chromium trioxide, forms a hydroxy-

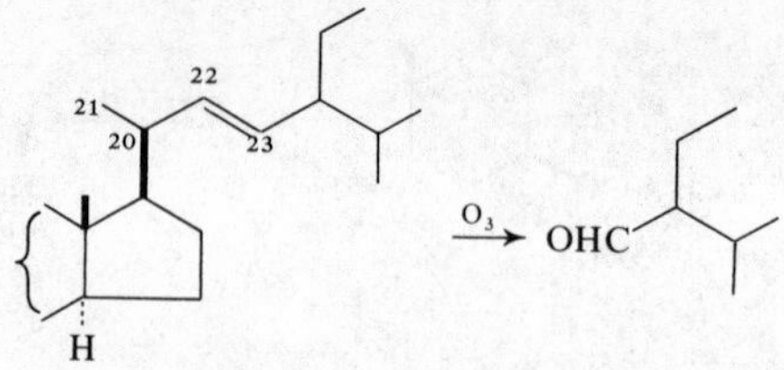

(I)

diketone. This, on dehydration followed by reduction, forms a dione which combines with hydrazine to form a pyridazine derivative. These reactions can be explained as follows (*cf.* cholesterol, §3ii):

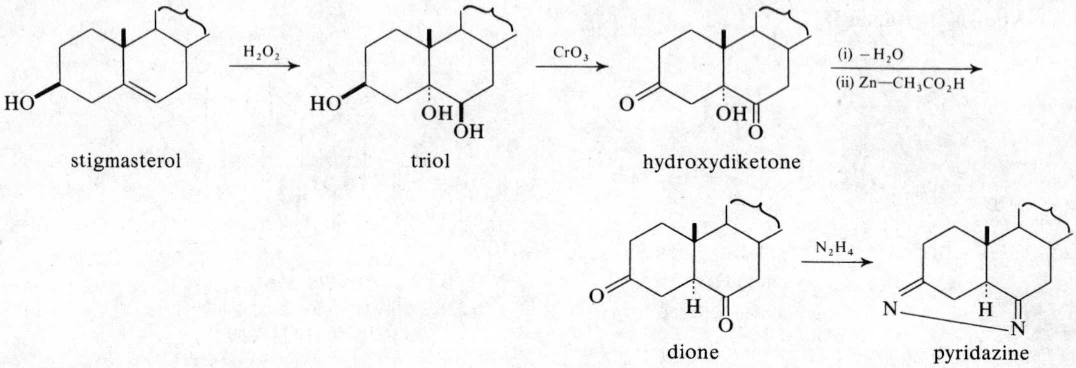

This position for the nuclear double bond is supported by other evidence. Also, the infrared spectrum of stigmasterol showed a band at 970 cm^{-1}. Hence, the 22,23-double bond has the *trans*-configuration (see Table 1.6). Thus stigmasterol has the structure shown.

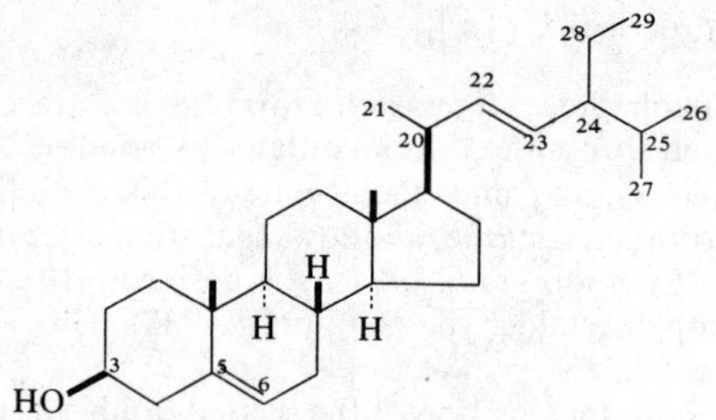

stigmasterol

A large number of other sterols occur naturally, *e.g.*,

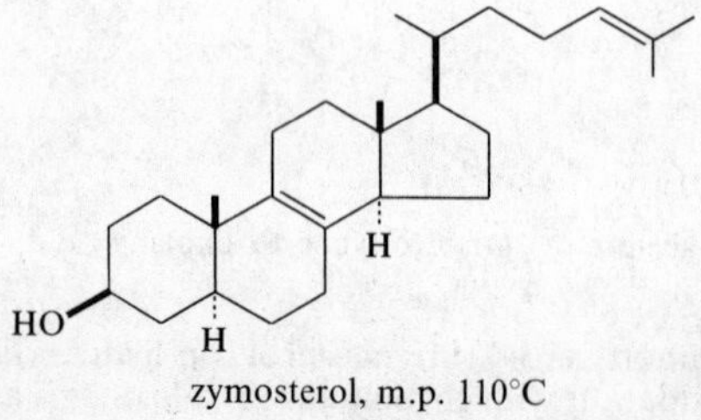

zymosterol, m.p. 110°C

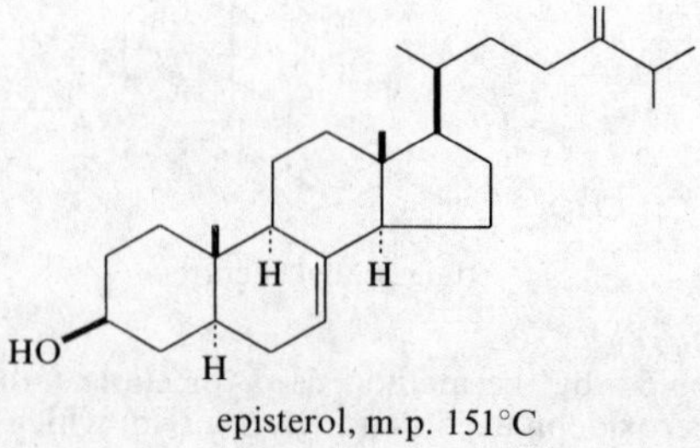

episterol, m.p. 151°C

lophenol, m.p. 151°C

brassicasterol, m.p. 148°C

Cephalosporin P$_1$. This is an antibiotic produced by a strain of *Cephalosporium*. Burton *et al.* (1956) showed it to be a tetracyclic monocarboxylic acid, $C_{32}H_{48}O_8$, m.p. 147°C, and that it was possibly a steroid, the parent skeleton containing 28 carbon atoms. It was also shown to be a tetrasubstituted α,β-unsaturated acid that contained two hydroxyl groups and two acetoxyl groups, one of which was readily removed by hydrolysis. One isolated double bond was also present. Further chemical work by Jones *et al.* (1961) showed the presence of an isopropylidene group; ozonolysis of the methyl ester gave acetone. The NMR spectrum of this ester showed a signal at τ 4·87, but this was absent in the NMR spectrum of dihydro-cephalosporin P$_1$ methyl ester. Furthermore, since this dihydro-compound still contained the α,β-unsaturated ester grouping, it therefore follows that cephalosporin P$_1$ contains a side-chain terminating in the grouping —CH=CMe$_2$. These authors proposed a structure based on further chemical evidence. The molecular formula $C_{32}H_{48}O_8$ (given above) had been determined by X-ray analysis. Jones *et al.* (1963), on the basis that fusidic acid (II), $C_{31}H_{48}O_6$, m.p. 192°C, a steroidal antibiotic similar to cephalosporin P$_1$, had a C_{29} carbon skeleton, redetermined the molecular weight of cephalosporin P$_1$ (as methyl ester) by mass spectrometry and now obtained the molecular formula $C_{33}H_{50}O_8$.

Helvolic acid (III), $C_{33}H_{44}O_8$, m.p. 215°C, an antibiotic produced by *Aspergillus fumigatus*, had been assigned a structure by Allinger *et al.* (1956, 1961) based on chemical work. Melera (1963) examined the NMR spectra of the methyl esters of fusidic acid, helvolic acid and cephalosporin P$_1$, and concluded that all three compounds had very closely similar structures, and pointed out that in helvolic acid and cephalosporin P$_1$ the additional carbon was present as an angular methyl group.

Jones *et al.* (1966) now re-examined the NMR spectrum of the methyl ester of cephalosporin P$_1$, and on the basis of their earlier chemical work (see above), on their interpretation of the NMR spectrum, and on the knowledge of the accepted structure of fusidic acid (Godtfredsen *et al.*, 1965), proposed (IV) as the structure of cephalosporin P$_1$ (but not the complete stereochemistry).

Oxley (1966), by chemical work and NMR spectral studies, deduced the stereochemistry of the

fusidic acid
(II)

helvolic acid
(III)

hydroxyl and acetoxyl groups in ring B of (IV). Further work by Chou *et al.* (1967) have confirmed (IV) as the structure of cephalosporin P_1.

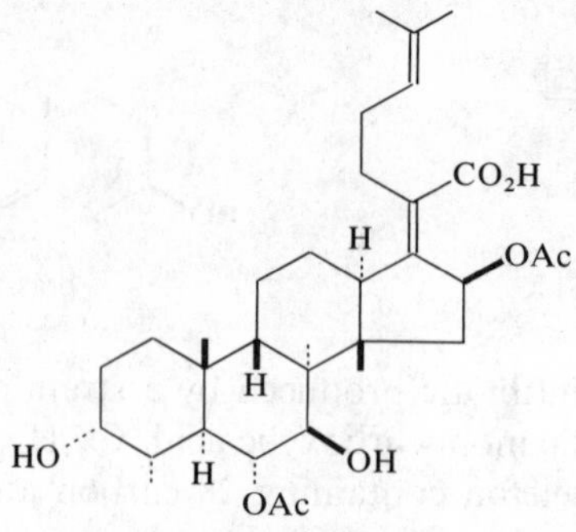

cephalosporin P_1
(IV)

Acansterol. This has been obtained by the preparative gas chromatography of the sterol portion of *Acanthaster planci*, and structure (V) has been assigned to it by Djerassi *et al.* (1971) based on spectral and chemical evidence.

The mass spectrum showed the molecular ion M^+ 426·3728. This corresponds to the molecular formula $C_{30}H_{50}O$ (this required M^+ 426·3861). There was also a peak at $M - CH_3$ 411·35937 (this required 411·36267). The compound had a m.p. 179–180°C and its infrared spectrum showed a band at 3 375 cm^{-1} which is typical of 7,8-unsaturated sterols. It also gave a positive Liebermann–Burchard reaction (see §3) and could be precipitated with digitonin; this is characteristic of 3β-hydroxysteroids (§3). The mass spectrum showed peaks at m/e 299–301, 271–273, 255–257, 231; these are characteristic of ring D fission (§4). Also present were the ions m/e 213 (231 − H_2O) characteristic of a steroidal nucleus with an unsaturated side-chain, m/e 411 ($M - CH_3$), m/e 383 ($M - C_3H_7$), m/e 355 ($M - C_5H_{11}$), m/e 326 ($M - C_7H_{16}$), and m/e 312 ($M - C_8H_{18}$) characteristic of the gorgosterol side-chain. The NMR spectrum (C_6D_6, 100 MHz) showed the presence of

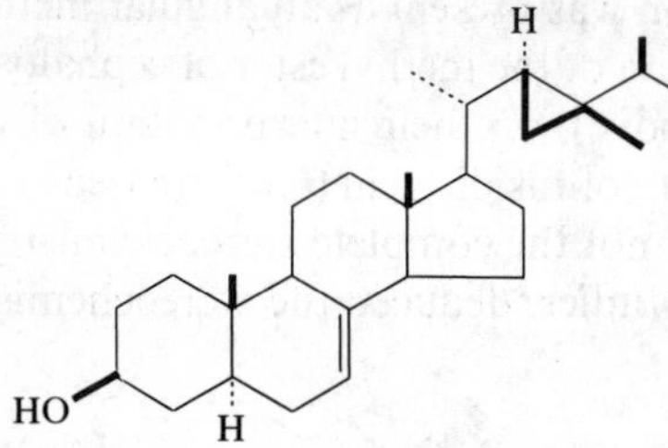

acansterol
(V)

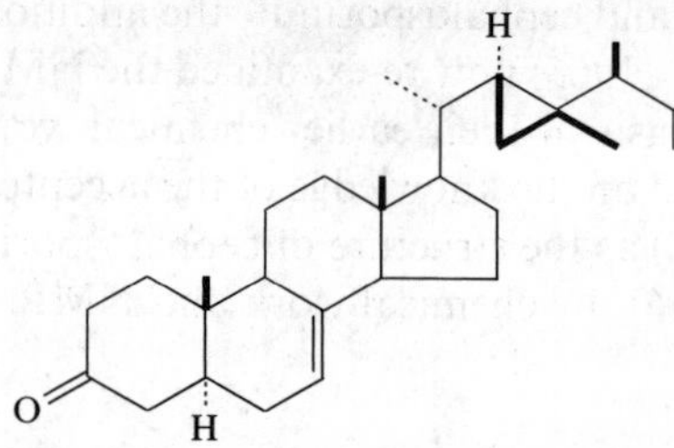

acansterone
(VI)

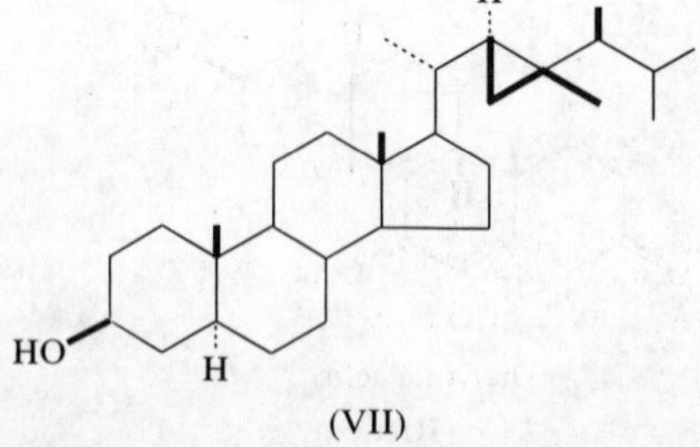

(VII)

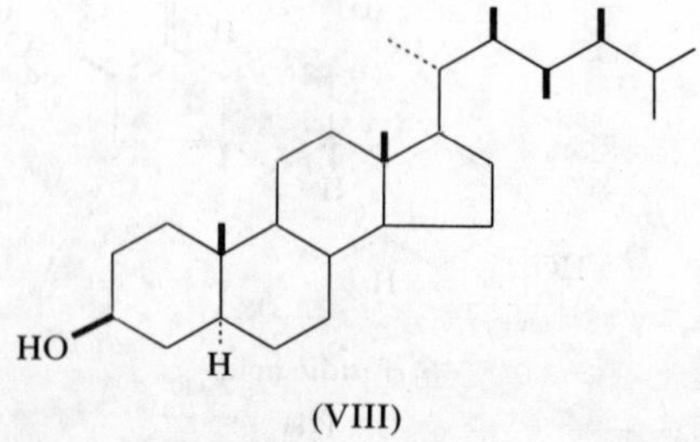

(VIII)

three quaternary methyl groups (τ 9·16, 9·03, and 8·87; all singlets), one isopropyl group (τ 8·89, d, J 6·0 Hz), two superimposed secondary methyl groups (τ 8·77, d, J 7 Hz), a secondary carbinol methine (τ 6·45, m), and an ethylenic proton (τ 4·51, dt). Other signals were at τ 9·89 (d,d), 9·70–9·50 (m), and 9·30 (d,d). As a result of decoupling experiments, it was believed that the protons were on a cyclopropane ring and that they had the same relationship to each other as in gorgosterol.

Oxidation of acansterol (V) with chromium trioxide in pyridine gave acansterone (VI). This had m.p. 192–194°C, m/e 424 ($M - H_2$), and a band at 1 705 cm^{-1} in its infrared spectrum (this corresponds to a carbonyl group). Since (VI) was transparent in the ultraviolet region and showed no base shift, it was therefore not a β,γ-unsaturated ketone. (VI) also showed the same fragmentation pattern as the parent sterol, but all peaks had shifted to lower mass-units by two. Furthermore, the ORD curve of (VI) was similar to that of ergost-7,8-en-3-one (see §10).

Prolonged catalytic hydrogenation (Pt) of (V) produced the dihydro-derivative (VII) and the tetrahydro-derivative (VIII). (VII), M^+ 428, showed identical GLC retention times and mass spectra to those of dihydrogorgosterol, whereas the mass spectrum of (VIII) showed M^+ 430, m/e 387 ($M - C_3H_7$), 359 ($M - C_5H_{11}$), 331 ($M - C_7H_{15}$), and 303 ($M - C_9H_{19}$), which suggested the presence of a C_{11} side-chain carrying methyl groups at every carbon atom (of the side-chain). All these data support (V) as the structure of acansterol.

§13. Biosynthesis of sterols

It has long been known that animals can synthesise cholesterol, but the possible pathways were unknown until biosynthetic cholesterol was prepared from acetic acid labelled isotopically (with ^{14}C) in either the methyl or the carboxyl group, or labelled in both groups ($^{13}CH_3{}^{14}CO_2H$). These tracer studies were carried out mainly by Bloch *et al.* (1942–) and by Cornforth *et al.* (1953–), and the results established that the distribution of the carbon atoms is as shown in (I), in which carbon atoms derived from the methyl group of acetic acid are indicated by dots. Thus acetic acid can be regarded as the fundamental unit. Evidence was also obtained that isovaleric acid can serve as a precursor for cholesterol, and then Tavormina *et al.* (1956), using labelled mevalonic acid (MVA), showed that this is converted almost completely into cholesterol by rat liver; the route from acetic acid to MVA has been described in **8** §34. The problem now is to discover the route whereby MVA is converted into cholesterol. As far back as 1926 Heilbron *et al.* suggested that squalene (**8** §33) is a precursor of cholesterol, and Robinson (1934) proposed a scheme for the cyclisation of the squalene molecule with the loss of three methyl groups. Biosynthetic experiments have established that squalene is produced by the linkage of two farnesyl residues joined tail to tail (**8** §34) and that the methyl group distribution is as shown in (II). Cyclisation with loss of the three methyl groups (indicated by broken lines) proposed by Robinson (*before* the labelled

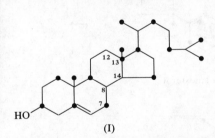

(I)

(II) ⟶ (III)

distribution in cholesterol was known) was formulated as (II) → (III). Comparison of formula (III) with (I) shows that the former is incorrectly labelled at C-7, C-8, C-12, and C-13. Furthermore, since Bloch *et al.* (1952) showed experimentally that squalene is a precursor of cholesterol, the Robinson scheme of cyclisation is untenable. Woodward *et al.* (1953), however, suggested that squalene is first cyclised to lanosterol, and then this loses three methyl groups to give cholesterol. Furthermore, Bloch *et al.* (1955) showed that lanosterol is converted into cholesterol in rats, and in 1956 carried out the biosynthesis of lanosterol from labelled acetate. Thus we have evidence for the suggested route from squalene to cholesterol. As mentioned above, Woodward *et al.* (1953) suggested that squalene ring-closes to form lanosterol, and proposed a 1,3-shift of the methyl group at C-8 to C-13. On the other hand, Ruzicka *et al.* (1955) and Bloch *et al.* (1957) proposed a 1,2-shift of the methyl group from C-14 to C-13 and another 1,2-shift from C-8 to C-14. Further work by Bloch *et al.* (1958) showed that the 1,2-shifts were correct; this is supported by the work of Cornforth *et al.*

(IIa)   (IV)

(V)   lanosterol

(I)
cholesterol

(1958). Also, van Tamelen *et al.* (1966, 1967) and Corey *et al.* (1967) have now shown that 2,3-epoxy-squalene is an intermediate in the conversion of squalene into lanosterol. The various steps (under the influence of the appropriate enzymes) are believed to be as shown.

In the conversion of lanosterol into cholesterol, the methyl groups at C-4′, 4′, and 14 are removed. Bloch *et al.* (1957) assumed these were eliminated as carbon dioxide *via* oxidation to carboxyl groups, the C-14 methyl group being removed first. There is now a great deal of evidence to support this sequence and for the removal of the C-4′ and 4′ methyl groups, but Barton *et al.* (1971, 1972) have shown that the C-14 methyl group is removed as formic acid *via* oxidation to the aldehyde. It is believed that (VI) is formed from lanosterol; this involves migration of the double bond from 8,9 to 7,8, oxidation of the CH_3 at C-14 to CH_2OH, and saturation of the double bond at 24,25 (R = —$CHMe(CH_2)_3CHMe_2$).

The biosynthesis of ergosterol from acetate has been carried out by Bloch *et al.* (1951), and the distribution pattern corresponds to that of cholesterol. Hanahan *et al.* (1953) showed that, except for CH_3-28, the carbon skeleton of ergosterol appears to be formed from the cyclisation of squalene. The carbon atom that produces CH_3-28, however, arises by an independent route. It has been found that formate and, better still, methionine (an amino-acid) are sources of CH_3-28.

Bile acids

§14. Introduction

The bile acids occur in bile (a secretion of the liver which is stored in the gall-bladder) of most animals combined as amides with either glycine ($NH_2CH_2CO_2H$) or taurine ($NH_2CH_2CH_2SO_3H$), *e.g.*, glycocholic acid (= glycine + cholic acid), taurocholic acid (= taurine + cholic acid). The

5β-cholanic acid
(cholanic acid)

5α-cholanic acid
(allocholanic acid)

bile acids are present as sodium salts, and they function as emulsifying agents in the intestinal tract, *e.g.*, fats, which are insoluble in water, are rendered 'soluble', and so may be absorbed in the intestine.

Most of the bile acids are hydroxy-derivatives of either 5β-cholanic acid or 5α-cholanic acid. Dehydration of a bile acid by heating in a vacuum, followed by catalytic reduction, gives either 5β-cholanic or 5α-cholanic acid.

About twenty natural bile acids have been characterised, and many others are synthetic. The positions of the hydroxyl groups are any of the following: 3, 6, 7, 11, 12 and 23, and in almost all of the natural bile acids the configurations of the hydroxyl groups are α (see §5). Some of the more important natural bile acids are:

Name	M.p. °C	Hydroxyl groups	Source	[α]_D °
Cholic acid	195	3α, 7α, 12α	Man, ox	+37
Deoxycholic acid	172	3α, 12α	Man, ox	+53
Lithocholic acid	186	3α	Man, ox	+32
Chenodeoxycholic acid	140	3α, 7α	Man, ox, hen	+11
α-Hyodeoxycholic acid	197	3α, 6α	Pig	+8

§15. The structures of 5β-cholanic acid (cholanic acid) and 5α-cholanic acid (allocholanic acid).

These acids may be derived from 5β-cholestane (coprostane) and 5α-cholestane, respectively, as follows (cf. §5). At the same time, these reactions show the relationship between the bile acids and the sterols (Windaus, 1919).

5β-Cholanic acid, m.p. 164°C, [α]_D +22°

cholesterol → (Oppenauer oxidation) → cholest-4-en-3-one → (H₂—Pt) → 5β-cholestan-3β-ol (coprostanol) → (i) CrO₃ (ii) Zn—Hg/HCl

5β-cholestane (coprostane) → (CrO₃) → 5β-cholanic acid

5α-Cholanic acid, m.p. 173°C, [α]_D +22°

cholesterol → (H₂—Pt) → 5α-cholestan-3β-ol → (CrO₃) → 5α-cholestan-3-one → (Zn—Hg HCl)

5α-cholestane → (CrO₃) → 5α-cholanic acid

§16. Structure of the bile acids

Since all the bile acids can be converted into either of the cholanic acids, the former are therefore hydroxy-derivatives of the latter, *e.g.*, lithocholic acid can be converted into 5β-cholanic acid as follows:

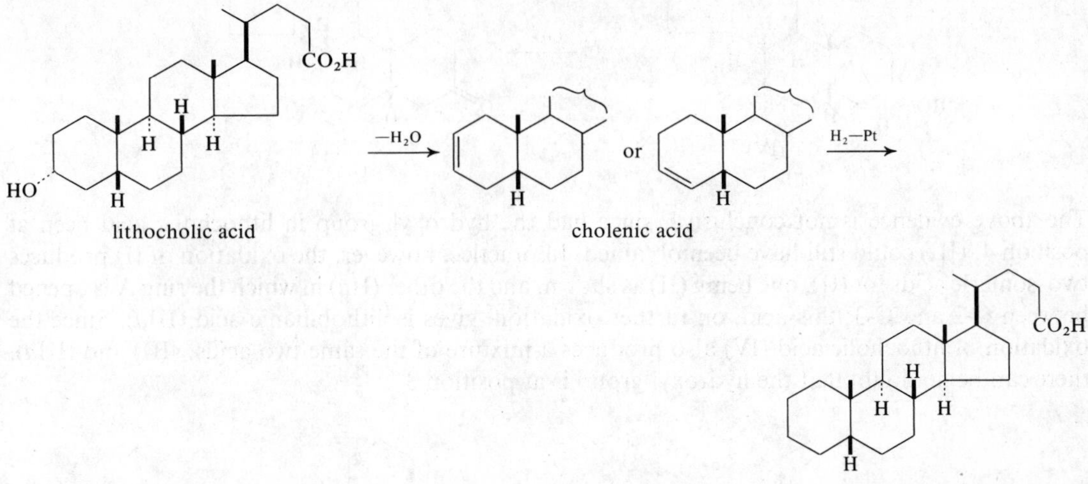

lithocholic acid   cholenic acid

5β-cholanic acid

According to Fieser *et al.* (1955), cholenic acid is a mixture of the two compounds shown, the chol-3-enic acid being the main constituent.

The positions of the hydroxyl groups in the bile acids have been determined by means of oxidative degradation, *e.g.*, the position of the hydroxyl group in lithocholic acid is shown to be at 3 as follows. Cholesterol can be converted into 5β-cholestan-3β-ol (I) which, on oxidation with chromium trioxide, forms a ketone and this, when oxidised with nitric acid, gives a dicarboxylic acid (II). (II), on further oxidation with nitric acid, produces the tricarboxylic acid, lithobilianic acid (III). Lithocholic acid (IV), on oxidation with chromium trioxide, forms dehydrolithocholic acid (V) and this, when oxidised with nitric acid, forms (III). It therefore follows that the hydroxyl group in lithocholic acid is probably in the same position as in 5β-cholestan-3β-ol, *viz.*, position 3. Thus:

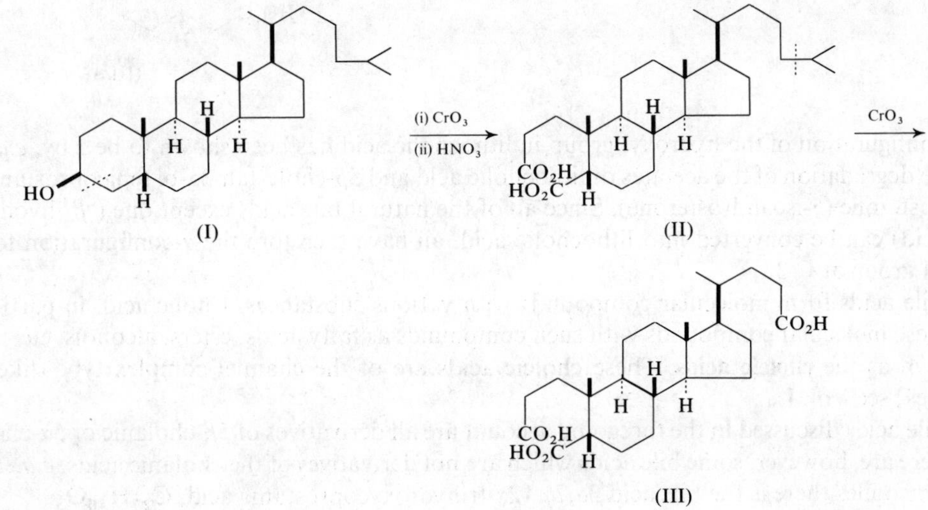

(I)   (II)

(III)

(IV)   (V)

The above evidence is not conclusive, since had the hydroxyl group in lithocholic acid been at position 4, (III) could still have been obtained. In practice, however, the oxidation of (I) produces two isomeric acids for (II), one being (II) as shown, and the other (II*a*) in which the ring A is opened between C-2 and C-3; this acid, on further oxidation, gives isolithobilianic acid (III*a*). Since the oxidation of lithocholic acid (IV) also produces a mixture of the same two acids, (III) and (III*a*), there can be no doubt that the hydroxyl group is at position 3.

(I)   (II*a*)

(III*a*)

The configuration of the hydroxyl group in lithocholic acid has been shown to be α by, *e.g.*, the oxidative degradation of the acetates of lithocholic acid and 5β-cholestan-3α-ol (epicoprostanol) to 5β-androsterone (5-isoandrosterone). Since all of the natural bile acids except one ('β' hyodeoxy-cholic acid) can be converted into lithocholic acid, all have therefore the α-configuration for the hydroxyl group at C-3.

The bile acids form molecular compounds with various substances. Cholic acid, in particular, forms these molecular compounds with such compounds as fatty acids, esters, alcohols, etc.; these are known as the **choleic acids**. These choleic acids are of the channel complex type (like urea complexes; see Vol. I).

The bile acids discussed in the foregoing account are all derivatives of 5β-cholanic or 5α-cholanic acid. There are, however, some bile acids which are not derivatives of the cholanic acids, *e.g.*, in the bile of crocodiles there is the bile acid 3α,7α,12α-trihydroxycoprostanic acid, $C_{27}H_{46}O_5$.

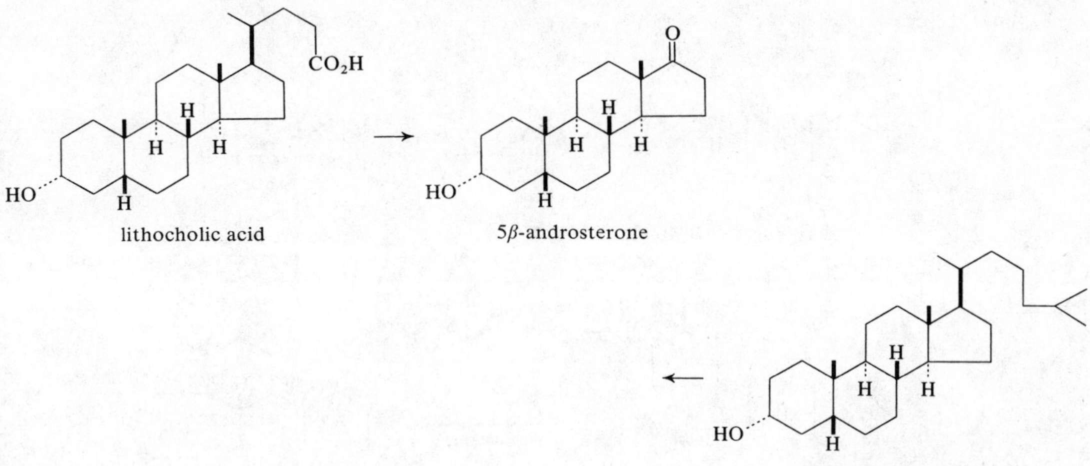

lithocholic acid

5β-androsterone

5β-cholestan-3α-ol

Steroid hormones

§17. Introduction

Hormones are substances which are secreted by the ductless glands, and only minute amounts are necessary to produce the various physiological reactions in the body. As a group, hormones do not resemble one another chemically, and their classification is based on their physiological activity. The sex hormones belong to the steroid class of compounds, and are produced in the gonads (testes in the male, and ovaries in the female). Their activity appears to be controlled by the hormones that are produced in the anterior lobe of the pituitary gland. Because of this, the sex hormones are sometimes called the secondary sex hormones, and the hormones of the anterior lobe of the pituitary (which are protein in nature) are called the primary sex hormones.

The sex hormones are of three types: the **androgens** (male hormones), the **oestrogens** (female or follicular hormones) and **gestogens** (the corpus luteum hormones). The sex hormones are responsible for the sexual processes, and for the secondary characteristics which differentiate males from females.

ANDROGENS

§18. Androsterone, $C_{19}H_{30}O_2$, m.p. 183°C, $[\alpha]_D$ +94°

It was first isolated by Butenandt *et al.* (1931) from male urine (about 15 mg from 15 000 litres of urine). Androsterone behaves as a saturated compound, and since it forms mono-esters, *one* oxygen atom is present as a hydroxyl group. The functional nature of the other oxygen atom was shown to be oxo, since androsterone forms an oxime, etc. The parent hydrocarbon of androsterone, $C_{19}H_{30}O_2$, is therefore $C_{19}H_{32}$, and since this corresponds to the general formula C_nH_{2n-6}, the molecule is tetracyclic (D.B.E. of $C_{19}H_{30}O_2 = 19 + 1 - 30/2 = 5$; 1 double bond due to C=O, and so there are four rings). This led to the suggestion that androsterone probably contains the steroid nucleus, and since it is a hydroxyketone, it was thought that it is possibly related to oestrone (§20). Butenandt (1932) therefore proposed a structure which was proved correct by Ruzicka (1934) as follows.

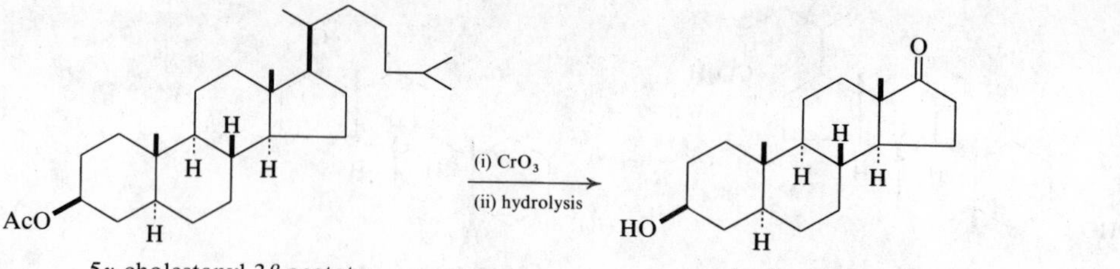

5α-cholestanyl 3β-acetate

$\xrightarrow[\text{(ii) hydrolysis}]{\text{(i) CrO}_3}$

epiandrosterone

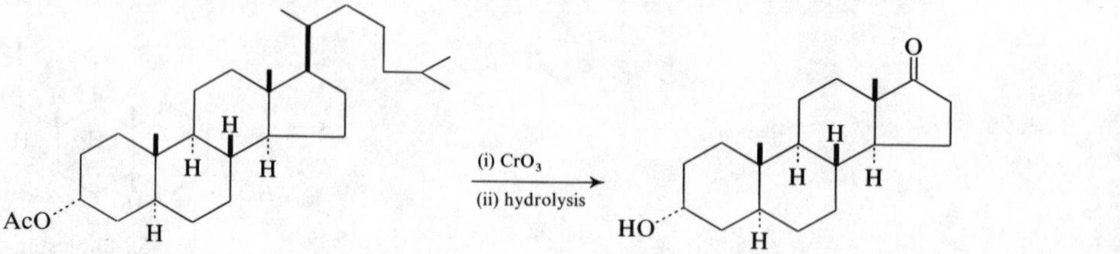

5α-cholestanyl 3α-acetate

$\xrightarrow[\text{(ii) hydrolysis}]{\text{(i) CrO}_3}$

androsterone

Ruzicka oxidised 5β-cholestanyl 3β-acetate with chromium trioxide in acetic acid to **epiandrosterone**, a hydroxyketone with the structure proposed for androsterone by Butenandt. When, however, 5α-cholestanyl 3α-acetate was oxidised, the product was androsterone. Thus the configuration of the hydroxyl group at C-3 is α and not β as Butenandt suggested. Epiandrosterone (formerly known as isoandrosterone), m.p. 174°C, $[\alpha]_D$ +88°, has about one-eighth of the activity of androsterone (see also §5).

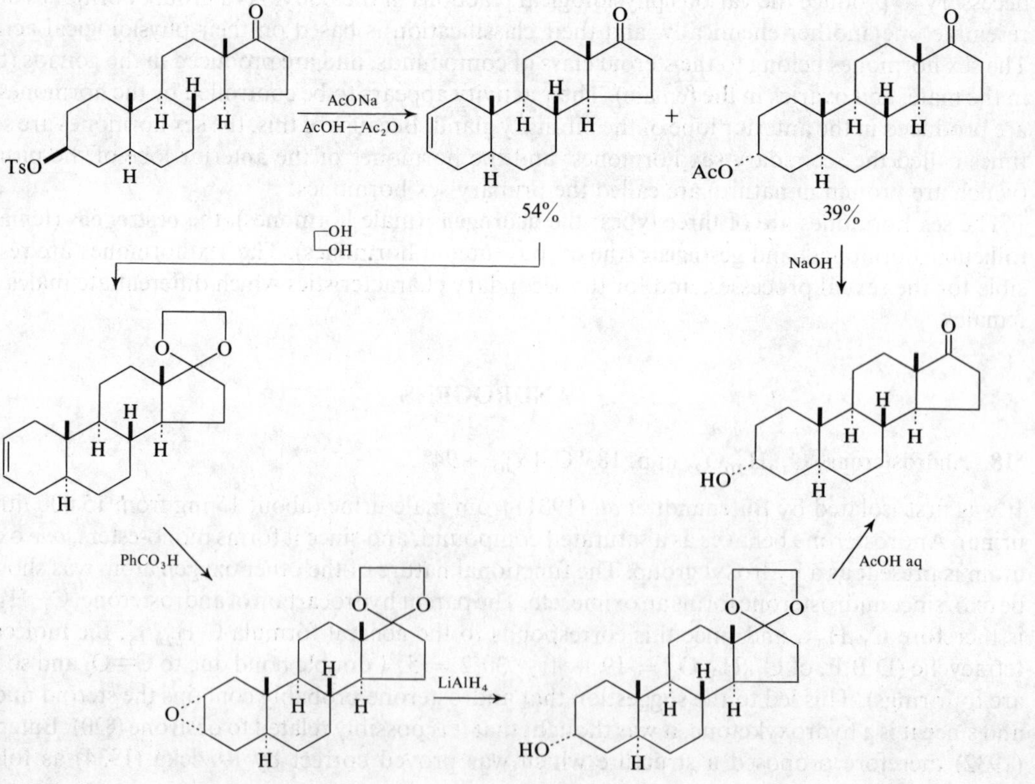

$\xrightarrow[\text{AcOH—Ac}_2\text{O}]{\text{AcONa}}$

54%

+

39%

Sondheimer *et al.* (1955) have converted epiandrosterone into androsterone, starting with epiandrosterone *p*-toluenesulphonate (*cf.* tosyl esters of sugars, 7 §9).

A convenient preparation of androsterone starts from dehydroepiandrosterone (Caglioti *et al.*, 1964).

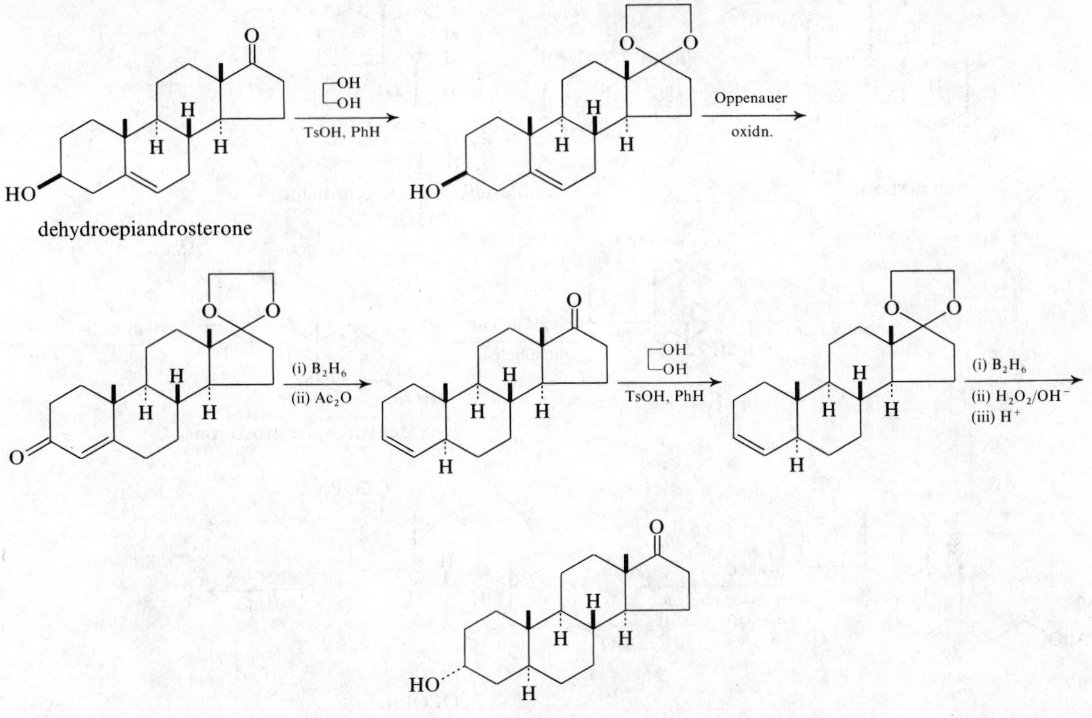

dehydroepiandrosterone

androsterone

A total synthesis of androsterone has been carried out by Woodward *et al.* (1952); they used the ester (XXIII) in the synthesis of cholesterol (§9).

Soon after the discovery of androsterone, Butenandt *et al.* (1934) isolated two other hormones from male urine, 5β-androsterone and dehydroepiandrosterone. Then Laqueur (1935) isolated the hormone testosterone from steer testes (10 mg from 100 kg of testes).

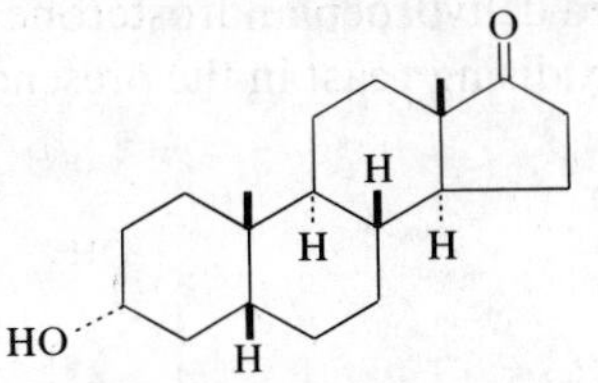

5β-androsterone
m.p. 151°C, [α]_D +105°

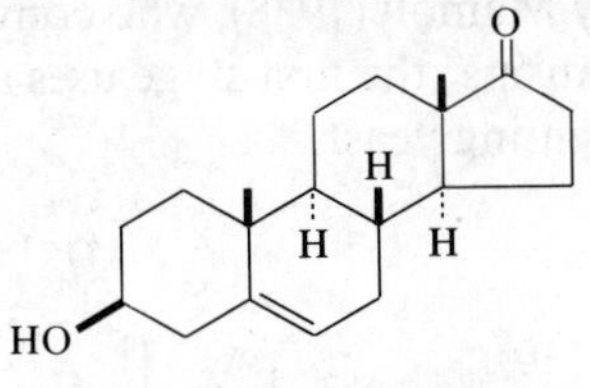

dehydroepiandrosterone
m.p. 153°C, [α]_D +11°

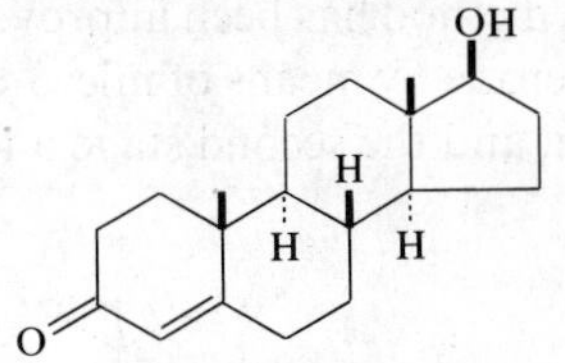

testosterone

§19. Testosterone, $C_{19}H_{28}O_2$, m.p. 155°C, [α]_D +109°, λ_{max} 240 nm

Testosterone has been produced commercially by the following method of Butenandt (1935) and Ruzicka (1935); the Oppenauer oxidation step in this method was introduced by Oppenauer (1937).

This preparation of testosterone establishes the structure of this hormone which had been shown to contain one hydroxyl group and an α,β-unsaturated ketone group.

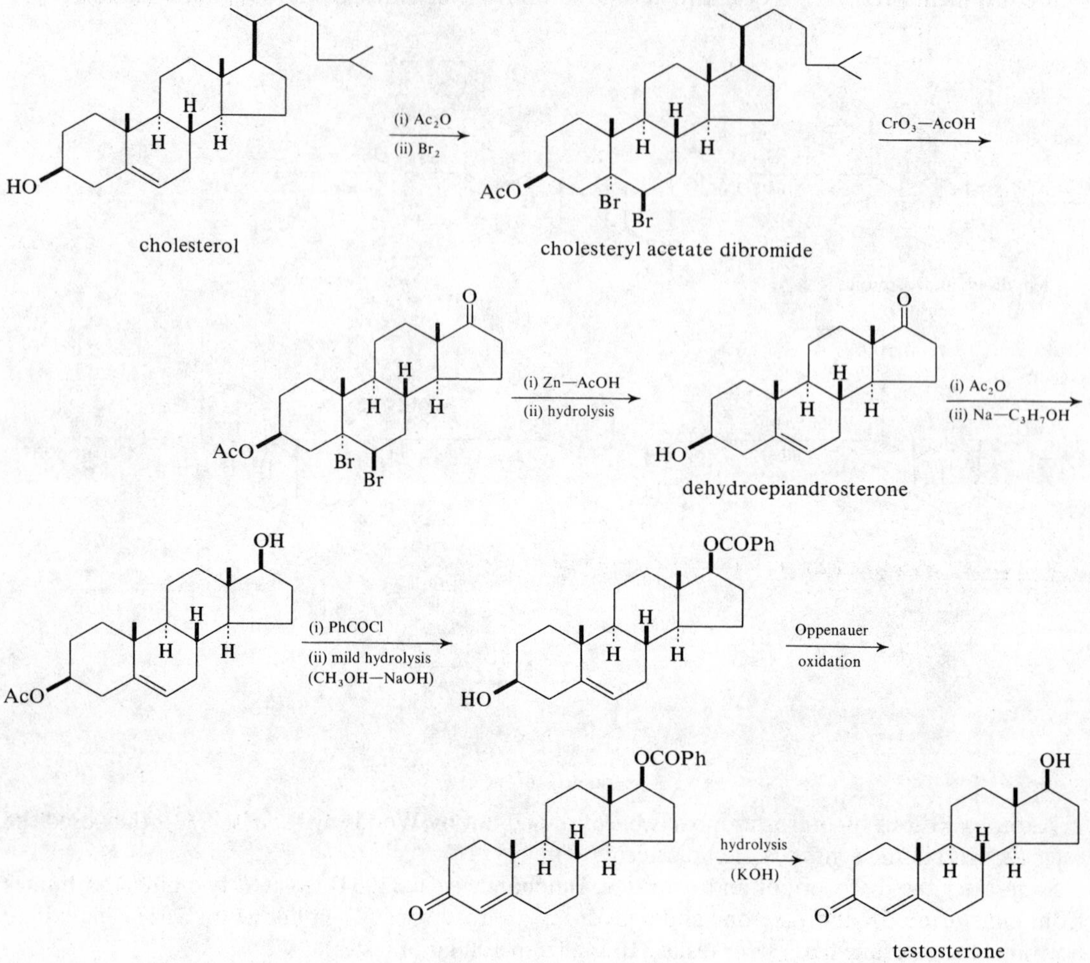

cholesterol

(i) Ac$_2$O
(ii) Br$_2$

cholesteryl acetate dibromide

CrO$_3$—AcOH

(i) Zn—AcOH
(ii) hydrolysis

dehydroepiandrosterone

(i) Ac$_2$O
(ii) Na—C$_3$H$_7$OH

(i) PhCOCl
(ii) mild hydrolysis
(CH$_3$OH—NaOH)

Oppenauer
oxidation

hydrolysis
(KOH)

testosterone

This method has been improved by Mamoli (1938), who converted dehydroepiandrosterone into testosterone by means of micro-organisms; the first stage uses an oxidising yeast in the presence of oxygen, and the second stage a fermenting yeast.

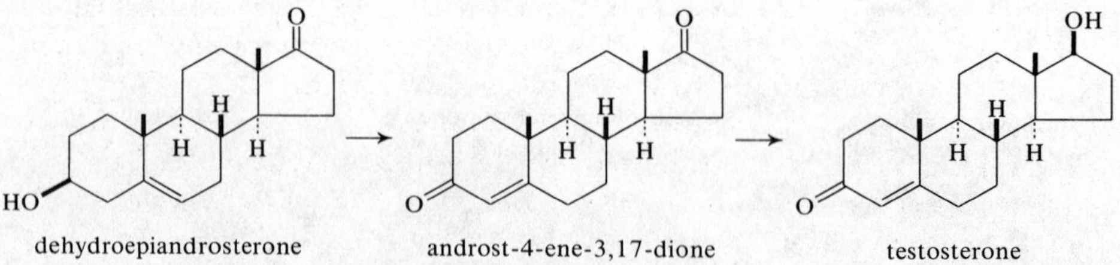

dehydroepiandrosterone   androst-4-ene-3,17-dione   testosterone

Elisberg *et al.* (1952) have shown that sodium borohydride selectively reduces the 3-keto group in the presence of others at 11, 12, 17 or 20. On the other hand, Norymberski *et al.* (1954) have shown that if there is a double bond in position 4,5, then the keto group at 17 or 20 is preferentially reduced to that at 3. Thus androst-4-ene-3,17-dione is reduced to testosterone by sodium borohydride. Johnson *et al.* (1960) have adapted Johnson's synthesis of equilenin (§17) to provide an improved synthesis of testosterone.

The stereochemisty of testosterone, except for the configuration of the hydroxyl group at C-17, is established by its preparation from cholesterol. The C-17 hydroxyl group was shown to have the β-configuration by molecular rotation measurements and by the examination of the rates of hydrolysis of various testosterone esters.

It appears that testosterone is the real male sex hormone in the body; the others are metabolic products of testosterone. The ketonic steroids are separated from the non-ketonic steroids (all from urine) by means of Girard's reagents (P and T); the ketonic compounds form *soluble* derivatives, and

$$Cl^-\{Me_3\overset{+}{N}CH_2CONHNH_2 \qquad Cl^-\{C_5H_5\overset{+}{N}CH_2CONHNH_2$$
reagent T   reagent P

may be regenerated by hydrolysis (see also Vol. I). Many other hormones have also been isolated from urine (see also §22).

Many commercial preparations are now carried out by means of microbiological transformations. The more important ones in steroid chemistry include *oxidations* (oxidation of alcohols, hydroxylation, epoxidation, dehydrogenation); *reductions* (carbonyl to hydroxyl, saturation of an ethylenic double bond); *esterification and hydrolysis*; *isomerisations*; *resolution of* (±)-modfications.

Mamoli's method described above has now been replaced by more efficient non-microbiological methods.

OESTROGENS

§20. Oestrone (estrone)

It has been known for a long time that there are hormones which control the uterine cycle, but it was not until 1929 that Butenandt and Doisy independently isolated the active substance **oestrone** from the urine of pregnant women. Oestrone is the first known member of the sex hormones, and soon after its discovery two other hormones were isolated, oestriol and oestradiol.

(+)-Oestrone, m.p. 259°C, $[\alpha]_D$ +170°, has the molecular formula $C_{18}H_{22}O_2$. It behaves as a ketone (forms an oxime, etc.), and contains one hydroxyl group (it forms a monoacetate and a monomethyl ether). Furthermore, this hydroxyl group is *phenolic*, since oestrone couples with diazonium salts in alkaline solution (this reaction is typical of phenols). When distilled with zinc dust, oestrone forms chrysene; this led to the suggestion that oestrone is related to the steroids (*cf.* §1). The X-ray analysis of oestrone also indicates the presence of the steroid nucleus, and at the same time showed that the keto group and the hydroxyl group are at the opposite ends of the molecule (Bernal, 1932). On catalytic hydrogenation, oestrone forms octahydrooestrone, $C_{18}H_{30}O_2$. This compound contains two hydroxyl groups (two hydrogen atoms are used for converting the keto group to an alcoholic group), and so six hydrogen atoms are used to saturate *three* double bonds. If these three double bonds are in one ring, *i.e.*, there is a benzenoid ring present, then the phenolic hydroxyl group can be accounted for. The presence of one benzene ring in the structure of oestrone is supported by measurements of the molecular refraction and the ultraviolet absorption spectrum (λ_{max} 280 nm).

When the methyl ether of oestrone is subjected to the Wolff–Kishner reduction, and the product distilled with selenium, 7-methoxy-1,2-cyclopentenophenanthrene is formed. The structure of this compound was established by the following synthesis (Cook *et al.*, 1934):

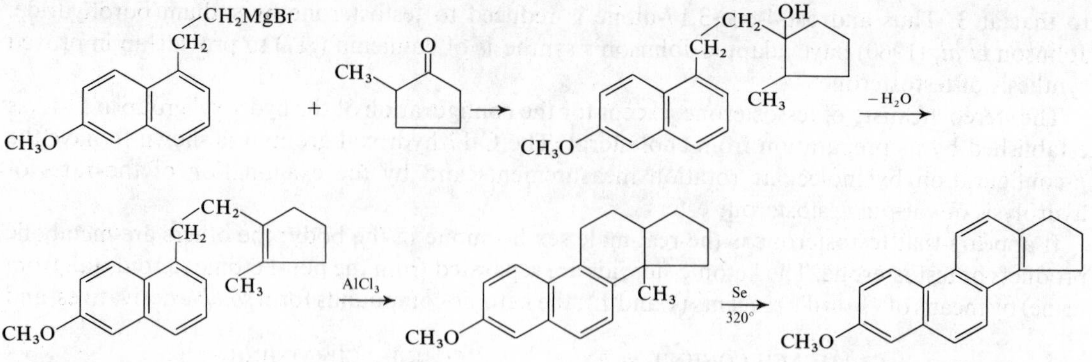

7-methoxy-1,2-
cyclopentenophenanthrene

Thus the benzene ring in oestrone is ring A, and the (phenolic) hydroxyl group is at position 3; hence the skeleton of oestrone is as shown. Into this skeleton we must fit the keto group, and since this skeleton contains only 17 carbon atoms, another carbon atom must also be placed. The position of the keto group was shown to be at 17, and the extra carbon atom was shown to be an angular methyl group at position 13, as follows (Cook *et al.*, 1935). When the methyl ether of oestrone (I) is treated with methylmagnesium iodide, compound (II) is obtained. When (II) is dehydrated with potassium hydrogen sulphate to (III), this catalytically reduced to (IV) and then (IV) distilled with selenium, the product is 7-methoxy-3′,3′-dimethyl-1,2-cyclopentenophenanthrene (V). The formation of (V) can be explained only if there is a keto group at position 17 and an angular methyl group at position 13. It should be noted that in the given equations, the dehydration is accompanied by the migration of the angular methyl group; this assumption is based on the analogy with known examples in which this occurs. Furthermore, this migration of a methyl group is characteristic of *trans*-fused hydrindanols of type (II), and so the configuration of rings C/D is *trans* (*cis*-C/D fusion leads to dehydration without rearrangement). In the *trans*-C/D fusion, the CH_3-18 group is in the axial position and so satisfies the stereoelectronic requirements for the 1,2-migration with loss of the hydroxyl group at C-17.

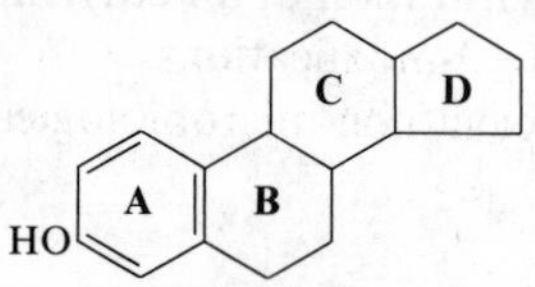

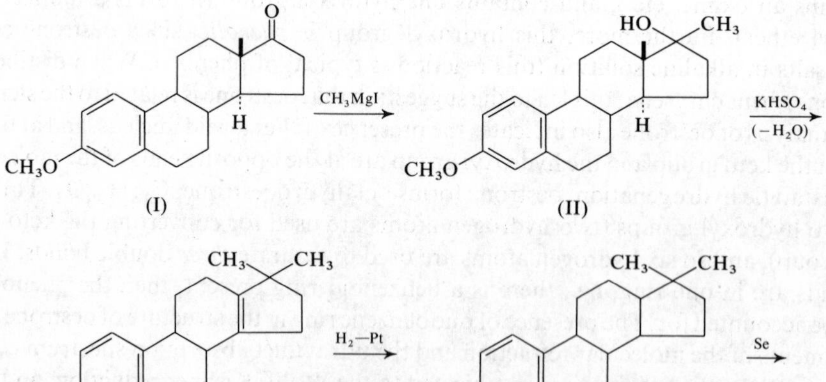

(I)   (II)

(III)   (IV)

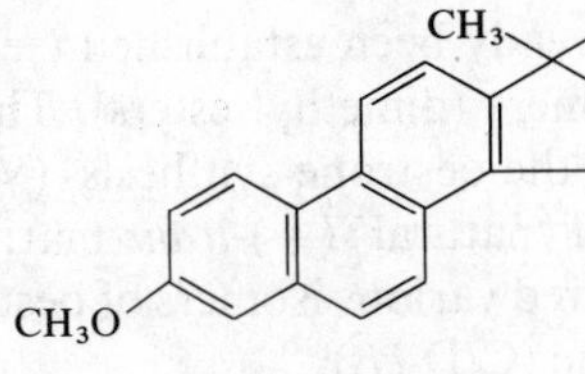

(V)

The structure of (V) has been confirmed by synthesis (Cook *et al.*, 1935). Thus the structure of oestrone is as shown (see also below).

This has been confirmed by the total synthesis of Anner and Miescher (1948). These authors started with the phenanthrene derivative (VI) which had been prepared previously by Robinson *et al.* (1938), and by Bachmann *et al.* (1942). The first step of the Anner–Miescher synthesis involves the Reformatsky reaction, and a later one the Arndt–Eistert synthesis.

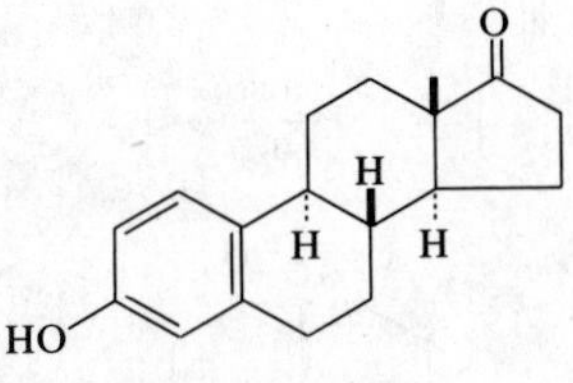

The stereochemical problems involved in the synthesis of oestrone are not so complicated as in cholesterol, since only four chiral centres are present in the hormone (*cf.* §5). (VI) contains 3 chiral centres and so four racemates are possible. Three have been isolated by Anner and Miescher, and one of these was converted into ($\pm$)-oestrone (C/D *trans*) and the stereoisomer (C/D *cis*), ($\pm$)-iso-oestrone. These were separated and the ($\pm$)-oestrone resolved with ($-$)-menthoxyacetic acid. The ($+$)-enantiomer that was obtained was shown to be identical with the natural compound. The *trans*-B/C fusion of the racemate used (for the oestrone synthesis) was deduced from other synthetic work, and the

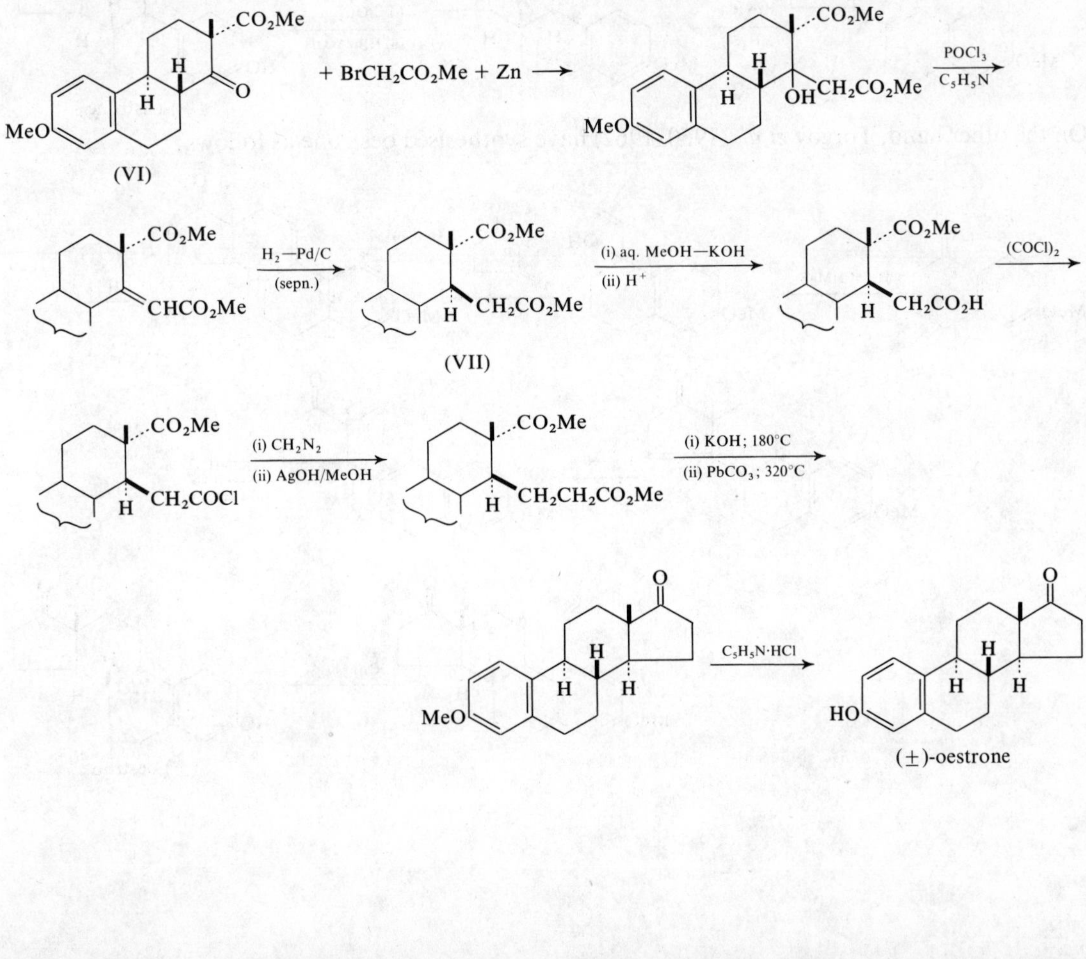

oestrone

(VI)   + $BrCH_2CO_2Me$ + Zn $\longrightarrow$ $\xrightarrow[C_5H_5N]{POCl_3}$

$\xrightarrow[\text{(sepn.)}]{H_2-Pd/C}$ (VII) $\xrightarrow[\text{(ii) } H^+]{\text{(i) aq. MeOH—KOH}}$ $\xrightarrow{(COCl)_2}$

$\xrightarrow[\text{(ii) AgOH/MeOH}]{\text{(i) } CH_2N_2}$ $\xrightarrow[\text{(ii) } PbCO_3;\ 320°C]{\text{(i) KOH; } 180°C}$

$\xrightarrow{C_5H_5N \cdot HCl}$

($\pm$)-oestrone

β-configuration of the CH$_3$-18 had already been established (see above). The catalytic reduction step produced a mixture of stereoisomers (dimethyl esters). These were separated by fractional crystallisation and the one chosen for the oestrone synthesis, (VII), was that which was identical with the methyl ether dimethyl ester of 'natural' (+)-*trans*-marrianolic acid (see formula II, §21).

Miescher and Anner have also prepared various isomers of oestrone by using other stereoisomers of (VI) and (VII), *e.g.*, (±)-iso-oestrone (C/D *cis*).

Johnson *et al.* (1958, 1962) have also carried out a total synthesis of oestrone; each step in their synthesis was stereospecific, but Hughes *et al.* (1960) have described total syntheses of oestrone which appear to be simpler than any previous method and just as efficient. The better method is as follows and involves a Mannick reaction and a Michael condensation (see Vol. I).

On the other hand, Torgov *et al.* (1960–1962) have synthesised oestrone as follows:

The parent hydrocarbon with a methyl group at C-13 and without a side chain at C-17 is now named *oestrane*, and unsaturation is indicated by the usual sytematic terminations, but ambiguity

5β-oestrane   5α-oestrane

in the numbering is avoided by inclusion of a number in brackets, *e.g.*, oestrone is oestra-1,3,5(10)-trien-17-one, and oestriol (§21) is oestra-1,3,5(10)-triene-3,16α,17β-triol (see also §7).

§21. Oestriol, $C_{18}H_{24}O_3$, m.p. 281°C, $[\alpha]_D$ +61°

Oestriol was isolated from human pregnancy urine by Marrian (1930). Since oestriol forms a tri-acetate, three hydroxyl groups must be present in the molecule. One was shown to be phenolic (*cf.* oestrone), and the other two secondary alcoholic, since, on oxidation, a diketone is produced. Furthermore, X-ray analysis indicates that the two alcoholic groups are in the *vicinal* position (*i.e.*, 1,2-). When oestriol is heated with potassium hydrogen sulphate, one molecule of water is removed and oestrone is produced. It therefore follows that oestriol has the same carbon skeleton as oestrone, and that the two alcoholic groups in oestriol are at positions 16 and 17. Structure (I) for oestriol fits the above facts, and is supported by the following evidence. When fused with potassium hydroxide, oestriol forms marrianolic acid (II) and this, on dehydrogenation with selenium, is converted into a hydroxydimethylphenanthrene (III) which on distillation with zinc dust, gives a dimethylphen-anthrene (IV). The structure of (IV) was shown to be 1,2-dimethylphenanthrene by synthesis, and since marrianolic acid forms an anhydride when heated with acetic anhydride, it therefore follows that oestriol contains a phenanthrene nucleus and a five-membered ring, the position of the latter being 1,2 (where the two methyl groups are in (IV)). Finally, the structure of (III) was shown to be 7-hydroxy-1,2-dimethylphenanthrene by synthesis (Haworth *et al.*, 1934), and so if (I) is the structure of oestriol, the degradation to the phenanthrene derivatives may be explained as follows:

(I)   (II)   (III)

(IV)

Since oestriol does not form an isopropylidene derivative with acetone, the adjacent hydroxyl groups must be *trans*. The configuration of the hydroxyl group at C-17 has been deduced as β from the synthesis of oestriol from oestrone (see below).

The chemical relationship between oestrone, oestriol and oestradiol (§22) is shown by the following reactions.

(i) Oestrone may be reduced to oestradiol by catalytic hydrogenation, by aluminium isopropoxide (the Meerwein–Ponndorf–Verley reduction), or by lithium aluminium hydride.

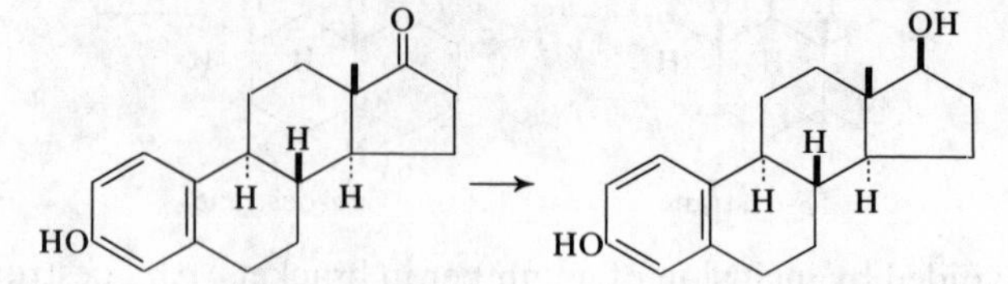

oestrone   oestradiol

(ii) Oestriol may be converted into oestrone by the action of potassium hydrogen sulphate (see above), and oestrone may be converted into oestriol as follows (Huffman *et al.*, 1947, 1948).

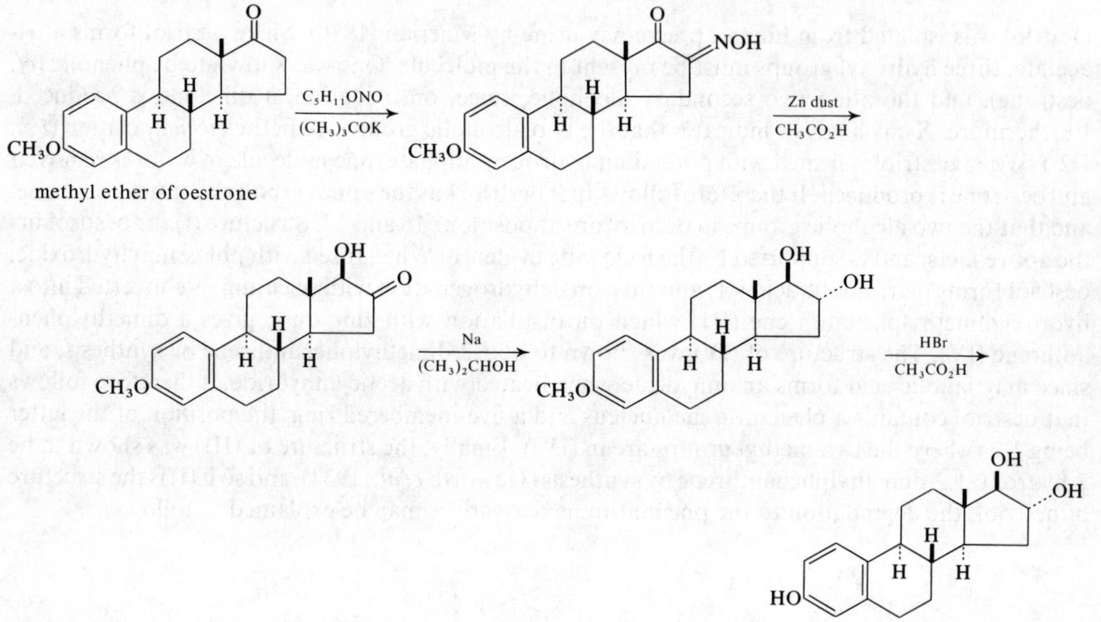

methyl ether of oestrone

Leeds *et al.* (1954) have converted oestrone into oestriol by a simpler method:

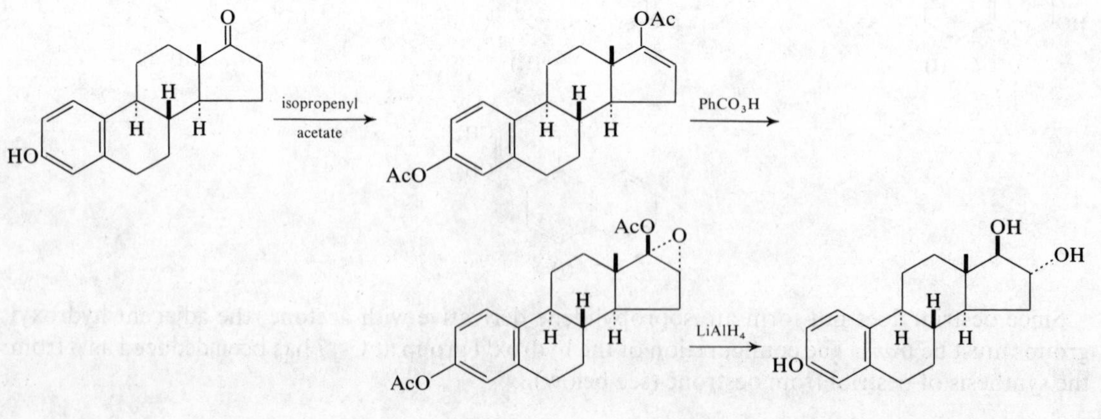

Oestriol is more soluble than oestrone in water, and is more potent than either oestrone or oestradiol when taken orally.

§22. Oestradiol, $C_{18}H_{24}O_2$

There are two stereoisomeric oestradiols, α and β; the α-isomer is much more potent than the β-. These names were based on the incorrect configuration at C-17, and to avoid confusion it is therefore better to refer to them as oestradiol-17β and oestradiol-17α, respectively.

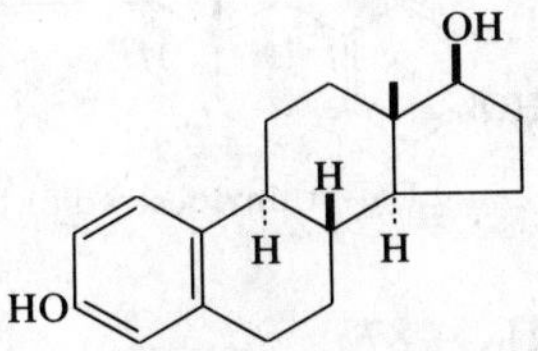

oestradiol-17β
(α-oestradiol)
m.p. 178°C, $[\alpha]_D$ +81°

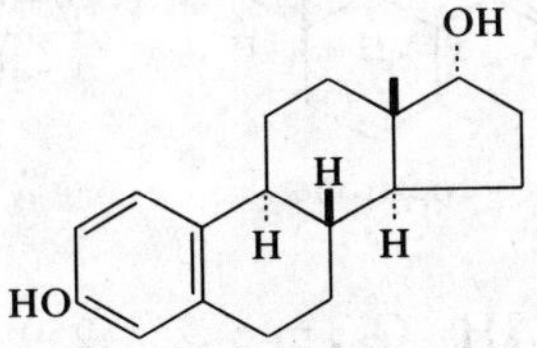

oestradiol-17α
(β-oestradiol)
m.p. 222°C, $[\alpha]_D$ +54°

Oestradiol-17β was first obtained by the reduction of oestrone (see §21), but later it was isolated from the ovaries of sows (Doisy et al., 1935). When the phenolic methyl ester of oestradiol is heated with zinc chloride, a molecular rearrangement occurs, the angular methyl group migrating to the cyclopentane ring D (cf. 10 §2viii). This compound, when dehydrogenated with selenium, produces

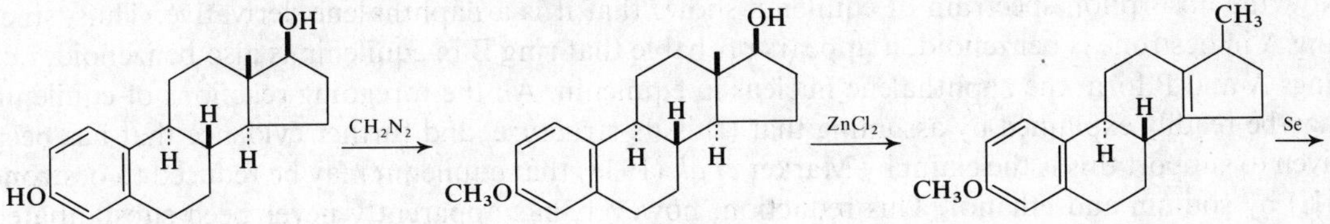

oestradiol-17β

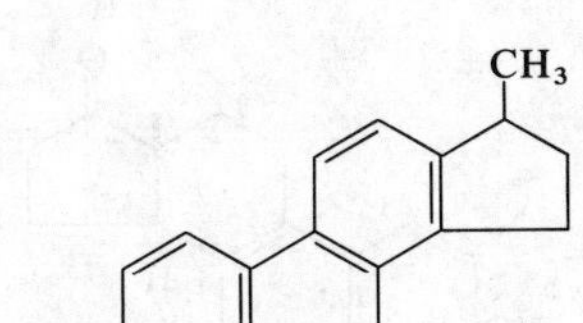

7-methoxy-3′-methyl-1,2-
cyclopentenophenanthrene

7-methoxy-3′-methyl-1,2-cyclopentenophenanthrene, the structure of which has been ascertained by synthesis (Cook et al., 1934). Thus the structure of oestradiol is established.

Velluz et al. (1960) have synthesised oestradiol starting from 6-methoxy-1-tetralone; this is therefore a total synthesis of the hormone.

Oestradiol-17α has been isolated from the pregnancy urine of mares (Wintersteiner et al., 1938). Oestradiol-17β is much more active than oestrone, whereas oestradiol-17α is much less active. It appears that oestradiol is the real hormone, and that oestrone and oestriol are metabolic products.

Thin-layer chromatography has been used by Struck (1961) and Lisboa et al. (1962) to investigate oestrogens, and Woltz et al. (1964), using combined thin-layer and gas chromatography, were able to identify the minor oestrogenic substances in female urine. On the other hand, Wang (1961) has shown that oestrone, oestriol, and oestradiol may be separated by adsorption chromatography (polyamide column).

A very active synthetic oestrogen is **17α-ethinyloestradiol**, and has the advantage that it is very active when taken orally. This synthetic compound has been prepared by the action of acetylene on oestrone in a solution of liquid ammonia containing potassium.

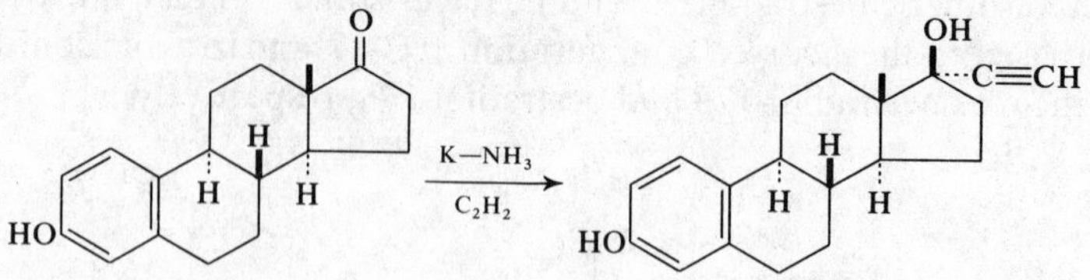

oestrone   17α-ethinyloestradiol

§23. (+)-Equilenin, $C_{18}H_{18}O_2$, m.p. 258–259°C. $[\alpha]_D$ +87°

This has been isolated from the urine of pregnant mares by Girard *et al.* (1932); it is not a very potent oestrogen. The reactions of equilenin show that a phenolic hydroxyl group and a ketonic group are present, and also that the molecule contains five double bonds (*cf.* oestrone, §20). When the methyl ether of equilenin is treated with methylmagnesium iodide, then the alcohol dehydrated, catalytically reduced and then dehydrogenated with selenium, the product is 7-methoxy-3′,3′-dimethyl-1,2-cyclopentenophenanthrene (II) [*cf.* oestrone, §20]. Thus the structure of equilenin is the same as that of oestrone, except that the former has two more double bonds than the latter (Cook *et al.*, 1935). Now the absorption spectrum of equilenin shows that it is a naphthalene derivative. Thus, since ring A in oestrone is benzenoid, it appears probable that ring B in equilenin is also benzenoid, *i.e.*, rings A and B form the naphthalene nucleus in equilenin. All the foregoing reactions of equilenin may be readily explained by assuming that (I) is its structure, and further evidence that has been given to support this is the claim by Marker *et al.* (1938) that equilenin may be reduced to oestrone (III) by sodium and ethanol. This reduction, however, has apparently never been substantiated (*cf.* Dauben *et al.*, 1956).

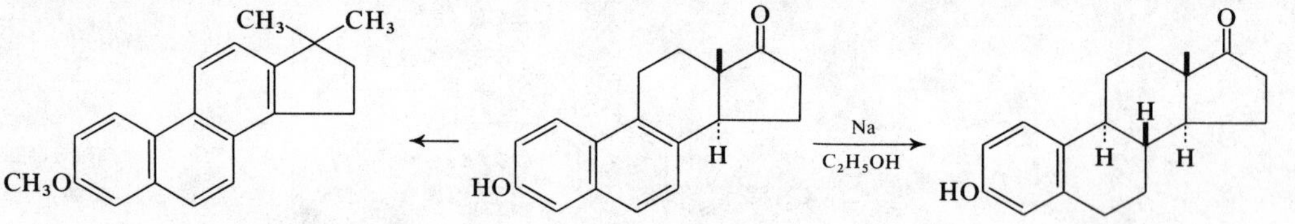

(II)   (I)   (III)
                                 equilenin   oestrone

The structure of equilenin has been confirmed by synthesis. The first synthesis was by Bachmann *et al.* (1940), but was somewhat improved by Johnson *et al.* (1947). In the following chart, compound (IV) is synthesised by the method of Bachmann, and the rest of the synthesis is that of Johnson, who started with compound (IV) [Johnson's synthesis involves fewer steps than Bachmann's].

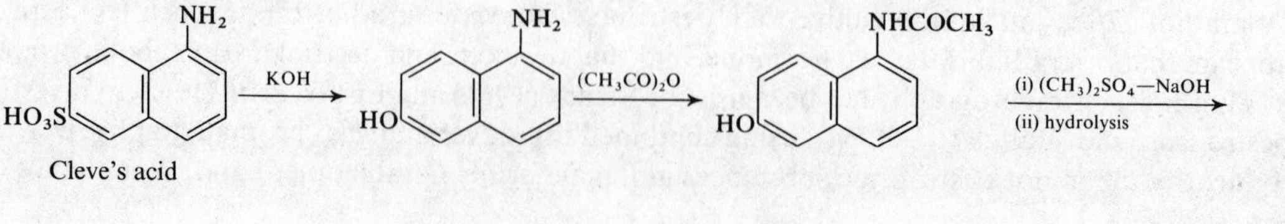

Cleve's acid

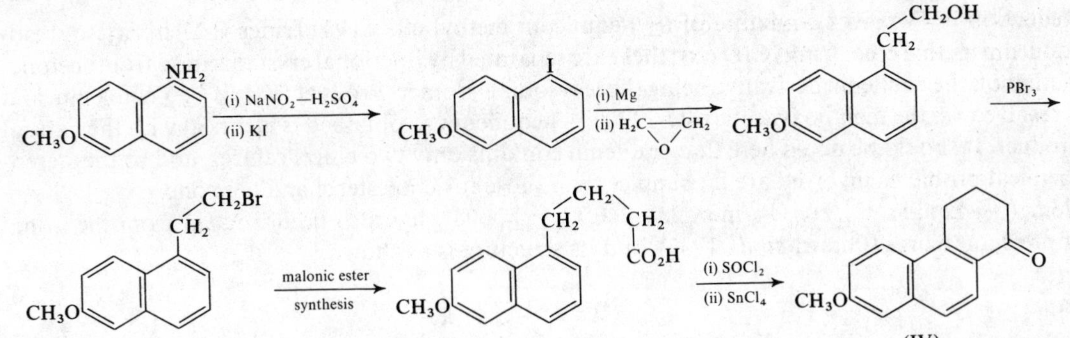

(IV)

Johnson's synthesis starting from (IV)

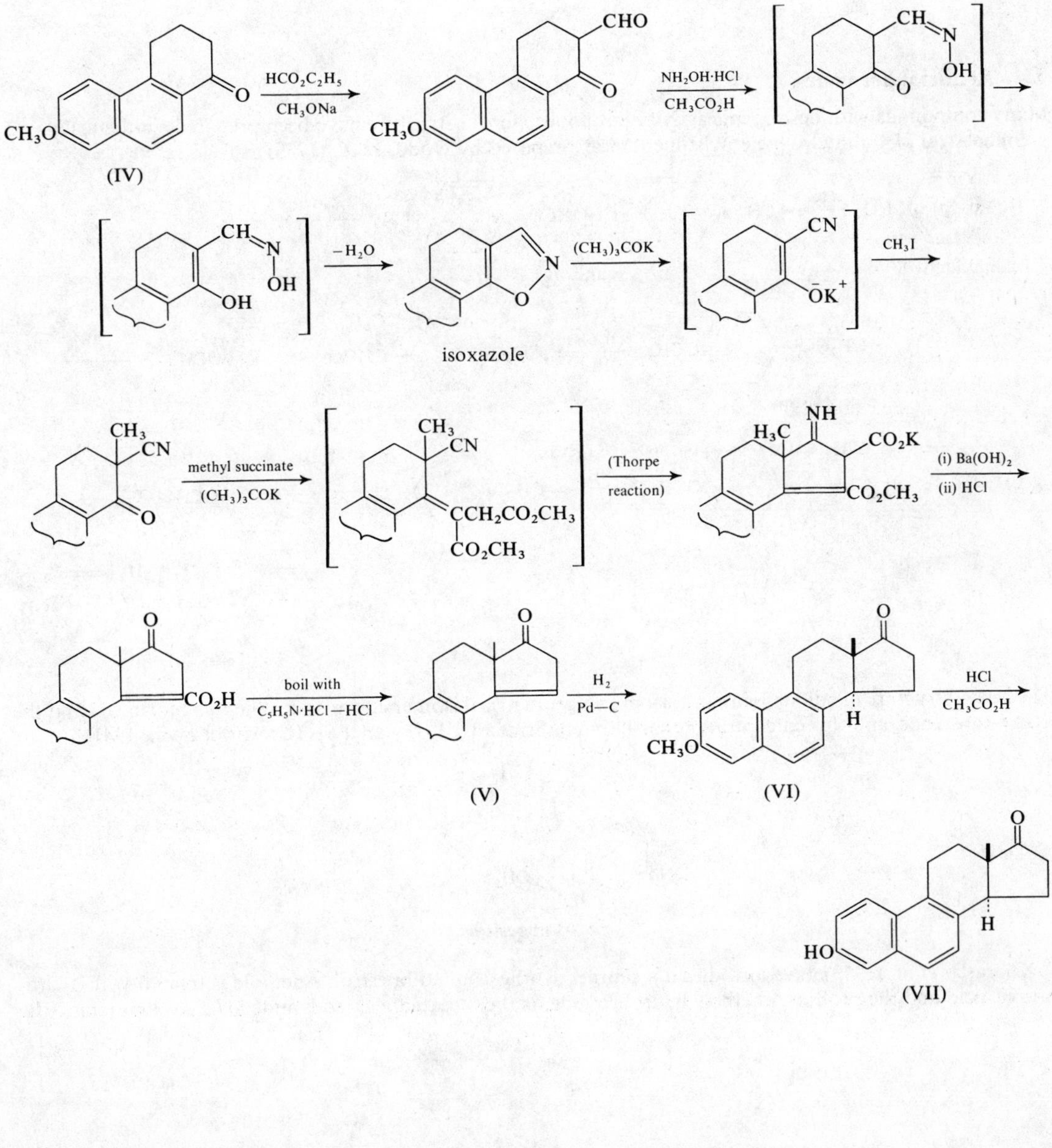

(IV)

isoxazole

(V)

(VI)

(VII)

Reduction of (V) gives a mixture of (±)-equilenin methyl ether (VI) [rings C/D *trans*], and iso-equilenin methyl ether (rings C/D *cis*); these are separated by fractional crystallisation from acetone-methanol, the equilenin derivative being the less soluble isomer. Product (VII) is (±)-equilenin, and is resolved *via* the menthoxyacetic ester. The (+)-equilenin so obtained is identical with the natural product. It should be noted here that equilenin contains only two chiral centres, and so the stereochemical problems involved are far simpler than those for cholesterol and oestrone.

§23a. (+)-**Equilin,** $C_{18}H_{20}O_2$, m.p. 238–240°C, $[\alpha]_D$ 308°, has also been isolated from the urine of pregnant mares (Girard *et al.*, 1932), and its structure is as shown.

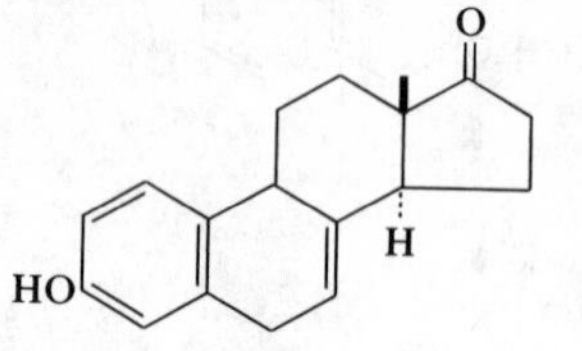

equilin

§24. Artificial hormones

Many compounds with oestrogenic activity but not of steroid structure have been prepared synthetically.
Stilboestrol (4,4′-dihydroxydiethylstilbene) was prepared by Dodds *et al.* (1939) as follows:

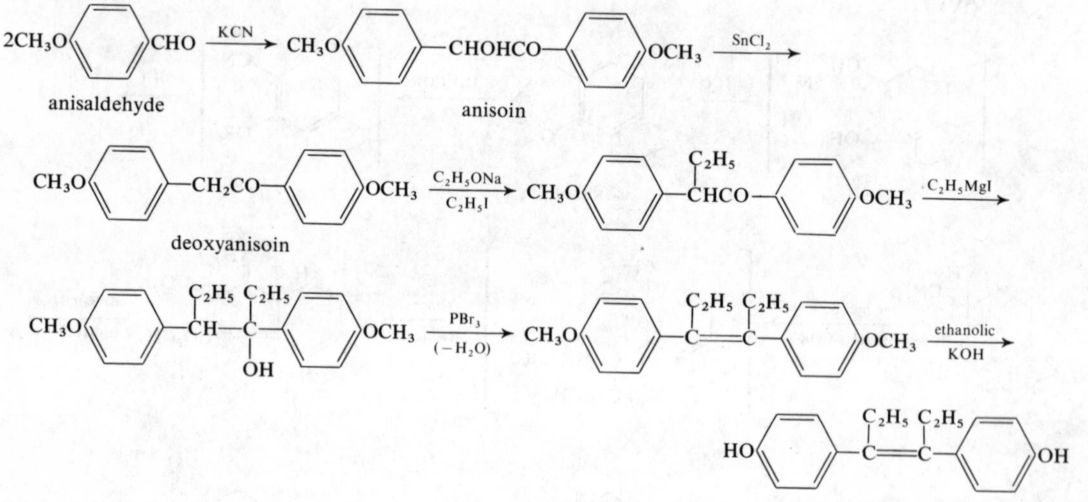

anisaldehyde

anisoin

deoxyanisoin

stilboestrol

The above structure of stilboestrol can exist in two geometrical isomeric forms; it is the *trans*-form which is the active substance, and this configuration has been confirmed by X-ray analysis (Crowfoot *et al.*, 1941).

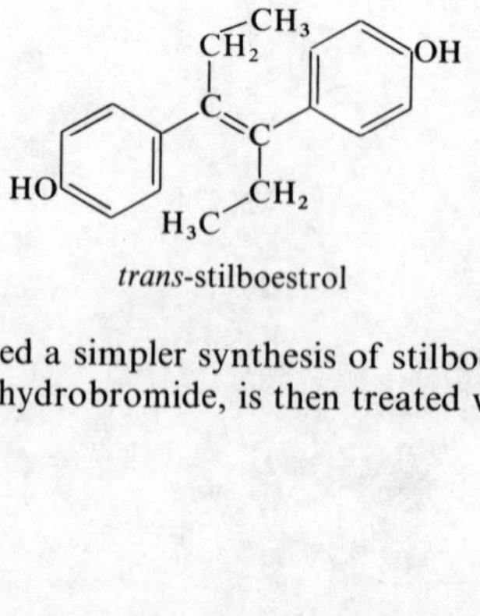

trans-stilboestrol

Kharasch *et al.* (1943) have introduced a simpler synthesis of stilboestrol. Anethole is treated with hydrobromic acid and the product, anethole hydrobromide, is then treated with sodamide in liquid ammonia. The resulting compound (I) gives stilboestrol on demethylation and isomerisation in the presence of alkali. The structure of (I) is uncertain, but it is believed to be the one given.

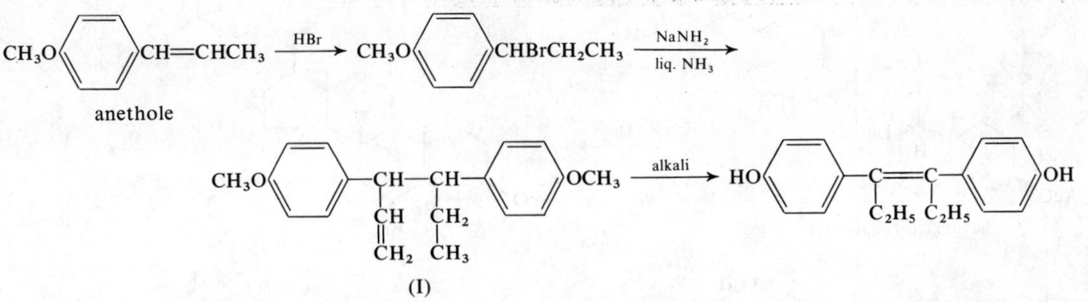

CH_3O—⟨⟩—$CH{=}CHCH_3$ $\xrightarrow{HBr}$ CH_3O—⟨⟩—$CHBrCH_2CH_3$ $\xrightarrow[\text{liq. } NH_3]{NaNH_2}$

anethole

CH_3O—⟨⟩—CH—CH—⟨⟩—OCH_3 $\xrightarrow{\text{alkali}}$ HO—⟨⟩—$C{=}C$—⟨⟩—OH
with branches $\overset{|}{CH}$, $\overset{|}{CH_2}$ and $\overset{|}{CH_2}$, $\overset{|}{CH_3}$; product bears C_2H_5 C_2H_5

(I)

Stilboestrol is more active than oestrone when administered subcutaneously, and it can also be given orally. **Hexoestrol** (dihydrostilboestrol) may be prepared from anethole hydrobromide as follows:

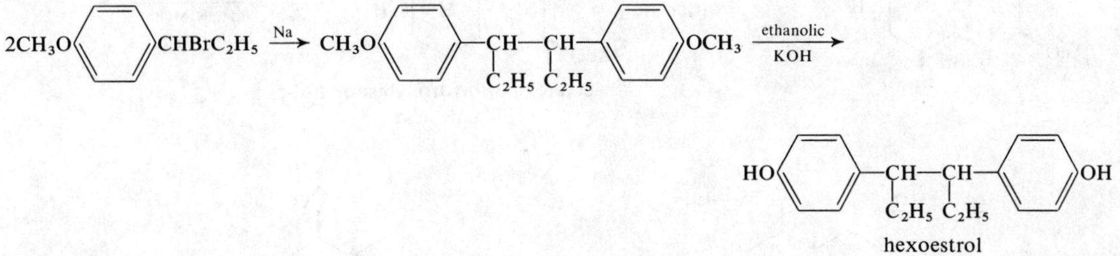

$2CH_3O$—⟨⟩—$CHBrC_2H_5$ $\xrightarrow{Na}$ CH_3O—⟨⟩—CH—CH—⟨⟩—OCH_3 $\xrightarrow[\text{KOH}]{\text{ethanolic}}$
with C_2H_5 C_2H_5

HO—⟨⟩—CH—CH—⟨⟩—OH
with C_2H_5 C_2H_5

hexoestrol

The active form is the *meso*-isomer (as shown by X-ray crystallography by Crowfoot *et al.*, 1941).

GESTOGENS

§25. Progesterone, $C_{21}H_{30}O_2$, m.p. 128°C, $[\alpha]_D$ +192°

This was first isolated in a pure form by Butenandt *et al.* (1934) from the *corpora lutea* of pregnant sows.

The chemical reactions of progesterone show that there are two keto groups present, and since on catalytic reduction three molecules of hydrogen are added to form the dialcohol $C_{21}H_{36}O_2$, it therefore follows that progesterone contains one double bond (four hydrogen atoms are used to convert the two keto groups to alcoholic groups). Thus the parent hydrocarbon of progesterone is $C_{21}H_{36}$, and since this corresponds to the general formula C_nH_{2n-6}, progesterone is therefore tetracyclic (D.B.E. of $C_{21}H_{36}O_2$ is $21 + 1 - 36/2 = 4$ rings). Furthermore, X-ray studies have shown that progesterone contains the steroid nucleus, and this is further supported by the fact that progesterone may be prepared from, *e.g.*, stigmasterol and cholesterol. These preparations also show the structure of progesterone, but do not provide conclusive evidence for the position of the double bond in progesterone, since the results can be interpreted equally well on the assumption that the double bond is 4,5 or 5,6. The absorption spectrum of progesterone, however, shows that it is an α,β-unsaturated ketone (λ_{max} 240 nm), and this suggests that the position of the double bond is 4,5 (see below). Finally, progesterone has also been synthesised from diosgenin and from pregnanediol, and the preparation from the latter, taken in conjunction with the others, definitely shows that the position of the double bond in progesterone is 4,5.

(i) **Progesterone from stigmasterol** (Butenandt *et al.*, 1934, with improvements by other workers).

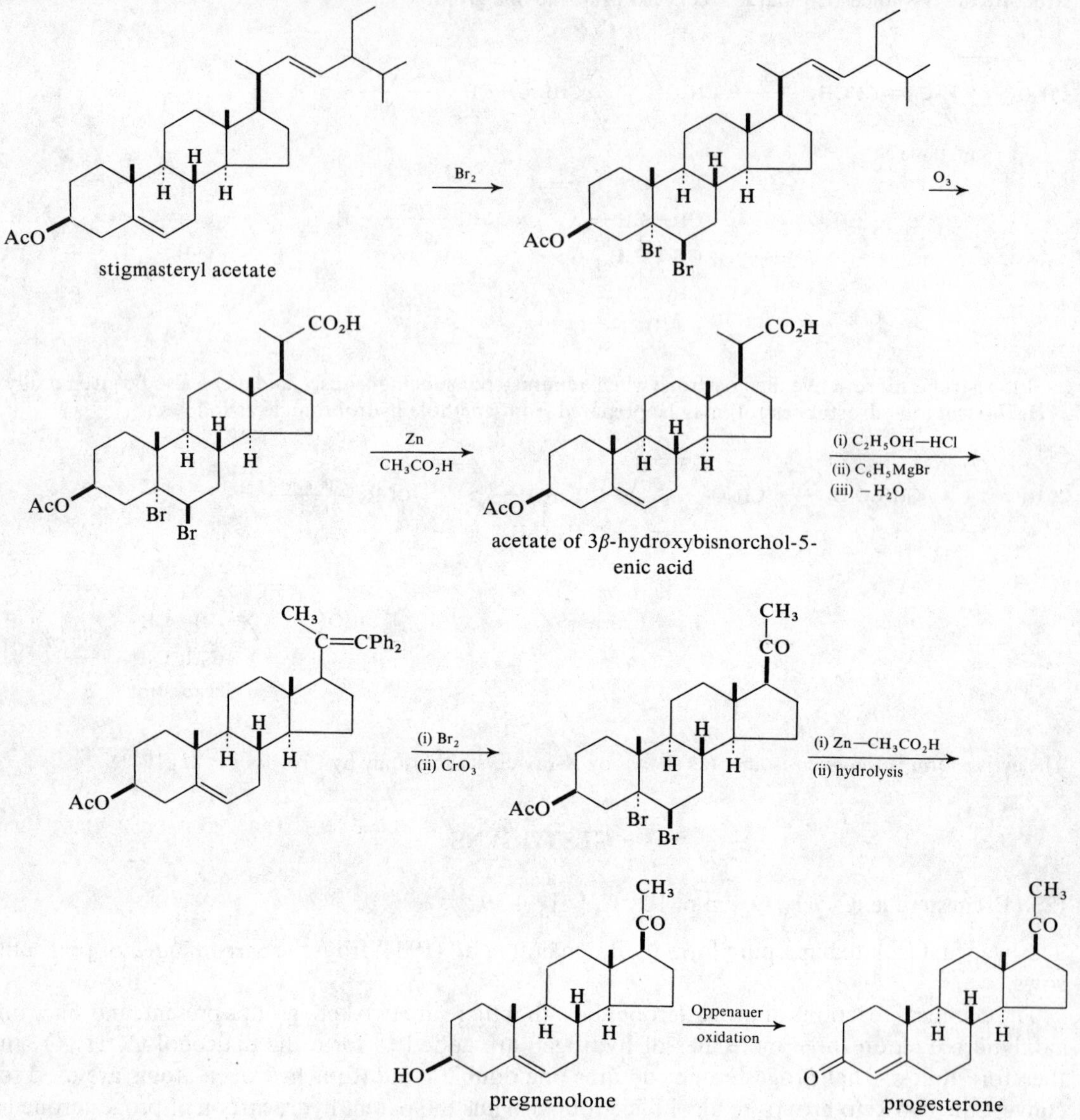

stigmasteryl acetate

acetate of 3β-hydroxybisnorchol-5-enic acid

pregnenolone

progesterone

Pregnenolone has also been isolated from the *corpus luteum*.

(ii) **Progesterone from cholesterol** (Butenandt *et al.*, 1939). Cholesterol is first converted into dehydroepiandrosterone (see §19), and then as follows:

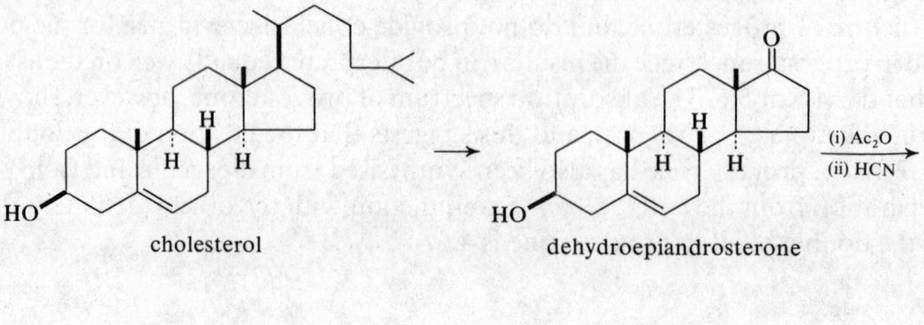

cholesterol

dehydroepiandrosterone

(iii) **Progesterone from diosgenin** (Marker *et al.*, 1940, 1941). Diosgenin (a sapogenin) occurs as a glycoside in the root of *Trillium erectum* (see §32).

(iv) **Progesterone from pregnanediol** (Butenandt *et al.*, 1934).

pregnanediol   →(CrO$_3$)→   pregnanedione   →(Br$_2$)→   [bromo intermediate]   →(C$_5$H$_5$N, (−HBr))→   progesterone

(v) **Progesterone from ergosterol** (Shepherd *et al.*, 1955). This appears to be the most practical synthesis (note the enamine step).

ergosterol   →(Oppenauer oxidation)→   ergosterone   →(HCl in MeOH)→   [MeO intermediate]   →(HCl heat)→   isoergosterone   →(H$_2$ / Pd—C)→

→(O$_3$)→   [CHO intermediate]   →(C$_5$H$_{10}$NH)→   [=CH—N enamine]   →(Na$_2$Cr$_2$O$_7$ / AcOH)→   progesterone

A total synthesis of progesterone has also been carried out; this uses the ester (XXIII) in the synthesis of cholesterol (§9).

§25a. 5β-Pregnane-3α,20α-diol, $C_{21}H_{36}O_2$, m.p. 242°C, $[\alpha]_D$ +27°, was isolated from human pregnancy urine by Marrian (1929), it is biologically inactive, and is the main metabolic product of progesterone. The functional nature of the two oxygen atoms was shown to be secondary alcoholic, and since pregnanediol is saturated, the parent hydrocarbon is $C_{21}H_{36}$, and so the molecule is tetracyclic (D.B.E. of $C_{21}H_{36}$ = 21 + 1 − 36/2 = 4 rings). Pregnanediol gives the haloform reaction; therefore a CH_3CHOH group is present (see Vol. I). When oxidised, pregnanediol is converted into the diketone pregnanedione and this, on the Clemmensen reduction, forms pregnane, $C_{21}H_{36}$. This is identical with 17-ethylaetiocholane, a compound of known structure. Thus pregnanediol contains the steroid nucleus, and the position of the side-chain is 17. Finally, the relationship between pregnanediol and progesterone shows that the former contains one hydroxyl group at position 3. Further work showed that the configuration of the 3-hydroxyl group is α. Thus:

pregnanediol   pregnanedione   pregnane

Homosteroids and norsteroids

§26. Introduction

These are mainly synthetic steroids which have been obtained by modification of the carbon skeleton of natural steroids. When any ring has been *increased* in size, the compound is called a **homosteroid**, and when *decreased* in size or an angular methyl group has been removed, the compound is called a **norsteroid** (see also §7).

§26a. Homosteroids.   The most widely studied compounds of this group are the D-homosteroids. Several of these have been isolated from the urine of pregnant mares, *e.g.*, uranediol (17α-methyl-5α-D-homoandrostane-3β,17aβ-diol). The new ring carbon atom introduced is designated by a number and the letter 'a' (and 'b', etc., as necessary), the number used being the highest numbered carbon atom in the ring enlarged, exclusive of ring junctions.

uranediol

One example of ring-D expansion is the conversion of androstenolone (dehydro-epiandrosterone) (I) into the 17aα-methyl-17aβ-hydroxy-D-homo-17-ketone (IV) or into the corresponding 17aα-epimer (V). (I) is ethynylated with potassium acetylide in liquid ammonia to give (II) and this, on hydration by means of aqueous mercuric chloride-aniline, gives (III). (III), under acidic conditions, rearranges to (IV) and under alkaline conditions rearranges to (V). Also note the rearrangement of (IIIa), the 17-epimer of (III). The mechanisms of these rearrangements are not yet fully understood.

(I)   (II)

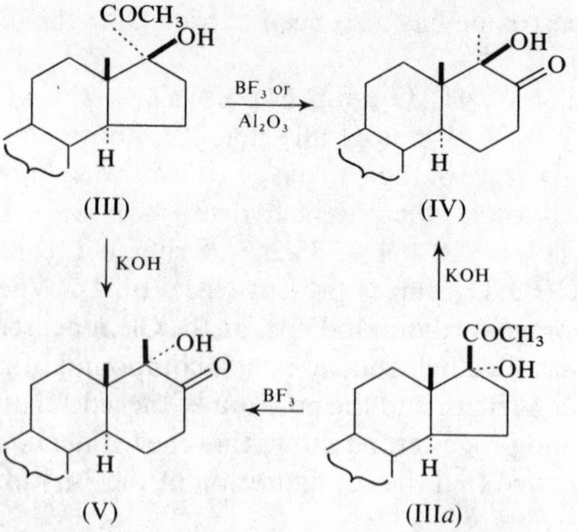

(III)   (IV)

(V)   (IIIa)

Another example of ring-D expansion is the conversion of the amino-alcohols (VI) and its 17-epimer (VIa) into a mixture of D-homo-17a-ketone (VII) and D-homo-17-ketone (VIII). In both cases, the major product is (VII); here also, the mechanism is not fully understood.

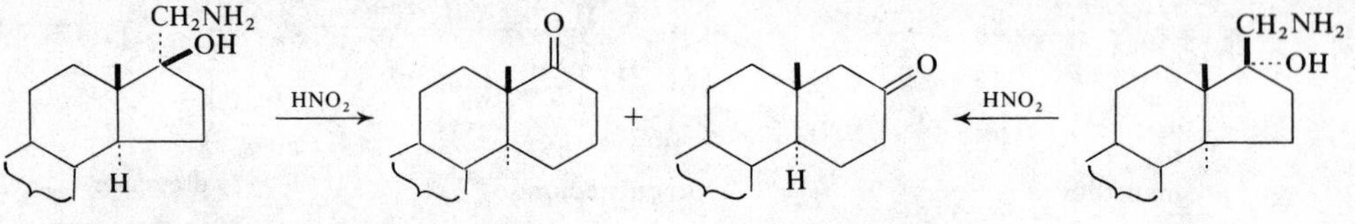

(VI)   (VII)   (VIII)   (VIa)

§**26b. Norsteroids.** Ring-norsteroids of types A-, B-, C-, and D-norsteroids are known, but the 19-norsteroids have been most widely studied. Some examples are:

(i) 19-Nortestosterone (II) from the 3-methyl ether of oestradiol (I) *via* a Birch reduction.

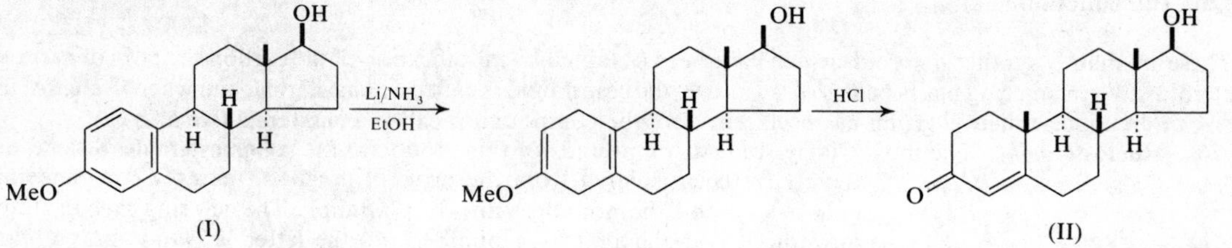

(I)   (II)

(ii) 19-Norprogesterone (IV) from the methyl ether of oestrone (III) *via* a Wittig reaction and hydroboration.

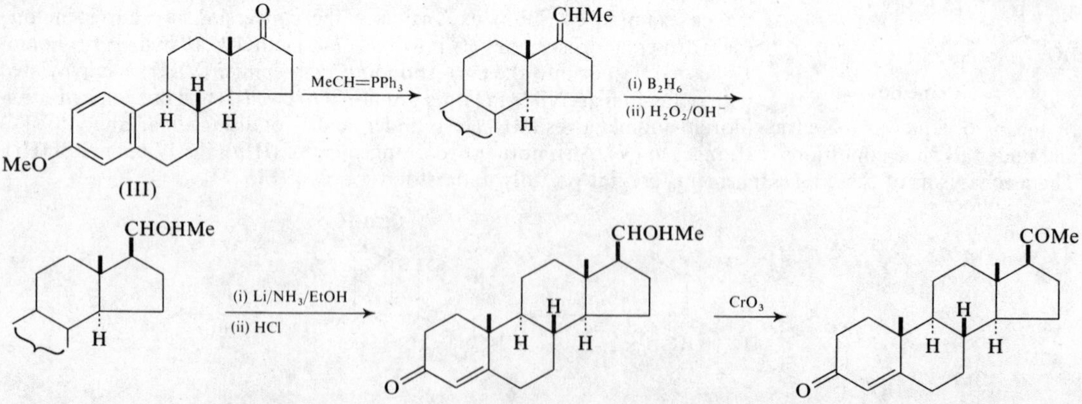

(III)

(IV)

Adrenocortical hormones

§27. Introduction

In the adrenal glands (of mammals) there are two regions, the *medulla* which produces adrenaline (see **14**§12), and the *cortex* which produces steroid hormones. The production of these adrenocortical hormones or *corticoids* is controlled by the hormone produced in the anterior lobe of the pituitary, the so-called adrenocorticotrophic hormone, ACTH. The corticoids have many physiological functions, but their main functions are the control of carbohydrate and protein metabolism and the control of the balance of water and electrolytes.

§28. Adrenocortical hormones

Many substances have been isolated from the extract of the adrenal cortex. Girard's reagent T was used to separate the keto from the non-keto compounds, and then each fraction was separated by adsorption or partition chromatography. Kendall *et al.* (1935) isolated 8, Wintersteiner *et al.* (1935–) 4, Reichstein *et al.* (1936–) 31, Kuizenga *et al.* (1945) 5, and Wettstein *et al.* (1959) 18 compounds. These substances were originally designated by letters (different workers using different letters for the same compound), but many are now known by trivial names. It appears that eight of these substances are highly physiologically active, and these are:

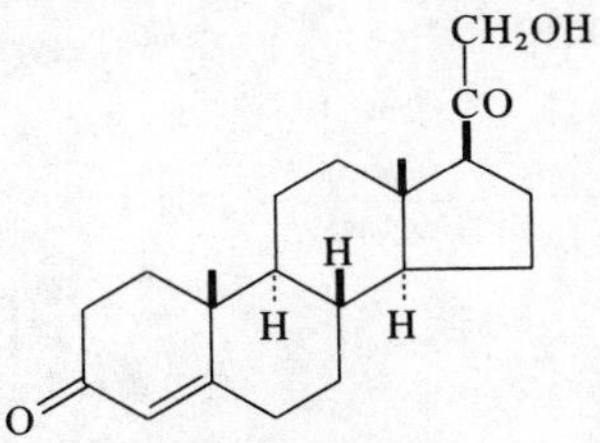

Substance Q;
11-Deoxycorticosterone;
21-Hydroxyprogesterone;
Cortexone

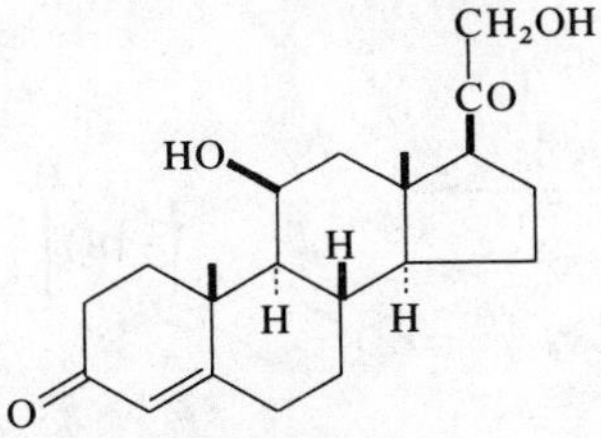

Substance H;
Corticosterone;
11,21-Dihydroxy-
progesterone

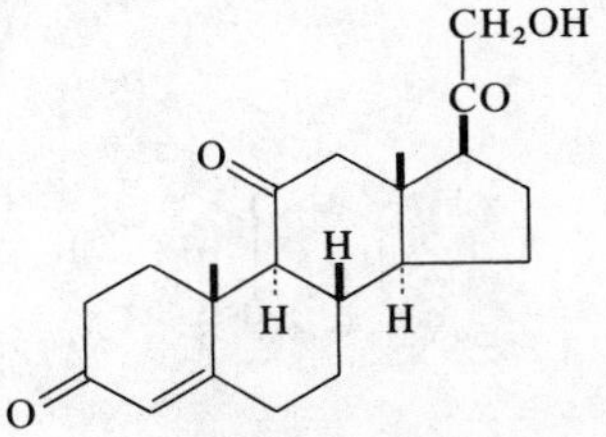

Compound A;
11-Dehydrocorticosterone;
21-Hydroxy-11-keto-
progesterone

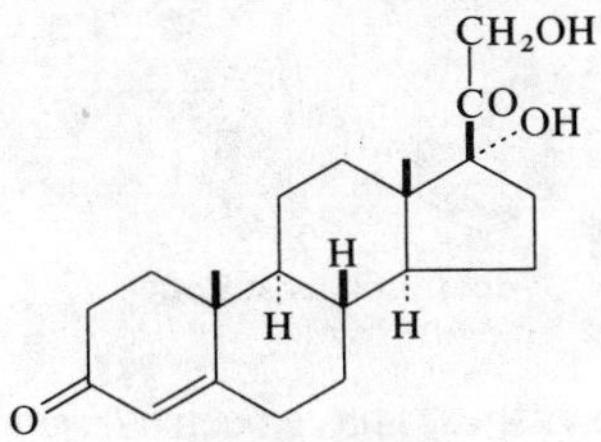

Substance S;
11-Deoxy-17-hydroxy-
corticosterone;
Cortexolone

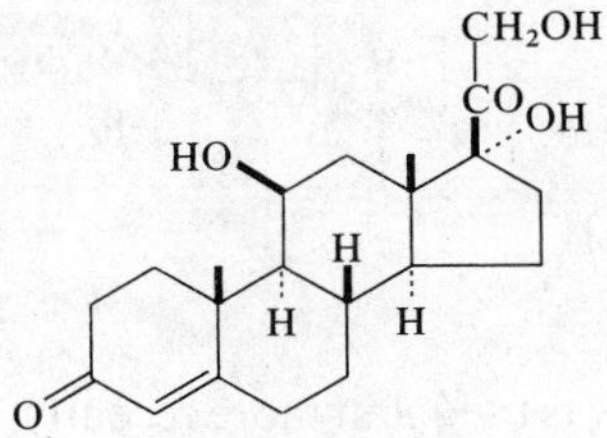

Substance M;
17-Hydroxy-
corticosterone;
Cortisol

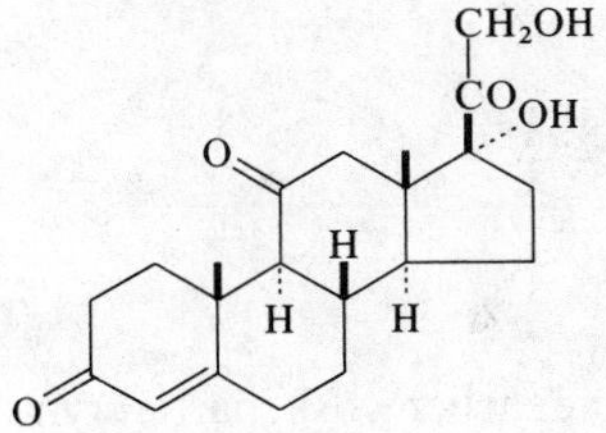

Substance F;
Compound E;
11-Dehydro-17-hydroxy-
corticosterone;
Cortisone

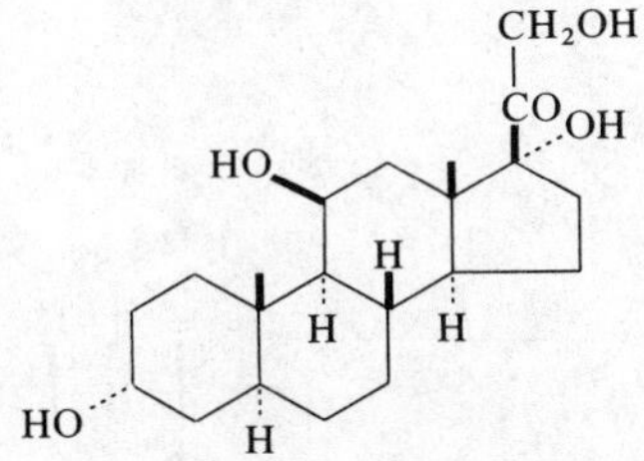

Substance C

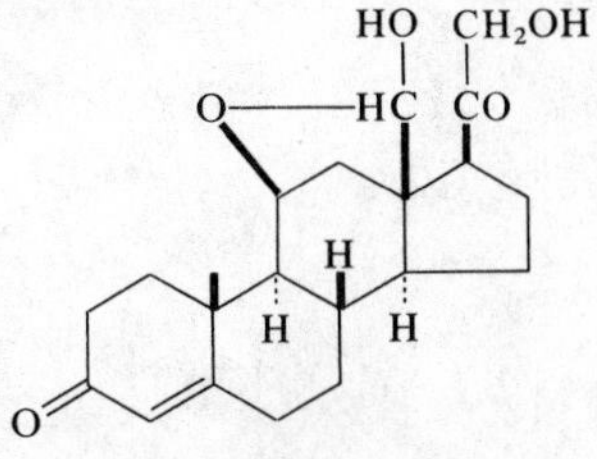

Aldosterone

Owing to the presence of the α-hydroxyketone group, the corticoids are strong reducing agents. The hydroxyl group at position 21 behaves in the usual way, but the 11-keto group does not form an oxime or a phenylhydrazone. The 11-keto group is resistant to catalytic reduction in neutral solution, but can be reduced in acid solution; it is readily reduced to a hydroxyl group by lithium aluminium hydride, and to a methylene group by the Clemmensen reduction (*cf.* §5).

The structures of the corticoids have been elucidated by degradation and by partial syntheses from sterols of known structure, *e.g.*, deoxycorticosterone from stigmasterol (Reichstein *et al.*, 1937, 1940). The first step is the conversion of stigmasterol to pregnenolone (see §25i).

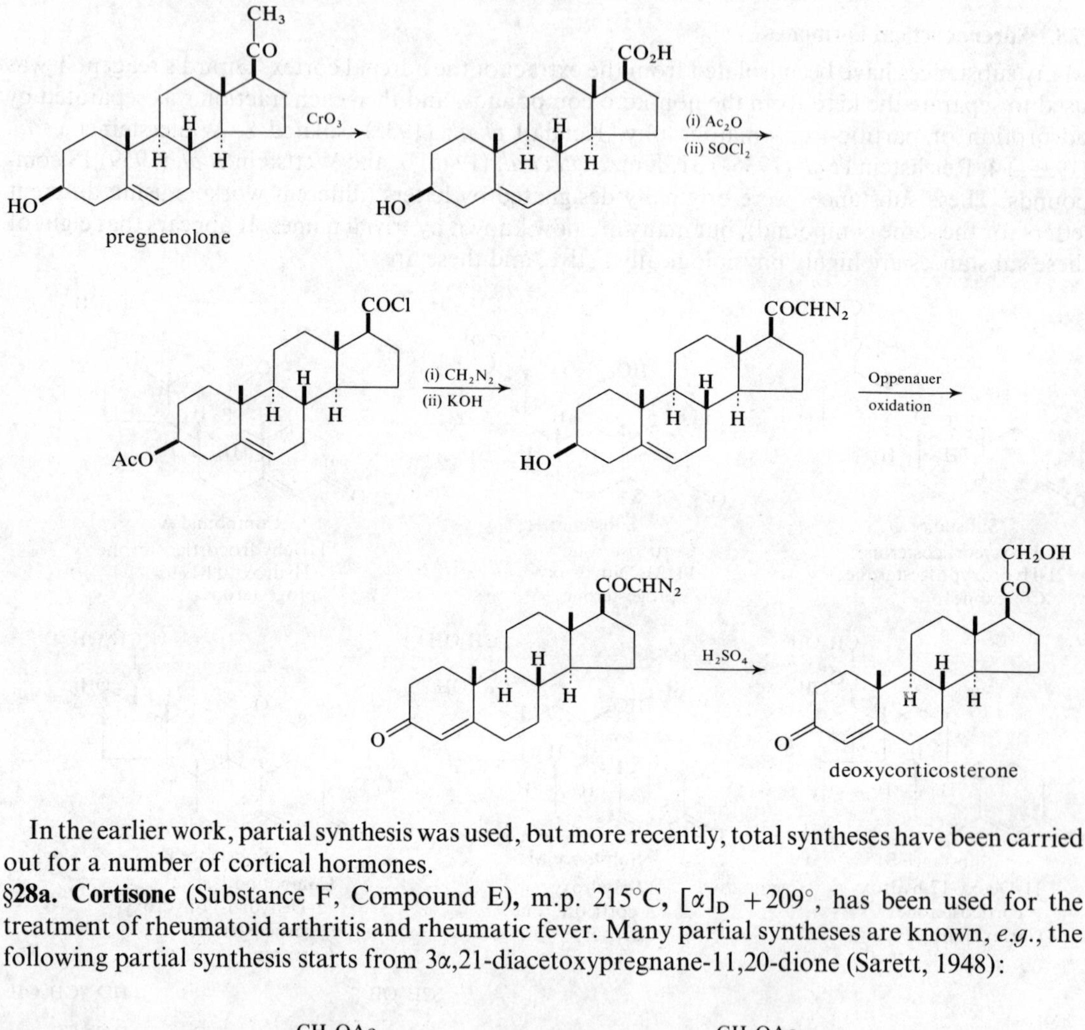

CH$_3$
CO

$\xrightarrow{\text{CrO}_3}$

CO$_2$H

$\xrightarrow[\text{(ii) SOCl}_2]{\text{(i) Ac}_2\text{O}}$

pregnenolone

COCl

AcO

$\xrightarrow[\text{(ii) KOH}]{\text{(i) CH}_2\text{N}_2}$

COCHN$_2$

HO

$\xrightarrow[\text{oxidation}]{\text{Oppenauer}}$

COCHN$_2$

O

$\xrightarrow{\text{H}_2\text{SO}_4}$

CH$_2$OH
CO

O

deoxycorticosterone

In the earlier work, partial synthesis was used, but more recently, total syntheses have been carried out for a number of cortical hormones.

§28a. Cortisone (Substance F, Compound E), m.p. 215°C, [α]$_D$ +209°, has been used for the treatment of rheumatoid arthritis and rheumatic fever. Many partial syntheses are known, *e.g.*, the following partial synthesis starts from 3α,21-diacetoxypregnane-11,20-dione (Sarett, 1948):

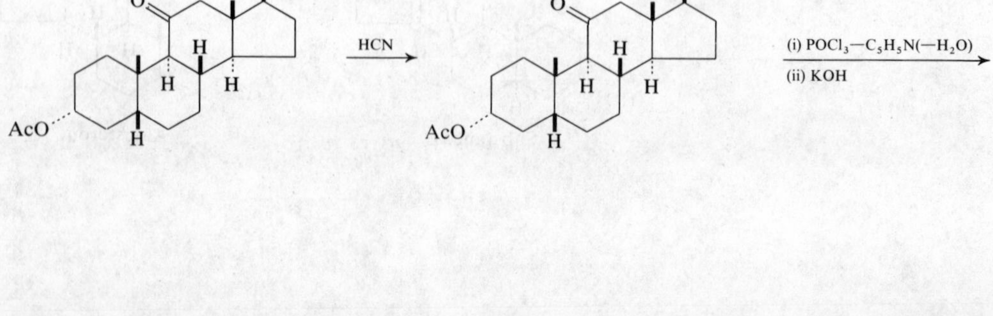

CH$_2$OAc
CO

O

AcO   H

$\xrightarrow{\text{HCN}}$

CH$_2$OAc
C(OH)CN

O

AcO   H

$\xrightarrow[\text{(ii) KOH}]{\text{(i) POCl}_3-\text{C}_5\text{H}_5\text{N}(-\text{H}_2\text{O})}$

CH$_2$OH
CCN
O
H
H H
HO
H

→ Ac$_2$O →

CH$_2$OAc
CCN
O
H
H H
HO
H

→ OsO$_4$ →

CH$_2$OAc
C—CN
C—O—OsO$_2$
O—O
O
H
H H
HO
H

(i) CrO$_3$
(ii) Na$_2$SO$_3$
→

CH$_2$OH
CO
OH
O
H
H H
O
H

(i) Ac$_2$O
(ii) Br$_2$
→

CH$_2$OAc
CO
OH
O
H
H H
O
Br
H

(i) −HBr
(ii) hydrolysis
→

CH$_2$OH
CO
OH
O
H
H H
O

cortisone

Several total syntheses of cortisone are known, *e.g.*, the very highly stereospecific synthesis by Sarett *et al.* (1952, 1953). This is of the type C → BC → ABC → ABCD (see §9). 3-Ethoxypenta-1,3-diene (I) underwent the Diels–Alder reaction with *p*-benzoquinone (II) to give the *cis*-fused diketone (III). This, on selective catalytic hydrogenation (Ni), gave the diketone (IV) which, on reduction with lithium aluminium hydride, formed the diol (V). (III)–(V) are all enol ethers. (V) when treated with acid, was hydrolysed to (VI) and this, on treatment with methyl vinyl ketone in the presence of alkali (Triton B; Me$_3$NCH$_2$Ph$^+$OH$^-$), underwent addition (Michael condensation) at the less hindered side followed by cyclisation to give the tricyclic ketone (VIII) with a β-methyl group (*cf.* cholesterol, §9). (VII) was converted into the ethylene ketal (VIII) [protection of the oxo group; this protection was kept until the final step of the synthesis], and this, by means of the Oppenauer oxidation, was selectively oxidised at the less hindered hydroxyl group to (IX). (IX) is formed with inversion to give the more stable *trans*-fused rings (inversion occurs at the carbon atom when enol formation is possible; *cf.* §5). (IX) was then converted into cortisone acetate (XXXI) as shown. The required configuration in (X) is obtained because the larger methallyl group is *trans* to the *meta* (11-) OH, thereby reducing 1,3-interactions; the hydroxyl group has the β (axial)-configuration (see §5). To avoid elimination of the 11β-hydroxyl group in step (XIII) to (XIV), (X) was oxidised to give (XI). Hydration of (XII) to (XIII) was carried out under mild conditions to avoid removal of the protecting group (3-position). Sodium borohydride reduction of (XV) gave (XVI) with an 11α (equatorial) hydroxyl group, and the next step reduced the α,β-double bond (XVI) → (XVII). It might also be noted that the α-configuration at position 11 produces the correct configuration (β) at C-14; the 11β-configuration would have produced the 14α-configuration. Resolution of (XXIV) was carried out with strychnine and the (+)-isomer was used in the next step ((XXIII) is the (±)-form). Ring extension of (VI) to (VII) is an example of the **Robinson annelation**.

(I)   (II)   (III) H_2—Ni   (IV)   LAH

(V) H_3O^+ (VI) $\overset{O}{\underset{OH^-}{\parallel}}$ (VII) $\overset{-OH}{\underset{H^+}{-OH}}$

(VIII)   Oppenauer oxidn.   (IX)   (i) MeI; Bu^{t}OK (ii) CH_2=$CMeCH_2I$; Bu^{t}OK

(X) CH_2CMe=CH_2 $\dfrac{CrO_3}{C_5H_5N}$ (XI) CH_2CMe=CH_2 EtOC≡CMgBr

(XII) CH_2CMe=CH_2 C≡COEt $\dfrac{HCl}{(+H_2O)}$ (XIII) CH_2CMe=CH_2 CH_2CO_2Et $-H_2O$

(XIV) CH_2CMe=CH_2 $CHCO_2Et$ (i) K_2CO_3 (ii) H_3O^+ (XV) CH_2CMe=CH_2 $CHCO_2H$ $NaBH_4$

(XVI) CH_2CMe=CH_2 $CHCO_2H$ $\dfrac{K/Me_2CHOH}{liq.\ NH_3}$ (XVII) CH_2CMe=CH_2 CH_2CO_2H $\dfrac{MeI}{K_2CO_3}$

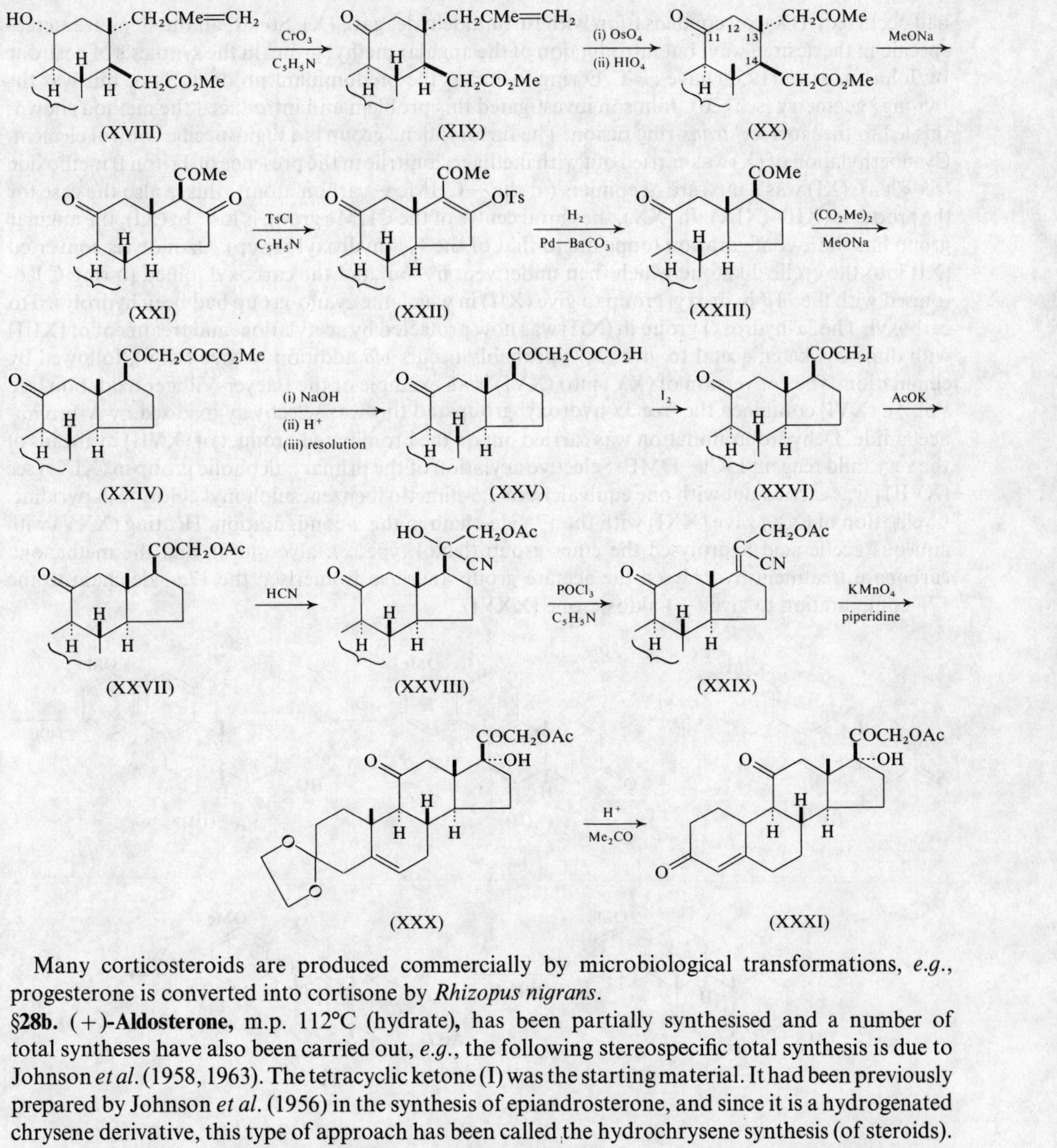

HO… CH₂CMe=CH₂

CH₂CO₂Me

(XVIII)

$\xrightarrow[C_5H_5N]{CrO_3}$

O CH₂CMe=CH₂

CH₂CO₂Me

(XIX)

$\xrightarrow[\text{(ii) HIO}_4]{\text{(i) OsO}_4}$

O 11 12 13 CH₂COMe

14 CH₂CO₂Me

(XX)

$\xrightarrow{MeONa}$

COMe

O O

(XXI)

$\xrightarrow[C_5H_5N]{TsCl}$

COMe OTs

O

(XXII)

$\xrightarrow[\text{Pd—BaCO}_3]{H_2}$

COMe

O

(XXIII)

$\xrightarrow[MeONa]{(CO_2Me)_2}$

COCH₂COCO₂Me

O

(XXIV)

$\xrightarrow[\text{(iii) resolution}]{\substack{\text{(i) NaOH} \\ \text{(ii) H}^+}}$

COCH₂COCO₂H

O

(XXV)

$\xrightarrow{I_2}$

COCH₂I

O

(XXVI)

$\xrightarrow{AcOK}$

COCH₂OAc

O

(XXVII)

$\xrightarrow{HCN}$

HO CH₂OAc CN

O

(XXVIII)

$\xrightarrow[C_5H_5N]{POCl_3}$

CH₂OAc CN

O

(XXIX)

$\xrightarrow[\text{piperidine}]{KMnO_4}$

COCH₂OAc OH

O

(XXX)

$\xrightarrow[Me_2CO]{H^+}$

COCH₂OAc OH

O

O

(XXXI)

Many corticosteroids are produced commercially by microbiological transformations, *e.g.*, progesterone is converted into cortisone by *Rhizopus nigrans*.

§28b. (+)-Aldosterone, m.p. 112°C (hydrate), has been partially synthesised and a number of total syntheses have also been carried out, *e.g.*, the following stereospecific total synthesis is due to Johnson *et al.* (1958, 1963). The tetracyclic ketone (I) was the starting material. It had been previously prepared by Johnson *et al.* (1956) in the synthesis of epiandrosterone, and since it is a hydrogenated chrysene derivative, this type of approach has been called the hydrochrysene synthesis (of steroids). (IV) is the 3α-ol and the action of lead tetra-acetate on the acetate of (IV) introduced an acetoxyl group at C-12 (of unknown configuration) to give (V). (VI), on treatment with perbenzoic acid, was converted into the epoxide which then underwent cleavage with benzoic acid to give (VII). This was subjected to the Birch reduction and the product, an enol ether, underwent hydrolysis to give (VIII). (VIII) was a mixture of two α,β-unsaturated ketones (only one has been shown). Catalytic hydrogenation of the mixture gave (IX), isomerisation occurring spontaneously to give the more stable *trans*-fused rings (*via* enolisation; see §5). (IX) now contained the 3α-hydroxyl group (hydrolysis had occurred). (IX), on condensation with furfuraldehyde, gave (X). So far, all the steps are stereo-specific in the desired way, but introduction of the angular methyl group in the synthesis of oestrone by Johnson *et al.* (1952) gave *cis*-C/D ring fusion as the predominant product. Since this was the 'wrong' geometry (see §20), Johnson investigated this problem and introduced the method shown; this led to the 'correct' *trans*-ring fusion. The furfurylidene group is a regiospecific control element. Cyanoethylation of (X) was carried out with methacrylonitrile in the presence of Triton B methoxide (see §28a). (XI) was a mixture of epimers (at the —CHMe— carbon atom); this is also the case for the products (XII)–(XIX). In (XX), the chiral centre of the CHMe group is lost. In (XI), the angular group has the α-configuration (opposite to that of the 11β-hydroxyl group). Ozonolysis converted (XI) into the cyclic diketone which then underwent fission, and the carboxyl joined to ring C lac-tonised with the 11β-hydroxyl group to give (XII) in which the cyano-group had been hydrolysed to carboxyl. The 3α-hydroxyl group in (XII) was now protected by acetylation, and treatment of (XIII) with dimethyl keten acetal to give (XV) probably occurs *via* addition to give (XIV), followed by elimination. The conversion of (XV) into (XVI) is an example of the Baeyer-Villiger oxidation (see Vol. I). (XVI) contained the free 3α-hydroxyl group and this was selectively oxidised by *N*-bromo-acetamide. Dehydrobromination was carried out on the brominated product of (XVII) by means of the very mild reagent LiCl—DMF. Selective acylation of the primary alcoholic group in (XIX) [see (XVII)] was carried out with one equivalent of 2,5-dimethylbenzenesulphonyl chloride in pyridine. Cyclisation of (XX) gave (XXI) with the 17-side-chain in the α-configuration. Heating (XXV) with aqueous acetic acid hydrolysed the ether group (lactol type; *cf.* glycosides), and the methanolic carbonate treatment hydrolysed the acetate group and also isomerised the 17α-side-chain to the 17β-configuration to give (±)-aldosterone (XXVI).

(IX)   (X)   (XI)

(XII)   (XIII)

(XIV)   (XV)

(XVI)   (XVII)

(XVIII)   (XIX)   (XX)

(XXI)   (XXII)   (XXIII)

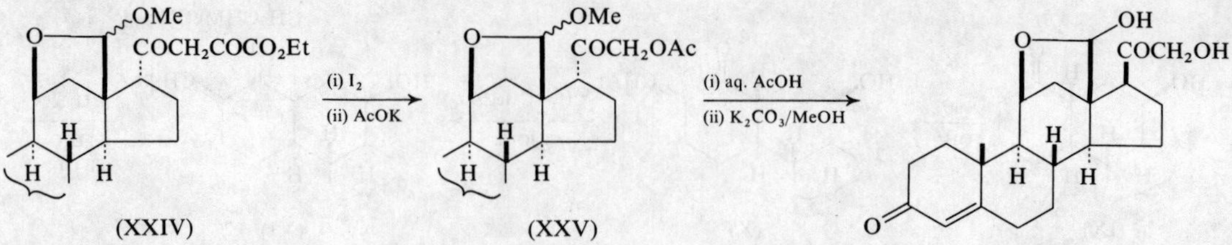

(XXIV)   (XXV)

(±)-aldosterone
(XXVI)

The structure of aldosterone has been a matter of argument. Ham *et al.* (1955) proposed that, in aqueous solution, aldosterone was an equilibrium mixture of three structural isomers, the 18-aldehyde (XXVII), the 18-hemiacetal (XXVI), and the 18-acetal-20-hemiacetal (XXVIII). The structure in solution, however, has usually been referred to as an equilibrium mixture of (XXVI) and

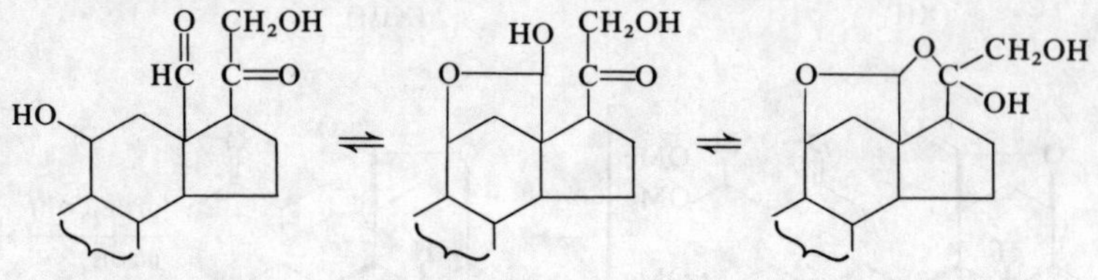

(XXVII)   (XXVI)   (XXVIII)

(XXVII) only. Duax *et al.* (1971) have examined the monohydrated crystalline form of aldosterone by X-ray analysis and showed that the structure is (XXVIII). This, however, need not be the only form in aqueous solution.

§29. Some methods used in steroid chemistry.

The following are some of the methods used in reactions involving adrenocortical hormones and, in some cases, steroids in general.

Keto groups may be protected to alkaline media by dioxolan (ethylene ketal) formation:

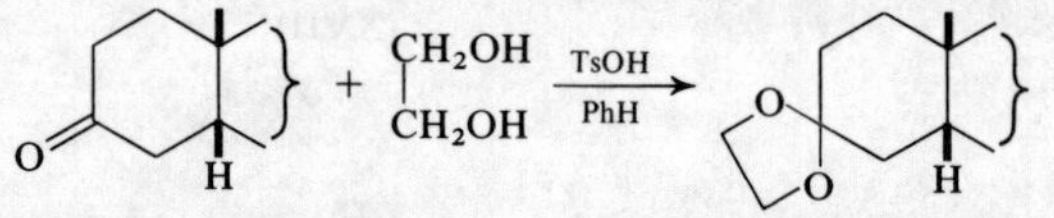

Under controlled conditions, it is often possible to selectively protect one group in a steroid containing several keto groups. The ease of dioxolan formation in saturated keto steroids is $3 > 20 > 17 > 11$, *e.g.*,

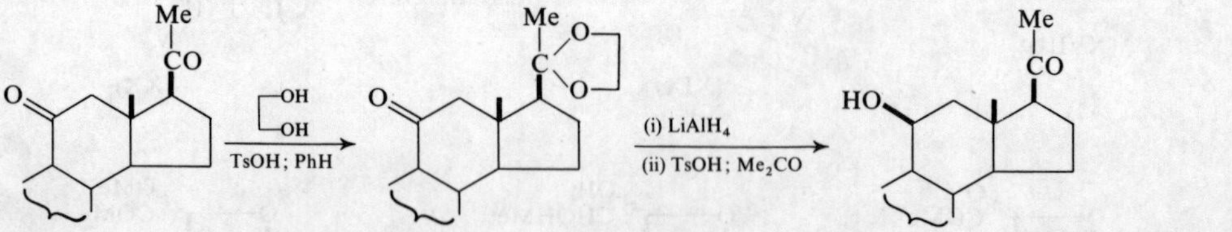

An interesting point in this connection is that in saturated keto steroids the order of reactivity of the keto group to Girard's reagent T (in MeOH—AcOH at 25°C) is $3 > 6 >> 20 > 12 >> 11$. The unreactive nature of the 11-keto group is due to large 1,3-interactions that would be experienced with the methyl groups at 18 and 19 if this keto group formed a derivative (see also §5).

Reactions involving the 17-acetoxyl group and/or the 17 positions are particularly important in adrenocortical hormone chemistry. Which method is used depends on the nature of the functional groups in the rest of the molecule and how they can be protected.

(a) Reichstein *et al.* (1939):

CH₃ / CO → (AcO)₄Pb / AcOH → CH₂OAc / CO → KOH → CH₂OH / CO

(b) Djerassi *et al.* (1953):

CH₃ / CO → Ac₂O / C₅H₅N → CH₂ ═ / OAc → *N*-iodosuccinimide in dioxan → CH₂I / CO → AcOK / AcOH → CH₂OAc / CO

(c) Ringold *et al.* (1958):

CH₃ / CO → I₂/CaO / THF, MeOH → CH₂I / CO → AcOK / Me₂CO → CH₂OAc / CO

Addition of peroxide in the first step improves the yield (Rothman *et al.*, 1960), and Amiard *et al.* (1961) have used calcium chloride instead of calcium oxide in the first step.

(d) Amos *et al.* (1959):

CH₃ / CO → —OH —OH / TsOH; PhH → CH₃ / C(O—O) → Br₂ / CH₂Cl₂ → CH₂Br / C(O—O) → MeOH / HCl → CH₂Br / CO

The keto-bromide may be converted into the acetate with potassium acetate in acetic acid (Marker *et al.*, 1942), but better yields are obtained with sodium acetate in dimethylformamide (Wettstein *et al.*, 1959).

(e) Wagner *et al.* (1949):

CH₃ / CO → 3Br₂ → CHBr₂ / COBr → (i) KOH—EtOH (ii) HCl → CO₂H / CBr → (i) CH₂N₂ (ii) LiAlH₄ → CH₂OH / CBr → Ac₂O →

CH₂OAc / CBr → OsO₄ → CH₂OAc / CO·OH

(*f*) Barton *et al.* (1962):

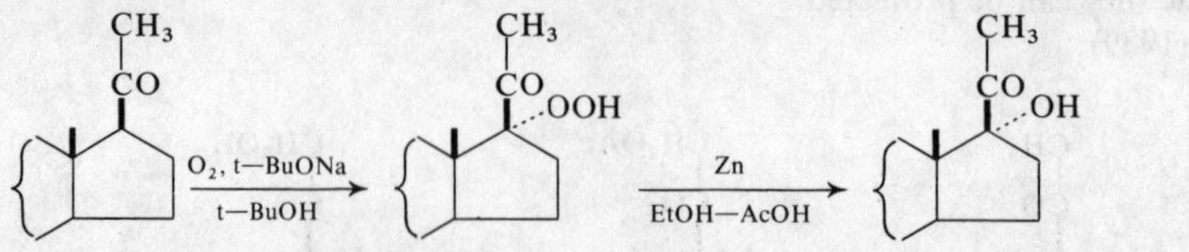

(*g*)

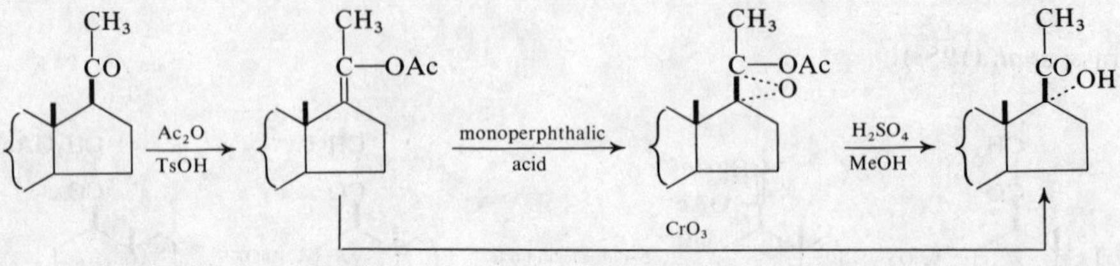

The first step was carried out by Chamberlin *et al.* (1955), but variations are the use of isopropenyl acetate, CH_2=CMeOAc, in sulphuric acid (Engel *et al.*, 1960) or acetic anhydride in perchloric acid-chloroform solution (Traub *et al.*, 1960). The chromium oxidation step is the method of Kritchevsky *et al.* (1949), and the alternative route (monoperphthalic acid) is the method of Attenburrow *et al.* (1961).

(*h*) The removal of the 17-acetyl group (*i.e.*, the complete removal of the side-chain) has been carried out in many ways. Two very good methods are by means of ethyl nitrite-sodium ethoxide (Fieser *et al.*, 1946) or by ozonolysis of the enol acetate (Marshall *et al.*, 1948):

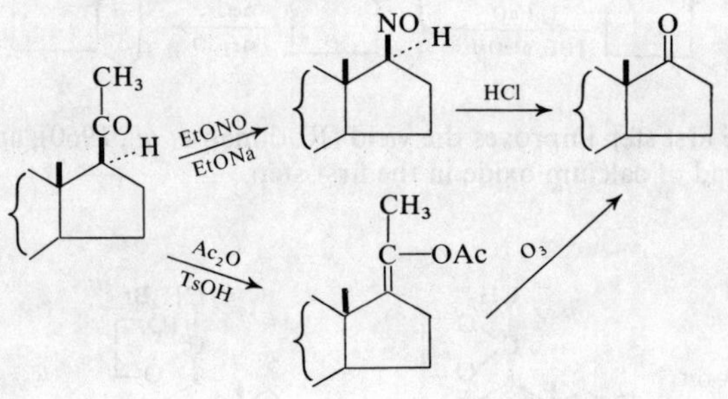

(*i*) The conversion of a 17-keto steroid to the 17-acetyl compound has been carried out by Krubiner *et al.* (1966) *via* a Wittig reaction:

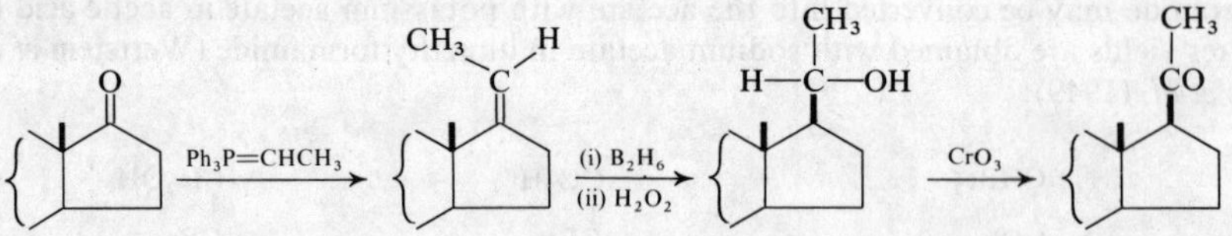

Steroidal glycosides and alkaloids

§30

There are many plant steroids which occur as glycosides (see 7 §24) and have the property of stimulating heart muscle. These are referred to as the **cardiac-active** or **cardiotonic glycosides**. Another group of steroidal glycosides has the property of forming foams in water (like soap solutions) and so are known as **saponins**. Finally, there is the group of **steroidal alkaloids**.

Only a very brief description of these compounds is given here. Their structures have been elucidated by the methods described for the steroids, *i.e.*, selenium dehydrogenation, graded oxidation, etc. Partial syntheses have also been carried out and, in a number of cases, total syntheses.

§31. Cardiotonic glucosides

When hydrolysed, these glycosides give one or more sugars and an aglycon or genin; in some cases, a dehydration product of the aglycon is produced. These aglycons are of two types. The more common type contains an α,β-unsaturated γ-lactone ring and is known as the **cardenolides**. All of these show a λ_{max} at 220 nm. The less common type contains a δ-ring which has a conjugated diene system and is known as the **bufadienolides** or **scilladienolides**. These show a λ_{max} at 300 nm. Both types of steroid aglycon have the normal configuration at C-8, C-9, C-10, C-13, and C-17, and both contain a C-3 and a 14β hydroxyl group. The two types may differ, however, in the configurations at C-3 and C-5, and in unsaturation and oxygen functions. Many different sugars have been isolated from these glycosides and are of various types. All, except glucose, are deoxyhexoses and methyl ethers. The sugar in the glycoside generally consists of several hexose residues and the glycosidic link to the steroid is always at C-3. Furthermore, it appears that the glycosidic linkage for a D-sugar is β, and is α for an L-sugar.

Some examples of these two types of cardiotonic glycosides are:

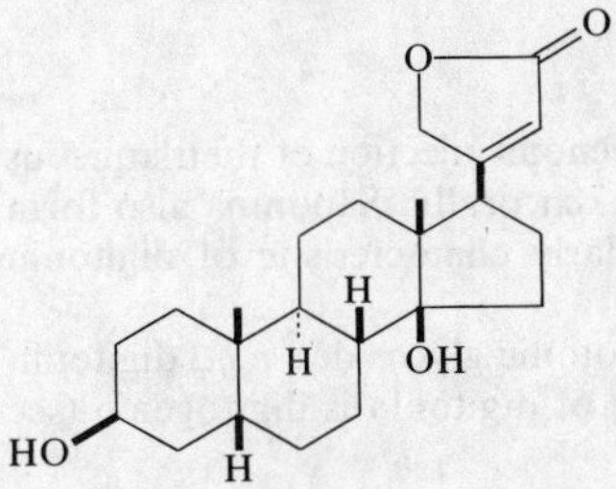

digitoxigenin 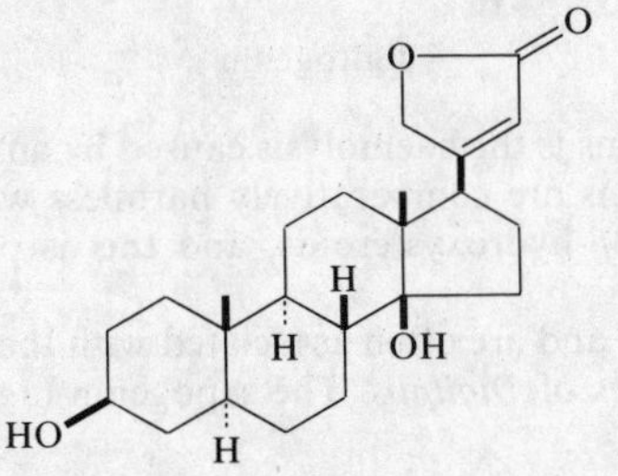   uzarigenin 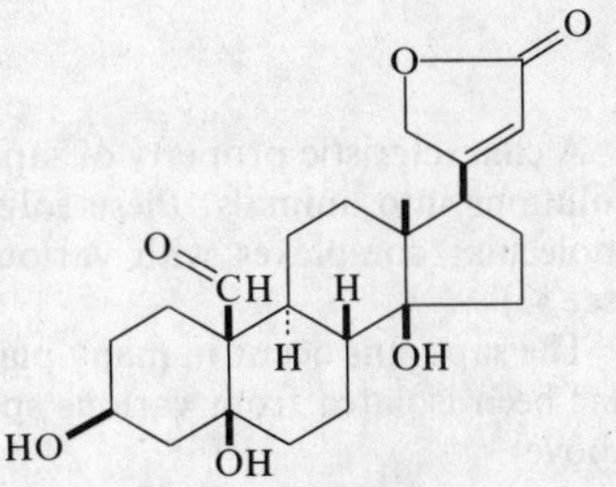   strophanthidin

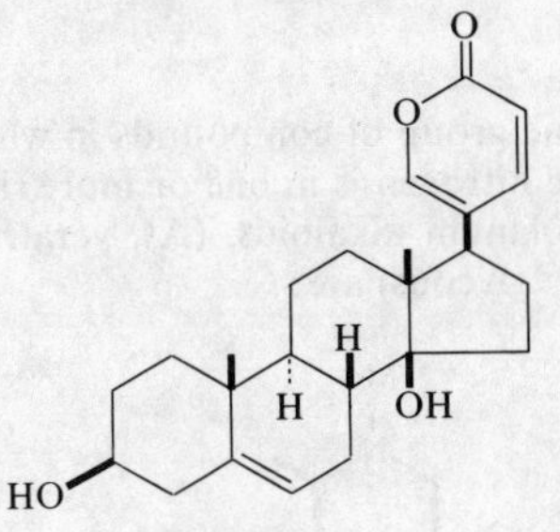

scillaren A 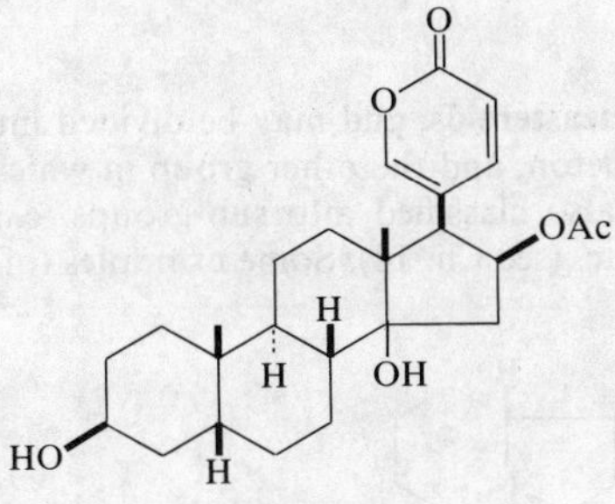   bufotalin 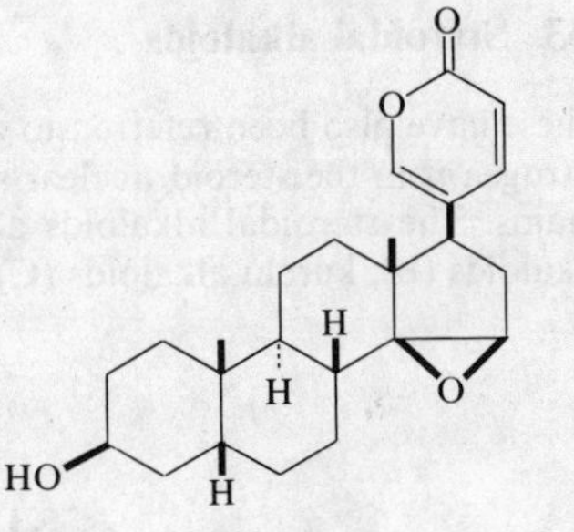   resibutogenin

The most common source of the cardenolides is the plants of the *Digitalis* (foxglove) family. On the other hand, the bufadienolides occur as glycosides in plants of the squill family and as esters of suberylarginine in the venom in the skin secretions of poisonous toads, *e.g.*, bufotoxin is the ester (terminal carboxyl group) of bufotalin (see structure above).

suberylarginine

§32. Sapogenins

These are the aglycons of the **saponins**, and are characterised by the presence of a spiroketal side-chain. One sapogenin, diosgenin, has been mentioned earlier (see §25); it is used as the starting material for the partial synthesis of progesterone. Some other examples are:

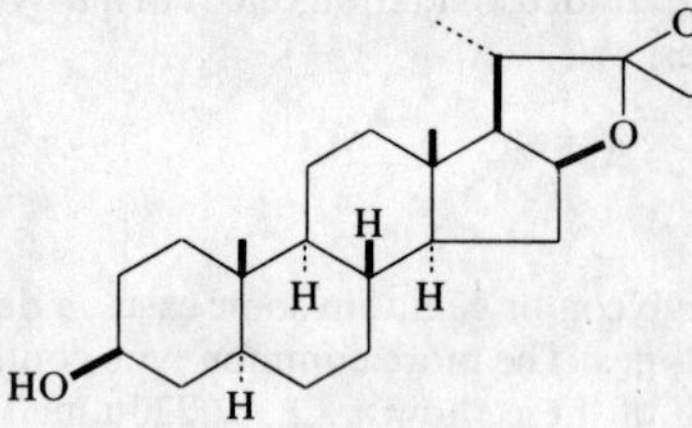

tigogenin

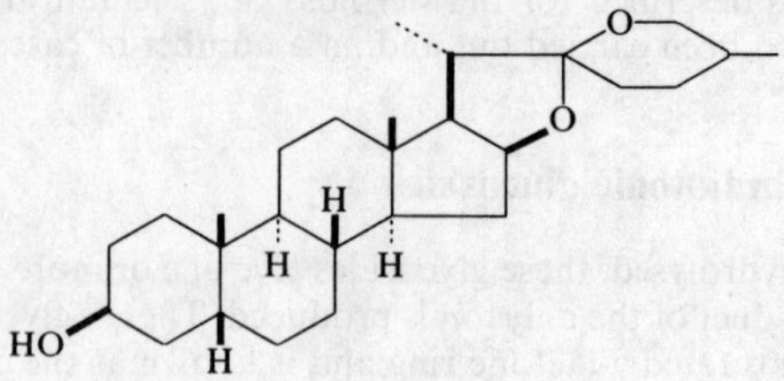

sarsasapogenin

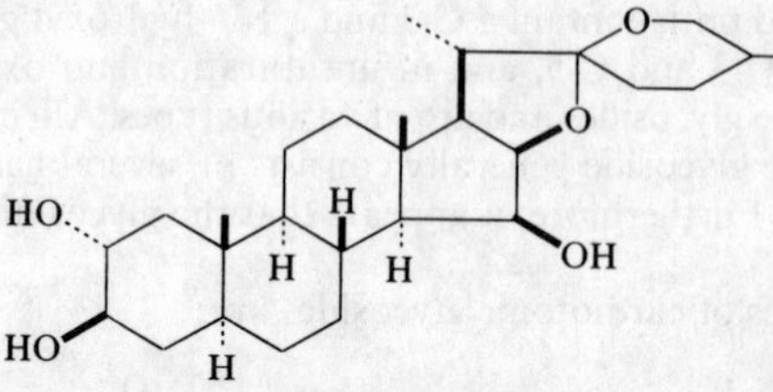

digitogenin

A characteristic property of saponins is the haemolysis caused by an intravenous injection of their aqueous solutions into animals; these solutions are comparatively harmless when taken orally. Saponins also form molecular complexes with various 3β-hydroxysteroids, and this is particularly characteristic of digitonin (see §3).

The saponins occur in many plants and are often associated with the cardiotonic glycosides, *e.g.*, digitonin has been isolated from various species of *Digitalis*. The sapogenin (aglycon) of digitonin is digitogenin (see above).

§33. Steroidal alkaloids

These have also been referred to as **azasteroids**, and may be divided into one group of compounds in which nitrogen is in the steroid nuclear skeleton, and the other group in which the nitrogen is in one or more side-chains. The steroidal alkaloids are also classified into sub-groups, *e.g.*, solanum alkaloids, (A), veratrum alkaloids (B), kurchi alkaloids (C), etc. (see Ch. 14). Some examples (of the aglycons) are:

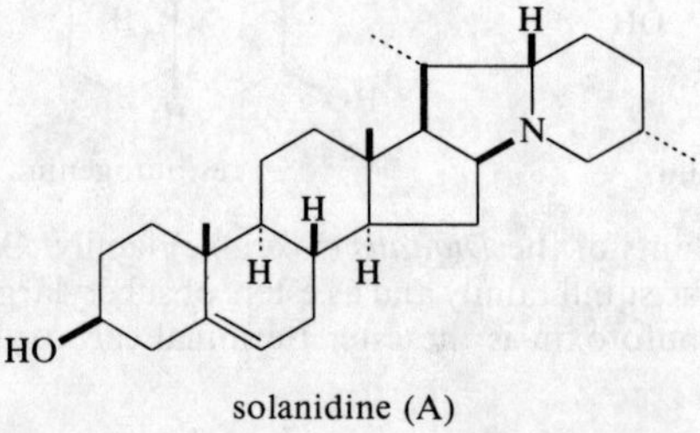

solanidine (A)

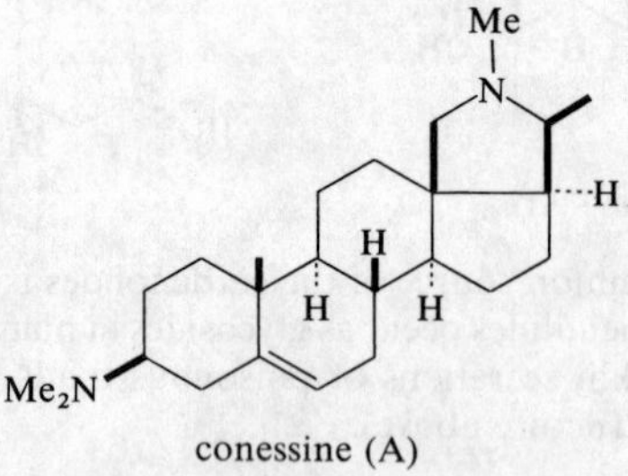

conessine (A)

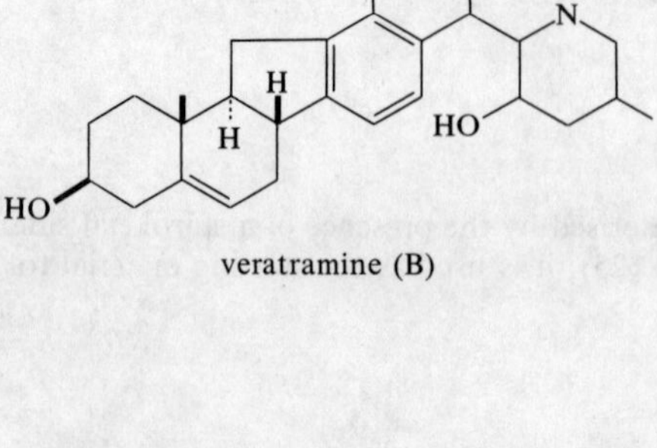

veratramine (B)

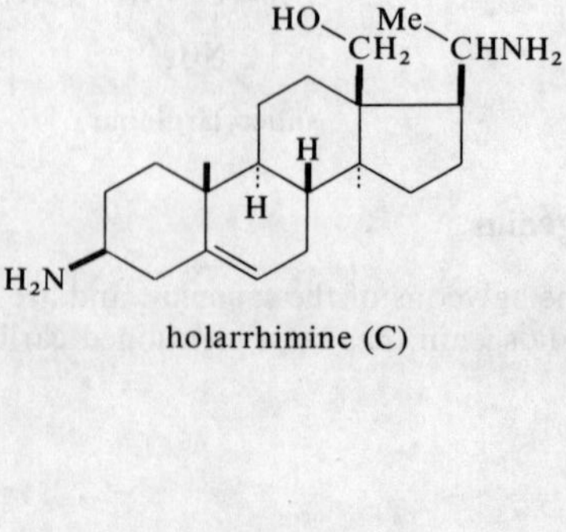

holarrhimine (C)

REFERENCES

FIESER and FIESER, *Steroids*, Reinhold (1959).

SHOPPEE, *Chemistry of the Steroids*, Butterworths (1964, 2nd edn.).

TEMPLETON, *An Introduction to the Chemistry of the Terpenoids and Steroids*, Butterworths (1969).

COFFEY (ed.), *Rodd's Chemistry of Carbon Compounds*, Elsevier. Vol. IID and IIE (1970). **Steroids** (see also Appendix. 'Nomenclature of Steroids').

Handbook for Chemical Society Authors, Special Publication No. 14. The Chemical Society. Ch. 4. 'Steroids'.

Terpenoids and Steroids, Specialist Periodical Reports. The Chemical Society, Vol. 1 (1971).

Recent Developments in the Chemistry of Natural Carbon Compounds. Vol. 1 (1965). Torgov, 'Achievements in the Total Synthesis of Natural Steroids'.

CHARNEY and HERZOG, *Microbial Transformations of Steroids*, Academic Press (1967).

DJERASSI (ed.), *Steroid Reactions: An Outline for Organic Chemists*, Holden-Day (1963).

KIRK and HARTSHORN, *Steroid Reaction Mechanisms*, Elsevier (1968).

BERNFELD (ed.), *Biogenesis of Natural Compounds*, Pergamon (1967, 2nd edn.).

GEISSMAN and GROUT, *Organic Chemistry of Secondary Plant Metabolism*, Freeman, Cooper and Co. (1969). Ch. XI. 'Higher Terpenoids'.

MULHEIRN and RAMM, 'The Biosynthesis of Sterols', *Chem. Soc. Rev.*, 1972, **1**, 259.

ELIEL, ALLINGER, ANGYAL, and MORRISON, *Conformational Analysis*, Interscience (1965). Chs. 3, 5.

MAYO (ed.), *Molecular Rearrangements*, Interscience. Part II (1964). Ch. 16. 'Rearrangements in Steroids.'

DJERASSI, *Optical Rotatory Dispersion*, McGraw-Hill (1960).

CRABBÉ, *Optical Rotatory Dispersion and Circular Dichroism in Organic Chemistry*, Holden-Day (1965).

ALLINGER and ELIEL (eds.), *Topics in Stereochemistry*, Interscience Publishers. Vol. 1 (1967), 'Recent Applications of ORD and OCD', p. 93.

COREY, 'General Methods for the Construction of Complex Molecules', *Pure Appl. Chem.*, 1967, **14**, 19.

TURNER, 'Control Elements in Organic Synthesis', *Chem. in. Britain*, 1971, **7**, 191.

JOHNSON et al., 'Steroid Total Synthesis—Hydrochrysene Approach. Racemic Conessine, Progesterone, Cholesterol, and Some Related Natural Products', *Tetrahedron*, 1966, Suppl. 8, Part II, p. 541.

DJERASSI et al., 'Acansterol: A Cyclopropane-containing Marine Sterol from Acanthaster planci', *Chem. Comm.*, 1971, 217.

CHOU et al., 'The Chemistry of Cephalosporin P_1', *Tetrahedron Letters*, 1967, 409 (see also references therein).

HERNDON, 'The Structure of Choleic Acids', *J. chem. Educ.*, 1967, **44**, 724.

BUDZIKIEWICZ, DJERASSI, and WILLIAMS, *Structure Elucidation of Natural Products by Mass Spectrometry*, Holden-Day. Vol. 2 (1964). Chs. 18–22.

Vitamins and Hormones, Academic Press (Vol. 1. 1943–).

12

Heterocyclic compounds containing two or more hetero-atoms

§1. Nomenclature

Many heterocyclic systems have trivial names (see text). The following is the systematic method of nomenclature.

(i) The names of monocyclic compounds are derived by a prefix (or prefixes) indicating the nature of the hetero-atoms present, and eliding the 'a' where necessary, *e.g.*, oxygen, **oxa**; sulphur, **thia**; nitrogen, **aza**; silicon, **sila**; phosphorus, **phospha**. When two or more of the same hetero-atoms are present, the prefixes di, tri, etc. are used, *e.g.*, dioxa, triaza. If the hetero-atoms are *different*, their order of citation starts with the hetero-atom of as high a group in the periodic table and as low an atomic number in that group. Thus, the order of naming will be O, S, N, P, Si, *e.g.*, thiaza (S then N).

(ii) The size of a monocyclic ring from 3 to 10 is indicated by a stem: 3, ir (tr*i*); 4, et (te*t*ra); 5, ol; 6, in; 7, ep (he*p*ta); 8, oc (*oc*ta); 9, on (n*on*a); 10, ec (d*ec*a) [see Table 12.1].

(iii) The state of hydrogenation is indicated in the suffix (see Table 12.1), or by the prefixes dihydro, tetrahydro, etc., or by prefixing the name of the parent unsaturated compound with the symbol *H* preceded by a number indicating the position of saturation.

Table 12.1

No. of members in the ring	Rings containing nitrogen		Rings containing no nitrogen	
	Unsaturation	Saturation	Unsaturation	Saturation
	(a)		(a)	
3	-irine	-iridine	-iren	-iran
4	-ete	-etidine	-et	-etan
5	-ole	-olidine	-ole	-olan
6	-ine	(b)	-in	-ane
7	-epine	(b)	-epin	-epan
8	-ocine	(b)	-ocin	-ocan
9	-onine	(b)	-onin	-onan
10	-ecine	(b)	-ecin	-ecan

(a) Corresponding to the maximum number of non-cumulative double bonds.
(b) Expressed by prefixing 'perhydro' to the name of the corresponding unsaturated compound.

(iv) (a) In a monocyclic compound containing only one hetero-atom, numbering starts at this atom.

(b) The ring is numbered to give substituents or other hetero-atoms the lowest numbers possible. If the hetero-atoms are different, then numbering starts at the atom cited first according to the rule in (i) and proceeds round the ring in order of precedence.

Examples (see text for the various trivial names).

| aziridine | azocine | 2*H*,6*H*-1,5,2-dithiazine | oxetan |

Fused heterocyclic systems. Only a very elementary account is given here. When one heterocyclic ring is present, this is chosen as the parent compound. If more than one heterocyclic ring is present, the order of preference is given to the nitrogen-containing component (nitrogen rings are the most common). For a component containing a hetero-atom other than nitrogen, the order of preference is that in (i) above (O before S, etc.). When the parent compound has been chosen, its name is prefixed by the name of the fused ring attached, *e.g.*, benz(o), naphth(o). Also, the parent compound chosen is the component containing the largest number of rings and has a simple name. For the purpose of numbering, the structure is written with the greatest number of rings in a horizontal position and a maximum number of rings above and to the right of the horizontal row (**10** §1). Numbering is then carried out (usually) in a clockwise direction starting with the uppermost ring farthest to right and omitting atoms at ring junctions. To distinguish isomers, the *peripheral sides of the parent compound* are lettered *a*, *b*, *c*, etc., beginning with *a* for the side 1,2, *b* for 2,3, etc. To the letter as early in the alphabet as possible, denoting the side where fusion occurs, are prefixed, if necessary, the numbers indicating the positions of fusion of the other component; their order conforms to the *direction of lettering* of the base component. It should be noted that these numbers apply to the *prefixed component* (as a separate entity) and *not* to the combined system (which is numbered according to the usual rules). Two examples are:

| benzo[*h*]isoquinoline | thieno[2,3-*b*]furan |

In addition to the foregoing rules, there are the rules that the component chosen is the one containing the largest possible individual ring, or containing the greatest number or variety of hetero-atoms, etc. Some examples are:

| 2*H*-furo[3,2-*b*]pyran | 1*H*-pyrazolo[4,3-*d*]oxazole | 5*H*-pyrido[2,3-*d*]-*o*-oxazine |

§1a. Spectral properties of heterocyclic compounds. Table 12.2 gives some spectral data: ultra-violet ($\pi \rightarrow \pi^*$; see **1** §12a); infrared, NMR, and also pK_a values in water for both base (proton gain) and acid (proton loss).

Table 12.2

Compound	λ_{max} (nm)	I.r. (cm^{-1})	τ (position)	pK$_a$ Proton gained	Proton lost
Pyrazole	210		2·45 (3,5), 3·75 (4)	2·47	14
Imidazole	207	1 550, 1 492, 1 451	2·30 (2), 2·86 (4,5)	7·03	14·5
Isoxazole	211	1 558, 1 431, 1 367		1·30	—
Oxazole	205				
Thiazole	235	1 615, 1 485, 1 385	1·12 (2), 2·02 (4), 2·59 (5)	2·53	—
Isothiazole	242	1 485, 1 390			
1,2,3-Triazole	210	1 520, 1 450, 1 410		1·17	9·42
1,2,4-Triazole	212		1·82 (3,5)	2·30	
Pyridazine	246	1 572, 1 565, 1 444, 1 414	0·83 (3), 2·32 (4)	2·33	—
Pyrimidine	243	1 610, 1 570, 1 467, 1 402	0·85 (2), 1·40 (4), 2·91 (5)	1·30	—
Pyrazine	260	1 584, 1 490, 1 418	1·50 (2,3)	0·70	—

The infrared spectra of many heterocyclic systems have been worked out in great detail. Contributions to the spectra due to various types of stretching, deformation, etc. (see **1** §12b) have been classified into regions. Table 12.2 lists ring-stretching vibrations which occur in the 1 600–1 350 cm^{-1} region. These bands are shown by most heterocyclic compounds and, in general, five-membered rings show three bands near 1 560, 1 480, and 1 400 cm^{-1}, whereas six-membered rings generally show four bands near 1 600, 1 570, and 1 480–1 420 cm^{-1}.

Some NMR spectral data have been given in Table 12.2. It will be seen that the ring protons have τ-values very much shifted downfield compared with benzene, and this downfield shift is more pronounced for hydrogens in the α-positions. These shifts are due to deshielding caused by the inductive effect of the hetero-atom (see also **1** §12e).

Mass spectrometry of heterocyclic compounds containing one hetero-atom has been studied in great detail, but this is not the case (so far) for heterocyclic compounds containing two or more hetero-atoms (see **1** §13m).

Azoles

PYRAZOLE GROUP

§2. Pyrazole

Pyrazole may be synthesised in a number of ways, some of the more convenient methods being the following:

(i) By passing acetylene into a cold ethereal solution of diazomethane (von Pechmann, 1898). This addition may be formulated:

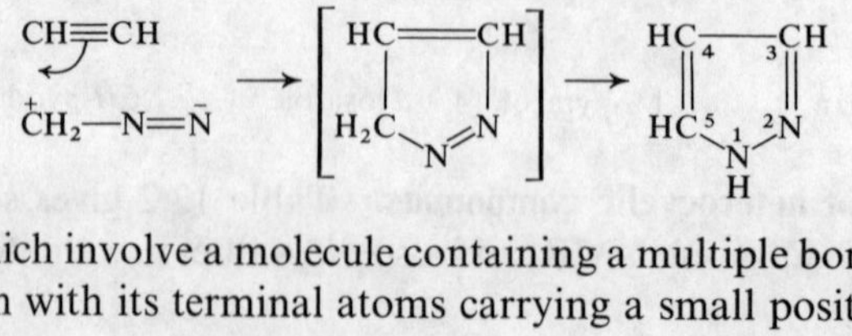

Additions such as this, which involve a molecule containing a multiple bond and molecule containing three atoms in a chain with its terminal atoms carrying a small positive and negative charge, respectively, are referred to as 1,3-*dipolar additions*; the cyclo-addition occurs in one step (*cf*. the Diels–Alder reaction; see also Vol. I).

(ii) The most convenient method of preparing pyrazole is by the condensation of 1,1,3,3-tetra-ethoxypropane (malondialdehyde diethyl acetal) with hydrazine dihydrochloride (Jones, 1949).

$$(EtO)_2CHCH_2CH(OEt)_2 \xrightarrow{(N_2H_4)2HCl}$$

(iii) By the decarboxylation of various pyrazolecarboxylic acid, *e.g.*, by heating pyrazole-3,4,5-tricarboxylic acid (see also §2a (ii)).

$$\xrightarrow{300°C} + 3CO_2$$

Properties of pyrazole. Pyrazole is a colourless solid, m.p. 70°C. This high value (compared with 1-alkyl or aryl substituted pyrazoles) is due to intermolecular hydrogen bonding which results in a dimer. Pyrazole is a tautomeric substance; the existence of tautomerism cannot be demonstrated in pyrazole itself, but it can be inferred by the consideration of pyrazole derivatives. If pyrazole is tautomeric, then the positions 3 and 5 will be identical; if pyrazole is not tautomeric, then these positions are different. Now Knorr *et al.* (1893) showed that on oxidation, both 3-methyl-1-phenylpyrazole and 5-methyl-1-phenylpyrazole gave the *same* product, *viz.*, methylpyrazole. Thus positions 3 and 5 must be equivalent in pyrazole, and this can only be explained by assuming that pyrazole is tautomeric ((I) and (II)). It therefore follows that

(I)   (II)

in pyrazole there can only be *two* carbon-alkyl derivatives, 3- (or 5-) and 4-. If, however, the imino hydrogen is replaced by an alkyl or aryl group, then *three* carbon-alkyl derivatives are possible, 3, 4 and 5, since tautomerism is now impossible, and so positions 3 and 5 are no longer equivalent.

In pyrazole itself the two tautomers will be expected to contribute equally to the equilibrium mixture, but in unsymmetrical pyrazoles it has been found that the contributions are unequal. Thus, Moore *et al.* (1965) have shown, by NMR spectra studies, that (III*a*) and (IV*a*) are the predominant structures.

(III)   (III*a*)   (IV)   (IV*a*)

Pyrazole exhibits aromatic properties, *e.g.*, it is readily halogenated, nitrated and sulphonated; the group enters at position 4. The following resonating structures are possible for pyrazole.

If these structures are contributed equally, then electrophilic attack should occur equally well at positions 3, 4 or 5 (in pyrazole itself, positions 3 and 5 are equivalent). As we have seen above, electrophilic attack occurs exclusively at position 4. The reason for this is not certain. Finar (1968) has shown (from simple Hückel MO calculations) that position 4 in pyrazole carries a larger π-electron charge than any of the other nuclear carbon atoms. Hence, from the point of view of the isolated molecule method (see Vol. I), position 4 will be the most likely site of attack by an electrophilic reagent. It was also shown that the localisation energy method (see Vol. I) also indicated that position 4 is the favoured site for electrophilic attack. On the other hand, in acid solution, e.g., in nitration, the pyrazole is protonated (see below) and again it was shown that position 4 is the favoured site for attack (by the nitronium ion). In this case, calculations showed that because of the positive charges on the nitrogen atoms the electrostatic repulsion between protonated substrate and the nitronium ion was much greater than that with the unprotonated species. Even so, position 4 was still the favoured site, but the rate of reaction is decreased (see also §2a).

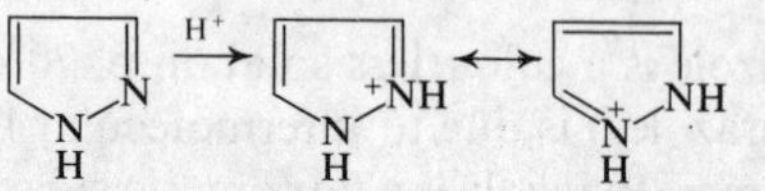

Pyrazole is feebly basic (see Table 12.2) and forms salts with inorganic acids; the imino hydrogen may be replaced by an acyl group. Pyrazole is very resistant to oxidising and reducing agents, but may be hydrogenated catalytically, first to pyrazoline, and then to pyrazolidine. Both of these compounds are stronger bases than pyrazole.

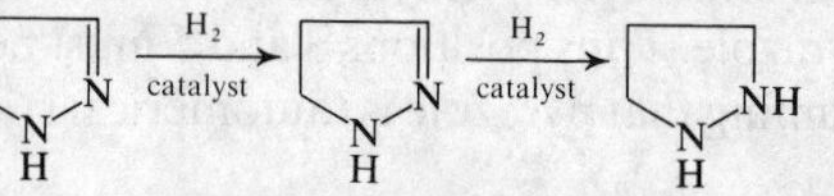

pyrazoline   pyrazolidine

§2a. Synthesis of pyrazole derivatives

(i) A very important method for preparing pyrazole derivatives is by the reaction between β-diketones and hydrazines (Knorr et al., 1883).

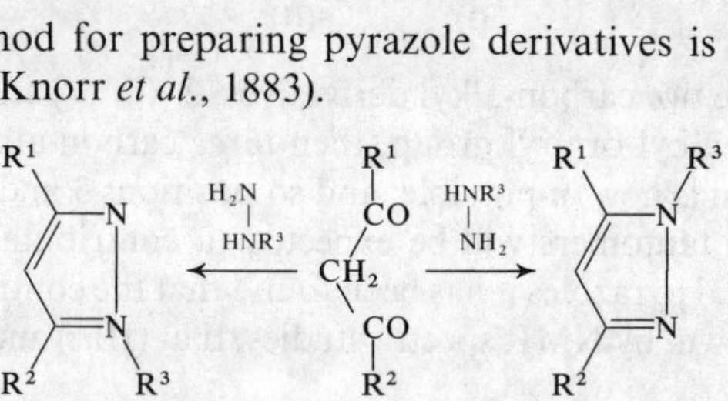

Thus, according to the above, a mixture of isomeric pyrazoles will be produced. Contrary to general opinion, the product is usually only one of the isomers, e.g., benzoylacetone and phenylhydrazine form only 3-methyl-1,5-diphenylpyrazole (Drumm, 1931). The mechanisms of these condensations are uncertain; a possibility is (cyclisation and proton transfer are shown as one step):

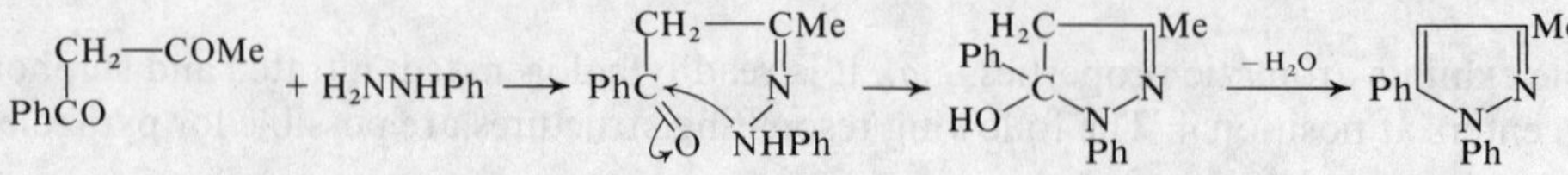

Since the phenyl group can conjugate with an adjacent carbonyl group far more so than can a methyl group, nucleophilic attack at the PhCO carbonyl group is hindered.

In some cases, two isomers have been isolated, e.g., 3-α-benzoylacetyl-1,5-diphenylpyrazole (I) reacts with phenylhydrazine to produce a mixture of 1,1′,5,5′-tetraphenyl-3,3′-bipyrazolyl (II) and 1,1′,3′,5-tetraphenyl-3,5′-bipyrazolyl (III) [Finar, 1955].

(I)   (II)   (III)

In this case, conjugation occurs at either end.

β-Ketoaldehydes may also be used (instead of β-diketones), particularly in the form of their vinyl ethers (enol ether), and again a mixture of isomers may be obtained.

If β-ketoesters are used then 5-pyrazolones are formed (Knorr *et al.*, 1883), *e.g.*, ethyl acetoacetate reacts with hydrazine to form 3-methylpyrazol-5-one.

(ii) Pyrazolecarboxylic acids are produced by the reaction between diazoacetic ester and acetylenic compounds, *e.g.*, with ethyl acetylenedicarboxylate, ethyl pyrazole-3,4,5-tricarboxylate is formed (by a 1,3-dipolar addition; *cf.* §2).

Similarly, propargylaldehyde reacts with diazomethane to form 3(5)-formylpyrazole (*cf.* (iv), below).

If an ethylenic compound is used instead of an acetylenic one, then a pyrazoline derivative is produced, *e.g.*, ethyl fumarate gives ethyl pyrazoline-3,4,5-tricarboxylate (by a 1,3-dipolar addition).

(iii) Pyrazoles are produced by the reaction between acetylenic carbonyl compounds and hydrazines (Moureu *et al.*, 1903); a mixture of isomers is said to be obtained.

(iv) Pyrazolines are obtained by the condensation of α,β-unsaturated ketones or aldehydes with hydrazines, *e.g.*, acraldehyde and hydrazine give pyrazoline.

Pyrazolines may be oxidised to pyrazoles by bromine or mercuric oxide.

If either carbon atom of the double bond is attached to a halogen atom, then a pyrazole is obtained, *e.g.*,

$$PhCH{=}CBrCOPh + PhNHNH_2 \longrightarrow \quad + HBr + H_2O$$

Properties of the pyrazole derivatives.   Pyrazoles with substituent methyl groups may be oxidised by potassium permanganate to the corresponding pyrazolecarboxylic acids, *e.g.*,

Pyrazole-3- and 5-carboxylic acids are readily decarboxylated by heating above their melting points; the pyrazole-4-carboxylic acids are more stable, but can nevertheless be decarboxylated at elevated temperatures, *e.g.*,

Although pyrazole itself is not reduced by sodium and ethanol, *N*-phenyl substituted pyrazoles are readily reduced to the corresponding pyrazolines, *e.g.*,

1-Unsubstituted pyrazoles apparently cannot be chloromethylated; carbinols are produced, *e.g.*, (Dvoretzky *et al.*, 1950):

On the other hand, 1-phenylpyrazole can readily be chloromethylated in the 4-position (Finar *et al.*, 1954).

4-Chloromethyl-1-phenylpyrazole can be converted into 1-phenylpyrazole-4-aldehyde by means of the Sommelet reaction (see Vol. I). The 4-aldehyde is more conveniently prepared by the direct formylation of 1-phenylpyrazole with dimethylformamide and phosphoryl chloride (Finar *et al.*, 1957). 1-Phenylpyrazole can also be mercurated in the 4-position (Finar *et al.*, 1954).

When boiled with concentrated aqueous potassium hydroxide, quaternary pyrazoles are converted into hydrazines (Knorr *et al.*, 1906), *e.g.*,

$$\text{(pyrazole, N-Ph)} + \text{MeI} \longrightarrow \{\text{(pyrazole, N-Ph, NMe)}\}^+ \text{I}^- \xrightarrow{\text{KOH}} \text{HCO}_2\text{H} + \text{PhNHNHMe}$$

Knorr used this reaction to prepare 1,2-disubstituted hydrazines; at the same time, this reaction proves the structure of the pyrazole-quaternary salts.

Esters of the pyrazolinecarboxylic acids eliminate nitrogen on heating to give cyclopropane derivatives; sometimes much better results are achieved if the compound is heated with copper powder.

$$\begin{array}{c}\text{RCH}\\ \| \\ \text{RCH}\end{array} + \begin{array}{c}\text{CHCO}_2\text{Et}\\ \| \\ \text{N}_2\end{array} \longrightarrow \begin{array}{c}\text{R}\\ \text{R}\end{array}\!\!\left[\text{pyrazoline, CO}_2\text{Et, NH}\right] \xrightarrow[\text{heat}]{\text{Cu}} \begin{array}{c}\text{RCH}\\ \text{RCH}\end{array}\!\!\text{CHCO}_2\text{Et} + \text{N}_2$$

Antipyrine (2,3-dimethyl-1-phenylpyrazol-5-one), m.p. 127°C, is very much used in medicine as a febrifuge. It is prepared industrially by condensing ethyl acetoacetate with phenylhydrazine, and methylating the product, 3-methyl-1-phenylpyrazol-5-one, with methyl iodide in alkaline ethanolic solution, or with methyl sulphate in the presence of sodium hydroxide.

$$\begin{array}{c}\text{MeC}\!-\!\text{CH}_2\\ \| \qquad | \\ \text{O} \quad \text{CO}_2\text{Et}\end{array} + \text{PhNHNH}_2 \longrightarrow \left[\begin{array}{c}\text{MeC}\!-\!\text{CH}_2\\ \| \qquad | \\ \text{N} \quad \text{CO}_2\text{Et}\\ \text{NH}\\ \text{Ph}\end{array}\right] \longrightarrow \underset{\substack{\text{3-methyl-1-phenyl-}\\ \text{pyrazol-5-one}}}{[\text{Me, N-N-Ph, O ring}]} + \text{EtOH} \xrightarrow{\text{MeI}} \underset{\text{antipyrine}}{[\text{Me, MeN-N-Ph, O ring}]}$$

At first sight one might have expected to obtain the *O*-methyl or the 4-methyl derivative, since the tautomeric forms (IV) (keto) and (V) (enol) are theoretically possible. Methylation of 3-methyl-1-phenylpyrazol-5-one with diazomethane results in the formation of the *O*-methyl derivative (this is also produced in a small amount when methyl iodide is used as the methylating reagent). This

$$\underset{\text{(IV)}}{[\text{Me, N-N-Ph, =O}]} \rightleftharpoons \underset{\text{(V)}}{[\text{Me, N-N-Ph, OH}]} \rightleftharpoons \underset{\text{(VI)}}{[\text{Me, HN-N-Ph, =O}]}$$

raised some doubts as to the structure of antipyrine, since for its formation, the tautomeric form (VI) must also be postulated. The structure of antipyrine was shown to be that given above by its synthesis from 1,2-methylphenylhydrazine and ethyl acetoacetate.

$$\begin{array}{c}\text{MeCOCH}_2\text{COOEt}\\ +\\ \text{MeNHNHPh}\end{array} \longrightarrow [\text{Me, MeN-N-Ph, O ring}] + \text{H}_2\text{O} + \text{EtOH}$$

The pyrazole nucleus has always been considered to be a synthetic one, but Fowden *et al.* (1959) have now isolated α-amino-β-1-pyrazolylpropionic acid from water-melon seed; this acid has been synthesised in good yield by Finar *et al.* (1960).

§2b. Indazoles (benzopyrazoles).   Indazole may conveniently be prepared by heating *o*-*N*-nitroso-*N*-benzoyltoluidine in benzene solution.

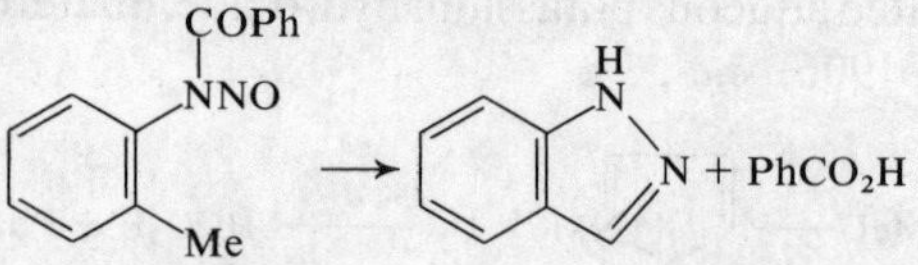

Another synthesis is that due to Ainsworth (1957):

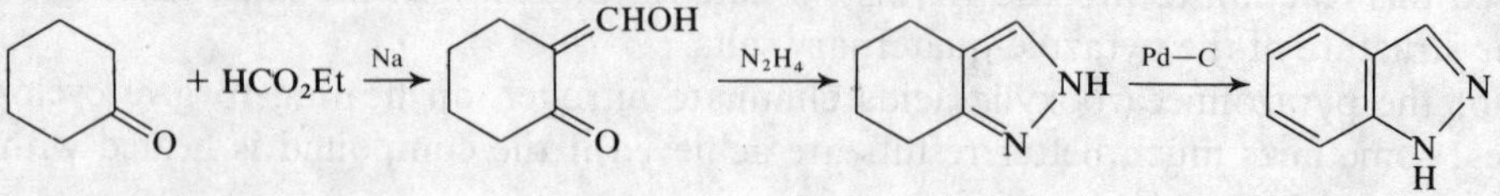

Indazole, m.p. 146°C, exhibits the same type of tautomerism that exists in pyrazole, since *two* series of *N*-derivatives (1 and 2) are known:

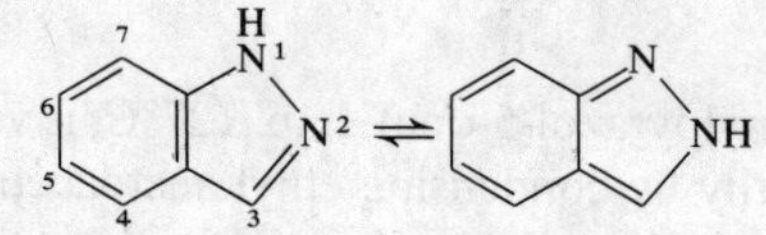

Nitration and sulphonation of indazole produce the 5-substitution product; bromination gives the 3,5-dibromo compound.

IMIDAZOLE GROUP

This group of compounds has also been known as the *iminazoles* or the *glyoxalines*.

§3. Imidazole (iminazole, glyoxaline)

This is isomeric with pyrazole, and occurs in the purine nucleus and in the amino-acid histidine; 4-amino-imidazole-5-carboxamide occurs naturally as a riboside (or ribotide).

Imidazole may be prepared by the action of ammonia on glyoxal. The mechanism of this reaction is uncertain, but one suggestion is that one molecule of glyoxal breaks down into formic acid and formaldehyde, and then the latter reacts as follows:

(i) $OHCCHO + H_2O \longrightarrow HCHO + HCO_2H$

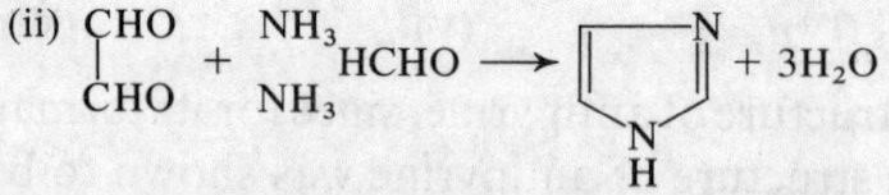

(ii) $\begin{array}{c} CHO \\ | \\ CHO \end{array} + \begin{array}{c} NH_3 \\ \\ NH_3 \end{array} HCHO \longrightarrow$ [imidazole structure] $+ 3H_2O$

A certain amount of support for this mechanism is given by the fact that imidazole may be prepared directly from glyoxal, ammonia and formaldehyde.

A general method for preparing imidazoles is by the reaction between an α-dicarbonyl compound, ammonia and an aldehyde (Radziszewsky, 1882).

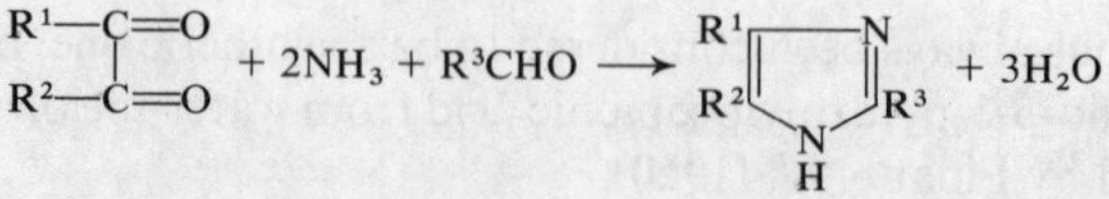

$$\begin{array}{c} R^1—C=O \\ R^2—C=O \end{array} + 2NH_3 + R^3CHO \longrightarrow \begin{array}{c} R^1 \\ R^2 \end{array} \text{[imidazole ring]} R^3 + 3H_2O$$

This method has been improved by Bredereck *et al.* (1959), who heated α-diketones with formamide and formaldehyde (or other aldehydes) at 180–200°C.

Imidazole itself is best prepared by the action of ammonia on a mixture of formaldehyde and tartaric ácid dinitrate ('dinitrotartaric acid'), and then heating the dicarboxylic acid in quinoline in the presence of copper.

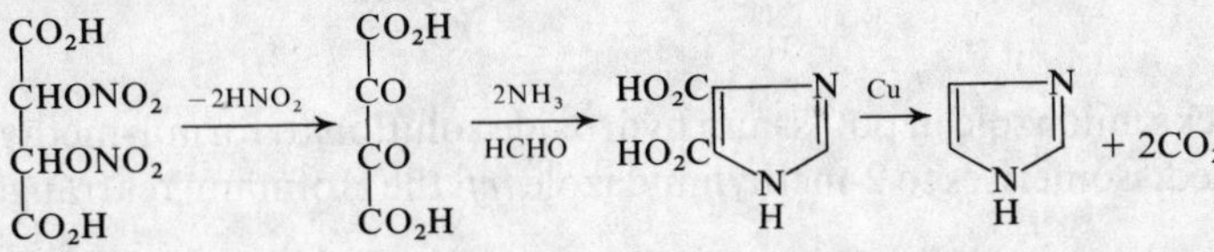

Another good method is to brominate paraldehyde in ethylene glycol and to heat the product, 2-bromomethyl-1,3-dioxolan, with formamide in the presence of ammonia (Bredereck *et al.*, 1958); bromoacetaldehyde is probably an intermediate:

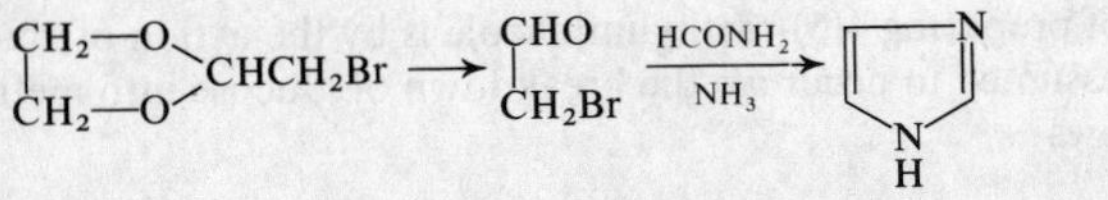

Although there are many methods available for synthesising imidazoles, all are limited in scope. The most general method is the action of potassium thiocyanate on α-aminoaldehydes of ketones (as hydrochlorides) and the product, an imidazoline thione, is desulphurised with Raney nickel or by oxidation with nitric acid.

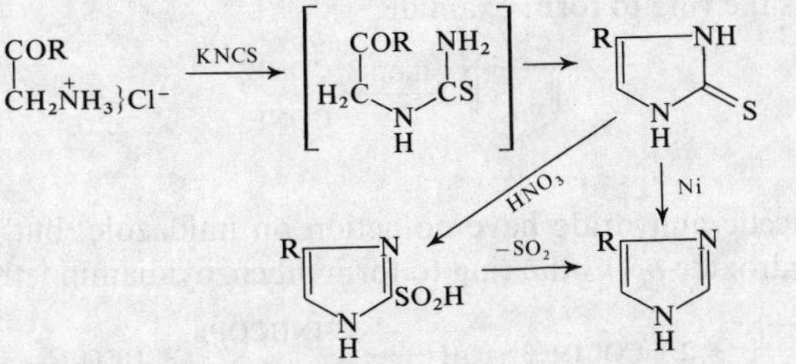

A shorter route starts with the α-bromoketone and an amidine:

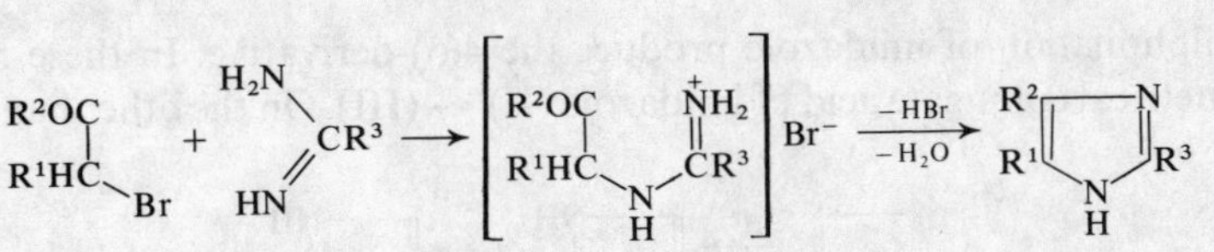

A much less general method is the cyclisation of α-acylaminoketones (which behave as 1,4-diketo compounds), *e.g.*,

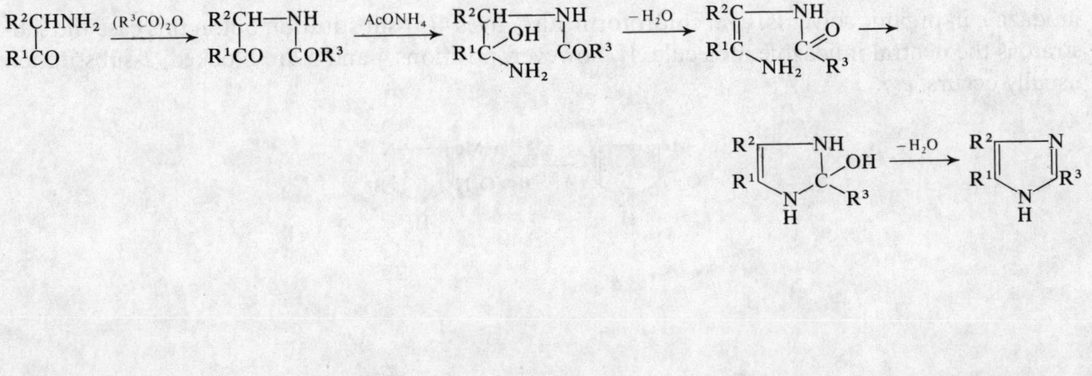

Imidazole, m.p. 90°C, is a weak base, but it is more basic than pyrazole (see Table 12.2). Imidazole is a tautomeric substance, since positions 4 and 5 are equivalent (positions 5, 4 and 2 have also been designated α, β and μ, respectively).

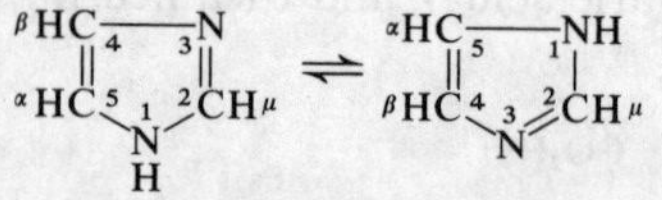

Methyl iodide attacks imidazole in potassium hydroxide solution to form 1-methylimidazole which, when strongly heated, isomerises to 2-methylimidazole (*cf.* the Hofmann rearrangement; see Vol. I).

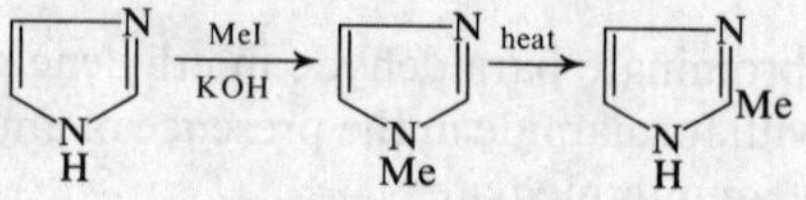

An interesting method of preparing 4(5)-methylimidazole is by the action of zinc hydroxide and ammonia on glucose; the reaction is assumed to occur *via* the breakdown of glucose into methylglyoxal and formaldehyde, which then react as follows:

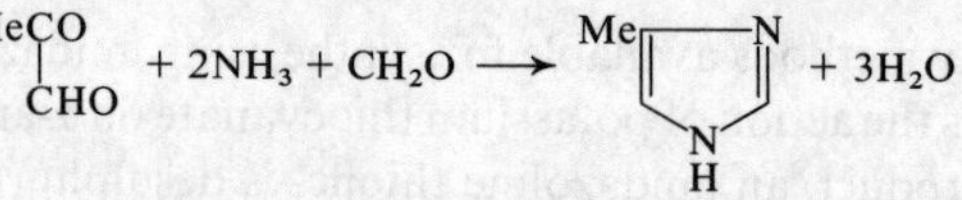

The imidazole ring is extremely stable towards oxidising and reducing agents; hydrogen peroxide, however, readily opens the ring to form oxamide.

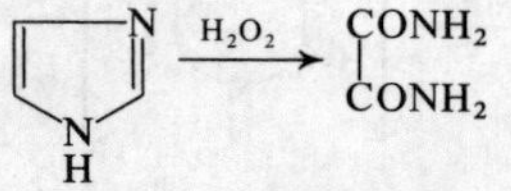

Acetyl chloride and acetic anhydride have no action on imidazole, but benzoyl chloride in the presence of sodium hydroxide *opens* the ring to form dibenzoyldiaminoethylene.

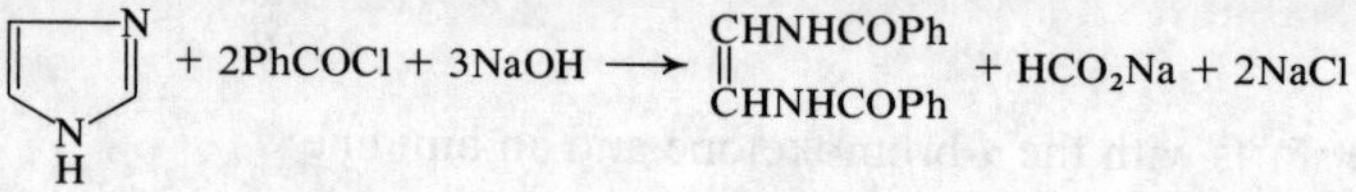

Nitration and sulphonation of imidazole produce the 4(5)-derivative. In these reactions the substrate is the symmetrical conjugate acid of imidazole (II) ↔ (III). On the other hand, bromination of

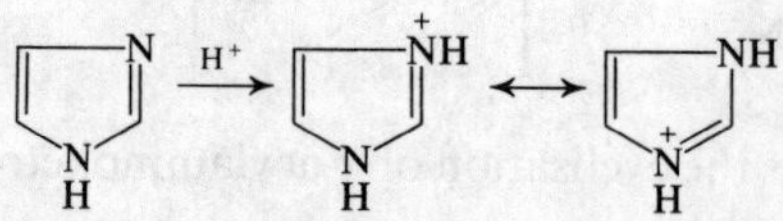

imidazole in organic solvents, *e.g.*, chloroform, also gives 4(5)-substitution but in this case the substrate is the neutral imidazole molecule. If, however, positions 4 and 5 are blocked, 2-substitution usually occurs, *e.g.*,

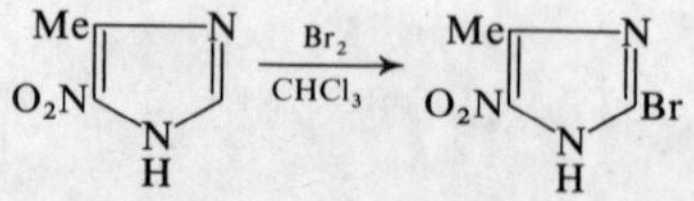

Thus, with bromine, imidazole forms 2,4,5-tribromoimidazole, presumably as shown:

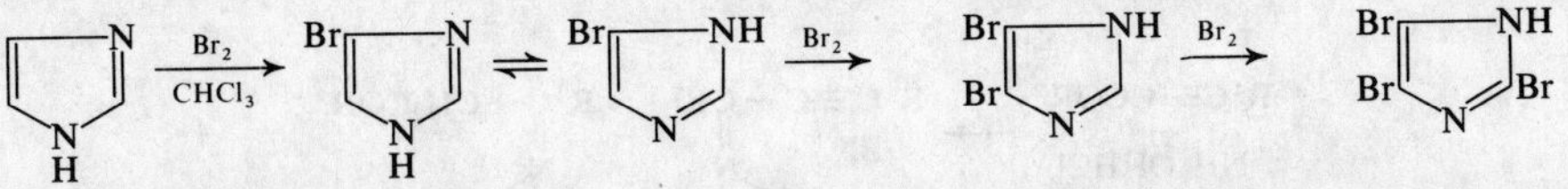

Imidazole couples with diazonium salts in the 2-position, but 1-alkylimidazoles do not couple at all.

§3a. Benzimidazoles (benziminazoles). These are readily formed by heating *o*-phenylenediamines with carboxylic acids, *e.g.*, benzimidazole itself (m.p. 170°C) is produced by heating *o*-phenylenediamine with 90 per cent formic acid.

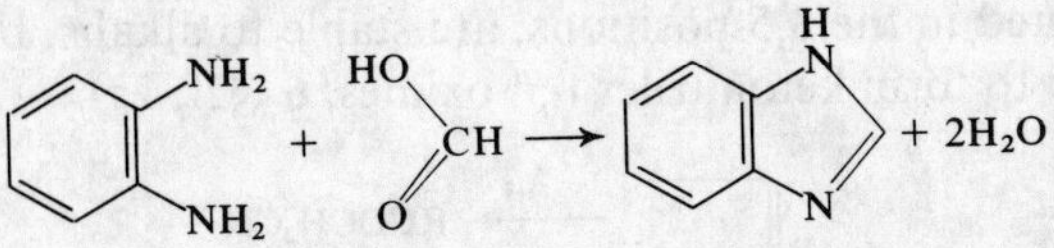

Benzimidazoles occur in vitamin B_{12} and in other biologically active compounds.

OXAZOLE GROUP

§4. Isoxazoles

These may be prepared by reaction between hydroxylamine and a β-dicarbonyl compound (*cf.* pyrazoles, §2). The mechanism of the reaction is not fully understood; it proceeds *via* the formation of an oxime and this possibly undergoes cyclisation as shown.

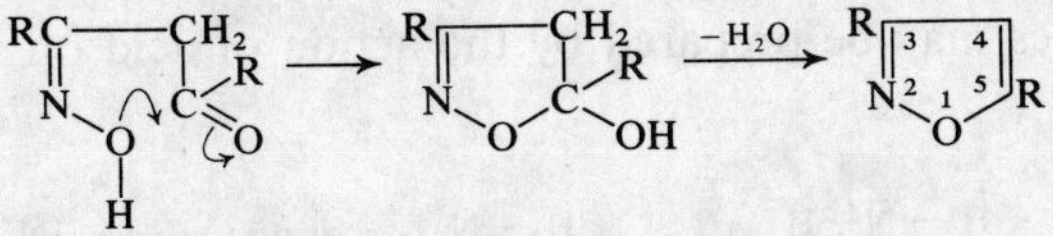

Isoxazole itself may be prepared by the action of hydroxylamine on propargylaldehyde.

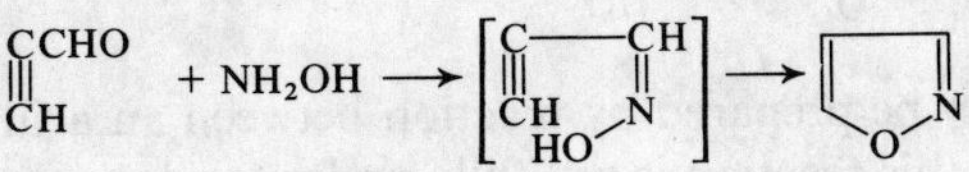

The most convenient preparation is by the reaction between 1,1,3,3-tetraethoxypropane and hydroxylamine hydrochloride (*cf.* pyrazole, §2).

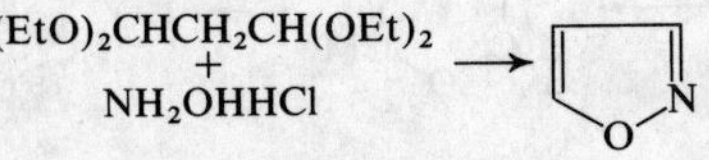

$$(EtO)_2CHCH_2CH(OEt)_2$$
$$+$$
$$NH_2OHHCl$$

Other methods of preparing isoxazoles are also similar to those used for preparing pyrazoles (see also above), *e.g.*,

(*a*) By the 1,3-dipolar addition of a nitrile oxide to an acetylene:

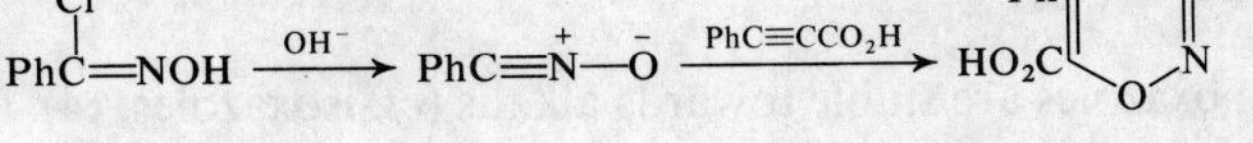

(*b*) By the condensation between acetylenic carbonyl compounds and hydroxylamine hydro-chloride:

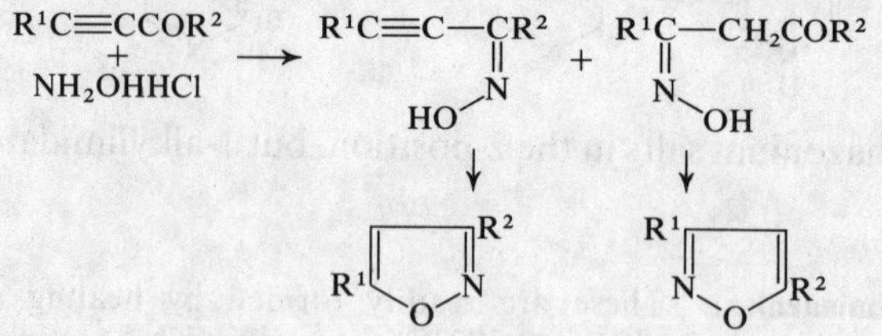

Isoxazole is a colourless liquid, b.p. 96°C, and smells like pyridine; it is weakly basic (see Table 12.2). Isoxazoles, when substituted in the 3,5-positions, are stable to alkalis, but when the 3-position is vacant, the ring is opened to form ketonitriles (*cf.* oximes, **6** §§2f, 2g).

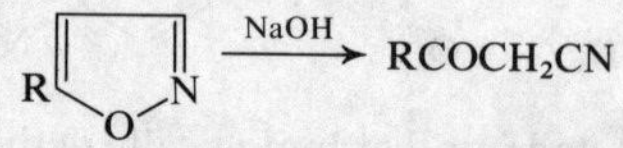

Isoxazoles undergo electrophilic substitution at the 4-position, and quaternisation of the tertiary nitrogen atom readily occurs on treatment with alkyl halides. The quaternary salts undergo ring-cleavage in the presence of alkali (*cf.* above), *e.g.*,

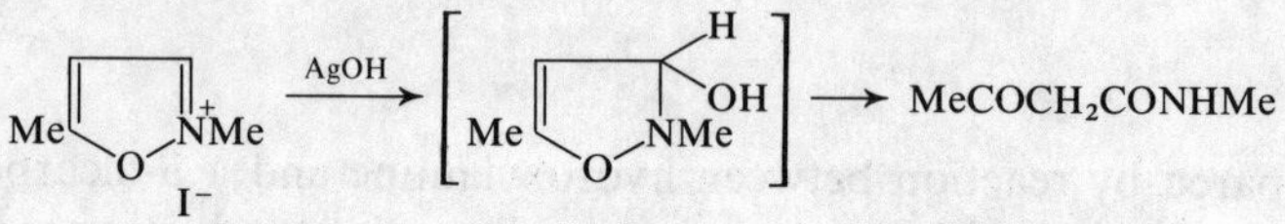

§**4a. Oxazoles.** Oxazoles may be prepared by the action of acid on an α-acylaminoketone (*cf.* imidazoles, §3), *e.g.*,

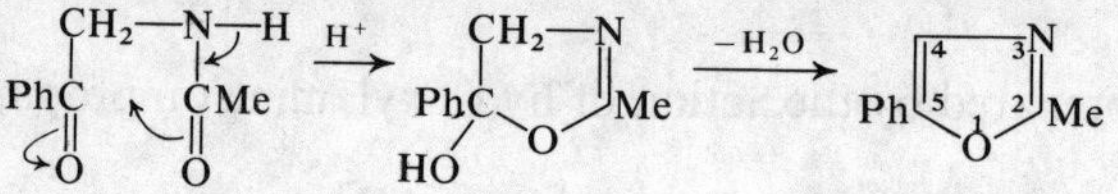

Alternatively, oxazoles may be prepared by reaction between an acid amide and an α-halogeno-ketone. The mechanism of this reaction is not fully understood; a poossibility is alkylation of the imido-form; *e.g.*,

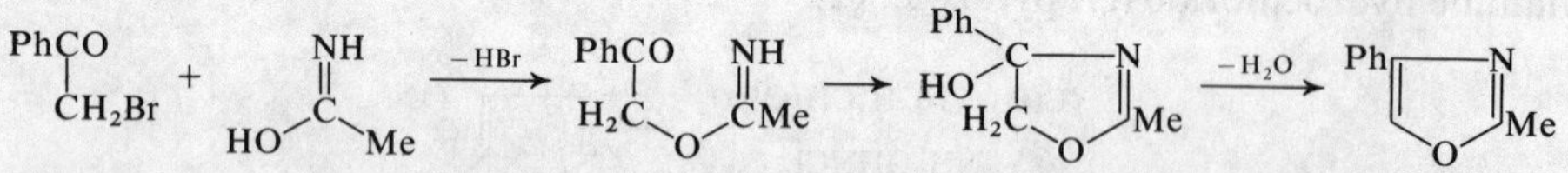

Oxazoles are basic (see Table 12.2) and possess aromatic properties, and the stability of the ring towards concentrated acids depends on the nature of the substituents in the ring, *e.g.*,

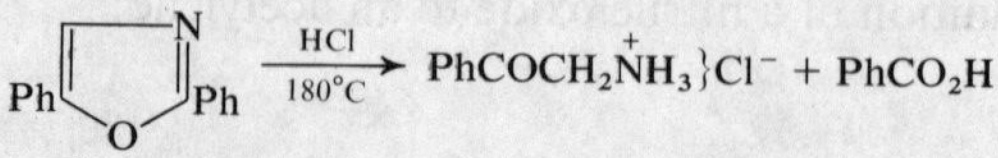

On the other hand, oxazoles are stable towards alkalis (*cf.* isoxazoles, §4).

Oxazole (b.p. 69°C) has been prepared by Cornforth *et al.* (1947, 1948) as follows:

$$EtO_2CCH_2NH_2 + Cl^- \{H_2\overset{+}{N}\!\!=\!\!CHOCHMe_2 \longrightarrow EtO_2CCH_2N\!\!=\!\!CHOCHMe_2 \xrightarrow[EtOK]{HC(OEt)_3}$$

5-Oxazolones. The oxazolones are keto derivatives of the oxazolines, the most important group being the 5-oxazolones or **azlactones**. These azlactones are very important intermediates in the preparation of α-amino-acids (see **13** §2*va*) and keto-acids (see Vol. I).

§4b. Benzoxazoles. These may be prepared by the reaction between *o*-aminophenols and carboxylic acids, *e.g.*, *o*-aminophenol and formic acid form benzoxazole, m.p. 31°C.

Bunnett *et al.* (1963) have prepared 2-methylbenzoxazole by the action of potassamide in liquid ammonia on *o*-chloroacetanilide. This reaction is believed to proceed *via* an aryne intermediate (see also Vol. I).

THIAZOLE GROUP

§5. Thiazoles

A general method for preparing thiazoles is the condensation between α-halogenocarbonyl compounds (particularly the chloro-derivatives) and thioamides; the mechanism of the reaction is uncertain, but it may possibly be (*cf.* oxazoles, §4a):

Thiazole itself may be prepared from chloroacetaldehyde and thioformamide.

If thiourea or its substitution products are used instead of thioamides, then 2-aminothiazoles are produced, *e.g.*, thiazole may be prepared from chloroacetaldehyde and thiourea as follows:

Another general method for preparing thiazoles is by the action of phosphorus pentasulphide on α-acylamidocarbonyl compounds (*cf.* imidazoles, §3):

$$\underset{\substack{| \\ R^1CO \quad COR^2}}{CH_2-NH} \xrightarrow{P_2S_5} \underset{\substack{| \\ R^1C \quad C-R^2 \\ S \quad O}}{H-CH-NH} \longrightarrow \underset{R^1}{\overset{NH}{\underset{S}{\bigcirc}}}\overset{R^2}{\underset{OH}{C}} \xrightarrow{-H_2O} R^1\overset{N}{\underset{S}{\bigcirc}}R^2$$

2-Mercaptothiazoles may be prepared by the condensation between α-chloroketones and ammonium dithiocarbamate.

$$\underset{\substack{R^1CO \\ | \\ R^2CHCl}}{} + \underset{\substack{NH_2 \\ C \\ S}}{CSNH_4} \longrightarrow \underset{R^2}{\overset{R^1}{\underset{S}{\bigcirc}}}\overset{N}{\underset{SH}{}} + H_2O + NH_4Cl$$

Thiazole is a weakly basic liquid, b.p. 117°C (see Table 12.2); it occurs in vitamin B_1. It is a very stable compound, and is not affected by the usual reducing agents; sodium and ethanol, however, open the ring to form thiols (or hydrogen sulphide) and amines. Thiazole is very resistant to substitution reactions, but if a hydroxyl group or an amino group is in position 2, then the molecule is

$$\underset{S}{\overset{Me}{\bigcirc}}\overset{N}{\underset{OH}{}} + Br_2 \xrightarrow{CHCl_3} \underset{Br}{\overset{Me}{\underset{S}{\bigcirc}}}\overset{N}{\underset{OH}{}} + HBr$$

readily attacked by the usual electrophilic reagents to form 5-substitution products, *e.g.*, 2-hydroxy-4-methylthiazole is readily brominated in chloroform solution to give 5-bromo-2-hydroxy-4-methylthiazole. Under vigorous conditions, thiazole may be nitrated (c. HNO_3 + c. H_2SO_4) and sulphonated (with oleum) to the corresponding 5-derivative.

§5a. Thiazolines. These may be prepared by the reaction between β-halogenoamines and thio-amides, *e.g.*,

$$\underset{\substack{CH_2NH_2 \\ | \\ CH_2Br}}{} + \underset{\substack{NH_2 \\ C \\ S}}{CR} \longrightarrow \overset{N}{\underset{S}{\bigcirc}}CR + NH_4Br$$

A characteristic reaction of the thiazolines is their ring opening by the action of acids, *e.g.*,

$$\overset{N}{\underset{S}{\bigcirc}}CMe \xrightarrow{HCl} \underset{\substack{CH_2NH_2 \\ | \\ CH_2SH}}{}$$

2-methylthiazoline   2-aminoethanethiol

§5b. Thiazolidines. These are readily formed by the condensation of carbonyl compounds with cysteine.

$$\underset{\substack{HO_2CCHNH_2 \\ | \\ CH_2SH}}{} + RCOR \longrightarrow \underset{\substack{HO_2C \\ | \\ S}}{\overset{NH}{\bigcirc}}CR_2 + H_2O$$

The thiazolidine ring is very easily opened, sometimes by boiling with water, or with an aqueous solution of mercuric chloride (see also penicillin, **18** §6a).

§5c. Benzothiazoles. These may be prepared by the action of acid anhydrides or chlorides on o-aminothiophenols, *e.g.*, benzothiazole from o-aminothiophenol and formic acid in the presence of acetic anhydride.

$$\overset{NH_2}{\underset{SH}{\bigcirc}} + \underset{\substack{O \\ \| \\ CH \\ | \\ HO}}{} \xrightarrow{(CH_3CO)_2O} \overset{N}{\underset{S}{\bigcirc}} + 2H_2O$$

Benzothiazoles are also formed by the action of phosphorus pentasulphide on *o*-acylamidophenols, *e.g.*,

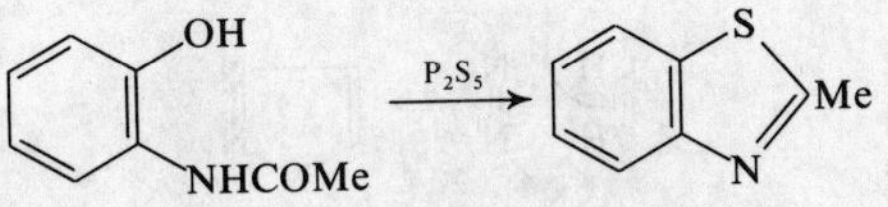

2-Mercaptobenzothiazole is a vulcanisation accelerator (**8** §35a); it may be prepared as follows:

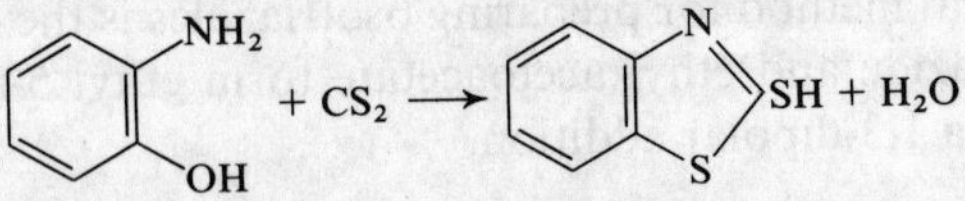

§5d. **Isothiazoles.** Benzisothiazoles have been known for many years, but no derivatives of isothiazole itself have been obtained until recently when Adams *et al.* (1959) prepared the parent compound and a number of its simple derivatives, *e.g.*,

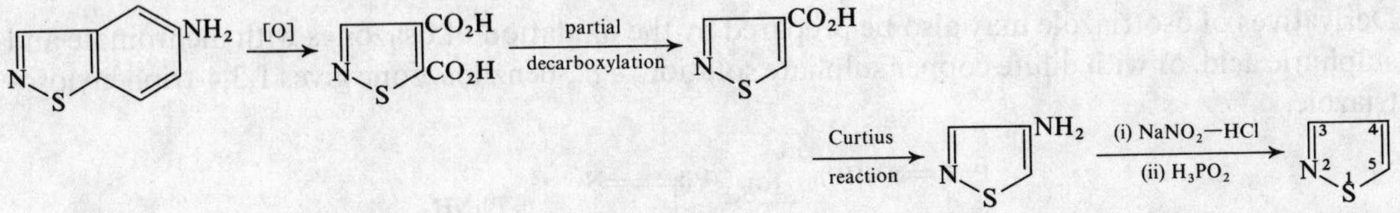

More recent syntheses of isothiazoles are, *e.g.*,

(*a*)

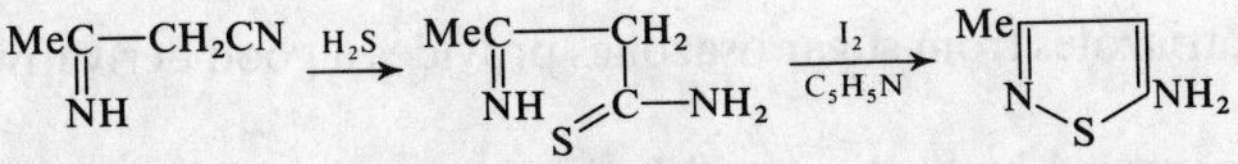

(*b*)

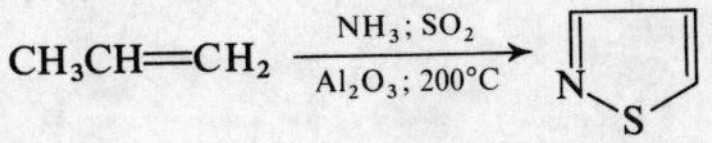

(*c*)

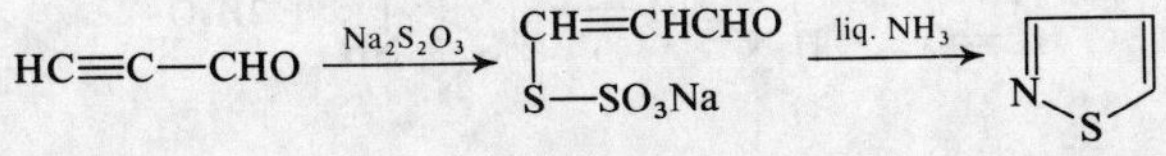

Isothiazole, b.p. 112°C, is a weak base (see Table 12.2) and undergoes electrophilic substitution in the 4-position.

TRIAZOLE GROUP

§6. **Osotriazoles and triazoles**

Triazoles are five-membered rings which contain two carbon and three nitrogen atoms. Two structural isomeric triazoles are known, the 1,2,3-(1,2,5-) and the 1,2,4-(1,3,4-), the former being known as *osotriazole*, and the latter as *triazole*. Each exists in two dissimilar tautomeric forms.

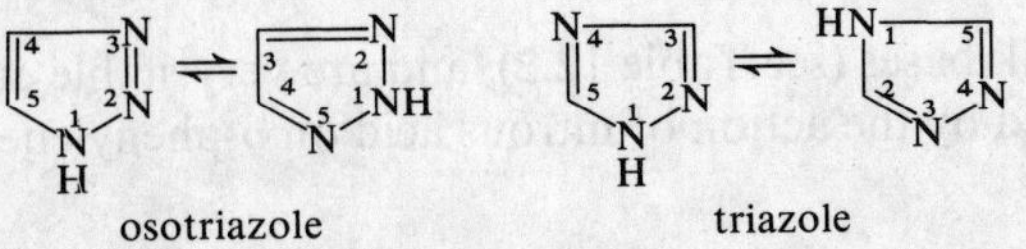

Replacement of the imino hydrogen atom by an alkyl or aryl group prevents tautomerism, and thereby gives rise to the possibility of *two* 1-substituted triazoles and *two* 1-substituted osotriazoles. All four types of compounds have been prepared.

Osotriazole may be prepared by the reaction between acetylene and hydrazoic acid. This is a 1,3-dipolar addition (§2):

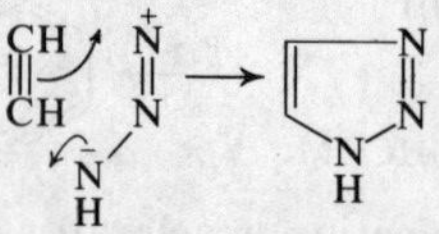

On the other hand, a general method for preparing osotriazoles is the condensation of azides with β-ketoesters, *e.g.*, phenyl azide and ethyl acetoacetate form ethyl 5-methyl-1-phenylosotriazole-4-carboxylate. This is also a 1,3-dipolar addition.

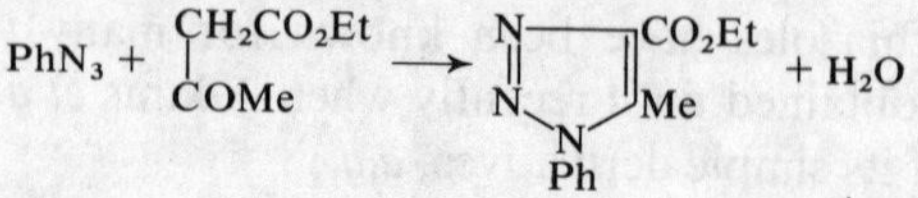

Derivatives of osotriazole may also be prepared by the oxidation of osazones with dichromate and sulphuric acid, or with dilute copper sulphate solution, *e.g.*, benzilosazone gives 1,3,4-triphenyloso-triazole.

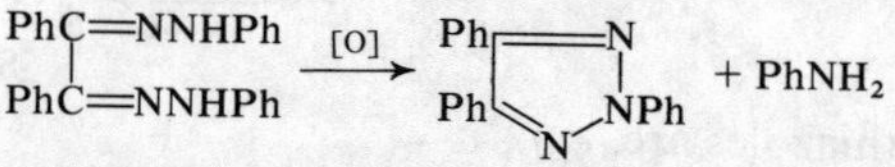

The formation of osotriazoles from sugar osazones provides a good derivative for the characterisation of sugars.

Triazoles may be prepared by heating acid hydrazides with amides, *e.g.*, formyl hydrazide and formamide give triazole.

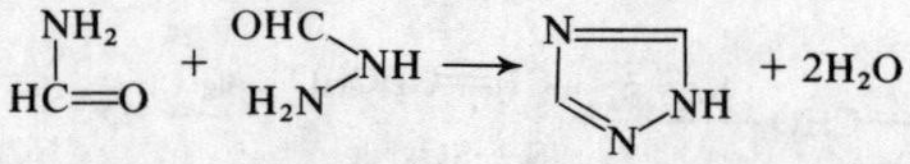

Triazoles are also formed when 1,2-diacylhydrazines are heated with ammonia or amines in the presence of zinc chloride, *e.g.*, 1,2-diacetylhydrazine and methylamine give 1,2,5-trimethyltriazole.

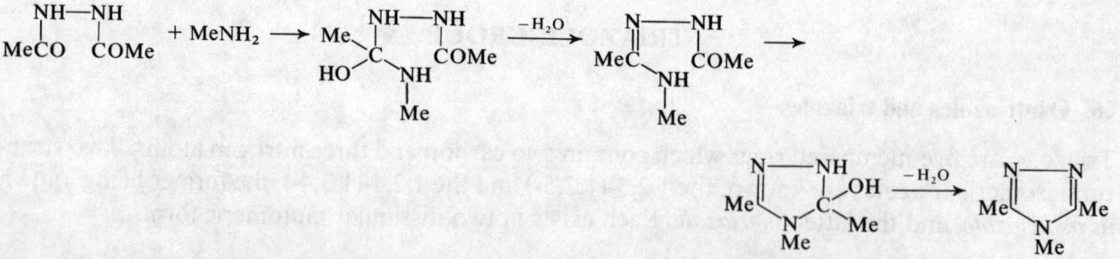

Both triazoles are weak bases (see Table 12.2), and are very stable compounds.
Benzotriazole is formed by the action of nitrous acid on *o*-phenylenediamine.

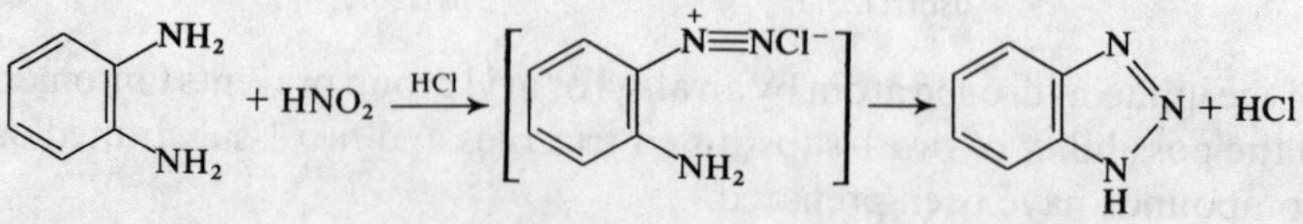

§7. Oxadiazoles

These are five-membered rings containing two carbon and two nitrogen atoms and one oxygen atom; four types are known.

| 1,2,3-oxadiazole | 1,2,4-oxadiazole | 1,2,5-oxadiazole | 1,3,4-oxadiazole |

The **furazans** (1,2,5-oxadiazoles) may be prepared by the action of sodium hydroxide on the dioximes of α-diketones.

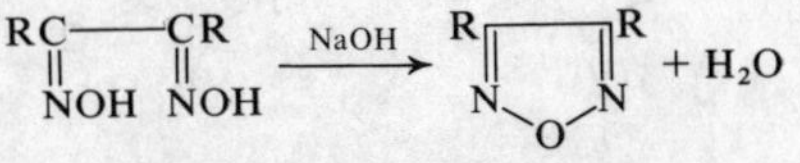

The corresponding thiadiazoles are also known: 1,2,3-, 1,2,4-, 1,2,5-, and 1,3,4-.

§8. Sydnones

The sydnones were first prepared by Earl *et al.* (1935) by the action of cold acetic anhydride on *N*-nitroso-*N*-phenylglycines; Earl formulated the reaction as follows:

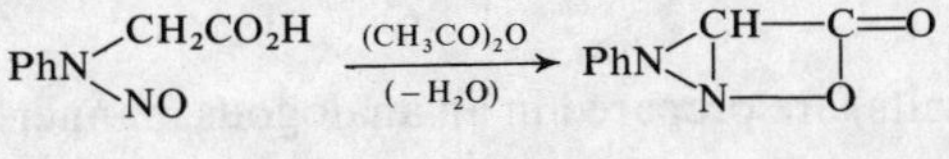

Earl (1946) proposed the name *sydnone* for compounds of this type; thus the above compound is *N*-phenylsydnone.

The structure proposed by Earl is similar to that of a β-lactone, but Baker *et al.* (1946, 1949) offered a number of objections to this structure, *e.g.*,

(i) A system containing fused three- and four-membered rings would be highly strained, and consequently is unlikely to be produced by dehydration with acetic anhydride; β-lactones are not produced under these conditions.

(ii) Many β-lactones are unstable to heat; sydnones are stable and so the β-lactone structure is unlikely.

(iii) If the β-lactone structure is correct, then sydnones should be capable of existing in optically active forms. Kenner and Baker (1946) prepared (+)-*N*-nitroso-*N*-phenylalanine, and when this was converted into a sydnone, the product was optically inactive.

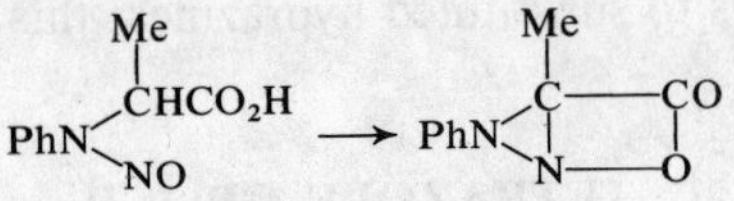

(iv) The aryl nucleus in sydnones is very resistant to substitution by electrophilic reagents. Since the above structure is similar to that of an arylhydrazine, this resistance is unexpected.

Baker *et al.* (1946) therefore proposed a five-membered ring which cannot be represented by any one purely covalent structure; they put forward a number of charged structures, the sydnone being a resonance hybrid, *e.g.*, three charged resonating structures are (I)–(III):

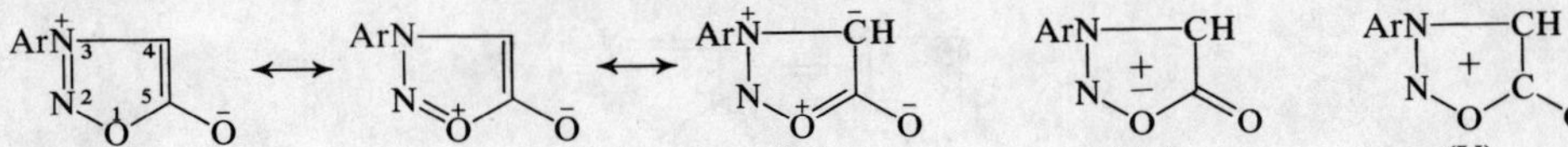

| (I) | (II) | (III) | (IV) | (V) |

Measurements have shown that sydnones have a large dipole moment, N-3 being the positive end (Sutton *et al.*, 1947, 1949; Le Fèvre *et al.*, 1947). Baker *et al.* (1949) suggested structure (IV), but later (1955) proposed (V) and called sydnones *meso-ionic compounds* to describe their aromatic properties and charge separation. More recent physical measurements such as NMR spectra (Stewart *et al.*, 1963), and also molecular orbital calculations (Coulson, 1961) have shown that in sydnones the positive charge is localised mainly on N-3 and the negative charge mainly on the exocyclic oxygen atom. It would therefore appear that sydnones are best represented as resonance hybrids of structures (I), (VI) and (VII).

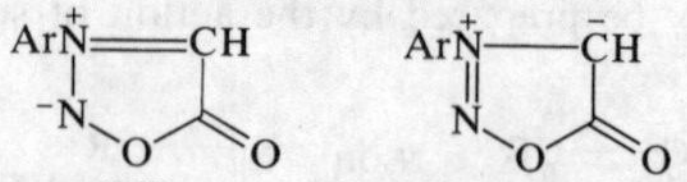

(VI)   (VII)

Such a hybrid molecule will be planar, would not be optically active (*cf.* (iii), above) and accounts for the lack of reactivity of the benzene ring towards electrophilic substitution.

Sydnones contain the 1,2,3-oxadiazole system, and their formation from *N*-nitroso-derivatives may be formulated as:

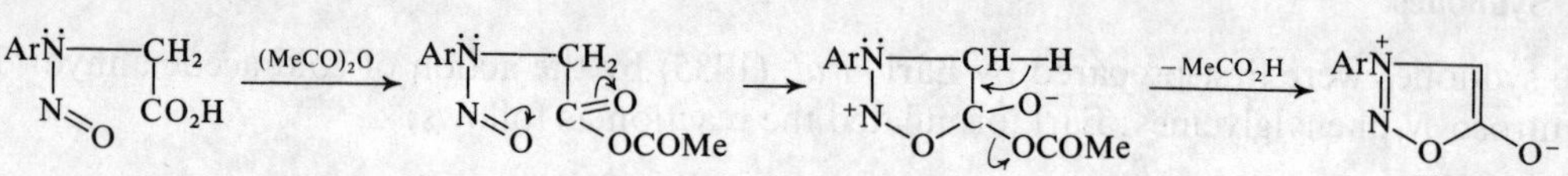

Iminosydnones (as their salts) are prepared in an analogous manner from *N*-nitrosoaminoaceto-nitriles:

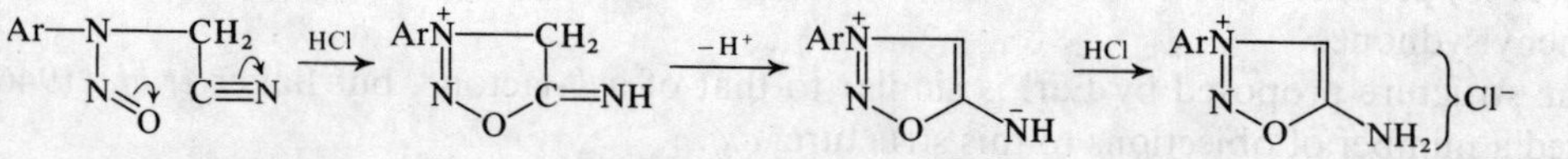

Most of the alkyl sydnones are liquids or low-melting solids, but the aryl sydnones are generally crystalline solids with m.ps. ranging to above 300°C. Sydnones are normally insoluble in water, but are readily soluble in the common organic solvents. Their most characteristic feature is the very strong band shown by the C=O stretch in the range 1 770–1 718 cm^{-1}.

3-Phenylsydnones readily undergo electrophilic substitution at position 4, *e.g.*, bromine in acetic acid and nitration with nitric acid below 0°C produce the corresponding 4-derivatives. These sydnones are also readily mercurated to the 4-mercuri chloride with mercuric chloride, and acetylated to the 4-acetyl compound by means of acetic anhydride in the presence of the BF_3OEt_2 complex. Strong acids hydrolyse sydnones to substituted hydrazines; this is often a convenient method of preparing such compounds.

TETRAZOLE GROUP

§9. Tetrazole

Tetrazole is a five-membered ring which contains one carbon and four nitrogen atoms. There are two tautomeric forms of tetrazole, and replacement of the imino hydrogen by, *e.g.*, an alkyl group gives rise to *two* 1-alkyltetrazoles (*cf.* triazoles, §6).

Tetrazole may be prepared by heating hydrogen cyanide with hydrazoic acid in benzene solution at 100°C; this is a 1,3-dipolar addition (§2).

Derivatives of tetrazole may be prepared by the condensation of phenyl azide with phenylhydrazones of aldehydes in the presence of ethanolic sodium ethoxide, e.g., benzaldehyde phenylhydrazone and phenyl azide form 1,4-diphenyltetrazole.

$$PhCH{=}N{-}NHPh + Ph{-}\bar{N}{-}N{=}\overset{+}{N} \xrightarrow{EtONa} \begin{bmatrix} PhC{=}N{-}NHPh \\ N{=}N{-}NHPh \end{bmatrix} \longrightarrow \underset{N{-}N}{\overset{Ph{-}N}{|}}NPh + PhNH_2$$

A less hazardous route is by reaction between an imidic chloride and sodium azide:

$$PhCONHPh \xrightarrow{PCl_5} PhC\overset{Cl}{\underset{NPh}{\diagdown}} \xrightarrow{NaN_3} PhC\overset{\bar{N}{-}N{=}\overset{+}{N}}{\underset{NPh}{\diagdown}} \longrightarrow \underset{PhN{-}N}{\overset{Ph{-}N}{|}}N$$

Tetrazole is a colourless solid, m.p. 156°C; it has no basic properties, but the imino hydrogen is acidic, e.g., tetrazole forms a silver salt $[CHN_4]^- Ag^+$.

Azines

DIAZINE GROUP

§10. Introduction

The diazines are six-membered rings containing two nitrogen atoms. Three isomeric diazines are theoretically possible, and all three are known.

o-diazine;   m-diazine;   p-diazine;
pyridazine   miazine;   piazine;
                    pyrimidine   **pyrazine**

§11. Pyridazines

These may be prepared by the action of hydrazine on unsaturated 1,4-diketones:

$$\underset{R}{\overset{R \quad O}{\diagdown}}\diagup\overset{O}{\underset{R}{|}} + N_2H_4 \longrightarrow \underset{R}{\overset{R}{\diagup}}\begin{array}{c}N \\ N\end{array} + 2H_2O$$

The cis-isomer (of the diketone) reacts faster than the trans. Pyridazine itself may be prepared from maleic dialdehyde and hydrazine hydrate.

$$\begin{array}{c} HC{\diagup}^{CHO} \\ HC{\diagdown}_{CHO} \end{array} + \begin{array}{c} NH_2 \\ | \\ NH_2 \end{array} \longrightarrow \underset{N}{\overset{N}{\bigcirc}} + 2H_2O$$

Saturated 1,4-diketones have also been used; the intermediate dihydro-compound may be oxidised by chromium trioxide in acetic acid. However, the main product of this reaction is often a 1-aminopyrrole.

Pyridazine, b.p. 208°C, is a weak base (see Table 12.2) and forms the pyridazinium mono-cation with acids. Pyridazine undergoes electrophilic substitution with great difficulty, but conversion into the 1-oxide offers a means of preparing various pyridazine substitution products (*cf.* pyridine; see Vol. I); *e.g.*,

PYRIMIDINES

§12. Ureides

Ureides are acylureas, and may be prepared by the action of an acid anhydride or acid chloride on urea, *e.g.*,

The simple ureides resemble the amides in properties.

Allophanic acid, $NH_2CONHCO_2H$, is not known in the free state, but many of its esters have been prepared:
(i) By the action of chloroformates on urea.

$$NH_2CONH_2 + ClCO_2R \longrightarrow NH_2CONHCO_2R + HCl$$

(ii) By the reaction between urethans and cyanic acid.

$$HNCO + NH_2CO_2R \longrightarrow NH_2CONHCO_2R$$

The alkyl allophanates are well-defined crystalline compounds, and so are frequently used to identify alcohols. They are prepared by passing cyanic acid vapour into the dry alcohol; urethans are intermediate products.

$$ROH + HNCO \longrightarrow NH_2CO_2R \xrightarrow{HNCO} NH_2CONHCO_2R$$

§13. Cyclic ureides

Many cyclic ureides are known; some occur naturally and others are synthetic (a number of cyclic ureides—alloxan, allantoin, parabanic acid and hydantoin—are discussed in **16** §2 in connection with the purines, which are cyclic diureides).

The cyclic ureides containing a *six-membered ring* behave, in a number of ways, as pyrimidine derivatives.

§13a. Barbituric acid.

A very important pyrimidine derivative is barbituric acid (malonylurea). It was originally prepared by condensing urea with malonic acid in the presence of phosphoryl chloride (Grimaux, 1879).

$$OC\begin{smallmatrix}NH_2 \\ NH_2\end{smallmatrix} + \begin{smallmatrix}HO_2C \\ HO_2C\end{smallmatrix}CH_2 \xrightarrow{POCl_3}$$ (barbituric acid structure)

A much better synthesis is to reflux ethyl malonate with urea in ethanolic solution in the presence of sodium ethoxide.

$$OC\begin{smallmatrix}NH_2 \\ NH_2\end{smallmatrix} + \begin{smallmatrix}EtO_2C \\ EtO_2C\end{smallmatrix}CH_2 \xrightarrow{C_2H_5ONa} \text{(barbituric acid)} + 2EtOH$$

Barbituric acid is a solid, m.p. 253°C, and is not very soluble in water. Structure (IV) represents barbituric acid as 2,4,6-trihydroxypyrimidine, and this structure has been proposed because of the acidic nature of barbituric acid. On the other hand, barbituric acid contains an active methylene

(I) ⇌ (II) ⇌ (III) ⇌ (IV)

group, since it readily forms an oximino derivative with nitrous acid. Thus barbituric acid behaves as if it had structure (I), (II) or (III). Furthermore, it is very difficult to acylate hydroxypyrimidines containing hydroxyl groups in the 2-, 4- or 6-positions, thus indicating that structure (I) is more probable than (II) or (III). This is supported by the fact that methylation of hydroxypyrimidines with, e.g., methyl iodide in the presence of sodium hydroxide, results in the formation of N-methyl derivatives; this indicates the probable presence of imino groups. On the other hand, it is possible to replace three hydroxyl groups by three chlorine atoms by means of phosphoryl chloride; this suggests barbituric acid behaves as (IV). However, X-ray analysis has indicated that (I) is the predominant form (in the solid state) but, even so, the molecule is planar (Jeffrey *et al.*, 1961; see also §15).

Barbituric acid can be nitrated and brominated in the 5-position, and also forms metallic derivatives (at position 5). By means of the sodio-derivative, one or two alkyl groups may be introduced at position 5 (this reaction is characteristic of the —CH_2CO— group). Barbituric acid and 5,5-dimethyl-barbituric acid have no hypnotic action. On the other hand, 5,5-diethylbarbituric acid (*Barbitone, Veronal*) has a strong hypnotic action; it is best prepared as follows:

$$OC\begin{smallmatrix}NH_2 \\ NH_2\end{smallmatrix} + \begin{smallmatrix}EtO_2C \\ EtO_2C\end{smallmatrix}C(C_2H_5)_2 \xrightarrow{EtONa} \text{(5,5-diethylbarbituric acid)}$$

5-Cyclohexyl-3,5-dimethylbarbituric acid (*Evipan*) is a better hypnotic than *Barbitone* and is not so toxic. 5-Ethyl-5-phenylbarbituric acid (*Luminal*) is also used in medicine.

§13b. Derivatives of barbituric acid.   Violuric acid (5-oximinobarbituric acid) is formed when barbituric acid is treated with nitrous acid;

X-ray analysis has shown that violuric acid exists in the oxime form (in the solid state), *i.e.*, as the oxime of alloxan (see **16** §2). It gives a violet colour in water, and forms deeply coloured salts with various metals, *e.g.*, the potassium salt is blue and the magnesium and barium salts are purple.

Dilituric acid (5-nitrobarbituric acid) may be prepared by nitrating barbituric acid with fuming nitric acid, or by the oxidation of violuric acid with nitric acid.

Uramil (5-aminobarbituric acid) is formed by the reduction of either dilituric acid or violuric acid.

Uramil may also be prepared by the action of ammonium hydrogen sulphite on alloxan, and then boiling the product, **thionuric acid**, with water.

Dialuric acid (5-hydroxybarbituric acid) is produced by the action of nitrous acid on uramil; it is also formed when alloxan is reduced with hydrogen sulphide or with zinc and hydrochloric acid.

X-ray analysis has shown that dialuric acid exists as the diketodihydroxy form (in the solid state).

§14. Pyrimidine, m.p. 22·5°C, b.p. 124°C/758 mm

This was first prepared from barbituric acid as follows (Gabriel, 1900).

Pyrimidine has been numbered in two ways, (A) and (B). (A) was used before (B) was proposed by IUPAC. (B) has been used in this book (see also the Purines, **16** §1).

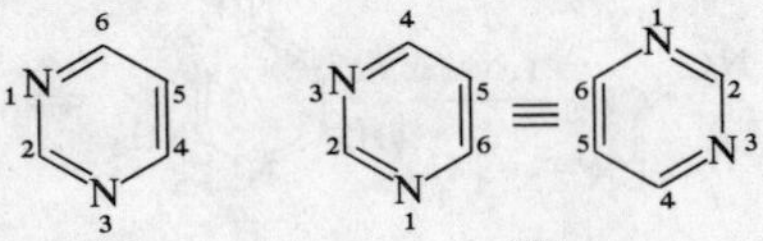

(A)   (B)

Pyrimidine may also be prepared by the oxidation of alkylpyrimidines, followed by decarboxylation. Another preparation is the catalytic reductive dechlorination of 2,4-dichloropyrimidine; the latter is heated with hydrogen under pressure in the presence of Pd—C and magnesium oxide (Whittaker, 1953).

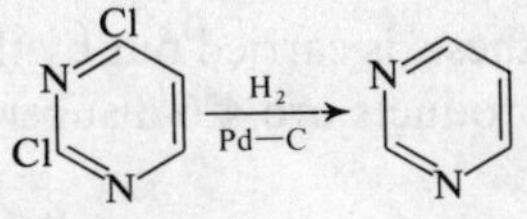

A convenient preparation of pyrimidine is by reaction between 1,1,3,3-tetraethoxypropane and formamide (*cf.* pyrazole, §2):

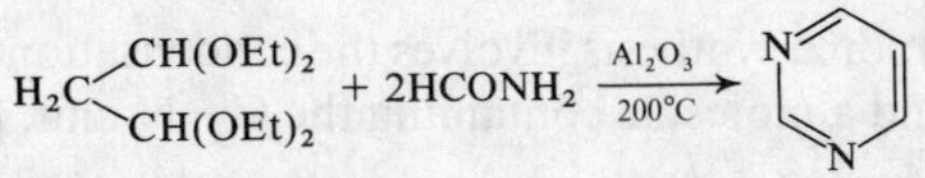

Pyrimidine is neutral in solution, but forms salts with acid (see Table 12.2). Pyrimidine is probably a resonance hybrid of the following resonating structures:

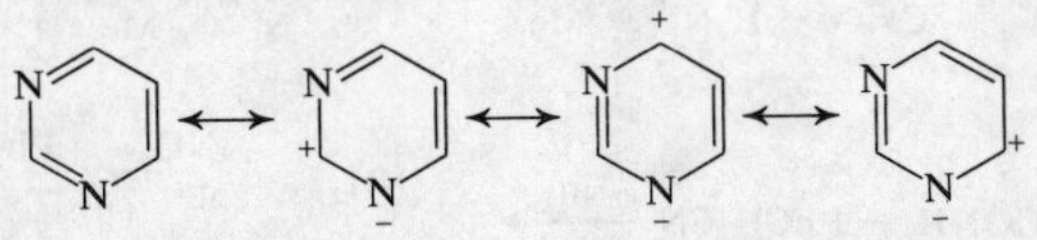

Thus the ring is deactivated, and position 5 has the greatest electron density (*cf.* nitrobenzene and pyridine, Vol. I). It can therefore be expected that attack by electrophilic reagents will be difficult, but attack by nucleophilic reagents (at positions 2, 4 and 6) will be facilitated. Chlorine atoms at 2, 4 or 6 are readily replaced by hydroxyl or amino groups, and an amino group in position 2 or 4 is readily replaced by a hydroxyl group merely on boiling with water (*cf.* vitamin B$_1$, **17** §3).

When a hydroxyl or an amino group is present in the pyrimidine nucleus, the compound no longer behaves entirely as an aromatic derivative. Thus, 2-hydroxypyrimidine behaves as the keto form. The introduction of hydroxyl or amino groups into positions 2, 4 and 6 progressively diminishes the aromatic properties of the compound (*cf.* barbituric acid, §13a, and uracil, §15).

Pyrimidine derivatives. A very important general method for preparing pyrimidines is the condensation between a three carbon compound of the type YCH$_2$Z, where Y and Z = COR, CO$_2$R, CN, and compounds having the amidine structure RC (= NH)NH$_2$, where R = R (an amidine), OH (urea), SH or SR (thiourea or its *S*-derivative), NH$_2$ (guanidine); the condensation is carried out in the presence of sodium hydroxide or sodium ethoxide. This general reaction may be illustrated by the condensation of acetamidine with ethyl acetoacetate to form 4-hydroxy-2,6-dimethylpyrimidine.

Other examples are the formation of (i) 4,6-diamino-2-mercaptopyrimidine from thiourea and malononitrile:

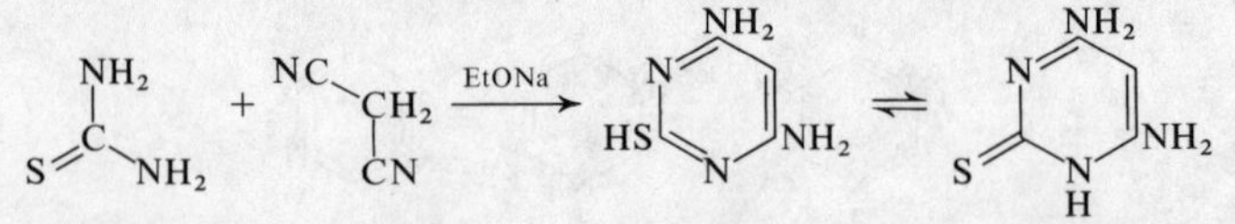

(ii) 2,6-diamino-4-hydroxypyrimidine from guanidine and ethyl cyanoacetate:

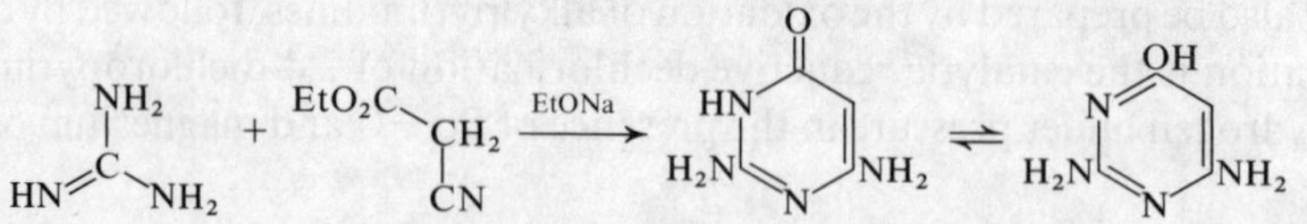

Another important pyrimidine synthesis is carried out by the condensation between β-diketones and formamide at 180–200°C. The products are 4,6-disubstituted pyrimidines, *i.e.*, position 2 is unsubstituted.

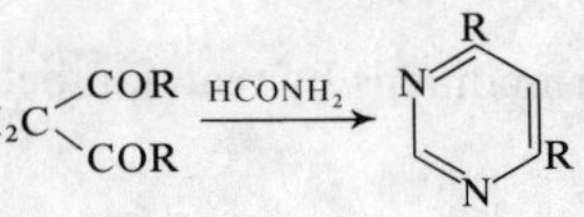

One other important pyrimidine synthesis involves the condensation between a molecule containing the unit C—C—C—N and a molecule containing the C—N unit, *e.g.*,

(a)

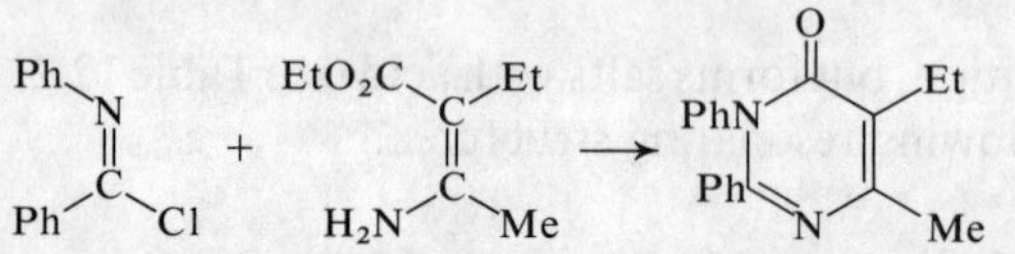

(b)

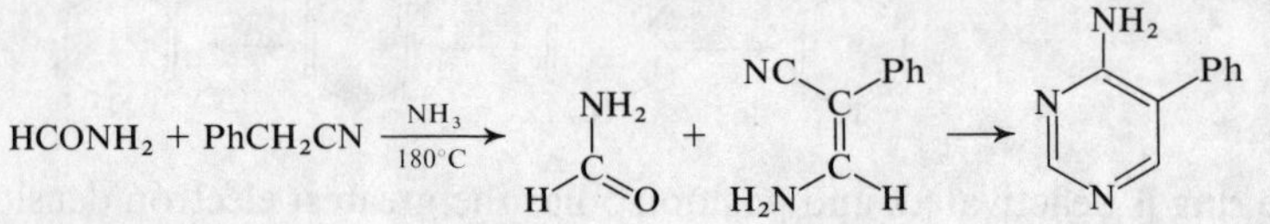

(c)

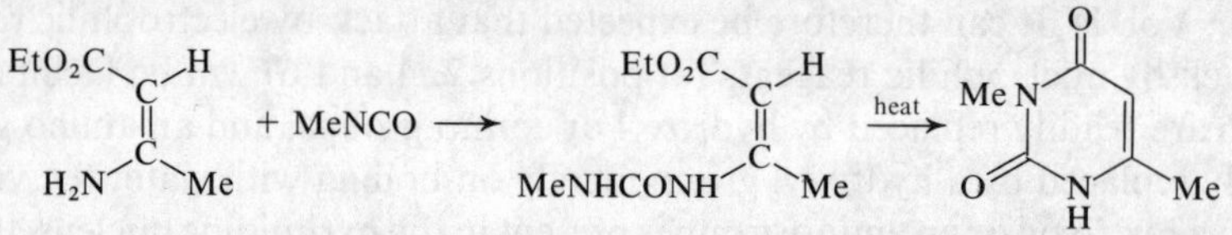

5,6-Diaminopyrimidines, which are intermediates in purine synthesis (see **16** §4), may be prepared by condensing formamidine with phenylazomalononitrile (Todd *et al.*, 1943).

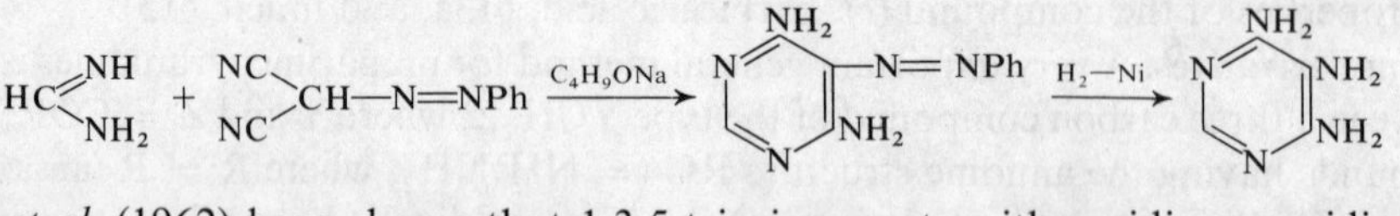

Schaeffer *et al.* (1962) have shown that 1,3,5-triazine reacts with amidines, amidine salts and imidates having α-acidic methylene groups to produce 5,6-disubstituted pyrimidines (yield: 51–100 per cent):

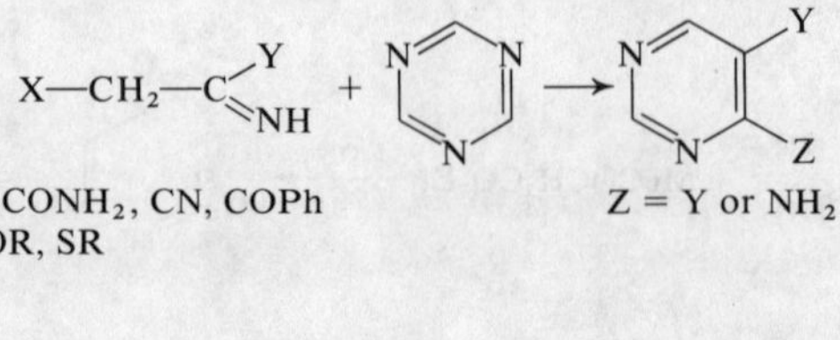

X = CO$_2$R, CONH$_2$, CN, COPh   Z = Y or NH$_2$
Y = NH$_2$, OR, SR

§15

Uracil (2,4-dihydroxypyrimidine) is a hydrolytic product of the nucleic acids (**16** §§13, 13b). It has been synthesised in many ways, *e.g.*,

(i) Fischer and Roeder (1901).

urea   ethyl acrylate   dihydrouracil

(ii) Wheeler and Liddle (1908).

thiourea   sodioformyl-
           acetic ester

(iii) The best method of preparation is to heat a solution of malic acid and urea in fuming sulphuric acid (Davidson *et al.*, 1926).

Four tautomeric structures are theoretically possible for uracil.

(I)   (II)   (III)   (IV)

The problem of pyrimidines containing hydroxyl, amino and mercapto groups in positions 2, 4 or 6 is still not absolutely clear as far as their structures are concerned. It seems quite certain that such compounds can exist in tautomeric forms, but conflicting results have been reported about which form predominates. Mason *et al.* (1955) have examined the infrared and ultraviolet spectra of these compounds and compared them with those of *O*- and *N*-derivatives synthesised by unambiguous methods. Their results have shown that hydroxypyrimidines exist in the keto form, mercapto derivatives as thiones and amino derivatives exist as such. Thus uracil is (I) [see also **16** §13b].

§16. Thymine (5-methyluracil, 2,4-dihydroxy-5-methylpyrimidine)

Thymine is a hydrolytic product of the nucleic acids. It has been synthesised by methods similar to those used for uracil.

(i) Fischer and Roeder (1901); in this case ethyl methacrylate is used instead of ethyl acrylate.

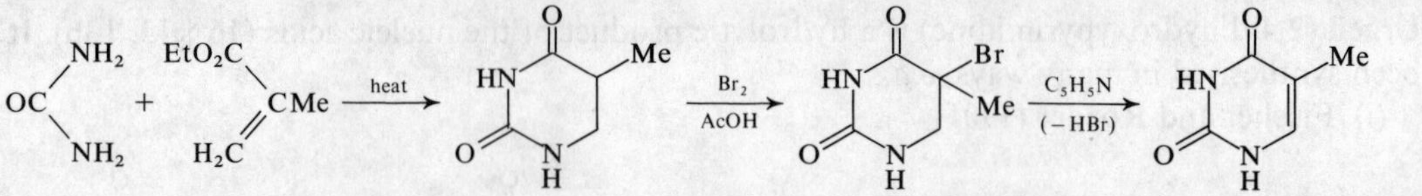

(ii) Wheeler and Liddle (1908); in this case sodioformylpropionic ester is used instead of sodio-formylacetic ester.

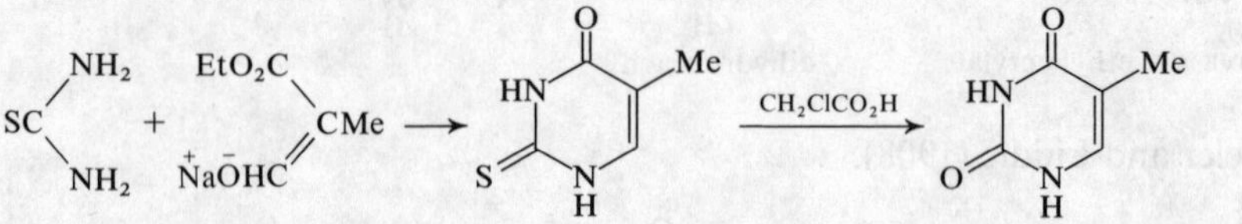

(iii) A very good method is that of Bergmann *et al.* (1933):

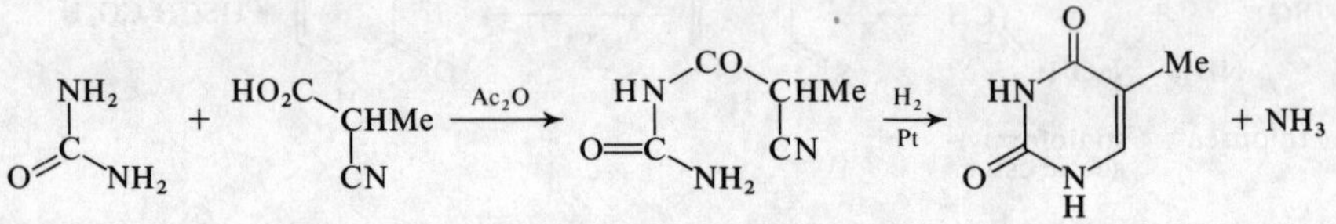

§17. Cytosine (4-aminouracil, 4-amino-2-hydroxypyrimidine)

A hydrolytic product of the nucleic acids, it has been synthesised by Wheeler and Johnson (1903) starting from *S*-ethylisothiourea and sodioformylacetic ester (see also **16** §13b).

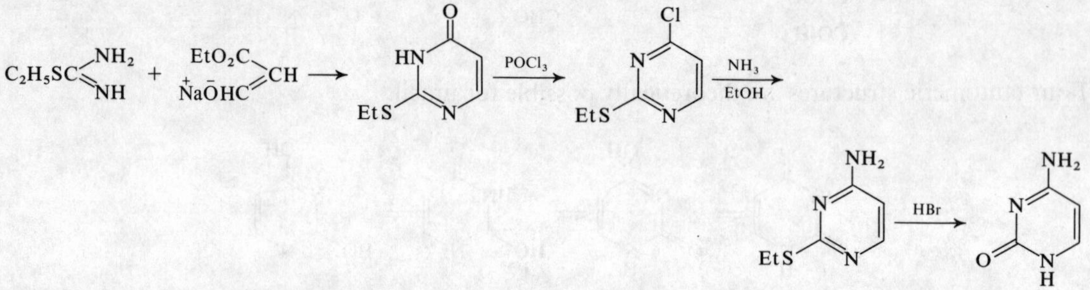

The best synthesis appears to be that of Tarsio *et al.* (1957):

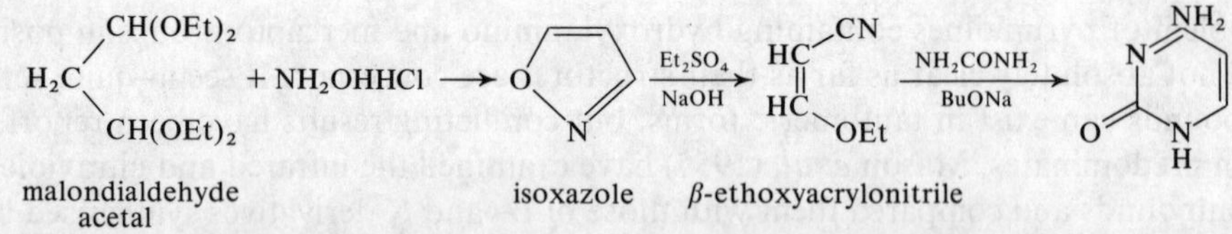

malondialdehyde acetal   isoxazole   β-ethoxyacrylonitrile

Katritzky *et al.* (1963) have examined the ultraviolet and NMR spectra of aqueous solutions of cytosine, and have concluded that the following two species are present (*cf.* §15).

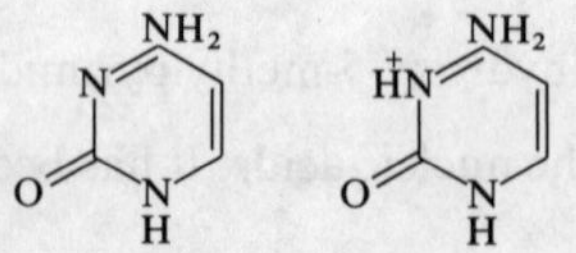

§17a.   Two cytosine derivatives that have been found in nucleic acids (**16** §13b) are 5-methyl- and 5-hydroxymethylcytosine. There appears to be no satisfactory synthesis of 5-methylcytosine, but Hitchings *et al.* (1949) have prepared it from thymine (§16) as follows:

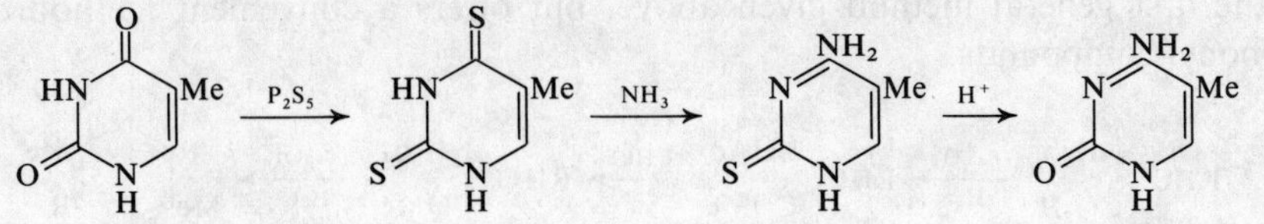

Ulbricht *et al.* (1955, 1956) have prepared 5-hydroxymethylcytosine starting from ethyl ethoxymethylenecyanoacetate:

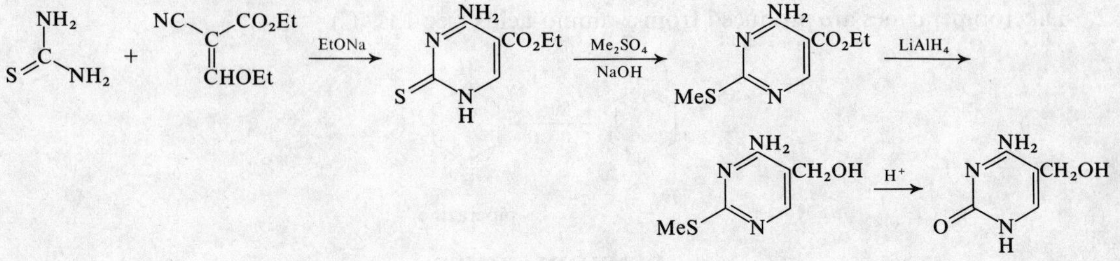

PYRAZINES

§18

Pyrazines may be prepared by the self-condensation of an α-aminoketone in the presence of an oxidising agent such as mercuric chloride; the intermediate dihydro compound is readily oxidised to the pyrazine (Gabriel *et al.*, 1893).

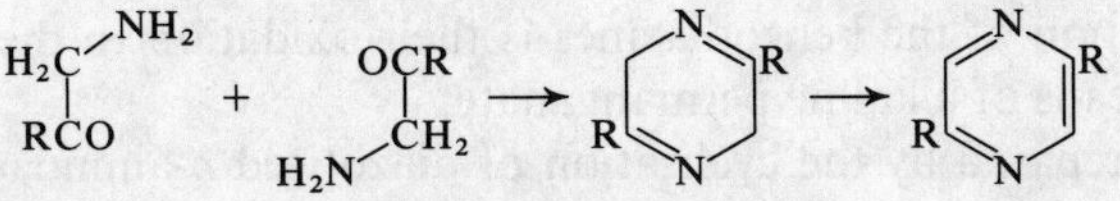

Actually, only the salts of α-aminoketo compounds are known; addition of alkali liberates the free base which immediately forms a pyrazine in the presence of mercuric chloride.

Pyrazine itself may be prepared from aminoacetaldehyde (R = H in the above equations) or as follows (Wolff *et al.*, 1908).

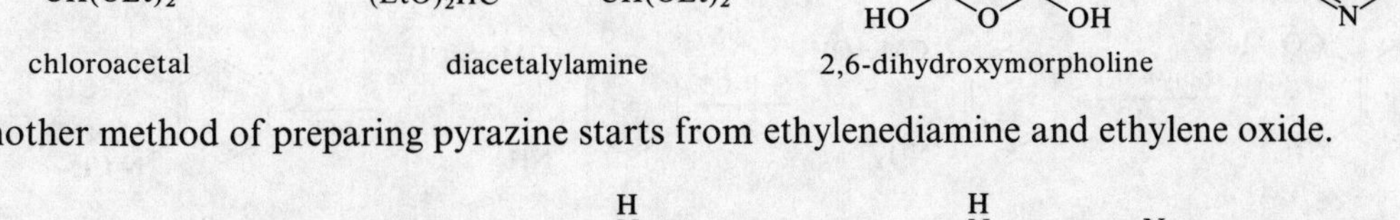

chloroacetal   diacetalylamine   2,6-dihydroxymorpholine

Another method of preparing pyrazine starts from ethylenediamine and ethylene oxide.

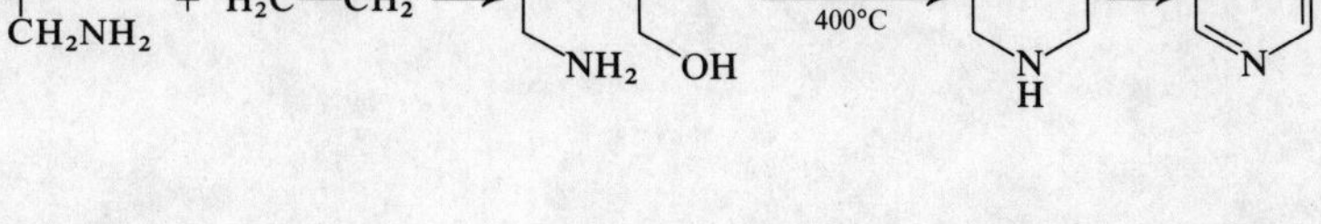

A convenient general method for preparing pyrazines is to heat an α-amino-acid with acetic anhydride in the presence of pyridine, hydrolyse the product (an acetamidoketone) with acid and then warm with sodium hydroxide in the presence of mercuric chloride (Dakin *et al.*, 1928). This method is thus similar to the first general method given above, but offers a convenient method of preparing α-aminocarbonyl compounds.

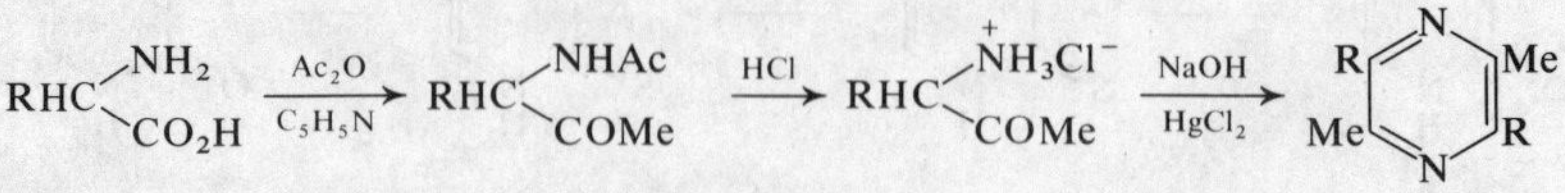

Pyrazine is a solid, m.p. 55°C; pyrazines (and pyrazine) are readily reduced by sodium and ethanol to hexahydropyrazines or **piperazines**. Piperazine, m.p. 104°C, is a strong diacid base (see Table 12.2). 2,5-Diketopiperazines are produced from α-amino-acids (see **13** §4C).

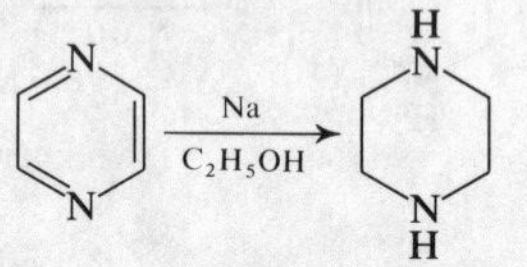

piperazine

BENZODIAZINES

§19

The following benzodiazines are theoretically possible, and all are known; the first two are derived from pyridazine, the third from pyrimidine and the fourth from pyrazine.

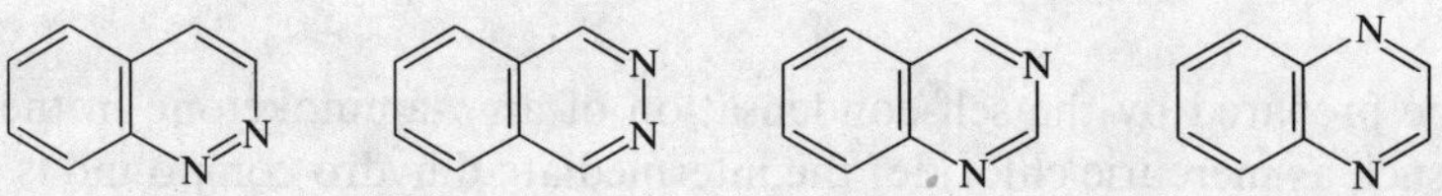

cinnoline   phthalazine   quinazoline   quinoxaline

A characteristic reaction of the benzodiazines is their oxidation to the corresponding diazine-dicarboxylic acid by means of alkaline permanganate.

Cinnolines may be prepared by the cyclisation of diazotised *o*-aminoacetophenones (Schofield *et al.*, 1948), *e.g.*,

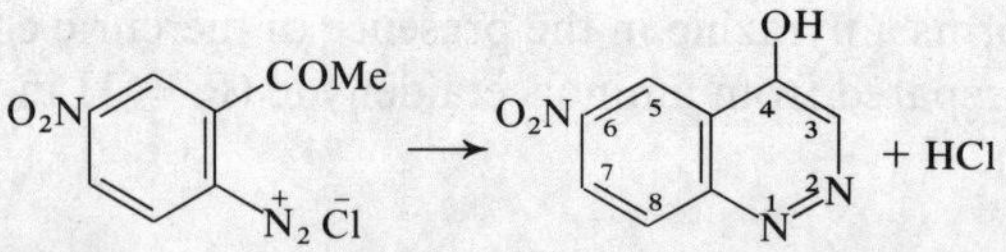

The most characteristic method of synthesising cinnolines starts from esters of anthranilic acid, *e.g.*,

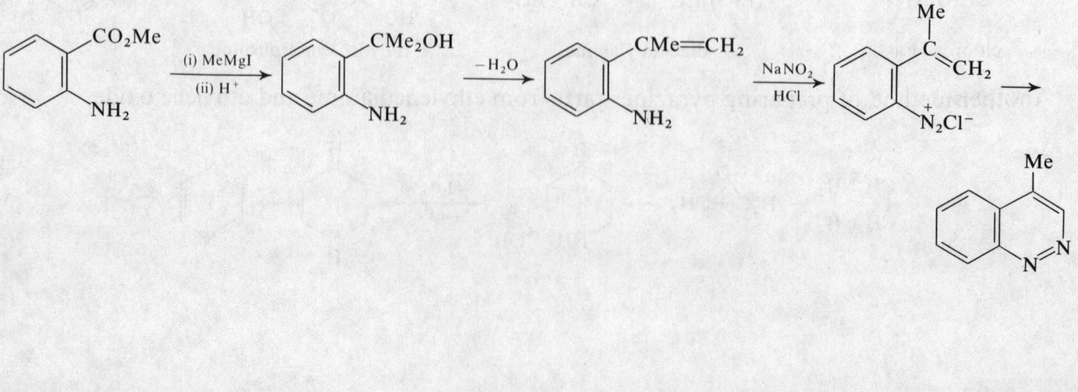

This method, however, fails in the preparation of a cinnoline unsubstituted in the 4-position.

Phthalazines are conveniently prepared by condensation between *o*-dioxobenzenes or *o*-acyl-benzoic acids and hydrazines, *e.g.*,

(*a*)

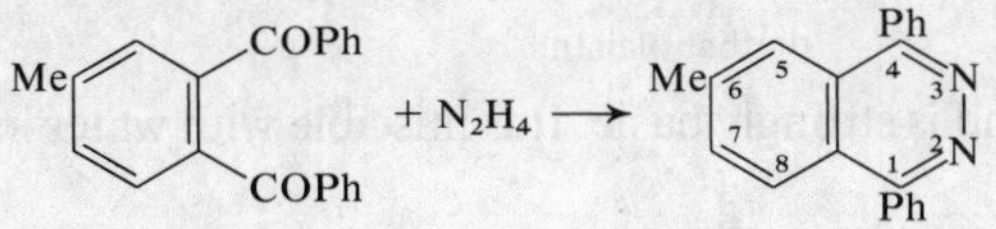

(*b*)

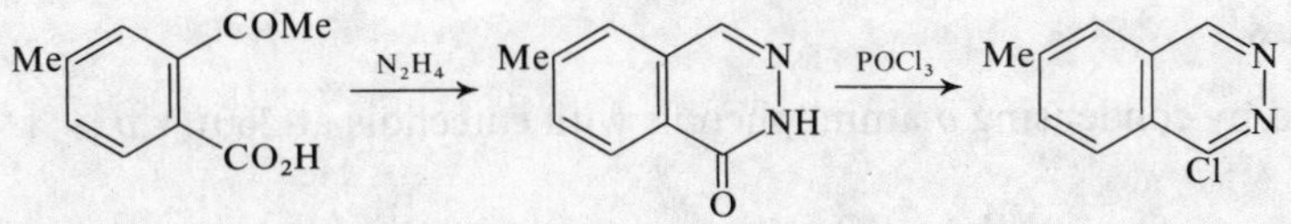

Quinazolines may be prepared by the action of ammonia on acylated *o*-aminobenzaldehydes *or* *o*-aminoacetophenones (Isensee *et al.*, 1948), *e.g.*,

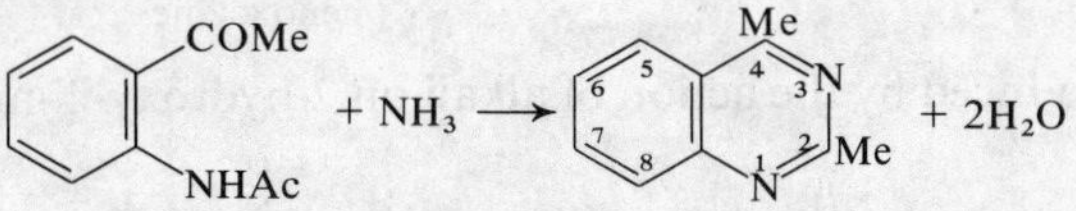

Quinoxalines are formed by the condensation of *o*-phenylenediamines with α-dioxo compounds, *e.g.*,

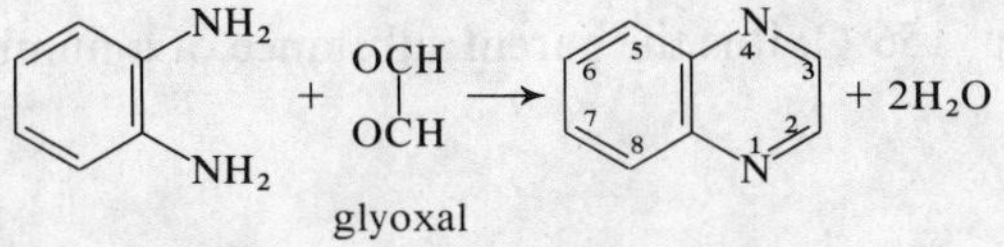

The formation of quinoxalines is used to identify aromatic *o*-diamines and 1,2-diketones (see, *e.g.*, **17** §9).

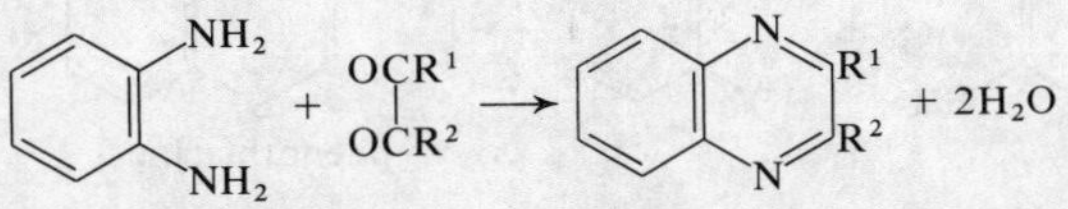

Of the *dibenzodiazines*, only the **phenazines** (*dibenzopyrazines*) are important. Phenazine, m.p. 171°C, may be prepared by condensing *o*-phenylenediamine with catechol in the presence of air.

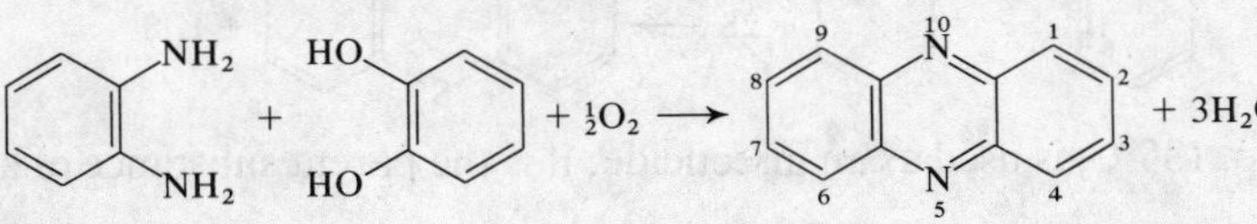

Phenazine forms unstable salts (coloured red or yellow) in excess of strong acids. Many dyes are derived from phenazine, *e.g.*, the safranines (see Vol. I).

DIAZINES CONTAINING ONE NITROGEN ATOM AND AN OXYGEN OR SULPHUR ATOM

§20. Oxazines

Morpholine is tetrahydro-1,4-oxazine, and it may be prepared as follows:

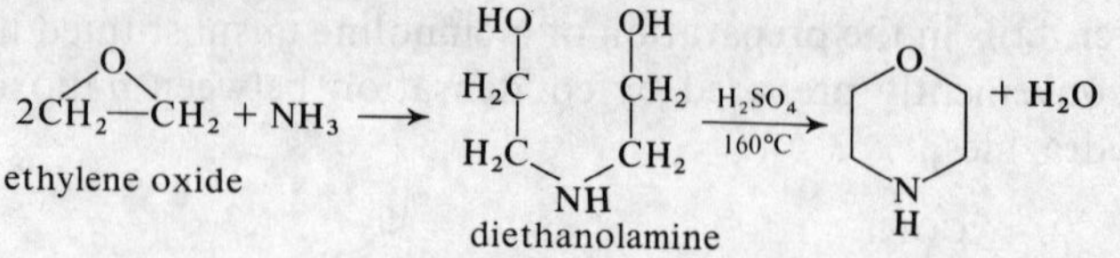

$$2CH_2\text{---}CH_2 + NH_3 \longrightarrow \quad \xrightarrow[160°C]{H_2SO_4} \quad + H_2O$$

ethylene oxide

diethanolamine

Morpholine is a liquid, b.p. 128°C, and is strongly basic. It is miscible with water in all proportions, and is widely used as a solvent.

§21. Phenoxazines

These are formed by condensing *o*-aminophenols with catechols at 260°, *e.g.*,

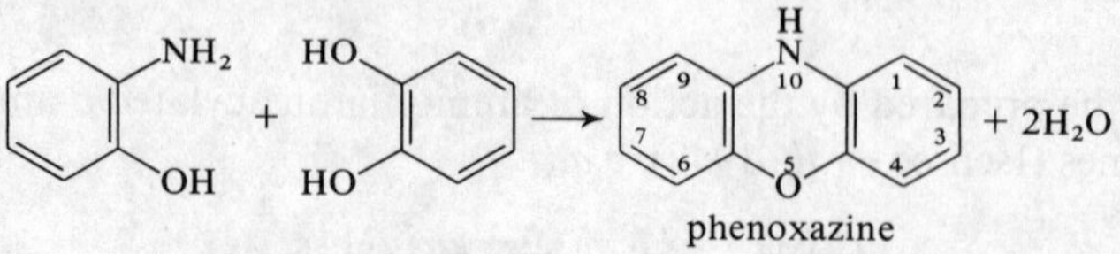

$$+ \quad \longrightarrow \quad + 2H_2O$$

phenoxazine

Phenoxazines are also produced by the action of alkali on 2-hydroxy-2′-nitrodiphenylamines, *e.g.*,

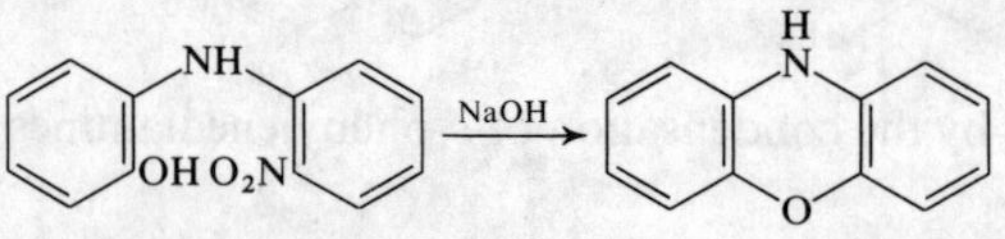

$$\xrightarrow{\text{NaOH}}$$

Phenoxazine is a solid, m.p. 156°C; it is the parent substance of a number of dyes.

§22. Thiazines

Phenothiazines may be prepared by heating *o*-aminothiophenols with catechols, *e.g.*,

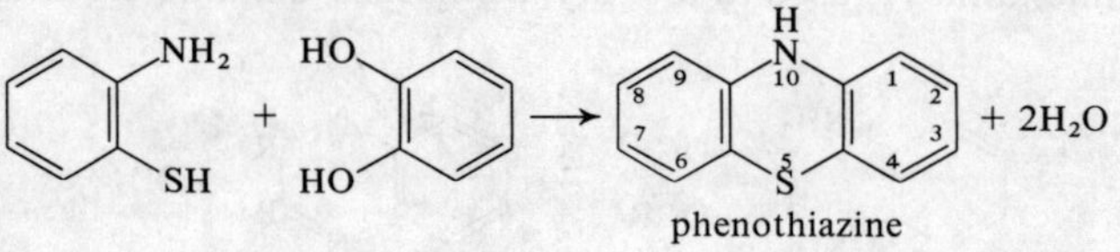

$$+ \quad \longrightarrow \quad + 2H_2O$$

phenothiazine

Phenothiazine may also be prepared by fusing diphenylamine with sulphur.

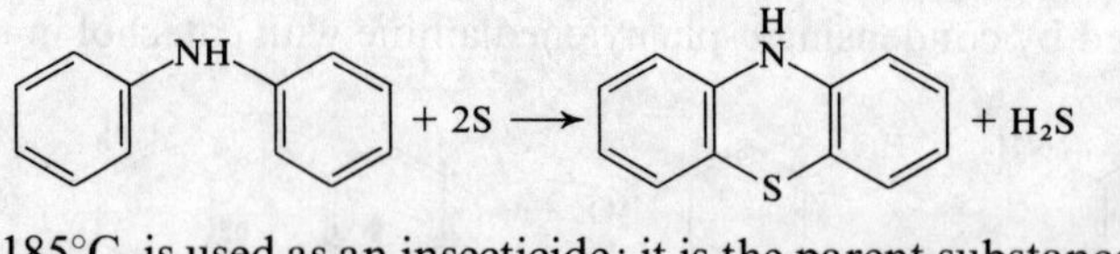

$$+ 2S \longrightarrow \quad + H_2S$$

Phenothiazine, m.p. 185°C, is used as an insecticide; it is the parent substance of a number of dyes.

TRIAZINES AND TETRAZINES

§23. Triazines

Three triazines are theorectically possible; only 1,3,5-triazine is known, but derivatives of each have been prepared.

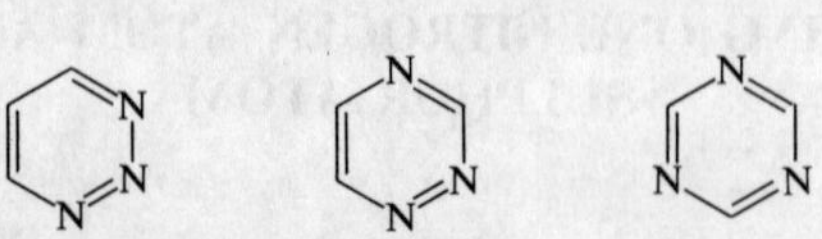

1,2,3-triazine;   1,2,4-triazine;   1,3,5-triazine;
β-triazine   α-triazine   cyanidine

Cyanuric acid, cyamelide and hexamethylenetetramine are derivatives of 1,3,5-triazine (see Vol. I).

§24. Tetrazines

Only derivatives of two tetrazines are known.

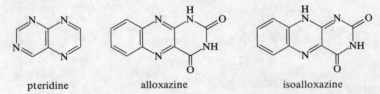

1,2,3,4-tetrazine   1,2,4,5-tetrazine

§25

Some important condensed systems containing *two* fused heterocyclic systems are:

pteridine   alloxazine   isoalloxazine

These occur in natural products (see Ch. 17, Vitamins). It appears that isoalloxazine, the tautomer of alloxazine, does not exist as such; only when the hydrogen atom is substituted is the isoalloxazine form retained (see 17 §6).

REFERENCES

ACHESON, *An Introduction to the Chemistry of Heterocyclic Compounds*, Interscience (1967, 2nd edn.).
BADGER, *The Chemistry of Heterocyclic Compounds*, Academic Press (1961).
RODD (ed.), *Chemistry of the Carbon Compounds*, Elsevier. Vol. IVA, B and C (1958–1960). Heterocyclic Compounds.
ELDERFIELD (ed.), *Heterocyclic Compounds*, Wiley (1951–).
Handbook for Chemical Society Authors, Chem. Soc. (1960). Pp. 90–106. 'Heterocyclic Systems.'
SIDGWICK, *The Organic Chemistry of Nitrogen*, Oxford Press (1966, 3rd edn. by Millar and Springall).
KATRITZKY and LAGOWSKI, *The Principles of Heterocyclic Chemistry*, Methuen (1967).
PALMER, *The Structure and Reactions of Heterocyclic Compounds*, Arnold (1967).
ALBERT, *Heterocyclic Chemistry*, Athlone Press (1968, 2nd edn.).
PAQUETTE, *Principles of Modern Heterocyclic Chemistry*, Benjamin (1968).
WEISSBERGER (ed.), *The Chemistry of Heterocyclic Compounds*, Interscience (1950–).
KATRITZKY and BOLTON (eds.), *Advances in Heterocyclic Chemistry*, Academic Press (1963–).
KATRITZKY (ed.), *Physical Methods in Heterocyclic Chemistry*, Academic Press (1963–).
JANSSEN (ed.), *Organosulphur Chemistry*, Interscience (1967).
SALMOND, 'Valence-shell Expansion in Sulphur Heterocycles', *Quart. Rev.*, 1968, **22**, 253.

Amino-acids and proteins

§1. **Classification of the amino-acids**

When hydrolysed by acids, alkalis or enzymes, proteins yield a mixture of amino-acids (see §6). The number of amino-acids so far obtained from proteins appears to be about twenty-five, all of which except two are α-amino-acids; the two exceptions are proline and hydroxyproline, which are imino-acids (see Table 13.1). Ten of the amino-acids are essential acids, *i.e.*, a deficiency in any one prevents growth in young animals, and may even cause death. The amino-acids are classified in several ways; Table 13.1 shows a convenient classification; the letters *g*, *l* and *e* which follow the name of the acids indicate that the acid is respectively of general occurrence, lesser occurrence and essential (to man). There are twenty amino-acids of general occurrence, *i.e.*, these are usually found in *all* proteins. However, plants, micro-organisms and antibiotics excreted by these organisms have continued to provide new amino-acids of diverse structures.

§2. **General methods of preparation of the amino-acids**

There are many general methods for preparing α-amino-acids, but usually each method applies to a small number of particular acids; many acids are also synthesised by methods special to an individual. It should also be noted that very often a synthesis is a more convenient way of preparing an amino-acid than preparing it from natural sources.

(i) **Amination of α-halogenated acids** (Perkin *et al.*, 1858).

(*a*) An α-chloro- or bromo-acid is treated with concentrated ammonia, *e.g.*,

$$\text{ClCH}_2\text{CO}_2\text{H} + 2\text{NH}_3 \longrightarrow \text{CH}_2(\text{NH}_2)\text{CO}_2\text{H} + \text{NH}_4\text{Cl}$$

This method is convenient for the preparation of glycine, alanine, serine, threonine, valine, leucine and norleucine.

(*b*) The yields obtained by the above method are variable because of side-reactions. Better yields are obtained by using **Gabriel's phthalimide synthesis** (1889) with α-halogeno-acids (see also Vol. I), *e.g.*,

(ii) **Strecker synthesis** (1850). A cyanohydrin is treated with concentrated ammonia, and the resulting amino-nitrile is then hydrolysed with acid. In practice the amino-nitrile is usually prepared from the oxo compound in one step by treating the latter with an equimolecular mixture of ammonium chloride and potassium cyanide (this mixture is equivalent to ammonium cyanide), e.g.,

This method is useful for preparing the following amino-acids: glycine, alanine, serine, valine, methionine, glutamic acid, leucine, isoleucine, norleucine and phenylalanine.

The mechanism of the Strecker synthesis is uncertain, but the one given above is very highly favoured. Optically active α-amino-acids have been prepared when the reaction is carried out in the presence of an optically active base, e.g., an alkaloid (see asymmetric synthesis, 3 §7).

(iiia) **Malonic ester synthesis.** This method is really an extension of (ia); it offers a means of preparing α-halogeno-acids, e.g.,

$$CH_2(CO_2C_2H_5)_2 \xrightarrow[RX]{C_2H_5ONa} RCH(CO_2C_2H_5)_2 \xrightarrow[(ii)\ HCl]{(i)\ KOH} RCH(CO_2H)_2 \xrightarrow{Br_2} RCBr(CO_2H)_2 \xrightarrow{heat}$$
$$RCHBrCO_2H \xrightarrow{NH_3} RCH(NH_2)CO_2H$$

This method offers a means of preparing, from readily accessible materials, the following acids: phenylalanine, proline, leucine, isoleucine, norleucine and methionine.

The malonic ester synthesis may also be combined with the Gabriel phthalimide synthesis to prepare phenylalanine, tyrosine, proline, cystine, serine, aspartic acid, methionine and lysine, e.g.,

Cystine.

(a) $C_6H_5CH_2SH + HCHO + HCl \longrightarrow C_6H_5CH_2SCH_2Cl$
    benzylthiol   benzylthiomethyl chloride

(b) $CH_2(CO_2C_2H_5)_2 \xrightarrow{Br_2} CHBr(CO_2C_2H_5)_2$

$H_2NCHCH_2SCH_2C_6H_5 \xrightarrow[\text{liquid } NH_3]{Na} H_2NCHCH_2SH \xrightarrow{air} H_2NCHCH_2SSCH_2CHNH_2$
(with CO_2H groups on the α-carbons)
S-benzylcysteine   (±)-cysteine   (±)-cystine

Proline.

Acylamido derivatives of malonic ester may also be used to synthesise amino-acids; the usual derivative employed is ethyl acetamidomalonate (Albertson, 1946).

$$CH_2(CO_2C_2H_5)_2 \xrightarrow{HNO_2} HON{=}C(CO_2C_2H_5)_2 \xrightarrow[Ni]{H_2} H_2NCH(CO_2C_2H_5)_2 \xrightarrow{CH_3COCl}$$

$$\underset{\text{ethyl acetamidomalonate}}{CH_3CONHCH(CO_2C_2H_5)_2} \xrightarrow[RBr]{C_2H_5ONa} CH_3CONHCR(CO_2C_2H_5)_2 \xrightarrow{HBr} RCH(NH_2)CO_2H$$

The following acids may be prepared by this method: serine, leucine, valine, methionine, lysine, glutamic acid and ornithine.

A special application of this method is the preparation of tryptophan from benzamidomalonic ester and gramine methosulphate (Albertson *et al.*, 1945; Tishler *et al.*, 1945).

A more recent method of preparing ethyl acetamidomalonate is to reduce oximinomalonic ester in a mixture of acetic anhydride, pyridine and sodium acetate with hydrogen in the presence of Raney nickel (Vignau, 1952).

(iii*b*) α-Amino-acids may be synthesised by means of the **Curtius reaction** (see also Vol. I).

Glycine, alanine, phenylalanine and valine can be prepared by this method.

Instead of malonic ester, the starting material can be ethyl cyanoacetate.

$$H_2C \begin{array}{c} CN \\ \\ CO_2C_2H_5 \end{array} \xrightarrow[RX]{C_2H_5ONa} RHC \begin{array}{c} CN \\ \\ CO_2C_2H_5 \end{array} \xrightarrow{N_2H_4} RHC \begin{array}{c} CN \\ \\ CONHNH_2 \end{array} \xrightarrow{HNO_2} RHC \begin{array}{c} CN \\ \\ CON_3 \end{array} \xrightarrow{C_2H_5OH}$$

$$RHC \begin{array}{c} CN \\ \\ NHCO_2C_2H_5 \end{array} \xrightarrow{HCl} RCH(NH_2)CO_2H$$

Phenylalanine and tyrosine are conveniently prepared by this method.

Another variation is the use of the Hofmann degradation on ester amides (see also Vol. I).

$$RHC \begin{array}{c} CO_2C_2H_5 \\ \\ CONH_2 \end{array} \xrightarrow[KOH]{Br_2} RHC \begin{array}{c} CO_2C_2H_5 \\ \\ NH_2 \end{array} \longrightarrow RCH(NH_2)CO_2H$$

(iiic) **The Darapsky synthesis** (1936). In this method an aldehyde is condensed with ethyl cyano-acetate and simultaneously hydrogenated; the product, an alkylcyanoacetic ester, is then treated as above (for the cyanoacetic ester method).

$$RCHO + H_2C \begin{array}{c} CN \\ \\ CO_2C_2H_5 \end{array} \xrightarrow[Ni]{H_2} RCH_2HC \begin{array}{c} CN \\ \\ CO_2C_2H_5 \end{array} \xrightarrow[(ii)\ HNO_2]{(i)\ N_2H_4} RCH_2HC \begin{array}{c} CN \\ \\ CON_3 \end{array} \xrightarrow[(ii)\ HCl]{(i)\ C_2H_5OH} RCH_2CH(NH_2)CO_2H$$

(iv) Amino-acids may be prepared by reducing α-ketonic acids in the presence of ammonia; the reduction may be performed catalytically or with sodium and ethanol. The mechanism of the reaction is not certain but it probably occurs *via* the imino-acid.

$$RCOCO_2H + NH_3 \xrightarrow[Pd]{H_2} \left[\begin{array}{c} RCCO_2H \\ \| \\ NH \end{array} \right] \longrightarrow RCH(NH_2)CO_2H$$

This method works well for alanine and glutamic acid.

Oximes of α-keto-acids may also be reduced to α-amino-acids. The advantage of this method is that the oximes may readily be prepared in good yield by the action of sulphuric acid on a mixture of an alkylacetoacetic ester and an alkyl nitrite (Hartung *et al.*, 1942).

$$CH_3COCHRCO_2C_2H_5 + RONO \xrightarrow{H_2SO_4} \begin{array}{c} RCCO_2C_2H_5 \\ \| \\ NOH \end{array} + CH_3CO_2H + ROH$$

The reduction of phenylhydrazones made by the action of a diazonium salt on an alkylacetoacetic ester also may be used to prepare α-amino-acids (*cf.* the Japp–Klingermann reaction, Vol. I); *e.g.*,

$$CH_3\underset{\underset{COCH_3}{|}}{CH}CO_2C_2H_5 + C_6H_5\overset{+}{N_2}\bar{Cl} \longrightarrow CH_3CO_2H + CH_3\underset{\underset{NNHC_6H_5}{\|}}{C}CO_2C_2H_5 \xrightarrow{Zn—C_2H_5OH} CH_3\underset{\underset{NH_2}{|}}{CH}CO_2C_2H_5 \xrightarrow{hydrolysis}$$

$$CH_3CH(NH_2)CO_2H$$

Thus alanine, phenylalanine, leucine, isoleucine, valine and hydroxyproline may be prepared in this way.

Alkylacetoacetic esters may also be converted into α-amino-acids by means of the Schmidt reaction (see also Vol. I).

$$CH_3COCHRCO_2C_2H_5 + HN_3 \xrightarrow{H_2SO_4} CH_3CONHCHRCO_2C_2H_5 + N_2 \xrightarrow{hydrolysis} RCH(NH_2)CO_2H$$

Table 13.1

Name	Systematic name	Formula
Neutral Amino-acids (one amino-group and one carboxyl group)		
1. Glycine (g)	Aminoacetic acid	$CH_2(NH_2)CO_2H$
2. Alanine (g)	α-Aminopropionic acid	$CH_3CH(NH_2)CO_2H$
3. Valine (g, e)	α-Aminoisovaleric acid	$(CH_3)_2CHCH(NH_2)CO_2H$
4. Leucine (g, e)	α-Aminoisocaproic acid	$(CH_3)_2CHCH_2CH(NH_2)CO_2H$
5. Isoleucine (g, e) j	α-Amino-β-methyl-n-valeric acid	$CH_3CH_2CH(CH_3)CH(NH_2)CO_2H$
6. Norleucine* (l)	α-Amino-n-caproic acid	$CH_3(CH_2)_3CH(NH_2)CO_2H$
7. Phenylalanine (g, e)	α-Amino-β-phenylpropionic acid	$C_6H_5CH_2CH(NH_2)CO_2H$
8. Tyrosine (g)	α-Amino-β-(p-hydroxyphenyl)propionic acid	HO—⟨ring⟩—$CH_2CH(NH_2)CO_2H$
9. Serine (g)	α-Amino-β-hydroxypropionic acid	$HOCH_2CH(NH_2)CO_2H$
10. Cysteine (g)	α-Amino-β-mercaptopropionic acid	$HSCH_2CH(NH_2)CO_2H$
11. Cystine (g)	Bis-(α-aminopropionic acid)-β-disulphide	$[—SCH_2CH(NH_2)CO_2H]_2$
12. Threonine (g, e)	α-Amino-β-hydroxy-n-butyric acid	$CH_3CHOHCH(NH_2)CO_2H$
13. Methionine (g, e)	α-Amino-γ-methylthio-n-butyric acid	$CH_3SCH_2CH_2CH(NH_2)CO_2H$
14. Iodogorgic acid† (l)	3,5-Di-iodotyrosine	HO—⟨ring⟩—$CH_2CH(NH_2)CO_2H$
15. Thyroxine† (l)	β-3,5-Di-iodo-4-(3',5'-di-iodo-4'-hydroxy)-phenyl-α-aminopropionic acid	$CH_2CH(NH_2)CO_2H$
16. Tryptophan (g, e)	α-Amino-β-indolepropionic acid	$CH_2CH(NH_2)CO_2H$
17. Proline (g)	Pyrrolidine-α-carboxylic acid	CO_2H

18. Hydroxyproline (g)   γ-Hydroxypyrrolidine-α-carboxylic acid

Acidic Amino-acids (one amino-group and two carboxyl groups)

19. Aspartic acid (g)	α-Aminosuccinic acid	$HO_2CCH_2CH(NH_2)CO_2H$
20. Asparagine (l)	α-Aminosuccinamic acid	$H_2NOCCH_2CH(NH_2)CO_2H$
21. Glutamic acid (g)	α-Aminoglutaric acid	$HO_2CCH_2CH_2CH(NH_2)CO_2H$
22. β-Hydroxyglutamic acid‡	α-Amino-β-hydroxyglutaric acid	$HO_2CCH_2CHOHCH(NH_2)CO_2H$
23. Glutamine (l)	α-Aminoglutaramic acid	$H_2NOCCH_2CH_2CH(NH_2)CO_2H$

Basic Amino-acids (two amino-groups and one carboxyl group)

24. Ornithine §	α,δ-Diamino-n-valeric acid	$H_2NCH_2CH_2CH_2CH(NH_2)CO_2H$
25. Arginine (g, e)	α-Amino-δ-guanidino-n-valeric acid	$NH{=}CNH(CH_2)_3CH(NH_2)CO_2H$ $\quad\;\;\vert$ $\quad NH_2$
26. Lysine (g, e)	α,ε-Diaminocaproic acid	$H_2N(CH_2)_4CH(NH_2)CO_2H$
27. Histidine (g, e)	α-Amino-β-imidazolepropionic acid	$CH_2CH(NH_2)CO_2H$

* The occurrence of norleucine in proteins is uncertain.
† See also §5.
‡ The occurrence of β-hydroxyglutamic acid in proteins is uncertain.
§ Ornithine is probably not present in proteins, but is formed by the hydrolysis of arginine.

Hiskey *et al.* (1961) have prepared optically active amino-acids from α-keto-acids by asymmetric synthesis. The keto-acid is catalytically hydrogenated in the presence of D(+)- or L(−)-α-methylbenzylamine (an azomethine is the intermediate), and hydrogenolysis of the benzylamine salt is carried out in the presence of palladous hydroxide ($BH^+ = PhCHMeNH_3^+$):

$$RCOCO_2H + 2PhCHMeNH_2 \longrightarrow \underset{\substack{\| \\ NCHMePh}}{RCCO_2^-}\}BH^+ \xrightarrow[Pd-C]{H_2} \underset{\substack{| \\ NHCHMePh}}{RCHCO_2^-}\}BH^+ \xrightarrow[Pd(OH)_2-C]{H_2} \underset{\substack{| \\ NH_2}}{RCHCO_2^-}\}NH_4^+ + 2PhCH_2CH_3$$

Thus, for example, pyruvic acid in the presence of the D-amine gave D(−)-alanine in 78 per cent yield and 91 per cent optical purity.

(v*a*) **The Azlactone synthesis** (*Erlenmeyer synthesis*, 1893). Azlactones are usually prepared by heating an aromatic aldehyde with hippuric acid (benzoylglycine) in the presence of acetic anhydride and sodium acetate, *e.g.*, benzaldehyde forms benzoyl-α-aminocinnamic azlactone (4-benzylidene-2-phenyloxazol-5-one).

$$C_6H_5CHO + \underset{\substack{| \\ NHCOC_6H_5}}{CH_2CO_2H} \xrightarrow[CH_3CO_2Na]{(CH_3CO)_2O} C_6H_5CH=C{\underset{N{\underset{C}{\overset{3}{\longleftarrow}}}{\overset{4 \quad 5}{\longrightarrow}}O}{\overset{}{\underset{|}{C_6H_5}}}}CO$$

This reaction is usually referred to as the **Erlenmeyer azlactone synthesis**. Aceturic acid (acetylglycine) may also be used instead of hippuric acid. Furthermore, it has been found that aliphatic aldehydes may condense with hippuric acid to form azlactones if lead acetate is used instead of sodium acetate (Finar *et al.*, 1949).

When azlactones are warmed with 1 per cent sodium hydroxide solution, the ring is opened, and if the product is reduced with sodium amalgam followed by hydrolysis with acid, an α-amino-acid is produced, *e.g.*,

$$C_6H_5CH=C{\underset{N{\underset{\underset{C_6H_5}{|}}{C}}O}{\overset{CO}{\longrightarrow}}} \xrightarrow{NaOH} \underset{\substack{| \\ NHCOC_6H_5}}{C_6H_5CH=CCO_2H} \xrightarrow{Na-Hg} \underset{\substack{| \\ NHCOC_6H_5}}{C_6H_5CH_2CHCO_2H} \xrightarrow{HCl}$$

$$C_6H_5CH_2CH(NH_2)CO_2H + C_6H_5CO_2H$$

The azlactone synthesis offers a convenient means of preparing phenylalanine, tyrosine, tryptophan and thyroxine.

(v*b*) Aromatic aldehydes also condense with hydantoin, and reduction of the product with sodium amalgam or ammonium hydrogen sulphide, followed by hydrolysis, gives an α-amino-acid, *e.g.*, tryptophan may be prepared by first converting indole into indole-3-aldehyde by means of the Reimer–Tiemann reaction (see Vol. I).

This method has been improved by using acetylthiohydantoin instead of hydantoin. The above method may be used to prepare phenylalanine, tyrosine, tryptophan and methionine.

$$
\begin{array}{c}
\text{OC}\!\!-\!\!\text{NH} \\
\qquad\qquad \text{CS} \\
\text{H}_2\text{C}\!\!-\!\!\text{NCOCH}_3
\end{array}
$$

acetylthiohydantoin

Another modification of the hydantoin synthesis is the **Bücherer hydantoin synthesis** (1934). In this method an oxo compound is converted into a 5-substituted hydantoin by means of ammonium carbonate and sodium cyanide in aqueous ethanol solution, followed by hydrolysis.

$$
\text{RCHO} \xrightarrow[\text{(NH}_4)_2\text{CO}_2]{\text{NaCN}} \quad
\begin{array}{c}
\text{RHC}\!\!-\!\!\text{CO} \\
\qquad\qquad \text{NH} \\
\text{HN}\!\!-\!\!\text{CO}
\end{array}
\xrightarrow{\text{NaOH}} \quad
\begin{array}{c}
\text{RCHCO}_2\text{H} \\
\text{NH}_2
\end{array}
$$

An example is the preparation of methionine:

$$
\text{CH}_2\!\!=\!\!\text{CHCHO} + \text{CH}_3\text{SH} \xrightarrow{\text{C}_5\text{H}_5\text{N}} \text{CH}_3\text{SCH}_2\text{CH}_2\text{CHO} \xrightarrow[\text{(NH}_4)_2\text{CO}_3]{\text{NaCN}}
$$

$$
\begin{array}{c}
\text{CH}_3\text{SCH}_2\text{CH}_2\text{HC}\!\!-\!\!\text{CO} \\
\qquad\qquad\qquad\qquad \text{NH} \\
\text{HN}\!\!-\!\!\text{CO}
\end{array}
\xrightarrow{\text{NaOH}} \quad
\begin{array}{c}
\text{CH}_3\text{SCH}_2\text{CH}_2\text{CHCO}_2\text{H} \\
\text{NH}_2
\end{array}
$$

(vc) Aromatic aldehydes may be condensed with diketopiperazine, and the product converted into an amino-acid by heating with hydriodic acid and red phosphorus, e.g.,

$$
2\text{C}_6\text{H}_5\text{CHO} + \quad
\begin{array}{c}
\text{O} \\
\text{HN} \\
\text{NH} \\
\text{O}
\end{array}
\xrightarrow{\text{(CH}_3\text{CO)}_2\text{O}} \quad
\begin{array}{c}
\text{O} \\
\text{HN} \quad \text{CHC}_6\text{H}_5 \\
\text{NH} \\
\text{C}_6\text{H}_5\text{CH} \\
\text{O}
\end{array}
\xrightarrow[\text{P}]{\text{HI}} \quad 2\text{C}_6\text{H}_5\text{CH}_2\text{CH(NH}_2)\text{CO}_2\text{H}
$$

Phenylalanine, tyrosine and methionine may be prepared by this method.

§3. Analysis of amino-acids from protein hydrolysates

Proteins are completely hydrolysed by acids, and this hydrolysis is usually carried out with 6N hydrochloric acid. This method largely destroys tryptophan and partially destroys cysteine and cystine (see also §9c). Serine and threonine are slowly destroyed, and asparagine and glutamine are hydrolysed to aspartic acid and glutamic acid, respectively. In spite of these difficulties, acid hydrolysis of proteins is the usual procedure.

Alkaline hydrolysis, which is generally carried out with 5N barium hydroxide, destroys arginine, cysteine, cystine, serine, and threonine. Since tryptophan is not destroyed, alkaline hydrolysis is useful for the analysis of this amino-acid. A serious disadvantage of alkaline hydrolysis is that it causes complete racemisation of the amino-acids.

Enzymic hydrolysis of proteins is slow and is usually incomplete. However, by use of a number of enzymes, each in turn, it is possible to degrade the protein into smaller and smaller fragments, and ultimately into the constituent amino-acids. This technique is very valuable for the elucidation of the amino-acid sequence in a protein (see §9c).

Analysis of mixtures of amino-acids may be carried out in various ways. Only those methods which are in current use are described here. A common method for the quantitative analysis of amino-acid mixtures is ion-exchange chromatography (**1** §15f). The column consists of a resin which may be a strongly acidic cation or a strongly basic anion exchanger. A common cation-exchange resin is sulphonated polystyrene. This is converted into its sodium salt and when an acid solution (at pH 3) of a mixture of amino-acids is added, the most basic acids are most tightly bound and the most acidic acids are most weakly bound. Elution is carried out with a series of buffer solutions, each in turn. The individual amino-acids are then identified from their elution positions (which have been previously determined by using the various amino-acids). This method has now been automated.

Another common method makes use of paper chromatography (**1** §15c). This may be carried out in several ways (Martin *et al.*, 1944). In *one-dimensional separations* the stationary phase is water and the mobile phase may be mixtures such as n-butanol-ethanol-water, n-butanol-acetic acid-water, etc. The paper is dried and sprayed with a dilute solution of ninhydrin in n-butanol or ethanol (see also §4C), and the coloured spots thereby produced show the positions of the amino-acids. Since the R_F values of the various amino-acids are known, it is therefore possible to deduce the identity of each acid present in the mixture. It is also possible to use this method for the quantitative estimation of the amino-acids since the colour is proportional to the amount of amino-acid present (the colour is measured photometrically and compared with standards).

In *two-dimensional separations*, the mixture of amino-acids is developed in one direction, the paper dried and developed in a perpendicular direction with another solvent. The solvents are mixtures and different combinations have been used, *e.g.*, (i) *first:* m-cresol-phenol; *second:* n-butanol-acetic acid-water; (ii) *first:* n-butanol-water-ammonium hydroxide; *second:* n-butanol-acetic acid-water.

Two-dimensional separations are also used with various derivatives of the amino-acids, *e.g.*, the DNP derivative (see §9b). These are eluted and determined spectrophotometrically. The DNP derivatives may also be separated by column chromatography on silica gel, kieselguhr, etc. (**1** §15a), or by two-dimensional TLC (**1** §15d).

Paper electrophoresis (**1** §15e) is widely used to identify amino-acids. GLC (**1** §15g) is also very useful for the quantitative estimation of amino-acids in mixtures. Volatile derivatives are used, particularly the *N*-trifluoroacetyl methyl ester.

NMR spectroscopy is now being used for the identification of amino-acids. The τ-values of amino-acid protons depend on the pH of the solution, and in neutral solution the dipolar-ion peak is characteristic of the amino-acid. At the same time, side-chain protons will show a characteristic pattern, *e.g.*,

$$\overset{2\cdot46 \, (b,m)}{NH_3^+}\!\!-\!\!\overset{5\cdot80 \, (q)}{CH_2}\!\!-\!\!CO_2^- \qquad \overset{NH_3^+ \, 2\cdot52(b)}{\underset{5\cdot54 \, (b,m)}{CH_3}\!\!-\!\!\overset{|}{\underset{}{CH}}\!\!-\!\!CO_2^-}$$

$$\overset{8\cdot15 \, (d)}{CH_3}$$

Mass spectrometry is increasing in use in the analysis of amino-acids, both as a means of identification and as a means of quantitative estimation (see §9e).

§4. General properties of the amino-acids

The amino-acids are colourless crystalline compounds which are generally soluble in water but sparingly soluble in organic solvents; most melt with decomposition, but Gross *et al.* (1955) have shown that sublimation is possible with a number of amino-acids. The infrared spectra of many amino-acids have been examined and it has been shown that the spectrum of the $(\pm)$-form of an amino-acid in the *solid state* differs markedly from that of either enantiomer (both of which show identical spectra). Enantiomers show absorption bands which are characteristic of NH_3^+ (3 130–3 000, 1 600–1 500, 1 550–1 480 cm^{-1}) and of CO_2^- (1 600–1 500 cm^{-1}). Other bands have also been observed, *e.g.*, 1 300, 880 cm^{-1}. On the other hand, of the common amino-acids, only three absorb in the ultraviolet region above 250 nm. These contain the benzene ring (the chromophore): phenylalanine ($\sim$260 nm), tyrosine ($\sim$275 nm), and tryptophan ($\sim$280 nm). When these amino-acids are present in a protein, it is possible to measure the concentration of that protein in solution by means of ultraviolet spectroscopy.

NMR spectroscopy has been mentioned in §3; mass spectrometry is dealt with in §9e.

All the amino-acids contain at least one chiral centre and all (except glycine) occur naturally in their optically active forms. It has been mentioned in **2** §5b that natural ($-$)-serine was chosen as the arbitrary standard for correlating the configurations of amino-acids, the relationship to this acid being indicated by D_s or L_s. It has now been shown that $L_g \equiv L_s$, *i.e.*, natural ($-$)-serine belongs to the L-series (with glyceraldehyde as absolute standard). The correlation between the two standards was established as follows. ($+$)-Alanine has been correlated with L($+$)-lactic acid (for the correlation of the latter with L($-$)-glyceraldehyde see **2** §5bi); and L($+$)-alanine has been correlated with L($-$)-serine:

(a) L($+$)-lactic acid ← (OH⁻) — (NaN₃) → — (H₂, cat.) → L($+$)-alanine

(b) L($-$)-serine → (MeOH / HCl) → (PCl₅) → (i) NaOH (ii) H₂–Pt → L($+$)-alanine

A recent method for determining the configuration of an α-amino-acid is by studying the rotatory dispersion curves of the dithiocarbamate derivatives of α-amino-acids, $RCH(CO_2H)NHC(=S)SC_2H_5$. Nine acids were studied by Djerassi *et al.* (1959), and positive Cotton effects were given by the acids with an L-configuration, and similar negative effects by those acids with a D-configuration. On the other hand, Klyne *et al.* (1965) have examined the ORD curves of a series of L-amino-acids and found that these give positive C.E. curves with peaks at about 216 nm (see also **1** §9a). It appears that all L-amino-acids will show positive Cotton effects with a peak at 216 nm or less, and so the study of ORD curves of amino-acids or of their suitable derivatives will lead to assignment of absolute configuration. It has been shown that the α-carbon atom, *i.e.*, the carbon atom attached to the amino-group, has, in almost all the amino-acids, the same configuration as L($-$)-glyceraldehyde. The specific rotation of the amino-acids depends on the *p*H of the solution, the temperature, the presence of salts and the nature of the solvent (see Table 13.2; also see §C, below). In aqueous solution, L-amino-acids generally show a positive shift in the sign of rotation (D-acids show an opposite shift) as the *p*H increases. Hence, this can be used (with caution) to determine the relative configuration of a new amino-acid.

The racemic amino-acids may be resolved by first formylating and then resolving the formyl derivatives *via* the salt with an optically active base, and finally removing the formyl group by hydrolysis (see also Ci). Alternatively, racemic amino-acids may be resolved by means of enzymes (see **2** §10iv). A more recent method is the selective destruction of one or other enantiomer of a racemate by a specific D- or L-oxidase (Parikh *et al.*, 1958); the optical purity of the product is greater than 99·9 per cent. Harada (1965) has resolved racemic amino-acids by the inoculation method (see **2** §10ii), and Contractor *et al.* (1965) have resolved DL-tryptophan, etc., by paper and thin-layer chromatography (the D-isomers have a greater R_F value than the corresponding L-isomers; see also **1** §§17c, 17d). On the other hand, Halpern *et al.* (1965) have resolved racemic amino-acids by first converting them into their diastereoisomeric L-α-chloroisovalerylamino-acid methyl esters, and then separating these by means of GLC (**1** §17g). These authors have also used the (−)-menthyl esters of amino-acids.

Because of their occurrence in one enantiomeric form, optical purity of amino-acids is extremely important in the synthesis of peptides. Hence, after having determined their chemical purity, the optical purity of amino-acids must be determined. Many methods are now available, but two of the most important techniques are chromatography (see above) and NMR spectroscopy. One application of the latter has been described in **2** §10a. Another application is that due to Pirkle *et al.* (1969). The NMR spectra of pairs of enantiomers of methyl esters of α-amino-acids are not identical when (R)-(−)-2,2,2-trifluoro-1-phenylethanol [PhCH(CF$_3$)OH] is used as solvent. The difference between the chemical shifts is sufficient to enable the optical purity of α-amino-acids to be determined. The explanation offered for these differences is the formation of short-lived diastereoisomeric solvates.

As pointed out above, most natural amino-acids are L; these are obtained by acid or enzymic hydrolysis of proteins. Alkaline hydrolysis of proteins gives the DL-amino-acids (§3), and so does the synthetic preparation; it is by resolution of the synthetic racemic modification that the D-amino-acids are frequently prepared. On the other hand, many of the amino-acids that have been discovered later, particularly those from metabolic products of micro-organisms, have the D-configuration, *e.g.*, the D-forms of 2, 3, 4, 5, 7, 9, 17, and 21 in Table 13.1.

The symbols D and L are used for the configuration of the α-carbon atom (see above), and the symbols (+) and (−) are used to indicate the direction of the rotation (*cf.* **2** §5). When two chiral centres are present, then D and L still refer to the α-carbon atom, and the *naturally occurring acid* is known as the L-amino-acid. The allo-form is the name given to the form in which the configuration of the *second chiral centre is inverted*, *e.g.*, L(−)-threonine (the naturally occurring form), D(+)-threonine, L-allothreonine and D-allothreonine.

L(−)-threonine   D(+)-threonine   L-allothreonine   D-allothreonine

Examination of the formulae shows that the L-acids belong to the L-series of amino-acids (since the α-carbon is configurationally related to L(+)-alanine), but the second chiral centre is configurationally related to the sugar series.

L-threonine   D-threose   L-allothreonine   L-threose

It has been pointed out above that the L-series of amino-acids has been correlated with L(−)-glyceraldehyde, and therefore the configuration of the α-carbon atom is the absolute one. This has also been established by Bijovet *et al.* (1954) by X-ray analysis of D-isoleucine hydrochloride and hydrobromide. It was shown that the D-acid had the absolute configuration given in the formula, and so it follows that the L-acid has the configuration shown (which is in agreement with the chemical correlation). The absolute configuration of L-threonine has also been confirmed by X-ray analysis.

$$
\begin{array}{cc}
\text{CO}_2\text{H} & \text{CO}_2\text{H} \\
\text{H—C—NH}_2 & \text{NH}_2\text{—C—H} \\
\text{H—C—CH}_3 & \text{CH}_3\text{—C—H} \\
\text{C}_2\text{H}_5 & \text{C}_2\text{H}_5 \\
\text{D-isoleucine} & \text{L-isoleucine}
\end{array}
$$

The specification of absolute configuration of α-amino-acids is carried out in the usual way (see also **2** §5d). All L-acids, represented by (I), will be equivalent to (II), and this is the (S)-form. Cysteine (III), however, is equivalent to (IV), and this is the (R)-form. Although the sequence rule

$$
\begin{array}{cccc}
\text{CO}_2\text{H} & b & \text{CO}_2\text{H} & c \\
\text{H}_2\text{N—}\text{—H} \equiv a\text{—}\text{—}d & & \text{H}_2\text{N—}\text{—H} \equiv a\text{—}\text{—}d & \\
\text{CH}_2\text{R} & c & \text{CH}_2\text{SH} & b \\
\text{(I)} & \text{(II) } (S)\text{-} & \text{(III)} & \text{(IV) } (R)\text{-}
\end{array}
$$

was designed so that D = R and L = S, it can be seen from the case of cysteine (and related substances containing the group —CH_2S—) that the implication is that this amino-acid belongs to the D-series (see **2** §5d).

Extending the specification to both carbon atoms, L-threonine is (2S,3R)-2-amino-3-hydroxy-butyric acid, and L-allothreonine is (2S,3S)-2-amino-3-hydroxybutyric acid.

Since they contain amino and carboxyl groups, the amino-acids possess the properties of both a base and an acid, *i.e.*, they are amphoteric.

A. Reactions due to the amino-group

(i) The amino-acids form salts with strong inorganic acids, *e.g.*, $\bar{\text{C}}\text{l}\{\text{H}_3\overset{+}{\text{N}}\text{CH}_2\text{CO}_2\text{H}$. These salts are usually sparingly soluble in water, and the free acid may be liberated by means of a strong organic base, *e.g.*, pyridine.

(ii) Amino-acids may be acetylated by means of acetyl chloride or acetic anhydride.

$$\text{RCH(NH}_2)\text{CO}_2\text{H} + (\text{CH}_3\text{CO})_2\text{O} \longrightarrow \text{RCH(NHCOCH}_3)\text{CO}_2\text{H} + \text{CH}_3\text{CO}_2\text{H}$$

Similarly, benzoyl chloride produces the benzoyl derivative. These acetylated derivatives are acidic, the basic character of the amino-group being effectively eliminated by the presence of the $-\text{I}$ group attached to the nitrogen. It should also be noted that the carboxyl group of one molecule can react with the amino-group of another molecule of an amino-acid to form a peptide (see §10). Sanger (1945) has shown that 1-fluoro-2,4-dinitrobenzene combines with amino-acids to form dinitro-phenyl derivatives (see §10).

(iii) Nitrous acid liberates nitrogen from amino-acids.

$$\text{RCH(NH}_2)\text{CO}_2\text{H} + \text{HNO}_2 \longrightarrow \text{RCHOHCO}_2\text{H} + \text{N}_2 + \text{H}_2\text{O}$$

The nitrogen is evolved quantitatively, and this forms the basis of the **van Slyke method** (1911) for analysing mixtures of amino-acids.

(iv) Nitrosyl chloride (or bromide) reacts with amino-acids to form chloro- (or bromo-) acids.

$$\text{RCH(NH}_2)\text{CO}_2\text{H} + \text{NOCl} \longrightarrow \text{RCHClCO}_2\text{H} + \text{N}_2 + \text{H}_2\text{O}$$

(v) When heated with hydriodic acid at 200°C, the amino-group is eliminated with the formation of a fatty acid.

$$RCH(NH_2)CO_2H \xrightarrow[200°C]{HI} RCH_2CO_2H + NH_3$$

B. Reactions due to the carboxyl group

(i) Amino-acids forms salts; the salts of the heavy metals are chelate compounds, *e.g.*, the copper salt of glycine (deep blue needles) is formed by heating copper oxide with an aqueous solution of glycine.

$$\begin{array}{ccc}
OC\!\!-\!\!-\!\!O & & NH_2\!\!-\!\!CH_2 \\
| & \searrow Cu \nwarrow & | \\
H_2C\!\!-\!\!NH_2 & & O\!\!-\!\!-\!\!CO
\end{array}$$

The amino-acids may be liberated from their alkali salts by treatment in ethanolic solution with ethyl oximinocyanoacetate (Galat, 1947).

(ii) When heated with an alcohol in the presence of dry hydrogen chloride, amino-acids form ester hydrochlorides, *e.g.*,

$$H_2NCH_2CO_2H + C_2H_5OH + HCl \longrightarrow \bar{C}l\{H_3\overset{+}{N}CH_2CO_2C_2H_5 + H_2O$$

The free ester may be obtained by the action of aqueous sodium carbonate on the ester salt. The esters are fairly readily hydrolysed to the amino-acid by aqueous sodium hydroxide (even at room temperature). These esters may be reduced to the amino-alcohols by means of sodium and ethanol, or hydrogenated in the presence of Raney nickel. Amino-acids may be reduced directly to the amino-alcohol with lithium aluminium hydride, and in this case no racemisation occurs (Vogel *et al.*, 1952).

$$RCH(NH_2)CO_2H \xrightarrow{LiAlH_4} RCH(NH_2)CH_2OH$$

(iii) When suspended in acetyl chloride and then treated with phosphorus pentachloride, amino-acids form the hydrochloride of the acid chloride.

$$RCH(NH_2)CO_2H \longrightarrow \bar{C}l\{H_3\overset{+}{N}CHRCOCl + POCl_3$$

(iv) Dry distillation, or better by heating with barium oxide, decarboxylates amino-acids to amines.

$$RCH(NH_2)CO_2H \longrightarrow RCH_2NH_2 + CO_2$$

(v) When heated with acetic anhydride in pyridine solution, amino-acids are converted into methyl α-acetamidoketones (Dakin *et al.*, 1928; see also **12** §18); this reaction is often referred to as the **Dakin–West reaction**.

$$RHC\begin{array}{c} \diagup NH_2 \\ \diagdown CO_2H \end{array} \xrightarrow[C_5H_5N]{(CH_3CO)_2O} RHC\begin{array}{c} \diagup NHCOCH_3 \\ \diagdown COCH_3 \end{array}$$

C. Reactions due to both the amino and carboxyl groups

(i) When measured in aqueous solution, the dipole moment of glycine (and other amino-acids) is found to have a large value. To account for this large value it has been suggested that glycine exists, in solution, as an *inner salt*. Such a double charged ion is also known as a *zwitterion, ampholyte* or a *dipolar ion*. This dipolar ion structure also accounts for the absence of acidic and basic properties of an amino-acid (the carboxyl and amino-groups of the *same* molecule neutralise each other to form a salt). The properties of crystalline glycine, *e.g.*, its high melting point and its insolubility in hydrocarbon solvents, also indicate that it exists as the inner salt in the solid state. Finally, X-ray analysis has shown that all amino-acids exist as dipolar ions.

In neutral solution, an amino-acid will be present in the following species, which are in equilibrium.

$$\underset{\text{conjugate acid}}{R\overset{+}{CHNH_3}CO_2H} \underset{-H^+}{\overset{+H^+}{\rightleftharpoons}} \underset{\text{dipolar ion}}{R\overset{+}{CHNH_3}CO_2^-} \underset{+H^+}{\overset{-H^+}{\rightleftharpoons}} \underset{\text{conjugate base}}{RCHNH_2CO_2^-}$$

The position of this equilibrium depends on the pH of the solution, in acid solution the conjugate acid predominating (see A(i)), and in alkaline solution the conjugate base predominating. For each amino-acid there is a particular pH value at which the concentration of the dipolar ion is a maximum. Since the net charge is zero, the dipolar ion is electrically neutral and consequently, in this condition, the amino-acid does not migrate when placed in an electric field. This pH at which migration does not occur is called the **isoelectric point** of that amino-acid.

Since they can behave both as an acid and as a base, monoamino-monocarboxylic acids have two pK values, one as an acid (when titrated with base) and the other as a base (when titrated with acid). By convention, pK_1 is the one corresponding to the group titrated at the most acid region, *i.e.*, the carboxyl group (the change is from carboxylate ion).

The following illustrates how the isoelectric point of a monoamino-monocarboxylic acid may be calculated. If we represent the isoelectric amino-acid as $H_3\overset{+}{N}—Z—CO_2^-$, we have the following equilibria:

$$\underset{cA}{H_3\overset{+}{N}—Z—CO_2H} \rightleftharpoons \underset{D.I.}{H_3\overset{+}{N}—Z—CO_2^-} + H^+$$

$$\underset{D.I.}{H_3\overset{+}{N}—Z—CO_2^-} \rightleftharpoons \underset{cB}{H_2N—Z—CO_2^-} + H^+$$

$$\therefore \quad K_1 = \frac{[\text{D.I.}][H^+]}{[cA]}; \qquad K_2 = \frac{[cB][H^+]}{[\text{D.I.}]}$$

$$\therefore \quad cA = \frac{[\text{D.I.}][H^+]}{K_1}; \qquad cB = \frac{K_2[\text{D.I.}]}{[H^+]}$$

At the isoelectric point (pH_i), [D.I.] is a maximum and since the net charge is zero,

$$\therefore \quad [cA] = [cB]$$

$$\therefore \quad \frac{[\text{D.I.}][H_i^+]}{K_1} = \frac{K_2[\text{D.I.}]}{[H_i^+]}$$

$$\therefore \quad [H_i^+]^2 = K_1 K_2$$

$$\therefore \quad 2pH_i = pK_1 + pK_2$$

$$\therefore \quad pH_i = (pK_1 + pK_2)/2$$

Let us use glycine as an example: $pK_1 = 2\cdot4$ and $pK_2 = 9\cdot6$. Hence the isoelectric point is $(2\cdot4 + 9\cdot6)/2 = 6\cdot0$ (see Table 13.2).

In the presence of salts, because these 'foreign' ions may combine with the dipolar ion, the pH for maximum concentration of dipolar ion may vary. Some authors prefer to use the term **isoionic point** for those cases where ions due to the amino-acid and hydrogen ions are present, and the term *isoelectric point* to those cases where ions other than hydrogen are also present, *i.e.*, the *p*H at which the dipolar-ion concentration is a maximum in the presence of salts.

Since the rotations of the dipolar ion, conjugate acid and conjugate base are different, the specific rotation of a given amino-acid will depend on the *p*H of the solution and the presence or absence of salts.

When an amino-acid contains two amino or two carboxyl groups, there are several possibilities for the structure of the dipolar ion at the isoelectric point. In all the α-amino-acids, it is the ionisation of the α-carboxyl group that is involved, but the amino-group, although often the α-amino, may also be the terminal amino-group, *e.g.*,

$$HO_2C(CH_2)_2CH(\overset{+}{N}H_3)CO_2^-$$
glutamic acid

$$H_3\overset{+}{N}(CH_2)_4CH(NH_2)CO_2^-$$
lysine

$$\underset{H_2N}{\overset{H_2N}{>}}CNH(CH_2)_3CH(NH_2)CO_2^-$$
arginine

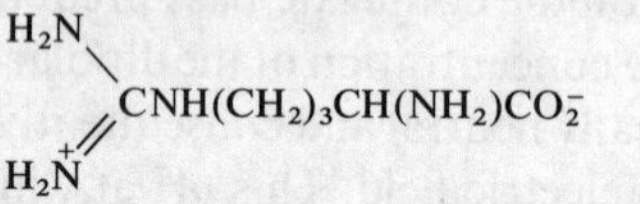

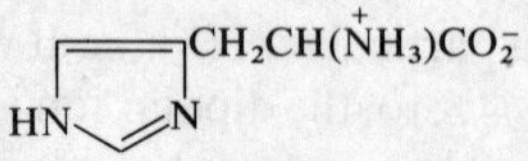

histidine

Titration of an amino-acid with alkali determines the pK_2 of that acid, *i.e.*, the group with the higher *pK* value is the positively charged NH_3^+ group (see above). In order to titrate the carboxyl group with alkali, the amino-group must be 'masked'. Thus, when a formalin solution is added to glycine, methylene-glycine is formed.

$$H_2NCH_2CO_2H + HCHO \longrightarrow CH_2{=}NCH_2CO_2H + H_2O$$

Table 13.2

Acid	Symbol	$[\alpha]_D^{25}$ (H$_2$O)	Isoelectric point
Glycine	Gly	—	6·0
Alanine	Ala	+2·7	6·1
Valine	Val	+6·4	6·0
Leucine	Leu	−10·8	6·0
Isoleucine	Ileu	+11·3	6·0
Phenylalanine	Phe	−35·1	5·9
Tyrosine	Tyr	−8·6	5·6
Serine	Ser	−6·8	5·7
Cysteine	CySH	+9·8	5·1
Cystine	CySSCy	−214·4*	5·0
Threonine	Thr	−28·3	5·7
Methionine	Met	−8·1	5·7
Tryptophan	Try	−31·5	5·9
Proline	Pro	−85·0	6·3
Hydroxyproline	Hypro	−75·2	5·8
Aspartic acid	Asp	+4·7	3·0
Asparagine	AspNH$_2$	−7·4	5·4
Glutamic acid	Glu	+11·5	3·1
Glutamine	GluNH$_2$	+9·1	5·7
Arginine	Arg	+12·6	10·8
Lysine	Lys	+14·6	9·5
Histidine	His	−39·0	7·6

* N HCl

Although some methyleneglycine is probably formed, it appears that the reaction is more complex; the main product appears to be dimethylolglycine.

$$H_2NCH_2CO_2H + 2HCHO \longrightarrow (CH_2OH)_2NCH_2CO_2H$$

This method of titrating amino-acids with alkali is known as the **Sörensen formol titration**.

(ii) When heated, α-amino-acids form 2,5-diketopiperazines; esters give better yields; e.g., diketopiperazine from glycine ester.

(iii) *N*-alkyl or arylamino-acids form *N*-nitroso derivatives with nitrous acid, and these may be dehydrated to sydnones by means of acetic anhydride (see **12** §8).

(iv) **Betaines.** These are the trialkyl derivatives of the amino-acids; betaine itself may be prepared by heating glycine with methyl iodide in methanolic solution. The betaines exist as dipolar ions; thus the formation of betaine may be written:

$$H_3\overset{+}{N}CH_2CO_2^- + 3CH_3I \longrightarrow (CH_3)_3\overset{+}{N}CH_2CO_2^- + 3HI$$

Betaine is more conveniently prepared by warming an aqueous solution of chloroacetic acid with trimethylamine.

$$(CH_3)_3N + ClCH_2CO_2H \longrightarrow (CH_3)_3\overset{+}{N}CH_2CO_2^- + HCl$$

Betaine is a solid, m.p. 300°C (with decomposition). It occurs in nature, especially in plant juices. It behaves as a base, e.g., with hydrochloric acid it forms the stable crystalline hydrochloride, $\bar{C}l\{(CH_3)_3\overset{+}{N}CH_2CO_2H$.

(v) Amino-acids react with phenyl isocyanate to form phenylhydantoic acids, and these, on treatment with hydrochloric acid, readily form hydantoins (see **16** §2):

If phenyl isothiocyanate is used instead of the isocyanate, then thiohydantoins are produced (see §9b).

(vi) **Ninhydrin reaction.** Ninhydrin (indane-1,2,3-trione hydrate) reacts with amino-acids to form a coloured product. The mechanism of the reaction is not certain; one possibility is:

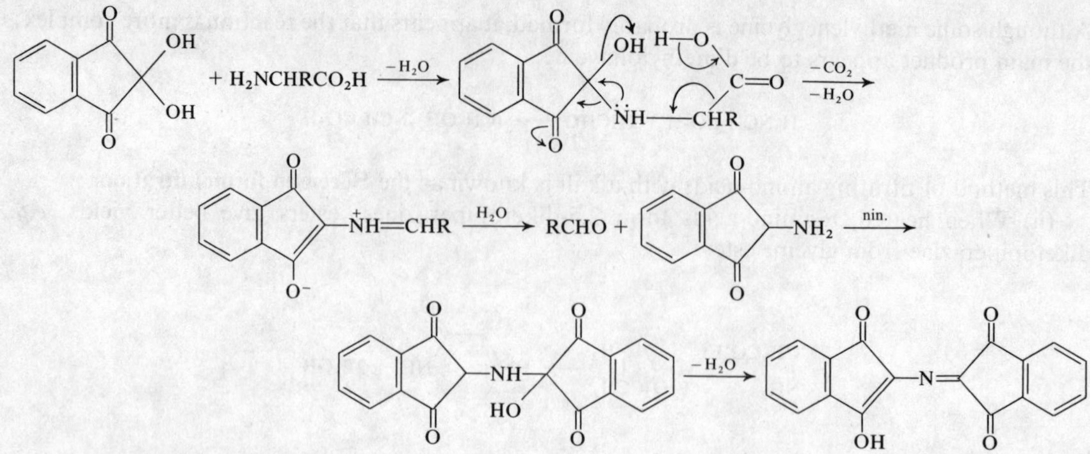

The ninhydrin reaction is used as a spraying reagent in the identification and quantitative estimation of amino-acids (see §3). All α-amino-acids give the same blue product; proline and hydroxyproline, however, give a yellow product. Other reagents are also used, *e.g.*, sodium 2,4,6-trinitrobenzene-1-sulphonate (TNBS). Also, specific reagents may be used to detect particular amino-acids, *e.g.*, diazotised sulphanilic acid couples with tyrosine and histidine in alkaline solution to give a red colour.

§5. Thyroxine (thyroxin)

Thyroxine is a hormone; it is an iodine derivative found in the protein *thyroglobulin* which occurs in the thyroid gland and was first isolated by Kendall (1919). It was later isolated by Harington (1930) as a white crystalline solid, m.p. 235°C, $[\alpha]_D$ −4·4. Hydrolysis of thyroglobulin yields the common amino-acids and also thyroxine and various iodinated derivatives—L-histidine (4-), L-tyrosine (3- and 3,5-) and L-thyronine. Three iodothyronines are present: 3,3′; 3,3′,5′-; 3,3′,5-. Of these the last shows the greatest biological activity.

The structure of thyroxine was established by Harington (1926). This author showed that the molecular formula of thyroxine is $C_{15}H_{11}I_4NO_4$. When treated in alkaline solution with hydrogen in the presence of colloidal palladium, the iodine in thyroxine is replaced by hydrogen to form **thyronine** (thyronin), $C_{15}H_{15}NO_4$. This behaves as a phenol and an α-amino-acid. On fusion with potassium hydroxide in an atmosphere of hydrogen, thyronine gives a mixture of *p*-hydroxybenzoic acid, quinol, oxalic acid and ammonia. When fused with potassium hydroxide at 250°C, thyronine gives *p*-hydroxybenzoic acid, quinol and a compound with the molecular formula $C_{13}H_{12}O_2$ (II). A structure for thyronine which would give all these products is (I).

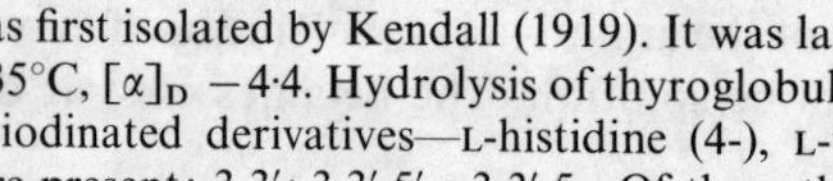

(I)
thyronine

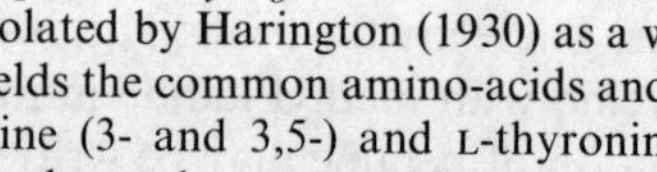

(III)

Thyronine (provisionally structure (I)) was subjected to the Hofmann exhaustive methylation (see **14** §4) and the product thereby obtained was then oxidised. The final product would be (III) [on the assumption that (I) is thyronine]. The structure of (III) was confirmed by synthesis, starting from *p*-bromoanisole and *p*-cresol (see also below).

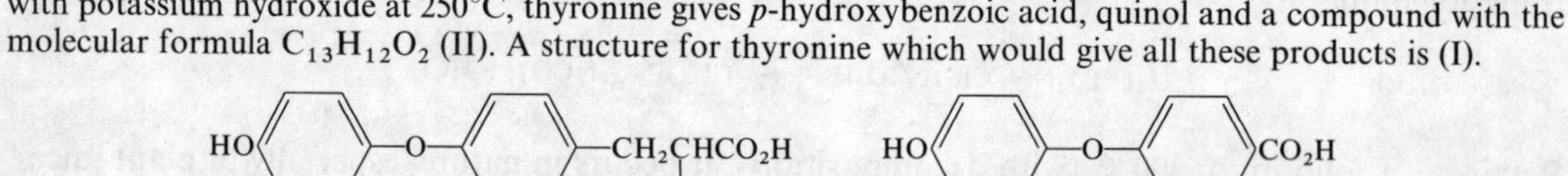

Furthermore, when 4-methoxy-4′-methyldiphenyl ether is heated with hydriodic acid, compound (II) [$C_{13}H_{12}O_2$; see above] is obtained; thus the structure of (II) is also established.

$$CH_3O-\!\!\!\bigcirc\!\!\!-O-\!\!\!\bigcirc\!\!\!-CH_3 \xrightarrow{HI} HO-\!\!\!\bigcirc\!\!\!-O-\!\!\!\bigcirc\!\!\!-CH_3$$
(II)

Now, when thyroxine is fused with potassium hydroxide, no *p*-hydroxybenzoic acid is obtained; instead, compounds of the pyrogallol type are formed. These fact suggest that two atoms of iodine are adjacent to the hydroxyl group, and that the two remaining iodine atoms are in the other benzene ring. This, together with the analogy with di-iodotyrosine, leads to the suggestion that thyroxine is (IV).

$$HO-\!\!\!\bigcirc\!\!\!-O-\!\!\!\bigcirc\!\!\!-CH_2CHCO_2H$$
$$\underset{NH_2}{}$$
(IV)
thyroxine

This structure for thyroxine has been confirmed by synthesis (Harington *et al.*, 1927).

$$NH_2\!\!\!-\!\!\!\bigcirc\!\!\!-NO_2 \xrightarrow{I_2} NH_2\!\!\!-\!\!\!\bigcirc\!\!\!-NO_2 \xrightarrow[\text{(ii) KI}]{\text{(i) NaNO}_2-\text{HCl}} I\!\!\!-\!\!\!\bigcirc\!\!\!-NO_2 \xrightarrow[\substack{K_2CO_3 \text{ in} \\ \text{butanone}}]{CH_3O-\bigcirc-OH}$$

$$CH_3O-\!\!\!\bigcirc\!\!\!-O-\!\!\!\bigcirc\!\!\!-NO_2 \xrightarrow[\text{(ii) C}_5\text{H}_{11}\text{ONO}-\text{HCl}]{\text{(i) SnCl}_2-\text{HCl}} CH_3O-\!\!\!\bigcirc\!\!\!-O-\!\!\!\bigcirc\!\!\!-\overset{+}{N_2}\bar{C}l \xrightarrow{CuCN}$$

$$CH_3O-\!\!\!\bigcirc\!\!\!-O-\!\!\!\bigcirc\!\!\!-CN \xrightarrow{SnCl_2-HCl} CH_3O-\!\!\!\bigcirc\!\!\!-O-\!\!\!\bigcirc\!\!\!-CHO \xrightarrow{C_6H_5CONHCH_2CO_2H}$$

$$CH_3O-\!\!\!\bigcirc\!\!\!-O-\!\!\!\bigcirc\!\!\!-CH=C\underset{N=CC_6H_5}{\overset{CO-O}{<}} \xrightarrow[P]{HI} HO-\!\!\!\bigcirc\!\!\!-O-\!\!\!\bigcirc\!\!\!-CH_2\underset{NH_2}{CHCO_2H} \xrightarrow[\substack{\text{conc.} \\ NH_3/H_2O}]{I_2}$$
azlactone

$$HO-\!\!\!\bigcirc\!\!\!-O-\!\!\!\bigcirc\!\!\!-CH_2\underset{NH_2}{CHCO_2H}$$
($\pm$)-thyroxine

The racemic modification was resolved *via* the formyl derivative (Harington, 1928), and later (1934) it was shown that this amino-acid belonged to the L-series.

Some points that may be noted in connection with this synthesis are: (i) protection by methylation of the hydroxyl group required in the final product; (ii) nucleophilic displacement of only the activated iodine atom (*para* to the nitro-group); (iii) reduction of the cyanide to aldehyde by means of the Stephen reaction; (iv) iodination *ortho* to phenoxide ion (see Vol. I).

The synthesis of thyroxine has been improved, *e.g.*, by Hems *et al.* (1949).

Proteins

§6. General nature of proteins

The name *protein* was introduced by Mulder (1839), who derived it from the Greek word *proteios* (meaning *first*). Proteins are nitrogenous substances which occur in the protoplasm of all animal and plant cells. Their composition varies with the source: carbon, 46–55 per cent; hydrogen, 6–9 per cent; oxygen, 12–30 per cent; nitrogen, 10–32 per cent; sulphur, 0·2–0·3 per cent. Other elements may also be present, *e.g.*, phosphorus (nucleoproteins), iron (haemoglobin).

As we have seen (§3), proteins can be broken down into smaller and smaller fragments until the final products are the amino-acids. This sequence may be written as (see also §7):

$$\text{protein} \rightarrow \text{polypeptides} \rightarrow \text{peptides} \rightarrow \text{amino-acids}$$

There is no sharp dividing line between peptides, polypeptides and proteins. One arbitrary convention designates proteins as those molecules with a molecular weight above $\sim 10\,000$ and peptides (poly-peptides) as those molecules with a molecular weight below $\sim 10\,000$. In general, proteins and peptides differ in physical and chemical properties which can be correlated with the differences in molecular size. Both groups often exhibit physiological activity, behaving as, *e.g.*, enzymes, hormones, growth factors, etc.

Synthetic peptides of very high molecular weight are often referred to as polypeptides, and their methods of preparation and the study of their properties have provided a great deal of information on the structure and properties of proteins.

Proteins are amphoteric, their behaviour as an anion or a cation depending on the pH of the solution. At some definite pH, characteristic for each protein, the positive and negative charges are exactly balanced, *i.e.*, there is no net charge on the protein molecule, and the molecules will not migrate in an electric field. In this condition the protein is said to be at its *isoelectric point*, and at this pH the protein has its least solubility, *i.e.*, it is most readily precipitated (*cf.* amino-acids, §4Ci). The osmotic pressure and viscosity of the protein solution are also a minimum at the iso-electric point. The amphoteric nature of proteins is due to the presence of a large number of free acidic and basic groups arising from the amino-acid units in the molecule. These groups can be titrated with alkali or acid, and by this means it has been possible to identify acidic and basic groups belonging to the various amino-acid units.

All proteins are optically active, and may be coagulated and precipitated from aqueous solution by heat, the addition of acids, alkalis, salts, organic solvents miscible with water, etc. Proteins in this precipitated state are said to be **denatured**, and the process of reaching this state, **denaturation**, occurs most readily near the isoelectric point. Denaturation is now believed to be the result of changes in *conformation* or *unfolding* of the protein molecule (see §12b). Associated with denaturation are changes in optical rotation and (usually) the loss of biological activity, *e.g.*, enzymes (all are proteins) become inactive when denatured.

Denaturation is generally irreversible, but many examples are now known where the process has been reversed. This reversal of denaturation has been called **renaturation** or **refolding**. When denaturation is effected by heat, renaturation does not usually result on rapid cooling. If, however, cooling is carried out very slowly, renaturation often occurs. In these circumstances the process of renaturation has been referred to as **annealing** (see also §12b).

Proteins exhibit a variety of colour reactions, *e.g.*,

(i) **Biuret reaction.** Addition of a very dilute solution of copper sulphate to an alkaline solution of a protein produces a red or violet colour. This reaction is due to the presence of the grouping —CO—NH—CHR—CO—NH—. At least two peptide linkages (—CONH—) must be present (dipeptides do not give the test).

(ii) **Xanthoproteic reaction.** Proteins usually produce a yellow colour when warmed with concentrated nitric acid, and the colour becomes orange when the solution is made alkaline. This reaction is due to the nitration of the benzene ring in phenylalanine, tyrosine and tryptophan.

(iii) **Millon's reaction.** Millon's reagent (mercuric nitrate in nitric acid containing a trace of nitrous acid) usually produces on addition to a protein solution a white precipitate which turns red on heating. This reaction is characteristic of phenols, and so is given by proteins containing tyrosine (this is the only phenolic amino-acid that occurs in proteins).

(iv) **Ninhydrin test.** Proteins (and peptides) give this test, but the colours are different from that of the amino-acids (see §4Cvi).

The molecular weights of proteins have been determined by means of ultracentrifugal sedimentation, osmotic pressure measurements, X-ray diffraction, light scattering effects, molecular sieves (gel filtration), and by chemical analysis (see also **7** §21). Chemical methods are based on the estimation of a particular amino-acid. Thus, suppose the percentage composition of amino-acids in a protein has been determined. From these values it is possible to calculate the mole proportions of each amino-acid by dividing its percentage weight by its molecular weight. We now choose the amino-acid present in the *least* molar amount and on the assumption that only *one* of these amino-acid residues is present in the protein, the molecular weight, M_1 of the protein, is given by

$$M_1 = \frac{100}{x} \times m \quad \text{or} \quad x = \frac{m}{M_1} \times 100$$

where x is the percentage weight and m is the molecular weight of the amino-acid. If *two* molecules of the amino-acid are present per molecule of protein, the percentage weight is still x, but now we have

$$x = \frac{2m}{M_2} \times 100 = \frac{2m}{2M_1} \times 100$$

i.e., the molecular weight M_2 is $2M_1$. Hence, if n molecules (where n must be an integral number) of the amino-acid are present, the molecular weight of the protein is nM_1. Therefore M_1 is the *minimum molecular weight* of the protein and nM_1 is its true molecular weight.

As an example, let us consider the protein bovine insulin. The amino-acid that occurs in the smallest molar amount is threonine: 2 per cent, $m = 119$.

$$\therefore \quad M_1 = \frac{100}{2} \times 119 = 5\,950$$

Now, bovine insulin has been shown to contain one molecule of threonine and hence its true molecular weight is also 5 950 (see also §11).

Since the modern methods of estimating amino-acids have a high degree of accuracy, a knowledge of the minimum molecular weight is extremely valuable. This is because many of the methods used for the determination of molecular weights of proteins (and peptides) are apparently accurate only within the limits of about 3–5 per cent. It should be noted that elemental analysis as a means of obtaining molecular formulae of proteins is unsatisfactory because of their very high molecular weights.

The average molecular weight of the common amino-acids is about 141·5, and since one molecule of water is lost in the formation of the peptide bond, a peptide containing n amino-acid residues has an approximate molecular weight $141·5n - 18n = 123·5n$. Hence $n = M/123·5$. For the purpose of simplifying the calculation (and with little effect on the approximation), we may replace 123·5 by 125.

The values of molecular weights recorded for proteins vary considerably, ranging from about 5 000 to many millions.

One of the difficulties in protein chemistry (including peptides) is to be able to decide whether the specimen being investigated is pure. Although many proteins (and peptides) have been obtained crystalline, these have no characteristic melting points. Various criteria are therefore used to show homogeneity, *e.g.*, constant solubility, chromatography (column, paper, and ion-exchange), paper electrophoresis, etc.

Since the solubility of a protein depends on *p*H, the presence or absence of salts, etc. (*cf.* above), by controlling these factors it is possible to separate proteins. Thus, for example, by adjusting the *p*H of a solution containing a mixture of proteins (or peptides) to the isoelectric point of each protein in turn, each of these will be precipitated in turn. Alternatively, the *salting out* method may be used to separate proteins. The solubility of many proteins is increased in the presence of small concentrations of various neutral salts. This is referred to as *salting in*, and bivalent cations are more effective than univalent cations. As the concentration of the ion is increased, the solubility of the protein passes through a maximum, then begins to decrease and at a sufficiently high concentration (of ion) the protein is precipitated, *i.e.*, salted out. Not only can cations precipitate proteins (as salts), but so can suitable anions, *e.g.*, tungstic acid, phosphotungstic acid, trichloroacetic acid, etc.

A third method of separation of proteins based on solubility is the controlled precipitation by organic solvents miscible with water (see §7).

From the foregoing account it can be seen that, in general, methods used for isolating proteins are also used for their separation and purification.

Many proteins are not composed of a single peptide chain but consist of a number of subunits. Furthermore, these subunits may or may not be identical (see also §9d).

Peptides have been classified as **homeomeric** when the products of hydrolysis are amino-acids only, and as **heteromeric** when other products in addition to amino-acids are obtained (see also §7). A large number of peptides are linear but many are cyclic. Cyclic peptides have been classified as **homodetic** when their structures contain only peptide linkages. On the other hand, when the rings contain both amide (peptide) and other types of linkages, *e.g.*, disulphide, the cyclic peptides are classified as **heterodetic**, *e.g.*, oxytocin (see §11). This latter class has also been called **cyclodepsipeptides**, but apparently some authors restrict this term to those heteromeric cyclic peptides composed of amino-acids and hydroxyacids linked by amide and ester bonds. In this case, the compounds have been referred to as the **peptolides**. They have been isolated from bacteria, fungi, etc., and many show biological activity.

§7. Classification of proteins

Several arbitrary classifications of the proteins are in use. One method divides the proteins into two groups, *fibrous proteins*, which are insoluble in common solvents, but are soluble in concentrated acids and alkalis, and *globular proteins*, which are soluble in water and in dilute acids, alkalis and salts (see also §12b).

A more common method of classification is the division of proteins into the three main groups: simple, conjugated, and derived proteins. Each group is subdivided into a number of classes designated by general names. Each class contains sub-classes of proteins of similar but not identical physical and chemical properties, *e.g.*, in A(i), below, one sub-class of albumin is serum albumin. The term serum indicates that this group of albumins occurs in the blood serum of vertebrates, *e.g.*, man, horse, sheep, dog, etc. However, all these serum albumins differ from each other.

A. Simple proteins.   These give only amino-acids or their derivatives on hydrolysis.

(i) *Albumins.* These are soluble in water (and in acids and alkalis), and are coagulated by heat. They are precipitated by saturating their solutions with ammonium sulphate.

Albumins are usually low or deficient in glycine; some albumins are serum albumin, egg albumin and lactalbumin.

(ii) *Globulins*. These are insoluble in water, but are soluble in dilute salt solution and in dilute solutions of strong inorganic acids and alkalis. They are precipitated by half saturating their solutions with ammonium sulphate, and they are coagulated by heat.

Globulins usually contain glycine; some typical globulins are serum globulin, tissue globulin and vegetable globulin.

(iii) *Prolamins*. These are insoluble in water or salt solution, but are soluble in dilute acids and alkalis, and in 70–90 per cent ethanol.

Prolamins are deficient in lysine, and contain large amounts of proline; some prolamins are zein (from maize), gliadin (from wheat) and hordein (from barley).

(iv) *Glutelins*. These are insoluble in water or dilute salt solution, but are soluble in dilute acids and alkalis; they are coagulated by heat. They are comparatively rich in arginine, proline and glutamic acid.

Some glutelins are glutenin (from wheat) and oyrzenin (from rice).

(v) *Scleroproteins* (*albuminoids*). These are insoluble in water or salt solution, but are soluble in concentrated acids or alkalis.

Examples: keratin (from hair, hoof), fibroin (from silk); these are not attacked by enzymes.

Submembers of the scleroproteins are:

(*a*) *Collagens* (in skin, tendons and bones); these form gelatin (a water-soluble protein) when boiled with water. Collagens are attacked by pepsin or trypsin.

(*b*) *Elastins* (in tendons and arteries); these are not converted into gelatin, and are attacked slowly by trypsin.

(vi) *Basic proteins*. These are strongly basic, and fall into two groups.

(*a*) *Histones*. These are soluble in water or dilute acids, but are insoluble in dilute ammonia. They are not coagulated by heat, and contain large amounts of histidine and arginine, but contain no tryptophan and very little cystine or methionine; they are hydrolysed by pepsin and trypsin. Histones are the proteins of the nucleic acids, haemoglobin, etc.

(*b*) *Protamins*. These are more basic than the histones and have a simpler structure. They are soluble in water, dilute acids and dilute ammonia; they are not coagulated by heat, and are precipitated from solution by ethanol. They contain large amounts of arginine, and occur in various nucleic acids. They do not contain sulphur, and are hydrolysed by various enzymes, *e.g.*, trypsin, papain, but not by pepsin.

B. Conjugated proteins. These are proteins which contain a non-protein group (*i.e.*, a compound not containing amino-acid residues) attached to the protein part. The non-protein group is known as the *prosthetic group*, and it may be separated from the protein part by careful hydrolysis.

(i) *Nucleoproteins*. The prosthetic group is a nucleic acid.

(ii) *Chromoproteins*. These are characterised by the presence of a coloured prosthetic group. Examples: chlorophyll and haemoglobin. These examples contain metals (see also (vi), below), but in many cases the prosthetic group is organic, *e.g.*, in visual purple (see **9** §7a) the prosthetic group is a carotenoid pigment.

(iii) *Glycoproteins*. In these the prosthetic group contains a carbohydrate or a derivative of the carbohydrates. They are also known as *mucoproteins*.

(iv) *Phosphoproteins*. These are conjugated proteins in which the prosthetic group contains phosphoric acid in some form other than in the nucleic acids or in the lipoproteins.

(v) *Lipoproteins*. In these the prosthetic group is lecithin, kephalin, etc.

(vi) *Metalloproteins*. These all contain a metal which is an integral part of the structure. Many metals occur, *e.g.*, iron, magnesium, copper, manganese. Examples are haemoglobin and chlorophyll which, as we have seen, may also be classed as chromoproteins (see (ii), above).

C. Derived proteins are degradation products obtained by the action of acids, alkalis or enzymes on proteins.

Protein ⟶ *Denatured proteins;* insoluble proteins formed by the action of heat, etc., on proteins (see
   ↓   also §6).
Primary proteoses (*metaproteins*); insoluble in water or dilute salt solution, but are soluble in acids or alkalis.
   ↓   They are precipitated by half-saturation with ammonium sulphate.
Secondary proteoses; soluble in water, not coagulated by heat, and are precipitated by saturation with
   ↓   ammonium sulphate.
Peptones
   ↓
Polypeptides   These are soluble in water, not coagulated by heat, and are not precipitated by saturation
   ↓   with ammonium sulphate.
Simple peptides
   ↓
Amino-acids

§8. The peptide linkage

As we have seen (§3), proteins are hydrolysed by acids, alkalis, or enzymes to a mixture of amino-acids. Fischer (1902) and Hofmeister (1902) suggested that amino-acids in proteins are joined in a *linear* fashion by *peptide* linkages, *i.e.*, by the —CONH— group, the carboxyl group of one amino-acid molecule forming an amide by combination with the amino-group of the next amino-acid molecule, etc. Thus, on this basis, a protein molecule may be represented as a *linear polymer* of amino-acid molecules.

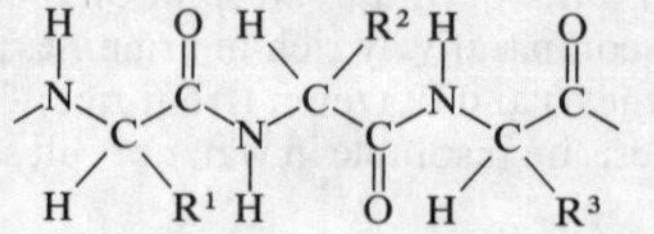

The infrared spectra of amides have been extensively studied and many assignments associated with the —CONH—group have been made. Thus, for example, polypeptides and proteins show bands near 3 300 and 3 100 cm^{-1}, which are characteristic of the hydrogen-bonded N—H group (str.) in secondary amides (RCONHR). Also shown are bands near 1 650 and 1 550 cm^{-1}, which are characteristic of the C=O (str.) in secondary amides. Ultraviolet spectra studies have shown that the peptide bond absorbs in the region 180–220 nm (see also §4).

Pauling *et al.* (1953) have carried out X-ray studies on a number of crystalline peptides and deduced the various bond lengths (in Å) and bond angles in these compounds (Fig. 13.1).

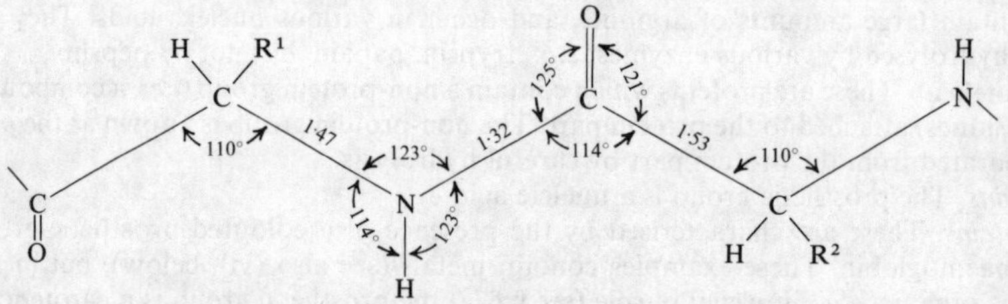

Fig. 13.1

The conclusions reached from these results were:

(i) The atoms in the group, —CONH—, are planar and the O and H are *trans*.

(ii) Since the peptide C—N bond length (*i.e.*, C—N of —CONH—), 1·32 Å is shorter than the usual C—N bond length (~1·47 Å), this bond has some double bond character.

We can explain the double bond character as being due to resonance, and hence hindered rotation about this C—N bond permits the possibility of geometrical isomerism, the *trans*-isomer being

trans   *cis*

the more likely because of the much larger steric repulsion operating in the *cis*-isomer. On the other hand, rotation can occur about the R^1CH—CO and the R^2CH—NH bond. It is therefore possible to describe the conformation of the protein molecule in terms of rotations about the C^α—C' bond (ψ) and about the N—C^α bond (ϕ). Thus, the conformation of a protein molecule containing *n* amino-acid residues is described by the parameters:

$$(\phi_1\psi_1)(\phi_2\psi_2)\cdots(\phi_n\psi_n)$$

This problem of conformation is considered further in §12a.

§9. The primary structure of peptides

The **primary structure** of a peptide (or protein) is the sequence of the amino-acid residues in the molecule. First, let us consider a dipeptide composed of two different amino-acids, **A** and **B**. These may be combined in two different ways:

$$\underset{\text{(I)}}{H_2N—A—CONH—B—CO_2H} \qquad \underset{\text{(II)}}{HO_2C—A—NHCO—B—NH_2} \qquad \underset{\text{(II}a\text{)}}{H_2N—B—CONH—A—CO_2H}$$

Inspection of either (I) or (II) shows that the two ends of each molecule are different. The 'amino-end' is said to be *N*-**terminal** and the 'carboxyl-end' is said to be *C*-**terminal**. The general method of writing the sequence of amino-acids in a peptide (polypeptide or protein) is with the terminal amino-group on the left. (I) is in accordance with this convention, but not (II), which should therefore be written as (IIa). The peptides are then named as acylated derivatives of the *terminal amino-acid residue on the right hand side*.

Table 13.2 (§4C(i)) gives a list of symbols used for amino-acids; they are usually the first three letters of the name. When the sequence of the amino-acids is not known, the symbols are enclosed in brackets and are separated by commas. When the sequence is known, the units are separated by dots or dashes, or by arrows which indicate the direction of linkage from carboxyl to amino. Since the conventional way of writing peptide formulae has the terminal amino-group on the left (see (I) and (IIa)), the arrow will point left-to-right. A terminal amino-group may be indicated by H and a terminal carboxyl group by OH. Finally, carbonamido-groups may be indicated by the addition of NH_2 to the symbol, *e.g.*, asparagine and glutamine (these have proposed alternatives): $AspNH_2$ (Asn) and $GluNH_2$ (Gln). Also, a proposed alternative for tryptophan is Trp. The following formulae illustrate the conventions:

(Ala, Gly, Tyr)   Thr·(Val, Arg)   Ala·Glu·Val   or

$$\text{H·Ala·Glu·Val·OH} \quad \text{or} \quad \text{Ala} \rightarrow \text{Glu} \rightarrow \text{Val} \quad \text{or} \quad \text{Ala—Glu—Val}$$

Returning now to the problem of amino-acid sequence, it can be shown that, in general, for *n* different acids *n*! different combinations are possible. Furthermore, had not the common amino-acids been all L-acids, the total number of possible combinations would have been very much larger.

As a simple example let us consider a tripeptide. The first thing to do in this case is to determine the nature of the amino-acid residues. This is usually carried out by acid hydrolysis and chromatography (see §3). Suppose the amino-acids are shown to be A, B and C. These can be written in six (3!) different combinations:

$$\text{A·B·C} \qquad \text{A·C·B} \qquad \text{B·A·C} \qquad \text{B·C·A} \qquad \text{C·A·B} \qquad \text{C·B·A}$$

The problem then is: how do we ascertain which is the actual combination of the tripeptide under investigation? Inspection of the formulae shows that if we were able to determine the *N*-terminal amino-acid (*N*—T—AA), we would be able to group the six possibilities into three pairs, *i.e.*, we would now know that our tripeptide was either one or other of a pair. We would also be in this situation if we were able to determine the *C*-terminal amino-acid (*C*—T—AA). Thus:

N-Terminal	*C*-Terminal
(*a*) A·B·C and A·C·B	(*d*) B·C·A and C·B·A
(*b*) B·A·C and B·C·A	(*e*) A·C·B and C·A·B
(*c*) C·A·B and C·B·A	(*f*) A·B·C and B·A·C

Since this results in *different* pairing, the determination of *both* N- and C-terminal groups will give the amino-acid sequence of the tripeptide, *e.g.*, if the N—T—AA determination showed that the tripeptide was in group (*b*) and the C—T—AA determination showed that the tripeptide was in group (*d*), the tripeptide is therefore B·C·A.

Now let us assume that the N— and C—T—AA methods are such that their application results in the *removal* of the respective terminal amino-acid. In these circumstances we would be left with different fragments according to the order of application (of the methods), *e.g.*, for B·C·A:

(i) N—T—AA first: fragment C·A.
(ii) C—T—AA first: fragment B·C.

By repeating *either* of these determinations, the amino-acid sequence is solved. Thus, the sequence may be determined by use of one method twice or by use of each method once.

Now let us consider the tetrapeptide whose acids have been shown to be (A, B, C, D). There are 24 (4!) possible combinations (as shown). Suppose the N— and C—T—AA determinations

A·B·C·D	B·A·C·D	C·A·B·D	D·A·B·C
A·B·D·C	B·A·D·C	C·A·D·B	D·A·C·B
A·C·B·D	B·C·A·D	C·B·A·D	D·B·A·C
A·C·D·B	B·C·D·A	C·B·D·A	D·B·C·A
A·D·B·C	B·D·A·C	C·D·A·B	D·C·A·B
A·D·C·B	B·D·C·A	C·D·B·A	D·C·B·A

showed respectively B and D. The tetrapeptide is therefore B·A·C·D or B·C·A·D. As for the tripeptide, the fragments obtained will depend on the order of application:

(i)   N—T—AA first: fragments A·C·D or C·A·D.
(ii) C—T—AA first: fragments B·A·C or B·C·A.
(iii) *Both* N— and C—T—AA (irrespective of order): fragments A·C or C·A.

Hence, the amino-acid sequence of the tetrapeptide may be determined by using *either* the N—T—AA or the C—T—AA method *three* times, or by a combination of these methods (also *three* operations). The general method of amino-acid sequence analysis, however, does not use both end-group analyses on the original peptide. Only one end-group is determined and this is then followed by fragmentation of the peptide in at least two different ways. The smaller peptides are then subjected to amino-acid sequence determination by end-group analysis. In this way, the various small peptides 'overlap' and so it becomes possible to deduce the complete sequence of the amino-acids in the original peptide (see §9c).

§9a. *C*-Terminal amino-acid determination.   The most widely used method is that of **hydrazinolysis** (Akabori *et al.*, 1956). The peptide (or protein) is heated with anhydrous hydrazine at 100°C. This converts all amino-acid residues except the C-terminal one into amino-acid hydrazides.

$$\text{---NHCHR}^1\text{CONHCHR}^2\text{CONHCHR}^3\text{CO}_2\text{H}$$

$$\text{--- + H}_2\text{NCHR}^1\text{CONHNH}_2 + \text{H}_2\text{NCHR}^2\text{CONHNH}_2 + \text{H}_2\text{NCHR}^3\text{CO}_2\text{H}$$

The mixture of products is subjected to chromatography on a column of a strong cation-exchange resin. On elution the strongly basic hydrazides are retained, but the free amino-acid is eluted and can be identified.

Another chemical method involves the reduction of the peptide (or protein) with lithium borohydride or lithium aluminium hydride. This converts the free terminal carboxyl group to a primary alcoholic group. Hydrolysis produces a mixture of amino-acids and an aminoalcohol, the latter being separated and identified by paper chromatography.

A widely used method makes use of the enzyme carboxypeptidase. This enzyme attacks peptides (or proteins) only at the end which contains the free α-carboxyl group. When this terminal amino-acid residue is liberated, the new terminal free carboxyl group is attacked by the enzyme. Thus, in the peptide $\cdots X \cdot Y \cdot Z$, after a given time of hydrolysis, a number of 'successive' terminal amino-acids will have been liberated, but in amounts $Z > Y > X > \cdots$. Hence, by identification and quantitative determination of the amino-acids, their sequence can be established.

§9b. *N*-Terminal amino-acid determination. The **Edman method** (1950) is very widely used and its basis is the reaction between phenyl isothiocyanate and the peptide (or protein) to form the phenyl-thiocarbamyl (PTC)-peptide (or protein) in the presence of dilute alkali. When treated with dilute acid (hydrochloric or trichloroacetic acid), the PTC-peptide is converted into a phenylthiohydantoin (PTH) and a peptide which now has lost the N—T—AA of the original of the peptide. The mechanism of this step is uncertain. The PTH may be separated and identified by paper chromatography,

$$C_6H_5NCS + H_2NCHR^1CONHCHR^2CONHCHR^3CO_2H \xrightarrow{OH^-}$$

$$C_6H_5NHCSNHCHR^1CONHCHR^2CONHCHR^3CO_2H \xrightarrow{H^+}$$

and the process can now be repeated on the degraded peptide. The Edman N-terminal amino-acid determination has now been automated, and because of this, can be used to determine the amino-acid sequence in polypeptides, *i.e.*, the step involving the splitting of peptides (or proteins) into smaller fragments may be unnecessary in many cases, particularly where the peptide is relatively small.

Another widely used method is the **DNP method** (Sanger, 1945). 1-Fluoro-2,4-dinitrobenzene (FDNB) very readily reacts with amino-groups in the presence of sodium hydrogen carbonate solution (mildly alkaline) at room temperature to form 2,4-dinitrophenyl (DNP) derivatives which are stable to acids. Hence, hydrolysis with acid of the DNP-peptide produces the DNP-amino-acid and a mixture of free amino-acids.

DNP-derivatives are formed with any free amino-group. Thus the basic amino-acid, lysine, will react even if it is not an *N*-terminal group (see Table 13.1). The hydroxyl group of tyrosine, the thiol group of cysteine, and the imidazole nucleus of histidine also react (although more slowly than an amino-group). Hence, the DNP method may give rise to a number of DNP derivatives. These, however, may be readily isolated and identified by chromatography (particularly TLC). If the basic amino-acid is *not* *N*-terminal, then it will form the mono-DNP derivative; if *N*-terminal, the di-DNP derivative. The DNP derivatives of most of the amino-acids have been prepared and characterised. The DNP method cannot be used repetitively, since its use requires complete hydrolysis of the DNP derivative (*cf.* the Edman method).

A recent modification of the DNP method is the use of 5-dimethylaminonaphthalene-1-sulphonyl chloride, 'dansyl' chloride (DNS-Cl), in place of FDNB. This modification is called the 'dansyl method', and its use is similar to that of the DNP method (replace FDNP by DNS-Cl in the above equation).

dansyl chloride
or DNS—Cl

DNS-derivative

This dansyl method is now being widely used because the dansyl group, being highly fluorescent, permits the detection and estimation of dansyl amino-acids in minute amounts by fluorimetric methods.

Apart from some other chemical methods, an enzymic method is also available for *N*-terminal amino-acid determination. The enzyme leucine aminopeptidase attacks peptides (or proteins) only at the end which contains the free amino-group and proceeds to liberate, in succession, each new terminal amino-acid. Hence, after a given time of hydrolysis, estimation of the amounts of free amino-acids will give their sequence (see carboxypeptidase, §9a).

§9c. Partial hydrolysis of peptides.   Since the 'overlapping procedure' (§9) is generally used for the elucidation of the amino-acid sequence, methods are necessary to bring about partial hydrolysis of peptides (or proteins). Different hydrolytic paths are possible because of the different susceptibilities of the various peptide bonds to attack by hydrolytic reagents.

First, let us consider the application of the overlapping procedure. Suppose we have a hexapeptide whose amino-acids have been shown to be (A, B, C, D, E, F) and whose *N*-terminal amino-acid has been shown to be C. The hexapeptide may therefore be written as C(A, B, D, E, F). Now suppose that on partial hydrolysis the small peptides obtained were (as shown by amino-acid analysis):

C—A, (B, E), (B, D), C·(A, E), (B, D, F) and (B, D, E, F)

Since we have C—A, C·(A, E) must be C—A—E. Hence (B, E) is E—B, and we now have C—A—E—B. Therefore (B, D) is B—D, and so we have C—A—E—B—D. Finally, since only F is missing, the hexapeptide is C—A—E—B—D—F; this explains fragment (B, D, E, F).

These results may be tabulated as shown.

N—T—AA			*C*—T—AA		
C	A				
C	A	E			
		E	B		
			B	D	
		E	B	D	F
C	A	E	B	D	F

As the peptide becomes more complex, the amino-acids usually occur more than once. This will increase the difficulty in elucidating the amino-acid sequence, *e.g.*, both hexapeptides C—A—E—B—D—E and C—A—E—E—B—D might possibly give rise to fragments C—A, (B, E), (B, D), C(A, E), (B, D, E) and (B, D, E, E). Since two (B, D, E) are possible, it will be necessary to use end-group analysis to decide which is correct; overlapping is of no help here. Suppose we found it to be E(B, D). This could still have been derived from either hexapeptide. If, however, we found it to be B(D, E), then the hexapeptide cannot be C—A—E—E—B—D. It also follows that (B, E) is E—B and so B(D, E) is B—D—E. The order in (B, E) would be confirmed by end-group analysis, and this would also show (B, D, E, E) is E(B, D, E). Hence, the hexapeptide is C—A—E—B—D—E. From this example it can be seen that it will usually be necessary to carry out end-group analysis on each fragment-peptide obtained. It can also be seen that had the fragment (E, E) appeared in the partial hydrolysate, solution to the problem would have been easier. Its absence suggests that the particular method of hydrolysis used readily splits the E—E bond. Hence, it is better to use different hydrolytic reagents which can selectively break peptide bonds.

Partial hydrolysis with acids is generally unsatisfactory, since bond-breaking tends to occur randomly and also results in a large number of small peptides which may be very difficult to separate. Even so, this approach is often successful for relatively small peptides. On the other hand, enzymic hydrolysis is extremely useful because each enzyme hydrolyses only certain types of peptide bond. Trypsin splits peptide bonds in which the carbonyl group is part of a lysine or an arginine residue. Chymotrypsin splits peptide bonds in which the carbonyl group is part of a phenylalanine, tyrosine, or tryptophan residue. Hence, the separate use of these two enzymes will result in splitting of the peptide (or protein) in different ways to give relatively large fragments.

Other enzymes are also available, e.g., carboxypeptidase (§9a), leucine aminopeptidase (§9b), pepsin (NH group of Leu, Asp, Glu, etc.), papain (CO group of Gly, Arg, Lys, etc.), etc. Since the specificity of the various enzymes differs considerably, the less specific enzymes are generally more satisfactory when used with relatively small peptides. Large peptides require the use of the specific enzymes; otherwise a large number of fragment-peptides will be obtained (see acidic hydrolysis, above).

Chemical methods have also been introduced to split peptides (or proteins) at specific peptide bonds. One of the most successful is the reaction between cyanogen bromide and the peptide in aqueous formic acid at room temperature. Only peptides in which the CO group is that of a methionine residue are split, the products being a homoserine lactone and the 'rest' of the peptide.

$$—NHCHR^1CONHCHCONHCHR^2CO— \quad \xrightarrow[\text{aq. } HCO_2H]{\text{BrCN}}$$
$$\underset{CH_2CH_2SMe}{|}$$

$$—NHCHR^1CONH—CH—C{=}O \quad + \; H_2NCHR^2CO— \; + \; MeSCN + Br^-$$
$$\underset{H_2C}{|} \qquad \underset{O}{}$$
$$\underset{CH_2}{}$$

It should also be remembered that this step of cleaving peptides into smaller fragments may be avoided in many cases (see §9b).

§9d. Protein subunits, cyclic structures, and disulphide bonds. In this section we shall deal with some further problems involved in the determination of amino-acid sequence. If the protein consists of a single linear peptide chain, then the methods described above may be readily applied. Thus, end-group analysis will show the presence of a single N—T—AA or of a single C—T—AA (or one of each if both end-group analyses are performed). In many cases, however, the results indicate the presence of n end groups (N or C). This usually means that the protein is composed of n peptide chains (see also §12c). If there are no end groups (i.e., no free α-NH_2 or α-CO_2H), this is strong evidence that the protein has a cyclic structure. Other evidence that may be used to show the presence of a cyclic peptide is the neutrality towards electrophoresis and the failure to give the ninhydrin test (§6).

When the subunits in a protein are not cross-linked by covalent bonds, they are readily dissociated into the individual units by, e.g., dissolving in a urea solution (see §12). These units are then separated, purified (§6), and examined by the methods described above. On the other hand, if cystine is present the subunits may be held together by the disulphide bond and/or a single chain may contain an intramolecular disulphide ring. These bonds are usually split before the primary structure is determined. One common method is oxidation of the molecule with performic acid to give cysteic acid (the sulphonic acid). Alternatively, the disulphide bond may be reduced to thiol by means of, *e.g.*, sodium borohydride, and the products treated with, *e.g.*, iodoacetic acid.

$$
\begin{array}{ccccc}
\overset{|}{\underset{|}{\text{NH}}} & & \overset{|}{\underset{|}{\text{NH}}} & \overset{|}{\underset{|}{\text{NH}}} & \overset{|}{\underset{|}{\text{NH}}} & \overset{|}{\underset{|}{\text{NH}}} \\
2\,\text{CHCH}_2\text{SO}_3\text{H} & \xleftarrow{\text{HCO}_3\text{H}} & \text{CHCH}_2\text{SSCH}_2\text{CH} & \xrightarrow{\text{NaBH}_4} & 2\,\text{CHCH}_2\text{SH} & \xrightarrow{\text{ICH}_2\text{CO}_2\text{H}} & 2\,\text{CHCH}_2\text{SCH}_2\text{CO}_2\text{H} \\
\overset{|}{\underset{|}{\text{CO}}} & & \overset{|}{\underset{|}{\text{CO}}} & & \overset{|}{\underset{|}{\text{CO}}} & & \overset{|}{\underset{|}{\text{CO}}}
\end{array}
$$

The primary structures of these products are then determined and the positions of the disulphide linkages are deduced from the positions (in the sequence) of the cysteic acid residues or of the carboxymethylcysteine residues. It should also be noted that performic acid oxidises methionine to the corresponding sulphone and also destroys tryptophan.

§9e. More recently, the primary structures of peptides and proteins have been elucidated by means of mass spectrometry. Because the volatility of the amino-acids is so low, special techniques were developed to examine their mass spectra. Even so, this led to a number of inaccuracies and so more volatile derivatives have been used. Me and Et esters have been examined in great detail and one fragment pattern usually observed is that due to fissions at *a* and *b*. The molecular ion is generally

$$
\text{R} \cdot + \overset{+}{\text{N}}\text{H}_2\!=\!\text{CHCO}_2\text{Et} \xleftarrow{b} \text{R}\!-\!\!\overset{b}{\vdots}\!-\!\text{CH}\overset{+}{\text{N}}\text{H}_2\!-\!\overset{a}{\vdots}\!-\!\text{CO}_2\text{Et} \xrightarrow{a} \cdot\text{CO}_2\text{Et} + \text{RCH}\!=\!\overset{+}{\text{N}}\text{H}_2
$$

$$
(m/e\ 102) \qquad\qquad\qquad (M^+) \qquad\qquad\qquad (73) \qquad (M-73)
$$

observed, but its intensity is usually weak. On the other hand, the intensity of the ion $[\overset{+}{\text{N}}\text{H}_2\!=\!\text{CHCO}_2\text{Et}]$, m/e 102, is usually strong or medium. Also, the intensity of the 'amine ion' $[\text{RCH}\!=\!\overset{+}{\text{N}}\text{H}_2]$ $(M-73)$ is generally strong or medium and so it is often possible to deduce the size of R (subtract 29 mass units (CHNH_2) from $M-73$, *i.e.*, $M-102$). This means that it is often possible to identify the amino-acid.

The peak at m/e 102 is always accompanied by a peak at m/e 74. This arises from the McLafferty rearrangement (**1** §13a) as follows:

$$
\overset{+}{\text{N}}\text{H}_2\!=\!\text{CH}\!-\!\text{C}\underset{\text{O}-\text{CH}_2}{\overset{\text{O}\quad\text{H}}{\diagup\diagdown\text{CH}_2}} \longrightarrow \text{C}_2\text{H}_4 + \overset{+}{\text{N}}\text{H}_2\!=\!\text{CH}\!-\!\text{C}\underset{\text{O}}{\overset{\text{OH}}{\diagup\diagdown}}
$$

$$
(m/e\ 102) \qquad\qquad\qquad (28) \qquad\qquad (m/e\ 74)
$$

The McLafferty rearrangement can also occur in amine ions when R contains more than two carbon atoms. This gives rise to a strong peak at m/e 30.

$$
\underset{\text{R}-\text{CH}-\text{CH}_2}{\overset{\text{H}\quad\text{CH}=\overset{+}{\text{N}}\text{H}_2}{\diagdown}} \longrightarrow \text{RCH}\!=\!\text{CH}_2 + \text{CH}_2\!=\!\overset{+}{\text{N}}\text{H}_2
$$

$$
(M-73) \qquad\qquad (M-103) \qquad (m/e\ 30)
$$

This, together with other peaks, may often be a means of identifying valine, leucine and isoleucine.

N-Trifluoroacetylamino-acids, as their methyl esters, are very good derivatives for the separation of amino-acid mixtures by GLC, and these derivatives can be identified by mass spectrometry.

Now let us consider the application of mass spectrometry to the determination of the primary structures of peptides (and proteins). Here also, because peptides are involatile, they are first modified chemically. One method is the reduction with lithium aluminium hydride or lithium borohydride to give a more volatile product (peptide bonds are reduced, as is also a terminal carboxyl group, to give a polyaminoalcohol).

$$
\underset{\text{R}^1}{\text{H}_2\text{N}-\overset{\text{R}^1}{\underset{|}{\text{CH}}}-\text{CO}-\text{NH}-\overset{\text{R}^2}{\underset{|}{\text{CH}}}-\text{CO}-\text{NH}-\overset{\text{R}^3}{\underset{|}{\text{CH}}}-\text{CO}_2\text{H} \xrightarrow{\text{LiAlH}_4}
$$

$$
\text{H}_2\text{N}-\overset{\text{R}^1}{\underset{f\cdots|\cdots}{\underset{|}{\text{CH}}}}\overset{}{\underset{c}{\text{CH}_2}}-\text{NH}-\overset{\text{R}^2}{\underset{g\cdots|\cdots}{\underset{|}{\text{CH}}}}\overset{}{\underset{d}{\text{CH}_2}}-\text{NH}-\overset{\text{R}^3}{\underset{h\cdots|\cdots}{\underset{|}{\text{CH}}}}\overset{}{\underset{e}{\text{CH}_2\text{OH}}}
$$

When this product is subjected to electron bombardment, it tends to undergo fission at bonds c, d, and e (these are at the most highly branched carbon atoms; $cf.$ **1** §13a), $e.g.$, fission at c gives:

$$
\overset{+}{\text{H}_2\text{N}}=\text{CH} + \cdot\text{CH}_2-\overset{\text{R}^2}{\underset{|}{\text{CH}}}-\text{CH}_2-\text{NH}-\overset{\text{R}^3}{\underset{|}{\text{CH}}}-\text{CH}_2\text{OH}
$$

Thus, the peak for the amine ion will show the size of R^1, and from this can be deduced the size of $(\text{R}^2 + \text{R}^3)$. Similarly, fission at d will give the sizes of $(\text{R}^1 + \text{R}^2)$ and R^3. Hence the sizes of R^1, R^2, and R^3, and therefore the corresponding amino-acids are now known, as is also their sequence. With more complicated peptides, peaks due to additional fissions at f, g, h, etc. will also have to be considered.

A later approach is the use of methyl, ethyl, and higher esters of peptides acylated at free amino-groups, $e.g.$, acetyl, trifluoroacetyl, etc. ($cf.$ amino-acids, above). In these acyl derivatives, the major fragmentations occur at the peptide bond (CO—NH) and also at the RC—CO bond.

It might also be noted that interpretation of the mass spectra of peptides is facilitated if the nature of the constituent amino-acids has been determined first.

§9f. **Summary of primary structure determination.**   Here, we shall summarise the strategy adopted to determine the primary structure of peptides and proteins, but it should be realised that there may be variations which depend on the nature of the molecule under consideration.

(i) The peptide or protein must be isolated in a pure state (§6).

(ii) It is first necessary to ascertain whether the protein consists of a single peptide chain or whether it is composed of a number of subunits. If the latter, then the subunits are separated (§§6, 9d), and each chain is examined separately.

(iii) The protein is completely hydrolysed into its constituent amino-acids and their nature and amounts are determined (§§3, 4).

(iv) The minimum molecular weight is determined from the amino-acid percentage composition (§6) and the molecular weight is also determined by a physical method (§6).

(v) End-group analysis is carried out to determine the nature of the N- and C-terminal groups (§§9a, 9b).

(vi) The amino-acid sequence may be determined by the Edman automated N-terminal method where possible. Alternatively, if the protein is relatively small, it may be subjected to controlled hydrolysis to give a number of simple peptides. These are isolated and purified, and end-group analysis is then applied to these and the amino-acid sequence in the protein may be deduced by the overlapping procedure (§9c). When the protein is relatively large, partial hydrolysis is effected in at least two different ways. The amino-acid sequence in each purified fragment is determined and the amino-acid sequence in the protein is deduced by the overlapping procedure.

Mass spectrometry may also be used to determine the amino-acid sequence in the protein or in the various fragments obtained by partial hydrolysis (§9e).

§10. Synthesis of peptides

The general principles may be illustrated by consideration of the synthesis of a dipeptide. As we have seen (§9), two different amino-acids, L—**A** and L—**B**, may be combined in two different ways (2!):

$$\text{H}_2\text{NACONHBCO}_2\text{H} \qquad\qquad \text{H}_2\text{NBCONHACO}_2\text{H}$$
$$\text{(I)} \qquad\qquad\qquad\qquad\qquad \text{(II)}$$

To prepare (I), the amino-group of **A** must be protected (regiospecific control; **11** §9) and the carboxyl group of **A** must be activated so that it readily reacts with the free amino-group of **B**. Similarly, to prepare (II), the amino-group of **B** must be protected and the carboxyl group of **B** must be activated. Hence, if Y is the protecting group and Z is the activating group, we have:

(I) $\text{H}_2\text{NACO}_2\text{H} \xrightarrow{\text{Y}} \text{YNHACO}_2\text{H} \xrightarrow{\text{Z}} \text{YNHACOZ} \xrightarrow{\text{H}_2\text{NBCO}_2\text{H}}$

$$\text{YNHACONHBCO}_2\text{H} \longrightarrow \text{H}_2\text{NACONHBCO}_2\text{H}$$
$$\text{(I)}$$

(II) $\text{H}_2\text{NBCO}_2\text{H} \xrightarrow{\text{Y}} \text{YNHBCO}_2\text{H} \xrightarrow{\text{Z}} \text{YNHBCOZ} \xrightarrow{\text{H}_2\text{NACO}_2\text{H}}$

$$\text{YNHBCONHACO}_2\text{H} \longrightarrow \text{H}_2\text{NBCONHACO}_2\text{H}$$
$$\text{(II)}$$

In each case, the final step involves the removal of the protecting group Y to give the dipeptide.

Other routes to dipeptides are as follows. The amino-group of the amino-acid which is to be *N*-terminal is protected and so is the carboxyl group of the amino-acid which is to be *C*-terminal. These two protected amino-acids may then be combined directly by means of a suitable reagent to give a dipeptide protected at both its *N*- and *C*-terminals. Thus (I) may be synthesised as follows (R is the carboxyl protecting group):

$$\text{YNHACO}_2\text{H} + \text{H}_2\text{NBCO}_2\text{R} \xrightarrow{-\text{H}_2\text{O}} \text{YNHACONHBCO}_2\text{R} \xrightarrow{\text{2 steps}} \text{H}_2\text{NACONHBCO}_2\text{H}$$
$$\text{(I)}$$

Alternatively, the carboxyl group of the *N*-terminal protected amino-acid is converted into an activated group and, after combination of the two amino-acid derivatives, a dipeptide is obtained which again has both its *N*- and *C*-terminals protected, *e.g.*, the synthesis of (II):

$$\text{YNHBCOZ} + \text{H}_2\text{NACO}_2\text{R} \longrightarrow \text{YNHBCONHACO}_2\text{R} \xrightarrow{\text{2 steps}} \text{H}_2\text{NBCONHACO}_2\text{H}$$
$$\text{(II)}$$

To extend the length of the peptide chain, *one* of the protecting groups in the dipeptide is selectively removed and the peptide is built up from this end. Thus, a peptide chain may be extended, one amino-acid residue at a time, from *either* end of its precursor. On the other hand, a number of suitable *simple* peptides may be synthesised, these then linked together to give the required protected peptide (or protein), from which the protecting groups are finally removed (see also §11).

One other point that requires consideration is that if the amino-acid *side-chain* contains reactive groups, these must be protected. Such reactive groups are, *e.g.*, amino (lysine), carboxyl (aspartic acid), hydroxyl (tyrosine), thiol (cysteine).

Many protecting groups have been introduced and their number is continually increasing. Fischer (1901–1907) introduced methods which, although they led to the synthesis of an octadeca-peptide, are no longer used.

Since peptide synthesis involves protecting N- and C-terminals (and also reactive side-chains), it is necessary to use protecting groups which can be selectively removed one at a time. It is also important that protecting groups should be easily introduced and should be removable under sufficiently mild conditions that the peptide bond is not hydrolysed and that no racemisation or rearrangements occur.

Five useful amino protecting groups are: benzyloxycarbonyl (carbobenzyloxy), t-butyloxy-carbonyl (Boc; carbo-t-butyloxy), trityl (triphenylmethyl), phthaloyl, and tosyl (Ts; p-toluene-sulphonyl). The usual method of protecting a carboxyl group is esterification, the common esters being methyl, ethyl, benzyl, and t-butyl. Reactive side-chain protecting groups are, $e.g.$, benzyl for thiol and hydroxyl, acetyl for hydroxyl, etc. Activation of the carboxyl group has been carried out in various ways, $e.g.$, by conversion into the acid chloride, acid azide, or p-nitrophenyl ester. Finally, the direct combination between an end amino-group and an end carboxyl group is effected by means of dicyclohexylcarbodi-imide (DCC) in an organic solvent (methylene dichloride, THF, etc.). The following account illustrates the applications of these techniques.

Bergmann (1932) introduced benzyloxycarbonyl chloride (also known as carbobenzyloxy chloride) as an amino protecting group, and this appears to be the most widely used method of protection. It is readily prepared by the action of carbonyl chloride on benzyl alcohol in toluene solution.

$$C_6H_5CH_2OH + COCl_2 \longrightarrow C_6H_5CH_2OCOCl + HCl$$

The procedure is then as follows:

$$C_6H_5CH_2OCOCl + R^1CH(NH_2)CO_2H \xrightarrow{OH^-} C_6H_5CH_2OCONHCHR^1CO_2H \xrightarrow{PCl_5}$$

$$C_6H_5CH_2OCONHCHR^1COCl \xrightarrow[NaOH]{R^2CH(NH_2)CO_2H} C_6H_5CH_2OCONHCHR^1CONHCHR^2CO_2H \xrightarrow{H_2-Pd}$$

$$C_6H_5CH_3 + CO_2 + NH_2CHR^1CONHCHR^2CO_2H$$

If the amino-acid contains sulphur, then catalytic reduction cannot be used, since the sulphur poisons the catalyst; the removal of the blocking group, however, may be successfully accomplished by means of sodium in liquid ammonia.

A later method of removing this group is to treat the derivative with hydrogen bromide in acetic acid or nitromethane (Ben-Ishai $et\ al.$, 1952; Anderson $et\ al.$, 1952):

$$C_6H_5CH_2OCONHCHR^1CONHCHR^2CO_2H \xrightarrow{HBr} C_6H_5CH_2Br + CO_2 + \overset{-}{Br}\overset{+}{N}H_3CHR^1CONHCHR^2CO_2H$$

The use of N-benzyloxycarbonyl derivatives causes no appreciable racemisation.

There are other ways in which this peptide synthesis may be carried out, $e.g.$, the p-nitrophenyl ester method (Z = benzyloxycarbonyl group):

$$ZNHCHR^1CO_2C_6H_4NO_2 \xrightarrow{NH_2CHR^2CO_2H} ZNHCHR^1CONHCHR^2CO_2H + HOC_6H_4NO_2 \xrightarrow[CH_3CO_2H]{HBr} \cdots$$

The use of this ester, an $activated$ ester, depends on the fact that it readily reacts with an amino group; the corresponding ethyl ester combines much more slowly. p-Nitrophenyl esters are prepared in high yield by the addition of dicyclohexylcarbodi-imide ($C_6H_{11}N{=}C{=}NC_6H_{11}$), a dehydrating agent, to a solution of the benzyloxycarbonyl derivative of the amino-acid and p-nitrophenol in ethyl acetate (du Vigneaud $et\ al.$, 1959).

On the other hand, the azide method may be used instead of acid chlorides or esters:

$$ZNHCHR^1CO_2Me \xrightarrow{N_2H_4} ZNHCHR^1CONHNH_2 \xrightarrow{HNO_2} ZNHCHR^1CON_3 \xrightarrow{NH_2CHR^2CO_2C_2H_5}$$

$$ZNHCHR^1CONHCHR^2CO_2C_2H_5 \xrightarrow{acid} ZNHCHR^1CONHCHR^2CO_2H \xrightarrow{H_2-Pd} NH_2CHR^1CONHCHR^2CO_2H$$

The azide synthesis is not accompanied by racemisation.

The t-butyloxycarbonyl reagent is not used as its chloride, since this is unstable, but is used as its *p*-nitrophenyl ester:

$$(CH_3)_3COCO_2C_6H_4NO_2 + NH_2CHRCO_2H \longrightarrow (CH_3)_3COCONHCHRCO_2H + HOC_6H_4NO_2$$

This group is readily removed by $HBr—CH_3CO_2H$, and also by $HCl—CH_3CO_2H$, the latter being particularly useful in that the benzyloxycarbonyl group is not removed by this reagent. The best reagent for removing the t-butyloxycarbonyl group appears to be trifluoroacetic acid.

The trityl reagent is simple to use, and may be removed by heating in acetic acid or catalytically $(H_2—Pd)$, *e.g.*,

$$(C_6H_5)_3CCl + NH_2CHRCO_2CH_3 \xrightarrow{Et_3N} (C_6H_5)_3CNHCHR^1CO_2CH_3 \xrightarrow[\text{(ii) } CH_3CO_2H]{\text{(i) NaOH}}$$

$$(C_6H_5)_3CNHCHR^1CO_2H \xrightarrow[\text{(ii) } NH_2CHR^2CO_2H]{\text{(i) } SOCl_2} (C_6H_5)_3CNHCHR^1CONHCHR^2CO_2H \xrightarrow{CH_3CO_2H}$$

$$(C_6H_5)_3COOCCH_3 + NH_2CHR^1CONHCHR^2CO_2H$$

Sheehan *et al.* (1940) have used the phthaloyl group as a means of protecting an end amino-group (*cf.* Gabriel's phthalimide synthesis, §2ib).

Phthaloylation occurs without racemisation provided the temperature does not exceed about 150°C. On the other hand, Nefkens (1960) has introduced a much milder method of phthaloylation starting from *N*-carbethoxyphthalimide (prepared from potassium phthalimide and ethyl chloroformate). This reagent reacts with amino-acids in aqueous sodium hydrogen carbonate solution at room temperature to form the optically pure phthaloyl derivative in excellent yield.

Weygand *et al.* (1961) have also prepared phthaloyl derivatives of amino-acids (without racemisation) by heating the acid with diethyl phthalate and triethylamine in phenol.

An example of the use of tosyl chloride as a protecting reagent is (Fischer, 1915):

$$TsCl + NH_2CHR^1CO_2H \xrightarrow[\text{(ii) } CH_3CO_2H]{\text{(i) NaOH}} TsNHCHR^1CO_2H \xrightarrow{SOCl_2} TsNHCHR^1COCl \xrightarrow{NH_2CHR^2CO_2H}$$

$$TsNHCHR^1CONHCHR^2CO_2H \xrightarrow[\text{liq. } NH_3]{Na} NH_2CHR^1CONHCHR^2CO_2H$$

No racemisation occurs in this synthesis.

Sheehan *et al.* (1956) showed that a protected *N*-amino-acid combines directly with an amino-acid ester in the presence of dicyclohexylcarbodi-imide in an inert solvent (methylene chloride, THF, etc; Phth = phthaloyl group; see also above):

$$PhthNHCHR^1CO_2H + NH_2CHR^2CO_2C_2H_5 + C_6H_{11}N{=}C{=}NC_6H_{11} \longrightarrow$$
$$PhthNHCHR^1CONHCHR^2CO_2C_2H_5 + C_6H_{11}NHCONHC_6H_{11}$$

The mechanism of this reaction is believed to be:

$$R^1CO_2H + C_6H_{11}N{=}C{=}NC_6H_{11} \longrightarrow C_6H_{11}N{=}\overset{\displaystyle OCOR^1}{\underset{\displaystyle}{C}}{-}NHC_6H_{11} \xrightarrow{R^2NH_2} R^1CONHR^2 + C_6H_{11}NHCONHC_6H_{11}$$

This reaction occurs with very little racemisation, but there are usually side-reactions which make difficult the purification of the desired product.

A different approach to peptide synthesis is the **anhydride method**. One application is as follows, the cyclic anhydride, *N*-carboxyanhydride (NCA) being the unit for polymerisation. The NCA derivative may be prepared in a number of ways. A common method is to convert the amino-acid into its *N*-benzyloxycarbonyl derivative and then to proceed as shown.

$$PhCH_2OCONHCHRCO_2H \xrightarrow{PCl_5} PhCH_2OCONHCHRCOCl \xrightarrow[60°C]{heat\ in\ vacuo} \begin{array}{c} RHC{-}CO \\ | \qquad\quad \diagdown \\ \quad\qquad O + PhCH_2Cl \\ | \qquad\quad \diagup \\ HN{-}CO \end{array}$$
$$(NCA)$$

Polymerisation is effected by heating the NCA derivative in an organic solvent (dimethylformamide, dioxan, etc.) in the presence of a catalyst, *e.g.*, water, amines, etc.

$$n \begin{array}{c} RHC{-}CO \\ | \qquad\quad \diagdown \\ \quad\qquad O \\ | \qquad\quad \diagup \\ HN{-}CO \end{array} + H_2O \longrightarrow n\,CO_2 + H_2NCHRCO{-}(NHCHRCO)_{n-1}OH$$

If a mixture of different anhydrides is used, the product is a polymer containing different residues in random distribution.

The NCA derivative can also be used to build up a peptide chain, one amino-acid residue at a time. NCA combines with an amino-acid in alkaline solution (*p*H 10), and after acidification the product is a dipeptide.

$$\begin{array}{c} R^1HC{-}CO \\ | \qquad\quad \diagdown \\ \quad\qquad O \\ | \qquad\quad \diagup \\ HN{-}CO \end{array} + H_2NCHR^2CO_2^- \xrightarrow{OH^-} \bar{O}_2CNHCHR^1CONHCHR^2CO_2^- \xrightarrow{H^+} H_2NCHR^1CONHCHR^2CO_2H + CO_2$$

This dipeptide may then be coupled with another NCA derivative, and so on.

A different approach to the anhydride method makes use of a mixed anhydride derived from ethyl chloroformate as follows (*cf.* the activated ester method):

$$ZNHCHR^1CO_2H \xrightarrow[Et_3N]{ClCO_2Et} ZNHCHR^1COOCO_2Et \xrightarrow{H_2NCHR^2CO_2Me} ZNHCHR^1CONHCHR^2CO_2Me + EtOH + CO_2$$

Examples have been given above where the carboxyl group has been protected as the methyl or ethyl ester. A difficulty here is that alkaline hydrolysis of the peptide ester may cause racemisation. This difficulty may be avoided by use of benzyl esters, since these can be split by catalytic hydrogenolysis (H$_2$—Pd) to give toluene.

$$RCO_2CH_2Ph \xrightarrow{H_2-Pd} RCO_2H + PhCH_3$$

The thiol group (in cysteine) may be protected by *S*-benzylation (benzyl chloride in the presence of aqueous ethanolic sodium hydroxide). This group is not removed by HBr—AcOH but is by sodium in liquid ammonia. Benzylation may also be used to protect hydroxyl groups, *e.g.*, in tyrosine, and is removed by HBr—AcOH.

t-Butyl esters are also useful since they may readily be prepared by the action of isobutene on the amino-acid in the presence of a small amount of concentrated sulphuric acid. Furthermore, the t-butyl group is easily removed by treating the ester with anhydrous trifluoroacetic acid or with dry hydrogen chloride.

Since racemisation is always possible in some of the methods described for peptide synthesis, it is desirable to be able to ascertain whether this has happened. One way is to attempt hydrolysis of the synthetic peptide with enzymes (which are highly stereospecific; see §16). It may be possible to separate mixtures of diastereoisomeric peptides by paper and thin-layer chromatography, etc. Weinstein *et al.* (1972) have used NMR spectroscopy to determine the amount of racemisation (see also **2** §9a).

Cyclic peptides may be synthesised in various ways. Small peptides may be cyclodimerised, and relatively long peptides cyclised (by self condensation) in dilute solution. A common method starts with peptide active esters. Relatively large rings may be formed by cyclising the peptide under the influence of dicyclohexylcarbodi-imide. The mixed anhydride method has also been used.

Solid-phase peptide synthesis.   Merrifield (1964) has introduced the 'solid phase' method in which an amino-acid or a peptide is bound chemically to an insoluble synthetic resin and then the chain is built up, one amino-acid residue at a time, at the free end. When the desired peptide has been synthesised, it is liberated from the solid support. The principles used for the peptide synthesis are those which have been described above. The method has been automated, *i.e.*, each addition of the appropriate amino-acid is carried out automatically at a predetermined time (*cf.* the Edman method, §9b). Some outstanding advantages of this solid phase method are: (i) because of the use of the insoluble solid support, purification of products is not necessary, excess of reagents being removed by thorough washing with suitable solvents; (ii) high yields; (iii) the time has been considerably shortened for synthesising peptides (and proteins).

The method may be illustrated with the following example. The resin, which is a copolymer of styrene and divinylbenzene, is chloromethylated. This results in the formation of 'benzyl chloride groups' through which the 'first' amino-acid becomes attached as the benzyl ester. This 'first' amino-acid, which is to be the *C*-terminal end of the peptide, is protected at its amino-group by, *e.g.*, the t-butyloxycarbonyl group, is heated with the resin in the presence of triethylamine in a suitable solvent. The protecting group is selectively removed by HCl—AcOH and the hydrochloride of the amino-group is converted into the free amino-group by the addition of excess of triethylamine. This benzyl ester of the 'first' amino-acid residue is now coupled with the *N*-t-butyloxycarbonyl derivative of the 'second' amino-acid by means of dicyclohexylcarbodi-imide. The cycle is then repeated with the *N*-protected 'third' amino-acid, and so on. When the desired peptide has been synthesised, the ester bond linking it to the resin may be split by dry hydrogen bromide in trifluoro-acetic acid.

$$\text{H}_2\text{N}-\text{A}^3-\text{CONH}-\text{A}^2-\text{CONH}-\text{A}^1-\text{CO}_2\text{CH}_2 \bigcirc \text{Res.} \xrightarrow[\text{CF}_3\text{CO}_2\text{H}]{\text{HBr}}$$

$$\text{H}_2\text{N}-\text{A}^3-\text{CONH}-\text{A}^2-\text{CONH}-\text{A}^1-\text{CO}_2\text{H}$$
$$\text{tripeptide}$$

§11. Oxytocin, insulin, thyrotropin releasing hormone, and antaminide

Oxytocin. As an illustration of the principles involved in the determination of the sequence of amino-acids, we shall first consider **oxytocin**, the hormone which occurs in the posterior pituitary gland and is responsible for uterine contraction. The structure was established independently by du Vigneaud *et al.* (1953, 1954) and Tuppy *et al.* (1953). Oxytocin is extracted from the gland by acetic acid and is purified by chromatography or electrophoresis.

The isoelectric point of oxytocin is 7·7, a value which suggests the presence of a free amino group and no free carboxyl group. Complete hydrolysis with acid and the quantitative estimation of the amino-acids (chromatography on starch) showed the presence of an equimolecular mixture of eight acids: cystine, glycine, leucine, isoleucine, proline, aspartic acid, glutamic acid and tyrosine. Ammonia was also obtained, the ratio of this to any one amino-acid being 3:1. The production of ammonia in this proportion suggests the presence of three carbonamido groups. Also, the molecular weight of oxytocin (determined by physical methods) was about 1 000, a value which indicates that the molecule is an octapeptide.

Tuppy's procedure was as follows. Since oxidation of oxytocin with performic acid gives a di-sulphonic acid with a molecular weight corresponding to an oxytocin disulphonic acid, this suggests that oxytocin is a ring compound, the ring therefore including the S—S bond of cystine (§9d). On controlled hydrolysis of oxidised oxytocin with hydrochloric acid, four dipeptides and two tri-peptides were isolated, together with two molecules of cysteic acid.

(I) Asp $\longrightarrow$ CySO$_3$H (II) CySO$_3$H $\longrightarrow$ Tyr (III) Leu $\longrightarrow$ Gly (IV) Ileu $\longrightarrow$ Glu (V) Tyr·(Glu, Ileu)
(VI) CySO$_3$H·(Leu, Pro)

The sequence in each dipeptide (I)–(IV) was established by the DNP method, *i.e.*, treatment of the dipeptide with FDNB followed by hydrolysis with acid, and identification of the dinitrophenyl derivative (the 'end group') by chromatography (§9b). End-group analysis of (V) showed tyrosine was the amino-terminal residue, and it therefore follows from the sequence in (IV) that the sequence in (V) is Tyr → Ileu → Glu (this must be so, since only *one* amino-acid residue of each kind is present in oxytocin). Furthermore, from the sequence in (II) it follows that in oxytocin the sequence of four amino-acids is CySO$_3$H → Tyr → Ileu → Glu. Also, from the sequence in (III), the sequence in (VI) must be CySO$_3$H → Pro → Leu, since Leu must be the terminal residue in order that (III) may be obtained. Hence the sequence of these four amino-acids is CySO$_3$H → Pro → Leu → Gly.

Partial hydrolysis of oxidised oxytocin with the proteinase isolated from *Bacillus subtilis* gave glycine amide and tetrapeptides (VII) and (VIII), the amino-acids in which were identified by

(VII) CySO$_3$H·(Glu, Tyr, Ileu) (VIII) Asp·(CySO$_3$H, Leu, Pro)

hydrolysis and chromatography, and also the end-group was determined. The sequence in (VII) has already been established to be CySO$_3$H → Tyr → Ileu → Glu (see above), and since the addition of Asp to (VI) gives (VIII), it follows that the sequence in (VIII) is Asp → CySO$_3$H → Pro → Leu (Leu shown to be the end-group).

Isolation of glycine amide (from the enzyme hydrolysis) shows that it is an end-group, and from (III) and (VIII) it follows that there is the following sequence:

$$Asp \longrightarrow CySO_3H \longrightarrow Pro \longrightarrow Leu \longrightarrow GlyNH_2$$

Since the amino-terminal group in (VII) is $CySO_3H$, combining the two sequences now established, the sequence in oxidised oxytocin that accounts for all the facts is:

$$CySO_3H \longrightarrow Tyr \longrightarrow Ileu \longrightarrow \overset{\overset{\displaystyle NH_2}{|}}{Glu} \longrightarrow \overset{\overset{\displaystyle NH_2}{|}}{Asp} \longrightarrow CySO_3H \longrightarrow Pro \longrightarrow Leu \longrightarrow GlyNH_2$$

The carbonamido groups have been placed as shown because (a) oxytocin contains three such groups (see above); (b) the terminal glycine amide accounts for one (see above); (c) glutamic and aspartic acids are the only two acids which each possess two carboxyl groups, and since in the others, all monocarboxylic acids, the carboxyl group must be involved in the peptide link, then only these two dicarboxylic acids can have carbonamido groups. There is, however, the problem of deciding which carboxyl group is the carbonamido group, i.e., whether it is the α or γ one of Glu and the α or β one of Asp.

Finally, since oxidised oxytocin is produced without chain fission, it suggests the presence of the S—S ring (see above). Assuming that α-carboxyl groups (of Glu and Asp) are involved in the peptide linkages, then the structure of oxytocin is:

$$\underset{\underset{\displaystyle S}{|}}{Cy} \longrightarrow Tyr \longrightarrow Ileu \longrightarrow \overset{\overset{\displaystyle NH_2}{|}}{Glu} \longrightarrow \overset{\overset{\displaystyle NH_2}{|}}{Asp} \longrightarrow \underset{\underset{\displaystyle S}{|}}{Cy} \longrightarrow Pro \longrightarrow Leu \longrightarrow GlyNH_2$$

Du Vigneaud's procedure is different from Tuppy's in that the structure of oxytocin was determined mainly as the result of the examination of many fragments obtained by the partial hydrolysis of oxytocin, performic acid-oxidised oxytocin oxidised with bromine-water, and desulphurised oxytocin. The resulting peptides were separated into acidic and neutral components by means of ion-exchange resins, and were then further separated by paper chromatography. It was shown that oxidised oxytocin had only one N-terminal group (DNP method) and that this was cystine. When oxidised oxytocin was treated with bromine-water, a dibromopeptide and a heptapeptide were obtained. Hydrolysis and end-group analysis of the dipeptide showed it to be $CySO_3H \rightarrow TyrBr_2$ (3,5-dibromo derivative). Hydrolysis of the heptapeptide gave $CySO_3H$, Leu, Ileu, Pro, Glu, Asp, Gly and ammonia, and end-group analysis showed that the N-terminal residue was isoleucine. Since oxytocin has only one terminal amino group (see above), the amino group in isoleucine must have formed the peptide link with tyrosine. Thus, the sequence of three residues is established: $CySO_3H \rightarrow Tyr \rightarrow Ileu$.

Controlled hydrolysis of the heptapeptide produced four fragments, (XIII)–(XVII), and hydrolysis of desulphurised oxytocin (by means of Raney nickel) gave four fragments, (XVIII)–(XXI).

(IX) Asp, $CySO_3H$ (X) $CySO_3H$, Pro   (XI) $CySO_3H$, Pro, Leu   (XIII) $CySO_3H$, Pro, Leu, Gly
(XIII) $CySO_3H$, Asp, Glu   (XIV) Leu, Gly, Pro   (XV) CySSCy, Asp, Glu   (XVI) Tyr, CySSCy, Asp, Glu
(XVII) Tyr, CySSCy, Asp, Glu, Leu, Ileu   (XVIII) Ala, Asp   (XIX) Glu, Ileu   (XX) Ala, Asp, Glu
(XXI) Ala, Asp, Glu, Leu, Ileu

In peptides (XVII) and (XXI), differentiation between Leu and Ileu was not made, i.e., these peptides contain only one of these acids, but which one was not determined (both acids appeared together on the chromatogram).

Application of the DNP method to (IX) showed that its sequence was Asp → $CySO_3H$. Consideration of the acids in (IX)–(XII) shows that the sequence of five residues in oxidised oxytocin is therefore (XXII):

$$\text{(XXII) Asp} \longrightarrow \text{CySO}_3\text{H} \longrightarrow \text{Pro} \longrightarrow \text{Leu} \longrightarrow \text{Gly}$$

This accounts for (XIV) and at the same time shows its sequence. On the other hand, since (XIII) contains (IX), it follows that Glu may be added to form the sequence (XXIII).

$$\text{(XXIII) Glu} \longrightarrow \text{Asp} \longrightarrow \text{CySO}_3\text{H} \longrightarrow \text{Pro} \longrightarrow \text{Leu} \longrightarrow \text{Gly}$$

Now, in desulphurisation, the —CH$_2$S— group is converted into the —CH$_3$ group. Thus, instead of cystine, two molecules of alanine (which is *not* present in oxytocin) will be produced. Hence, (XVIII) corresponds to (IX) and (XX) to (XIII). Also, the isolation of (XIX) shows that Glu is linked to Ileu, and since Glu is linked to Asp as shown in (XXIII), Ileu must be in the sequence (XXIV).

$$\text{(XXIV) Ileu} \longrightarrow \text{Glu} \longrightarrow \text{Asp} \longrightarrow \text{CySO}_3\text{H} \longrightarrow \text{Pro} \longrightarrow \text{Leu} \longrightarrow \text{Gly}$$

Since Ileu is now assigned, it follows that (XVII) is Tyr, CySSCy, Asp, Glu, Ileu, and (XXI) is Ala, Asp, Glu, Ileu.

If Tyr is joined to one half of the cystine residue, with Asp joined to the other half, then (XVI) is accounted for, *i.e.*, oxytocin contains the sequence

$$\begin{array}{c} \text{Tyr} \longrightarrow \text{CyS} \\ | \\ \text{Ileu} \longrightarrow \text{Glu} \longrightarrow \text{Asp} \longrightarrow \text{CyS} \longrightarrow \text{Pro} \longrightarrow \text{Leu} \longrightarrow \text{Gly} \end{array}$$

This accounts for the eight amino-acids, and since the only free amino group present is in cystine (see above), and since oxidation does not bring about fission, oxytocin must be cyclic, and this is satisfied by joining Tyr to Ileu. The Gly end is not satisfactory, since this residue is present as carbonamide. This was confirmed by application of the Edman method of end-group analysis to oxidised oxytocin. The first *four* acids were removed, the order of removal being: CySO$_3$H, Tyr, Ileu and Glu.

The carbonamido groups were placed as described above (in Tuppy's method), and the structure for oxytocin was therefore the same as that established by Tuppy.

The structure of oxytocin has been confirmed by a number of syntheses. The one described here is that of du Vigneaud *et al.* (1959). In the following equations, the symbols used are OEt = ethyl ester, NP = *p*-nitrophenyl ester, Bzl = benzyl, Z = benzyloxycarbonyl:

$$\text{H·GlyOEt} \xrightarrow{\text{ZLeuNP}} \text{ZLeu·GlyOEt} \xrightarrow{\text{HBr—AcOH}} \text{HLeu·GlyOEt} \xrightarrow{\text{ZProNP}} \text{ZPro·Leu·GlyOEt} \xrightarrow[\text{MeOH}]{\text{NH}_3}$$

$$\text{ZPro·Leu·GlyNH}_2 \xrightarrow[\text{(ii) ZCyS(Bzl)NP}]{\text{(i) HBr—AcOH}} \overset{\text{Bzl}}{\underset{|}{\text{ZCyS}}}\text{·Pro·Leu·GlyNH}_2 \xrightarrow[\text{(ii) ZAsp(NH}_2)\text{NP}]{\text{(i) HBr—AcOH}} \overset{\text{NH}_2\ \ \text{Bzl}}{\underset{|\ \ \ \ \ |}{\text{ZAsp·CyS}}}\text{·Pro·Leu·Gly·NH}_2 \xrightarrow[\text{(ii) ZGlu(NH}_2)\text{NP}]{\text{(i) HBr—AcOH}}$$

$$\overset{\text{NH}_2\ \text{NH}_2\ \text{Bzl}}{\underset{|\ \ \ \ |\ \ \ \ |}{\text{ZGlu·Asp·CyS}}}\text{·Pro·Leu·GlyNH}_2 \xrightarrow[\text{(ii) ZIleuNP}]{\text{(i) HBr—AcOH}} \overset{\text{NH}_2\ \text{NH}_2\ \text{Bzl}}{\underset{|\ \ \ \ |\ \ \ \ |}{\text{ZIleu·Glu·Asp·CyS}}}\text{·Pro·Leu·GlyNH}_2 \xrightarrow[\text{(ii) ZTyr(Bzl)NP}]{\text{(i) HBr—AcOH}}$$

$$\overset{\text{Bzl}\ \ \ \ \ \ \ \ \ \text{NH}_2\ \text{NH}_2\ \text{Bzl}}{\underset{|\ \ \ \ \ \ \ \ \ \ |\ \ \ \ |\ \ \ \ |}{\text{ZTyr·Ileu·Glu·Asp·CyS}}}\text{·Pro·Leu·GlyNH}_2 \xrightarrow[\text{(ii) ZCyS(Bzl)NP}]{\text{(i) HBr—AcOH}} \overset{\text{Bzl}\ \ \ \ \ \ \ \ \ \ \ \ \ \text{NH}_2\ \text{NH}_2\ \text{Bzl}}{\underset{|\ \ \ \ \ \ \ \ \ \ \ \ \ \ |\ \ \ \ |\ \ \ \ |}{\text{ZCyS·Tyr·Ileu·Glu·Asp·CyS}}}\text{·Pro·Leu·GlyNH}_2 \xrightarrow[\text{(ii) O}_2\text{ (air)}]{\text{(i) Na—NH}_3}$$

$$\overset{\text{NH}_2\ \text{NH}_2}{\underset{|\ \ \ \ |}{\text{Cy·Tyr·Ileu·Glu·Asp·Cy·Pro·Leu·GlyNH}_2}}$$
$$\underset{S\text{————————}S}{|\ |}$$

Insulin.   This is the hormone which occurs in the pancreas and was the first protein whose amino-acid sequence was worked out (Sanger *et al.*, 1951–1955). Measurement of the molecular weight of insulin gave values which varied with the concentration. The values were multiples of 12 000, *viz.*

12 000, 24 000, and 36 000. The minimum molecular weight of insulin, determined from amino-acid analysis, was about 6 000 (see §6). It was originally believed that 12 000 was the true molecular weight, but later work based on osmotic pressure and sedimentation measurements in organic solvents showed that the 'monomer' of insulin actually did have the molecular weight 6 000.

N-Terminal amino-acid determination (DNP method) showed the presence of one glycine residue and one phenylalanine residue. Hence, insulin contains *two* peptide chains linked together (§9d). Since amino-acid analysis had shown the presence of cystine, it was *assumed* that the two chains were joined by disulphide bonds. Insulin was therefore oxidised with performic acid. This produced two peptides, which were separated (by electrophoresis or by chromatography) and examined individually. The peptide with the *N*-terminal glycine residue was called the A-chain and that with the *N*-terminal phenylalanine residue was called the B-chain. Each chain was subjected to partial hydrolysis with acids and with enzymes. The A-chain gave about 35 fragments with acid hydrolysis and about 10 fragments with enzymic hydrolysis; the B-chain gave respectively about 50 and about 10. The fragments were separated (by electrophoresis or by chromatography) and examined by end-group analysis (DNP method) and for amino-acid residues. Then, by means of the overlapping procedure, the primary structure of each chain was deduced. The A-chain was shown to contain 21 amino-acid residues and the B-chain 30. The A-chain contained four cysteic acid residues and the B-chain two. Hence, the A-chain contains a disulphide ring and is linked to the B-chain by two disulphide bonds.

Insulins from different sources, *e.g.*, cattle, sheep, horses, etc., differ slightly, but all show identical hormonal activity. The formula shown is that of bovine insulin. It will be seen that there is a small

```
                    H2N  S————————S            NH2        NH2        NH2
                      |   |        |             |          |          |
        HGly·Ileu·Val·Glu·Glu·Cy·Cy·Ala·Ser·Val·Cy·Ser·Leu·Tyr·Glu·Leu·Glu·Asp·Tyr·Cy·Asp
                              |                                                  |
                              S                                                  S
                              |                                                  |
               H2N  NH2       S                                                  S
                 |    |       |                                                  |
        HPhe·Val·Asp·Glu·His·Leu·Cy·Gly· Ser·His·Leu·Val·Glu·Ala·Leu·Tyr·Leu·Val·Cy
                                                                                   |
                              HOAla·Lys·Pro·Thr·Tyr·Phe·Phe·Gly·Arg·Glu·Gly
```

ring system containing cystine, alanine, serine and valine. The differences in the insulins from various sources appear to concern this ring only. Thus, the sequence Ala → Ser → Val in bovine insulin is replaced by Ala → Gly → Val in sheep insulin, and by Thr → Gly → Ileu in horse insulin (Brown *et al.*, 1955; Harris *et al.*, 1956). Katsoyannis *et al.* (1966) have synthesised human and sheep insulins; Merrifield *et al.* (1968) have synthesised the A- and B-chains by the solid phase method (§10).

Thyrotropin releasing hormone (TRH).   Schally *et al.* (1966, 1969) isolated (by means of electrophoresis and chromatography) a few milligrams of this hormone in an impure state from about a quarter of a million porcine hypothalami. Because of the small amount available, the general strategy of determining primary structures of proteins was very much restricted. Acid hydrolysis of the hormone gave three amino-acids, histidine, glutamic acid and proline, in essentially equimolecular proportions. It was also shown that these three amino-acids were derived from the sequence Glu·His·Pro (I) as a probable part of TRH. (I) and other synthetic tripeptides of these three amino-acids in several alternative sequences, however, showed no hormonal activity (Schally *et al.*, 1968). It was also shown that TRH had neither a free amino nor a free carboxyl group. One possibility is that the tripeptide is cyclic (§9d). Folkers *et al.* (1969) carried out synthetic experiments on (I), modifying both the amino and carboxyl groups and tested the hormonal activity of each product. In this way it was shown that methylation (carboxyl groups) and ammonation of (I) gave a compound which was identical with TRH biologically and chromatographically. The structure of

$$HO_2CCH_2CH_2CHCONHCHCON \longrightarrow (II)$$

with NH₂ below the CHCON and CH₂ / CO₂H below, imidazole ring with HN—N

(I)

TRH was thought to be (II), L-pyroglutamyl-L-histidyl-L-proline amide, (pyroGlu·His·ProNH₂), and this was confirmed by (i) hydrolysis to the three amino-acids (Glu, His and Pro); (ii) its NMR

(II) structure: O=pyrrolidone ring N—H, CONHCHCON, CH₂, CONH₂, imidazole HN—N

(II)

spectrum. Assignable signals were (τ-values): 2·39 bs (2-H His); 3·10 bs (4-H His); 5·55 m (α-H His); 5·80 m (α-H pyroGlu); 6·35 m (α-H Pro); 7·0 m (CH₂ His); 7·0 m (5-CH₂ Pro); 7·7 m (CH₂CH₂ pyroGlu); 8·1 bm (CH₂CH₂ Pro) [b = broad; see also Table 1.9]; (iii) seventeen R_F values obtained in different solvent systems were identical with the R_F values of TRH under the same conditions.
Antamanide. This is an antitoxin which has been isolated from the fungus *Amanita phalloides* by chromatographic methods. Its structure has been elucidated by Wieland *et al.* (1968) who used a combination of gas chromatography and mass spectrometry.

Hydrolysis of antamanide (HCl—AcOH) gave a mixture of the amino-acids alanine, phenyl-alanine, proline, and valine in the molar ratio 1:4:4:1. Since it did not give the ninhydrin test and also was electrophoretically neutral, antamanide was assumed to be a cyclic peptide (§9d). The mass spectrum showed the presence of molecular ion at $M = 1\,146$. This corresponds to ~9·2 amino-acid residues (see §6), and taking this in conjunction with the molar ratio given above, antamanide is most probably a cyclic decapeptide. This cyclic structure was supported by the fact that the molecular ion had a very high intensity. It was also established that all the amino-acids had the L-configuration (*cf.* **2** §10a).

The first approach to the determination of the primary structure was purely chemical. Hydrolysis of antamanide with HCl—AcOH under controlled conditions gave a mixture of linear peptides and unchanged cyclopeptide. These were separated by preparative TLC. Amino-acid analysis of the quickest migrating component showed it was composed of two Phe, one Ala, one Val, and four Pro residues. Application of the Edman method (§9b) showed the sequence:

Phe·Phe·Ala·Val·Pro·Pro·(Pro·Pro)

This leaves two Phe residues to be accounted for, and these were originally placed at the beginning of the chain to give (—Phe₄·Ala·Val·Pro₄—) as the sequence in the cyclic decapeptide. The octapeptide: Phe·Phe·Ala·Val·Pro·Pro·Pro·Pro was synthesised (standard methods were used), but it was found to be chromatographically different from the octapeptide obtained by fragmentation of antamanide (see above). Since further chemical work failed to elucidate the amino-acid sequence, mass spectrometry was used. As already mentioned, $M = 1\,146$, and an unusual feature of the mass spectrum was the absence of intense fragment ions above m/e 588 and m/e 560, the only exception being an ion at $M - 91$ (91 = benzyl from Phe). On the basis of the ions observed, it was possible to deduce two probable pentapeptide sequences (see also §9e).

                    PhCH₂   PhCH₂   Me₂CH

HN——CHCO—N——CHCO┼NHCH┼CO┼NHCH┼CO┼NHCH┼CO—
              m/e 195│   314│ 342│   461│ 489│   560│

                    Me   PhCH₂   PhCH₂

HN——CHCO—N——CHCO┼NHCH┼CO┼NHCH┼CO┼NHCH┼CO—
              m/e 195│   238│ 266│   385│ 413│   532│

The absence of characteristic fragment ions between m/e 588 and m/e 1 055 ($M - 91$) may be readily explained by the immediate decomposition of the antamanide molecule into two pentapeptides, each of which then decomposes stepwise.

On the basis of the above observations and deductions, it was concluded that the structure of antamanide is derived by coupling the two sequences Pro·Pro·Phe·Phe·Val and Pro·Pro·Ala·Phe·Phe. These sequences were confirmed by a combination of gas chromatography and mass spectrometry. Antamanide was treated with MeOH—HCl and the methyl esters of the peptides thereby produced were separated, as their N-trifluoroacetyl derivatives, by gas chromatography. Over 30 peptide fragments were obtained and their amino-acid sequences were elucidated by mass spectrometry. Some of the more important fragments were (written so as to show overlapping):

                    Val·Pro·Pro·Ala
                      Ala·Phe·Phe
                        Phe·Phe·Pro
                          Phe·Pro·Pro
                            Pro·Pro·Phe
                                  Phe·Phe·Val
                                    Phe·Val·Pro

Hence, the structure of antamanide which is in agreement with the facts is (III).

```
        Pro ——→ Phe ——→ Phe ——→ Val ——→ Pro
(III)    ↑                                   │
        Pro ←—— Phe ←—— Phe ←—— Ala ←—— Pro
```

This structure has been confirmed by synthesis (Wieland *et al.*, 1969). The decapeptide (IV) was synthesised by the solid phase method and cyclised by means of dicyclohexylcarbodi-imide.

$$\text{Phe·Pro·Pro·Phe·Phe·Val·Pro·Pro·Ala·Phe} \xrightarrow{\text{DCC}} \text{(III)}$$
                    (IV)

THE SPATIAL ARRANGEMENT OF PROTEIN MOLECULES

§12. Introduction

The spatial arrangement of the polypeptide chain in a protein molecule is determined by the **primary structure** (amino-acid sequence) of that protein (§9). The conformation that the polypeptide 'backbone' assumes is called the **secondary structure**, and the way in which the entire molecule folds to produce a specific shape is called the **tertiary structure** of the protein. Finally, there is the **quaternary structure** of a protein. This is concerned with those proteins which contain subunits and is a description of the arrangement and ways in which the subunits are held together (see also §9d).

Various types of bonds and/or forces are responsible for the stabilisation of these protein 'structures' other than the primary structure.

The hydrogen bond. This is an extremely important factor in the stabilisation of protein conformations. The most common type of hydrogen bonding occurs between the carbonyl oxygen of one peptide bond and the hydrogen atom of the amino group of another peptide bond. Although this bond is weak (**1** §3), because a large number of them are involved, the overall stabilisation is considerable (see §12a). The strength of the hydrogen bond is a maximum when the three atoms (O, H, and N) are collinear, and a result of hydrogen bonding is a shortening of the distance between O and N (*i.e.*, less than that calculated from the sum of the van der Waals radii). This shortening has been used as a means of establishing the presence of these bonds in crystalline proteins (X-ray analysis). Infrared spectroscopy is also a means of showing the presence of hydrogen bonds.

$$\!>\!C\!=\!O\cdots\cdots H\!-\!N\!<$$

Electrostatic forces. These may be forces of repulsion or attraction, depending on the charge on the polar groups. The two polar groups are carboxylate, $-CO_2^-$, and ammonium, $-NH_3^+$. When like-charged polar groups are close together, the repulsive forces will destabilise the protein conformation. When the polar groups carry unlike charges, the attractive forces will stabilise the conformation; these attractive forces are often referred to as 'salt linkages' or ionic bonds. Unlike hydrogen bonds, these electrostatic forces are independent of the orientation of the two polar groups with respect to each other. In aqueous solution, the polar groups will be hydrated and this will considerably decrease the electrostatic forces. Also, since the charges ($-CO_2^-$ and $-NH_3^+$) depend on the pH of the solution (§6), the conformation can also depend on the pH.

Other forces that may operate are dipole-dipole interactions (**1** §10) and van der Waals forces (**1** §2).

Inter- and intramolecular chemical bonds. The disulphide bond has already been discussed in connection with the primary structure of a protein (§9d). Since, however, the primary structure influences the other types of 'structure', the presence of disulphide bonds will affect the conformation of the protein.

The hydrophobic bond. The exact nature of this 'bond' is still a matter of debate and, in any case, the term 'bond' is misleading since no type of bond (in the usual meaning of the term) is involved. According to one theory, hydrophobic bonds are a consequence of the hydrophobic character (*i.e.*, non-polar and have little attraction for water) of alkyl side-chains of the amino-acids and also a consequence of the structure of water. Water molecules form hydrogen bonds among themselves, but this produces only *three-dimensional clusters*. This cluster-formation results in a decrease in the entropy of the system. Furthermore, since hydrophobic side-chains can fit into suitable types of clusters of water molecules, the clusters are further stabilised and so the entropy of the system is further decreased. On the other hand, if different hydrophobic side-chains in the protein molecule come into contact with one another (through folding of the chain), the area now exposed to water is decreased and so the number of 'cages' is reduced. This results in an *increase* in entropy, *i.e.*, the formation of hydrophobic bonds, *viz. contact* between hydrophobic side-chains, increases the stability of the system. Hence, maximum stability is achieved by the hydrophobic side-chains lying *inside* the protein molecule. At the same time, hydrophilic groups (*i.e.*, polar groups, and have a high attraction for water) will tend to lie on the *surface* of the protein molecule.

The orders of hydrophobic and hydrophilic character are:

Hydrophobic: Phe > Ala > Val > Gly > Leu > Cys.
Hydrophilic: Tyr > Ser > Asp > Glu > AspNH$_2$ > GluNH$_2$ > Arg.

§12a. Secondary structure of proteins.   The α-Helix. The α-helix model for the conformation of proteins was proposed by Pauling *et al.* (1951). This was suggested on theoretical grounds, and its presence was subsequently verified by experimental evidence. Some of the arguments on which this model was based were:

(i) The peptide group is planar (see §8).

(ii) The dihedral angles ψ and ϕ taken about the C^{α}—C' and N—C^{α} bonds, respectively, are close to those corresponding to potential minima in the system (see also §8).

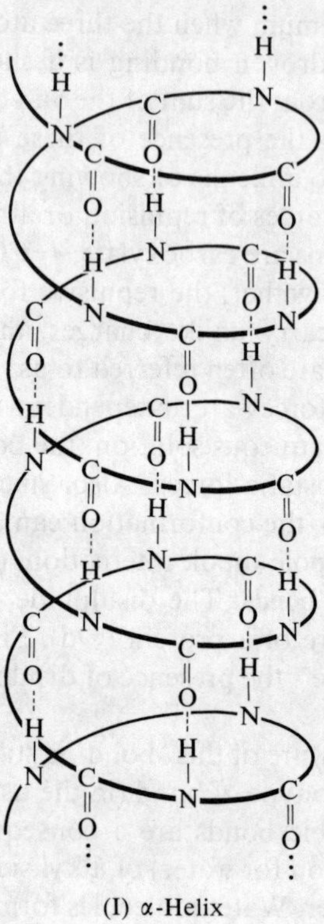

(I) α-Helix

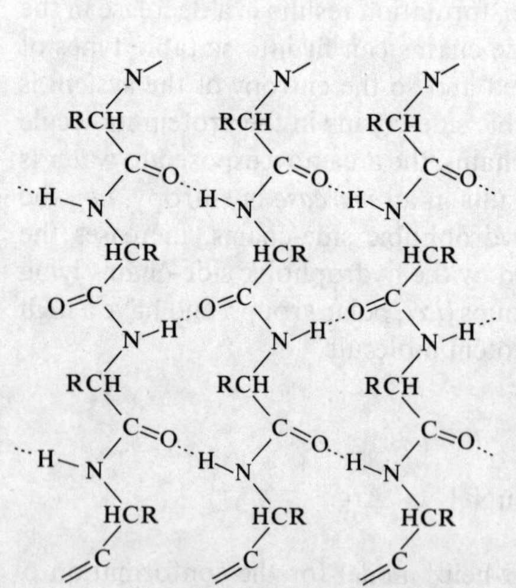

(IIa) (Parallel)

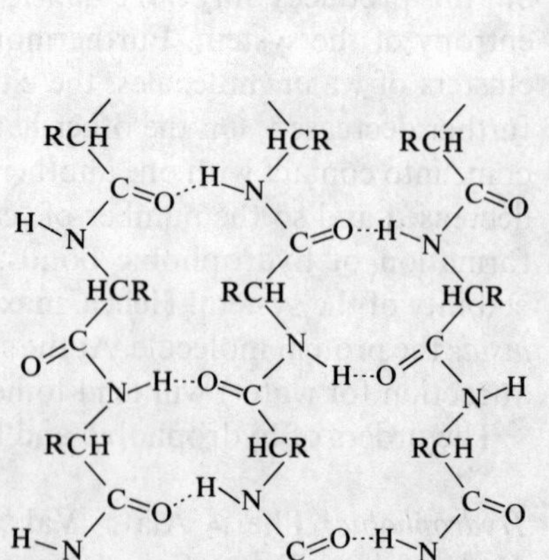

(IIb) (Anti-parallel)

(iii) Hydrogen bonding stabilises the conformation, and the strength of this bond is a maximum when the atoms concerned (C=O—H—N) are collinear or, failing this ideal situation, do not deviate by more than $30°$ (from collinearity).

(iv) The model to be chosen permits the maximum number of hydrogen bonds (of the type in (iii)).

The model which best satisfied these requirements was the α-helix. Pauling then proposed a helix in which each turn contained either 3·7 or 5·1 amino-acid residues. Further considerations (largely stereochemical) showed that a helix with 3·7 residues per turn was more stable than any other. This α-helix is represented by (I) and it should be noted that each hydrogen bond is formed between the CO group of one residue and the NH group of the fourth residue in the chain. This hydrogen bonding prevents free rotation and so the helix is rigid. Furthermore, at least three adjacent hydrogen bonds must be broken before free rotation can occur in a segment of the helix.

The α-helix may be left- or right-handed. The common amino-acids, except glycine, are optically active and all have the L-configuration (§4). Moffitt (1956) deduced theoretically that the right-handed helix (for L-amino-acids) is more stable than the left-handed helix. Hence, the right-handed helix is the one that would be expected to occur naturally.

The β-conformation. Pauling *et al.* (1951) also proposed another conformation, the **β-conformation** or **pleated sheet**. In this the polypeptide chain is *extended* and chains are held together by *intermolecular* hydrogen bonds. Two types of pleated sheets are possible, parallel (II*a*) in which all the chains run in the same direction, and anti-parallel (II*b*) in which the chains run alternately in opposite directions.

The existence of the α-helix in proteins in the *solid* state has been established by X-ray analysis. Also, X-ray data have shown that the α-helix has two types of repeat units, one being the *pitch* or distance between two successive turns ($\sim 5\cdot0$–$5\cdot5$ Å), and the other being the distance, in the direction of the helical axis, between two like atoms in the chain (1·5 Å), *e.g.*, the 'rise' from the first N to the second N in NHCOCHRNH. The diameter of the helix has been estimated to be about 10 Å.

Not all polypeptide chains are capable of forming the α-helix, since the stability of this helix depends on the nature and sequence of the side-chains (R groups) in the polypeptide chain, *e.g.*, proline inhibits the formation of a helical conformation. This is due to the fact that the peptide bond is of the type —CO—N<, *i.e.*, there is no hydrogen on the nitrogen atom and hence hydrogen bonding is not possible (for proline). Thus, the α-helix ends at this point (the proline molecule), proceeds in some conformation other than the helix and can then start again as a helix. The amount of the helix form varies in proteins, ranging from zero to about 100 per cent.

X-ray analysis has also established the existence of the pleated sheet structure in *solid* proteins. The chains are parallel in, *e.g.*, keratin, and are anti-parallel in, *e.g.*, fibroin. The calculated distance between two CHR groups on the same side of a chain is 7·2 Å, but the actually measured repeat unit is 7·0 Å. This shortening has been attributed to crowding caused by the side-chains (R), thereby preventing the chain from being fully extended.

Although X-ray analysis may be used to determine the conformations of proteins in the solid state, other methods must be used to investigate the conformations in solution. As we have seen, the stability of the α-helix is largely dependent on hydrogen bonding. Thus, in solvents which cannot form hydrogen bonds with the protein solute, *e.g.*, chloroform, there will be no competition and so a helical protein will tend to retain this conformation. On the other hand, if the solvent can form hydrogen bonds with the protein solute, *e.g.*, water, acetic acid, etc., the conformation of the protein will now depend on the relative strengths of the 'chain' hydrogen bonds, those between the protein and solvent, and those between solvent and solvent. With water as solvent, all these hydrogen bonds have about the same strength and so the α-helix is relatively stable. On the other hand, with dichloroacetic acid as solvent, hydrogen bonding between protein and solvent occurs to a large extent, resulting in extensive loss of the helical conformation and the appearance of the randomly coiled configuration. Complete loss of the α-helix occurs when the helical protein is dissolved in water containing urea. Urea is a resonance hybrid and the negatively charged oxygen atom can

$$
\begin{array}{ccc}
\mathrm{H_2\ddot{N}} & \mathrm{H_2\overset{+}{N}} & \mathrm{H_2\ddot{N}} \\
\diagdown & \diagdown\diagdown & \diagdown \\
\quad\ \ \mathrm{C{=}O} \ \longleftrightarrow & \quad\ \ \mathrm{C{-}\bar{O}} \ \longleftrightarrow & \quad\ \ \mathrm{C{-}\bar{O}} \\
\diagup & \diagup & \diagup\diagup \\
\mathrm{H_2\ddot{N}} & \mathrm{H_2\ddot{N}} & \mathrm{H_2\overset{+}{N}}
\end{array}
$$

therefore form hydrogen bonds with the protein molecule which are stronger than the 'chain' hydrogen bonds.

The random coil conformation is, unlike the α-helix, very flexible and the change from one form into the other, *i.e.*, the *helix-coil transition*, can be effected by changes in temperature or *p*H.

Optical rotatory studies (**1** §9) have provided a valuable means of estimating the helical content of proteins in solution. As we have seen (§4), the common amino-acids have the L-configuration and so it can be anticipated that proteins will exhibit optical rotations which will have some relationship to the constituent amino-acid residues (the value of the rotation for proteins is always negative). In relatively short peptides, the optical rotation is approximately the sum of the contributions of the amino-acid residues present (see Rule of optical superposition; **1** §9). As the peptide chain increases in length, the deviations from this 'addition rule' may become considerable. In the randomly coiled configuration, the addition rule holds reasonably well, but when the chain assumes a helical conformation, because *this* structure is chiral the optical rotation of the protein will consist of the sum of two contributions, that due to the rotation of the amino-acid residues (negative) and that due to the helix. Furthermore, the contribution by the helix will depend on its length. Thus, it may be possible to estimate approximately the amount of helical content present in the protein from the optical rotations (observed and estimated from the addition rule).

Better quantitative results have been achieved by means of optical rotatory dispersion studies (**1** §9a). Both the amplitude and the shape of ORD curves are very sensitive to changes in the helical content of proteins.

Other methods are also available for the determination of helical content. Infrared spectroscopic studies have shown that the frequency of the absorption band due to hydrogen bonding depends on the C=O---H—N angle. Since these are quite different in the α-helix and pleated sheet, these two conformations can be distinguished.

Deuterium exchange experiments have been used to estimate helical content. When dissolved in deuterium oxide, rapid exchange would be expected to occur between deuterium (of D_2O) and protein hydrogen atoms attached to oxygen or nitrogen (see **1** §12e). Experimental results, however, have shown that for most proteins the exchange rates are much lower than expected. This slow exchange has been attributed to the hydrogen atoms of the peptide groups (CONH) in the *helical regions* of the protein molecule. The reason for this is uncertain, but it is possible to estimate helical contents, the values of which are in reasonable agreement with those obtained by ORD studies.

NMR spectroscopy has recently been used to distinguish between the α-helix and random coil configurations. The NMR spectrum of a single 'straight-chain' polypeptide is essentially that derived from the superposition of its constituent amino-acid residues (see §3). As a result of experimental work, it has been found that the signal of an α-proton (α-CH—NH—) in a helix occurs upfield with respect to that in the random coil and that the NH signal in the helix occurs downfield with respect to that in the random coil. Hence, it is possible to detect helix-coil transitions by NMR spectroscopy (see above).

§12b. Tertiary structure of proteins.   As we have seen (§12a), hydrogen bonding is of extreme importance in the stabilisation of the secondary structures, the α-helix and pleated sheets. On the other hand, folding of the entire molecule, *i.e.*, the tertiary structure, involves hydrogen bonding, ionic, chemical, and hydrophobic bonds (see §12). The tertiary structure that a protein assumes under normal conditions of temperature and *p*H will be its most stable arrangement. This has been referred to as the *native conformation* of that protein. Two major molecular shapes occur naturally, *fibrous* and *globular* (see also §7). Fibrous proteins have a large helical content and are essentially rigid molecules of rod-like shape. On the other hand, globular proteins have a polypeptide chain which consists partly of helical sections and folded about the random coil sections to give a 'spherical' shape. In globular proteins, most polar groups lie on the surface of the molecule and most hydrophobic side-chains lie inside the molecule (see §12).

The tertiary structures of proteins have been elucidated by methods which give information on the shapes of molecules, *e.g.*, X-ray analysis, viscosity measurements, diffusion, light-scattering, ultracentrifuge method, electron microscopy (*cf.* molecular weights of proteins, §6).

When a protein undergoes denaturation (see §6). the changes that occur involve changes in secondary and/or tertiary structures of proteins. This has been established by, *e.g.*, large changes in optical rotation and in the ORD curves of the protein.

α-keratin, which is found in hair and wool, consists of three (or seven) α-helices wound round each other like strands in a rope. On the other hand, silk fibroin consists of pleated sheats in which the polypeptide chains are anti-parallel (§12a). These two are fibrous proteins. Two globular proteins are mycoglobin and haemoglobin, both of which contain haem (they are chromoproteins; §7B).

§12c. Quaternary structure of proteins. Both fibrous and globular proteins (§12b) may consist of only one polypeptide chain or of several chains. In the latter case, the protein is said to be *oligomeric*, the individual chains being known as *protomers* or *subunits*. These subunits may or may not be identical, and when they are held together by hydrogen bonds, they may be separated by, *e.g.*, dissolving in water containing urea (see §12a). Mycoglobin consists of a single polypeptide chain which contains about eight straight segments (α-helices) which are folded in an irregular manner at the random-coil sections. Haemoglobin, however, contains four subunits, two identical α-chains and two identical β-chains. Each subunit has a tertiary structure similar to that of mycoglobin.

Enzymes

§13. General nature of enzymes

Enzymes are biological catalysts which bring about chemical reactions in living cells. They are produced by the living organism, and are usually present in only very small amounts in the various cells (about 0·01 per cent). They can also exhibit their activity even when they have been extracted from their source. All enzymes are globular proteins, many have been identified and a large number have been obtained in crystalline form.

§14. Nomenclature and classification

A common method of naming enzymes is to add the suffix *ase* to the name of the *substrate*, *i.e.*, the substance being acted upon, *e.g.*, esterase acts on esters, amylase on starch (amylum), protease on proteins, urease on urea, etc. Some enzymes, however, have retained their trivial names, *e.g.*, emulsin, pepsin, trypsin, etc. Names are also used for *particular* enzymes, *e.g.*, urease, amylase, or as *general* names for *groups* of enzymes, *e.g.*, esterases, proteases, etc.

The above nomenclature is still widely used, but it has led to difficulties as more and more enzymes have been isolated. Because of this, the International Commission on Enzymes (1961) has recommended a systematic method of nomenclature and classification. According to this system, enzymes are divided into six main groups according to the nature of the reaction that is catalysed, and each main group is given a code number. The main groups are:

1. **Oxidoreductases.** These enzymes catalyse oxidation-reduction reactions, and include oxidases (direct oxidation with molecular oxygen), dehydrogenases (removal of hydrogen from substrates), etc.

2. **Transferases.** This group of enzymes catalyses the transfer of various functional groups, *e.g.*, transaminase.

3. **Hydrolases.** These catalyse hydrolytic reactions, *e.g.*, proteases (proteins), esterases (esters), etc.

4. **Lyases.** There are two types of lyases, one which catalyses addition to double bonds and the other which catalyses removal of groups and leaves double bonds.

5. **Isomerases.** These catalyse various types of isomerisation, *e.g.*, racemases, epimerases, etc.

6. **Ligases.** These enzymes catalyse the formation of a bond between two molecules and is accompanied by the breaking of a pyrophosphate bond of ATP or similar triphosphate (see, *e.g.*, §15).

Each of these main groups is divided into subgroups which take the number of their main group followed by another number which specifies the type of group in the substrate that undergoes reaction. The subgroups are also divided into sub-subgroups. These are indicated by a third figure which gives more detailed information on the groups involved in the reaction. Finally, a *fourth* figure indicates the serial number of the enzyme in its sub-subgroup. Thus, an enzyme is specified by four numbers (separated by points), *e.g.*, $1 \cdot 1 \cdot 1 \cdot 1$ is the oxidoreductase which is involved in hydrogen transfer from a CHOH group to NAD^+ or $NADP^+$ as acceptor (see §15). The trivial name of this enzyme is alcohol dehydrogenase.

The systematic names of enzymes consist of two parts, the first part specifying the substrate (or substrates) and the second part, which ends in 'ase', indicates the nature of the reaction that is catalysed. For example, let us consider the reaction:

$$\text{L-alanine} + \text{2-oxoglutarate} \longrightarrow \text{pyruvate} + \text{L-glutamate}$$

This reaction is catalysed by the enzyme transaminase (see also §18). Since this is a subgroup of the main group of enzymes, the transferases, the common name transaminase has been changed to the more systematic name aminotransferase. Thus, this enzyme is named as L-alanine:2-oxoglutarate aminotransferase; its Enzyme Commission number is $2 \cdot 6 \cdot 1 \cdot 2$. The trivial name of this enzyme is alanine aminotransferase, and was formerly called glutamic-pyruvic transaminase.

§15. Cofactors

Many enzymes require the presence of non-protein compounds in order to perform their catalytic action. These compounds are collectively known as **cofactors** or **activators**, and fall into three main groups. **Coenzymes** are organic molecules which may be separated from the enzyme by, *e.g.*, dialysis. On the other hand, some cofactors are bound to the enzyme and then referred to as the **prosthetic group** of its enzyme (see also §7B). Finally, cofactors may be inorganic ions. In some cases the metal is tightly bound to the enzyme which is then referred to as a **metalloenzyme**. In other cases the enzymes are 'metal-activated'. Metal activators are uni- or bi-valent metal cations, *e.g.*, Na^+, K^+, Mg^{2+}, Zn^{2+}, Ca^{2+}.

The complex, enzyme-cofactor, is known as a **holoenzyme**, and when the cofactor has been removed the protein that remains is known as an *apoenzyme*. This has no enzymic activity.

Some enzymes are synthesised in the organism in an inactive form; this is known as a **zymogen**.

Thus, *e.g.*, the enzyme pepsin is synthesised as its zymogen, pepsinogen. This is converted into pepsin in the presence of hydrochloric acid.

Coenzymes and prosthetic groups generally act as carriers of specific functional groups or specific atoms. In order to act in this manner, these cofactors must exist in two forms, one form being converted into the other during a catalysed reaction, and the latter being reconverted into the former by a coupled reaction. These two reactions may, or may not, follow each other. Here, we shall discuss three coenzymes which are nucleotides (see **16** §13d).

Nicotinamide-adenine dinucleotide (NAD⁺). This was formerly known as diphosphopyridine nucleotide (DPN) and has the structure shown.

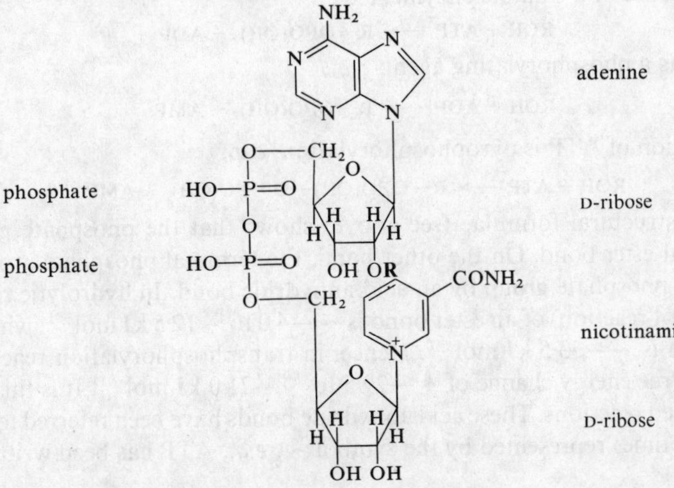

NAD⁺:R = H; NADP⁺:R = PO₃H₂

This coenzyme functions as an acceptor of hydrogen atoms and electrons in the presence of dehydrogenases and is thereby converted into the reduced form **NADH**. Since only the nicotinamide moiety is involved in this transfer, the reaction may be written as shown (note the hydride ion transfer from the substrate; see also **8** §34).

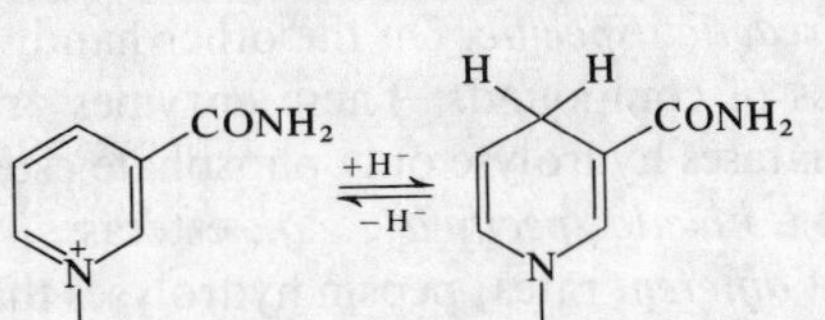

Nicotinamide-adenine dinucleotide phosphate (NADP⁺). This was formerly known as triphosphopyridine nucleotide (TPN) and has the structure shown (see above). This also behaves as an acceptor of hydrogen atoms and electrons, thereby being converted into the reduced form, **NADPH** (see also **8** §34). It appears that NAD⁺ and NADH are usually involved in degradative processes, whereas NADP⁺ and NADPH are usually involved in synthetic processes.

Adenosine triphosphate (ATP) has the structure shown. It is involved in enzyme-catalysed transphosphorylation reactions, transferring one phosphate group to the substrate, itself being converted into **adenosine diphosphate (ADP)**. This, in turn, can also transfer a phosphate group and is thereby converted into **adenosine monophosphate (AMP)** [see also **8** §34].

For chemical reactions to proceed, energy must be supplied to overcome the energy barriers. In biosynthetic processes, this energy is supplied by ATP when it is involved in transphosphorylation reactions in the presence of a suitable enzyme, *e.g.*,

$$\text{ROH} + \text{ATP} \longrightarrow \text{R—OPO(OH)}_2 + \text{ADP}$$

ADP also behaves as a phosphorylating agent, *e.g.*,

$$\text{ROH} + \text{ADP} \longrightarrow \text{R—OPO(OH)}_2 + \text{AMP}$$

A less usual reaction of ATP is pyrophosphorylation, *e.g.*,

$$\text{ROH} + \text{ATP} \longrightarrow \text{R—OPO(OH)—O—PO(OH)}_2 + \text{AMP}$$

Inspection of their structural formulae (see above) shows that the phosphate group in AMP is linked by the normal ester bond. On the other hand, the terminal phosphate groups in ADP and ATP are linked to a phosphate group by an acid anhydride bond. In hydrolytic reactions, the free energy change (heat of reaction) of an ester bond is $\sim -4{\cdot}0$ to $-12{\cdot}5\,\text{kJ mol}^{-1}$, whereas that for the acid anhydride bond is $\sim -33{\cdot}5\,\text{kJ mol}^{-1}$. Hence, in transphosphorylation reactions by ATP or ADP, there is a net free energy change of $\sim -29{\cdot}5$ to $\sim -21{\cdot}0\,\text{kJ mol}^{-1}$. It is this energy which is used to 'drive' coupled reactions. These acid anhydride bonds have been referred to as 'energy-rich' bonds, and are sometimes represented by the symbol $\sim$, *e.g.*, ATP has been written as:

$$\text{adenine-ribose—O—PO(OH)} \sim \text{O—PO(OH)} \sim \text{O—PO(OH)}_2$$

§16. Specificity of enzyme action

One of the most characteristic properties of enzymes is their specificity of action. This specificity may be manifested in one of three ways:

(i) An enzyme may catalyse a particular type of reaction, *e.g.*, esterases hydrolyse only esters. Such enzymes are said to be *reaction specific*. On the other hand, an enzyme may be specific for a particular compound or class of compounds. These enzymes are *substrate specific*, *e.g.*, urease hydrolyses only urea; phosphatases hydrolyse only phosphate esters.

(ii) Many enzymes exhibit a *kinetic specificity*, *e.g.*, esterases, although hydrolysing all esters, hydrolyse the various esters at *different* rates; pepsin hydrolyses the peptide link, but is most active for those links in which, among other things, the amino group belongs to an aromatic amino-acid and the carboxyl group is one of a dicarboxylic amino-acid.

(iii) Many enzymes are *stereospecific*, *e.g.*, maltase hydrolyses α-glycosides but not β-glycosides, whereas emulsin hydrolyses the latter but not the former (*cf.* **7** §3).

It should be noted, however, that a given enzyme can exhibit more than one of the specificities, *e.g.*, esterases, while hydrolysing only esters, may also hydrolyse one enantiomer (of an optically active ester) more rapidly than the other.

§17. Mechanism of enzyme action

It has been shown that the rate of enzyme-catalysed reactions depends on a number of factors. The *p*H of the solution has a great effect on enzyme activity, and it has been found that an enzyme behaves efficiently as a catalyst over a narrow range of pH. This optimum pH is characteristic of a particular enzyme and is determined experimentally; it is usually between pH 5 and pH 9. As we have seen (§6), extremes of pH denature proteins and so it is reasonable to suppose that the spatial arrangement of the molecular structure plays a part in enzymic activity (§12).

Like all chemical reactions, enzyme-catalysed reactions are affected by changes in temperature, the rate being increased as the temperature rises. However, since enzymes can be denatured by heat (§6), too high a temperature destroys the activity of the enzyme. Many enzymes have an optimum temperature between 40° and 50°C, but the range may be higher, particularly for plant enzymes.

The rate of an enzyme-catalysed reaction depends on the concentration of the substrate and that of the enzyme. If the substrate is in excess, the rate is directly proportional to the concentration of the enzyme. On the other hand, if the enzyme concentration is kept constant, then the rate increases rapidly as the substrate concentration increases slowly. However, as the substrate concentration increases further, the rate increases much more slowly and finally reaches a maximum at a high substrate concentration (the rate *versus* substrate concentration gives a hyperbolic curve). This behaviour has been interpreted as follows. The substrate 'combines' with a particular region on the enzyme surface to form a complex. These regions are the **active sites**, and the complex is known as the **Michaelis complex** (1913). An enzyme may have one or more active sites. When all of these sites are occupied, the enzyme is now 'saturated' and consequently no further rate increase is possible. The substrate concentration (of the hyperbolic curve) corresponding to half the maximum rate is called the **Michaelis constant**, K_m. Its reciprocal $(1/K_m)$ is a measure of the affinity of an enzyme for the substrate, *e.g.*, if K_m is large, $1/K_m$ is small; this indicates that the substrate concentration must be large in order to achieve half the maximum rate.

The general belief is that enzyme-catalysed reactions proceed through a number of steps. If we represent the enzyme (together with its cofactor) as E, the substrate as S, and the products as P, the reaction may be written (in simple terms) as:

$$E + S \rightleftharpoons ES \rightleftharpoons EP \rightleftharpoons E + P$$

The existence of these intermediates has been established by various means, *e.g.*, their isolation in some cases, spectroscopic studies, isotopic labelling experiments, etc. The nature of the interactions between enzyme and substrate can be of various types: hydrogen bonds, electrostatic forces, hydrophobic bonds, and chemical bonds (see §34).

Like 'chemical' catalysts, enzymes lower the energy of activation (E) of the reactions which they catalyse but they are far more efficient than the former, *i.e.*, they lower the energy of activation to a much greater extent, *e.g.*, the decomposition of hydrogen peroxide:

$$H_2O_2 \xrightarrow{\text{cat.}} H_2O + \tfrac{1}{2}O_2$$

When platinum is the catalyst, E is $\sim 50 \cdot 2$ kJ mol^{-1}, whereas for the enzyme catalase (as catalyst), E is $\sim 2 \cdot 5$ kJ mol^{-1}.

The mechanism whereby enzymes effect these large rate accelerations is still uncertain. It is generally accepted, however, that mechanisms in which enzymes participate involve the usual types of reactions, *i.e.*, nucleophilic, electrophilic, homolytic, rearrangements, etc. Several contributing factors have been suggested to account for the high efficiency of enzyme-catalysed reactions.

(i) *Proximity effect*. Binding of the reactant molecules (substrate and cofactor) to the enzyme results in an 'increased concentration' of the reactant molecules.

(ii) Binding causes the reactant molecules to be correctly oriented and consequently the transition state is reached more readily.

(iii) Binding produces a strain effect in the reactant molecules and consequently the bonds to be broken are 'deformed', thereby being brought to a state close to those existing in the transition state. Thus, the energy of activation of the reaction is lowered.

It is well established that the catalytic effects of enzymes are due to their three-dimensional structure (see also above). X-ray studies have shown that certain amino-acids, which are not necessarily adjacent in the primary structure, are 'brought together' through folding, thereby producing an active site. Since the mode of folding is dependent on the sequence of the amino-acids (primary structure), the latter must be one factor that contributes to the specificity of enzyme action (§16), *i.e.*, there is a steric relationship between the enzyme and the substrate. This was the basis of the 'lock-and-key' theory proposed by Fischer (1894) to explain enzyme specificity. According to this theory, the geometry of the enzyme, the 'lock', is complementary to that of the substrate, the 'key', the result being that the latter fits into the former as a key fits into a lock.

The stereospecificity of an enzyme may be explained on the lock-and-key theory as follows. If we assume that an optically active compound can be bound to the enzyme through a minimum of three points (Bergmann *et al.*, 1935), then the 'fit' will occur with either the D- or L-enantiomer, but

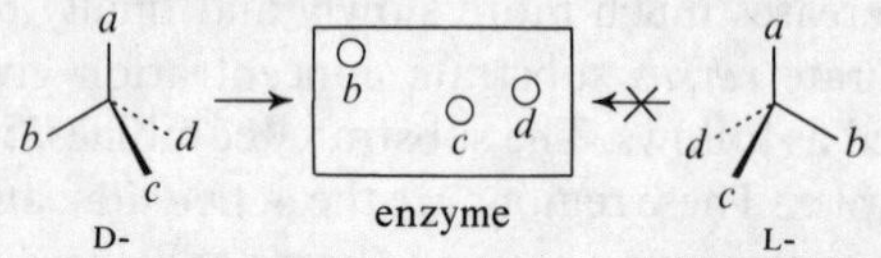

not with both, *e.g.*, if the D-enantiomer fits, the L will not (and *vice versa*). Similarly, reduction of, *e.g.*, pyruvic acid to lactic acid, will occur on one side (enantiotopic or prochiral faces; **2** §7a) to produce one enantiomer of lactic acid. The pyruvic acid molecule fits into the enzyme in one way

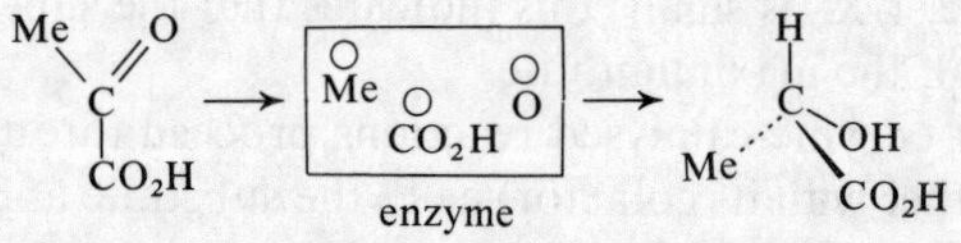

only and consequently hydrogen transfer must occur to one face only, thereby resulting in the formation of only one enantiomer of lactic acid.

Now let us consider the cofactor NAD^+ (see §15). This has a pair of enantiotopic (prochiral) faces and when a hydride ion is accepted, NADH is formed and this contains enantiotopic (prochiral) hydrogens at the 4-position:

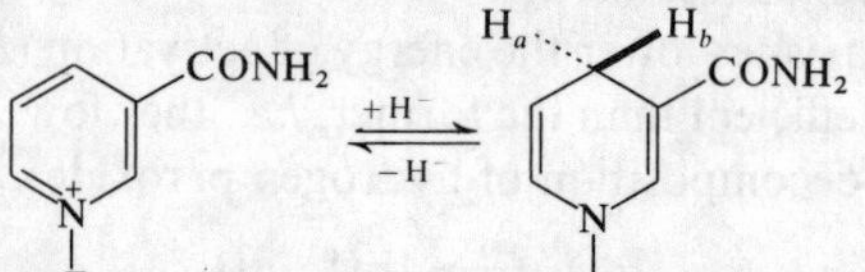

Experimental work has shown that the NAD^+–enzyme complex is usually stereospecific, only one hydrogen (H_a or H_b) reacting exclusively. Which face of NAD^+ is attacked and which hydride ion from NADH is transferred depends on the nature of the enzyme (see also §18).

Enzyme inhibitors. Enzyme activity can be reduced or inhibited by the presence of various compounds. There are two major types of inhibition: *competitive* and *irreversible*. In competitive inhibition, the inhibitor is a compound whose structure and geometry closely resemble that of the normal substrate. Competition occurs between the two (for the active site), but inhibition can be reversed by increasing the concentration of the normal substrate. It therefore follows that the enzyme-inhibitor complex readily regenerates the two molecules in competitive inhibition. On the other hand, in irreversible inhibition the inhibitor forms a highly stable enzyme-inhibitor complex (*via* a covalent bond), and if sufficient inhibitor is present, the catalytic effect of the enzyme towards its normal substrate is completely lost.

The inhibitors discussed above are believed to exhibit inhibition (competitive or irreversible) by combining with the enzyme at its active site. There are however, some compounds which inhibit (or increase) enzyme activity by changing the conformation of the active site of the enzyme. Enzymes which behave this way are called **allosteric enzymes**, and are inhibited (or activated) by combination with the **allosteric effector** at some position of the enzyme which is *not* the active site. Allosteric effectors are usually small molecules which bear no chemical resemblance to the normal substrate (*cf.* competitive inhibitors, above).

§18. Biosynthesis of amino-acids

As we have seen (§1; Table 13.1), man can synthesise some amino-acids but not others; the latter must be provided in the diet. On the other hand, plants and many micro-organisms are capable of synthesising all the amino-acids in proteins. However, the pathways followed in plants and animals may be different for the non-essential amino-acids.

$$CH_3COCO_2H + CO_2 \longrightarrow HO_2CCH_2COCO_2H$$

Tricarboxylic acid cycle

The common amino-acids are derived from a relatively small number of precursors and, in some cases, an amino-acid may be produced from two different precursors. Histidine is exceptional in that it is produced by a pathway not involved in the biosynthesis of any other common amino-acid.

The **glutamate family** is derived from 2-oxoglutaric acid (α-ketoglutaric acid) which is synthesised from acetic acid by way of the **Krebs cycle** (1937), also known as the **tricarboxylic acid cycle**. One step is the conversion of a hexose molecule into two molecules of pyruvic acid *via* phosphoglyceric acid (see also **7** §23a). Pyruvic acid is converted into oxaloacetic acid which then enters into the tricarboxylic acid cycle.

Inspection of the citric acid structural formula shows that the two CH_2CO_2H groups are enantiotopic (prochiral). Potter *et al.* (1949) synthesised, by means of enzymes, citric acid labelled with ^{14}C at *one* CH_2CO_2H group and showed that the enzymic conversion of this compound gave 2-oxoglutaric acid exclusively labelled at the carboxyl group attached to the carbonyl group (see also §16).

$$
\begin{array}{c}
\overset{*}{C}H_2CO_2H \\
C(OH)CO_2H \\
CH_2CO_2H
\end{array}
\xrightarrow{-H_2O}
\begin{array}{c}
H\overset{*}{C}\!-\!CO_2H \\
\parallel \\
C\!-\!CO_2H \\
CH_2CO_2H
\end{array}
\xrightarrow{+H_2O}
\begin{array}{c}
\overset{*}{C}HOHCO_2H \\
CHCO_2H \\
CH_2CO_2H
\end{array}
\xrightarrow{-2H}
\begin{array}{c}
\overset{*}{C}OCO_2H \\
CH_2 \\
CH_2CO_2H
\end{array}
\;+\;CO_2
$$

The glutamate family contains *four* amino-acids: glutamic acid, glutamine, proline, and arginine. Here, we shall deal with the non-essential acids; this excludes arginine (see Table 13.1). The pathways are shown in the chart, and starts with 2-oxoglutaric acid (P_i is a molecule of phosphoric acid). The various enzymes involved are not given in the charts.

$$HO_2CCH_2CH_2COCO_2H$$
2-oxoglutaric acid
$$\downarrow NH_3, NADPH$$
$$HO_2CCH_2CH_2CH(NH_2)CO_2H$$
——— L-glutamic acid ———

$$H_2NOCCH_2CH_2CH(NH_2)CO_2H$$ (via NH₃, ATP)
L-glutamine
+ ADP + P_i

$$OHCCH_2CH_2CH(NH_2)CO_2H$$ (via NADPH, ATP)
L-glutamic-4-semialdehyde

spontaneous cyclisation ($-H_2O$)

L-Δ'-pyrroline-5-carboxylic acid

↓ NADPH

L-proline

An extremely important feature of the pathway leading to glutamic acid is the utilisation of ammonia in the conversion of the 2-oxo-acid to the amino-acid. All experimental work has shown that 2-oxo-acids are produced in the biosynthesis of all the common amino-acids and that these oxo-acids are aminated by means of L-glutamic acid (see also tryptophan, below). This transamination proceeds under the influence of aminotransferases. This may be illustrated with aspartic acid and asparagine of the aspartate family (which also includes lysine, threonine, and methionine).

(i) $CH_2{=}C(OP)CO_2H + ADP \longrightarrow ATP \longrightarrow CH_3COCO_2H \xrightarrow[ATP]{CO_2} HO_2CCH_2COCO_2H + ADP + P_i$

(ii)

$$\begin{array}{ccc}
CO_2H & CO_2H & \\
| & | & \\
CO & CHNH_2 & \\
| \quad + & | & \xrightarrow{\text{aminotransferase}} \\
CH_2 & CH_2 & \\
| & | & \\
CO_2H & CH_2CO_2H & \\
\text{oxaloacetic} & \text{L-glutamic} & \\
\text{acid} & \text{acid} &
\end{array}
\qquad
\begin{array}{ccc}
CO_2H & CO_2H \\
| & | \\
CHNH_2 & CO \\
| \quad + & | \\
CH_2 & CH_2 \\
| & | \\
CO_2H & CH_2CO_2H \\
\text{L-aspartic} & \text{2-oxoglutaric} \\
\text{acid} & \text{acid}
\end{array}$$

$$\Big\downarrow \text{NH}_3, \text{ATP}$$

$$\begin{array}{c}
CO_2H \\
| \\
CHNH_2 \\
| \\
CH_2 \\
| \\
CONH_2 \\
\text{L-asparagine}
\end{array}$$

It should also be noted that amino-acid amides are produced by amination of acids with ammonia.

The aminotransferases involved in transamination require the presence of a cofactor (§15); this is pyridoxal 5′-phosphate or pyridoxamine 5′-phosphate (see also vitamin B_6, **17** §10).

$$\text{HO} \diagdown \quad \overset{R}{\underset{\underset{Me \quad N}{\diagup}}{\diagup}} \diagdown CH_2OPO(OH)_2$$

pyridoxal 5′-phosphate: R = CHO
pyridoxamine 5′-phosphate: R = CH_2NH_2

If we represent the enzyme–cofactor complex as E—CHO and E—CH_2NH_2, we can write the mechanism of the transamination as follows:

(i) $\displaystyle E{-}CHO + H_2N\overset{\overset{\textstyle CO_2H}{|}}{C}H(CH_2)_2CO_2H \underset{+H_2O}{\overset{-H_2O}{\rightleftharpoons}} E{-}CH{=}N{-}\overset{\overset{\textstyle CO_2H}{|}}{C}H(CH_2)_2CO_2H \rightleftharpoons$

$\displaystyle E{-}CH_2N{=}\overset{\overset{\textstyle CO_2H}{|}}{C}(CH_2)_2CO_2H \underset{-H_2O}{\overset{+H_2O}{\rightleftharpoons}} E{-}CH_2NH_2 + O{=}\overset{\overset{\textstyle CO_2H}{|}}{C}(CH_2)_2CO_2H$

(ii) $\displaystyle E{-}CH_2NH_2 + O{=}\overset{\overset{\textstyle CO_2H}{|}}{C}CH_2CO_2H \underset{+H_2O}{\overset{-H_2O}{\rightleftharpoons}} E{-}CH_2N{=}\overset{\overset{\textstyle CO_2H}{|}}{C}CH_2CO_2H \rightleftharpoons E{-}CH{=}N{-}\overset{\overset{\textstyle CO_2H}{|}}{C}HCH_2CO_2H \underset{-H_2O}{\overset{+H_2O}{\rightleftharpoons}}$

$\displaystyle E{-}CHO + H_2N\overset{\overset{\textstyle CO_2H}{|}}{C}HCH_2CO_2H$

This mechanism involves the formation of a Schiff base which rearranges to the isomeric Schiff base (see Vol. I).

As we have seen, the common amino-acids containing a benzene ring are essential acids (Table 13.1). These acids—phenylalanine, tyrosine, and tryptophan—constitute the **aromatic family**. The aromatic amino-acids are synthesised by micro-organisms by the **shikimic acid route**, and there is some evidence to show that this route is also followed in higher plants. Two distinct routes to the benzene ring are possible: (i) from acetate; (ii) from carbohydrates. The latter is known as the shikimic acid route. Both the acetate and the shikimic acid route are followed in the biosynthesis of flavonoids (**15** §16).

The shikimic acid route starts from D-glucose which is converted into phosphoenolpyruvic acid

(PEP) and erythrose-4-phosphate (see also **7** §23a). These combine to form 3-deoxy-D-arabino-heptulosonic acid 7-phosphate which is then transformed in a series of steps to shikimic acid which, in turn, is converted into chorismic acid (see chart). Up to this point, the pathway is common to the three aromatic amino-acids (the amino-acids have been written as such and not as the carboxylate form).

Shikimic acid route leading to chorismic acid

Shikimic acid is $3\alpha,4\alpha,5\beta$-trihydroxycyclohex-1-ene-1-carboxylic acid, m.p. 190–191°C, $[\alpha]_D$ $-157°$, and λ_{max} 213 nm (ε 8 900) [see **11** §5 for the meanings of α and β]. Its structure and stereochemistry have been determined by a number of workers, and Hall (1964) has shown, from his NMR spectral studies, that the acid exists predominantly in the half-chair conformation, the boat form contributing only to a very small extent (*cf.* **4** §13).

half-chair   boat

Davis *et al.* (1951–1958) showed that shikimic acid was an intermediate in the biosynthesis of the three aromatic amino-acids and Gibson *et al.* (1962) established that chorismic acid is another intermediate that was derived from shikimic acid. These workers also proposed the structure of chorismic acid given (in the chart) and this has been confirmed by NMR studies (Gibson *et al.*, 1963). The stereochemistry of chorismic acid, however, was based on that of (−)-shikimic acid, which had been established by Fischer *et al.* (1937).

The stereochemistry of the elimination of phosphoric acid from shikimic acid 5-phosphate to give chorismic acid has been shown, by means of tritium labelled experiments, to be stereospecifically *trans* (Hill *et al.*, 1969; Onderka *et al.*, 1969). Thus it is H_b which is eliminated, which is the opposite of what would be expected for a *concerted* reaction.

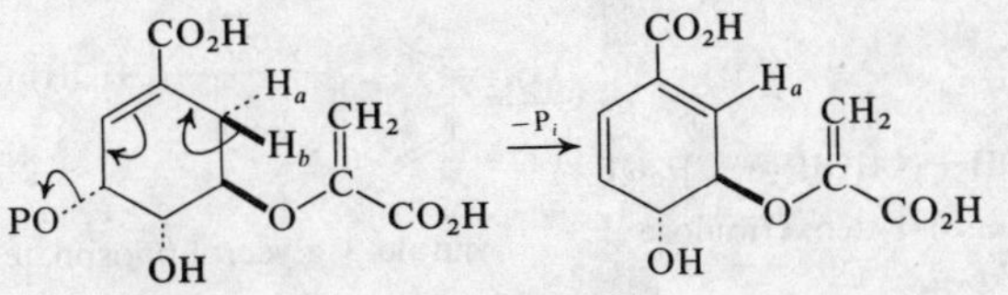
CO₂H
Ha
Hb
CH₂
PO
OH
−Pi
CO₂H

We now return to the conversion of chorismic acid into the aromatic amino-acids. The pathways are shown in the charts.

Phenylalanine and tyrosine

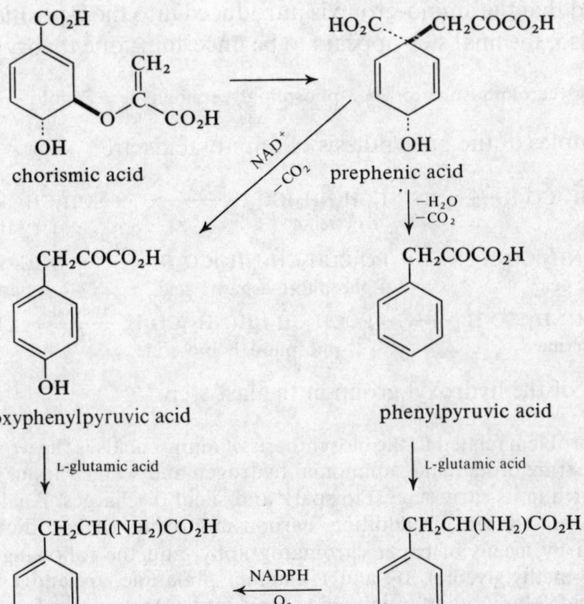
chorismic acid
prephenic acid
NAD⁺
−CO₂
−H₂O
−CO₂
p-hydroxyphenylpyruvic acid
phenylpyruvic acid
L-glutamic acid
L-glutamic acid
NADPH
O₂
L-tyrosine
L-phenylalanine

Tryptophan

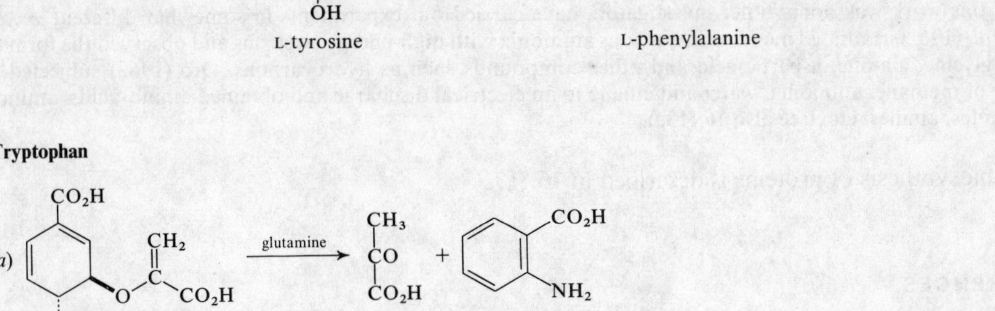
(a)
glutamine
chorismic acid
pyruvic acid
anthranilic acid
(b)
+ POCH₂—CH(CHOH)₂CHOPOP
5-phosphoribosyl-1-pyrophosphate
NH—CH(CHOH)₂CHCH₂OP
N′-(5′-phosphoribosyl) anthranilate

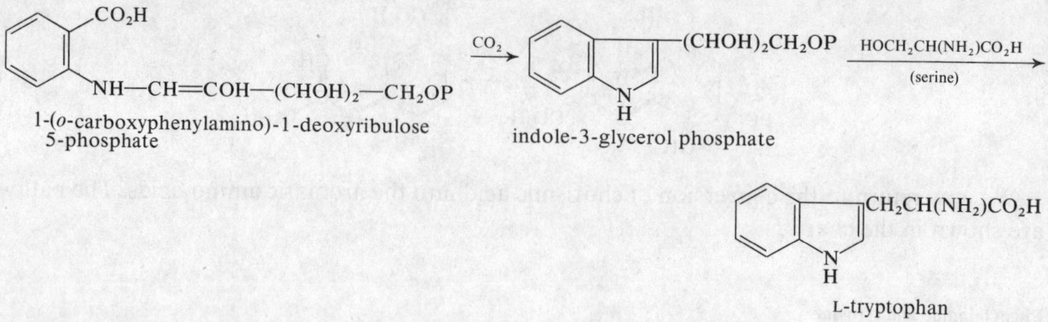

1-(o-carboxyphenylamino)-1-deoxyribulose
5-phosphate

indole-3-glycerol phosphate

L-tryptophan

It should be noted that the amino-group is introduced into the 2-position of chorismic acid to give anthranilic acid. Also, the final step appears to be uncertain; one theory is that it occurs as follows:

$$\text{indole-3-glycerol phosphate} \longrightarrow \text{3-phosphoglyceraldehyde + indole} \xrightarrow{\text{serine}} \text{tryptophan}$$

Some other examples of the biosynthesis of amino-acids are:

(a) $HOCH_2CH(NH_2)CO_2H \xrightarrow{H_2S} HSCH_2CH(NH_2)CO_2H \xrightarrow{NAD^+} [—SCH_2CH(NH_2)CO_2H]_2 + NADH$
       L-serine   L-cysteine   L-cystine

(b) $HO_2CCH_2CH(NH_2)CO_2H \xrightarrow{ATP} PO_2CCH_2CH(NH_2)CO_2H \xrightarrow{NADH} OHCCH_2CH(NH_2)CO_2H \xrightarrow{NADH}$
       L-aspartic acid   4-phospho-L-aspartic acid   L-aspartic acid 3-aldehyde

$HOCH_2CH_2CH(NH_2)CO_2H \xrightarrow{NADH} POCH_2CH_2CH(NH_2)CO_2H \xrightarrow[H_2O]{\text{Pyridoxal-P}} CH_3CHOHCH(NH_2)CO_2H$
       L-homoserine O-phospho-L-homoserine   L-threonine

Note the migration of the hydroxyl group in the last step.

A very interesting problem related to the biosynthesis of amino-acids is the work of Miller (1953, 1955). This author subjected a mixture of methane, ammonia, hydrogen and water vapour (which possibly made up the atmosphere of the Earth in its early stages) to spark and silent discharges. Analysis of the gases showed that the initial gases were present and, in addition, carbon monoxide, carbon dioxide and nitrogen. The solid product was analysed by means of paper chromatography, and the following aminoacids were identified: glycine, sarcosine (N-methylglycine), D- and L-alanine, β-alanine, D- and L-α-amino-n-butyric acid and α-amino-isobutyric acid. Many other amino-acids (unidentified) were also formed, as well as formic, acetic propionic, glycollic and lactic acids.

Since this work was done, other investigators have carried out experiments in somewhat different ways. Palm *et al.* (1962) irradiated methane in aqueous ammonia with high-energy electrons and observed the formation of glycine, alanine, aspartic acid and other compounds such as hydrocarbons. Oró (1963) subjected a mixture of methane, ammonia, water and ethane to an electrical discharge and obtained amino-acids, amino-acid amides, amines, etc. (see also 16 §13e).

The biosynthesis of proteins is described in 16 §17.

REFERENCES

Advances in Protein Chemistry, Academic Press (1944–).
GREENSTEIN and WINITZ, *Chemistry of the Amino Acids*, Wiley (1961).
HAUROWITZ, *The Chemistry and Function of Proteins*, Academic Press (1963, 2nd edn.).
NEURATH (ed.), *The Proteins*, Academic Press (1963–).
FLORKIN and STOTZ (eds.), *Comprehensive Biochemistry*, Elsevier. Vols. 7 and 8 (1963). 'Proteins.'
ELMORE, *Peptides and Proteins*, Cambridge University Press (1968).
BAILEY, *Techniques in Protein Chemistry*, Elsevier (1967, 2nd edn.).
Specialist Periodical Reports, The Chemical Society, 'Aminoacids, Peptides and Proteins.' Vol. 1 (1969). Vol. 2 (1970).

ELIEL and ALLINGER (eds.), *Topics in Stereochemistry*, Wiley-Interscience. Vol. 5 (1970). 'Polypeptide Stereochemistry,' p. 69.

SHELDRICK, 'Application of Computers in Chemical Analysis: Amino-acid Analysis and Sequence Determination', *Quart. Rev.*, 1970, **24**, 454.

FREEDMAN, 'Applications of the Chemical Reactions of Proteins in Studies of their Structure and Function', *Quart. Rev.*, 1971, **25**, 431.

BUDZIKIEWICZ, DJERASSI and WILLIAMS, *Structure Elucidation of Natural Products by Mass Spectrometry*, Holden-Day. Vol. 2 (1964). Ch. 26. 'α-Amino Acids and Peptides.'

JONES, 'The Mass Spectra of Amino-acid and Peptide Derivatives', *Quart Rev.*, 1968, **22**, 302.

SHEMYAKIN, 'Primary Structure Determination of Peptides and Proteins by Mass Spectrometry', *Pure appl. Chem.*, 1968, **17**, 313.

LEDERER, 'Mass Spectrometry of Natural and Synthetic Peptide Derivatives', *Pure appl. Chem.*, 1968, **17**, 489.

FOLKERS *et al.*, 'The Identity of Chemical and Hormonal Properties of the Thyrotropin Releasing Hormone and Pyroglutamyl-Histidyl-Proline Amide', *Biochem. biophys. Res. Commun.*, 1969, **37**, 705.

WIELAND *et al.*, 'The Discovery, Isolation, Elucidation of Structure, and Synthesis of Antamanide', *Angew. Chem. Int. Edn.*, 1968, **7**, 204.

MAYO (ed.), *Molecular Rearrangements*, Interscience. Part II (1964). Ch. 15. 'Rearrangements in the Chemistry of Amino Acids and Peptides.'

DIXON and WEBB, *Enzymes*, Longmans, Green (1964, 2nd edn.).

WILLIAMS, *Introduction to the Chemistry of Enzyme Action*, McGraw-Hill (1969).

WALEY, 'Mechanism of Enzyme Action', *Quart. Rev.*, 1967, **21**, 379.

WILLIAMS, 'Mechanism of Action and Specificity of Proteolytic Enzymes', *Quart. Rev.*, 1969, **23**, 1.

CORNFORTH, 'Exploration of Enzyme Mechanisms by Asymmetric Labelling', *Quart. Rev.*, 1969, **23**, 125.

LIPSCOMB, 'Three-dimensional Structures and Chemical Mechanisms of Enzymes', *Chem. Soc. Rev.*, 1972, **1**, 319.

14 Alkaloids

§1. Definition of an alkaloid

Originally the name **alkaloid** (which means alkali-like) was given to *all organic bases isolated from plants*. This definition covers an extraordinary wide variety of compounds, and as the study of 'alkaloids' progressed, so the definition changed. Königs (1880) suggested that alkaloids should be defined as naturally occurring organic bases which contain a pyridine ring. This definition, however, embraces only a limited number of compounds, and so the definition was again modified a little later by Ladenburg, who proposed to define alkaloids as natural plant compounds having a basic character and containing at least one nitrogen atom in a heterocyclic ring. Ladenburg's definition excludes any synthetic compounds and any compounds obtained from animal sources. One must admit that even today it is still difficult to define an alkaloid. The term is generally limited to organic bases formed in plants. Not all authors do this, and so they specify those alkaloids obtained from plants as *plant alkaloids* (or *vegetable alkaloids*). On the whole, alkaloids are very poisonous, but are used medicinally in very small quantities. Thus we find that the basic properties, (usually) complex structures, physiological action and plant origin are the main characters which define plant alkaloids. Even so, the class of compounds known as the *purines* (Ch. 16), which possess the above characters, are not usually included under the heading of alkaloids (some purines are also obtained from animal sources).

It is interesting to note in this connection that Sertürner (1806) isolated a basic compound from opium. Up to that time it was believed that plants produced only acids or neutral compounds.

§2. Extraction of alkaloids

Alkaloids are usually found in the seeds, root, leaves, or bark of the plant, and generally occur as salts of various plant acids, *e.g.*, acetic, oxalic, citric, malic, tartaric acid, etc. A common method of isolation of alkaloids is as follows. The plant is dried, then finely powdered and extracted with boiling methanol. The solvent is distilled off, and the residue treated with inorganic acids, where-upon the bases are extracted as their soluble salts. The free bases are liberated by the addition of sodium carbonate and extracted with various solvents, *e.g.*, ether, chloroform, etc. The mixtures of bases thus obtained are separated by various methods into the individual compounds. More recent methods of separation involve the use of chromatography. Lee (1960) has converted plant alkaloids into their reineckates, dissolved these in acetone, and passed this solution through an ion-exchange column, and thereby obtained the alkaloids in a high state of purity. (Reinecke's solution is $H[Cr(NH_3)_2(SCN)_4]$.) Most alkaloids are obtained from natural sources, but a few are synthesised commercially, *e.g.*, ephedrine and papaverine.

§3. General properties

The alkaloids are usually colourless, crystalline, non-volatile solids which are insoluble in water, but are soluble in ethanol, ether, chloroform, etc. Some alkaloids are liquids which are soluble in water, *e.g.*, coniine and nicotine, and a few are coloured, *e.g.*, berberine is yellow. Most alkaloids have a bitter taste and are optically active (laevorotatory). They are generally tertiary nitrogen compounds and contain one or two nitrogen atoms usually in the tertiary state in a ring system; most of the alkaloids also contain oxygen. The optically active alkaloids are very useful for resolving racemic acids. The alkaloids form insoluble precipitates with solutions of phosphotungstic acid, phospho-molybdic acid, picric acid, potassium mercuri-iodide, etc. Many of these precipitates have definite crystalline shapes and so may be used to help in the identification of an alkaloid. Some of these reagents are also used as a means of detecting alkaloids in paper and thin layer chromatography.

§4. General methods for determining structure

As we have seen in earlier chapters, structure determination involves the use of a variety of chemical and physical methods. Many of the following chemical methods, although part of the general approach in structure determination, are those which have been particularly useful in alkaloid chemistry.

(i) After a pure specimen has been obtained it is subjected to qualitative analysis (invariably the alkaloid contains (carbon), hydrogen and nitrogen; most alkaloids also contain oxygen). This is then followed by quantitative analysis and thus the empirical formula is obtained; determination of the molecular weight finally leads to the molecular formula. If the alkaloid is optically active, its specific rotation is also measured.

(ii) When an alkaloid contains oxygen, the functional nature of this element is determined:

(*a*) *Hydroxyl group*. The presence of this group may be ascertained by the action of acetic anhydride, acetyl chloride or benzoyl chloride on the alkaloid (acylation must usually be considered in conjunction with the nature of the nitrogen also present in the molecule; see (iii)). When it has been ascertained that hydroxyl groups are present, then their number is also estimated (by acetyla-tion, etc.). The next problem is to decide whether the hydroxyl group is alcoholic or phenolic. It is phenolic if the alkaloid is soluble in sodium hydroxide and reprecipitated by carbon dioxide; also a coloration with ferric chloride will indicate the presence of a phenolic group. If the compound does not behave as a phenol, the hydroxyl group may be assumed to be alcoholic, and this assumption may be verified by the action of dehydrating agents (most alkaloids containing an alcoholic group are readily dehydrated by sulphuric acid or phosphorus pentoxide). The behaviour of the compound towards oxidising agents will also disclose the presence of an alcoholic group.

(*b*) *Carboxyl group*. The solubility of the alkakloid in aqueous sodium carbonate or ammonia indicates the presence of a carboxyl group. The formation of esters also shows the presence of a carboxyl group.

(*c*) *Oxo group*. The presence of an oxo group is readily ascertained by the formation of an oxime, semicarbazone and phenylhydrazone.

(*d*) Hydrolysis of the alkaloid and an examination of the products led to information that the compound is an ester, lactone, amide, lactam or a betaine.

(*e*) The *Zerewitinoff active hydrogen determination* may be applied to the alkakloid (see Vol. I).

(*f*) *Methoxyl group.* The presence of methoxyl groups and their number may be determined by the *Zeisel method.* The alkaloid is heated with concentrated hydriodic acid at its boiling point (126°C); the methoxyl groups are thereby converted into methyl iodide, which is then absorbed by ethanolic silver nitrate and the silver iodide is weighed.

(*g*) *Methylenedioxyl group* ($-OCH_2O-$). The presence of this group is indicated by the formation of formaldehyde when the alkaloid is heated with hydrochloric or sulphuric acid.

(iii) *The functional nature of the nitrogen.*

(*a*) The general reactions of the alkaloid with acetic anhydride, methyl iodide and nitrous acid often show the nature of the nitrogen, *e.g.*, if all the reactions are negative, then the nitrogen is most probably tertiary. The difficulty here is that some alkaloids may undergo ring fission, the product being an *N*-acylated derivative. If the alkaloid forms an amine oxide with 30 per cent hydrogen peroxide, then the nitrogen atom is tertiary.

(*b*) Distillation of an alkaloid with aqueous potassium hydroxide usually leads to information regarding the nature and number of alkyl groups attached to nitrogen. The formation (in the volatile products) of methylamine, dimethylamine or trimethylamine indicates respectively the attachment of one, two or three methyl groups to a nitrogen atom; the formation of ammonia shows the presence of an amino group.

(*c*) The presence of *N*-methyl groups and their number may be determined by means of the *Herzig–Meyer method.* When the alkaloid is heated with hydriodic acid at 150–300°C under pressure, *N*-methyl groups are converted into methyl iodide (*cf.* the Zeisel method, ii*f*)).

(*d*) The results of hydrolysis will show the presence of an amide, lactam or betaine (*cf.* (ii*d*)).

(*e*) *Hofmann's exhaustive methylation method* (1883) is a very important process in alkaloid chemistry, since by its means heterocyclic rings are opened with the elimination of nitrogen, and the nature of the carbon skeleton is thereby obtained. The general procedure is to hydrogenate the heterocyclic ring (if this is unsaturated), convert this compound to the quaternary methylammonium hydroxide which is then heated. In this last stage a molecule of water is eliminated, a hydrogen atom *in the β-position* with respect to the nitrogen atom combining with the hydroxyl group, and the ring is opened at the nitrogen atom on the *same* side as the *β*-hydrogen atom eliminated. The process is repeated on the product; this results in the complete removal of the nitrogen atom from the molecule, leaving an unsaturated hydrocarbon which, in general, isomerises to a *conjugated* diene (see Vol. I for a discussion of the mechanism); *e.g.*, pyridine gives piperylene.

Although the general procedure for exhaustive methylation is to heat the quaternary hydroxide at about 200°C, in a number of cases the reaction may be carried out by refluxing an aqueous or ethanolic solution of potassium hydroxide containing the methiodide or methosulphate of the base. This procedure is usually satisfactory for bases which contain a benzene ring in the *β*-position to the nitrogen atom. This may be explained on the basis that benzylic hydrogen has an increased acidity (and so is more readily removed) because of stabilisation of the transition state by conjugation (with the benzene ring). An interesting example of this is the case of laudanosine. When either *β*-hydrogen atom is eliminated, a styrene derivative is formed, but in one there is more extended conjugation than in the other, and so the former is the product.

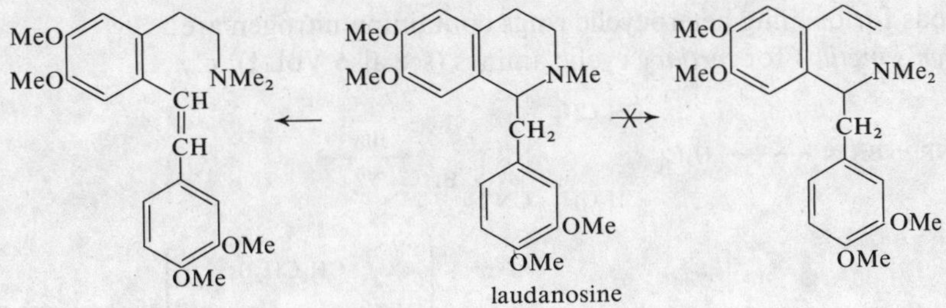

laudanosine

Even though the compound contains a β-hydrogen atom, the exhaustive methylation method may fail, *e.g.*, tetrahydroquinoline.

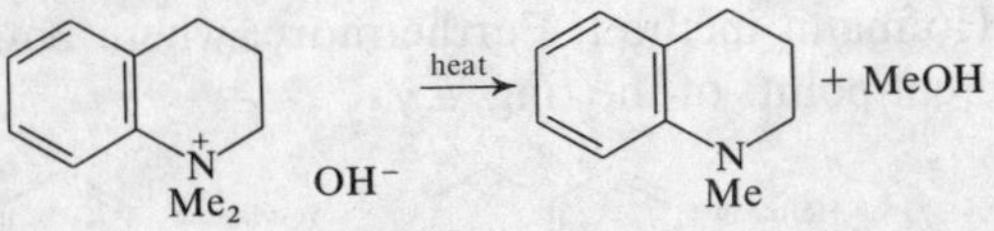

Alcohols are often obtained as a by-product in this elimination reaction, and in some cases no alkene is obtained at all (as in the above example).

When the base does not contain a β-hydrogen atom, the exhaustive methylation method fails. In such cases the Emde modification (1909, 1912) may be used. In this method the quaternary ammonium halide is reduced with sodium amalgam in aqueous ethanol or with sodium in liquid ammonia, or is catalytically hydrogenated, *e.g.*,

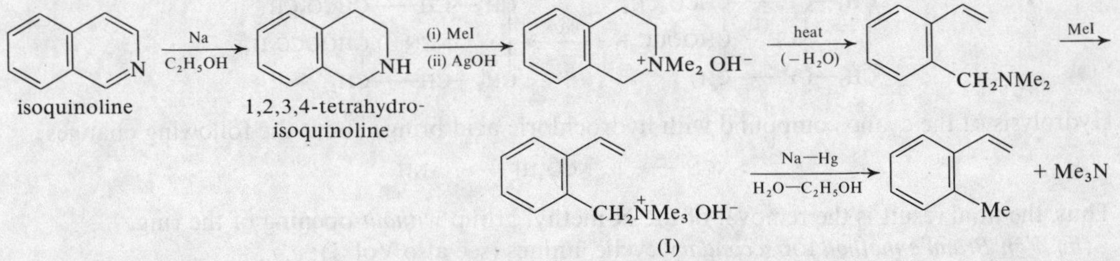

isoquinoline   1,2,3,4-tetrahydro-
                        isoquinoline

(I)

Examination of (I) shows that β-hydrogen is absent; hence Hofmann's method cannot be used.

It has been mentioned above that exhaustive methylation fails with tetrahydroquinoline. The heterocyclic ring, however, is opened by the Emde degradation.

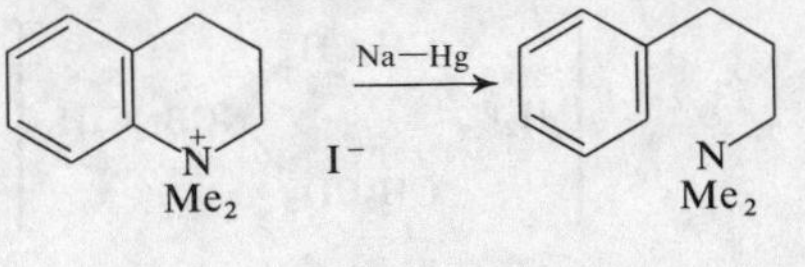

The Emde degradation on tetrahydroisoquinoline is also interesting:

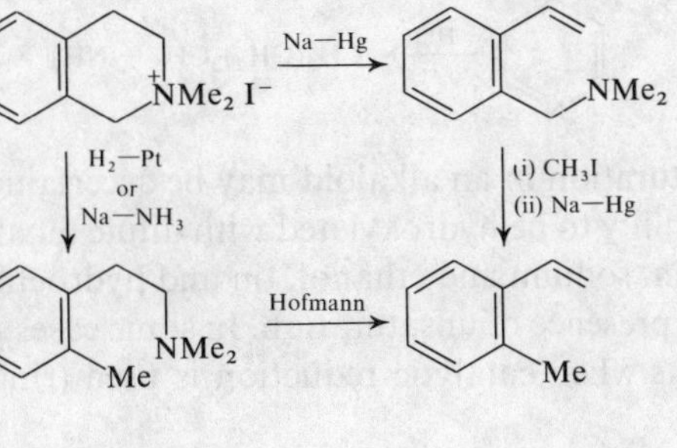

Other methods for opening heterocyclic rings containing nitrogen are:

(*i*) *Von Braun's method* for *tertiary* cyclic amines (see also Vol. I); *e.g.*,

$$
\underset{\displaystyle \text{CH}_2\text{CH}_2}{\overset{\displaystyle \text{CH}_2\text{CH}_2}{\text{H}_2\text{C}}}\!\!\!\!\text{NR} + \text{BrCN} \longrightarrow \left\{\underset{\displaystyle \text{CH}_2\text{CH}_2}{\overset{\displaystyle \text{CH}_2\text{CH}_2}{\text{H}_2\text{C}}}\!\!\!\!\overset{+}{\underset{\displaystyle \text{CN}}{\text{NR}}}\right\}\text{Br}^- \xrightarrow[\text{boil}]{\text{HBr}}
$$

$$
\left[\underset{\displaystyle \text{CH}_2\text{CH}_2\text{NRCN}}{\overset{\displaystyle \text{CH}_2\text{CH}_2\text{Br}}{\text{H}_2\text{C}}}\right] \longrightarrow \text{CH}_2\text{Br(CH}_2)_4\text{NHR}
$$

A point of interest about the cyanogen bromide method is that it is often successful with compounds that fail with the Hofmann method. Furthermore, where both methods are applicable, ring-opening occurs at different points of the ring, *e.g.*,

[structure] ←——Hofmann——— [structure NMe] ———von Braun——→ [structure]

In general, fission of unsymmetrical amines by cyanogen bromide occurs to give the bromide of the 'shorter' bromide (see example given).

In the above examples, the ring is opened, but in other cases dealkylation occurs with formation of the cyclic *N*-cyano derivative, *e.g.*, cocaine (§23):

$$
\begin{array}{ccc}
\text{CH}_2\text{—CH—CHCO}_2\text{CH}_2 & & \text{CH}_2\text{—CH—CHCO}_2\text{CH}_3 \\
\quad\ \ \text{NCH}_3 \ \ \text{CHOOCC}_6\text{H}_5 & \xrightarrow{\ \text{BrCN}\ } & \quad\ \ \text{NCN} \ \ \text{CHOOCC}_6\text{H}_5 \\
\text{CH}_2\text{—CH——CH}_2 & & \text{CH}_2\text{—CH——CH}_2
\end{array}
$$

Hydrolysis of the cyano compound with hydrochloric acid brings about the following changes:

$$>\!\text{NCN} \longrightarrow [\,>\!\text{NCO}_2\text{H}\,] \longrightarrow \ >\!\text{NH}$$

Thus, the final result is the removal of the N-methyl group *without* opening of the ring.

(*ii*) *Von Braun's method* for *secondary* cyclic amines (see also Vol. I); *e.g.*,

$$
\underset{\displaystyle \text{CH}_2\text{CH}_2}{\overset{\displaystyle \text{CH}_2\text{CH}_2}{\text{H}_2\text{C}}}\!\!\!\!\text{NH} + \text{C}_6\text{H}_5\text{COCl} \xrightarrow{\ \text{NaOH}\ } \underset{\displaystyle \text{CH}_2\text{CH}_2}{\overset{\displaystyle \text{CH}_2\text{CH}_2}{\text{H}_2\text{C}}}\!\!\!\!\text{NCOC}_6\text{H}_5 \xrightarrow{\ \text{PBr}_3\text{—Br}_2\ }
$$

$$
\left[\underset{\displaystyle \text{CH}_2\text{CH}_2}{\overset{\displaystyle \text{CH}_2\text{CH}_2}{\text{H}_2\text{C}}}\!\!\!\!\text{NCBr}_2\text{C}_6\text{H}_5\right] \xrightarrow[\substack{\text{reduced} \\ \text{pressure}}]{\text{distil under}} \text{Br(CH}_2)_5\text{Br} + \text{C}_6\text{H}_5\text{CN}
$$

(*iii*) In a number of cases the ring may be opened by heating with hydriodic acid at 300°C, *e.g.*,

[pyridine structure] $\xrightarrow[300°\text{C}]{\text{HI}}$ $\text{CH}_3(\text{CH}_2)_3\text{CH}_3 + \text{NH}_3$

(iv) The presence of unsaturation in an alkaloid may be ascertained by the addition of bromine or halogen acids, or by the ability to be hydroxylated with dilute alkaline permanganate. Reduction by means of sodium amalgam, sodium and ethanol, tin and hydrochloric acid, hydriodic acid, etc., also may be used to show the presence of unsaturation. In some cases, reduction may decompose the molecule. This often happens when catalytic reduction is used (ring cleavage occurs), and hence milder methods of reduction are desirable. Two particularly mild reducing reagents are lithium aluminium hydride and sodium borohydride. Sodium in liquid ammonia gives the Emde type of degradations (see (iii)).

(v) *Oxidation*. This is one of the most valuable means of determining the structure of alkaloids (*cf.* terpenes, **8** §3). By varying the 'strength' of the oxidising agent, it is possible to obtain a variety of products:

(*a*) Mild oxidation is usually effected with hydrogen peroxide, ozone, iodine in ethanolic solution, or alkaline potassium ferricyanide.

(*b*) Moderate oxidation may be carried out by means of acid or alkaline potassium permanganate, or chromium trioxide in acetic acid.

(*c*) Vigorous oxidation is usually effected by potassium dichromate–sulphuric acid, chromium trioxide–sulphuric acid, concentrated nitric acid, or manganese dioxide–sulphuric acid.

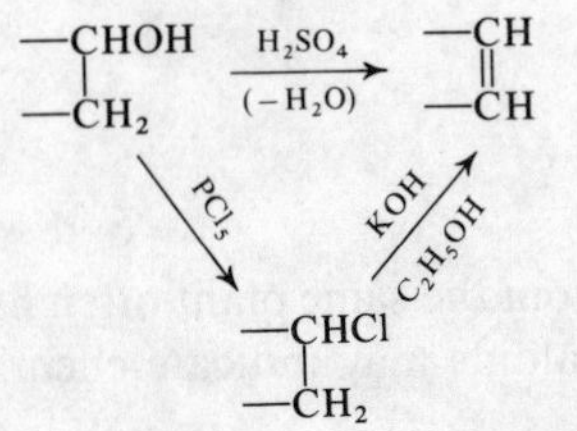

This classification is by no means rigid; the 'strength' of an oxidising agent depends to some extent on the nature of the compound being oxidised. In those cases where it can be done, better results are sometimes achieved by first dehydrating the compound and then oxidising the unsaturated compound thus obtained; oxidation is readily effected at a double bond. More recently, mercuric acetate has been used to dehydrogenate certain alkaloids, thereby introducing olefinic bonds.

(vi) Fusion of an alkaloid with solid potassium hydroxide often produces relatively simple fragments, the nature of which will give information on the type of nuclei present in the molecule (*cf.* (iii*b*)).

(vii) *Zinc dust distillation*. This usually gives the same products as (vi) except that when the alkaloid contains oxygen this is removed.

(viii) Physical methods are now being used, in conjunction with chemical methods, to elucidate structure, *e.g.*, infrared spectra studies are used to identify many functional groups; ultraviolet spectra are used to indicate the likely type of structure present; and X-ray analysis has offered a means of distinguishing between alternative structures that appear to fit equally well the alkaloid in question. Owing to the introduction of computers, it is now possible to quickly perform the calculations from X-ray data, and so the complete stereochemical structure can be obtained from a single crystal. A very good example is that of thelepogine, $C_{20}H_{31}NO$, the structure of which has been determined by X-ray analysis; no chemical work was carried out (Fridrichsons *et al.*, 1960).

NMR spectroscopy is a more recent method for detecting many functional groups, *e.g.*, olefinic protons, *N*-, *O*-, and *C*-methyl groups, and heterocyclic rings such as pyridine, pyrrole, indole, etc. More recently still, mass spectrometry has been used for structure elucidation of various groups of alkaloids. It is often possible to determine the type of nucleus—aromatic and heterocyclic—and the size and structure of side-chains. Mass spectrometry may also be used on the products formed from, *e.g.*, zinc dust distillation.

The stereochemistry of alkaloids has been solved by classical methods, X-ray analysis, and more recently by means of optical rotatory dispersion and circular dichroism where these are applicable (*i.e.*, only with optically active alkaloids).

(ix) *Synthesis*. The foregoing analytical work will ultimately lead to the proposal of a tentative structure (or structures) for the alkaloid under consideration. Because of the increasing value of physical methods in elucidating structure, synthesis of the compound as a means of final proof of structure is less important than it used to be. Nevertheless, synthesis will always give additional evidence for the structure assigned, and may also provide a much better way of obtaining a particular alkaloid (than from natural sources).

§5. Classification of the alkaloids

Long before the structures of the alkaloids were known, the source of the alkaloid was considered the most important characteristic of the compound. Thus there could not be a rational classification. Even today, with the structures of so many known (over 2 000), the classification of the alkaloids is still somewhat arbitrary owing to the difficulty of classifying into distinct groups. Even so, it is probably most satisfactory (chemically) to classify the alkaloids according to the nature of the nucleus present in the molecule. Members of the following groups are described in this book (different classifications are possible):

  (i) Phenylethylamine group.

  (ii) Pyrrolidine group.

  (iii) Pyridine and piperidine groups.

  (iv) Pyrrolidine-pyridine group.

  (v) Quinoline group.

  (vi) Isoquinoline group.

  (vii) Phenanthrene group.

 (viii) Indole group.

It should be noted that in many cases different alkaloids obtained from the same plant often have similar chemical structures, and so sometimes the source of the alkaloids may indicate chemical similarity.

There is no systematic nomenclature of alkaloids. Trivial names are used and these end in 'ine' (indicating a base) and usually indicate the source of the alkaloid.

Structural formulae of alkaloids have been written in various ways in the literature. 'Square' formulae have been quite common in the past, but the tendency now is to use pentagons, hexagons, etc., and also conformational representations, e.g., tropine:

tropine

PHENYLETHYLAMINE GROUP

Many compounds of this group are known, some natural and others synthetic. Their outstanding physiological action is to increase the blood-pressure; hence they are often referred to as the *pressor drugs*.

§6. β-Phenylethylamine

This is the parent substance of this group of alkaloids, and occurs in putrid meat (it is formed by the decarboxylation of phenylalanine, an amino-acid). It also occurs in mistletoe. β-Phenylethylamine may be readily synthesised as follows:

$$C_6H_5CH_2Cl + KCN \longrightarrow C_6H_5CH_2CN \xrightarrow[C_2H_5OH]{Na} C_6H_5CH_2CH_2NH_2$$

β-Phenylethylamine is a colourless liquid, b.p. 197°C.

§7. D(−)-Ephedrine, m.p. 38·1°C, $[\alpha]_D$ −6·3°

D(−)-Ephedrine occurs in the genus *Ephedra*; it is one of the most important drugs in *Ma Huang* (a Chinese drug). Physiologically, its action is similar to that of adrenaline (§12), and it can be taken orally. Ephedrine has also been used in the treatment of hay fever, bronchial asthma, etc.

The molecular formula of ephedrine is $C_{10}H_{15}NO$, and since on oxidation ephedrine forms benzoic acid, the structure therefore contains a benzene ring with only one side-chain. When treated with nitrous acid, ephedrine forms a nitroso-compound; therefore the compound is a secondary amine. Since ephedrine forms a dibenzoyl derivative, one hydroxyl group must be present (one benzoyl group is accounted for by the imino group). Finally, when heated with hydrochloric acid, ephedrine forms methylamine and propiophenone.

$$C_{10}H_{15}NO \xrightarrow{HCl} CH_3NH_2 + C_6H_5COCH_2CH_3$$

The formation of these products can be explained if the structure of ephedrine is either (I) or (II).

$$C_6H_5CHOHCH_2CH_2NHCH_3 \qquad \underset{\underset{NHCH_3}{|}}{C_6H_5CHOHCHCH_3}$$

$$\text{(I)} \qquad\qquad\qquad \text{(II)}$$

It has been observed, however, that compounds of structure (II) undergo the *hydramine fission* to form propiophenone when heated with hydrochloric acid. Thus (II) is more likely than (I). This is supported by the fact that when subjected to the Hofmann exhaustive methylation method, ephedrine forms 1,2-methylphenylethylene oxide (III); this cannot be produced from (I) but is to be expected from (II).

$$\underset{\text{(II)}}{C_6H_5CHOHCH(CH_3)NHCH_3} \xrightarrow[\text{(ii) AgOH}]{\text{(i) } CH_3I} C_6H_5CHOHCH(CH_3)N(CH_3)_3\}^+OH^- \xrightarrow[(-H_2O)]{\text{heat}}$$

$$\overset{O}{\overset{/\backslash}{C_6H_5CHCHCH_3}} + (CH_3)_3N$$

$$\text{(III)}$$

Further support for (II) is afforded by the following evidence. Structure (I) contains one chiral centre and so replacement of the hydroxyl group by hydrogen will result in the formation of an optically inactive compound. Structure (II), however, contains two chiral centres and so the replacement of the hydroxyl group by hydrogen should still give a compound that can be optically active. Experimentally it has been found that when this replacement is effected in (−)-ephedrine, the product, deoxyephedrine is optically active. Thus (II) agrees with all the known facts, and this structure has been confirmed by synthesis, *e.g.*, Nagai *et al.* (1929):

$$C_6H_5CHO + C_2H_5NO_2 \xrightarrow{K_2CO_3} C_6H_5CH(OH)CH(CH_3)NO_2 \xrightarrow{H_2/Pt} \underset{\text{(IV)}}{C_6H_5CH(OH)CH(CH_3)NH_2} \xrightarrow{\text{separate}} \text{(IV)}$$

$$\text{(IV)} + \text{(V)}$$

$$\xrightarrow{CH_3I} \underset{\text{(VI)}}{C_6H_5CH(OH)CH(CH_3)NHCH_3}$$

(IV) is (±)-norephedrine, (V) is (±)-nor-ψ-ephedrine, and (VI) is (±)-ephedrine (this was resolved). (V), on methylation, gives (±)-ψ-ephedrine.

(±)-Ephedrine itself has been synthesised by Manske *et al.* (1929) by the catalytic reduction of 1-phenylpropane-1,2-dione (benzoylacetyl) in the presence of methylamine in methanol solution.

$$C_6H_5COCOCH_3 + CH_3NH_2 \longrightarrow C_6H_5COC(=NCH_3)CH_3 \xrightarrow{H_2-Pt} \underset{\text{(±)-ephedrine}}{C_6H_5CHOHCH(CH_3)NHCH_3}$$

The racemic ephedrine was resolved by means of mandelic acid. Some $(\pm)$-ψ-ephedrine was also obtained in this synthesis.

This is an example of a stereoselective synthesis; both pairs of diastereoisomers, $(\pm)$-ephedrine and $(\pm)$-ψ-ephedrine, are produced, but the former is the predominant product.

Since the ephedrine molecule contains two dissimilar chiral centres, four optically active forms (two pairs of enantiomers) are theoretically possible. According to Freudenberg (1932), the configurations of ephedrine and ψ-ephedrine (m.p. 118°C, $[\alpha]_D \pm 51\cdot2°$) are:

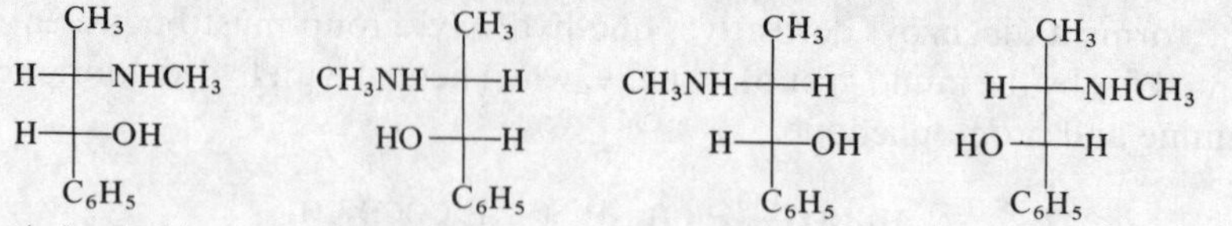

The four Fischer projection structures:
$D(-)$-ephedrine $L(+)$-ephedrine $D(-)$-ψ-ephedrine $L(+)$-ψ-ephedrine

Ephedrine has the *erythro*-configuration, and ψ-ephedrine the *threo*-, and these have been confirmed by Fodor *et al.* (1949, 1950) as follows. The N-carbobenzoxy derivative (13 §9) of nor-ψ-ephedrine rearranges to the O-derivative in acid solution. If nor-ψ-ephedrine has the *threo*-configuration, then this leads to the favourable *trans* orientation of the phenyl and methyl groups

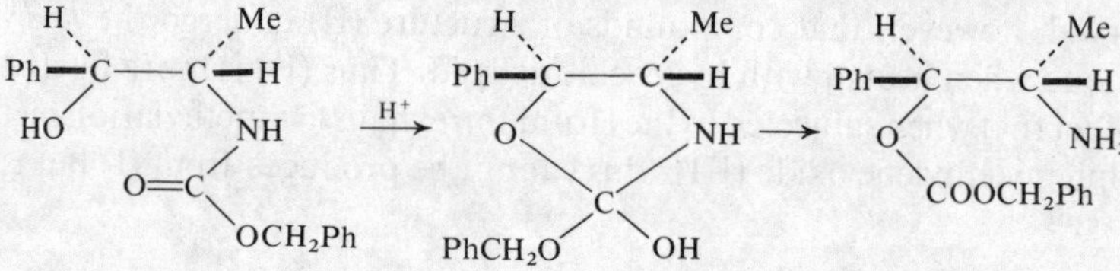

in the cyclic intermediate, *i.e.*, steric repulsions are a minimum. On the other hand, nor-ephedrine will therefore have the *erythro*-configuration, and it was found that its N-carbobenzoxy derivative does not readily rearrange to the O-derivative under acidic conditions. Thus, the steric repulsion which would occur between the phenyl and methyl groups in the cyclic intermediate is apparently too great to permit its formation. Hence it is possible, on this basis, to distinguish between the stereoisomers ephedrine and ψ-ephedrine.

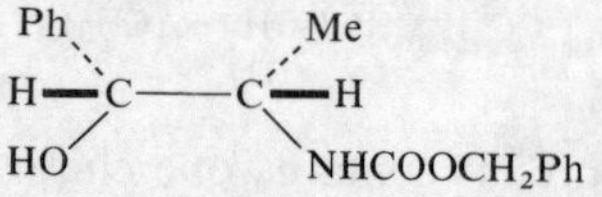

nor-ephedrine

Another point of interest is that $(-)$-ephedrine (pK_a 9·14) is a weaker base than $(+)$-ψ-ephedrine (pK_a 9·22). This can be explained in terms of conformational analysis. In the conjugate acid of ψ-ephedrine hydrogen bonding is possible (as shown), and consequently this conjugate acid is more

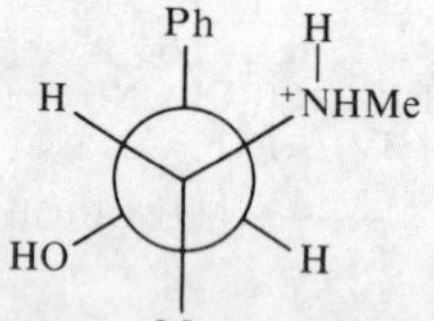

$(-)$-ephedrine (conjugate acid) $(+)$-ψ-ephedrine (conjugate acid) 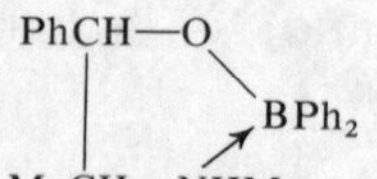   (VII)

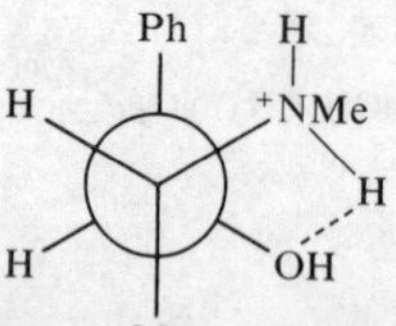

stable than that of ephedrine. In ephedrine, rotation about the single bond could bring the OH and $^+NH_2Me$ groups into the skew position, but this conformation is opposed by the strong steric interactions which would now be present.

These assignments of configurations are further supported by the fact that both ephedrine and

ψ-ephedrine react with diphenylborinic acid (Ph_2BOH) to form ring compounds of type (VII). The rate of formation of (VII) from ψ-ephedrine was much faster than that from ephedrine. This can be explained on the basis that the ephedrine molecule must undergo rotation to give the unfavourable conformation (OH and NHMe skew; *cf.* above).

Confirmation of the configuration of ($-$)-ephedrine, as its hydrochloride, has been obtained from X-ray analysis (Phillips, 1954).

Various mechanisms have been proposed for the hydramine fission. Chatterjee *et al.* (1961) have suggested two different mechanisms according to whether the aryl nucleus contains (i) an electron-releasing group in the *o*- and/or *p*-position, *e.g.*, R = OMe, OH, Me:

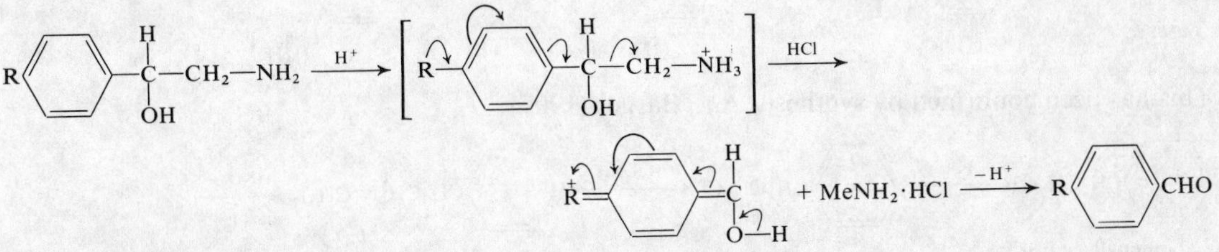

(ii) R in the *m*-position:

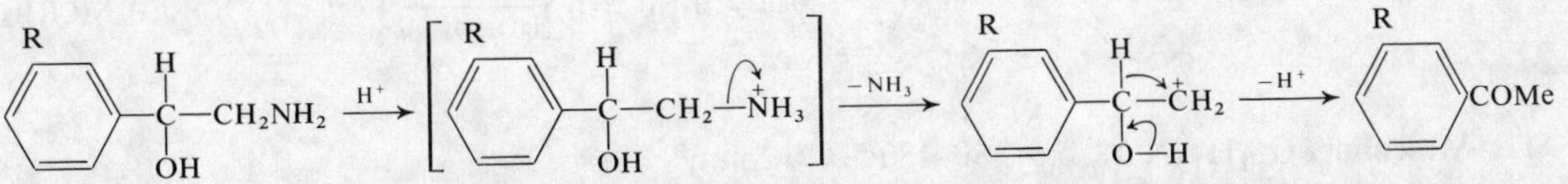

Thus hydramine fission gives an aldehyde or a ketone according to the nature and position of groups in the aryl nucleus. With a 4-nitro group the product is 4-nitroacetophenone (yield: very poor).

§8. Benzedrine (*Amphetamine*)

Originally introduced as a substitute for ephedrine, it is now used in its own right since it apparently produces a feeling of confidence. Benzedrine has been synthesised in many ways, *e.g.*, Mingoia (1940):

$$C_6H_5CH_2COCH_3 \xrightarrow[150-190°C]{HCONH_2} C_6H_5CH_2CH(CH_3)NHCHO \xrightarrow{HCl} C_6H_5CH_2CH(CH_3)NH_2$$
$$(+)\text{-benzedrine}$$

The benzedrine molecule contains one chiral centre and the ($+$)-form is known as Dexedrine (Dexamphetamine).

§9. β-*p*-Hydroxyphenylethylamine (*tyramine*), m.p. $160°C$

This occurs in ergot, and is produced by the putrefaction of proteins (by the decarboxylation of tyrosine). Tyramine has been synthesised in various ways, *e.g.*,

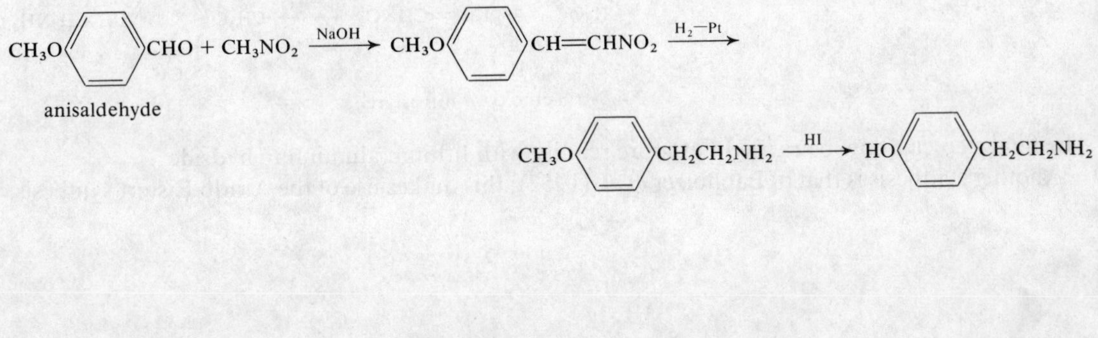

§10. Hordenine (β-p-hydroxyphenylethyldimethylamine, *Anhaline*), m.p. 117–118°C

This occurs naturally in germinating barley. The molecular formula of hordenine is $C_{10}H_{15}NO$; the routine tests show that hordenine is a tertiary base and that it contains a phenolic group. Since the methylation of hordenine, followed by oxidation (with alkaline permanganate), gives anisic acid (I), it therefore follows that the hydroxyl group is in the *para*-position with respect to the side-chain. Furthermore, since the methylated compound gives p-vinylanisole (II) after the Hofmann exhaustive methylation, the structure of hordenine is probably (III).

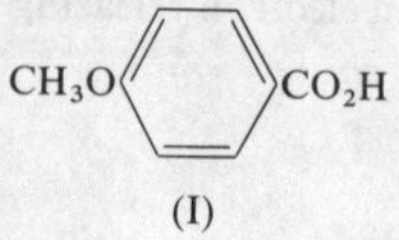

$$CH_3O\langle\ \rangle CO_2H \qquad CH_3O\langle\ \rangle CH{=}CH_2 \qquad HO\langle\ \rangle CH_2CH_2N(CH_3)_2$$

$$\text{(I)} \qquad\qquad\qquad \text{(II)} \qquad\qquad\qquad \text{(III)}$$

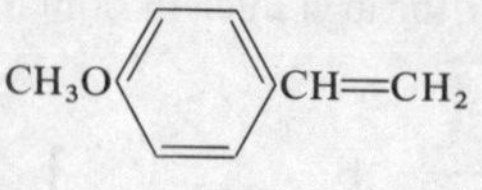

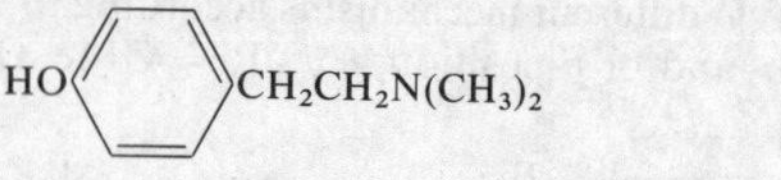

This has been confirmed by synthesis, *e.g.*, Barger (1909):

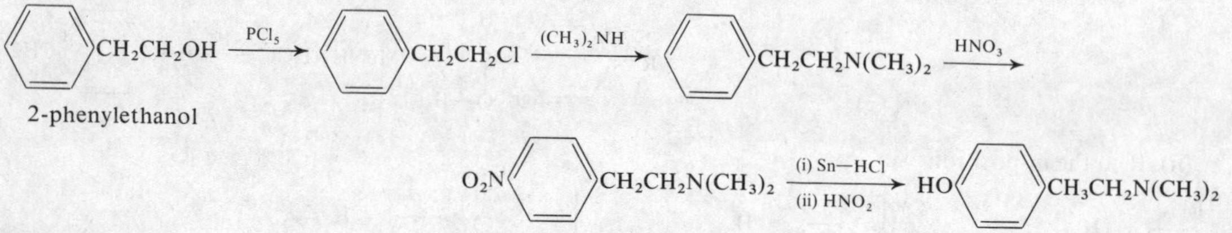

$$\langle\ \rangle CH_2CH_2OH \xrightarrow{PCl_5} \langle\ \rangle CH_2CH_2Cl \xrightarrow{(CH_3)_2NH} \langle\ \rangle CH_2CH_2N(CH_3)_2 \xrightarrow{HNO_3}$$

2-phenylethanol

$$O_2N\langle\ \rangle CH_2CH_2N(CH_3)_2 \xrightarrow[\text{(ii) HNO}_2]{\text{(i) Sn—HCl}} HO\langle\ \rangle CH_3CH_2N(CH_3)_2$$

§11. Mescaline, $C_{11}H_{17}NO_3$, b.p. 180–180·5°C/12 mm

This occurs naturally in 'mescal buttons'. The routine tests show that mescaline contains a primary aliphatic amino-group and three methoxyl groups. On oxidation with alkaline permanganate,

$$CH_3O\langle\ \rangle CH_2CH_2NH_2$$

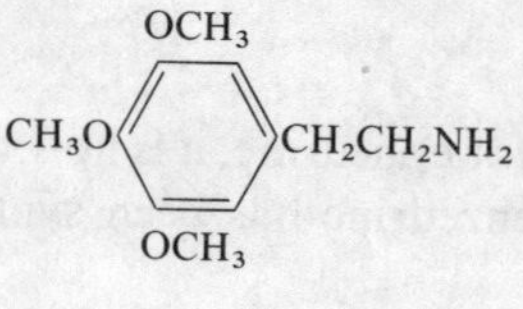

(I)

mescaline gives 3,4,5-trimethoxybenzoic acid, and thus the probable structure of mescaline is (I). This has been confirmed by synthesis (Späth, 1919):

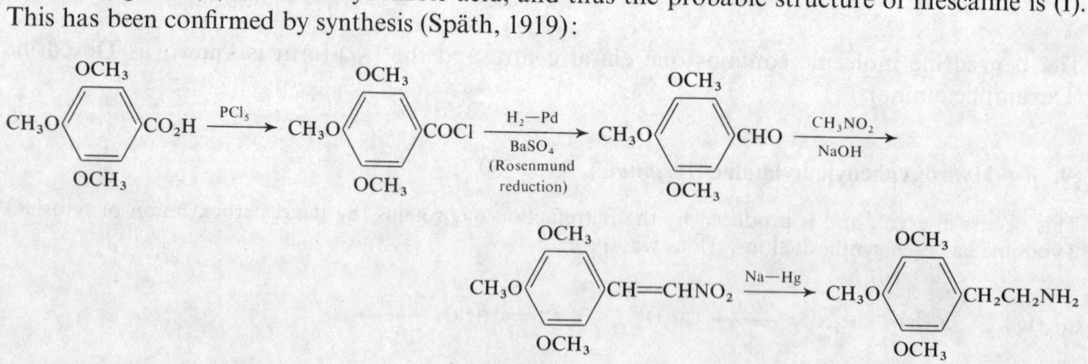

$$CH_3O\langle\ \rangle CO_2H \xrightarrow{PCl_5} CH_3O\langle\ \rangle COCl \xrightarrow[\substack{\text{BaSO}_4\\ \text{(Rosenmund}\\ \text{reduction)}}]{H_2-Pd} CH_3O\langle\ \rangle CHO \xrightarrow[\text{NaOH}]{CH_3NO_2}$$

$$CH_3O\langle\ \rangle CH{=}CHNO_2 \xrightarrow{Na-Hg} CH_3O\langle\ \rangle CH_2CH_2NH_2$$

3,4,5-trimethoxy-ω-nitrostyrene

The final step can now be carried out more readily with lithium aluminium hydride.
  Another synthesis is that of Banholzer *et al.* (1952); this makes use of the Arndt–Eistert synthesis.

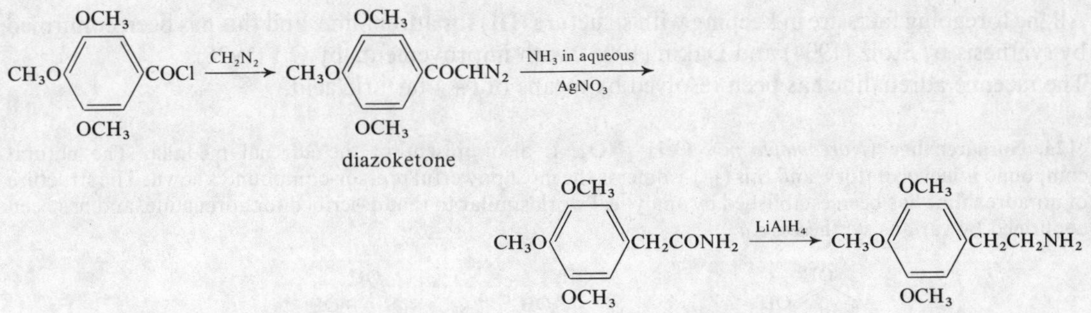

At the top, a reaction scheme:

A 2,4,5-trimethoxybenzoyl chloride (CH_3O / OCH_3 / OCH_3 ring with $COCl$) $\xrightarrow{CH_2N_2}$ the diazoketone (CH_3O ring with $COCHN_2$) $\xrightarrow[\text{AgNO}_3]{\text{NH}_3 \text{ in aqueous}}$

then CH_3O (OCH_3, OCH_3) ring with CH_2CONH_2 $\xrightarrow{LiAlH_4}$ CH_3O (OCH_3, OCH_3) ring with $CH_2CH_2NH_2$

N-Methylmescaline and *N*-acetylmescaline also occur naturally in mescal buttons.

§12. Adrenaline (*Epinephrine*), $C_9H_{13}NO_3$

This is a non-steroid hormone. The adrenal medulla is the source of the hormones adrenaline and nor-adrenaline. Adrenaline was the first hormone to be isolated in a crystalline form (Takamine, 1901; Aldrich, 1901), and is active only when given by injection; it raises the blood-pressure, and is used locally to stop haemorrhage.

Adrenaline is a colourless crystalline solid, m.p. 211°C, and dissolves in acids and alkalis (it is insoluble in water); it is also optically active, $[\alpha]_D -53.5°$.

The phenolic character of adrenaline is indicated by its solubility in sodium hydroxide and its reprecipitation by carbon dioxide. Since it gives a green colour with ferric chloride, this led to the suggestion that adrenaline is a catechol derivative. When boiled with aqueous potassium hydroxide, adrenaline evolves methylamine; thus a methylamino group is probably present. On the other hand, when fused with potassium hydroxide, the product is protocatechuic acid (I) [Takamine, 1901];

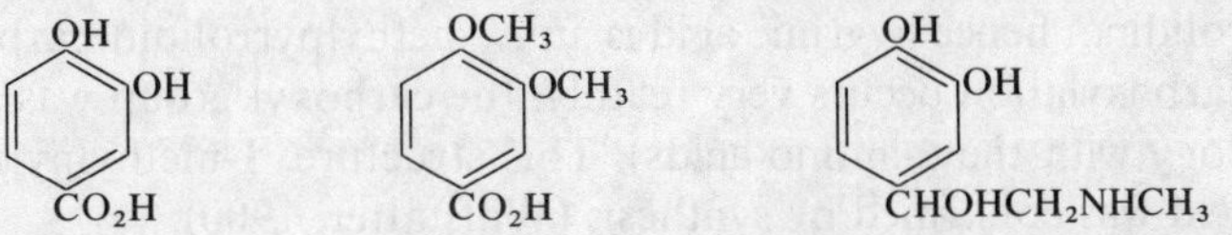

(I) is a benzene ring with OH, OH and CO_2H (protocatechuic acid).
(II) is a benzene ring with OCH_3, OCH_3 and CO_2H (veratric acid).
(III) is a benzene ring with OH, OH and $CHOHCH_2NHCH_3$.

methylation, followed by fusion with potassium hydroxide, gives veratric acid (II) and trimethyl-amine (Jowett, 1904). The formation of trimethylamine indicates that the nitrogen atom must occur at the *end* of the side-chain. Since adrenaline is optically active, it must contain at least one chiral centre. Now, adrenaline contains three hydroxyl groups, two of which are phenolic (as shown by the formation of (I) and (II)). The third hydroxyl group was shown to be secondary alcoholic by the fact that when adrenaline is treated with benzenesulphonyl chloride, a tribenzenesulphonyl deriva-tive is obtained which, on oxidation, gives a ketone (Friedmann, 1906). To account for the oxidation of adrenaline to the benzoic acid derivative, the —CHOH— group must be attached directly to the nucleus; had it been —CH₂CHOH, then a phenylacetic acid derivative would have been obtained.

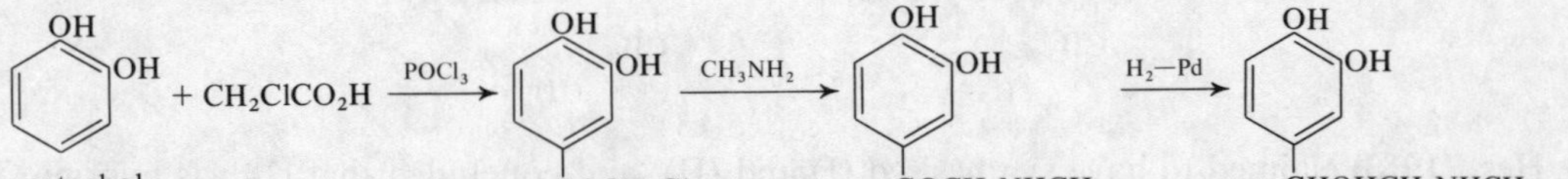

Reaction scheme at bottom:

catechol (benzene ring with OH, OH) $+ CH_2ClCO_2H$ $\xrightarrow{POCl_3}$ ω-chloro-3,4-dihydroxyacetophenone (ring with OH, OH and $COCH_2Cl$) $\xrightarrow{CH_3NH_2}$ (ring with OH, OH and $COCH_2NHCH_3$) $\xrightarrow{H_2—Pd}$ (±)-adrenaline (ring with OH, OH and $CHOHCH_2NHCH_3$)

All the foregoing facts are in keeping with structure (III) for adrenaline, and this has been confirmed by synthesis by Stolz (1904) and Dakin (1905), with improvements by Ott (1926).
The racemic adrenaline has been resolved by means of ($+$)-tartaric acid.

§12a. **Noradrenaline** (*Norepinephrine*), $C_8H_{11}NO_3$, is also present in the adrenal medulla. The natural compound is laevorotatory, and this ($-$)-isomer is the most powerful pressor-compound known. The structure of noradrenaline has been established by analytical work similar to that described for adrenaline, and has been confirmed by various syntheses, *e.g.*,

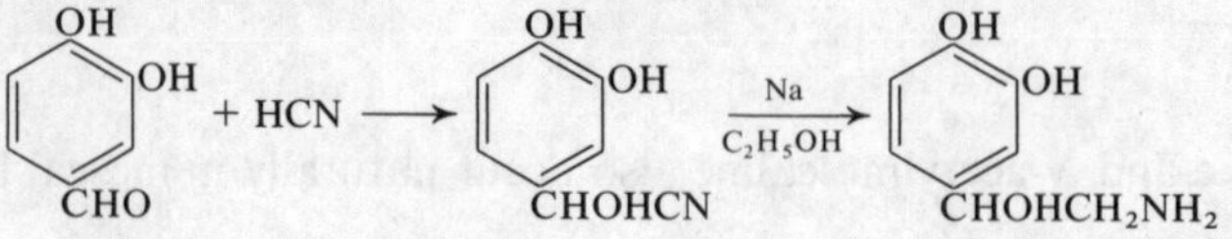

($\pm$)-noradrenaline

PYRROLIDINE GROUP

§13. Hygrine, $C_8H_{15}NO$, b.p. 193–195°C, $[\alpha]_D -1\cdot3°$

This is one of the coca alkaloids. Its reactions show the presence of a keto group and a tertiary nitrogen atom, and when oxidised with chromic acid, hygrnic (hygric) acid is formed.

$$C_8H_{15}NO \xrightarrow{[O]} C_6H_{11}NO_2$$
hygrinic acid

Hygrinic acid was first believed to be a piperidinecarboxylic acid, but comparison with the three piperidine acids showed that this was incorrect. When subjected to dry distillation, hygrinic acid gives *N*-methylpyrrolidine; hence hygrinic acid is an *N*-methylpyrrolidinecarboxylic acid. Furthermore, since the decarboxylation occurs very readily, the carboxyl group was assumed to be in the 2-position (by analogy with the α-amino-acids). This structure, 1-methylpyrrolidine-2-carboxylic acid, for hygrinic acid was confirmed by synthesis (Willstätter, 1900).

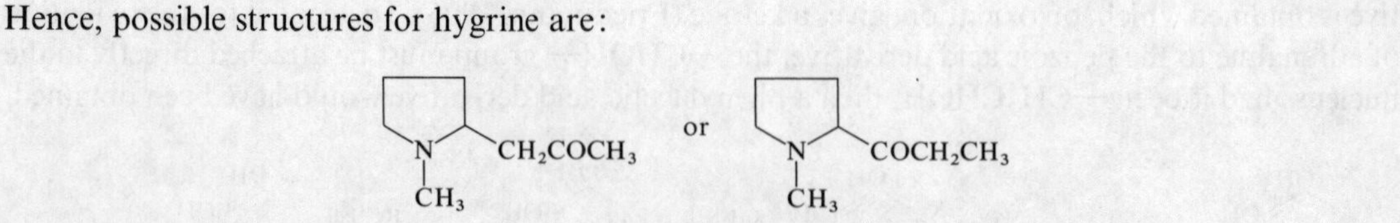

($\pm$)-hygrinic acid

Hence, possible structures for hygrine are:

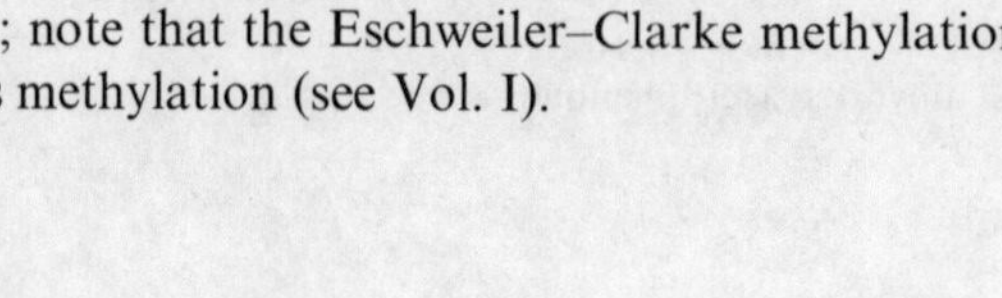

Hess (1913) claimed to have synthesised (I) and (II), and concluded that (I) was hygrine. This 'synthesis' is shown here; note that the Eschweiler–Clarke methylation involves oxidation of the alcoholic group as well as methylation (see Vol. I).

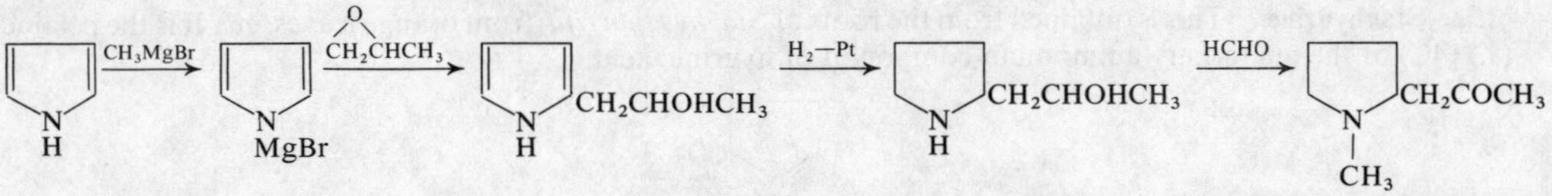

Lukeš *et al.* (1959) have repeated Hess's work and have shown that the product is not hygrine but the tetrahydro-oxazine (III); it is the last stage of Hess's interpretation that has been shown to be incorrect.

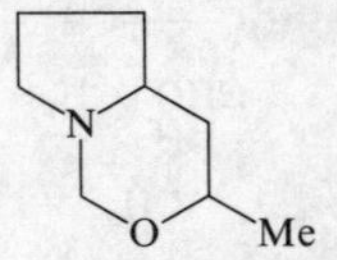

(III)

Anet *et al.* (1949) have synthesised ($\pm$)-hygrine by condensing γ-methylaminobutyraldehyde with ethyl acetoacetate in a buffered solution at a *p*H of 7 (physiological conditions).

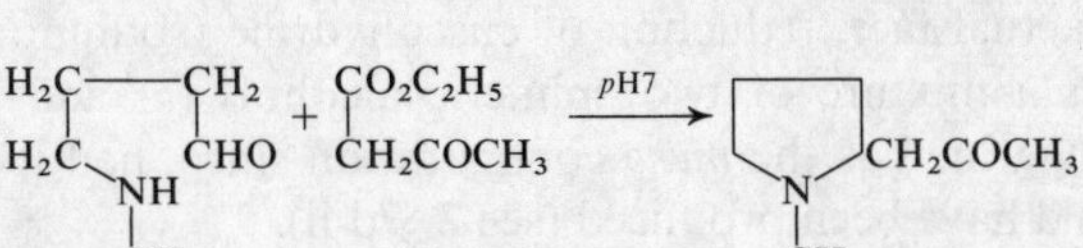

The absolute configuration of hygrine has been established as follows. Karrer *et al.* (1948) showed that ($-$)-hygrinic acid was configurationally related to L($+$)-glutamic acid and L($-$)-proline by the series of reactions shown:

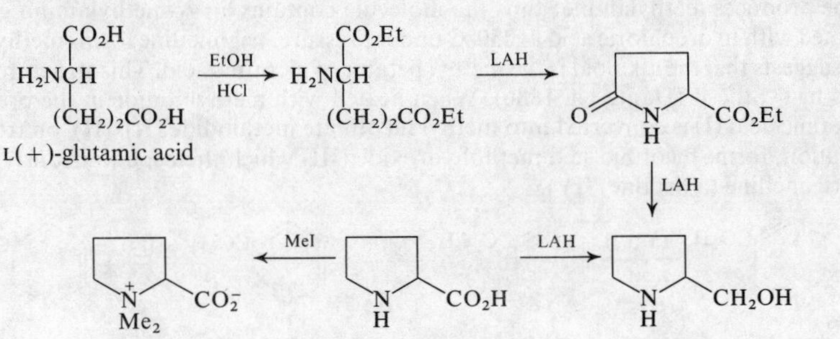

L($+$)-glutamic acid

($-$)-stachydrine   L($-$)-proline (as ester)

Lukeš *et al.* (1960) then showed that the hygrinic acid obtained by the oxidation of hygrine (CrO_3—AcOH—H_2SO_4) had the same direction of rotation as that of its precursor (*i.e.*, hygrine). Furthermore, ($-$)-hygrinic acid was converted into ($-$)-stachydrine (§13a) on methylation, and this compound was also obtained by the methylation of L($-$)-proline.

($-$)-Hygrine, as the free base, rapidly racemises; the mechanism is believed to involve ring-opening.

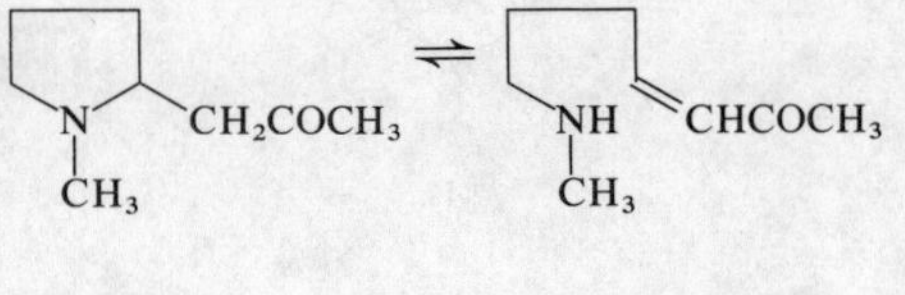

§13a. **Stachydrine.**   This is obtained from the roots of *Stachys tuberifa*, from orange leaves, etc. It is the betaine (13 §4C) of the quaternary ammonium compound of hygrinic acid.

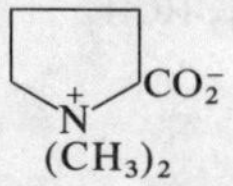

§14. Cuscohygrine (*Cuskhygrine*), b.p. 169–170°C/23 mm

This occurs with hygrine. Its structure is established by the following synthesis (Anet *et al.*, 1959); γ-methylaminobutyraldehyde is condensed with acetonedicarboxylic ester:

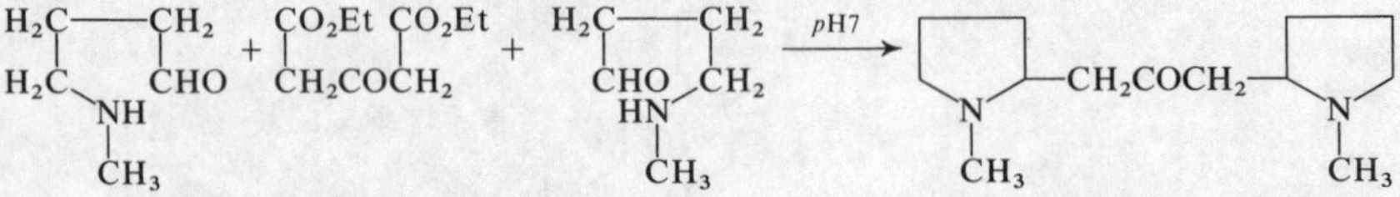

cuscohygrine

Cuscohygrine contains two identical chiral centres and so can exist as a pair of enantiomers and a *meso*-form (*cf.* tartaric acid). Natural cuscohygrine is optically inactive, and hence may be either a racemate or a *meso*-form. Failure to resolve might be taken as evidence for a *meso*-form, but this is negative evidence. In actual fact, reduction of cuscohydrine (sodium and ethanol) to the corresponding alcohol gives a mixture of two epimeric alcohols (α- and β-dihydrocuscohygrine). Therefore natural cuscohygrine has the *meso*-configuration since, had it been the racemate, only one racemic alcohol would have been produced (see 2 §7d ii).

PYRIDINE AND PIPERIDINE GROUPS

§15. Trigonelline, $C_7H_7NO_2$, m.p. 130°C

This is widely distributed in plants; the best source is the coffee bean. When boiled with barium hydroxide solution trigonelline produces methylamine; thus the molecule contains an *N*-methylamino group. On the other hand, when heated with hydrochloric acid at 250°C under pressure, trigonelline forms methyl chloride and nicotinic acid; this suggests that the alkaloid is the methyl betaine of nicotinic acid. This structure for trigonelline has been confirmed by synthesis (Hantzsch, 1886). When heated with methyl iodide in the presence of potassium hydroxide, nicotinic acid (I) is converted into methyl nicotinate methiodide (II). (II), on treatment with 'silver hydroxide' solution, forms nicotinic acid methohydroxide (III) which then spontaneously loses a molecule of water to give trigonelline (a betaine) (IV).

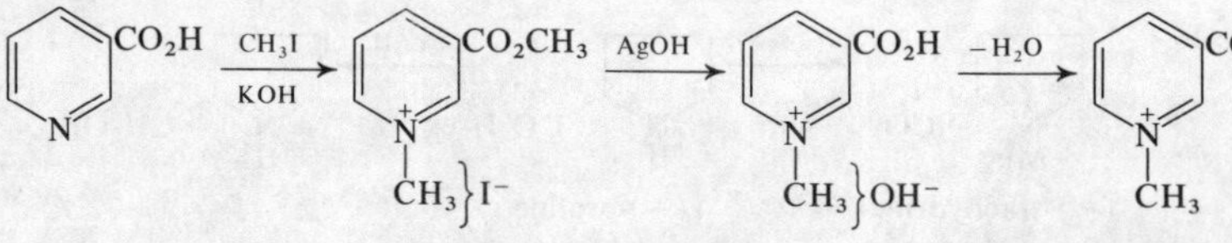

(I)   (II)   (III)   (IV)

§16. Ricinine, $C_8H_8N_2O_2$, m.p. 201·5°C

This has been isolated from castor-oil seed; it is not a very toxic alkaloid. Degradative and synthetic work led to the suggestion that (I) is the structure of ricinine.

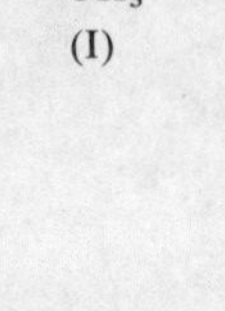

(I)

This has been confirmed by synthesis, *e.g.*, Späth *et al.* (1923):

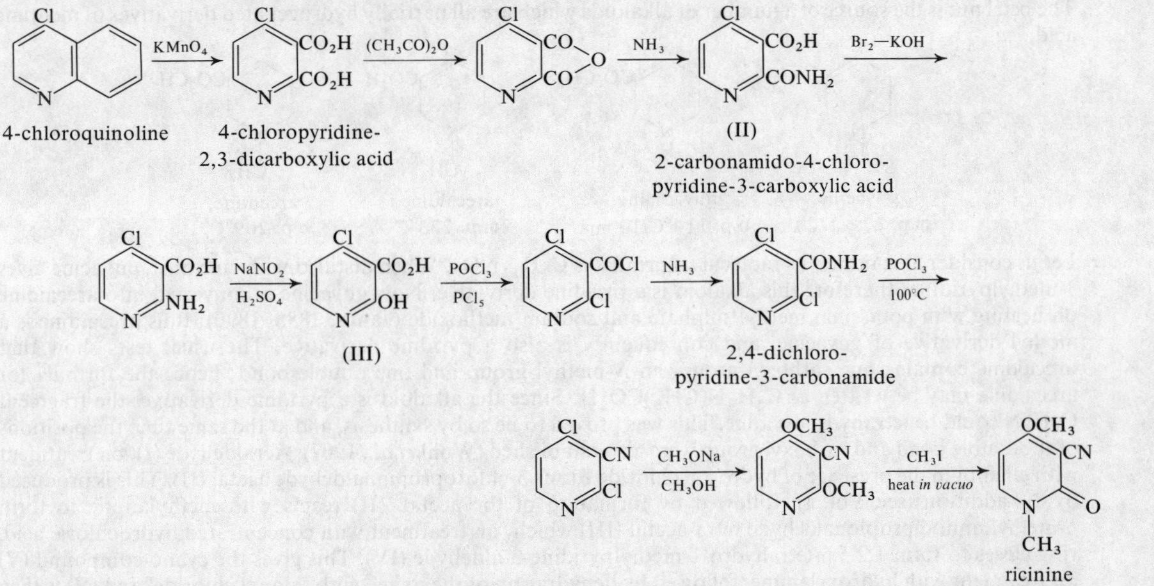

4-chloroquinoline   4-chloropyridine-
                         2,3-dicarboxylic acid

(II)

2-carbonamido-4-chloro-
pyridine-3-carboxylic acid

(III)

2,4-dichloro-
pyridine-3-carbonamide

ricinine

This is not an unambiguous synthesis, since (II) could have been 3-carbonamido-4-chloropyridine-2-carboxylic acid (II*a*) and consequently (III) would have been (III*a*).

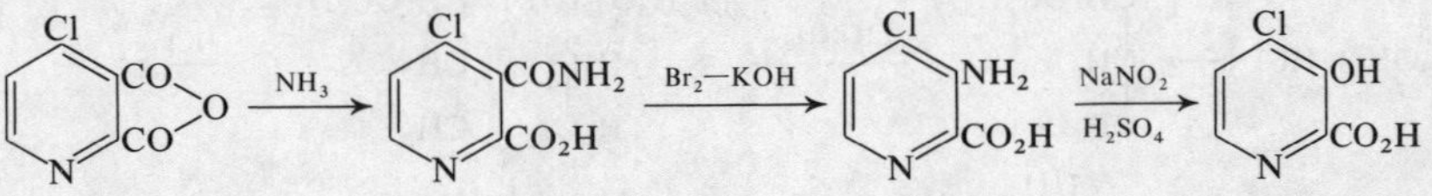

(II*a*)   (III*a*)

The structure of (III) was proved by the fact that on hydrogenation in the presence of Pd—BaSO₄, it gave 2-hydroxypyridine-3-carboxylic acid (IV).

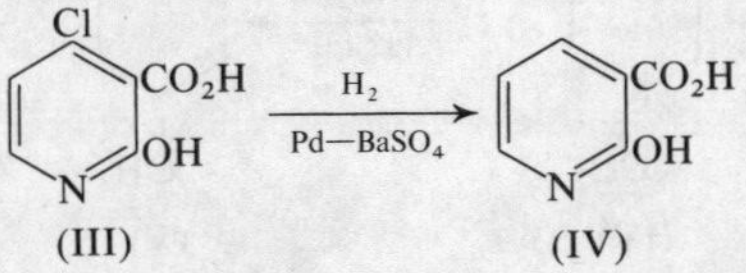

(III)   (IV)

Another synthesis of ricinine is that of Taylor *et al.* (1956). It should be noted that use has been made of the reactivity of the 4-position (towards electrophiles) in pyridine-1-oxide, and the ready displacement of the 4-nitro-group by nucleophiles (see Vol. I).

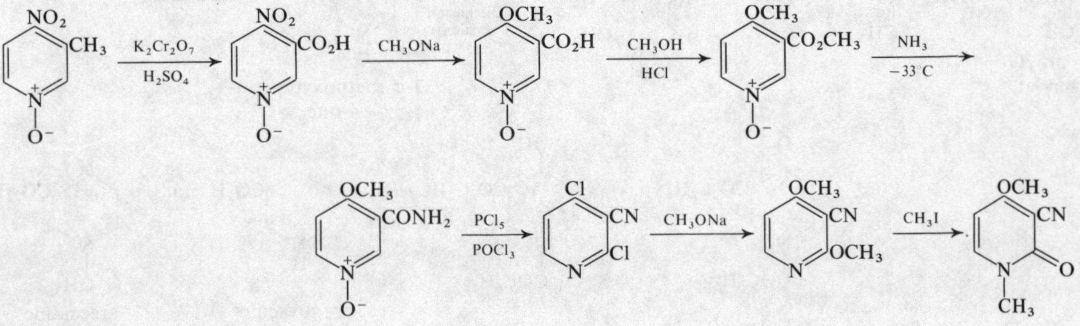

§17. Areca (or Betel) nut alkaloids

The betel nut is the source of a number of alkaloids which are all partially hydrogenated derivatives of nicotinic acid, *e.g.*,

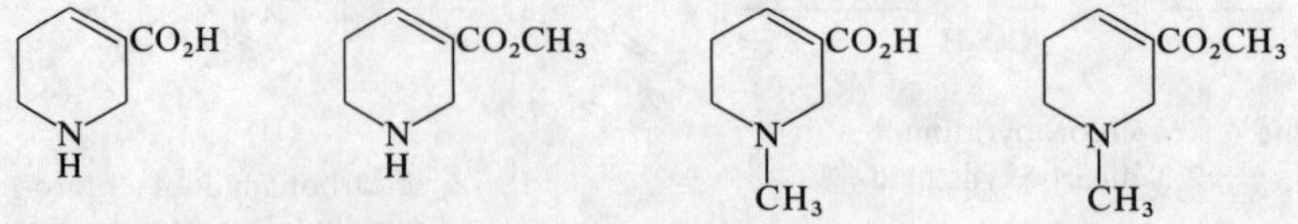

guvacine,   guvacoline,   arecaidine,   arecoline,
m.p. 271-272°C   b.p. 114°C/13 mm   m.p. 223°C   b.p. 209°C

Let us consider arecaidine; its molecular formula is $C_7H_{11}NO_2$. When distilled with zinc dust, guvacine gives 3-methylpyridine; therefore this alkaloid is a pyridine derivative. Now guvacine is converted into arecaidine on heating with potassium methyl sulphate and sodium methoxide (Jahns, 1888, 1890); thus arecaidine is a methyl derivative of guvacine, and consequently is also a pyridine derivative. The usual tests show that arecaidine contains one carboxyl group, an *N*-methyl group and one double bond; hence the formula for arecaidine may be written as $C_5H_7N(CH_3)CO_2H$. Since the alkaloid is a pyridine derivative, the fragment C_5H_7N could be tetrahydropyridine. This was proved to be so by synthesis, and at the same time the positions of the double bond and carboxyl group were also established (Wohl *et al.*, 1907). Acraldehyde (I), on treatment with ethanol in the presence of hydrogen chloride forms 3-chloropropionaldehyde acetal (II). This is produced by 1,4-addition (see Vol. I), followed by formation of the acetal. (II) reacts with methylamine to form β-methyliminodipropionaldehyde tetra-acetal (III) which, on treatment with concentrated hydrochloric acid, ring closes to form 1,2,5,6-tetrahydro-1-methylpyridine-3-aldehyde (IV). This gives the cyano compound (V) on treatment with hydroxylamine, followed by dehydration of the oxime with thionyl chloride, and (V) is then converted into arecaidine by hydrolysis. Arecaidine is (VI) or possibly (VI*a*), the dipolar ion structure (*cf.* amino-acids and betaines).

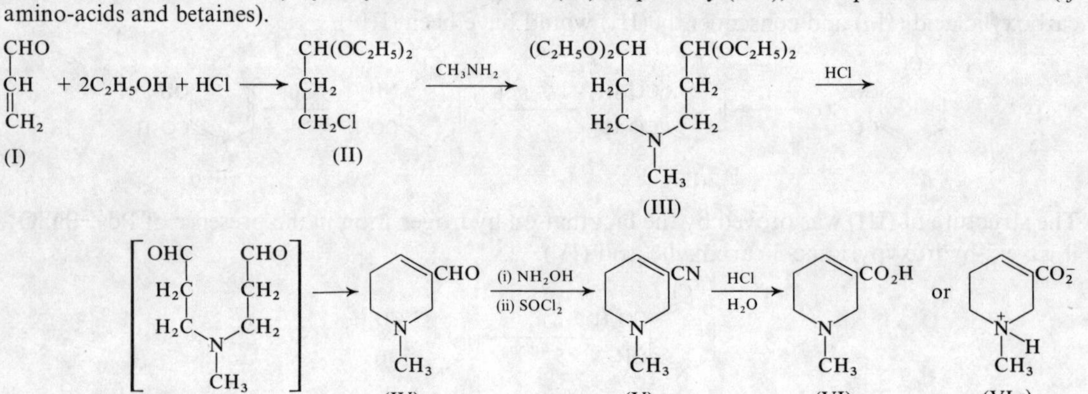

Another synthesis of arecaidine (and guvacine) is that of McElvain *et al.* (1946).

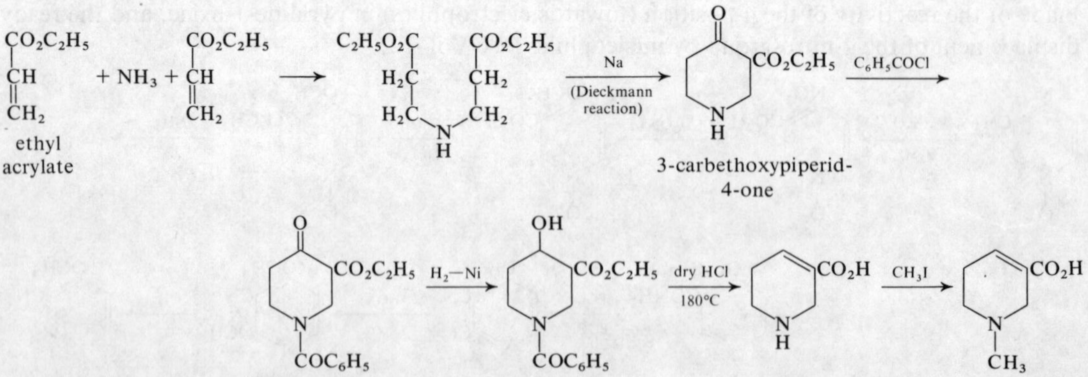

ethyl
acrylate

3-carbethoxypiperid-
4-one

guvacine   arecaidine

§18. Hemlock alkaloids

The most important alkaloid of this group is **coniine**; it was the first alkaloid to be synthesised. Oil of hemlock was drunk by Socrates when he was condemned to death in 399 B.C.

(+)-**Coniine**, $C_8H_{17}N$, b.p. 166–167°C, $[\alpha]_D$ +15·7°, is the form that occurs in oil of hemlock. When distilled with zinc dust, coniine is converted into conyrine, $C_8H_{11}N$ (Hofmann, 1884). Since the oxidation of conyrine with permanganate gives pyridine-2-carboxylic acid (α-picolinic acid), it follows that a pyridine nucleus is present with a side-chain in the 2-position. Thus coniine is probably a piperidine derivative with a side-chain in the 2-position. This side-chain must contain three carbon atoms, since two are lost when conyrine is oxidised. This side-chain is therefore either n-propyl

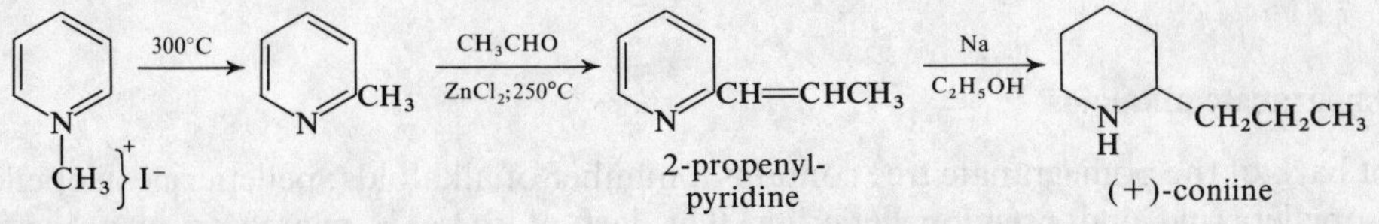

2-propenyl-
pyridine

(+)-coniine

or isopropyl, and it was actually shown to be n-propyl by the fact that when heated with hydriodic acid at 300°C under pressure, coniine forms n-octane. Had the side-chain been isopropyl, then the expected product would be iso-octane. From this evidence it therefore follows that coniine is 2-n-propylpiperidine, and this has been confirmed by synthesis (Ladenburg, 1886). The racemic coniine was resolved by means of (+)-tartaric acid, and the (+)-coniine so obtained was found to be identical with the natural compound.

The reactions of coniine described above can therefore be formulated as follows:

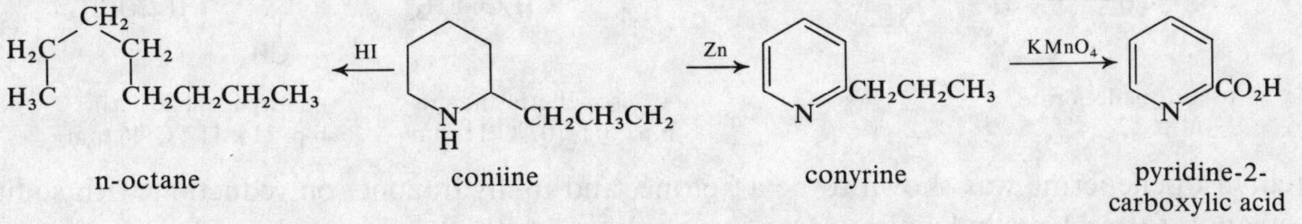

n-octane   coniine   conyrine   pyridine-2-
                                                                            carboxylic acid

Coniine has also been synthesised from 2-methylpyridine and phenyllithium as follows (Bergmann *et al*., 1932):

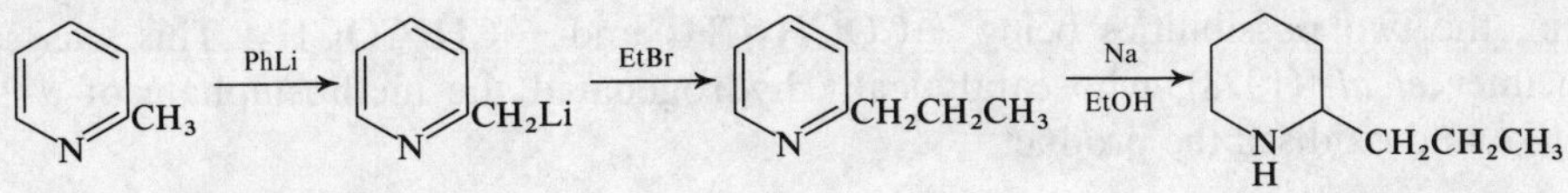

Other hemlock alkaloids are:

conhydrine   γ-coniceine
m.p. 121°C, $[\alpha]_D$ +10°   b.p. 171°C/746 mm

Conhydrine forms coniine when heated with hydriodic acid and red phosphorus (Hofmann, 1885; Lellmann, 1890), and gives piperidine-2-carboxylic acid when oxidised with chromic acid (Willstätter, 1901). Thus, in conhydrine, it is the side-chain that contains the hydroxyl group. The γ-position (in the side-chain) is excluded because piperidine-2-propionic acid would be the expected oxidation product. Willstätter suggested that the hydroxyl group was in the β-position, but Löffler *et al*. (1909) synthesised this, and since the compound did not resemble conhydrine, the α-hydroxy structure was proposed (as shown). This has been supported by other work, and Galinovsky *et al.* (1948) have synthesised conhydrine, showing that it has the α-hydroxy structure. The configuration of the chiral centre in the ring of (+)-conhydrine has been shown to be L (King *et al.*, 1950).

γ-Coniceine, on hydrogenation, gives (±)-coniine, and on dehydrogenation produces 2-n-propylpyridine. Its apparent behaviour as a secondary base, and some of its reactions led Lellmann *et al.* (1890) to propose that the double bond was in the 2,3-position. Beyerman *et al.* (1961), however, have concluded from spectroscopic studies that the double bond is in the 1,2-position. The infrared spectrum of γ-coniceine showed a band at $1\,663$ cm^{-1} (attributed to C=N; $\sim 1\,670$ cm^{-1} (s): RCH=NR), whereas the *synthetic* 2,3-compound (with the *N*-methyl group) showed a band at $1\,645$ cm^{-1} (C=C; $1\,655$–$1\,640$ cm^{-1} (w): unconjugated).

§19. Pomegranate alkaloids

The root bark of the pomegranate tree contains a number of alkaloids: pelletierine, isopelletierine, methylisopelletierine and pseudopelletierine. The last of these is related to atropine, and its structure was elucidated in a similar manner in that oxidation, then exhaustive methylation (twice), and finally catalytic reduction give suberic acid, $(CH_2)_6(CO_2H)_2$ (*cf.* §22). Pseudopelletierine has been synthesised by Schöpf *et al.* (1935), who used the Robinson method (see §22) with glutardialdehyde instead of succindialdehyde.

pseudopelletierine
m.p. 53–54 °C

isopelletierine
b.p. 102–107°C/11 mm

methylisopelletierine
b.p. 114–117°C/26 mm

Methylisopelletierine was shown to be a ketone, and its hydrazone, on reduction with sodium and ethanol, forms 1-methylconiine. Also, on oxidation with chromic acid, methylisopelletierine gives 1-methylpiperidine-2-carboxylic acid. Thus the structure of this alkaloid is 1-methylpiperidine with a side-chain at position 2. The problem that remains is the position of the keto group in the side-chain, the two possibilities being —COCH₂CH₃ and —CH₂COCH₃. This was solved by Meisenheimer *et al.* (1928), who catalytically hydrogenated the methosulphate of α-2-pyridyl-propan-β-ol and oxidised the product.

On the other hand, treatment of the base itself gave isopelletierine, which may be methylated to methylisopelletierine. Wibaut *et al.* (1944) have also synthesised isopelletierine as follows:

Pelletierine is very interesting from the point of view of the history of the elucidation of its structure. The molecular formula of this alkaloid is $C_8H_{15}NO$; this is the same as that for isopelletierine. Tanret (1878–1880) isolated both of these compounds (as well as pseudopelletierine and methyl-isopelletierine) and pointed out that pelletierine was optically active and that isopelletierine was not. Hess *et al.* (1917) were unable to isolate an optically active base from pomegranate bark, and renamed isopelletierine as pelletierine, but in 1919 Hess *did* isolate isopelletierine. Hess *et al.* (1909) established that pelletierine had structure (I) on the basis of the following evidence. The alkaloid behaves as a secondary amine and contains an aldehyde group because it forms an oxime which, on dehydration with phosphorus pentachloride, forms a cyanide which, on hydrolysis, produces an

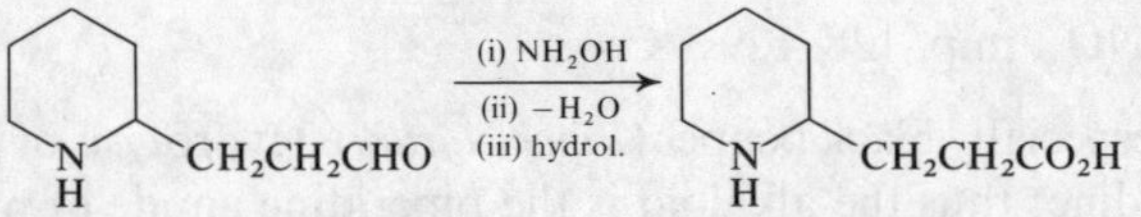

$$\text{(I)} \quad \xrightarrow[\text{(iii) hydrol.}]{\substack{\text{(i) NH}_2\text{OH} \\ \text{(ii) } -\text{H}_2\text{O}}} \quad$$

acid the ethyl ester of which, according to the authors, was identical with ethyl piperidine-2-propionate, a compound prepared by Löffler *et al.* (1909). Hess also attempted to oxidise the alkaloid directly to the acid, but failed to obtain the acid.

A number of syntheses of pelletierine have been attempted, but all failed. Spielman *et al.* (1941) prepared 'pelletierine acetal' as follows:

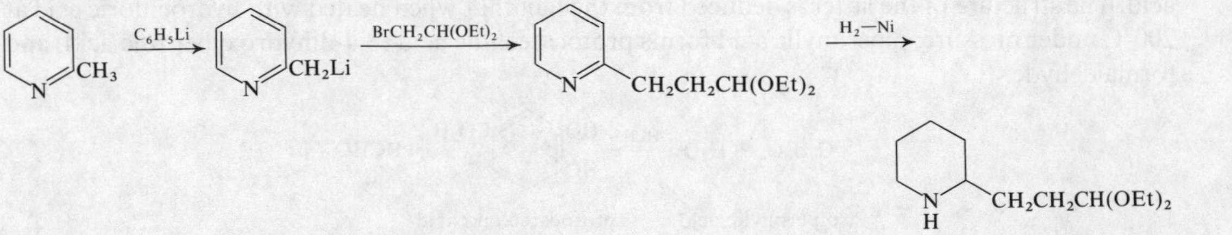

The authors failed to hydrolyse this compound to the aldehyde. Wibaut *et al.* (1940) also prepared the acetal and failed to obtain the free aldehyde. Beets (1943) therefore suggested that pelletierine probably exists as some bicyclic structure such as (II).

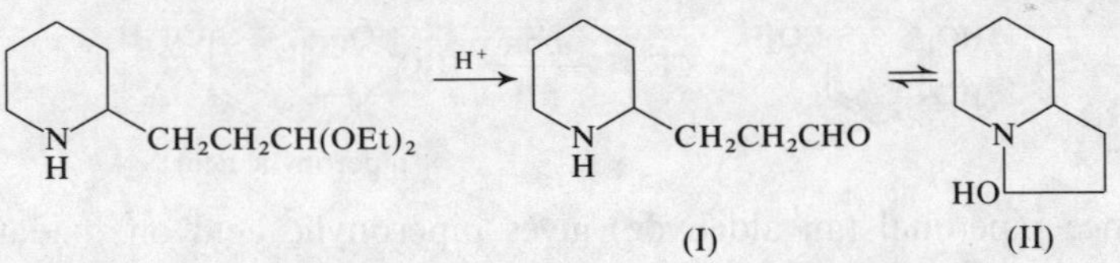

Galinovsky *et al.* (1952) finally obtained the free aldehyde and found that the compound did not behave like 'pelletierine'. It was also observed that the physical constants of Hess's pelletierine and its derivatives were very similar to those described for isopelletierine. The authors therefore compared the m.p.s. of 1-benzoylpelletierine (from 'natural' pelletierine) and 1-benzoylisopelletierine (synthetic), and found that the two compounds were identical. Thus 'pelletierine' and isopelletierine appear to be identical, and this was confirmed by Galinovsky *et al.* (1954) who, using partition chromatography, isolated isopelletierine (characterised as its picrate). However, Wibaut *et al.* (1954) have isolated from pomegranate bark extracts, by means of paper chromatography, an alkaloid of unknown constitution. Wibaut *et al.* (1955) showed that this compound was not identical with isopelletierine, and attempts to synthesise 'pelletierine' again failed. These authors also showed that natural 'pelletierine' was identical with isopelletierine. Finally, Beyerman *et al.* (1965) showed that 'pelletierine' is the $(-)$-form of isopelletierine. The latter undergoes ready racemisation *via* the open-chain form (*cf.* hygrine, §13).

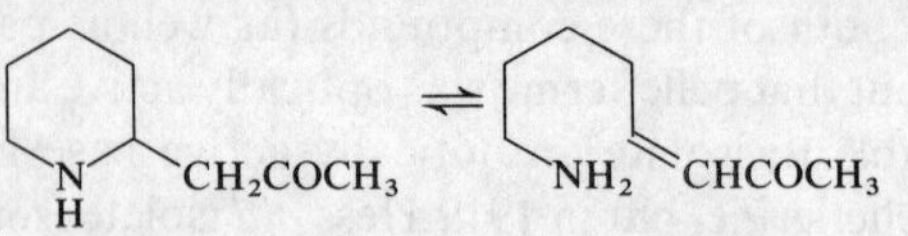

The absolute configuration of $(-)$-pelletierine picrate (stable compound) has been shown to be D; this is the opposite of the amino-acids (**13** §4).

§20. Piperine, $C_{17}H_{19}NO_3$, m.p. 128–129·5°C

This occurs in pepper, especially black pepper (*Piper nigrum*). Hydrolysis of piperine with alkali gives piperic acid and piperidine; thus the alkaloid is the piperidine amide of piperic acid (Babo *et al.*,

$$C_{17}H_{19}NO_3 + H_2O \xrightarrow{\text{KOH}} C_{12}H_{10}O_4 + C_5H_{11}N$$
$$\text{piperic acid} \quad \text{piperidine}$$

1857). Since piperidine is hexahydropyridine, the structure of piperine rests on the elucidation of that of piperic acid. The routine tests show that piperic acid contains one carboxyl group and two double bonds. When oxidised with permanganate, piperic acid gives first piperonal and then piperonylic acid. The structure of the latter is deduced from the fact that when heated with hydrochloric acid at 200°C under pressure, piperonylic acid forms protocatechuic acid (3,4-dihydroxybenzoic acid) and formaldehyde.

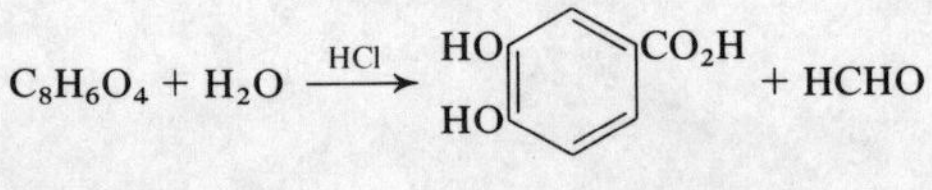

$$C_8H_6O_4 + H_2O \xrightarrow{\text{HCl}}$$

piperonylic acid   protocatechuic acid

Since one atom of carbon is eliminated, and there are no free hydroxyl groups in piperonylic acid, the structure of this acid is probably the methylene ether of protocatechuic acid, *i.e.*, piperonylic acid is 3,4-methylenedioxybenzoic acid; this has been confirmed by synthesis:

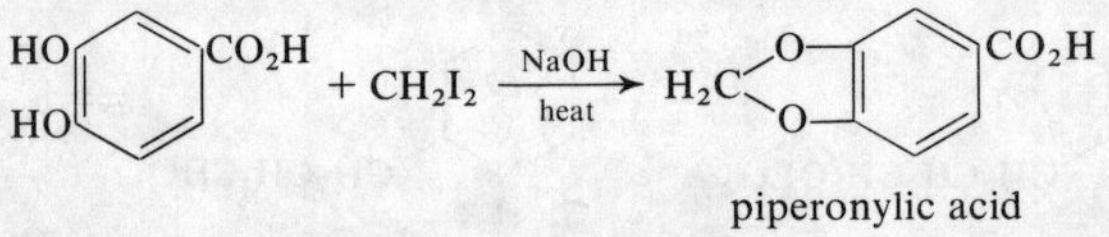

piperonylic acid

Furthermore, since piperonal (an aldehyde) gives piperonylic acid on oxidation, piperonal is therefore 3,4-methylenedioxybenzaldehyde.

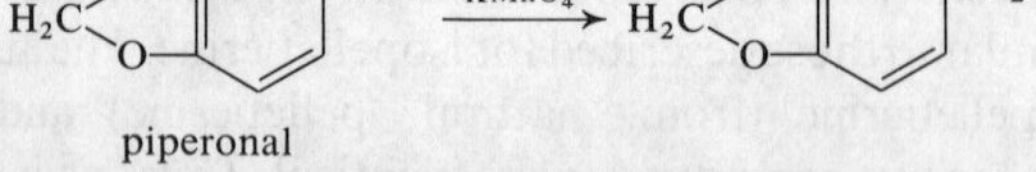

piperonal

From these results of oxidative degradation, it therefore follows that piperic acid is a benzene derivative containing only one side-chain. It is this side-chain that contains the two double bonds (the ready addition of four bromine atoms shows the presence of two *ethylenic* bonds), and since the careful oxidation of piperic acid gives tartaric acid in addition to piperonal and piperonylic acid, the side-chain is a 'straight' chain. If we assume (I) as the structure of piperic acid, then all of the foregoing products of oxidation may be accounted for.

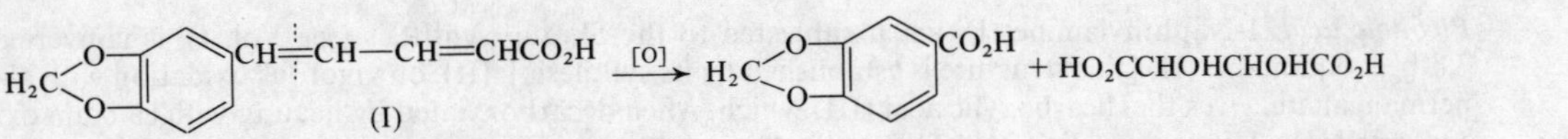

(I)

This has been confirmed by synthesis (Ladenburg *et al.*, 1894); piperonal (prepared *via* the Reimer–Tiemann reaction) is condensed with acetaldehyde in the presence of sodium hydroxide (Claisen–Schmidt reaction), and the product (a cinnamaldehyde derivative) is then heated with acetic anhydride in the presence of sodium acetate (Perkin reaction).

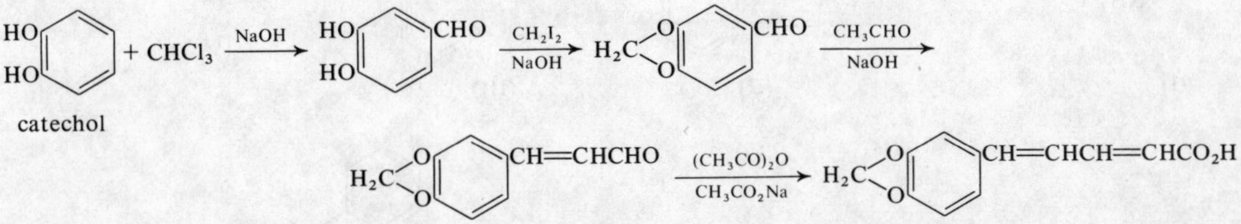

catechol

When the acid chloride of piperic acid (prepared by the action of phosphorus pentachloride on the acid) is heated with piperidine in benzene solution, piperine is formed; thus piperine is the piperidine amide of piperic acid.

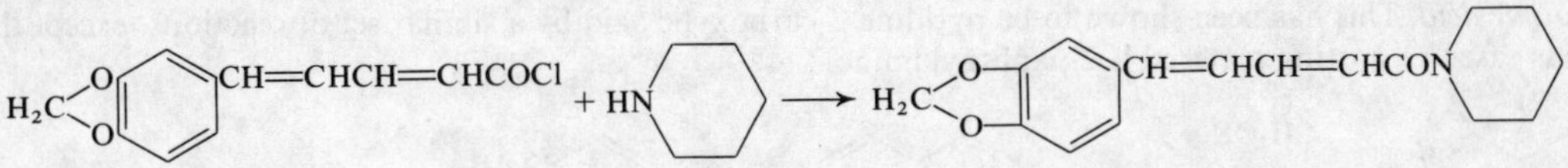

piperine

The stereochemistry of piperine has been shown to be *trans,trans* about the double bonds (see also 2 §4). The *cis,cis* stereoisomer is **chavicine** (it gives chavicinic acid on hydrolysis); it also occurs in pepper.

PYRROLIDINE–PYRIDINE GROUP

§21. Tobacco alkaloids

Many alkaloids have been isolated from the tobacco leaf, *e.g.*, nicotine, nicotimine (anabasine), nornicotine, etc.

Nicotine, $C_{10}H_{14}N_2$, b.p. 247°C, is the best known and most widely distributed of the tobacco alkaloids; it occurs naturally as the (−)-form, $[\alpha]_D$ −169°. When oxidised with dichromate–sulphuric acid (or permanganate or nitric acid), nicotine forms nicotinic acid (Huber, 1867).

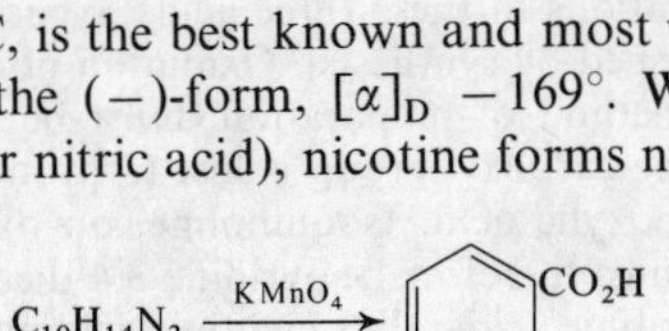

nicotine   nicotinic acid

It is instructive, at this point, to see how the orientations of the three isomeric pyridinecarboxylic acids have been elucidated.

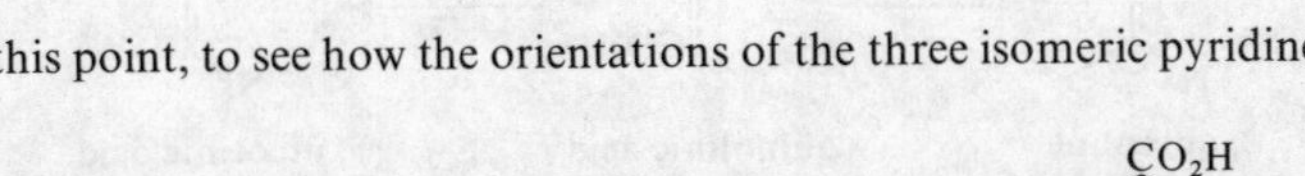

picolinic acid,   nicotinic acid,   isonicotinic acid,
m.p. 137°C   m.p. 234–237°C   m.p. 317°C

Picolinic acid. 1-Naphthylamine (I), when subjected to the Skraup synthesis (see Vol. I), is converted into 7,8-benzoquinoline (II) [this structure is established by its synthesis]. (II), on vigorous oxidation with alkaline permanganate, gives the dicarboxylic acid (III) which, when decarboxylated by heating with calcium oxide, is converted into 2-phenylpyridine (IV). This, on further oxidation with permanganate, gives a pyridinecarboxylic acid which must, from the structure of (IV), be the 2-acid, *i.e.*, picolinic acid (V).

Nicotinic acid. This has been shown to be pyridine-3-carboxylic acid by a similar set of reactions, except that in this case the starting material is 2-naphthylamine.

nicotinic acid

Isonicotinic acid. This third isomer is therefore pyridine-4-carboxylic acid.

An alternative proof for the orientations of these three acids is based on the structures of quinoline and isoquinoline (which have been established by synthesis). Oxidation of quinoline with alkaline permanganate gives quinolinic acid which, by its method of preparation, must be pyridine-2,3-dicarboxylic acid. When quinolinic acid is heated to 190°C, one carboxyl group is lost to produce nicotinic acid; thus nicotinic acid must be either pyridine-2- or -3-carboxylic acid. Isoquinoline, on oxidation with alkaline permanganate, produces cinchomeronic acid, which must therefore be pyridine-3,4-dicarboxylic acid. This, on gentle heating, gives a mixture of nicotinic and isonicotinic acids; thus nicotinic acid must be the 3-acid, and isonicotinic acid the 4-acid. Hence picolinic acid is pyridine-2-carboxylic acid.

quinoline   quinolinic acid   nicotinic acid

isoquinoline   cinchomeronic acid   isonicotinic acid

Returning to the structure of nicotine, since nicotinic acid is a product of oxidation, the alkaloid therefore contains a pyridine nucleus with a complex side-chain in the 3-position. Thus we may write the formula of nicotine as (VI). Because of its formula, this side-chain was originally believed to be piperidine, but further work showed that this was incorrect. When nicotine zincichloride is distilled, the products are pyridine, pyrrole and methylamine (Laiblin, 1879). This suggests that the side-chain $C_5H_{10}N$ is a pyrrole derivative. Furthermore, when nicotine is heated with concentrated hydriodic acid at 150°C (Herzig–Meyer method), methyl iodide is formed. Thus the side-chain contains an *N*-methyl group. It therefore appears that the side-chain could be *N*-methylpyrrolidine, but its point of attachment to the pyridine nucleus could be either 2 or 3 on the evidence obtained so far:

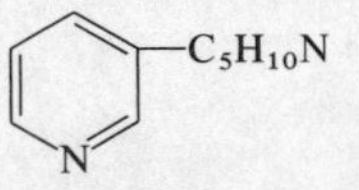

(VI)

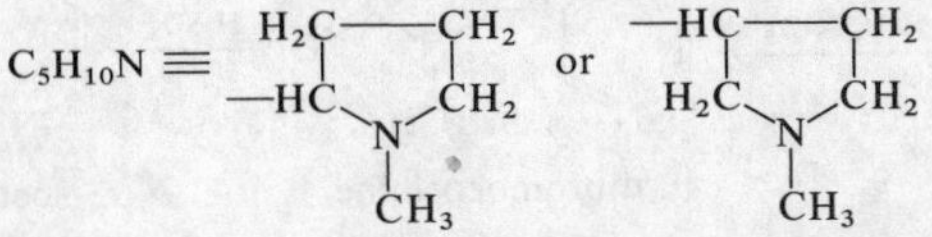

The correct structure of nicotine was obtained by Pinner (1892, 1893). Treatment of nicotine with bromine in acetic acid gives, among other products, the hydrobromide perbromide, $C_{10}H_{10}Br_2N_2O \cdot HBr \cdot Br_2$, which, when treated with aqueous sulphurous acid, is converted into dibromocotinine, $C_{10}H_{10}Br_2N_2O$. This, on heating with a mixture of sulphurous and sulphuric acids at 130–140°C, forms 3-acetylpyridine, oxalic acid and methylamine. Thus the structure of nicotine must account for the following skeleton structures:

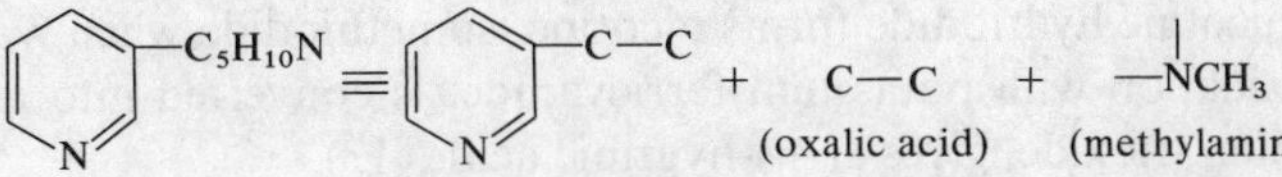

(oxalic acid) (methylamine)

(3-acetylpyridine)

Now bromine, in the presence of hydrobromic acid, converts nicotine into dibromoticonine, $C_{10}H_8Br_2N_2O_2$, which, on heating with barium hydroxide solution at 100°C, forms nicotinic acid, malonic acid and methylamine. Hence the structure of nicotine must also account for the following skeleton structures:

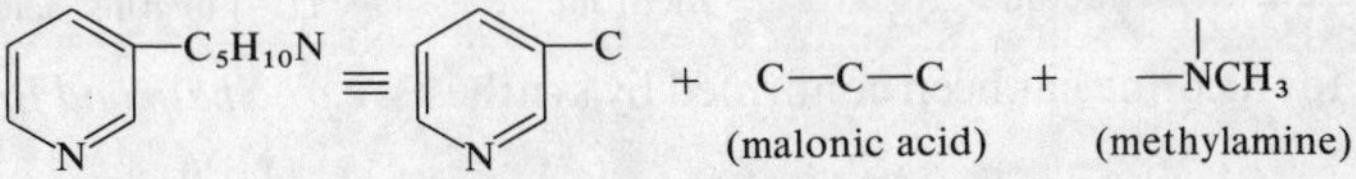

(malonic acid) (methylamine)

(nicotinic acid)

These two sets of reactions, taken in conjunction with one another, are satisfied by the following skeleton for nicotine:

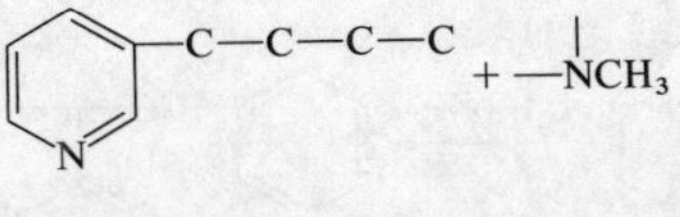

The problem now is: Where is the position of the *N*-methyl group? Nicotine behaves as a *di-tertiary base*, and forms two isomeric 'methyl iodide addition products'. Thus the nitrogen atom in the side-chain must be of the type —C—N(CH_3)—C—. Furthermore, it is extremely difficult to reduce nicotine beyond hexahydronicotine (the pyridine part is reduced to piperidine). Hence the side-chain must be saturated, and this can only be so if it is cyclic, *i.e.*, *N*-methylpyrrolidine ($C_5H_{11}N$: D.B.E. $= 5 + 1 - (11 - 1)/2 = 1$. Hence one ring is present since the side-chain is saturated). The presence of this pyrrolidine nucleus also accounts for the formation of pyrrole when nicotine zincichloride is distilled (see above). All the foregoing facts are satisfied by the following structure for nicotine.

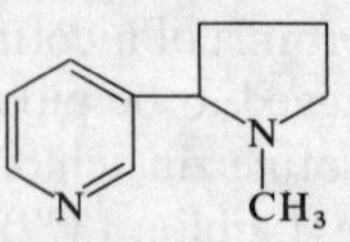

nicotine

Pinner's dibromo structures have now been revised as shown (Quin *et al.*, 1973).

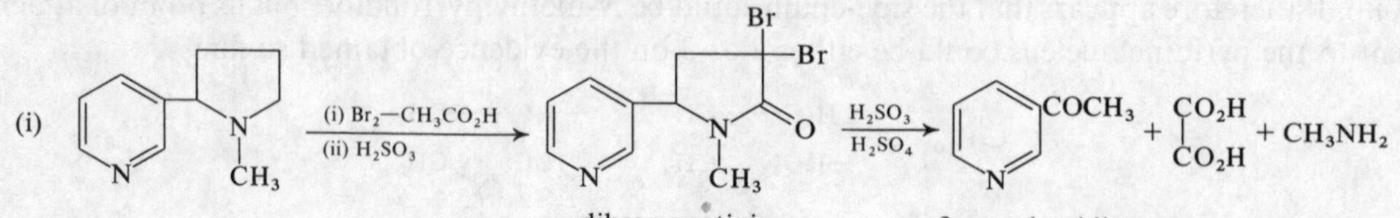

(i)

(i) Br$_2$—CH$_3$CO$_2$H
(ii) H$_2$SO$_3$

dibromocotinine

H$_2$SO$_3$
H$_2$SO$_4$

+ 3-acetylpyridine + $\begin{matrix}CO_2H\\CO_2H\end{matrix}$ + CH$_3$NH$_2$

3-acetylpyridine

(ii)

Br$_2$
HBr

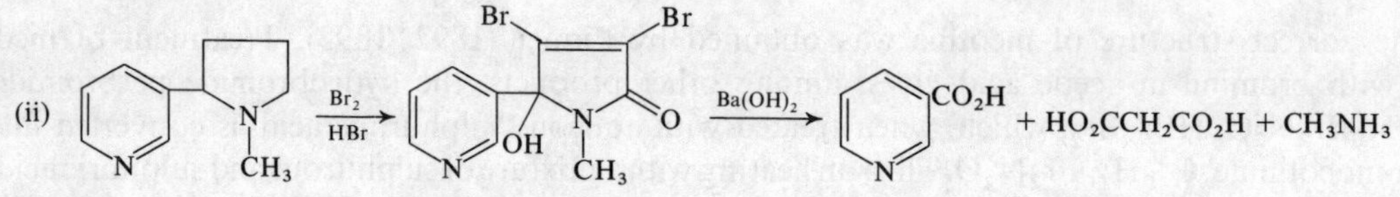

dibromoticonine

Ba(OH)$_2$

+ HO$_2$CCH$_2$CO$_2$H + CH$_3$NH$_3$

The most direct analytical evidence for the presence of the pyrrolidine nucleus has been given by Karrer (1925, 1926); nicotine hydriodide forms nicotine isomethiodide when warmed with methyl iodide and this, on oxidation with potassium ferricyanide, is converted into nicotone which, on oxidation with chromium trioxide, gives L(−)-hygrinic acid (§13).

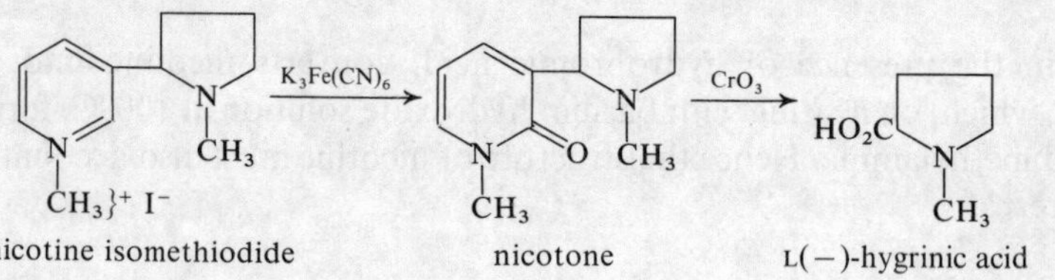

K$_3$Fe(CN)$_6$ CrO$_3$

nicotine isomethiodide   nicotone   L(−)-hygrinic acid

Pinners formula for nicotine has been confirmed by synthesis, *e.g.*, *Späth and Bretschneider* (1928).

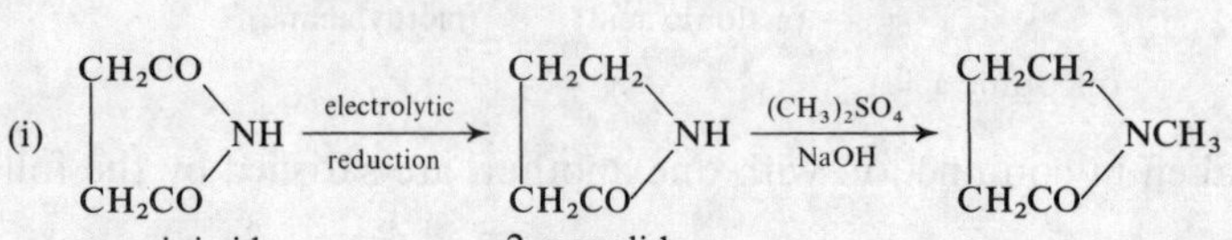

(i)

$\begin{matrix}CH_2CO\\CH_2CO\end{matrix}$ NH

electrolytic reduction

$\begin{matrix}CH_2CH_2\\CH_2CO\end{matrix}$ NH

(CH$_3$)$_2$SO$_4$
NaOH

$\begin{matrix}CH_2CH_2\\CH_2CO\end{matrix}$ NCH$_3$

succinimide   2-pyrrolidone

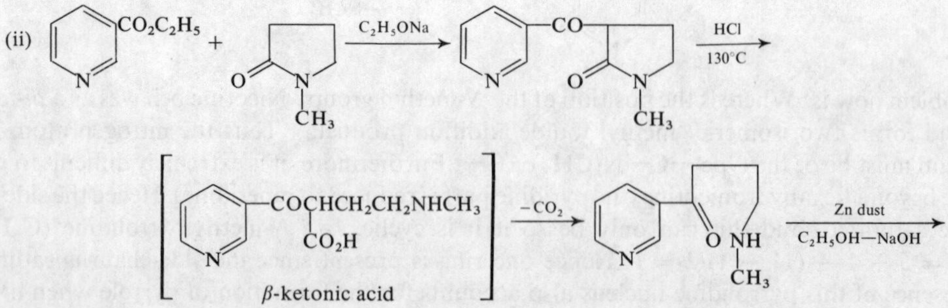

(ii)

CO$_2$C$_2$H$_5$ +

C$_2$H$_5$ONa

HCl
130°C

—COCHCH$_2$CH$_2$NHCH$_3$
          CO$_2$H

β-ketonic acid

−CO$_2$

Zn dust
C$_2$H$_5$OH—NaOH

This was resolved by means of (+)-tartaric acid; the synthetic (−)-nicotine is identical with the natural compound.
Craig (1933).

Späth *et al.* (1936) have resolved (±)-nornicotine; methylation of the (−)-form with formaldehyde and formic acid gave (−)-nicotine, identical with the natural product.

§22. Solanaceous alkaloids

This group includes atropine, hyoscyamine and scopolamine (hyoscine).

Atropine, $C_{17}H_{23}NO_3$, m.p. 118°C, occurs in deadly nightshade (*Atropa belladonna*) together with hyoscyamine. Hyoscyamine is optically active $[\alpha]_D$ −22°, but readily racemises to atropine when warmed in an ethanolic alkaline solution; thus atropine is (±)-hyoscyamine.

When warmed with barium hydroxide solution, atropine is hydrolysed to (±)-tropic acid and tropine (an alcohol); thus atropine is the tropine ester of tropic acid. When (−)-hyoscyamine is hydrolysed with cold water, tropine and (−)-tropic acid are obtained.

(±)-Tropic acid, $C_9H_{10}O_3$, m.p. 117°C, $[\alpha]_D$ ±81·5°, is a saturated compound (it does not add on bromine); the usual tests show that it contains one carboxyl group and one alcoholic group. When heated strongly, tropic acid loses a molecule of water to form atropic acid, $C_9H_8O_2$, and this, on

$$C_6H_5CH=CHCO_2H$$
(I)

(II)

oxidation, gives benzoic acid. Thus tropic and atropic acids contain a benzene ring with one side-chain. It therefore follows that atropic acid could be either (I) or (II). Since, however, (I) is known to be cinnamic acid, (II) must be atropic acid. This is supported by the fact that oxidation of atropic acid with permanganate gives phenylglyoxylic acid ($PhCOCO_2H$). Addition of a molecule of water to (II) would therefore give tropic acid which, consequently, must be either (III) or (IV).

$$
\begin{array}{cc}
\overset{\displaystyle OH}{\underset{\displaystyle CH_3}{C_6H_5-C-CO_2H}} & \overset{\displaystyle H}{\underset{\displaystyle CH_2OH}{C_6H_5-C-CO_2H}} \\
(III) & (IV)
\end{array}
$$

Tropic acid has been shown to be (IV) by synthesis, *e.g.*, Mackenzie and Wood (1919), starting from acetophenone.

(III) is atrolactic acid, and its dehydration to (II) confirms the structure of atropic acid. It should also be noted that the addition of hydrogen chloride takes place contrary to Markownikoff's rule (see unsaturated acids, Vol. I); had the addition been in accordance with the rule, then atrolactic acid would have again been obtained. It is tropic acid that contains the chiral centre which gives rise to the optically active hyoscyamine. The above synthesis results in ($\pm$)-tropic acid, and this has been resolved by means of quinine.

Blicke *et al.* (1952) have synthesised tropic acid by boiling phenylacetic acid with isopropyl-magnesium chloride in ethereal solution, and then treating the product, a Grignard reagent, with formaldehyde.

Fodor *et al.* (1961) have established the absolute configuration of ($-$)-tropic acid by its correlation with ($-$)-alanine. According to the Cahn–Ingold–Prelog convention (**2** §5d), natural tropic acid is (S)-($-$)-tropic acid.

$$
\begin{array}{c}
Ph \\
| \\
H-\!\!\!-CO_2H \\
| \\
CH_2OH
\end{array}
$$

Tropine (tropanol), $C_6H_{15}NO$, m.p. 63°C, behaves as a saturated compound which contains an alcoholic group. The structure of tropine was investigated by Ladenburg (1883, 1887), who showed that the molecule contained a reduced pyridine nucleus:

Tropine iodide is formed by the replacement of the alcoholic group in tropine by an iodine atom, which is then replaced by hydrogen to form dihydrotropidine (tropane). The formation of methyl chloride indicates the presence of an N-methyl group, and the isolation of 2-ethylpyridine shows the presence of this nucleus (in a reduced form). Largely on this evidence, Ladenburg was led to suggest the following alternative formulae for tropine:

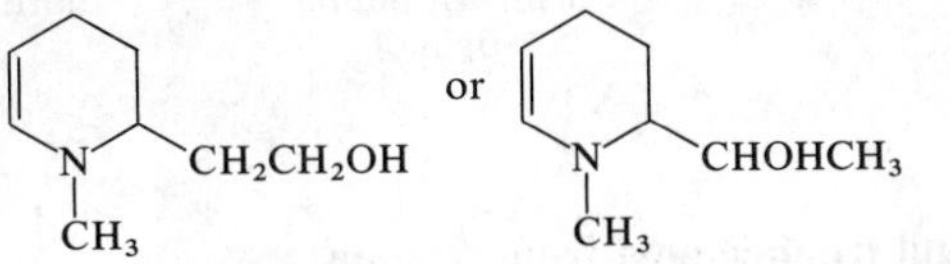

$$\text{(ring)}\quad N(CH_3)\text{—}CH_2CH_2OH \qquad \text{or} \qquad \text{(ring)}\quad N(CH_3)\text{—}CHOHCH_3$$

Merling (1891), by the oxidation of tropine with chromium trioxide, obtained ($\pm$)-tropinic acid.

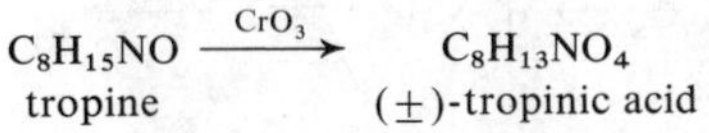

$$\underset{\text{tropine}}{C_8H_{15}NO} \xrightarrow{\text{CrO}_3} \underset{(\pm)\text{-tropinic acid}}{C_8H_{13}NO_4}$$

Tropinic acid is a dicarboxylic acid, and since there is no loss of carbon in its formation, the hydroxyl group in tropine must therefore be in a ring system. Thus Ladenburg's formula is untenable, and so Merling proposed the following structures for tropine:

$$\begin{array}{c} CH \\ H_2C \quad CHOH \quad CH_2 \\ CH_3N \quad CH_2 \quad CH_2 \\ CH \end{array} \quad \text{or} \quad \begin{array}{c} CH \\ H_2C \quad CH_2 \quad CH_2 \\ CH_3N \quad CHOH \quad CH_2 \\ CH \end{array}$$

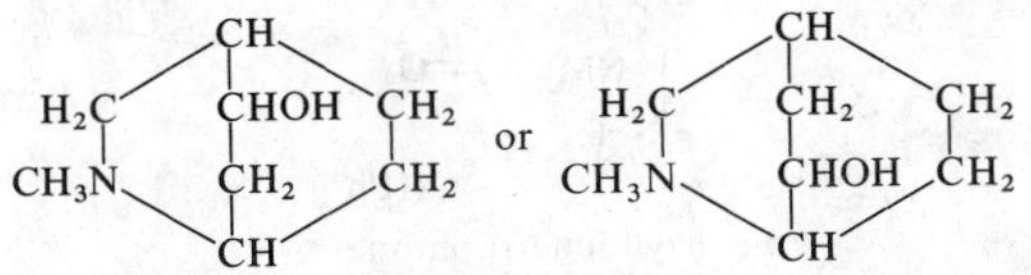

Willstätter (1895–1901) then examined the oxidation products of tropine obtained as follows:

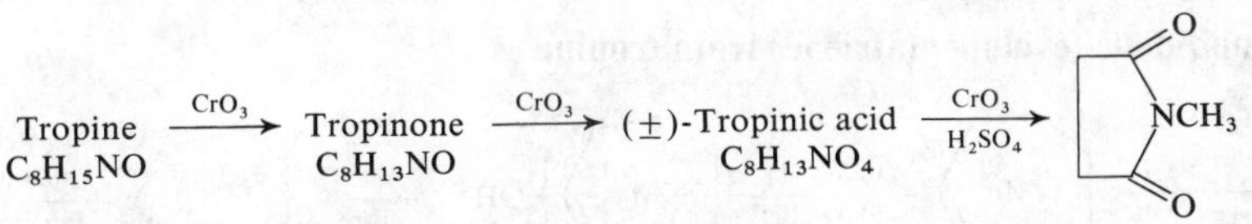

$$\underset{C_8H_{15}NO}{\text{Tropine}} \xrightarrow{\text{CrO}_3} \underset{C_8H_{13}NO}{\text{Tropinone}} \xrightarrow{\text{CrO}_3} \underset{C_8H_{13}NO_4}{(\pm)\text{-Tropinic acid}} \xrightarrow[\text{H}_2\text{SO}_4]{\text{CrO}_3} \text{(N-methylsuccinimide)}$$

Tropinone behaved as a ketone; thus tropine is a secondary alcohol (cf. Merling's formula). Willstätter (1897) also showed that tropinone forms a dibenzylidene derivative with benzaldehyde, and a di-oximino derivative when treated with amyl nitrite and hydrochloric acid. Thus tropinone contains the CH_2COCH_2 grouping, and so it follows that Merling's formula is also untenable. Willstätter therefore proposed three possible structures for tropine, but eliminated two by the consideration of various reactions of tropine, and was left with the following (which contains a pyridine and a pyrrole nucleus with the nitrogen atom common to both):

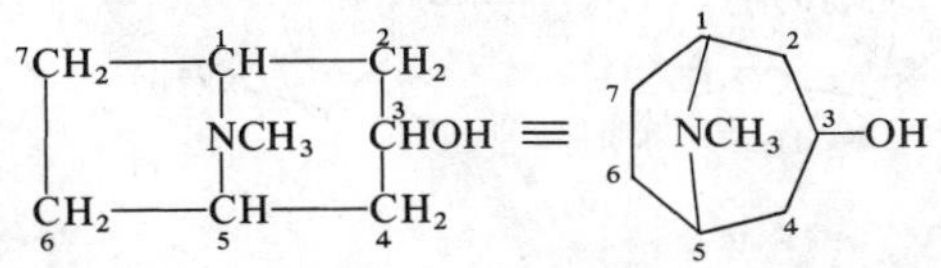

$$\begin{array}{ccc} {}^{7}CH_2 & {}^{1}CH & {}^{2}CH_2 \\ & NCH_3 \quad {}^{3}CHOH \\ CH_2 & CH & CH_2 \\ {}_{6} & {}_{5} & {}_{4} \end{array} \equiv \quad \text{(bicyclic: }NCH_3\text{, }{}^{3}\text{—OH, positions }1,2,4,5,6,7\text{)}$$

Not only did this fit the facts best, but it was also supported by the following evidence: (i) Exhaustive methylation of tropine gives tropilidene (cycloheptatriene), C_7H_8. (ii) Exhaustive methylation of tropinic acid gives an unsaturated dicarboxylic acid which, on reduction, forms pimelic acid. (iii) Tropinone, on oxidation with CrO_3—H_2SO_4, gives N-methylsuccinimide. This indicates the presence of a pyrrolidine ring in tropinone.

All the foregoing reactions of tropine can be readily explained on the Willstätter formula.

Formation of 2-ethylpyridine from tropine

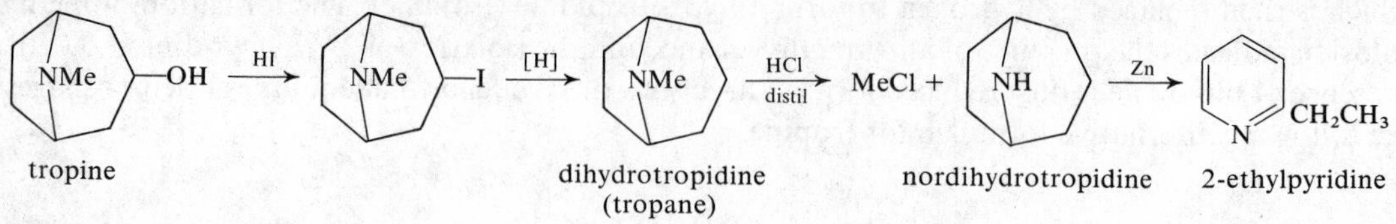

tropine   dihydrotropidine   nordihydrotropidine   2-ethylpyridine
                                                   (tropane)

Formation of tropinone and tropinic acid from tropine

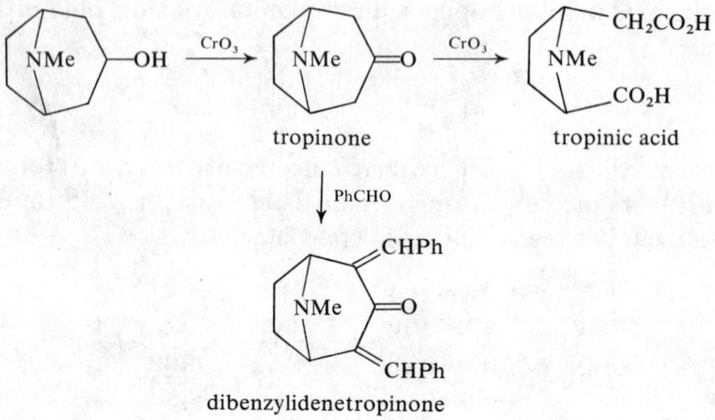

tropinone   tropinic acid

dibenzylidenetropinone

Formation of tropilidene (cycloheptatriene) from tropine

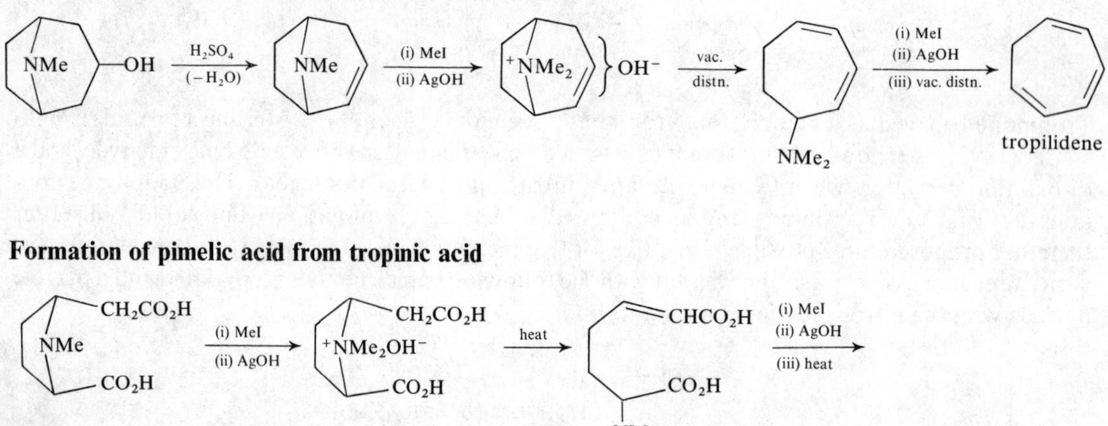

tropilidene

Formation of pimelic acid from tropinic acid

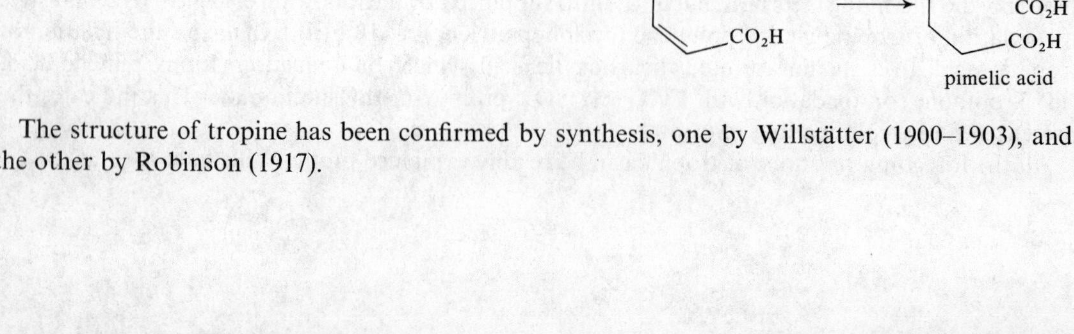

pimelic acid

The structure of tropine has been confirmed by synthesis, one by Willstätter (1900–1903), and the other by Robinson (1917).

Willstätter's synthesis

Robinson's synthesis

Robinson imagined that the skeleton of tropinone could, by means of hydrolysis, be broken down into the three units: succindialdehyde, methylamine and acetone.

Furthermore, Robinson thought that these three units could be 'joined' by means of double Mannich reaction (see §32) to form tropinone *in one step*. When this mixture was allowed to stand in water for thirty minutes, tropinone was produced in very small yield. The reaction may be formulated as shown.

A much better yield (40 per cent) is obtained by using calcium acetonedicarboxylate or ethyl acetone-dicarboxylate instead of acetone; the calcium salt or ester so produced is converted into tropinone by warming with hydrochloric acid, *e.g.*, (ca = Ca/2):

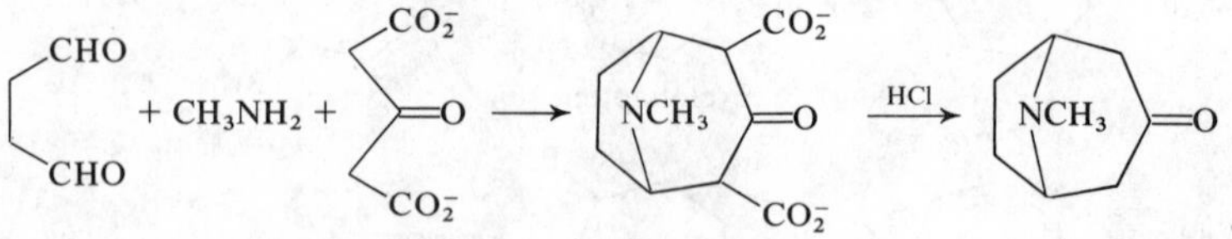

In acetonedicarboxylic acid, because each methylene group is flanked by two carbonyl groups, there is a greater amount of the enol form (see Vol. I).

Schöpf *et al.* (1935) have obtained a yield of 70–85 per cent by carrying out Robinson's synthesis at a *p*H of 7. Elming *et al.* (1958) have also synthesised tropinone using methylamine hydrochloride, acetonedicarboxylic acid and generating succinaldehyde *in situ* by the action of acid on 2,5-di-methoxytetrahydrofuran (see also Vol. I):

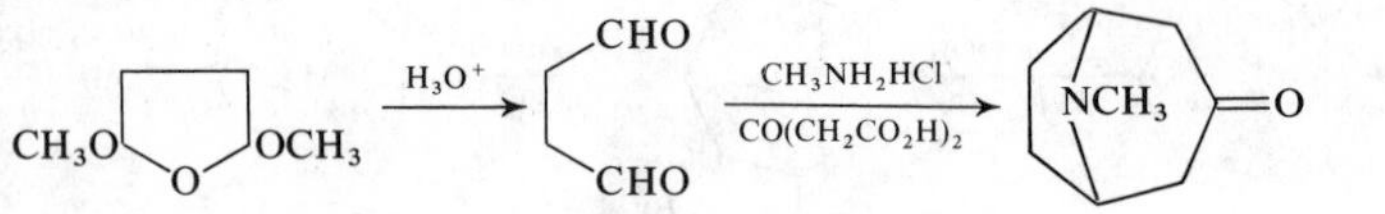

The yield was 81 per cent, but in this case 'physiological conditions' were not necessary.

The final problem is to combine tropine with tropic acid; this has been done by heating the two together in the presence of hydrogen chloride (Fischer–Speier esterification; see Vol. I).

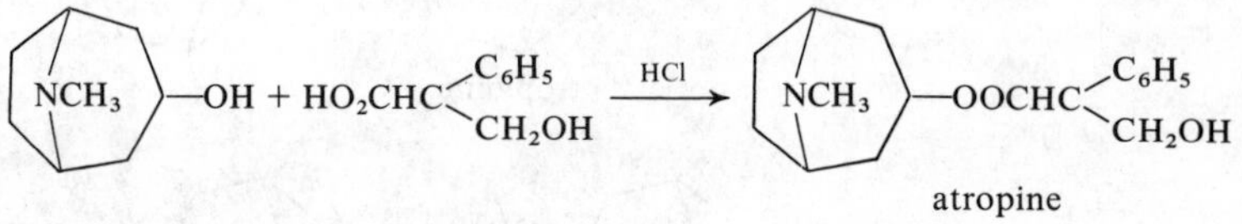

atropine

If (+)- or (−)-tropic acid is used, the product is (+)- or (−)-hyoscyamine, respectively.

Stereochemistry of the tropines

Tropinone can be reduced to a mixture of two alcohols, tropine and ψ-tropine (pseudotropine), the relative amounts of the two depending on the nature of the reducing agent. Catalytic hydrogenation (Pt), electrolytic reduction, and zinc dust and hydriodic acid produce tropine, whereas sodium amalgam and sodium in ethanol give ψ-tropine. Lithium aluminium hydride and sodium borohydride give a mixture of the two, with ψ-tropine predominating.

Tropine and ψ-tropine are epimers, one epimer having the hydrogen atom on C-3 on the same side as the nitrogen bridge, and the other isomer has this hydrogen atom on the opposite side (*cf.* the borneols, **8** §23b); Fig. 14.1 shows the two possible forms. Neither of these forms is optically

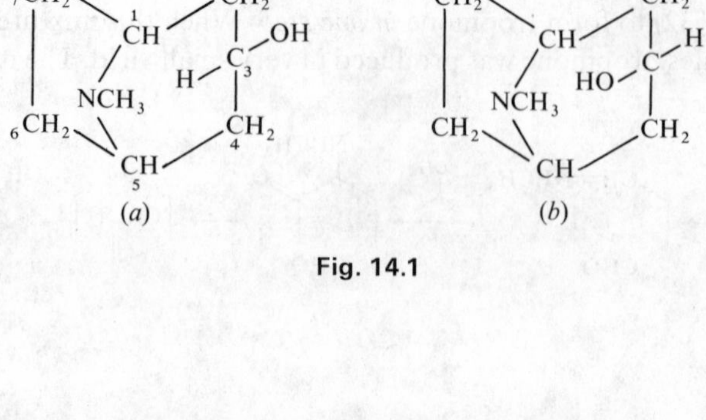

Fig. 14.1

active, since the molecule has a plane of symmetry. C-1 and C-5 are chiral centres, but the molecule is optically inactive by internal compensation (see **2** §7b), and so each isomer is a *meso*-form; C-3 is pseudo-asymmetric (see **4** §8).

The problem now is to decide which geometrical isomer (of the two forms shown in Fig. 14.1) is tropine and which is ψ-tropine. Fodor (1953) has given evidence to show that ψ-tropine is the *syn*-compound (nitrogen bridge and hydroxyl groups are in the *cis*-position; Fig. 14.1b), and that tropine is the *anti*-compound (nitrogen bridge and hydroxyl group are in the *trans*-position; Fig. 14.1a). The problem, however, is more involved than this, since the conformation of the piperidine ring has also to be considered. Thus, the two questions to be answered are: (a) whether the piperidine ring is in the chair or boat conformation, and (b) the orientations (axial or equatorial) of the hydroxyl and methyl groups. Fodor (1953) proposed the boat conformation in both isomers, the axial orientation of the methyl group in both isomers, but axial hydroxyl in ψ-tropine and equatorial hydroxyl in tropine (Fig. 14.2). The evidence was based on rearrangements similar to those used for ephedrine

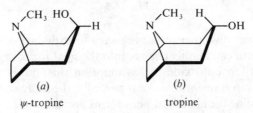

(a)   (b)
ψ-tropine   tropine

Fig. 14.2

and ψ-ephedrine (§7). It was shown that *N*-acetyl- or *N*-benzoyl-nor-ψ-tropine readily undergoes $N \rightarrow O$ acyl migration *via* a cyclic intermediate, whereas the corresponding derivatives of nortropine do not. These results can be explained if the piperidine ring is a boat and the hydroxyl group in the ψ-isomer is axial. Fodor also showed that tropane derivatives yield, on quaternisation, principally or exclusively the derivative in which the entering group takes up the equatorial position. Thus

ψ-isomer

the *N*-methyl group would appear to be axial. However, in view of the fact that the tertiary nitrogen atom will be in a state of oscillation (see **6** §2c), the *N*-methyl group will be constantly changing from axial to equatorial and vice versa. Thus the quaternisation results cannot decide the orientation of the *N*-methyl group (see also below).

Zenitz *et al.* (1952) and Clemo *et al.* (1953) support these configurations from evidence obtained by measurements of the dipole moments of these two isomers; ψ-tropine has been shown to have a higher dipole moment than tropine. Zenitz *et al.* also concluded from their infrared absorption spectra measurements that there is intramolecular hydrogen bonding in ψ-tropine (this would imply that the *N*-methyl group is equatorial), but House *et al.* (1963) believe that only intermolecular hydrogen bonding occurs. Bose *et al.* (1953), however, have assumed the chair form for the piperidine ring by analogy with the chair conformation of cyclohexane compounds and pyranosides (see **4** §11). Thus these authors have suggested that ψ-tropine is Fig. 14.3(a), in which the hydroxyl group is equatorial, and that tropine is Fig. 14.3(*b*), in which the hydroxyl group is axial. Support for this is the fact that when heated in amyl alcohol containing sodium amyloxide, tropine is isomerised to ψ-tropine. Thus, the latter is the thermodynamically stable isomer and this is in keeping with the equatorial hydroxyl group being a more stable conformation than the axial hydroxyl group.

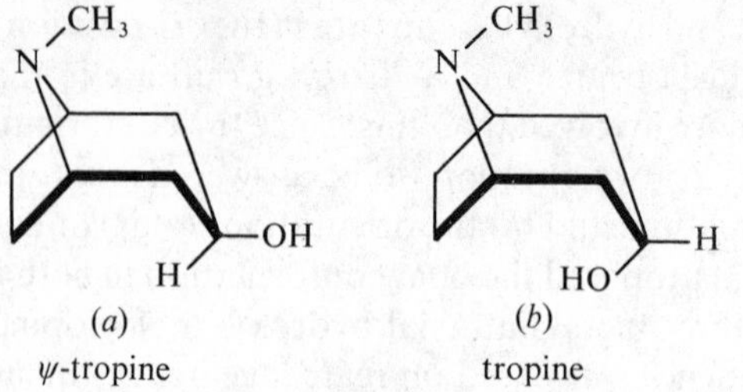

(*a*)   (*b*)
ψ-tropine   tropine

Fig. 14.3

If these are the conformations, then it is necessary to explain Fodor's results. Sparke (1953) suggested that the chair form can readily change into the boat form, and Archer and Lewis (1954) also adopted this explanation but made the assumption that the bond energy involved in the hydrogen bond is sufficient to transform, at least partially, the more stable chair form into the less stable boat form; in ψ-tropine the chair and boat forms are in mobile equilibrium, the latter being the predominant form. It should be remembered that the equatorial hydroxyl in the chair form of ψ-tropine (Fig. 14.3*a*) becomes axial in the boat form (Fig. 14.2*a*).

Closs (1959) examined the NMR spectra of some tropane deuterohalides and concluded that the *N*-substituent in tropanes is predominantly equatorial. He also suggested that the quaternisation could lead to the kinetically controlled product if the conformer with the *N*-substituent axial was present in small proportion, but reacted much faster than the equatorial conformer (see also the Curtin-Hammett principle, **4** §5m). X-ray analysis of tropine hydrobromide has shown the presence of the chair conformation (Visser *et al.*, 1954), and Le Fèvre *et al.* (1962) have concluded, from dipole-moment and Kerr-constant measurements of a number of tropane derivatives, that the piperidine ring is in the chair form with the *N*-methyl equatorial. Fodor *et al.* (1966) have examined the dipole moments and NMR spectra of some tropane derivatives, and have confirmed that the piperidine ring is in the chair conformation with the *N*-methyl group predominantly equatorial. Thus, as the matter stands at present, ψ-tropine is predominantly Fig. 14.4(*a*).

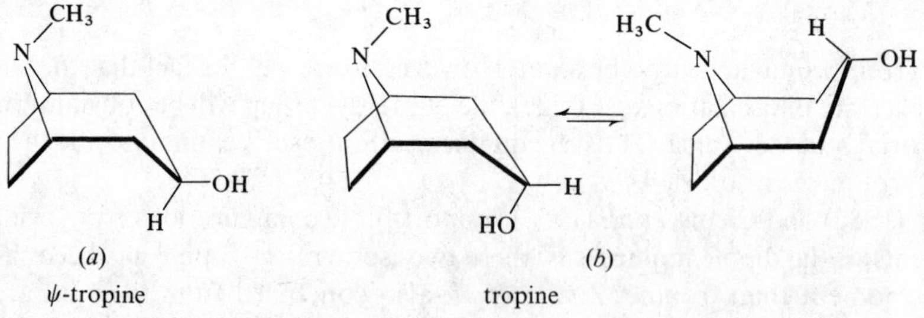

(*a*)   (*b*)
ψ-tropine   tropine

Fig. 14.4

In tropine, however, the predominant conformation is the piperidine ring in a deformed chair form, together with a minor amount in the boat form (Fig. 14.4*b*).

§22a. Tropeines and pseudotropeines. These are synthetic esters formed respectively from tropine and ψ-tropine with various organic acids. The tropeines (including atropine itself) are powerful mydriatics (pupil dilators) and feeble anaesthetics; the ψ-tropeines are the reverse. One of the most important tropeines is *homatropine* (*mandelyltropeine*), which is prepared by combining tropine with mandelic acid.

homatropine

§22b. Hyoscine (scopolamine), $C_{17}H_{21}NO_4$, a syrup, $[\alpha]_D - 18°$, is obtained from various sources, *e.g.*, *Datura Metel*. Hyoscine is a constituent of travel sickness tablets, and when administered with morphine, produces 'twilight sleep'. Hyoscine is the $(-)$-tropic ester of the amino-alcohol *scopine*; these two compounds are produced by the hydrolysis of hyoscine with aqueous ammonium hydroxide.

hyoscine　　　　　　　　　　scopine　　　　　tropic acid

More vigorous hydrolysis of hyoscine with acids or alkalis produces *oscine* (*scopoline*), which is formed by the isomerisation of scopine.

scopine　　　　　　　　　　oscine

It is interesting to note, in this connection, that the action of *ethanolic* sodium hydroxide on $(-)$-hyoscine at room temperature causes the latter to racemise to $(\pm)$-hyoscine.

Fodor *et al.* (1959) have carried out a total synthesis of $(\pm)$-hyoscine and have shown that its conformation is that given for scopine (replace OH by $OOCCHPhCH_2OH$).

§23. Coca alkaloids

In this group occur cocaine, benzoylecgonine, tropacocaine, hygrine (§13), cuscohygrine (§14), etc.

$(-)$-**Cocaine,** $C_{17}H_{21}NO_4$, m.p. 98°C, $[\alpha]_D - 16°$, occurs in coca leaves; it is sparingly soluble in water, but its hydrochloride is quite soluble and is used as a local anaesthetic. When heated with water, cocaine is hydrolysed to methanol and benzoylecgonine.

$$C_{17}H_{21}NO_4 + H_2O \longrightarrow C_{16}H_{19}NO_4 + CH_3OH$$
cocaine　　　　　　benzoylecgonine

Thus cocaine contains a carbomethoxyl group, and benzoylecgonine a carboxyl group. When benzoylecgonine is heated with barium hydroxide solution, further hydrolysis occurs, the products obtained being benzoic acid and ecgonine.

$$C_{16}H_{19}NO_4 + H_2O \xrightarrow{Ba(OH)_2} C_9H_{15}NO_3 + C_6H_5CO_2H$$
benzoylecgonine　　　　　　ecgonine

Ecgonine shows the reactions of an alcohol, and so benzoylecgonine is the benzoyl derivative of a hydroxycarboxylic acid. The structure of ecgonine has been deduced from the nature of the products obtained by oxidation, *viz.*,

$$\text{Ecgonine} \xrightarrow{CrO_3} \text{Tropinone} \xrightarrow{CrO_3} \text{Tropinic acid} + \text{Ecgoninic acid}$$
$$\quad\; C_9H_{15}NO_3 \qquad\qquad C_8H_{13}NO \qquad\qquad C_8H_{13}NO_4 \qquad\quad C_7H_{11}NO_3$$

From these results, it follows that ecgonine contains the tropane structure and that the alcoholic group must be in the same position as in tropine (§22). Now in the formation of tropinone from ecgonine, a carboxyl group is lost (as we have seen, ecgonine contains a carboxyl group). Thus the carboxyl group is in a position such that the oxidation of the secondary alcoholic group in ecgonine to a keto group is accompanied by the elimination of the carboxyl group. This type of elimination is characteristic of β-ketonic acids, and this interpretation of the results is confirmed by the fact that Willstätter *et al.* (1898) actually observed the formation of an unstable β-ketonic acid which lost carbon dioxide to give tropinone. Hence ecgonine is:

ecgonine

On this basis, the foregoing reactions may therefore be written:

cocaine   benzoylecgonine   ecgonine

tropinone   tropinic acid   ecgoninic acid

The structure of ecgonine has been confirmed by synthesis (Willstätter *et al.*, 1901); the starting point is tropinone (see §22 for its synthesis). Before describing this synthesis, let us first examine the structure of ecgonine from the stereochemical point of view; it will be seen that there are four dissimilar chiral centres present (*), and so there are $2^4 = 16$ optically active forms (eight pairs of enantiomers) possible (*cf.* tropine, §22). Since, however, only the *cis* fusion of the nitrogen bridge is possible in practice, C-1 and C-5 therefore have only one configuration (the *cis*-form), and so there are only eight optically active forms (four pairs of enantiomers) actually possible (*cf.* camphor, **8** §23a); three pairs of enantiomers have been prepared synthetically.

In the original synthesis of Willstätter, the racemic ecgonine obtained was not identical with the (−)-ecgonine from (−)-cocaine, but its chemical properties were the same (note the Kolbe–Schmitt type of reaction; see Vol. I).

tropinone   sodium tropinone-carboxylate   a (±)-ecgonine

Later, Willstätter *et al.* (1921) synthesised ecgonine by means of the Robinson method (see §22):

$$\text{CHO H} + \text{NCH}_3 + \quad \xrightarrow{\text{KOH}} \quad \xrightarrow{\text{heat}} \quad \xrightarrow[\text{(ii) hydrol.}]{\text{(i) Na/Hg}}$$

The final product was shown to be a mixture of three racemates, $(\pm)$-ecgonine, $(\pm)$-ψ-ecgonine and a third pair of enantiomers (Willstätter *et al.*, 1923). The racemic ecgonine was resolved, and the $(-)$-form esterified with methanol and then benzoylated; the product was $(-)$-cocaine.

$$\xrightarrow[\text{(ii) C}_6\text{H}_5\text{COCl}]{\text{(i) CH}_3\text{OH/HCl}}$$

$(-)$-ecgonine $(-)$-cocaine

In a similar way, the $(+)$- and $(-)$-ψ-cocaines were obtained from the corresponding ψ-ecgonines.

Fodor *et al.* (1953, 1954) and Findlay (1953, 1954) have established the conformations of ecgonine and ψ-ecgonine ($R^1 = CO_2H$; $R^2 = H$) and the corresponding cocaines ($R^1 = CO_2Me$; $R^2 = COPh$) (*cf.* §22):

cocaine ψ-cocaine
(and ecgonine)   (and ψ-ecgonine)

Hardegger *et al.* (1955) have correlated $(-)$-cocaine with L-glutamic acid and have shown that the formula represents the absolute configuration of L$(-)$-cocaine.

$(-)$-ecgonine $\xrightarrow{\text{CrO}_3}$ $(-)$-ecgoninic acid

L$(+)$-glutamic acid

(i) CH$_2$N$_2$ (ii) LAH ; (i) TsCl (ii) KCN ; (i) K (ii) MeI ; H$_2$O$_2$; OH$^-$; HNO$_2$

§23a. Tropacocaine, $C_{15}H_{19}NO_2$, m.p. 49°C, occurs in Java coca leaves. When heated with barium hydroxide solution, tropacocaine is hydrolysed to ψ-tropine and benzoic acid; thus the alkaloid is benzoyl-ψ-tropine.

tropacocaine ψ-tropine

§23b. Mass spectrometry of tropanes. Fragmentation patterns of tropanes and some of their derivatives have been investigated and so will enable information on structures of unknown tropanes to be obtained. Blossey *et al.* (1964) have proposed the following paths for the fragmentation of tropinone.

m/e 83   *m/e* 110

m/e 96

QUINOLINE GROUP

§24. Angostura alkaloids

A number of alkaloids have been isolated from angostura bark, *e.g.*; cusparine, galipine, galipoline, etc. **Cusparine,** $C_{19}H_{17}NO_3$, m.p. 90–91°C, has been shown to contain one methoxyl group (Zeisel method), and when fused with potassium hydroxide, protocatechuic acid is obtained.

On the other hand, controlled oxidation of cusparine gives piperonylic acid and 4-methoxyquinoline-2-carboxylic acid.

Consideration of this information led to the suggestion of the following structure for cusparine.

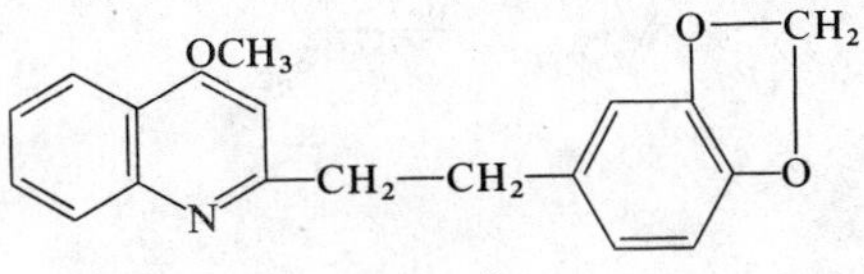

cusparine

This has been confirmed by synthesis (Späth *et al.*, 1924). Note the activated 2-methyl group.

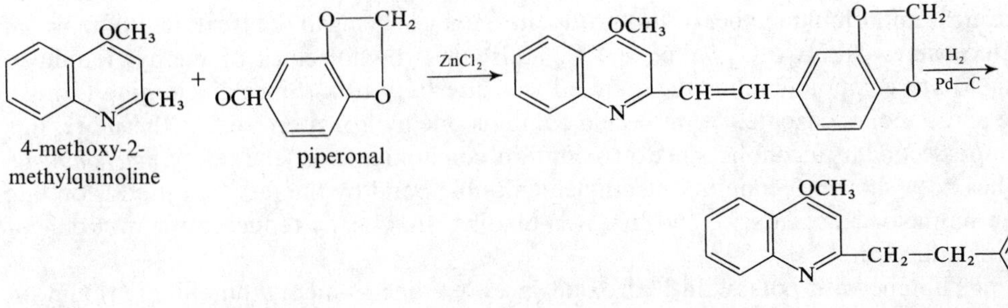

4-methoxy-2-
methylquinoline   piperonal

cusparine

Galipine, $C_{20}H_{21}NO_3$, m.p. 113°C, contains three methoxyl groups (Zeisel method). When oxidised with chromic acid, galipine produces 4-methoxyquinoline-2-carboxylic acid and veratric acid, and when fused with potassium hydroxide, galipine gives protocatechuic acid. Thus the formula of the alkaloid is probably:

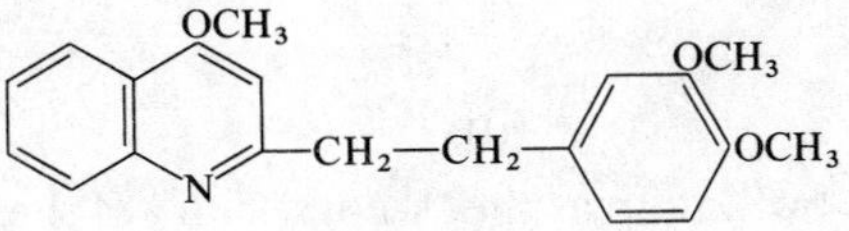

galipine

This has been confirmed by synthesis (Späth *et al.*, 1924).

veratraldehyde

galipine

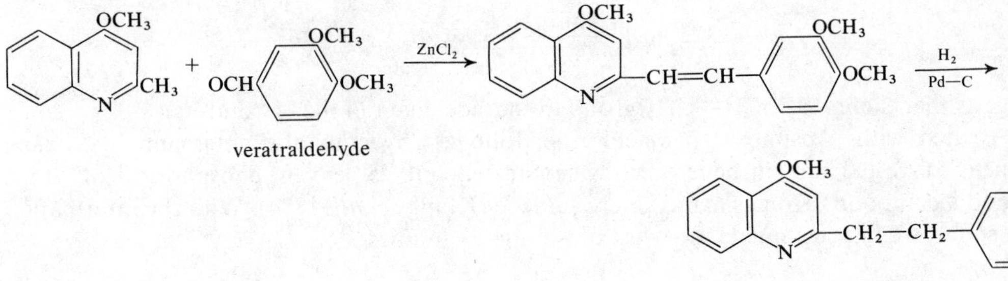

Galipoline, $C_{19}H_{19}NO_3$, m.p. 193°C, contains two methoxyl groups and one phenolic group. When methylated with diazomethane, galipoline is converted into galipine. Thus one of the methoxyl groups in the latter is a hydroxyl group in the former. The position of this phenolic hydroxyl was shown to be in the quinoline nucleus by synthesis (Späth *et al.*, 1924).

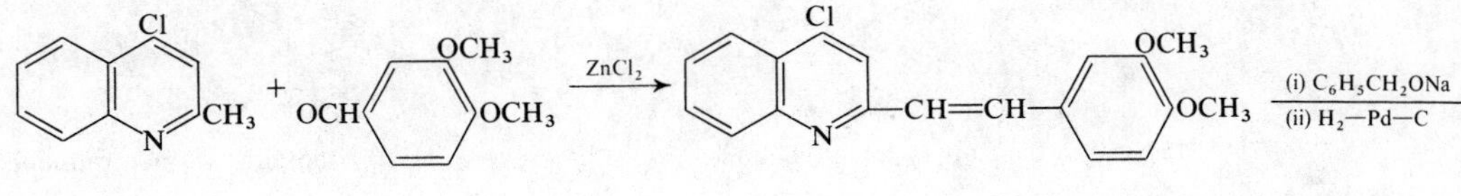

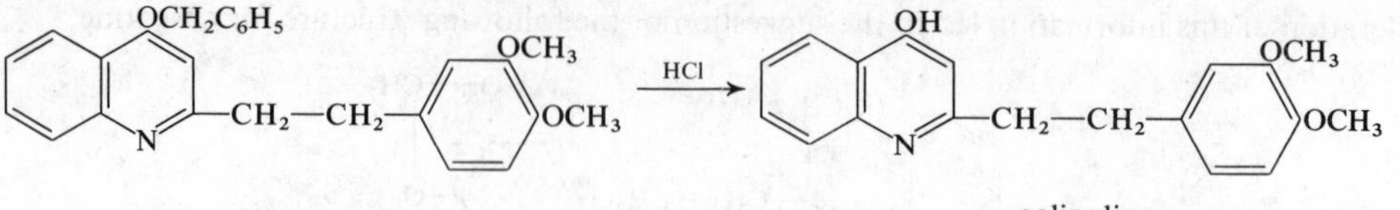

galipoline

§25. Cinchona alkaloids

Cinchonine and quinine, together with many other alkaloids, occur in the bark of various species of *Cinchona*. Cinchonine may be regarded as the parent substance of the cinchona alkaloids, but quinine is the most important member of this group, its main use being in the treatment of malaria.
§25a. (+)-Cinchonine, $C_{19}H_{22}NO_2$, m.p. 264°C, adds on two molecules of methyl iodide to form a diquaternary compound; thus the alkaloid is a ditertiary base. Since cinchonine forms a monoacetate and a monobenzoate, the molecule contains one hydroxyl group. Furthermore, this hydroxyl group is secondary alcoholic, since on oxidation, cinchonine forms the ketone *cinchoninone*. Cinchonine has been shown to contain one ethylenic double bond by the fact that it adds on one molecule of bromine or halogen acid, and that it is readily catalytically reduced, one molecule of hydrogen being added on.

Fusion of cinchonine with potassium hydroxide gives lepidine (4-methylquinoline) (I) and on vigorous oxidation with chromic acid in sulphuric acid solution, cinchoninic acid (II) is obtained (Königs, 1894). Thus cinchonine contains a quinoline nucleus with a side-chain in position 4 (III);

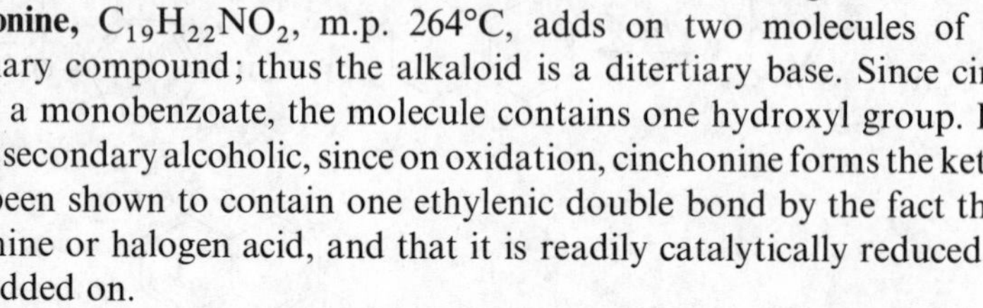

(I)   (II)   (III)

this side-chain was referred to by Skraup as the 'second-half' of the molecule. The hydroxyl group in cinchonine must be in this 'second-half', since if it were not, then a hydroxy derivative or a carboxy derivative (the hydroxyl is alcoholic) of cinchoninic acid would have been obtained.

Oxidation of cinchonine with permanganate gives cinchotenine and formic acid (Königs, 1879).

$$C_{19}H_{22}N_2O + 4[O] \xrightarrow{KMnO_4} C_{18}H_{20}N_2O_3 + HCO_2H$$
cinchotenine

This suggests that there is a $-CH{=}CH_2$ group in the side-chain in the 'second-half'.

When treated with phosphorus pentachloride, followed by ethanolic potassium hydroxide, cinchonine is converted into cinchene which, when heated with 25 per cent phosphoric acid, forms lepidine and a compound Königs named meroquinene (Königs *et al.*, 1884). With the information obtained so far, we may formulate the work of Königs as follows:

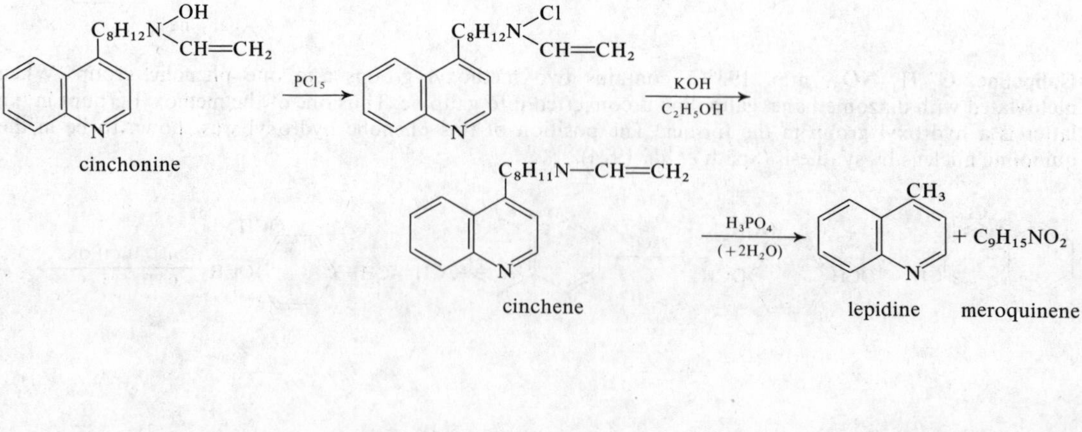

cinchonine

cinchene   lepidine   meroquinene

Meroquinene (meroquinenine) is also obtained, together with cinchoninic acid, when cinchonine is oxidised with chromic acid (König s, 1894).

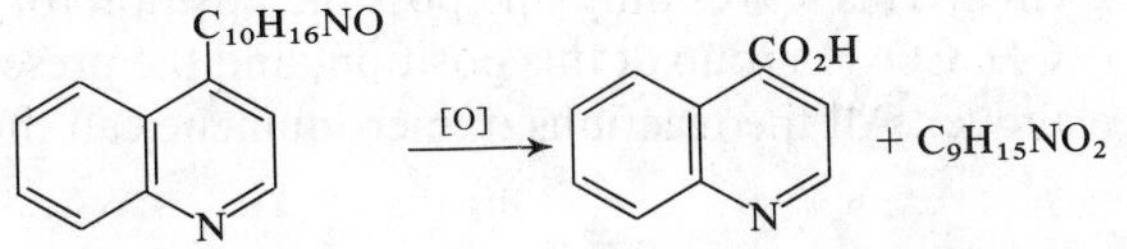

cinchonine   cinchoninic acid   meroquinene

Thus the key to the structure of the 'second-half' is the structure of meroquinene. The routine tests showed that meroquinene contains one carboxyl group and one double bond; the presence of the latter indicates that the —CH=CH$_2$ side-chain is still present in meroquinene. Oxidation of meroquinene with cold acid permanganate produces formic acid and cincholoiponic acid, the latter being a dicarboxylic acid (Königs, 1879). The formation of formic acid confirms the presence of the —CH=CH$_2$ side-chain in meroquinene. The presence of this group has also been demonstrated by

$$C_9H_{15}NO_2 \xrightarrow[\text{H}_2\text{SO}_4]{\text{KMnO}_4} C_8H_{13}NO_4 + HCO_2H$$

meroquinene   cincholoiponic acid

the ozonolysis of meroquinene; formaldehyde is produced (Seekles, 1923). Oxidation of cincholoiponic acid with acid permanganate produces loiponic acid, $C_7H_{11}NO_4$ (Königs, 1890). This is also a dicarboxylic acid, and since it contains one methylene group less than its precursor cincholoiponic acid, this suggests that the latter contains at least a side-chain —CH$_2$CO$_2$H.

The reactions of the above three acids indicated that they were all secondary bases; that they all contained a piperidine ring is shown by the following reactions.

(i) Meroquinene $\xrightarrow[240°C]{\text{HCl}}$

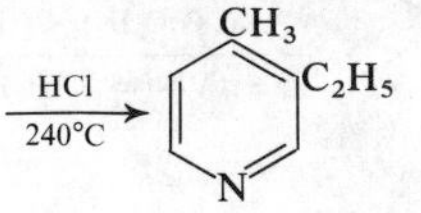

(ii) Cincholoiponic acid $\xrightarrow[\text{heat}]{\text{H}_2\text{SO}_4}$

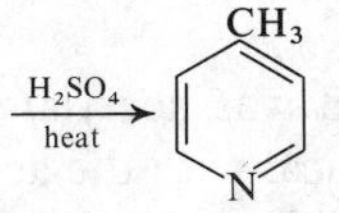

(iii) Loiponic acid $\xrightarrow[\text{isomerises}]{\text{KOH}}$

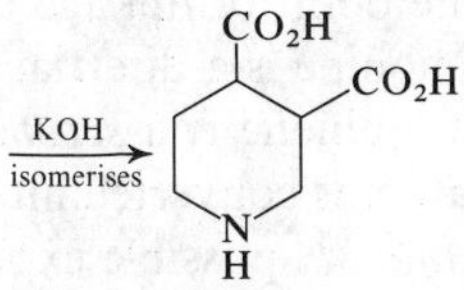

hexahydrocinchomeronic
acid

The structure of hexahydrocinchomeronic acid is known from its synthesis (*cf.* §21).

Consideration of the above results shows that a possible skeleton structure of meroquinene is as shown. The problem then is to find the position of the remaining carbon atom. This carbon atom

cannot be an *N*-methyl group, since all three acids are secondary bases. As we have seen, meroquinene contains a —CH=CH$_2$ group in the side-chain. A possible position for the extra carbon atom is the side-chain containing this unsaturated group, *i.e.*, the side-chain is an allyl group, —CH$_2$CH=CH$_2$. All the foregoing facts can be explained on this basis, but the following fact cannot, *viz.*, that reduction of meroquinene gives cincholoipon, $C_9H_{17}NO_2$, a compound which contains one carboxyl group and one *ethyl group*. Thus the unsaturated side-chain cannot be allyl (this should have given a propyl group on reduction); the side-chain is therefore vinyl. This leaves only one possible position for the extra carbon atom, *viz.*, 4; this would give a —CH_2CO_2H group at this position, and the presence of such a group has already been inferred (see above). All the reactions of meroquinene can therefore be explained on the following structures:

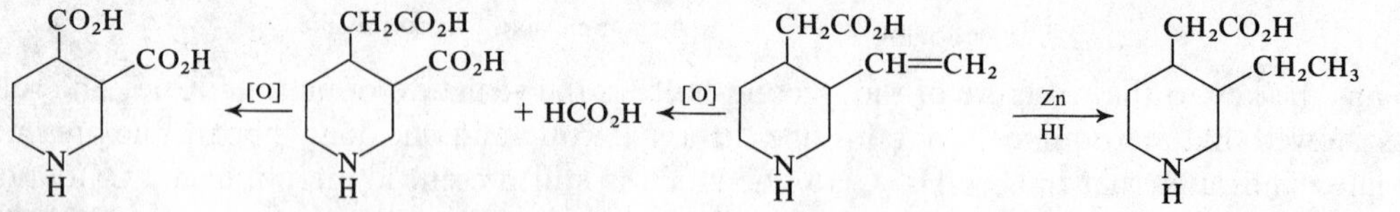

loiponic acid   cincholoiponic acid   meroquinene   cincholoipon

This formula for meroquinene is supported by the synthesis of cincholoiponic acid (Wohl *et al.*, 1907; *cf.* §17).

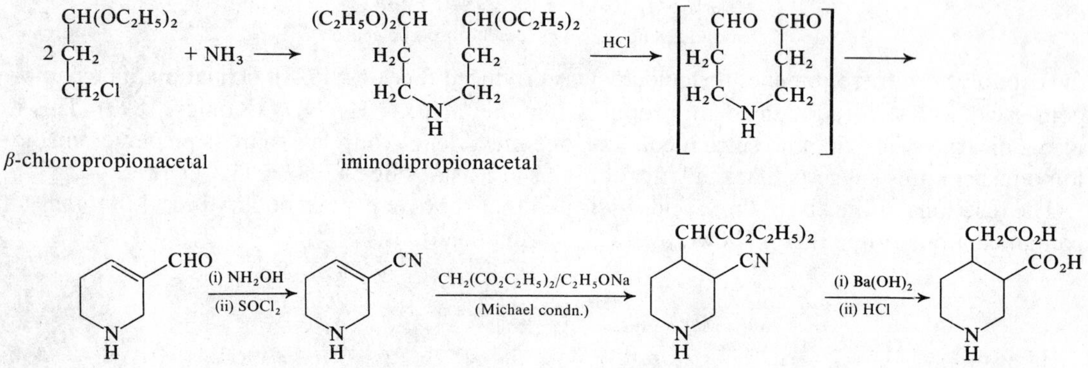

β-chloropropionacetal   iminodipropionacetal

($\pm$)-cincho-loiponic acid

The racemic cincholoiponic acid was acetylated, and this derivative was resolved by means of brucine; the ($+$)-form was identical with the acid obtained from meroquinene.

Since meroquinene is obtained from cinchonine by oxidation, the carbon atom of the carboxyl group in meroquinene will be the point of linkage to the 'quinoline-half' at which fission of the 'second-half' occurs. Since cinchonine is a ditertiary base, the 'second-half' therefore contains a tertiary nitrogen atom. But meroquinene is a *secondary* base, and it therefore follows that in its formation the tertiary nitrogen atom is converted into a secondary nitrogen atom, *a carboxyl group also being produced at the same time*. A possible explanation for this behaviour is that the tertiary nitrogen atom is a part of a bridged ring, one C—N bond being broken when cinchonine is oxidised:

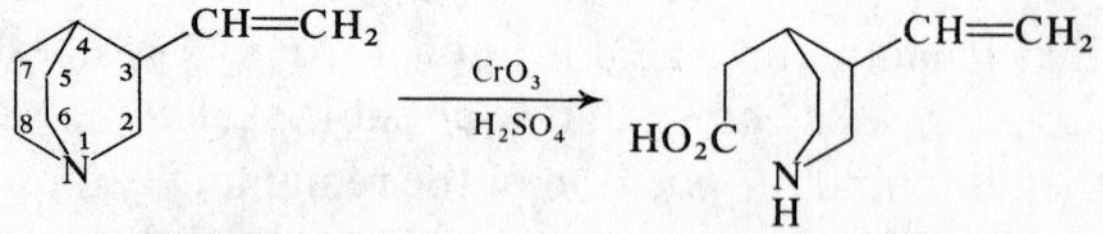

3-vinylquinuclidine   meroquinene

Thus, in cinchonine, the 'quinoline-half' must be joined *via* its side-chain at position 4 to the 'quinuclidine-half' at position 8. The remaining problem is to ascertain the position of the secondary alcoholic group in the 'second-half'. Rabe *et al.* (1906, 1908) converted cinchonine into the ketone cinchoninone by gentle oxidation (chromium trioxide). This ketone, in which both nitrogen atoms are still tertiary, on treatment with amyl nitrite and hydrogen chloride, gives cinchoninic acid and an oxime. The formation of an acid and an oxime indicates the presence of the group —COCH<, *i.e.*, a methine group adjacent to a carbonyl group:

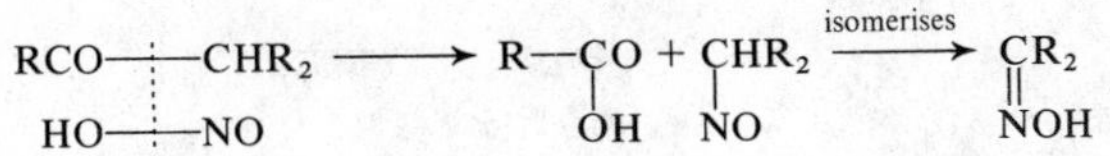

The structure of the oxime obtained from cinchoninone was shown to be 8-oximino-3-vinyl-quinuclidine by its hydrolysis to hydroxylamine and meroquinene. If we assume that the secondary alcoholic group connects the 'quinoline-half' to the quinuclidine nucleus, then the foregoing reactions may be written as follows, on the assumption that the structure of cinchonine is as given.

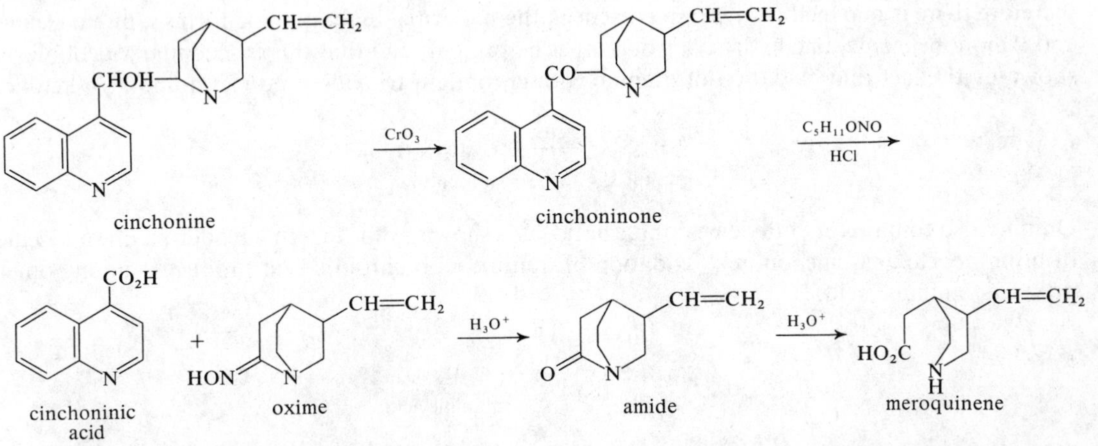

cinchonine   cinchoninone

cinchoninic   oxime   amide   meroquinene
acid

A partial synthesis of cinchonine has been carried out by Rabe (1911, 1913). This starts from cinchotoxine, which is prepared by the prolonged action of acetic acid on cinchonine; the latter isomerises (Rabe *et al.*, 1909).

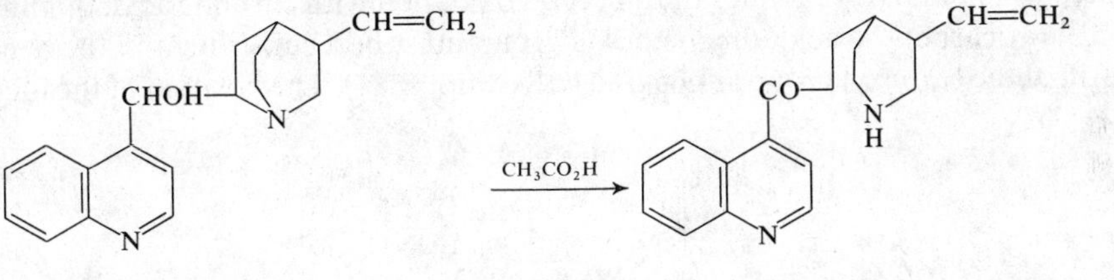

cinchonine   cinchotoxine

This isomerisation is an example of the *hydramine fission* (see §7). The conversion of cinchotoxine into cinchonine was carried out as follows:

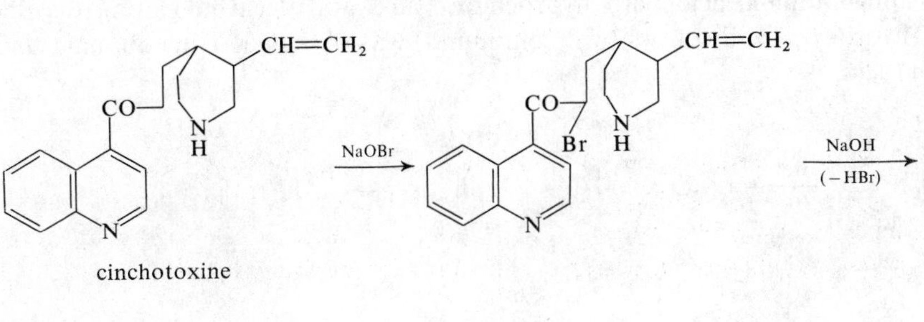

cinchotoxine

cinchoninone   (±)-cinchonine

§25b. (−)-Quinine, $C_{20}H_{24}N_2O_2$, m.p. 177°C, is used as a febrifuge and as an antimalarial. Since quinine adds on two molecules of methyl iodide to form a diquaternary salt, it is therefore a ditertiary base. When heated with hydrochloric acid, quinine eliminates one carbon atom as methyl chloride; therefore there is one methoxyl group present in the molecule. Since quinine forms a monoacetate and a monobenzoate, one hydroxyl group must be present, and that this is secondary alcoholic is shown by the fact that oxidation of quinine with chromium trioxide produces quinone, a ketone.

$$C_{20}H_{24}N_2O_2 \xrightarrow{CrO_3} C_{20}H_{22}N_2O_2$$
quinine   quininone

Quinine also contains one ethylenic double bond, as is shown by the fact that it adds on one molecule of bromine, etc. (cf. cinchonine). Oxidation of quinine with chromic acid produces, among other products, quininic acid.

$$C_{20}H_{24}N_2O_2 \xrightarrow[H_2SO_4]{CrO_3} C_{11}H_9NO_3$$
quinine   quininic acid

On the other hand, controlled oxidation of quinine with chromic acid gives quininic acid and meroquinene. Thus the 'second-half' in both quinine and cinchonine is the same, and so the problem is to elucidate the structure of quininic acid. When heated with soda-lime, quininic acid is de-carboxylated to a methoxyquinoline, and since, on oxidation with chromic acid, quininic acid forms pyridine-2,3,4-tricarboxylic acid, the methoxyl group must be a substituent in the benzene ring (of quinoline), and the carboxyl group at position 4 (Skraup, 1881). The position of the methoxyl group

quininic acid   pyridine-2,3,4-
                                 tricarboxylic acid

was ascertained by heating quininic acid with hydrochloric acid and decarboxylating the de-methylated product; 6-hydroxyquinoline (a known compound) was obtained. Thus quininic acid is 6-methoxycinchoninic acid.

quininic acid   6-hydroxyquinoline

This structure for quininic acid has been confirmed by synthesis (Rabe *et al.*, 1931).

The direct oxidation of 6-methoxy-4-methylquinoline to quininic acid is extremely difficult; oxidation of the methyl group is accompanied by the oxidation of the benzene ring, the final product being pyridine-2,3,4-tricarboxylic acid (see §26).

Thus, on the basis of the foregoing evidence, the structure of quinine is:

quinine

Rabe *et al.* (1918) carried out a partial synthesis of quinine starting from quinotoxine, which was prepared by heating quinine in acetic acid (*cf.* cinchotoxine). Woodward and Doering (1944) have synthesised (+)-quinotoxine, and so we now have a *total* synthesis of quinine. The following is Woodward and Doering's work up to (+)-quinotoxine, and from this to quinine is Rabe's work. *m*-Hydroxybenzaldehyde (I) was condensed with aminoacetal (II) and the product cyclised with sulphuric acid to give 7-hydroxyisoquinoline (III); this is an example of the Pomeranz-Fritsch reaction (see Vol. I). This was treated with formaldehyde in methanol solution containing piperidine (Mannich reaction; see §32). The complex formed (IV) was converted into 7-hydroxy-8-methyl-isoquinoline (V) by heating with methanolic sodium methoxide at 220°C. (V), on catalytic reduction (platinum) followed by acetylation, gave *N*-acetyl-7-hydroxy-8-methyl-1,2,3,4-tetrahydroiso-quinoline (VI), which, on further catalytic reduction by heating with a Raney nickel catalyst under pressure and then followed by oxidation with chromium trioxide was converted into *N*-acetyl-7-keto-8-methyldecahydroisoquinoline (VII). (VII) was a mixture of *cis*- and *trans*-isomers; these were separated (*via* their crystalline hydrates) and the *cis*-isomer ((VIIa); see 4§11d(a) for conventions) then treated with ethyl nitrite in the presence of sodium ethoxide to give the homomeroquinene derivative (VIII). This, on reduction, gave (IX), which may now be written more conveniently as shown. Exhaustive methylation of (IX), followed by hydrolysis, gave *cis*-(±)-homomeroquinene (X). (X), after esterification and benzoylation, gave (XI) which, on condensation with ethyl quininate (XII), produced (XIII) [a β-keto-ester]. This, on heating with 16 per cent hydrochloric acid, was hydrolysed and decarboxylated to (±)-quinotoxine (XIV). This was resolved *via* its dibenzoyl-tartrate (tartaric acid proved unsuccessful for resolution).

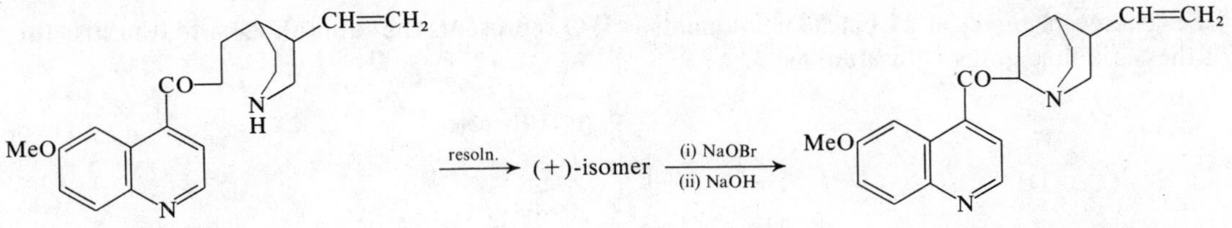

(XIV)
(±)-quinotoxine

(+)-quininone

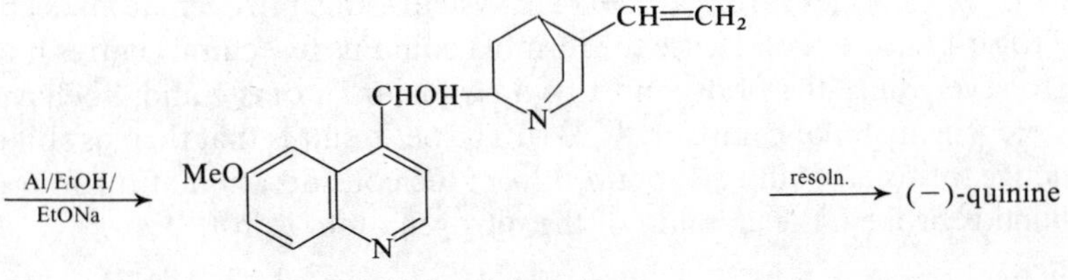

(±)-quinine

(−)-quinine

Conversion of (IV) into (V) failed with hydrogenolysis (H_2 + catalyst). The mechanism of the reaction with methoxide ion probably occurs by hydride ion transfer.

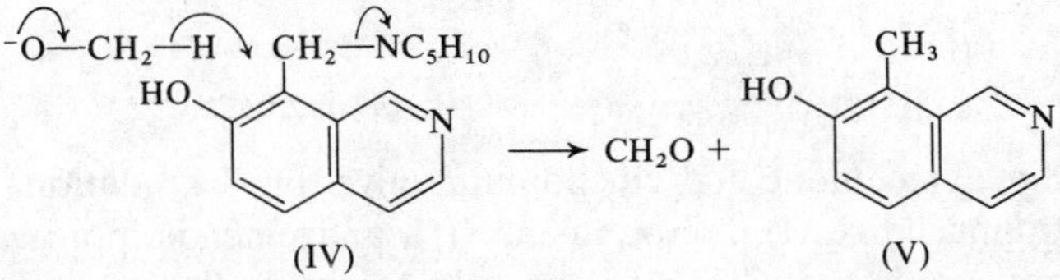

(IV)   (V)

The conversion of (VIIa) to (VIII) possibly occurs as follows (the tertiary hydrogen atom is removed in preference to the secondary):

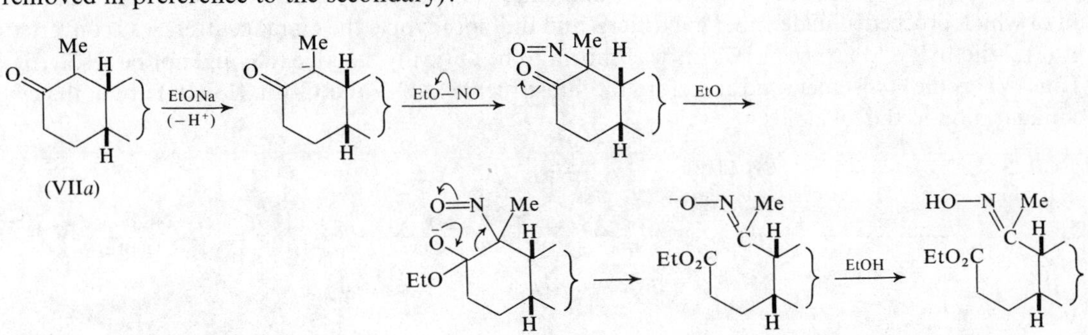

(VIIa)

(VIII)

(IX) contains a new chiral centre, but this is lost when the amino-acid side-chain is converted into the vinyl group. The exhaustive methylation step was carried out by heating (IX) with ethanolic methyl iodide in the presence of potassium carbonate, followed by heating the quaternary salt with 60 per cent potassium hydroxide solution at 140°C (note the formation of the Hofmann product). (X) proved difficult to isolate and so it was treated with potassium cyanate, followed by hydrolysis of the ureide:

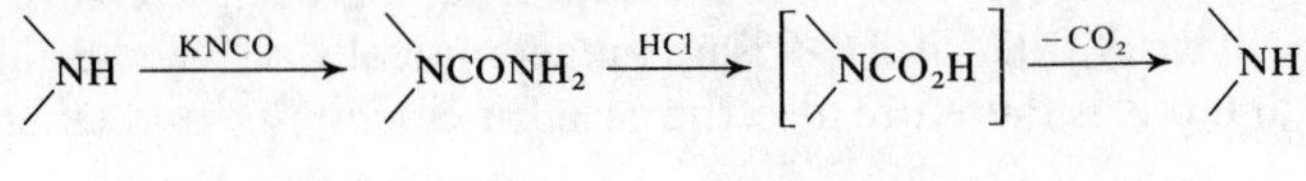

§25c. Stereochemistry of the cinchona alkaloids.   If Q represents the 'quinoline half', the structure of these alkaloids may be written as:

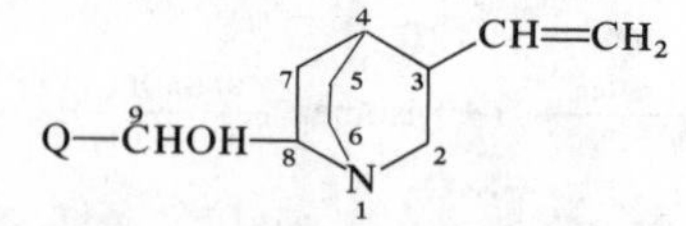

This formula contains four chiral centres: 3, 4, 8 and 9. Since the nitrogen atom is tertiary and all its three valencies form parts of ring systems, this nitrogen atom is chiral and cannot oscillate (*cf.* Tröger's base, **6** §2c). Hence the formula contains five chiral centres if we include the nitrogen atom. However, since the bridge must be a *cis* fusion, atoms 1 and 4 behave as 'one chiral unit' (*cf.* the stereochemistry of camphor, **8** §23a). The net result is that there is still the same number of optically active forms as would be obtained from the consideration of the four chiral centres. When the 1,8-bond is broken, the chirality of the nitrogen atom is lost.

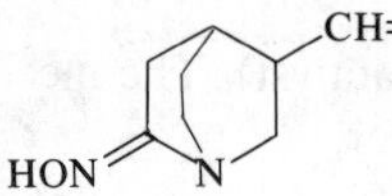

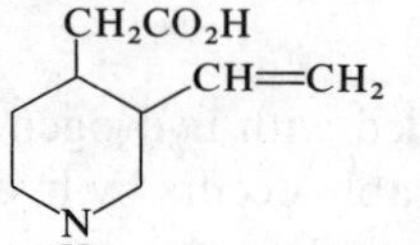

Quinine, quinidine, cinchonine and cinchonidine give, on degradation, the optically identical 8-oximino-3-vinylquinuclidine (I), meroquinene (II), and cincholoiponic acid (III). It therefore follows that the configurations of C-3 and C-4 are the same for all three compounds. The configuration at C-4 relative to that at C-3 was determined by Prelog *et al.* (1944) as follows. The ethyl ester of cincholoipon (IV) was converted into the dibromide (V) which, by means of a series of reactions, all of which proceeded under mild conditions and did not involve the chiral centres, was converted into 1,2-diethylcyclohexane (VI). This was shown to be optically inactive (it could not be resolved). Thus (VI) is the *cis*-isomer, and therefore the substituents at C-3 and C-4 in (I)–(III) are in the *cis*-configuration in the alkaloids.

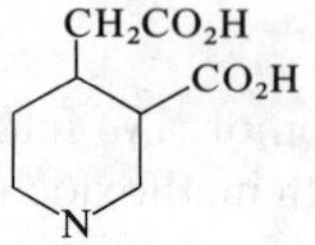

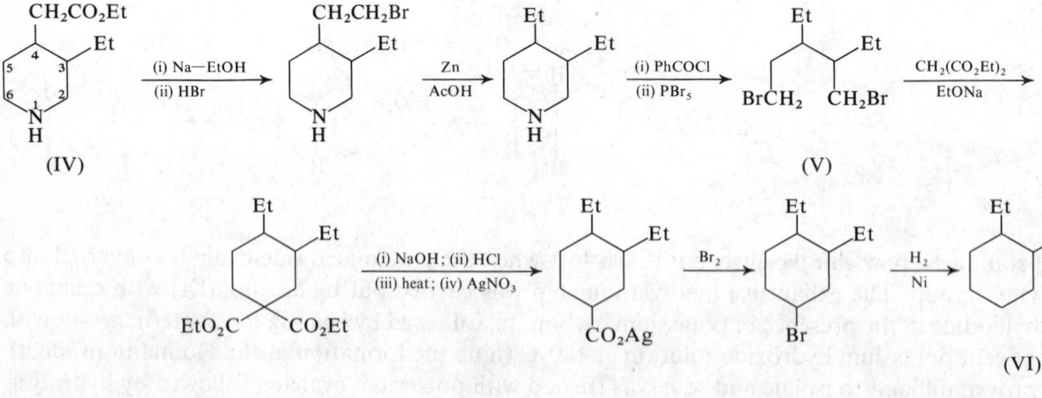

The 9-deoxy derivatives (*i.e.*, CH_2 has replaced CHOH) of cinchonine and cinchonidine have different specific rotations, $+179\cdot3°$ and $-29\cdot9°$, respectively. Since the configurations of C-3 and C-4 are the same in both bases, and since C-9 is no longer optically active, the difference between the two must be at C-8, and this is therefore also the case for cinchonine and cinchonidine. Similarly, since $[\alpha]_D$ of deoxyquinine is $-97\cdot7°$ and that of deoxyquinidine is $+211\cdot1°$, then quinine and quinidine differ at C-8.

Cinchonine, $[\alpha]_D +224\cdot4°$, and quinidine, $[\alpha]_D +243\cdot5°$, are both dextrorotatory, and both can be converted into their cyclic ethers (VII). On the other hand, cinchonidine, $[\alpha]_D -111°$, and quinine, $[\alpha]_D -158\cdot2°$, are both laevorotatory, and do not form cyclic ethers. The cyclic ether structure is

(VII)   (VIII)

only possible if the groups attached to C-3 and C-8 are in the *endo*-position (VIII). Thus, in cinchonine and quinidine, the hydrogen atoms at C-3 and C-8 are *cis* with respect to each other. Also, because C-4 and C-8 are *cis*-oriented, it follows that the hydrogen atoms at C-3, C-4 and C-8 are all *cis*-oriented in cinchonine and quinidine, whereas in cinchonidine and quinine, the hydrogens at C-3 and C-4 are *cis*, but the hydrogens at C-3 and C-8 are *trans*.

Before considering the configuration at C-9, we shall discuss the direction of rotation of this chiral centre. This makes use of the Rule of Optical Superposition (**1** §9). Degradation products (I)–(III) are all dextrorotatory, and since all contain only the same two chiral centres C-3 and C-4, then it may be concluded that the *total* contribution of C-3 and C-4 is dextrorotatory. King *et al.* (1922), using this and other data, concluded that the four chiral centres contributed to the final direction of rotation of each alkaloid as shown in the Table. Thus quinine is 6-methoxycinchonidine and quinidine is 6-methoxycinchonine.

Alkaloid	$[\alpha]_D°$	C-3 + C-4	C-8	C-9
Cinchonine	$+224$	$+$	$+$	$+$
Cinchonidine	-111	$+$	$-$	$-$
Quinine	-158	$+$	$-$	$-$
Quinidine	$+254$	$+$	$+$	$+$

Prelog *et al.* (1950) have deduced the configuration at C-9 by comparing the basicities of the alkaloids and their C-9-epimers, and the basicities of $(-)$-ephedrine and $(+)$-ψ-ephedrine. The configurations of ephedrine (*erythro*-configuration) and ψ-ephedrine (*threo*-configuration) have

(−)-ephedrine	(+)-ψ-ephedrine	(−)-quinine	(+)-epiquinine
pK_a 9·14	9·22	pK_a 7·73	8·44

been discussed in §7, and the structures of quinine and epiquinine have been drawn so that comparisons can be made for C-8 and C-9. Inspection of the pK_a values shows that ψ-ephedrine is a stronger base than ephedrine and that epiquinine is a stronger base than quinine. The authors then proposed that, by analogy, $(+)$-epiquinine is therefore probably related to $(+)$-ψ-ephedrine in configuration and $(-)$-quinine to $(-)$-ephedrine. Thus, the configurations (at C-8 and C-9) in $(-)$-quinine and $(+)$-epiquinine are probably those shown in the formulae.

If we accept these configurations, then the relative configurations at C-3, C-4, C-8 and C-9 are now known. If the *absolute* configuration of any *one* of these chiral centres could be established, the absolute configurations of the other three are also established. Actually, Prelog *et al.* had determined the absolute configuration of C-3 in 1944. Dibromide (V) [see above] was catalytically hydrogenated,

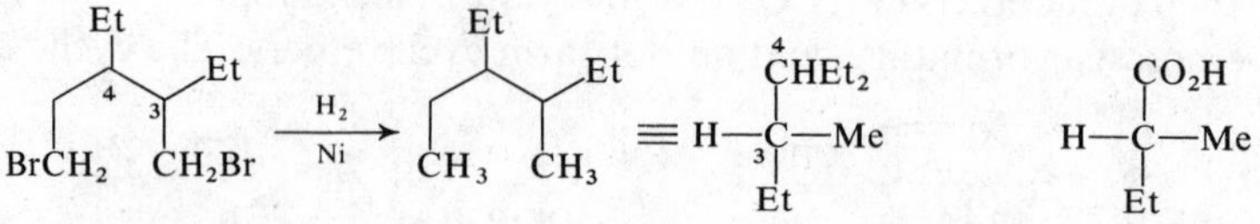

(V)   (IX)   (X)

and the product was shown to be (−)-3-methyl-4-ethylhexane (IX). The configuration of (IX) was established by its synthesis from (−)-ethylmethylacetic acid (X) which, in turn, has been correlated with glyceraldehyde. It is therefore now possible to write the absolute configurations.

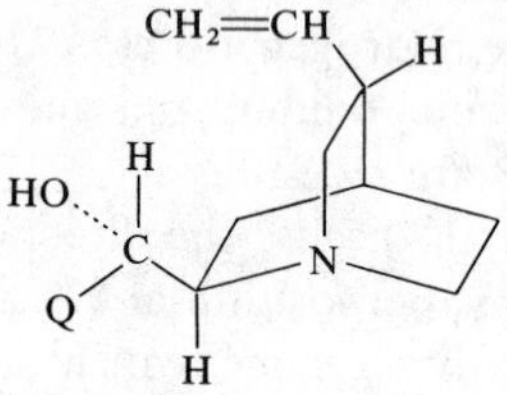

(+)-cinchonine
(+)-quinidine

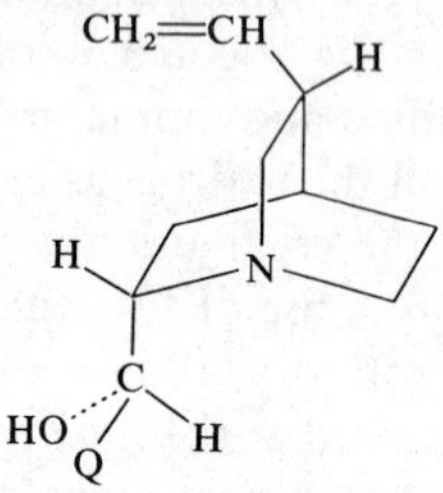

(−)-cinchonidine
(−)-quinine

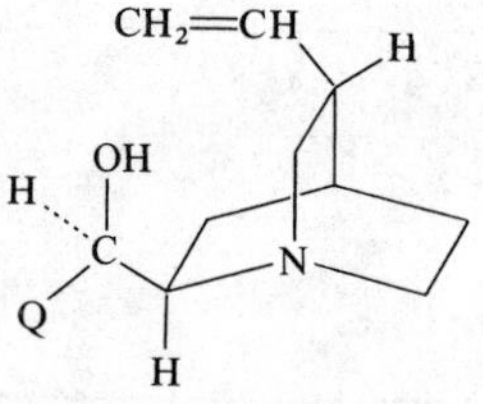

epiquinidine

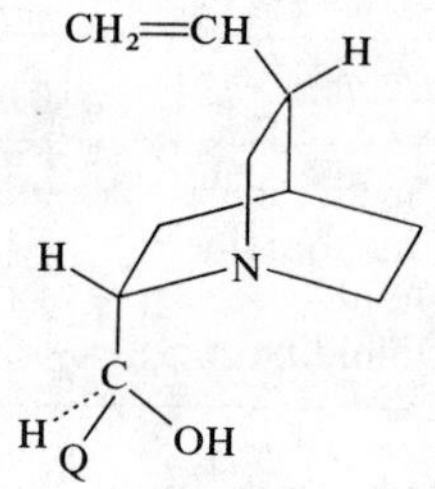

epiquinine

ISOQUINOLINE GROUP

Opium alkaloids.   Many alkaloids have been isolated from opium, and they are divided into two groups according to the nature of their structure:

   (i) *Isoquinoline group*, *e.g.*, papaverine, laudanosine, etc.
   (ii) *Phenanthrene group*, *e.g.*, morphine (see §27).

§26. Papaverine, $C_{20}H_{21}NO_4$, m.p. 147°

This is one of the optically inactive alkaloids; it does not contain any chiral centre. The structure of papaverine was established by Goldschmiedt and his co-workers (1883–1888), and their work is a very good example of the application of oxidative degradation to structure determination of the alkaloids.

   Since papaverine adds on one molecule of methyl iodide to form a quaternary iodide, the nitrogen atom in the molecule is in the tertiary state. The application of the Zeisel method shows the presence of four methoxyl groups; the demethylated product is known as papaveroline.

$$C_{20}H_{21}NO_4 + 4HI \longrightarrow 4CH_3I + C_{16}H_{13}NO_4$$
papaverine   papaveroline

When oxidised with cold dilute permanganate, papaverine is converted into the secondary alcohol papaverinol, $C_{20}H_{21}NO_5$. This, on more vigorous oxidation with hot dilute permanganate, is oxidised to the ketone papaveraldine, $C_{20}H_{19}NO_5$ (it is the formation of this *ketone* that shows that papaverinol is a *secondary* alcohol). Finally, the prolonged action of hot permanganate oxidises papaveraldine to papaverinic acid, $C_{16}H_{13}NO_7$. This is a dibasic acid and still contains the keto group present in its precursor—it forms an oxime, etc.; papaverinic acid also contains two methoxyl groups. The foregoing reactions led to the conclusion that papaverine contains a methylene group.

$$(C_{19}H_{19}NO_4)CH_2 \xrightarrow{\text{[O]}} (C_{19}H_{19}NO_4)CHOH \xrightarrow{\text{[O]}} (C_{19}H_{19}NO_4)CO$$
papaverine   papaverinol   papaveraldine

When oxidised with hot concentrated permanganate, papaverine (or the oxidised products mentioned above) is broken down into small fragments, *viz.*, veratric acid, metahemipinic acid, pyridine-2,3,4-tricarboxylic acid and 6,7-dimethoxyisoquinoline-1-carboxylic acid. Let us now consider the evidence for the structures of these compounds.

Veratric acid. When decarboxylated, veratric acid forms veratrole. Since this is *o*-dimethoxybenzene, veratric acid is therefore a dimethoxybenzoic acid. The position of the carboxyl group with respect to the two methoxyl groups (in the *ortho*-position) is established by the following synthesis.

veratric acid

Thus veratric acid is 3,4-dimethoxybenzoic acid.
Metahemipinic acid. This is a dicarboxylic acid, and when decarboxylated by heating with calcium oxide, veratrole is formed; thus metahemipinic acid contains two methoxyl groups in the *ortho*-position. Furthermore, since the acid forms an anhydride when heated with acetic anhydride, the two carboxyl groups must be in the *ortho*-position. Hence metahemipinic acid is either (I) or (II). Now metahemipinic acid forms only *one* mono-ester; (II) permits the formation of only one monoester, but (I) can give rise to two different monoesters. Thus (II) is metahemipinic acid; (I) is actually hemipinic acid (this isomer was known before metahemipinic acid).

(I)
hemipinic acid

(II)
metahemipinic acid

Pyridine-2,3,4-tricarboxylic acid. The routine tests showed that this contains three carboxyl groups, and since decarboxylation gives pyridine, the acid must be a pyridinetricarboxylic acid. The positions of the three carboxyl groups are established by the fact that this pyridinetricarboxylic acid is produced when lepidine (4-methyl-quinoline) is oxidised.

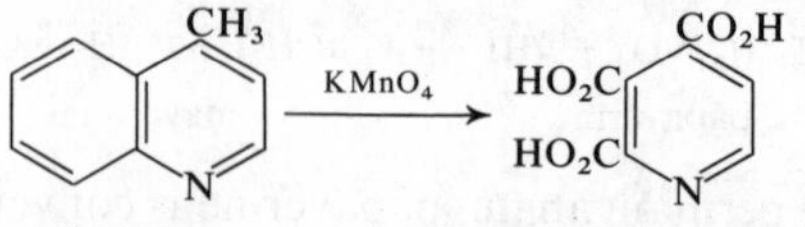

lepidine → (KMnO₄) → pyridine-2,3,4-tricarboxylic acid

6,7-Dimethoxyisoquinoline-1-carboxylic acid. The usual tests showed that this compound contains one carboxyl group and two methoxyl groups. On oxidation, this acid forms pyridine-2,3,4-tricarboxylic acid; when decarboxylated, the acid forms a dimethoxyisoquinoline which, on oxidation, gives metahemipinic acid; thus the structure is established.

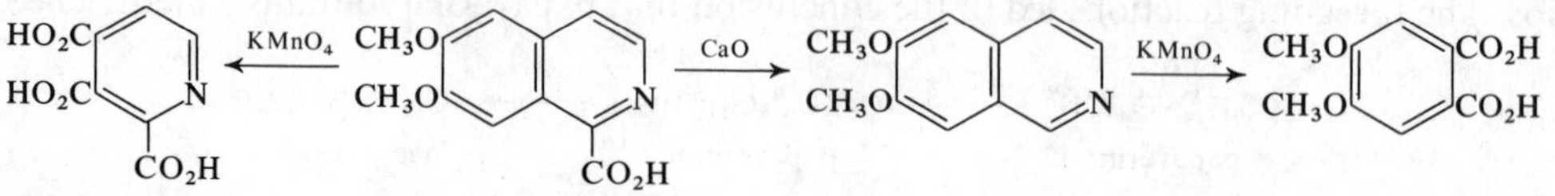

pyridine-2,3,4-tricarboxylic acid ← (KMnO₄) — 6,7-dimethoxy-isoquinoline-1-carboxylic acid — (CaO) → — (KMnO₄) → metahemipinic acid

We may now deduce the structure of papaverine as follows:

(i) The isolation of veratric acid indicates the presence of group (III) in papaverine.

(ii) The isolation of 6,7-dimethoxyisoquinoline-1-carboxylic acid indicates the presence of group (IV) in the molecule.

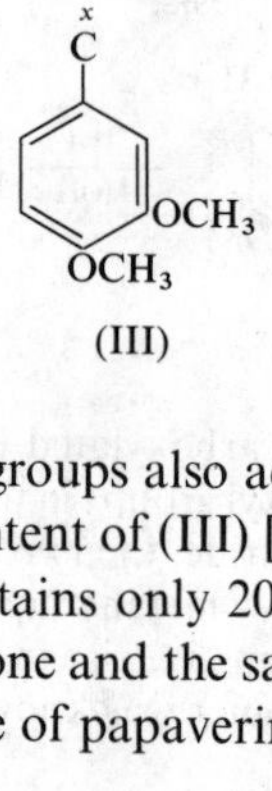

(III) 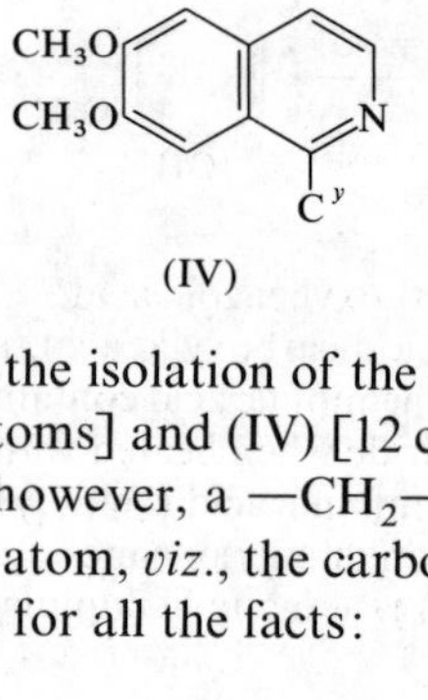   (IV)

The presence of these two groups also accounts for the isolation of the other two fragments.

(iii) The total carbon content of (III) [9 carbon atoms] and (IV) [12 carbon atoms] is 21 carbon atoms. But papaverine contains only 20. There is, however, a —CH_2— group present, and if we assume that C^x and C^y are one and the same carbon atom, viz., the carbon atom of the CH_2 group, then the following structure of papaverine accounts for all the facts:

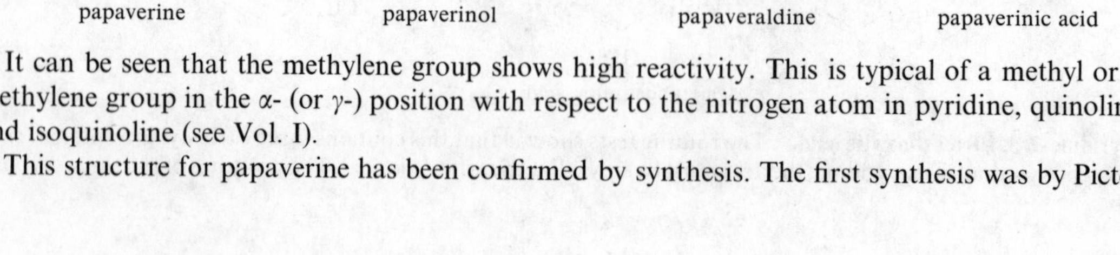

papaverine — [O] → papaverinol — [O] → papaveraldine — [O] → papaverinic acid

It can be seen that the methylene group shows high reactivity. This is typical of a methyl or a methylene group in the α- (or γ-) position with respect to the nitrogen atom in pyridine, quinoline and isoquinoline (see Vol. I).

This structure for papaverine has been confirmed by synthesis. The first synthesis was by Pictet and Gams (1909), but Bide and Wilkinson (1945) carried out a simpler one, and it is this that is described here.

(i) [CH₃O, CH₃O substituted benzene] $\xrightarrow[\text{HCl}]{\text{HCHO}}$ [CH₃O, CH₃O–benzene–CH₂Cl] $\xrightarrow{\text{KCN}}$ [CH₃O, CH₃O–benzene–CH₂CN]

$\xrightarrow{\text{H}_2-\text{Raney Ni}}$ [CH₃O, CH₃O–benzene–CH₂CH₂NH₂] homoveratrylamine

(i) HCl
(ii) PCl₅ $\rightarrow$ [CH₃O, CH₃O–benzene–CH₂COCl] homoveratroyl chloride

(ii) [CH₃O,CH₃O–benzene–CH(CH₂)–CH₂–NH₂ + COCl–CH₂–benzene–OCH₃,OCH₃] $\xrightarrow{\text{heat}}$ [amide: CH₃O,CH₃O–benzene–CH(CH₂)CH₂–NH–CO–CH₂–benzene–OCH₃,OCH₃] $\xrightarrow{\text{P}_2\text{O}_5}$ [CH₃O,CH₃O–benzene–CH(CH₂)CH₂–N=C(OH)–CH₂–benzene–OCH₃,OCH₃] $\xrightarrow{-\text{H}_2\text{O}}$

[dihydroisoquinoline: CH₃O,CH₃O–ring–CH₂CH₂–N=C–CH₂–benzene–OCH₃,OCH₃] $\xrightarrow[\text{asbestos; 200°C}]{\text{Pd on}}$ [CH₃O,CH₃O–isoquinoline–N=, –CH₂–benzene–OCH₃,OCH₃] papaverine

The cyclodehydration step is an example of the Bischler–Napieralski reaction (see Vol. I).

An interesting reaction of papaverine is its reduction by tin and hydrochloric acid to two products, norlaudanosine ((V); see also §26a) and pavine (VI). The formation of (V) is not unexpected in that

[MeO,MeO–isoquinoline–N, –CH₂–benzene–OMe,OMe] $\xrightarrow{\text{Sn/HCl}}$ [MeO,MeO–tetrahydroisoquinoline–NH, –CH₂–benzene–OMe,OMe] (V) + [MeO,MeO ... NH ... OMe,OMe bridged structure] (VI)

it is known that tin and hydrochloric acid reduce isoquinoline to 1,2,3,4-tetrahydroisoquinoline *via* the 1,2-dihydro-compound (see Vol. I). Pavine, however, must have been formed by some rearrangement. One suggestion is that the 1,2-dihydropapaverine is produced first. This has an enamine structure (see Vol. I) and, on protonation, forms an iminium salt which undergoes an intramolecular nucleophilic cyclisation.

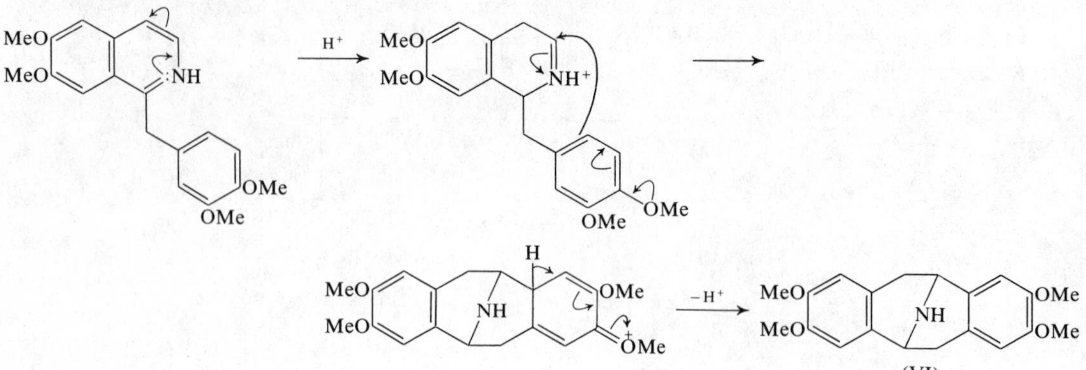

§26a. Some other alkaloids of the isoquinoline group are:

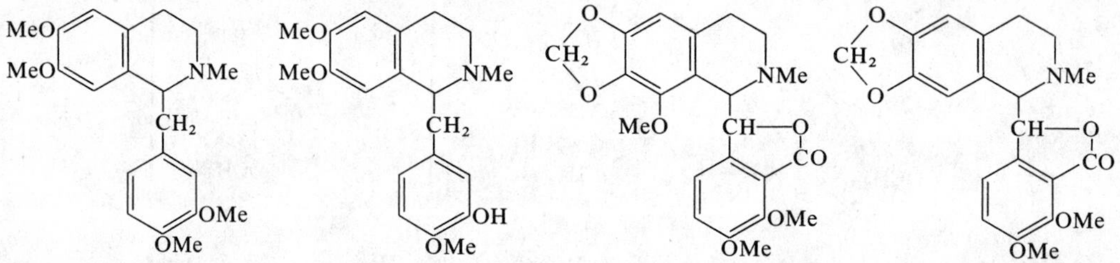

laudanosine   laudanine   narcotine   hydrastine

PHENANTHRENE GROUP

§27. Morphine, codeine and thebaine

These are three important opium alkaloids which contain the phenanthrene nucleus.

$(-)$-**Morphine**, $C_{17}H_{19}NO_3$, m.p. 254°C, $[\alpha]_D - 131°$, is the chief alkaloid in opium, and was the first alkaloid to be isolated (Sertürner, 1806). The usual tests show that the nitrogen atom is in the tertiary state, and since morphine forms a diacetate (known as **heroin**) and a dibenzoate, two hydroxyl groups are therefore present in the molecule. Morphine gives the ferric chloride test for phenols, and dissolves in aqueous sodium hydroxide to form a *monosodium* salt, and this is re-converted into morphine by the action of carbon dioxide; thus *one* of the hydroxyl groups is phenolic (Matthiessen *et al.*, 1869). The second hydroxyl group is secondary alcoholic, as is shown by the following reactions. Halogen acids convert morphine into a monohalogeno derivative, one hydroxyl group being replaced by a halogen atom. When heated with methyl iodide in the presence of aqueous potassium hydroxide, morphine is methylated to give $(-)$-**codeine**, $C_{18}H_{21}NO_3$, m.p. 155°C, $[\alpha]_D - 135°$ (Grimaux, 1881). Since codeine is no longer soluble in alkalis, it therefore follows that it is only the *phenolic* hydroxyl group in morphine that has been methylated. Further-more, codeine can be oxidised by chromic acid to *codeinone*, a ketone (Hesse, 1884). Thus the hydroxyl group in codeine (and this one in morphine) is secondary alcoholic, and so codeine is the monomethyl (phenolic) ether of morphine. Also, codeine absorbs one molecule of hydrogen on catalytic reduction (Pd), and therefore both codeine and morphine contain one ethylenic bond.

$(-)$-**Thebaine,** $C_{19}H_{21}NO_3$, m.p. 193°C, $[\alpha]_D$ $-219°$, produces two molecules of methyl iodide when heated with hydriodic acid (Zeisel method); hence thebaine is a dimethoxy derivative. When heated with sulphuric acid, thebaine eliminates one methyl group as methyl hydrogen sulphate, and forms codeinone (Knorr, 1906). The formation of a *ketone* led Knorr to suggest that thebaine is the methyl ether of the *enolic* form of codeinone. The foregoing work can thus be summarised by assigning the following formulae to the compounds described:

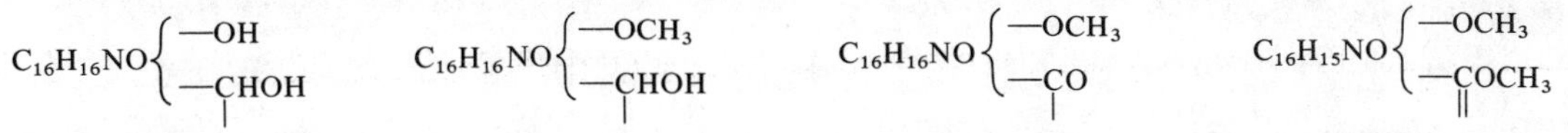

$$C_{16}H_{16}NO\begin{cases} -OH \\ -CHOH \\ | \end{cases}\qquad C_{16}H_{16}NO\begin{cases} -OCH_3 \\ -CHOH \\ | \end{cases}\qquad C_{16}H_{16}NO\begin{cases} -OCH_3 \\ -CO \\ | \end{cases}\qquad C_{16}H_{15}NO\begin{cases} -OCH_3 \\ -COCH_3 \\ \| \end{cases}$$

$$\quad\text{morphine}\qquad\qquad\qquad\text{codeine}\qquad\qquad\qquad\text{codeinone}\qquad\qquad\qquad\text{thebaine}$$

So far, we have accounted for the functional nature of two of the oxygen atoms; the unreactivity of the third oxygen atom suggests that it is probably of the ether type (Vongerichten, 1881).

All three alkaloids are tertiary bases (each combines with one molecule of methyl iodide to form a methiodide). When heated with hydrochloric acid at 140°C under pressure morphine loses one molecule of water to form *apomorphine*, $C_{17}H_{17}NO_2$. Codeine, under the same conditions, also gives apomorphine (and some other products). Thebaine, however, when heated with dilute hydrochloric acid, forms *thebenine*, $C_{18}H_{19}NO_3$ (a secondary base), and with concentrated hydrochloric acid, morphothebaine, $C_{18}H_{19}NO_3$ (a tertiary base). Thus in the formation of thebenine from thebaine, a tertiary nitrogen atom is converted into a secondary one. For this change to occur, the tertiary nitrogen must be of the type $>NR$, where the nitrogen is in a ring system; had the nitrogen been in the group $-NR_2$, then the formation of a *primary* base could be expected. The presence of a cyclic tertiary base system is supported by the fact that codeine, when subjected to exhaustive methylation, produces α-codeimethine, the formula of which contains one more CH_2 than codeine itself, and the nitrogen atom is not lost. If codeine contains an acyclic t-amine system, then the product would contain fewer carbon atoms and loss of nitrogen would occur. If codeine contains a t-cyclic base system, the results are then readily explained:

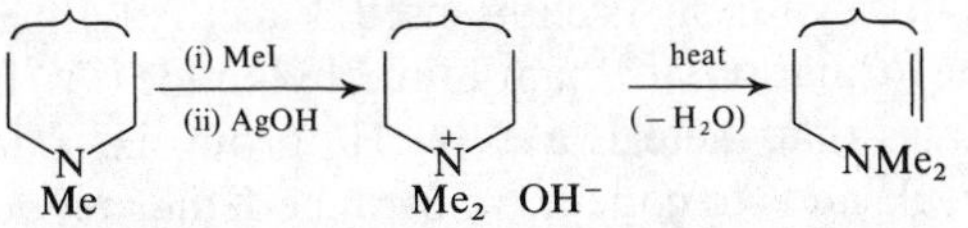

Evidence for the *N*-methyl group is given later, and it should be noted that α-codeimethine and its β-isomer are identical with α- and β-methylmorphimethine, respectively (see below).

When morphine is distilled with zinc dust, phenanthrene and a number of bases are produced (Vongerichten *et al.*, 1869). This suggests that a phenanthrene nucleus is probably present, and this has been confirmed as follows. When codeine methiodide (I) is boiled with sodium hydroxide solution, α-methylmorphimethine (II) is obtained and this, on heating with acetic anhydride, forms methylmorphol (III) and ethanoldimethylamine (IV) [some of (II) isomerises to β-methylmorphimethine].

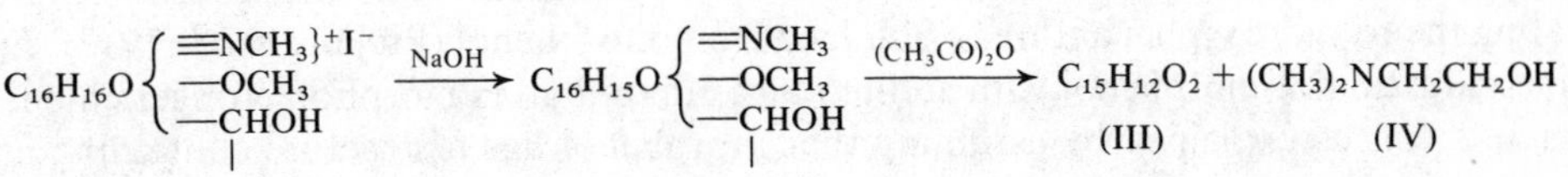

$$C_{16}H_{16}O\begin{cases} \equiv NCH_3\}^+I^- \\ -OCH_3 \\ -CHOH \\ | \end{cases}\xrightarrow{NaOH} C_{16}H_{15}O\begin{cases} =NCH_3 \\ -OCH_3 \\ -CHOH \\ | \end{cases}\xrightarrow{(CH_3CO)_2O} C_{15}H_{12}O_2 + (CH_3)_2NCH_2CH_2OH$$

$$\qquad\qquad\qquad\text{(I)}\qquad\qquad\qquad\qquad\qquad\text{(II)}\qquad\qquad\qquad\qquad\text{(III)}\qquad\qquad\text{(IV)}$$

The structure of methylmorphol (III) was ascertained by heating it with hydrochloric acid at 180°C under pressure; methyl chloride and a dihydroxyphenanthrene, *morphol*, were obtained. Oxidation of diacetylmorphol gives a diacetylphenanthraquinone; thus positions 9 and 10 are free. On further oxidation (permanganate), the quinone is converted into phthalic acid; therefore the two hydroxyl groups are in the same ring. Since the fusion of morphine with alkali gives protocatechuic acid, this shows that both hydroxyl groups in morphol are in the *ortho*-position. Finally, Pschorr *et al.* (1900) showed by synthesis that dimethylmorphol is 3,4-dimethoxyphenanthrene (*cf.* Pschorr synthesis, **10** §2vi*a*).

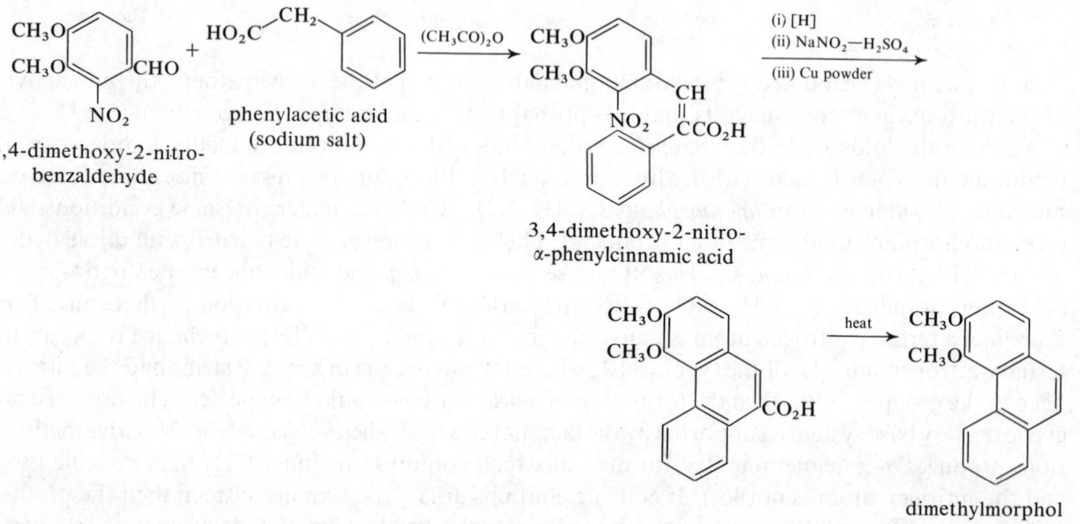

3,4-dimethoxy-2-nitro-
benzaldehyde

phenylacetic acid
(sodium salt)

3,4-dimethoxy-2-nitro-
α-phenylcinnamic acid

dimethylmorphol

Then Pschorr *et al.* (1902) synthesised methylmorphol (III), and showed it to be 4-hydroxy-3-methoxyphenanthrene (in this synthesis Pschorr used 3-acetoxy-4-methoxy-2-nitrobenzaldehyde).

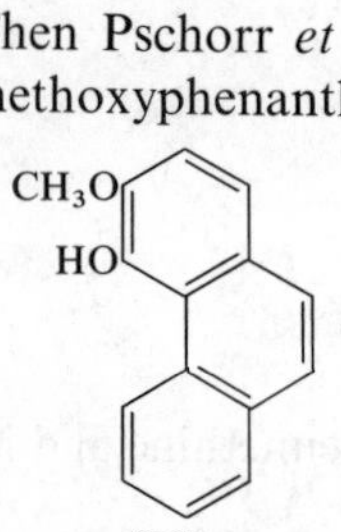

(III)
methylmorphol

The formation of ethanoldimethylamine (IV) from α-methylmorphimethine indicates that there is a $>NCH_3$ group in codeine (only *one* methyl iodide molecule adds to codeine to form codeine methiodide; it has also been shown above that this nitrogen is in a heterocyclic ring). This is confirmed by the following evidence. When codeine is subjected to the von Braun degradation (§4), three hydrogen atoms are lost and one nitrogen atom is added. This can readily be interpreted by the conversion of $>NCH_3$ into $>NCN$, and so it follows that all three alkaloids contain an *N*-methyl group.

When β-methylmorphimethine is heated with water, the products obtained are trimethylamine, ethylene and *methylmorphenol* (Vongerichten, 1896). Demethylation of this compound with hydrochloric acid produces *morphenol*, a compound which contains one phenolic hydroxyl group and an inert oxygen atom. On fusion with potassium hydroxide, morphenol gives 3,4,5-trihydroxyphenanthrene (Vongerichten *et al.*, 1906). The structure of this compound was shown by the synthesis of 3,4,5-trimethoxyphenanthrene, which was found to be identical with the product obtained by methylating the trihydroxyphenanthrene obtained from morphenol (Pschorr *et al.*, 1912). Furthermore, the reduction of morphenol with sodium and ethanol gives morphol (Vongerichten, 1898). These results can be explained by assuming that morphenol has a structure containing an ether linkage in positions 4,5 (of the phenanthrene nucleus).

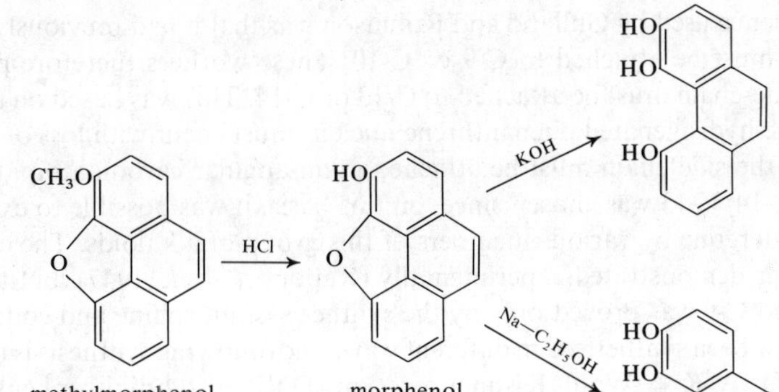

methylmorphenol

morphenol

morphol

Codeinone, on heating with acetic anhydride, gives ethanolmethylamine and the diacetyl derivative of 4,6-dihydroxy-3-methoxyphenanthrene.

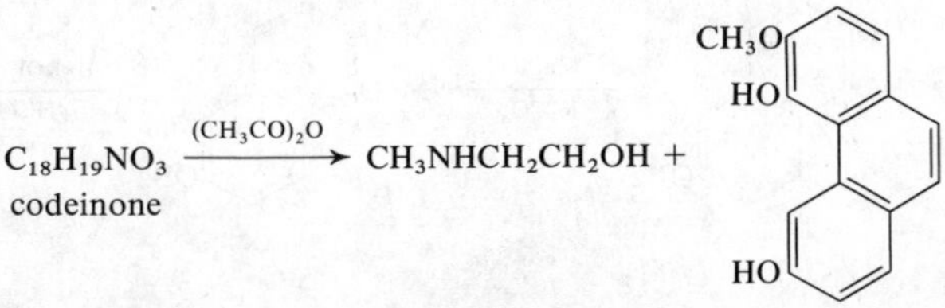

$$C_{18}H_{19}NO_3 \xrightarrow{(CH_3CO)_2O} CH_3NHCH_2CH_2OH +$$

codeinone

The position 3 of the methoxyl group and the position 4 of the hydroxyl group have already been accounted for; the hydroxyl group in the 6-position must therefore be produced from the oxygen of the keto group in codeinone.

Based on the foregoing evidence, and a large amount of other experimental work, Gulland and Robinson (1923, 1925) proposed the following structures; these have been written with the configurations assigned by later workers (see below).

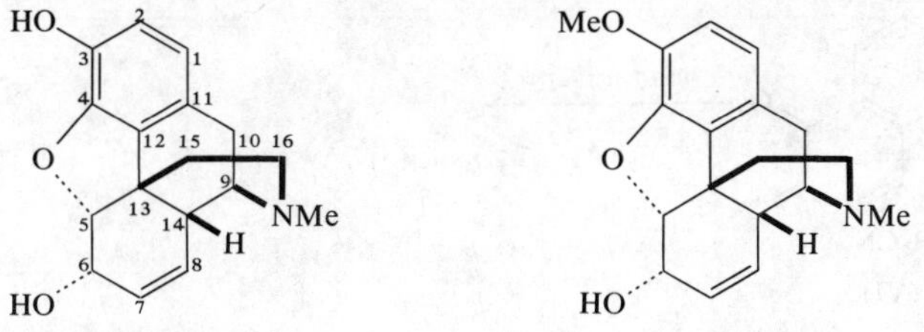

morphine

codeine

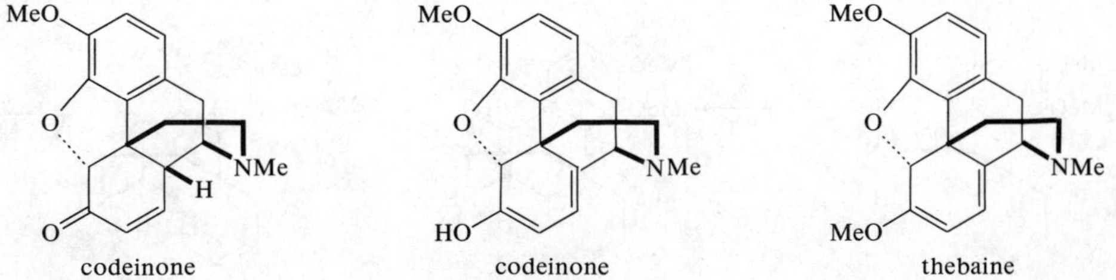

codeinone

codeinone
(an enol form)

thebaine

One piece of evidence used by Gulland and Robinson was that it had previously been shown that the nitrogen atom must be attached to C-9 or C-10. These workers therefore proposed that the nitrogen–carbon side-chain must be attached to C-13 or C-14. This was based on the argument that aromatisation of the hydrogenated phenanthrene nucleus must occur with loss or migration of that side-chain. Hence, the side-chain must be attached at an angular carbon atom. Of the two possibilities, C-13 and C-14, C-13 was chosen since, on this basis, it was possible to explain some of the rearrangements undergone by various members of this group of alkaloids. The correctness of this assignment was later demonstrated experimentally (Rapoport *et al.*, 1947), but the attachment of the nitrogen atom to C-9 was proved only by the synthesis of morphine and codeine.

Morphine has now been synthesised in different ways; the following synthesis is that of Gates *et al.* (1956) [Bz = PhCO; W-K = Wolff–Kishner reaction; DNP = 2,4-dinitrophenylhydrazine].

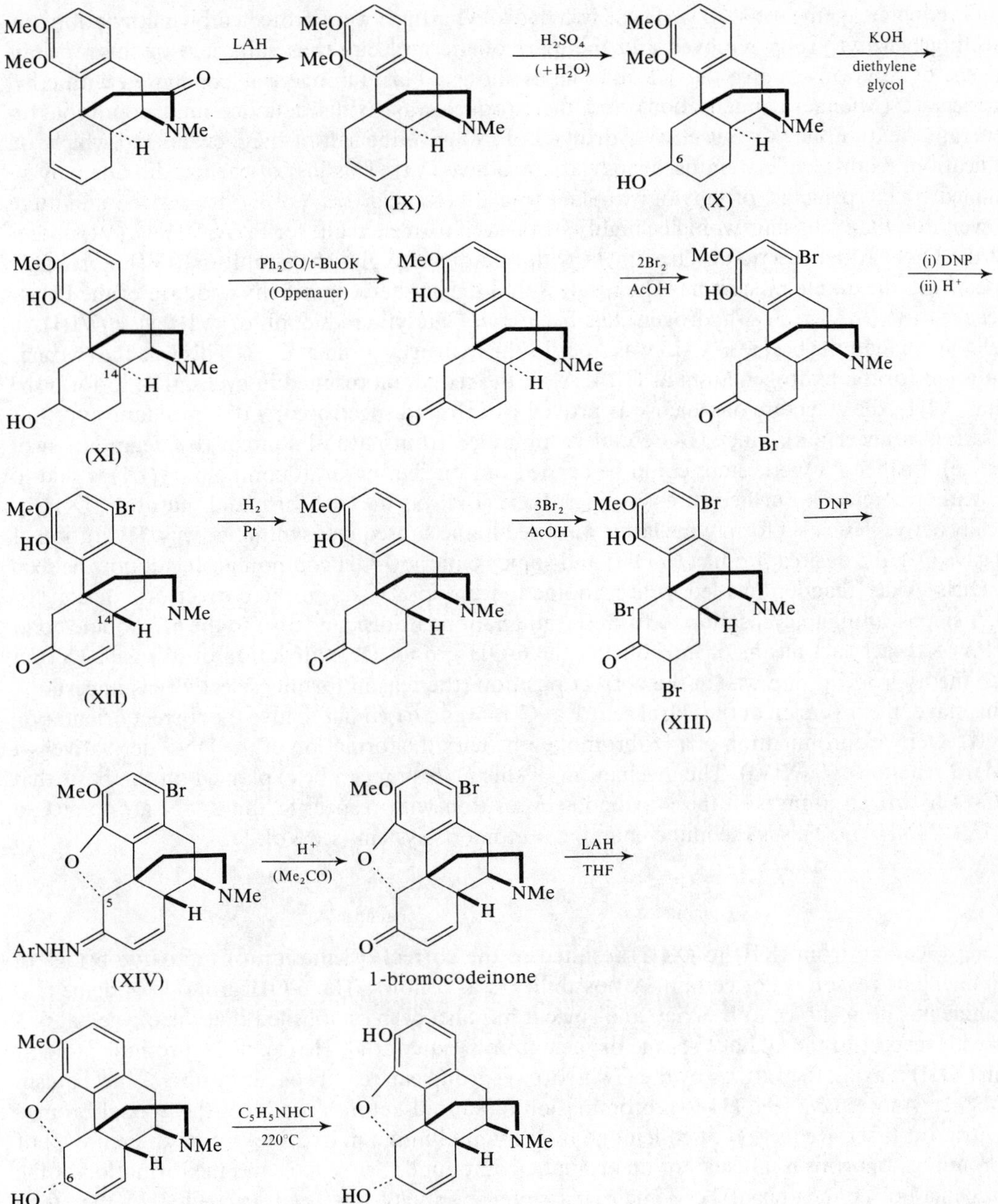

(IX)

(X)

(XI)

(XII)

(XIII)

(XIV)

1-bromocodeinone

codeine

morphine

The approach adopted by Gates was the synthesis of the hydrophenanthrene precursor. Since the Schotten–Baumann method of benzoylation (see Vol. I) produced the dibenzoate of 2,6-dihydroxy-naphthalene, the conditions for monobenzoylation had to be worked out. The object of this protection of one hydroxyl group was to permit the carrying out of the desired sequence of reactions at one part of the molecule at a time. Nitrosation gave the 1-nitroso-compound and oxidation of the 1-amino-2-hydroxy-derivative gave the 1,2-quinone which was readily reduced by sulphur dioxide (a mild reducing agent; see Vol. I). These two hydroxyl groups were protected by methylation, the protecting benzoyl group removed and this part of the molecule was subjected to the previous sequence of reactions to give the 1,2-quinone as shown. This quinone was condensed with ethyl cyanoacetate (Michael condensation) and the product was oxidised under mild conditions to regenerate the quinone (V). Selective hydrolysis of (V) gave the salt of the α-cyanoacid which, on acidification, readily underwent decarboxylation to give (VI). This loss of carbon dioxide may be explained by the principle of vinylogy applied to a β-keto-acid (see Vol. I). It must be admitted, however, that the cyclic state would be highly strained (if formed at all; see EAA, Vol. I). (VI) underwent the Diels–Alder reaction on treatment with butadiene to give the enol form ((VII); probably formed from the diketo precursor). The result is that the *cis*-stereospecificity addition of the Diels–Alder reaction (to give a *cis*-hydrogen) has been lost. Catalytic reduction of (VII) gave (VIII), in which the ethanamine bridge at C-13 was *trans* to the hydrogen atom at C-14. This was the 'wrong' orientation for the hydrogen atom at C-14. Also, the reduction resulted in cyclisation to form the lactam (VIII), the structure of which was proved by infrared spectroscopy (the mechanism of this cyclisation is uncertain). Since (IX) could be obtained from natural sources (by degradation of thebaine), further synthetic steps could be carried out on the 'natural' compound ((IX) is said to be a synthetic 'relay'). Furthermore, since synthetic (IX) was the ($\pm$)-form and 'natural' (IX) was optically active—the ($+$)-form—the latter was used in the subsequent synthetic steps. Hydration of (IX) gave (X), the desired product (6-OH) and some isomeric 7-OH compound. It can now be seen that Diels–Alder reaction has led to a cyanomethyl group at C-13 in the correct orientation for further steps leading to cyclisation to form the ethanamine bridge, and also to the 6,7-double bond which was to act as a means of introducing the 6-OH group. Demethylation of (X) gave (XI) in which the hydroxyl group was in the correct position (the reason for this selectivity is uncertain). At this stage, the inversion of the chiral centre at C-14 was carried out to give the correct orientation in (XII). Dehydrobromination of an α-bromoketone with the formation of the DNP derivative is a standard reaction (*cf.* (XIV)). The mechanism of this inversion can be explained on the basis that the C-14 hydrogen atom is in the vinylogous α-position with respect to the C=N group at C-6 (*i.e.*, C_6=NNHAr). This is the imine-enamine tautomeric system (see Vol. I):

$$N=C-C=C-CH \qquad\qquad HN-C=C-C=C$$

$$\text{imine}\qquad\qquad\qquad\qquad\qquad \text{enamine}$$

The steps leading from (XII) to (XIII) resulted in the correct orientation of the oxide bridge in morphine. The reason is not certain. A possibility is as follows. The 6-OH group in codeine and morphine has been shown to be axial, and since it has also been established that the oxygen at C-5 is *cis* with respect to the OH at C-6, the oxygen atom is equatorial. Hence, if the bromine atom at C-5 in (XIII) is axial, then attack by the C-4 hydroxyl group can readily occur by an S_N2 mechanism (see **4** §12). As we have seen (**11** §8), bromination of steroid ketones produces the α-axial bromo-derivative (at first). Reduction of codeinone by lithium aluminium hydride caused the removal of the bromine atom (this is unusual for an aromatic compound; See Vol. I) and the formation of the correct alcohol epimer (axial), codeine. This stereospecificity has been attributed to the steric hindrance caused by the benzene ring.

Stereochemistry of morphine and codeine. Each of these compounds contains five chiral centres (5, 6, 9, 13, and 14), but since the bridged ring system across positions 9, 13 must be *cis*, eight pairs of enantiomers are possible for each compound. A great deal of chemical work has been carried out to deduce the stereochemistry of codeine and has led to the configuration given above, *i.e.*, the hydrogen atoms at C-5, C-6, and C-14 are all *cis*, and the bridge at C-9 and C-13 is also *cis*. This stereochemistry has been confirmed by X-ray analysis (Mackay *et al.*, 1955), but it was not possible, however, to determine the absolute configuration by this method. This has been done as follows.

Degradation of thebaine gave the dicarboxylic acid (XV), thereby establishing the absolute stereochemistry at C-13 and C-14 (Kalvoda *et al.*, 1955). The conformational formulae of morphine and codeine may be written as (XVI). The chair form has been used for the cyclohexene ring and rings I, II, and the oxide bridge lie approximately in the plane of the paper and rings III and IV are approximately perpendicular to the plane of the paper.

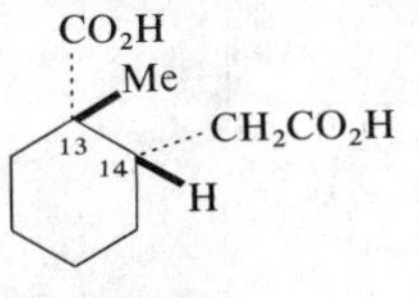

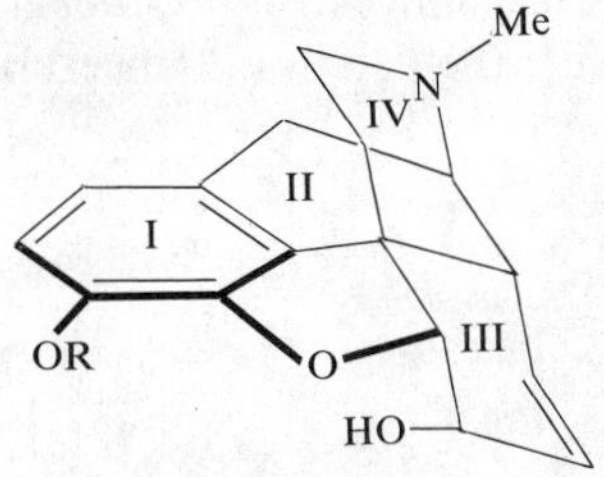

morphine: R = H

codeine: R = Me

(XV)   (XVI)

§27a. Molecular rearrangements.

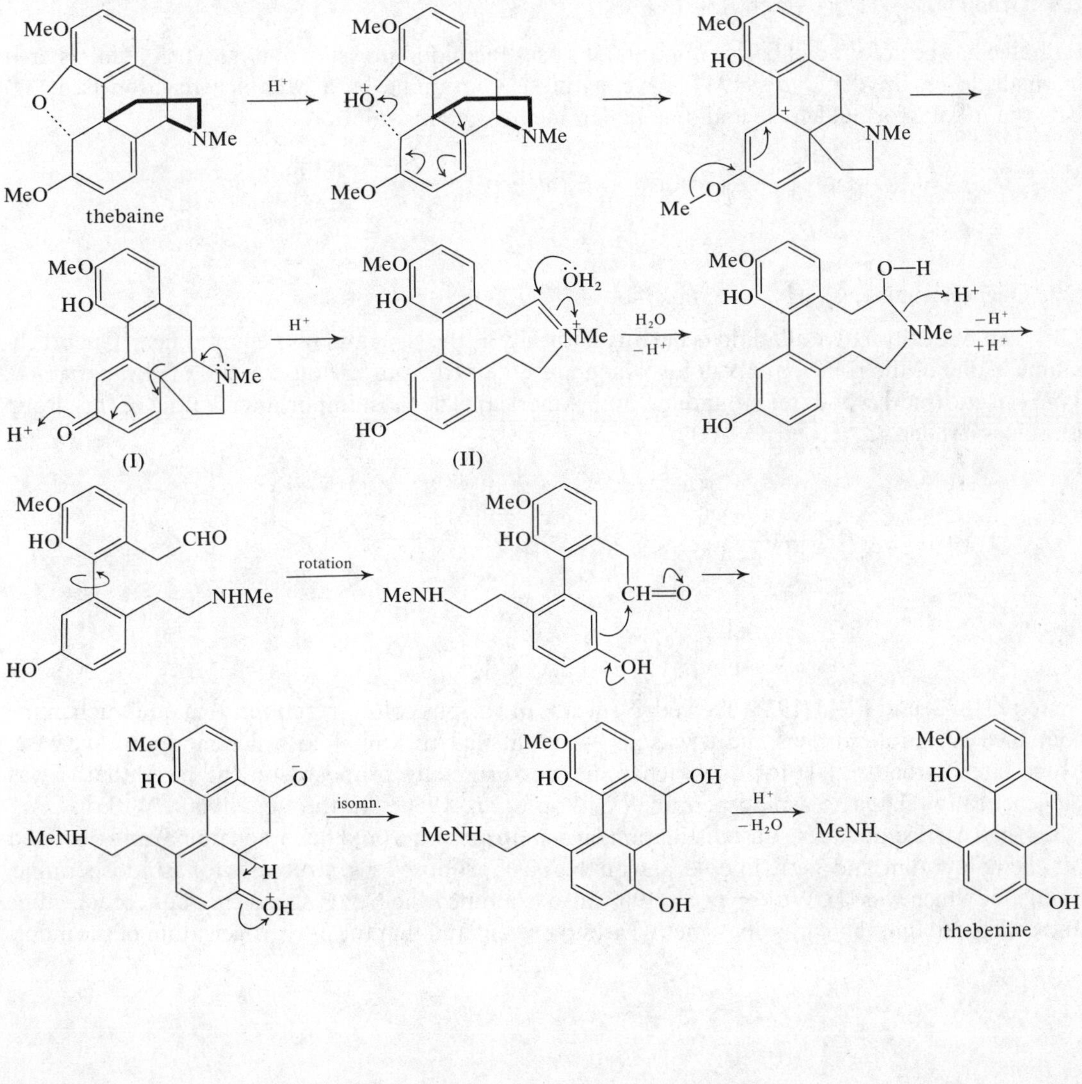

Thebaine and its derivatives undergo many types of rearrangement, most of which occur under the influence of acid, *e.g.*, when heated with dilute hydrochloric acid, thebaine rapidly undergoes rearrangement to form thebenine. One suggestion is that the change occurs *via* a dienone–phenol rearrangement, (I) → (II) [see also Vol. I]. Since changes of ring-size occur, this rearrangement may also be regarded as an example of the Wagner–Meerwein rearrangement (**8** §23d). Evidence for the existence of the dienone has been obtained. The salt of the Schiff base (II) is readily hydrolysed to the aldehyde (see Vol. I).

Morphine, when heated with concentrated hydrochloric acid, undergoes rearrangement to form apomorphine. It is possible that this change also occurs *via* a dienone–phenol rearrangement (and Wagner–Meerwein rearrangement); the details are uncertain.

morphine   apomorphine

INDOLE GROUP

§28. Gramine, $C_{11}H_{14}N_2$, m.p. 134°C

Gramine has been found in barley mutants; it raises the blood pressure in dogs when administered in small doses. Snyder *et al.* (1944) have synthesised gramine by a Mannich reaction (see §32) between indole, formaldehyde and dimethylamine in aqueous solution.

§29. Quebrachamine, $C_{19}H_{26}N_2$, m.p. 146–147°C

This is an optically active alkaloid occurring naturally as the (+)- and (−)-enantiomers. Quebrach-amine is one of the principal alkaloids which are obtained from various species of *Aspidosperma*, *Vallesia*, etc. (hard-wood trees found in South America). The most important alkaloid of this group is **aspidospermine**, $C_{22}H_{30}N_2O_2$, (I)

(I)   (II)

Hesse (1882) and Field (1924) showed, by means of various colour reactions, that quebrachamine contained an indole nucleus and it was also thought that this alkaloid was a monotertiary base. Much later, structure (II) for quebrachamine was originally proposed on the basis that it was biogenetically related to aspidospermine (Witkop *et al.*, 1960; Smith *et al.*, 1960). Witkop *et al.* (1954) had carried out a zinc dust distillation on aspidospermine (and quebrachamine) and obtained 3,5-diethylpyridine and 3-ethylindole, and on this basis proposed two structures for aspidospermine, neither of which was (I). Witkop *et al.* (1960) also examined the NMR spectrum of quebrachamine and concluded that there was no *N*-methyl group present and that the 2-hydrogen atom of the indole nucleus was absent (see (II)). Then Mills *et al.* (1960) proposed structure (I) for aspidospermine on the information obtained from X-ray analysis, and this structure has been confirmed by total syntheses (Stork *et al.*, 1963; Kutney *et al.*, 1969).

Biemann *et al.* (1961, 1962) re-examined the products of the zinc dust distillation of quebrachamine by means of mass spectrometry and observed peaks corresponding to substituted pyridines containing two, three and four carbon atoms and peaks corresponding to substituted indoles of m/e 131, 145, 159, and 173. A more detailed examination of these products by gas chromatography combined with mass spectrometry showed that the pyridine derivatives were 3-ethyl- ((III); 75 per cent), 3-methyl-5-ethyl- (12 per cent), 3-ethyl-4-methyl- (5 per cent), and 3,5-diethylpyridine (5 per cent). Four indoles (3-Me, 2-Et, 2,3-Me$_2$, and 2,3-Et$_2$) were also identified. Of these indole derivatives, 2,3-diethylindole (IV) has the highest molecular weight, and on the basis of this fragment and that of the predominant pyridine fragment, 3-ethylpyridine, Biemann deduced that the structure of quebrachamine was either (II) or (IIa), and chose (II) because of its relationship to aspidospermine (I).

(III)   (IV)

(II) R^1 = H; R^2 = Et
(IIa) R^1 = Et; R^2 = H

(V)

These assumptions were proved correct by making use of the *mass-spectrometric shift technique* (Biemann, 1960). This is based on the assumption that substitution in the benzene ring of indole- and dihydroindole-containing alkaloids does not change the pattern of fragmentation. The consequence of this is that all fragments which do *not* contain the substituent will appear in both spectra, whereas those *containing* the substituent will be shifted to a higher mass, *e.g.*, if one compound contains a methoxyl group, the methoxy-containing fragments will all have (m/e + 30) compared with m/e for the *non* methoxy-containing compound. Furthermore, the similarity of structures of two alkaloids is demonstrated by this method even though these structures are not actually known.

The mass spectra of quebrachamine (II) and its 17-methoxy-derivative ((V); see also (I) for numbering) prepared from aspidospermine (I) were found to be similar: (i) both exhibited a number of identical peaks which had about the same intensity; (ii) a number of peaks in (II) were shifted by 30 mass units in (V). Structure (II) for quebrachamine has been confirmed by total syntheses (Kutney *et al.*, 1969; Ziegler *et al.*, 1969).

The mass spectrum of deacetylaspidospermine ((I); replace the 1-COMe by 1-H) was also examined by Biemann. The important characteristics of the mass spectrum were the intense molecular ion ($M = 312$), a medium ion m/e 284, and a very intense ion m/e 124. The molecular ion is presumably formed by loss of an electron from the alicyclic nitrogen atom. A point of interest is that the ethyl group attached to a quaternary carbon atom is not lost; the ethylene is produced from

deacetylaspidospermine
$M = 312$

m/e 284

m/e 124

carbon atoms 3 and 4. This scheme is supported by the fragmentation patterns observed with de-acetylaspidospermine labelled with deuterium at C-2. This pattern of fragmentation, particularly the formation of the ion m/e 284, has been used to elucidate the structures of many alkaloids related to aspidospermine.

§30. Heptaphylline, $C_{18}H_{17}NO_2$, m.p. 170–171°C

An optically inactive alkaloid, it was isolated from the hexane extracts of the roots of *Clausena heptaphylla*, followed by chromatographic separation on silica-gel (Joshi *et al.*, 1967). These workers obtained its molecular formula from elemental analysis and mass spectrometry (M^+ 279), and elucidated its structure mainly by physical methods. The ultraviolet spectrum showed bands at 234, 278, 298, and 346 nm. This suggested the presence of a carbazole nucleus because of the close resemblance to a known carbazole compound, murrayanine. Moreover, the presence of the carb-azole nucleus was supported by the fact that heptaphylline gave a green colour reaction with concentrated sulphuric and nitric acids.

Examination of the infrared spectrum of heptaphylline indicated the presence of an imino (NH) and/or a hydroxyl group (3 300 cm^{-1}), a formyl atom (2 740 cm^{-1}), and an intramolecularly hydrogen-bonded carbonyl group (1 645 cm^{-1}). Bands at 1 618 and 1 590 cm^{-1} were assigned to an aromatic system.

Since heptaphylline gave a blue colour on treatment with an ethanolic solution of ferric chloride, a phenolic hydroxyl group was assumed to be present. Also, formation of a dinitrophenylhydrazone confirmed the presence of the carbonyl group, and reduction of ammoniacal silver nitrate showed the carbonyl group to be aldehydic. This formyl group was placed in the 3-position (of the carbazole nucleus) because examination of the ultraviolet spectra of 1-, 2-, 3-, and 4-formylcarbazole showed that the ultraviolet spectrum of heptaphylline closely resembled that of 3-formylcarbazole.

From the information obtained so far, we may write the structure of heptaphylline as (I).

(I)

The hydroxyl group must be in the 2 or 4 position in order to form an intramolecular hydrogen bond with the formyl group.

The NMR spectrum of heptaphylline showed the following peaks: (i) τ 8·34 (d, J 1 Hz; 3H); (ii) τ 8·17 (d, J 1 Hz; 3H); (iii) τ 6·40 (d, J 6 Hz; 2H); (iv) τ 4·65 (bt, J 6 Hz; 1H); (v) τ 2·9 − 1·7 (m; 4H); (vi) τ 1·75 (s; 1H); (vii) τ 0·1 (s; 1H); (viii) τ −1·4 (s; 1H); (ix) τ −1·6 (s; 1H).

These signals account for the seventeen hydrogen atoms in the molecule, and their possible assignments are as follows:

(II)

(i) and (ii). These are two methyl groups attached to an ethylenic carbon atom, *i.e.*, Me$_2$C= group (see **9** §1). Since the signals are doublets, this indicates the grouping —CH=CMe$_2$.

(iii). This is a benzylic methylene group, *i.e.*, Ar—CH$_2$.

(iv). This broad triplet suggests a vinyl proton, and so we may now account for the five carbon atoms as shown in (II). From this it follows that the carbazole nucleus contains an amino hydrogen atom. Structure (II) accounts for all of the carbon atoms in heptaphylline.

Hence, the nitrogen atom of the carbazole nucleus cannot be substituted by a carbon-containing group (see also below).

(v) and (vi). These indicate aromatic protons, and since (vi) is a singlet, this means that one benzene ring of carbazole contains a hydrogen atom that is not flanked by *ortho*-hydrogen atoms. Hence, the C_5-side-chain must be in the benzene ring containing the hydroxyl and formyl groups (see (I)).

(vii). This signal corresponds to the formyl hydrogen atom.

(viii) and (ix). One of these signals corresponds to the hydroxyl hydrogen atom, since this group is known to be present. Hence, the other signal must correspond to an imino hydrogen atom; this has already tentatively proposed above; see (iv). The presence of two protons capable of undergoing chemical exchange (see 1 §12e) was confirmed by the fact that in the NMR spectrum of deuterated heptaphylline the two signals (viii) and (ix) were now absent.

The problem now was to ascertain the positions of the hydroxyl group and the side-chain (in the same benzene ring). This was done by heating heptaphylline (III) with polyphosphoric acid. This produced an isomeric compound ((IV); $C_{18}H_{17}NO_2$), m.p. 250°C. The ultraviolet spectrum of (IV) differed very little from that of (III), but the infrared spectrum of (IV) now showed a band at $1\,670\ cm^{-1}$, which corresponds to the usual region of the carbonyl group in an aromatic aldehyde (*cf.* with (III), above).

The NMR spectrum of (IV) showed a singlet signal at $\tau\ 8.58$ ($6H = 2$ Me), and two triplets at $\tau\ 8.0$ and $\tau\ 7.05$. Hence, in (IV) the two methyl groups are now equivalent and there is no long-range coupling. Also, the two triplets suggest the presence of the grouping $Ar—CH_2—CH_2—$, since the singlet for the vinyl proton (in (III)) had now disappeared. These findings led Joshi *et al.* to propose that (IV) had been formed from (III) by cyclisation involving the hydroxyl group and the double bond in the side-chain. This is possible only if these two groups are in the *ortho*-position. Hence, the hydroxyl group must be in the 2-position and the side-chain in the 1-position. On this basis, heptaphylline was given structure (III).

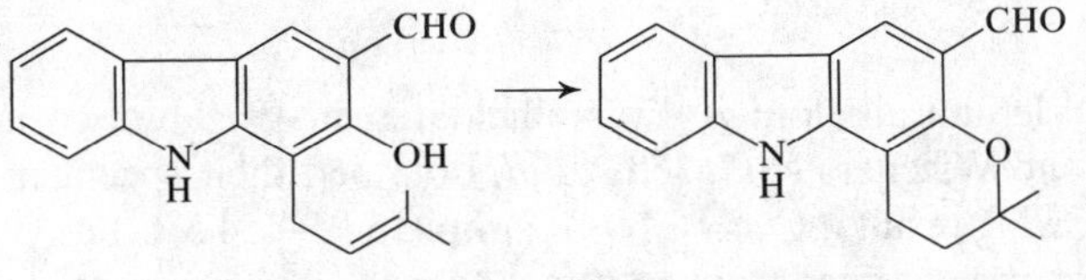

(III)   (IV)

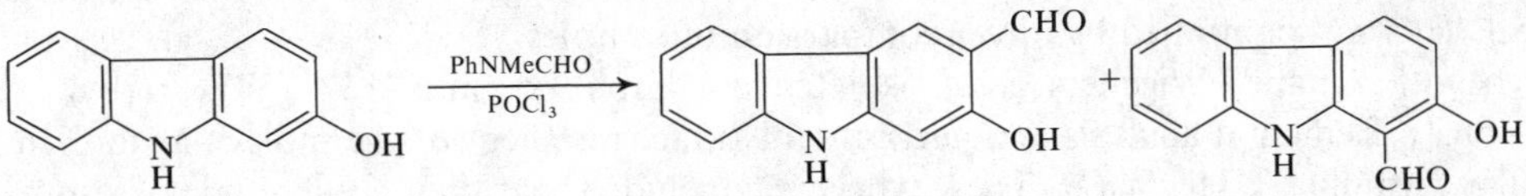

(V)   (VI)   (VII)

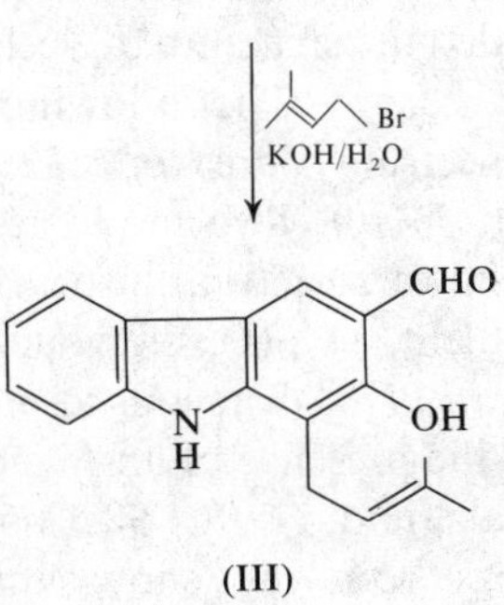

(III)

Joshi *et al.* (1968) confirmed structure (III) by synthesis. They used the Vilsmeier–Haak aldehyde synthesis (see Vol. I) on 2-hydroxycarbazole (V). This gave a mixture of the 3- (VI) and the 1-aldehyde (VII). These were separated chromatographically and (VI), on prolonged shaking with 3,3-dimethyl-allyl bromide in the presence of aqueous potassium hydroxide, gave heptaphylline (III).

§31. Sceletium alkaloid A_4

A number of alkaloids have been isolated from the *Sceletium* species, the most important of which is **mesembrine** (I). The structure of this alkaloid (which is based on the octahydroindole ring system) was established by Popelak *et al.* (1960) by degradative work, and was confirmed by a total synthesis by Shamma *et al.* (1965).

Popelak *et al.* also separated (by paper chromatography) a number of new alkaloids from the *Sceletium* species, among which was one they named Alkaloid Sceletium A_4, $C_{20}H_{24}N_2O_2$, m.p. 155–156°C (ethyl acetate). This was shown to contain two methoxyl groups and one N-methyl and, since it contained one more nitrogen atom than mesembrine (I), Popelak believed that the new alkaloid belonged to a separate structural group in the mesembrine series.

(I)	(II)	(III)	(IV)	(V)
mesembrine	Sceletium alkaloid A_4			

The structure of Sceletium alkaloid A_4 was elucidated in 1971 by two independent groups of workers—Jeffs *et al.* and Wiechers *et al.* Jeffs *et al.* obtained their specimen from *S. namaquense*, and recorded the following results: $C_{20}H_{24}N_2O_2$, m.p. 153·5–154·5°C (ethyl acetate), $[\alpha]_D$ +131°. The molecular formula was obtained from an accurate mass measurement of the molecular ion, and the similarity of their data to those reported by Popelak suggested that the two alkaloids were identical. This was confirmed by direct comparison of samples.

On the other hand, Wiechers *et al.* isolated a compound, m.p. 132–134°C (ethyl acetate), $[\alpha]_D$ −40·5°. Elemental analysis and accurate mass measurement of the molecular ion led to the molecular formula $C_{20}H_{24}N_2O_2$. These workers concluded that their compound corresponded to Sceletium alkaloid A_4 (of Popelak) and that their specimen was in the partially racemised form. Both groups of workers elucidated the structure of Sceletium alkaloid A_4 (II) by the application of i.r., u.v., NMR, and mass spectroscopy. The following is mainly the work of Wiechers. The most abundant ions in the mass spectrum were: m/e 323 ($M - 1$), 309, 296 ($C_{18}H_{20}N_2O_2$), 281 ($C_{18}H_{19}NO_2$), and 266 ($C_{17}H_{16}NO_2$). Two moderately abundant ions, m/e 219 ($C_{13}H_{17}NO_2$) and 57, however, provided the most structural information. All the mesembrane alkaloids which possess a 3α-dimethoxyl substituent, *e.g.*, (I), show an abundant peak at m/e 219, which has been attributed to ion (III) [Jeffs *et al.*, 1970]. The ions at m/e 281 ($M - C_2H_5N$), 266 ($M - C_3H_8N$), and 57 (IV) are consistent with the presence of an N-methylpyrrolidine ring.

The infrared spectrum of the alkaloid, 1 605, 1 582, 1 571, and 1 520 cm^{-1}, confirmed the presence of the benzene and pyridine rings (both rings show similar i.r. spectra).

The ultraviolet spectrum of Sceletium alkaloid A_4, λ_{max} 232, 268, 274, and 286 nm, closely matched the summation ultraviolet spectrum of 3,4-dimethoxytoluene and 2,3-dimethylpyridine. Jeffs *et al.* prepared (V) as a model and showed that its u.v. spectrum closely resembled that of Sceletium alkaloid A_4 (II).

The NMR spectrum at 100 MHz (Wiechers *et al.*) showed three three-proton singlets at τ 7·66 (NMe), 6·3 (OMe), 6·23 (OMe), and a multiplet at τ 3·52–3·28 corresponding to three aromatic protons. Also observed were signals at τ 1·52 (dd), 2·44 (dd), and 2·85 (dd) corresponding to a 2,3-disubstituted pyridine ring.

Taking into account all the spectral data and that two methylene groups in an additional ring would give the molecular formula $C_{20}H_{24}N_2O_2$, Wiechers *et al.* proposed (II) as the structure for Sceletium alkaloid A_4.

The evidence obtained by Jeffs *et al.* was substantially the same as that of Wiechers *et al.*, but the former group confirmed structure (II) by X-ray analysis, and also determined the stereochemistry of the alkaloid (as shown in (II)).

§32. Biosynthesis of alkaloids

As more and more structures of alkaloids were elucidated, it became increasingly probable that the precursors in the biosynthesis of many alkaloids were amino-acids and amino-aldehydes or amines derived from them. A particularly interesting point is that the consideration of biosynthesis has led to deductions in structure, *e.g.*, Woodward (1948) proposed a biosynthesis of strychnine, and from this Robinson (1948) deduced the structure of emetine which was later confirmed by the synthetic work of Battersby *et al.* (1950) [see also §29].

Because of the great diversity of structure, it is not possible to develop only one pathway for the biosynthesis of all alkaloids. Thus many pathways have been proposed, each one accounting for the biosynthesis of a number of alkaloids of related structure. What follows is only an indication of some of the pathways that are generally acceptable, and it should be noted that many of the intervening steps are uncertain and that the 'starting compounds' are substances which have been synthesised in the organism.

The most common amino-acids (see **13** §18 for their biosynthesis) that act as precursors in alkaloid biosynthesis are the following:

$$H_2N(CH_2)_3CH(NH_2)CO_2H$$
ornithine

$$H_2N(CH_2)_4CH(NH_2)CO_2H$$
lysine

phenylalanine: R = H
tyrosine: R = OH

tryptophan

$$MeSCH_2CH_2CH(NH_2)CO_2H$$
methionine

Many types of reactions have been postulated for the biosynthetic conversion of amino-acids into alkaloids. Some of the more important ones are described here, but the enzymes involved in these transformations are not discussed (see also **13** §13–§17).

(i) **Decarboxylation.** This results in the formation of an amine.

$$RCH(NH_2)CO_2H \longrightarrow RCH_2NH_2 + CO_2$$

(ii) **Oxidative deamination.** This type of reaction can take place in different ways (see also **13** §18).

$$\text{(a)}\quad RCH(NH_2)CO_2H \longrightarrow RCOCO_2H \longrightarrow RCHO$$

$$\text{(b)}\quad RCH(NH_2)CO_2H \longrightarrow RCH_2NH_2 \longrightarrow RCHO$$

(iii) **Schiff base formation** (see also Vol. I).

$$R^1CHO + R^2NH_2 \longrightarrow R^1CH{=}NR^2$$

(iv) **Mannich reaction.** This is the reaction between a molecule with an active hydrogen atom, an aldehyde, and an amine (see also Vol. I). A 'Mannich intermediate' is believed to be formed first, e.g.,

$$HCHO + Et_2NH \longrightarrow Et_2\overset{+}{N}{=}CH_2 + H_2O$$

This intermediate is a quaternary Schiff base. The following steps then occur.

$$R^1{-}\overset{\overset{O}{\|}}{C}{-}CH_3 \rightleftharpoons R^1{-}\overset{\overset{OH}{|}}{C}{=}CH_2 \quad CH_2{=}\overset{+}{N}R_2^2 \longrightarrow R^1{-}\overset{\overset{+}{O}H}{\underset{}{C}}{-}CH_2{-}NR_2^2 \longrightarrow R^1{-}\overset{\overset{O}{\|}}{C}{-}CH_2{-}\overset{+}{N}HR_2^2$$

These two reactions, (iii) and (iv), are extremely important in that they both lead to the formation of a carbon-nitrogen bond.

(v) **Oxidative phenol coupling.** This, basically, is the coupling between two phenolic compounds brought about by oxidising agents which produce free radicals. Coupling between the two molecules can be C—C, C—O, or O—O. The most important is the first, and can be *ortho-ortho*, *ortho-para*, or *para-para* (see Vol. I).

(vi) Other reactions involved in alkaloid biosynthesis are oxidation, reduction, hydration, dehydration, rearrangements, alkylation, acylation, etc.

The general technique for elucidating biosynthetic pathways is to test postulated routes by means of labelled precursors administered to plants. After a suitable time has elapsed, the alkaloid is isolated from the plant and the isotopic content is examined (see also **8** §34).

§32a. Phenylethylamine group (§§6–12a).   The starting point for these alkaloids is phenylalanine, and this is synthesised by the shikimic acid route (**13** §18). Methionine (represented as Me—S in the equations) has been shown to be the source of both *O*- and *N*-methyl groups of many alkaloids. Formate can also act as a source for *N*-methyl, and is the source for *C*-methyl groups.

phenylalanine   nor-ψ-ephedrine

ephedrine

tyrosine   tyramine   *N*-methyltyramine

Ephedrines have been shown to be metabolites of phenylalanine, whereas hordenine and mescaline are metabolites of tyrosine (which is itself derived from phenylalanine; see **13** §18). Introduction of *C*-methyl has been shown to occur *via* formic acid (labelled with ^{14}C) and not by reduction of the carboxyl group (in the precursor). Tyrosine labelled with ^{14}C at the α-carbon atom leads to the predicted labelled positions of *N*-methyltyramine, hordenine, and mescaline. Labelled dopa (3,4-dihydroxyphenylalanine) at the α-carbon atom also leads to the predicted labelled mescaline.

§32b. Pyrrolidine alkaloids (§§13–14). The starting compounds are *N*-methyl-Δ¹-pyrrolinium cation and acetoacetic acid. The former is derived from ornithine and related amino-acids (see §32d) and the latter from acetic acid (see **8** §34).

It should be noted that the pathways described involve Mannich reactions (see also §32c).

§32c. Piperidine alkaloids (§§18–19). There are several ways in which the piperidine nucleus can be synthesised in the plant, and the pathway depends on the nature of the alkaloid. The precursor for the pelletierines is lysine, which is first converted into the *N*-methyl-Δ¹-piperidinium cation (*cf*. §32b). This then undergoes a Mannich reaction with acetoacetic acid, etc.

The actual step involved in methylation is uncertain; it may occur later (isopelletierine also occurs naturally).

A difficulty with the biosynthetic pathway described above is the way in which lysine is converted into the cation. It has been shown that lysine labelled at C-6 (^{14}C) gave *N*-methylisopelletierine labelled at C-6. This is in keeping with the pathway given above (but see the pyrrolidine-pyridine group, §32d).

At first sight, it might have been anticipated that coniine, which closely resembles isopelletierine, follows the same biosynthetic route. When labelled experiments were carried out, it was found that lysine was a very poor precursor for coniine. Further work with labelled acetate (CH$_3$ĊO$_2$H) showed that coniine was derived from four acetate units, and so a polyketide intermediate has been suggested. Furthermore, since labelled γ-coniceine is incorporated by hemlock to give labelled coniine, the biosynthetic pathway shown has been proposed.

polyketide

γ-coniceine   coniine

§32d. Pyrrolidine–pyridine alkaloids (§§21–23a).

The pyridine ring has been shown, by means of labelled precursors, to be formed in plants by several routes. Nicotinic acid is the precursor of the pyridine ring of nicotine (§21), and there is a great deal of evidence to show that this acid is produced *via* quinolinic acid, *e.g.*, nicotinic acid and quinolinic acid are equally good precursors. The biosynthesis of the pyridine ring in nicotinic and quinolinic acids has been the subject of much debate, but it now appears that glycerol and aspartic acid are involved. One possible biosynthetic pathway is:

glycerol   glyceraldehyde   aspartic acid
                  3-phosphate

quinolinic acid   nicotinic acid

Tracer experiments have shown that the pyrrolidine ring may be derived from ornithine, putrescine (and its *N*-methyl derivative), and γ-methylaminobutyraldehyde. These are very efficient precursors; less efficient ones are glutamic acid and proline. Thus, a possible biosynthetic pathway to *N*-methyl-Δ¹-pyrrolinium cation, with ornithine as the precursor, is:

HO$_2$C   NH$_2$ NH$_2$ → NH$_2$ NH$_2$ → NH$_2$ NHMe → OHC   NHMe → (pyrrolinium with Me, positions 2 and 5)

ornithine   putrescine   Me

When 2-^{14}C-ornithine was used as precursor, nicotine was obtained which was labelled equally at positions 2 and 5 in the pyrrolidine ring. This is in keeping with the formation of a symmetrical intermediate, *viz.* putrescine. This would be expected to be methylated equally well at either amino-group.

A point of interest in this connection is the biosynthesis of the piperidine ring from lysine (§32c). Some workers have proposed that the pathway involves the formation of cadaverine [H$_2$N(CH$_2$)$_5$NH$_2$] as an intermediate, and that this follows the path given for pyrrolidine. However, as was pointed out, experiments with labelled lysine appear to have excluded the formation of a symmetrical intermediate.

H$_2$N   O   CO$_2$H   →✗→   H$_2$N   H$_2$N

lysine   cadaverine

The final problem with the biosynthesis of nicotine is how the two rings link together. Labelled experiments have shown that the carboxyl group in nicotinic acid is not incorporated into nicotine. A possible mechanism, based on the use of labelled nicotinic acid, is (note the loss of hydride ion):

(reaction scheme)   nicotine

Tropane alkaloids (§§22–23a). It has been shown that precursors of tropine are ornithine, *N*-methyl-putrescine, hygrine, etc. However, in this case, 2-^{14}C-ornithine gave rise to tropine labelled at C-1 (and not 1 and 5 as in nicotine; see above). Also, starting with *N*-methylputrescine labelled H$_2$N(CH$_2$)$_4$^{15}NH^{14}CH$_3$, produced tropine with ^{15}N^{14}CH$_3$. This establishes the fact that the nitrogen atom in the alkaloid is derived from the amino-acid precursor. A possible biosynthetic pathway is:

(i)   (reaction scheme with CO$_2$H, NMe, =O) → (NMe, CO$_2$H, =O) → (NMe, =O) hygrine →

(NMe, =O, CH$_2$) → (NMe, =O) tropinone →

(NMe, OH) tropine → (NMe, OOCH, CH$_2$OH, Ph) hyoscyamine

(ii)   (NMe, CO$_2$H, =O) ----→ (NMe, CO$_2$H, OH) ecgonine → (NMe, CO$_2$Me, OOCPh) cocaine

Labelled experiments have shown that phenylalanine is the precursor of tropic acid (in hyocyamine) and benzoic acid (in cocaine), the former being produced *via* a rearrangement (* and • indicate the positions of ^{14}C in *separate* labelled experiments).

$$Ph-\overset{*}{C}O_2H \longleftarrow Ph-\overset{*}{C}H_2-\underset{NH_2}{\overset{\bullet}{C}H}-CO_2H \xrightarrow{\text{rearr.}} Ph-\overset{*}{C}H-CH_2OH$$
$$\bullet CO_2H$$

§**32e. Quinoline alkaloids** (§§24–25).   The biosynthesis of the cinchona alkaloids has been shown to proceed from tryptophan as the precursor. Another precursor is believed to be **secologanin**, which is derived from **loganin**, a natural terpenoid of the iridoid group (**8** §18a), and has been shown to be derived from mevalonic acid (**8** §34). Thus (G = glucose):

mevalonic acid   loganin   secologanin

We may now give some of the steps involved in the biosynthesis of quinine (note the Pictet–Spengler reaction; see Vol. I).

(i)   tryptophan   tryptamine

(ii)   tryptamine   +   secologanin

quinine

§32f. Isoquinoline alkaloids (§§26–26a).   Tracer experiments have shown that papaverine is derived from tyrosine. This produces dopamine and 3,4-dihydroxyphenylacetaldehyde (or the pyruvic acid, —CH$_2$COCO$_2$H; see also §32a). These undergo condensation (Pictet–Spengler), etc.

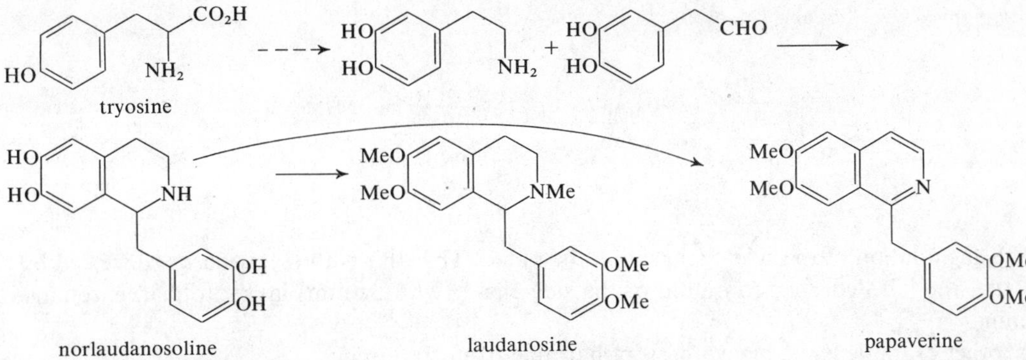

tryosine

norlaudanosoline   laudanosine   papaverine

§32g. Phenanthrene alkaloids (§27).   It is now believed that the opium alkaloids are biosynthesised from the alkaloid **reticuline** (which occurs in opium). Reticuline can be derived from norlaudanosoline (§32f) and leads to thebaine, codeine, and morphine *via* an oxidative phenol coupling step (see §32).

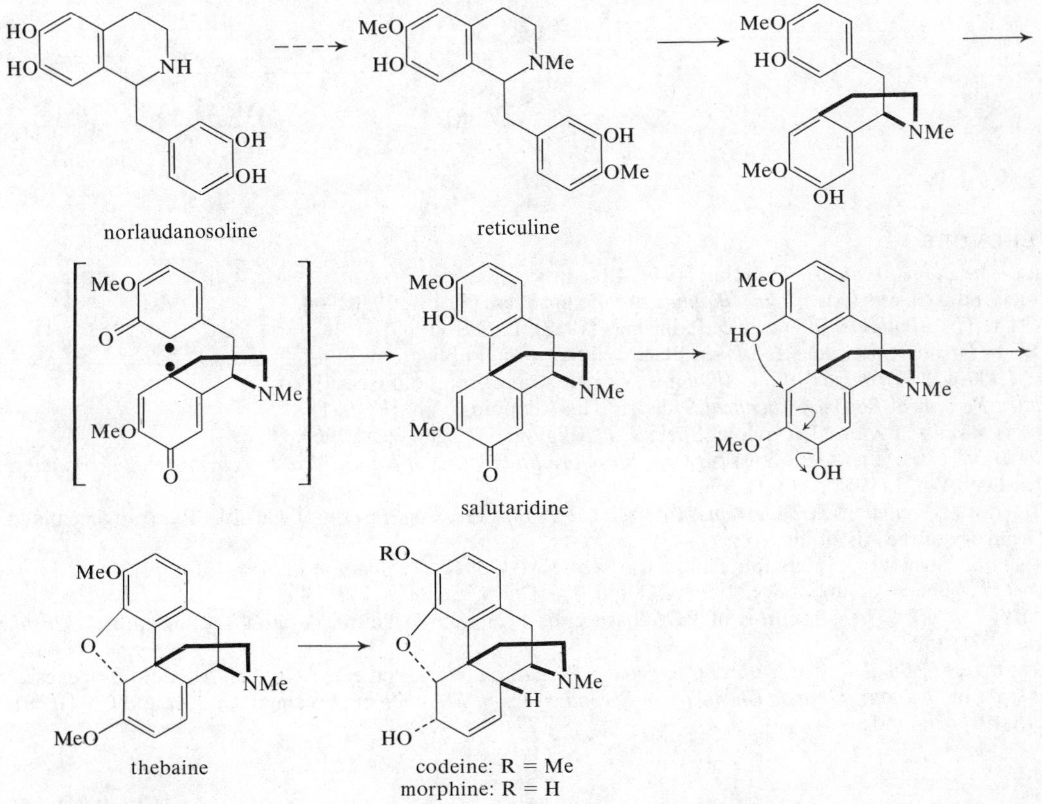

norlaudanosoline   reticuline

salutaridine

thebaine   codeine: R = Me
                            morphine: R = H

§32h. Indole alkaloids (§§28–31).   Most of the indole alkaloids are derived from tryptophan, *e.g.*, gramine (§28). In the chart, RCHO stands for pyridoxal phosphate (**13** §18).

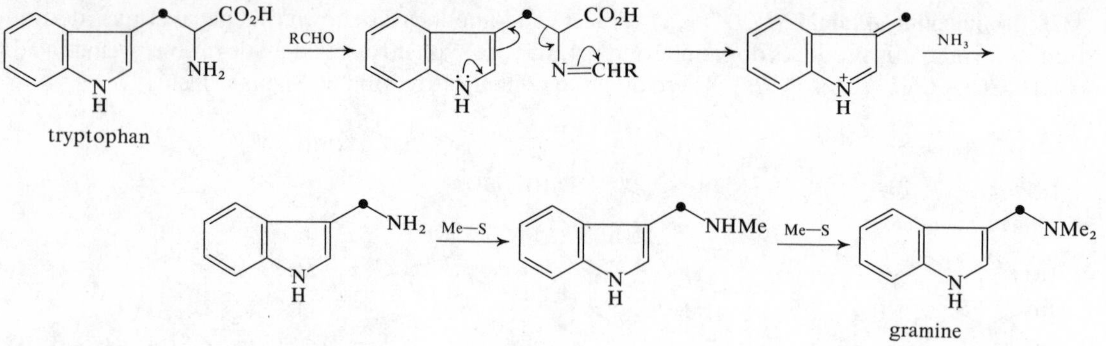

tryptophan

gramine

The degradation of the side-chain should be noted. That this is the sequence is suggested by the fact that the labelled β-carbon atom of the side-chain (with tritium) in tryptophan is retained in gramine.

Another example is the biosynthesis of harmine from tryptophan.

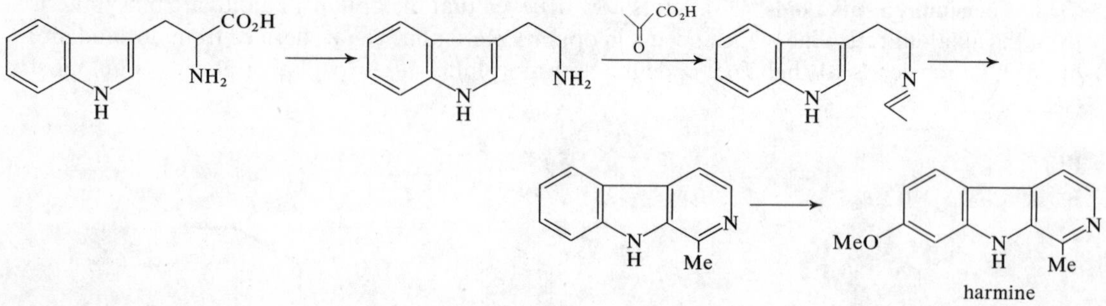

harmine

REFERENCES

HENRY, *The Plant Alkaloids*, Churchill (1949, 4th edn.).

MANSKE and HOLMES (eds.), *The Alkaloids*, Academic Press (Vol. 1, 1950; —).

BENTLEY, *The Alkaloids*, Interscience Publishers (1957). Part II (1965).

SWAN, *An Introduction to the Alkaloids*, Blackwell Scientific Publications (1967).

PELLETIER (ed.), *Chemistry of the Alkaloids*, Van Nostrand Reinhold Co. (1970).

Specialist Periodical Reports, Chemical Society. 'The Alkaloids.' Vol. 1 (1971).

SANGSTER and STUART, 'Ultraviolet Spectra of Alkaloids', *Chem. Rev.*, 1965, **65**, 69.

BUDZIKIEWICZ, DJERASSI and WILLIAMS, *Structure Elucidation of Natural Products by Mass Spectrometry*, Holden-Day. Vol. I (1964). Vol. II (1964).

MAYO (ed.), *Molecular Rearrangements*, Interscience Publishers. Part 11 (1964). Ch. 14. 'Rearrangements in the Chemistry of the Alkaloids.'

JOSHI *et al.*, 'Structure of Heptaphylline, a Carbazole Alkaloid', *Tetrahedron Letters*, 1967, 4019.

JEFFS *et al.*, 'The Structure of Sceletium Alkaloid A$_4$', *Chem. Comm.*, 1971, 1466.

WIECHERS *et al.*, 'The Structures of Partial Racemic Sceletium Alkaloid A$_4$ and Tortuosamine', *Chem. Comm.*, 1971, 1467.

BERNFELD (ed.), *Biogenesis of Natural Compounds*, Pergamon (1967, 2nd edn.). Ch. 17. 'Alkaloid Biogenesis.'

GEISSMAN and CROUT, *Organic Chemistry of Secondary Plant Metabolism*, Freeman, Cooper and Co. (1969). Chs. 15–19. 'Alkaloids.'

15 Anthocyanins

§1. Introduction

Anthocyanins are natural plant pigments; they are glycosides and their aglycons, *i.e.*, the sugar-free pigments, are known as the *anthocyanidins*. The anthocyanins, which are water-soluble pigments, generally occur in the aqueous cell-sap, and are responsible for the large variety of colours in flowers; red—violet—blue. Willstätter *et al.* (1913–) showed that the various shades of colour exhibited by all flowers are due to a very small number of different compounds. Furthermore, these different compounds were shown to contain the same carbon skeleton, and differed only in the nature of the substituent groups. The anthocyanin pigments are amphoteric; their acid salts are usually red, their metallic salts usually blue and in neutral solution the anthocyanins are violet (see also §5).

In addition to anthocyanins, the colour of flowers depends on the presence of co-pigments such as flavones, flavonols, etc., and to metal chelation, particularly with iron and aluminium. The colour (due to chelation) of the anthocyanins is affected to a large extent only when the molecule contains two hydroxyl groups in the *o*-position.

Geissman *et al.* (1952) have applied the term *flavonoids* to embrace all compounds whose structure is based on flavone (see §11). Thus the anthocyanins are one group of flavonoid compounds.

§2. General nature of the anthocyanins

The fundamental nucleus in anthocyanidins is benzopyrylium chloride, but the parent compound is 2-phenylbenzopyrylium chloride or **flavylium chloride**.

benzopyrylium chloride   flavylium chloride

The flavylium cation can be represented as a number of resonating structures, *e.g.*,

For convenience, flavylium salts will be represented as oxonium salts.

Most of the anthocyanidins are derivatives of 3,5,7-trihydroxyflavylium chloride. Thus, the hydroxylation patterns in the natural anthocyanidins fall into the three basic groups of pelargonidin, cyanidin and delphinidin. Table 15.1 lists the more common anthocyanidins (as chlorides). A far less common type is the 3-deoxyanthocyanidin group (the 3-hydroxyl group is absent), *e.g.*, luteolinidin (3-deoxycyanidin).

Table 15.1

Aglycon		
Trivial name	*Chemical name*	*Occurrence*
Pelargonidin	3,4′,5,7-Tetrahydroxyflavylium chloride	Present in orange-red to scarlet flowers, *e.g.*, scarlet *Pelargonium*, orange-red dahlia.
Cyanidin	3,3′,4′,5,7-Pentahydroxyflavylium chloride	Present in crimson to bluish-red flowers, *e.g.*, deep red dahlia, red roses, blue cornflower.
Delphinidin	3,3′,4,5,5′,7-Hexahydroxyflavylium chloride	Present in violet to blue flowers, *e.g.*, Delphinium.
Peonidin	3,4′,5,7-Tetrahydroxy-3′-methoxyflavylium chloride	Present in flowers less blue than the Cyanidin group, *e.g.*, red peony.
Malvidin (Syringidin)	3,4′,5,7-Tetrahydroxy-3′,5′-dimethoxyflavylium chloride	Present in flowers less blue than the Delphinidin group, *e.g.*, *Primula viscosa*.
Hirsutidin	3,4′,5-Trihydroxy-3′,5′,7-trimethoxyflavylium chloride	Present in *Primula hirsuta*.

Various sugars (mono-, di- and trisaccharides) have been found in anthocyanins; the most common are glucose, galactose and rhamnose, and the most important of these is glucose. Some pigments as well as being glycosides, are also acylated derivatives. The most common acids appear to be derivatives of cinnamic acid.

$$\text{HO} \underset{R}{\text{---}\!\!\bigcirc\!\!\text{---}} \text{CH}\!\!=\!\!\text{CH}\!\!-\!\!\text{CO}_2\text{H}$$

R = H; *p*-coumaric acid
R = OH; caffeic acid
R = OCH$_3$; ferulic acid

The isolation of anthocyanins depends on the plant source. The earlier methods used solvent extraction (ethanol, ether, acetone and light petroleum), but nowadays chromatography is the main method. With column chromatography (cellulose powder, silica gel, ion-exchange resins, etc.), the solvent used depends on the nature of the adsorbent. Furthermore, since anthocyanins are coloured, a series of bands is produced on the column. The identity of the bands may then be determined by specific colour tests for the anthocyanins. However, a better way of identifying these compounds is to use paper chromatography, together with known compounds for comparison. Moreover, paper chromatography is particularly useful for micro-scale work. Other methods used for separation are paper electrophoresis (*cf.* §5) and counter-current distribution.

The anthocyanins are characterised by two absorption bands: Band I, 475–560 nm (visible region), and Band II, 275–280 nm (ultraviolet region). The actual colour (Band I) depends on the number and positions of the hydroxyl and methoxyl groups, and when these are fixed, the colour then depends on *p*H and solvent (see also §5).

The various groups of flavonoids give rise to characteristic colour reactions, and so it is possible to assign a flavonoid to its class, *e.g.*,

Table 15.2

Class	Aqueous NaOH	Conc. H_2SO_4	Mg–HCl
Anthocyanins	Blue to violet	Yellowish-orange	Red (fades to pink)
Flavones	Yellow	Yellow to orange	Yellow to red
Flavonols	Yellow to orange	Yellow to orange	Red to magenta
Flavanones	Yellow to orange (cold); red to purple (hot)	Orange to crimson	Red, magenta, violet, blue
Isoflavones	Yellow	Yellow	Yellow
Leucoanthocyanins	Yellow	Crimson	Pink

§3. Structure of the anthocyanidins

The anthocyanin is first hydrolysed with hydrochloric acid and the anthocyanidin is isolated as the chloride. The usual analytical methods are applied to determine the number of hydroxyl and methoxyl groups present in the molecule. The structure of the anthocyanidin is ascertained by the nature of the products obtained by fusing the anthocyanidin with potassium hydroxide (Willstätter *et al.*, 1915); phloroglucinol or a methylated phloroglucinol and a phenolic acid are always obtained, *e.g.*, cyanidin chloride gives phloroglucinol and protocatechuic acid.

cyanidin chloride

This method suffers from the disadvantage that the fusion (or boiling with concentrated potassium hydroxide solution) not only degrades the anthocyanidin, but also often demethylates it at the same time. Thus the positions of the methoxyl groups in the original compound are now rendered uncertain. This difficulty was overcome by Karrer *et al.* (1927), who degraded the anthocyanidin with a 10 per cent solution of barium hydroxide or sodium hydroxide in an atmosphere of hydrogen; in this way, the methoxyl groups are left intact.

The next problem is to ascertain the positions of the sugar residues. After hydrolysis (of the anthocyanin), the sugar is identified by the usual methods of sugar chemistry, and this includes the use of paper chromatography. If two or more monosaccharide molecules are obtained for each molecule of anthocyanin, it is necessary to determine whether they were present as such, or as a disaccharide (or trisaccharide) which was hydrolysed. One method is first to methylate the anthocyanin and then hydrolyse with suitable enzymes. In this way, methylated disaccharides may be isolated intact.

(i) Karrer *et al.* (1927) methylated the anthocyanin, removed the sugar residues by hydrolysis (hydrochloric acid), and finally hydrolysed with barium hydroxide solution in an atmosphere of hydrogen; the positions of the *free* hydroxyl indicate the points of attachment of the sugar residues. In some cases, however, interpretation of the results is uncertain, *e.g.* (G represents a sugar residue):

(I) $\xrightarrow{\text{Me}_2\text{SO}_4 / \text{NaOH}}$ (II) $\xrightarrow{\text{HCl}}$

(III) $\xrightarrow{\text{Ba(OH)}_2 \ (\text{H}_2)}$ $+ \ \text{HO}_2\text{C}$

The problem is: Which of the two hydroxyl groups in monomethylphloroglucinol was originally attached to G? The above results do not lead to a definite answer, since had the structure of the anthocyanin been (IV) instead of (I), (III) would still have been obtained:

(IV)   ------→ $+ \ \text{HO}_2\text{C}$ (III)

(ii) Hydrogen peroxide (15 per cent) attacks anthocyanins as follows (Karrer *et al.*, 1927):

(V) $\xrightarrow{\text{H}_2\text{O}_2}$ (VI)

If the anthocyanin (V) has a glucose residue in the 3-position, then *this* glucose residue in (VI) is readily hydrolysed by dilute ammonia. If the glucose residue in (V) is in either the 5- or 7-position, then this glucose residue in (VI) is removed only by heating with dilute hydrochloric acid. Thus position 3 can be distinguished from positions 5 or 7, but the latter two cannot be distinguished from each other.

(iii) Anthocyanins with a free hydroxyl group in the 3-position are very readily oxidised by ferric chloride; the anthocyanins are rapidly decolorised in this oxidation (Robinson *et al.*, 1931).

The final problem is to determine whether the sugar linkage (to the anthocyanidin) is α or β. This is ascertained by hydrolysis with the enzymes maltase (α-linkage) and emulsin (β-linkage; see 7 §3).

Conclusive evidence for the positions and nature of the linkages of the sugar residues is afforded by the synthesis of the anthocyanins (see, *e.g.*, cyanin, §5). In general, it has been found that glucose residues are linked at positions 3 or 3,5 and that the linkage is usually β (but see also §12).

Now that a large number of structures have been elucidated, it has been possible to correlate, to a large extent, physical data with structure. Thus, the flavonoid is fairly easily assigned to its class by its absorption spectrum (visible and ultraviolet) and by colour reactions.

It has already been pointed out (§2) that the known anthocyanidins belong to three main types: cyanidin (λ_{max} 535 nm), pelargonidin (λ_{max} 520 nm), and delphinidin (λ_{max} 564 nm) [all measured in

MeOH–HCl solution]. Thus these may be distinguished from each other. Furthermore, the intro-duction of sugar residues into these anthocyanidins shifts the maxima towards the shorter wave-lengths, the shifts being characteristic for sugar residues in the 3- or 3,5-positions, and for the 5-position. Also, since 3-glycoside spectra show a pronounced shoulder (440–460 nm region), it is therefore possible to obtain information about the positions of sugar residues in anthocyanins.

Examination of the absorption spectra of anthocyanidins in the presence of certain reagents also gives information about structure. Thus aluminium chloride and sodium ethoxide shift the maxima to the longer wavelengths, the actual shift depending on the positions of the hydroxyl groups in the molecule, e.g., cyanidin (λ_{max} 535 nm) has its λ_{max} at 553 nm in the presence of aluminium chloride.

In this way, it may be possible to obtain some indication of the relationship of the compound under investigation to a flavonoid of known structure, thereby simplifying further structure determination. Also, since the R_F values of the known anthocyanins have been determined (Harborne, 1959), these compounds are quite readily identified.

§4. General methods of synthesising the anthocyanidins

(i) Willstätter (1914) synthesised anthocyanidins starting from coumarin.

coumarin   chrom-3-en-2-ol

This method has very limited application.

(ii) Robinson has introduced a number of methods whereby *all* anthocyanidins can be prepared. The basic reaction of these methods is the condensation between *o*-hydroxybenzaldehyde and acetophenone in ethyl acetate solution which is then saturated with hydrogen chloride.

chalcone

The original method of Robinson (1924) resulted in the formation of a product in which the sub-stituent groups were either all hydroxyl groups or all methoxyl groups, *e.g.*,

Robinson (1928, 1931) then modified this method so that the product could have both hydroxyl and methoxyl substituent groups, *e.g.*,

peonidin chloride

The following is a brief account of the methods used by Robinson and his co-workers for preparing the substituted acetophenones and substituted benzaldehydes.

ω,3,4-Triacetoxyacetophenone.

catechol $\xrightarrow{+ CH_2ClCO_2H}$ $\xrightarrow{POCl_3}$ $\xrightarrow[AcOK]{Ac_2O}$

ω,4-Diacetoxyacetophenone.

anisole $\xrightarrow{+ CH_2ClCOCl}$ $\xrightarrow{AlCl_3}$ $\xrightarrow[AcOK]{Ac_2O}$

ω,3,4-Trimethoxyacetophenone.

veratric acid $\xrightarrow{SOCl_2}$ (COCl) $\xrightarrow{CH_2N_2}$ (COCHN$_2$) diazoketone $\xrightarrow[HCO_2H]{aqueous}$ (COCH$_2$OH) $\xrightarrow[NaOH]{Me_2SO_4}$ (COCH$_2$OMe)

ω,4-Dimethoxyacetophenone.

(i) $CH_2O + Me_2SO_4 + KCN \longrightarrow MeOCH_2CN$
cyanodimethyl
ether

(ii) $MeOCH_2CN + $ (ArMgBr) $\longrightarrow$ $COCH_2OMe$

ω,3,4-Triacetoxy-5-methoxyacetophenone.

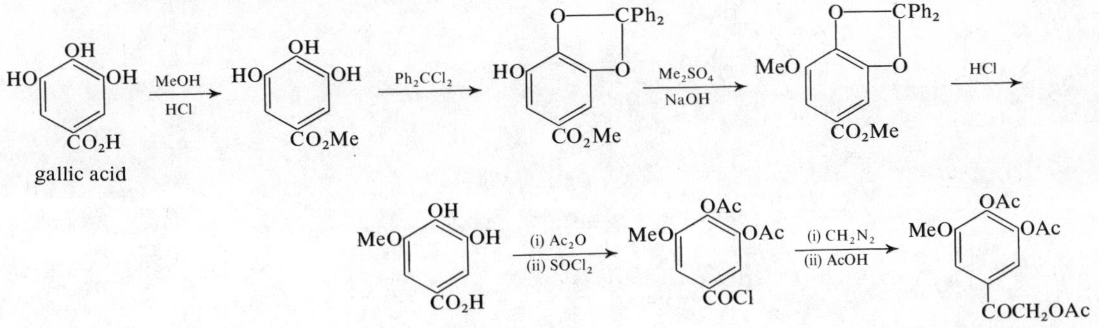

gallic acid

2,4,6-Trihydroxybenzaldehyde (phloroglucinaldehyde).

phloroglucinol

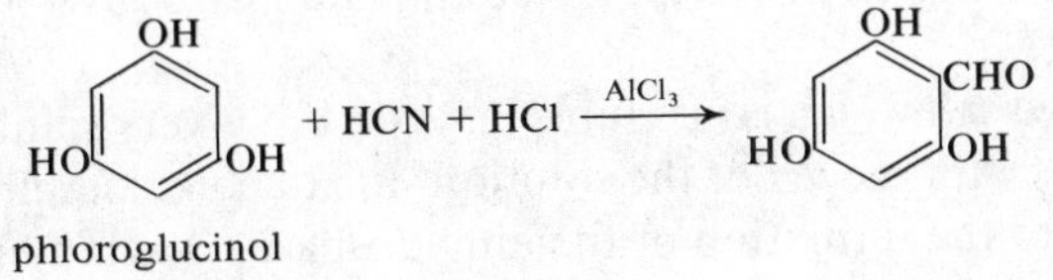

2-Hydroxy-4,6-dimethoxybenzaldehyde.

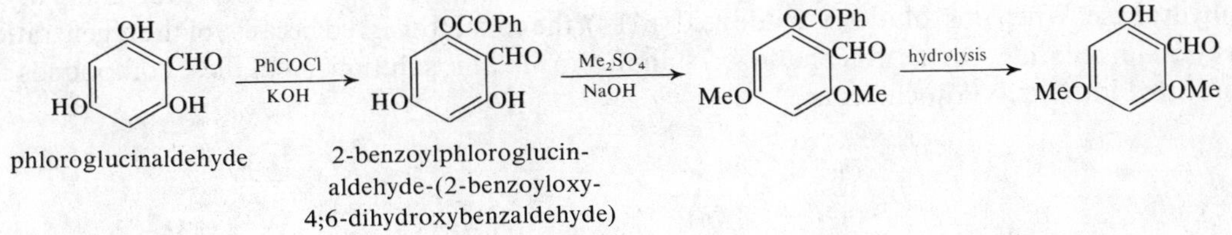

phloroglucinaldehyde   2-benzoylphloroglucin-
aldehyde-(2-benzoyloxy-
4;6-dihydroxybenzaldehyde)

§5. Cyanidin chloride, $C_{15}H_{11}ClO_6$

Cyanin chloride, on hydrolysis with hydrochloric acid, gives cyanidin chloride and two molecules of D-glucose.

$$C_{27}H_{31}ClO_{16} + 2H_2O \xrightarrow{\text{HCl}} C_{15}H_{11}ClO_6 + 2C_6H_{12}O_6$$

Since cyanidin chloride forms a penta-acetate, the molecule therefore contains five hydroxyl groups. No methoxyl groups are present, and so the potassium hydroxide fusion may be used to degrade this compound; this gives phloroglucinol and protocatechuic acid. Thus cyanidin chloride has the following structure:

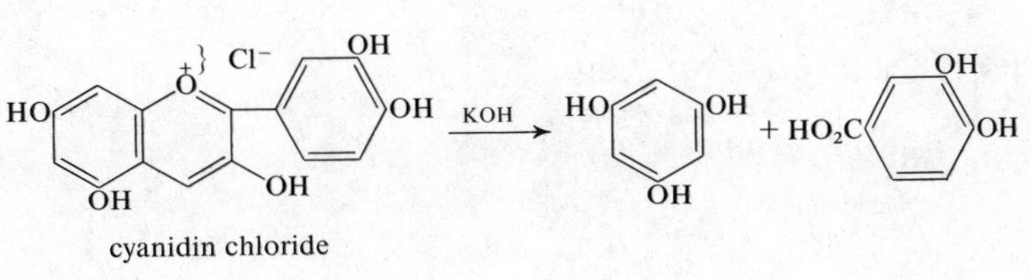

cyanidin chloride

This structure has been confirmed by synthesis (Robinson *et al.*, 1928):

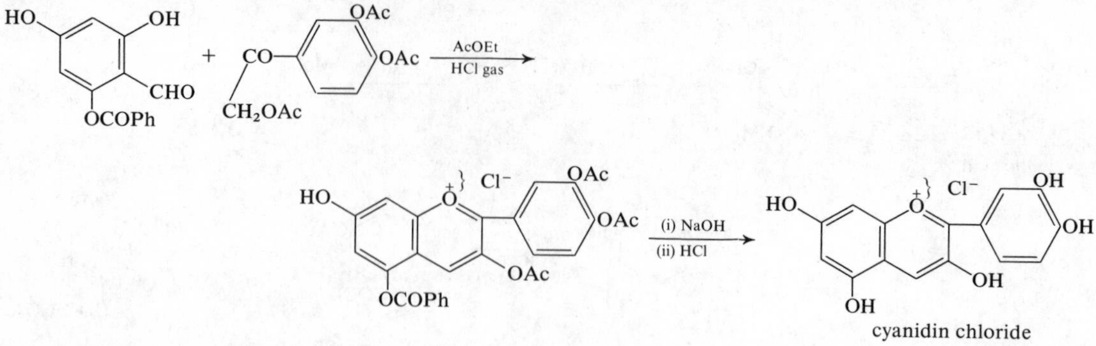

cyanidin chloride

The formation of phloroglucinol and protocatechuic acid by the alkaline fusion of cyanidin chloride suggests a relationship to quercetin, since the latter also gives the same fusion products (see §14).

Cyanidin chloride is a red salt which is insoluble in water but is very soluble in ethanol. The colour of the salt, however, varies with the *p*H of the solution. In aqueous sodium acetate solution (*p*H 8), the solution is violet due to the formation of the anhydrobase. On standing, the solution becomes colourless by conversion of the anhydrobase (quinonoid structure) into the colourless pseudobase (in which the quinonoid structure has been lost). When this colourless solution is made alkaline with sodium hydroxide (*p*H 12), the colour changes to blue due to the formation of the anion of the anhydrobase. When this solution is made acid (*p*H 4), the colour turns red because of the regeneration of cyanidin chloride. On the other hand, on standing in alkaline solution, all of these compounds are converted into the yellow chalcone.

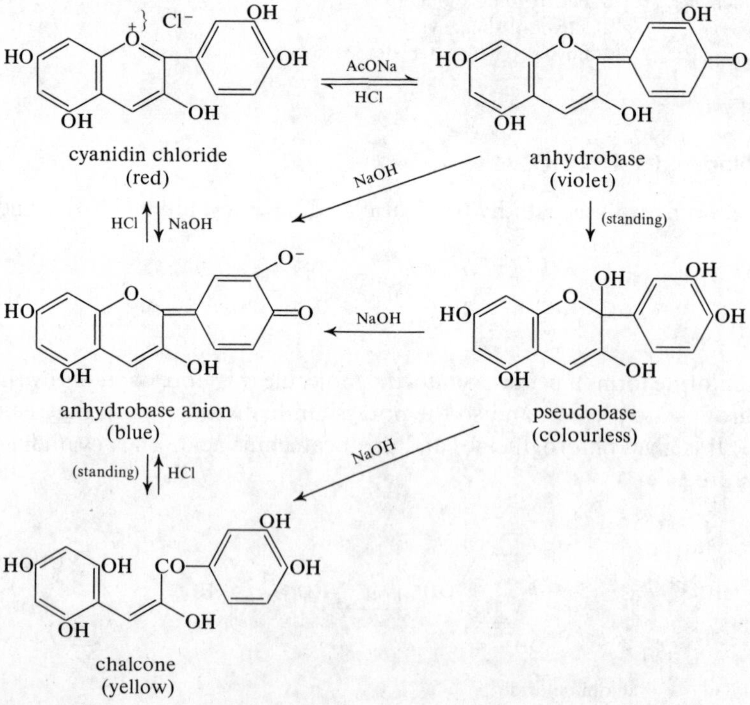

cyanidin chloride
(red)

anhydrobase
(violet)

anhydrobase anion
(blue)

pseudobase
(colourless)

chalcone
(yellow)

On the basis of these ionic structures (positive for oxonium salts and negative for salts of the colour bases), anthocyanins should migrate in an electric field. Markakis (1960) has shown that various anthocyanins, when placed within an electric field applied across filter paper, move to the anode or cathode according to the pH of the solution. Markakis also showed that isoelectric point (**13** §4c) and the pH of minimum colour display coincide. On the acidic side of the isoelectric point, the oxonium salt-form predominates; and when the pH is higher than that of the isoelectric point, the salt of the colour base predominates, and according to Markakis, it is the pseudobase which probably predominates at the isoelectric point.

Cyanin was the first anthocyanin to be isolated and its structure determined. It has been synthesised by Robinson *et al.* (1932). Phloroglucinaldehyde (I) was condensed with tetra-acetyl-α-bromo-glucose (II) [*cf.* **7** §24], in acetone solution to which has been added aqueous potassium hydroxide; the product was 2-*O*-tetra-acetyl-β-glucosidylphloroglucinaldehyde (III). ω-Hydroxy-3,4-diacetoxy-acetophenone (IV) was also condensed with tetra-acetyl-α-bromoglucose (II) in benzene solution to give ω-*O*-tetra-acetyl-β-glucosidoxy-3,4-diacetoxyacetophenone (V). Compounds (III) and (V) were then dissolved in ethyl acetate and the solution saturated with hydrogen chloride; the product (VI) was treated first with cold aqueous potassium hydroxide and then with hydrochloric acid, whereby cyanin chloride (VII) was produced.

§6. Pelargonidin chloride, $C_{15}H_{11}ClO_5$

This is formed, together with two molecules of glucose, when pelargonin chloride is hydrolysed with hydrochloric acid.

$$C_{27}H_{31}ClO_{15} + 2H_2O \xrightarrow{\text{HCl}} C_{15}H_{11}ClO_5 + 2C_6H_{12}O_6$$

Since pelargonidin chloride forms a tetra-acetate, the molecule contains four hydroxyl groups. Furthermore, since there are no methoxyl groups present, the potassium hydroxide fusion or boiling with concentrated potassium hydroxide solution may be used to degrade the compound; the products are phloroglucinol and *p*-hydroxybenzoic acid, and so the structure is probably as shown:

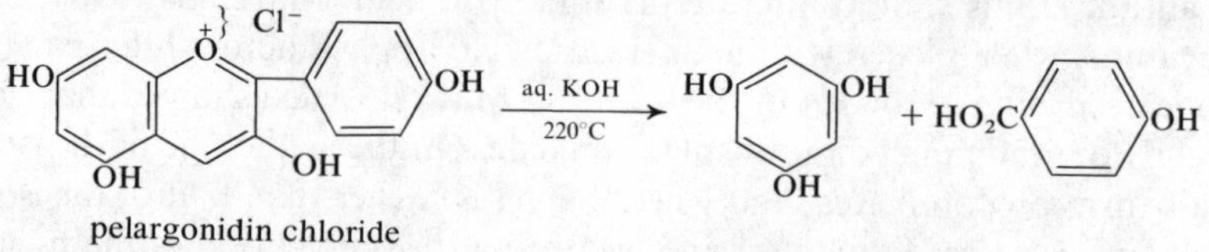

pelargonidin chloride

This structure has been confirmed by synthesis, *e.g.*, Robinson *et al.* (1928).

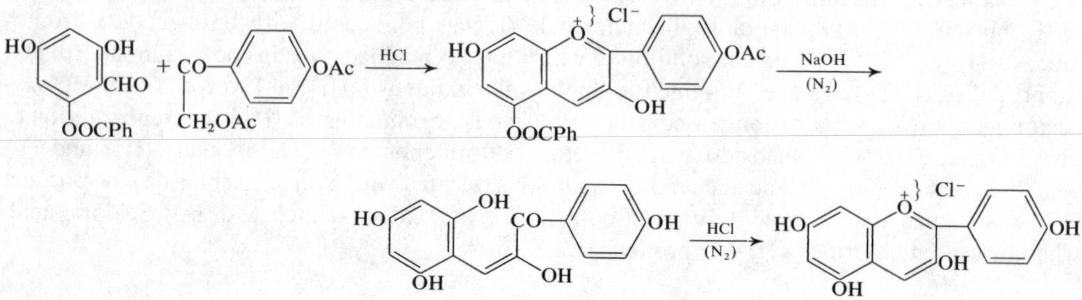

Pelargonin chloride (I) has been synthesised by Robinson *et al.* (1932) from 2-*O*-tetra-acetyl-*β*-glucosidylphloroglucinaldehyde (II) and *ω*-*O*-tetra-acetyl-*β*-glucosidoxy-4-acetoxyacetophenone (III) [*cf.* cyanin chloride, §5].

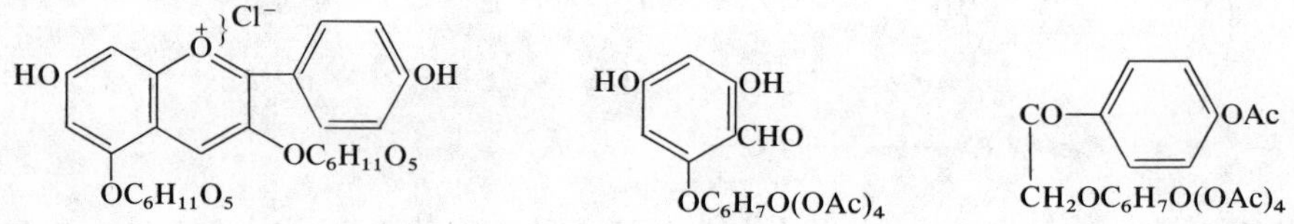

(I)   (II)   (III)

§7. Delphinidin chloride, $C_{15}H_{11}ClO_7$

This is obtained, together with two molecules of glucose and two molecules of *p*-hydroxybenzoic acid, when delphinin chloride is hydrolysed with hydrochloric acid.

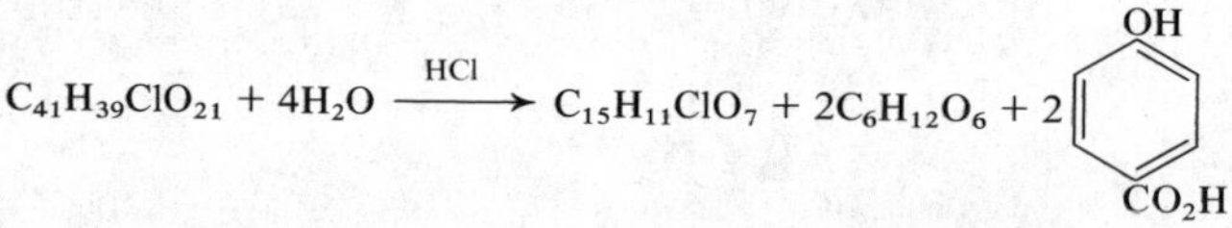

$$C_{41}H_{39}ClO_{21} + 4H_2O \xrightarrow{HCl} C_{15}H_{11}ClO_7 + 2C_6H_{12}O_6 + 2$$

Delphinidin chloride contains six hydroxyl groups, and no methoxyl groups; on fusion with potassium hydroxide, the products are phloroglucinol and gallic acid.

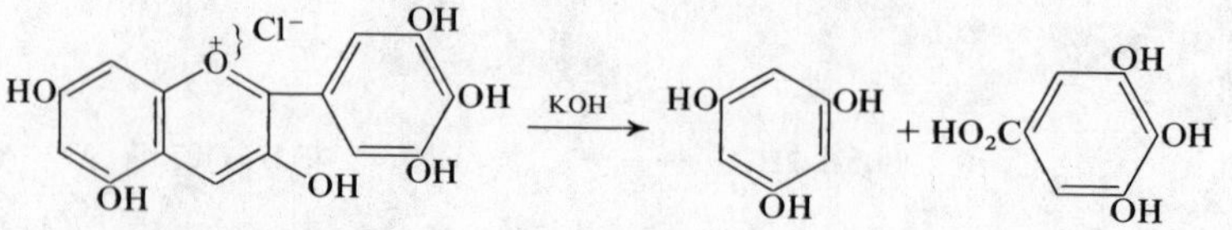

delphinidin chloride

This structure has been confirmed by synthesis, starting from 2-benzoylphloroglucinaldehyde and *ω*,3,4,5-tetra-acetoxyacetophenone (Robinson *et al.*, 1930).

Delphin chloride, $C_{27}H_{31}ClO_{17}$, is the 3,5-diglucoside of delphinidin chloride (no *p*-hydroxy-benzoic acid is present).

§8. Peonidin chloride, $C_{16}H_{13}ClO_6$

This is produced, together with two molecules of glucose, when peonin chloride is hydrolysed with hydrochloric acid.

$$C_{28}H_{33}ClO_{16} + 2H_2O \xrightarrow{HCl} C_{16}H_{13}ClO_6 + 2C_6H_{12}O_6$$

When heated with hydrogen iodide in the presence of phenol, peonidin chloride is demethylated to give cyanidin chloride. Thus peonidin is the monomethyl ether of cyanidin. Heating peonidin chloride with potassium hydroxide solution produces 4-hydroxy-3-methoxybenzoic acid and phloroglucinol. Thus:

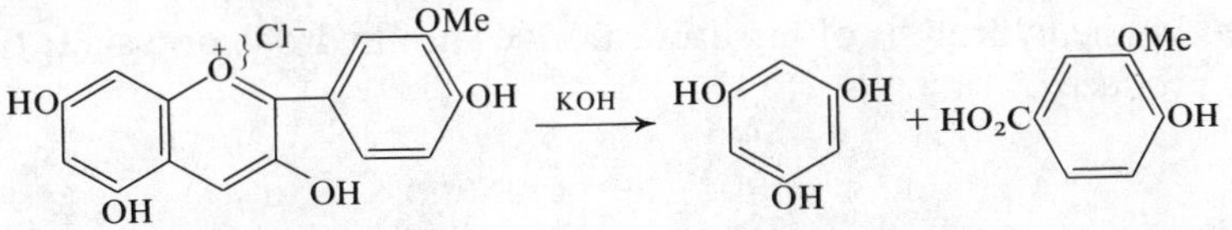

peonidin chloride

This structure has been confirmed by synthesis from 2-benzoylphloroglucinaldehyde and ω,4-diacetoxy-3-methoxyacetophenone (Robinson *et al.*, 1926).

Peonin chloride (I) has been synthesised by Robinson *et al.* (1931), using 2-*O*-tetra-acetyl-β-glucosidylphloroglucinaldehyde (II) and ω-tetra-acetyl-β-glucosidoxy-4-acetoxy-3-methoxyaceto-phenone (III).

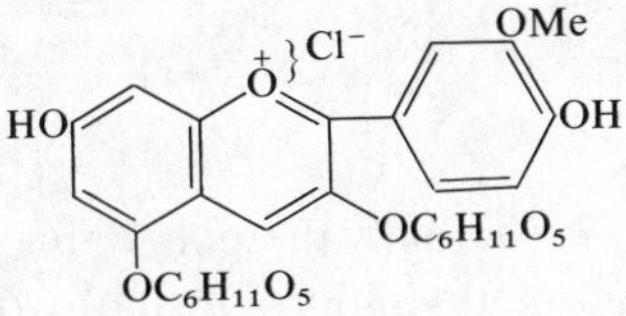

(I) 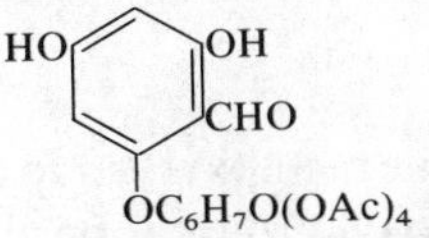   (II) 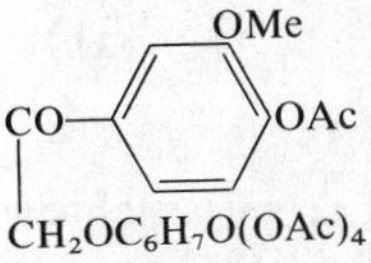   (III)

§9. Malvidin chloride, $C_{17}H_{15}ClO_7$

This is produced, together with two molecules of glucose, when malvin chloride is hydrolysed with hydrochloric acid.

$$C_{29}H_{35}ClO_{17} + 2H_2O \xrightarrow{HCl} C_{17}H_{15}ClO_7 + 2C_6H_{12}O_6$$

Malvidin chloride contains four hydroxyl groups and two methoxyl groups. When degraded by boiling barium hydroxide solution in an atmosphere of hydrogen, the products are phloroglucinol and **syringic acid** (4-hydroxy-3,5-dimethoxybenzoic acid). Thus:

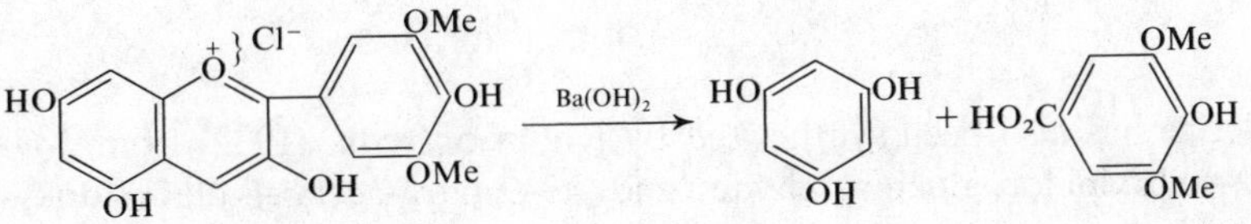

malvidin chloride

Robinson *et al.* (1928) confirmed this structure by synthesis, starting from 2-benzoylphloroglucin-aldehyde and ω-acetoxy-4-benzyloxy-3,5-dimethoxyacetophenone (*cf.* §10). Robinson *et al.* (1932) have also synthesised **malvin chloride** (I) by condensing 2-*O*-tetra-acetyl-β-glucosidylphloroglucin-aldehyde with ω-*O*-tetra-acetyl-β-glucosidoxy-4-acetoxy-3,5-dimethoxyacetophenone (II).

(I)   (II)

§10. Hirsutidin chloride, $C_{18}H_{17}ClO_7$

This is produced by the hydrolysis of hirsutin chloride with hydrochloric acid; two molecules of glucose are also produced.

$$C_{30}H_{37}ClO_{17} + 2H_2O \xrightarrow{\text{HCl}} C_{18}H_{17}ClO_7 + 2C_6H_{12}O_6$$

Hirsutidin chloride contains three hydroxyl groups and three methoxyl groups. Its structure is shown from the fact that on hydrolysis with barium hydroxide solution in an atmosphere of hydrogen the products are monomethylphloroglucinol and syringic acid. The formation of these products

hirsutidin chloride

does not prove conclusively that the methoxyl group at position 7 is actually there; had this position been interchanged with the hydroxyl group at position 5, monomethylphloroglucinol would still have been obtained (*cf.* §3). The formula given for hirsutidin chloride, however, has been confirmed by synthesis, starting from 2-benzoyl-4-*O*-methylphloroglucinaldehyde and ω-acetoxy-4-benzyloxy-3,5-dimethoxyacetophenone (Robinson *et al.*, 1930).

Hirsutin chloride has also been synthesised by Robinson *et al.* (1932) from 2-*O*-tetra-acetyl-β-glucosidyl-4-*O*-methylphloroglucinaldehyde and ω-*O*-tetra-acetyl-β-glucosidoxy-4-acetoxy-3,5-dimethoxyacetophenone.

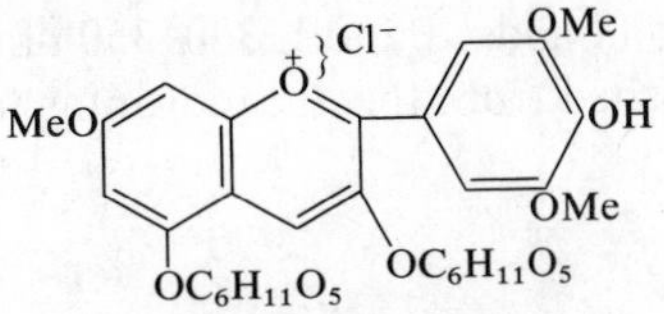

hirsutin chloride

§10a. **Leucoanthocyanidins and leucoanthocyanins.**   These groups of compounds are derivatives of flavan-3,4-diol (I).

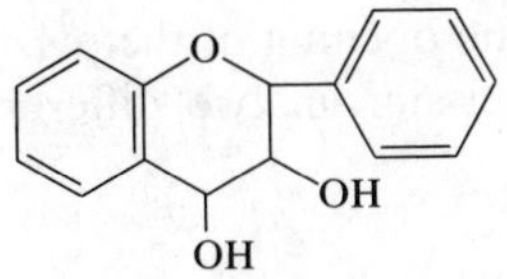

(I)

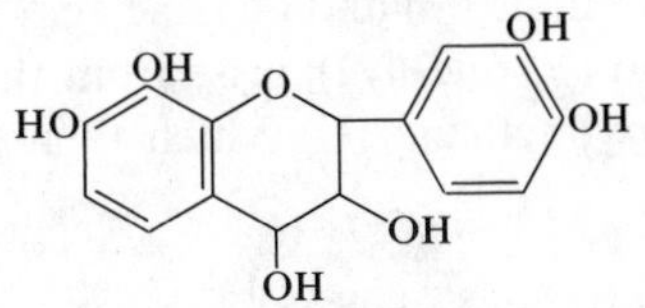

(II)

melacacidin

They are colourless compounds and are readily converted into anthocyanidins when heated with hydrochloric acid. **Melacacidin**, which has been isolated from Australian blackwood, is (II).

Flavones

§11. Introduction

The flavones, which are also known as the **anthoxanthins**, are yellow pigments which occur in the plant kingdom. Flavones occur naturally in the free state, or as glycosides (the aglycon is the *anthoxanthidin* and the sugar is glucose, etc.), or associated with tannins. Chemically, the flavones are very closely related to the anthocyanins; the flavones are hydroxylated derivatives of *flavone* (2-phenyl-4-chromone) which may be partially alkylated. In almost all cases positions 5 and 7 are hydroxylated, and frequently one or more of positions 3', 4' and 5'. Positions 5, 7 and 4' are generally

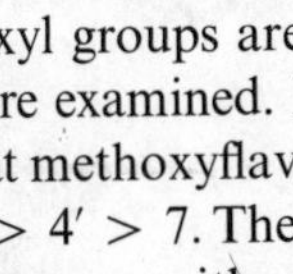

chromone

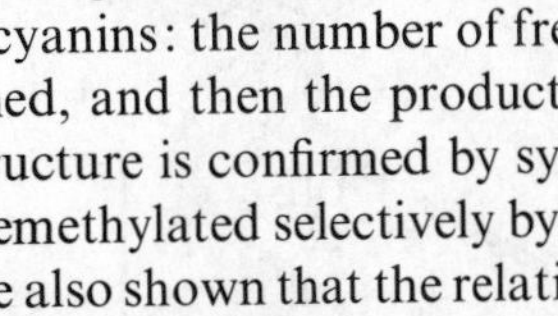

flavone

unmethylated, but 3' and 5' are often methylated. The general method of ascertaining the structure of the flavones is similar to that used for the anthocyanins: the number of free phenolic groups and the number of methoxyl groups are first determined, and then the products obtained by alkaline fusion or hydrolysis are examined. Finally, the structure is confirmed by synthesis. Simpson *et al.* (1954) have shown that methoxyflavones may be demethylated selectively by hydrobromic acid, the relative rates being 3' > 4' > 7. These authors have also shown that the relative rates of methylation of flavone-hydroxyl groups with methyl sulphate and sodium hydrogen carbonate in acetone solution are 7 > 4' > 3' > 3. With methyl sulphate and aqueous alcoholic sodium carbonate, the exact reverse of this order is obtained. These results thus offer a method of ascertaining the positions of methoxyl groups in various methoxyflavones.

Alkaline degradation may now be conveniently carried out on a microscale, and the products are examined by paper chromatography.

The flavones show two absorption bands: Band I, 330–350 nm, and Band II, 250–270 nm. Thus, these compounds may be distinguished from the anthocyanins (and also by means of colour reactions; see §2).

§12. Flavone, $C_{15}H_{10}O_2$

This occurs naturally as 'dust' on flowers, leaves, etc. When boiled with concentrated potassium hydroxide solution, flavone (I) gives a mixture of four products, salicylic acid (III), acetophenone (IV), o-hydroxyacetophenone (V) and benzoic acid (VI). The products, which are produced in the pairs (III) and (IV), and (V) and (VI), arise from the fact that the opening of the pyrone ring produces o-hydroxydibenzoylmethane (II) which then undergoes scission in two different ways ((II) is a β-diketone).

In general, all the flavones give a mixture of four products when degraded with potassium hydroxide. The intermediate o-hydroxy-β-diketone can be isolated if the flavone is heated with a methanolic solution of barium hydroxide (Müller, 1915), or better still, by the action of sodium peroxide on flavone in pyridine (Wheeler *et al.*, 1955).

The structure given for flavone has been confirmed by synthesis. Many syntheses are known, *e.g.*, **the Kostanecki synthesis** (1900). This is a general method for synthesising flavones, and consists in condensing the ester of an alkylated salicylic acid with an acetophenone in the presence of sodium (this is an example of the Claisen condensation; this synthesis is a reversal of the formation of (III) and (IV)). Thus, for flavone itself, the reaction is carried out with methyl o-methoxybenzoate and acetophenone.

The most useful general synthetic method for preparing flavones is that of Robinson (1924). This is a reversal of the formation of (V) and (VI); an o-hydroxyacetophenone is heated at about 180°C with the anhydride and sodium salt of a substituted benzoic acid, *e.g.*, flavone:

Another general method which is also a reversal of the formation of (V) and (VI) is illustrated by the preparation of **chrysin** (5,7-dihydroxyflavone) from 2,4,6-trimethoxyacetophenone and ethyl benzoate.

This preparation involves a Claisen condensation, and the following is also another general method which involves the **Baker–Venkataraman rearrangement**, in which an *o*-benzoyloxyacetophenone is isomerised to an *o*-hydroxy-β-diketone by a base. This rearrangement occurs by an internal Claisen condensation. This preparation of flavones is known as the **Baker–Venkataraman synthesis** (1933).

Another method for synthesising flavones is by the ring expansion of 2-benzylidenecoumaran-3-ones (Wheeler *et al.*, 1955), *e.g.*,

2-Benzylidenecoumaran-3-ones are known as **aurones**; many occur naturally.

Most flavones are yellow solids which are soluble in water, ethanol and dilute acids and alkalis. The oxonium salts are usually more highly coloured than the free bases; the flavones do not occur naturally as salts (*cf.* anthocyanins). The structure of flavone salts is not certain; they are probably best represented as the resonance hybrid (VII).

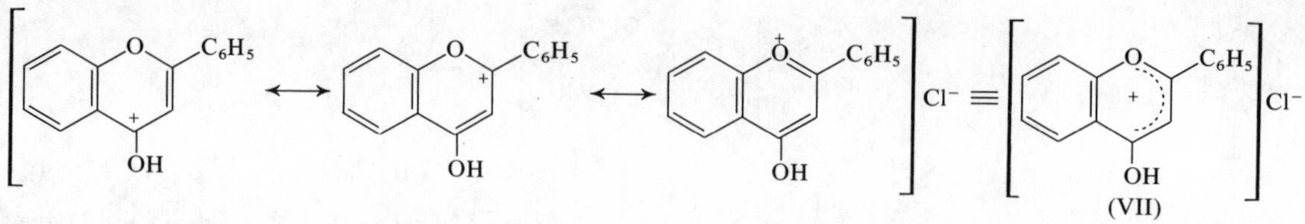

(VII)

An unusual feature of flavones is that they occur frequently as *C*-glycosyl derivatives as well as *O*-glycosides, *e.g.*,

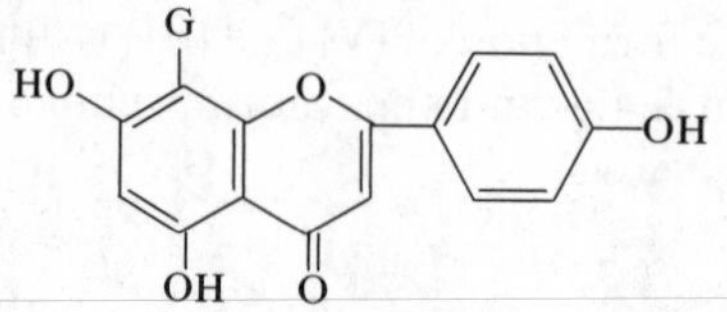

vitexin 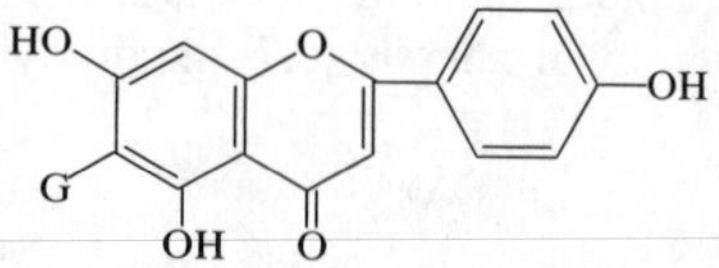   isovitexin

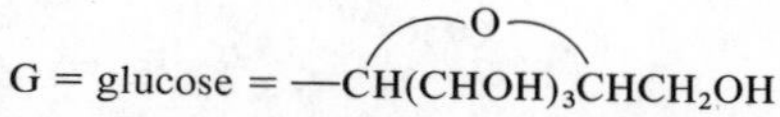

$$G = \text{glucose} = -CH(CHOH)_3\overset{\displaystyle\frown O \frown}{CHCH_2OH}$$

The structure of vitexin was established by Rao *et al.* (1962) and that of isovitexin by Seikel *et al.* (1966). One of the problems in this type of compound is the assignment of the position of the *C*-glycosyl group. Mass spectra (Prox, 1968) and NMR spectra (Gentili *et al.*, 1968) have been used to distinguish the C-6 and C-8 positions. On the other hand, Gaffield *et al.* (1972) have used CD measurements to distinguish between the two positions (see also **1** §9b). These authors showed that a positive Cotton effect at 250–275 nm indicates a C-6 glycosyl linkage and a negative Cotton effect at 250–275 nm indicates a C-8 linkage. These results apply to β-D-glucopyranosyl flavones.

§13. Flavonol (3-hydroxyflavone), $C_{15}H_{10}O_3$

Flavonol is widely distributed in the plant kingdom, usually in the form of glycosides. Flavonols show two absorption bands: Band I, 350–390 nm, and Band II, 250–270 nm. These, taken in conjunction with their specific colour reactions (§2), make it possible to identify this group of compounds.

When boiled with an ethanolic solution of potassium hydroxide, flavonol gives *o*-hydroxybenzoylmethanol and benzoic acid. This suggests that flavonol is 3-hydroxyflavone (3-hydroxy-2-phenyl-γ-chromone).

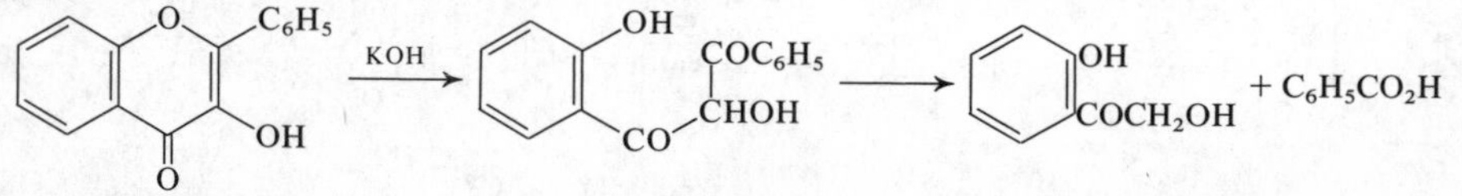

flavonol

This structure has been confirmed by various syntheses, *e.g.*, Kostanecki *et al.* (1904). This is a general method, and uses the Claisen reaction between *o*-hydroxyacetophenones and substituted benzaldehydes, *e.g.*, flavonol.

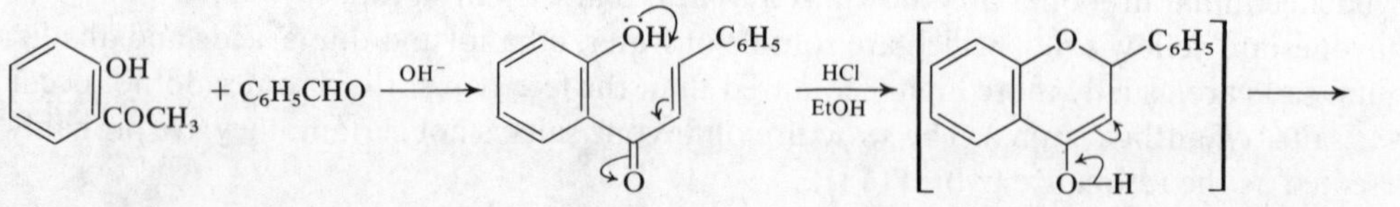

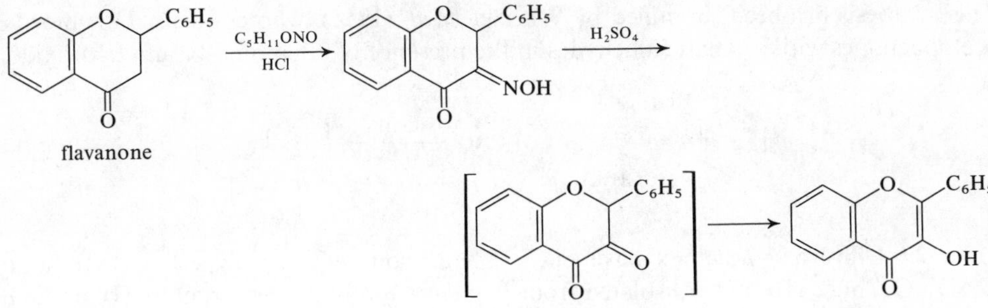

flavanone

keto form

enol form;
flavonol

The synthesis, starting from flavonone, has been adapted to the preparation of flavones.

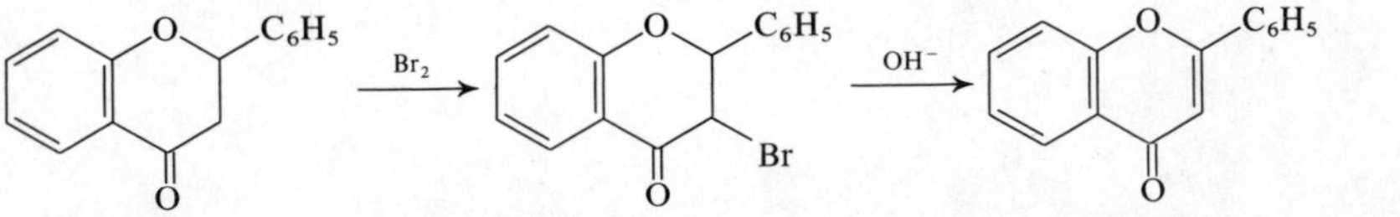

flavanone

flavone

This dehydrogenation of flavanones to flavones may be effected by a variety of reagents. Iodine in the presence of potassium acetate may be used instead of bromine (Seshadri *et al.*, 1955). Selenium dioxide may also be used (Venkataraman *et al.*, 1935, 1936), but not if the molecule contains free hydroxyl groups. If these are present, the dehydrogenation can be carried out *via* the acetylated derivative (Seshadri *et al.*, 1954). On the other hand, flavonol may be prepared by the **Algar–Flynn–Oyamada reaction** (1934). 2′-Hydroxychalcone, on treatment with alkaline hydrogen peroxide, is first converted into 3-hydroxyflavanone and then into flavonol.

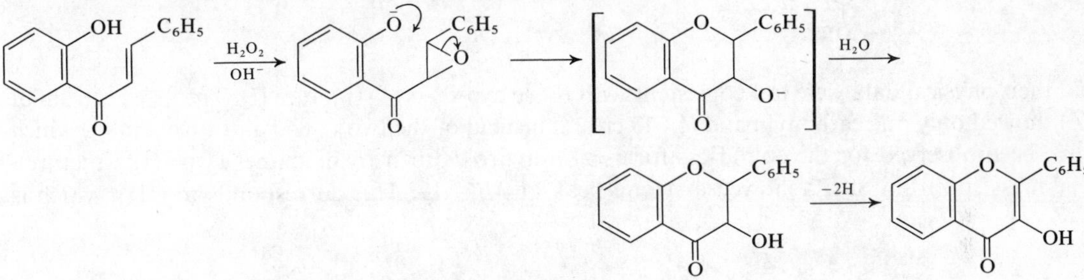

This reaction affords a very good general synthesis of flavonoids.

An alternative general method for preparing flavones based on the flavonol synthesis is as follows (Kostanecki *et al.*, 1898):

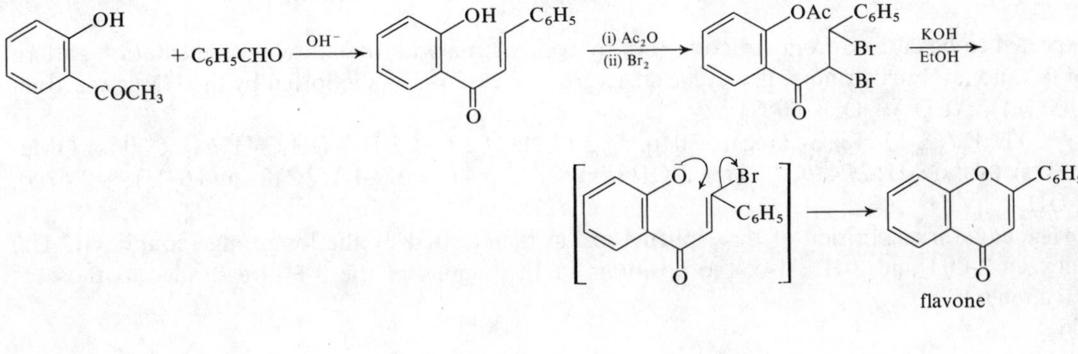

flavone

This synthesis has been simplified by Wheeler *et al.* (1955), who condensed ω-chloro-*o*-hydroxy-acetophenones with aromatic aldehydes in the presence of ethanolic sodium hydroxide, *e.g.*,

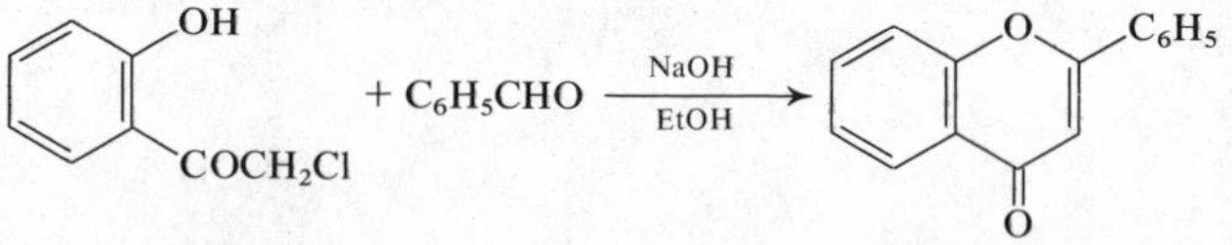

§13a. 2,5-Dihydroxy-7-methoxyflavanone. Chadenson *et al.* suggested that a compound, $C_{16}H_{15}O_5$, m.p. 170–172°C, isolated from *Populus nigra* buds had structure (I) on the basis that it readily gave the flavone (II) on cyclodehydration with acid. When Chadenson *et al.* (1972) treated

(II) with sodium peroxide in pyridine in the expectation of regenerating (I), the experiment failed (*cf.* flavone, §12). On the other hand, when (II) was heated with anhydrous potassium hydroxide in pyridine, the product was identical with the natural compound (believed to be (I)). A synthesis of benzoyl-(2,6-dihydroxy-4-methoxybenzoyl)methane (I) was then attempted by the Baker–Venkataraman method (see §12) as shown. The product (Z) was identical with the natural compound,

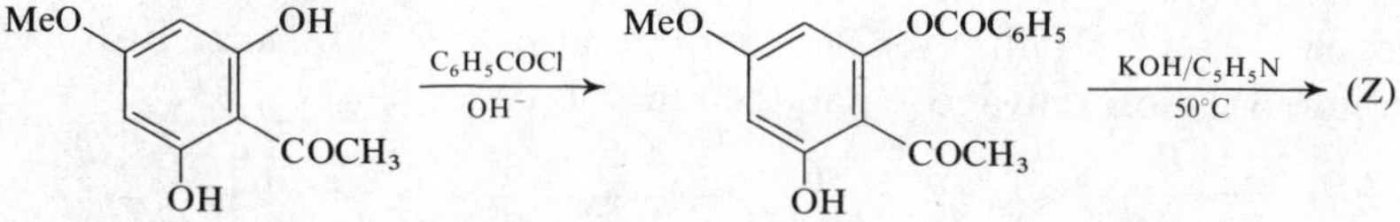

but their physical data were not consistent with those expected of structure (I). The i.r. spectrum of (Z) showed only one carbonyl band ($1\,640$ cm^{-1}) instead of the two ($1\,640$ and $1\,680$ cm^{-1}) which have been observed for the colourless forms of *o*-hydroxydibenzoylmethanes (type (I) structure). The mass spectrum of (Z) showed a strong peak at $M-17$. This corresponds to (III), which is

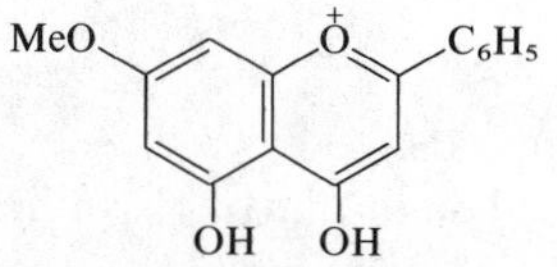

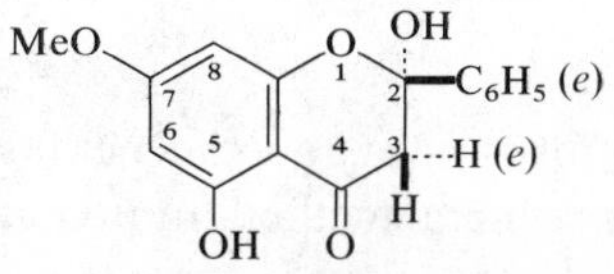

expected to be derived from structure (IV) by comparison with the known fragmentation pattern of flavanones. Furthermore, this cyclic structure, (IV)≡(Z), was supported by the NMR spectrum (100 MHz; $(CD_3)_2CO$; -60°C):

τ 7·21 (d, J_{gem} 17 Hz), 3-H (eq); 6·70 (q, J_{gem} 17 Hz, J 2 Hz), 3-H-2-OH, 3-H (*ax*); 6·20 (s), OMe; 2·91 (s), 6- and 8-H; 2·74 (d, J 2 Hz), 2-OH (*ax*); 2·5 (3′-, 4′-, and 5′-H); 2·2 (2′- and 6′-H); -2·40 (s), 5-OH.

The equatorial position of the 2-phenyl group is indicated by the long-range coupling (2 Hz) between 2-OH and 3-H. Also, the positions of the signals of the 3-H are similar to those of flavanones.

§14. Quercetin, $C_{15}H_{10}O_7$

This occurs as the glycoside *quercitrin* in the bark of *Quercus tinctoria*; quercitrin appears to be the most widely distributed natural pigment. On hydrolysis with acid, quercitrin forms quercetin and one molecule of rhamnose.

$$C_{21}H_{20}O_{11} + H_2O \xrightarrow{\text{HCl}} C_{15}H_{10}O_7 + CH_3(CHOH)_4CHO$$

Quercetin contains five hydroxyl groups; no methoxyl groups are present; on fusion with potassium hydroxide, phloroglucinol and protocatechuic acid are obtained (*cf.* cyanidin, §5). Also, when quercetin is methylated and the product, pentamethylquercetin, boiled with an ethanolic solution of potassium hydroxide, 6-hydroxy-ω,2,4-trimethoxyacetophenone and veratric acid are obtained. These results suggest that quercetin is 3,3',4',5,7-pentahydroxyflavone.

This structure has been confirmed by synthesis, *e.g.*, Kostanecki *et al.* (1904); see also §13.

Another synthesis is that of Robinson *et al.* (1926); it is a general method for flavonols (*cf.* flavone, §12): ω-methoxyphloroacetophenone is condensed with veratric anhydride in the presence of the potassium salt of veratric acid (3,4-dimethoxybenzoic acid; this has been written as $ArCO_2H$).

The position of the rhamnose residue in quercitrin has been shown to be 3 (Herzig *et al.*, 1912).

Before leaving this problem of quercetin, let us consider its relationship to cyanidin (§5). As we have seen, the relationship between the two compounds is suggested by the fact that both give the same products when fused with potassium hydroxide. Willstätter *et al.* (1914) reduced quercetin with magnesium in hydrochloric acid containing mercury, and thereby obtained a small amount of cyanidin chloride.

Bauer *et al.* (1954) have converted the penta-acetate of quercetin into cyanidin chloride by means of lithium aluminium hydride.

King *et al.* (1957) have shown that the reductive acetylation of a flavonol, followed by the action of hot hydrochloric acid, gives the corresponding anthocyanidin; thus:

$$\text{quercetin} \xrightarrow[\text{(ii) HCl}]{\text{(i) Zn}\rightarrow\text{AcONa; Ac}_2\text{O}} \text{cyanidin chloride}$$

This appears to be a useful general method.

Isoflavones

§15. Isoflavones

These are hydroxylated derivatives of isoflavone (3-phenyl-4-chromone) which may be partially alkylated. The isoflavones occur naturally, but are not so widespread as the flavones; they occur either in the free state or as glycosides. The general method of ascertaining the structure of isoflavones is similar to that used for the flavones (see §§3, 11). Thus fusion with potassium hydroxide breaks down the molecule into two fragments, and hydrolysis with ethanolic potassium hydroxide permits the isolation of intermediates. This may be illustrated with **daidzein** (Walz, 1931):

isoflavone

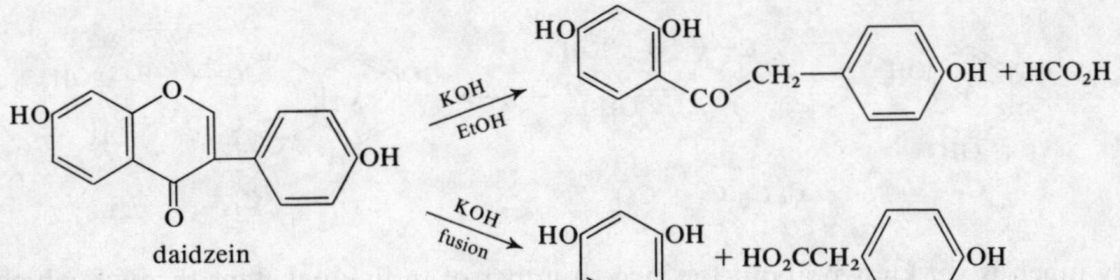

daidzein $\xrightarrow[\text{EtOH}]{\text{KOH}}$ (2,4-dihydroxyphenyl p-hydroxybenzyl ketone) + HCO_2H

daidzein $\xrightarrow[\text{fusion}]{\text{KOH}}$ (resorcinol) + $HO_2CCH_2C_6H_4OH$

Oxidation with alkaline hydrogen peroxide may also be used in degrading isoflavones; recognisable fragments are not usually obtained by this method, but sometimes information may be obtained about the substituents in the 3-phenyl nucleus, *e.g.*, **genistein** (4′,5,7-trihydroxyisoflavone) gives *p*-hydroxybenzoic acid.

The final proof of the structure of an isoflavone lies in its synthesis. A general method of synthesising isoflavones is that of Späth *et al.* (1930); *e.g.*, isoflavone itself may be synthesised from benzyl *o*-hydroxyphenyl ketone and ethyl formate:

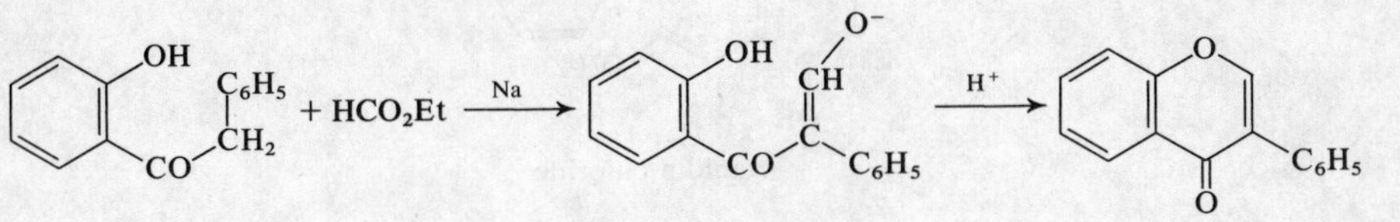

benzyl o-hydroxyphenyl ketone $+ HCO_2Et \xrightarrow{\text{Na}}$ (enolate intermediate) $\xrightarrow{\text{H}^+}$ isoflavone (C_6H_5)

By using substituted ketones, various isoflavones may be synthesised, *e.g.*, daidzein from 2,4-dihydroxyphenyl *p*-hydroxybenzyl ketone (Wessely *et al.*, 1933):

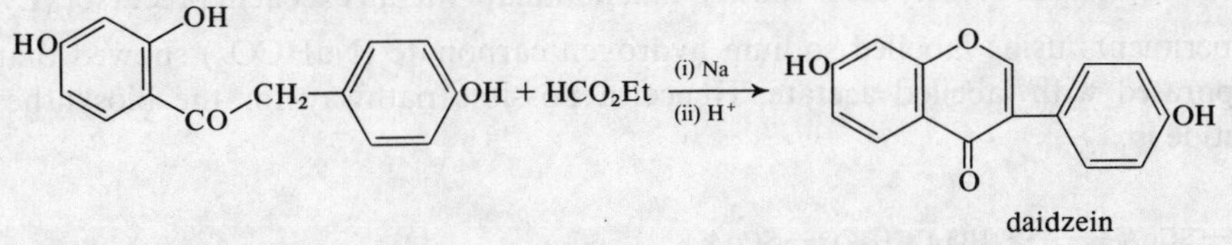

2,4-dihydroxyphenyl p-hydroxybenzyl ketone $+ HCO_2Et \xrightarrow[\text{(ii) H}^+]{\text{(i) Na}}$ daidzein

Another method of preparing isoflavones is the **Baker–Ollis synthesis** (1953). Benzyl *o*-hydroxyphenyl ketones react at room temperature with ethoxalyl chloride in pyridine, and the products, on alkaline hydrolysis followed by acidification and heating, produce isoflavones, *e.g.*, daidzein:

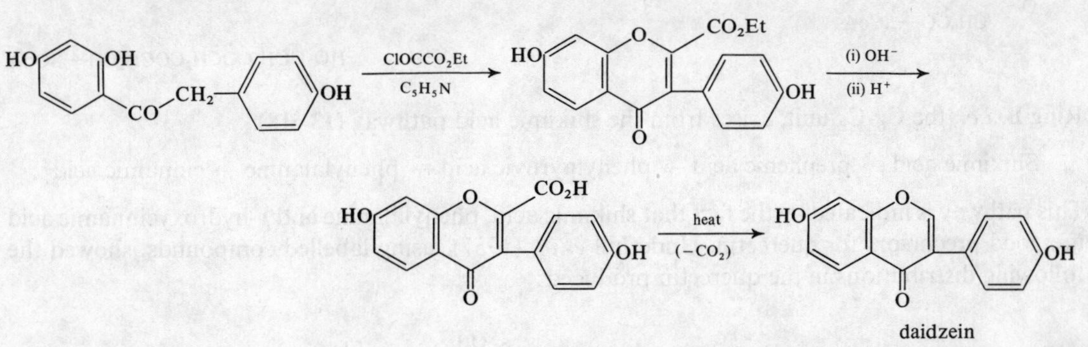

benzyl o-hydroxyphenyl ketone $\xrightarrow[\text{C}_5\text{H}_5\text{N}]{\text{ClOCCO}_2\text{Et}}$ (isoflavone-2-CO_2Et) $\xrightarrow[\text{(ii) H}^+]{\text{(i) OH}^-}$ (isoflavone-2-CO_2H) $\xrightarrow[(-CO_2)]{\text{heat}}$ daidzein

§16. Biosynthesis of the flavonoids

Robinson (1936) considered the C_{15} skeleton of flavonoids to be composed of two parts, C_6 and C_9:

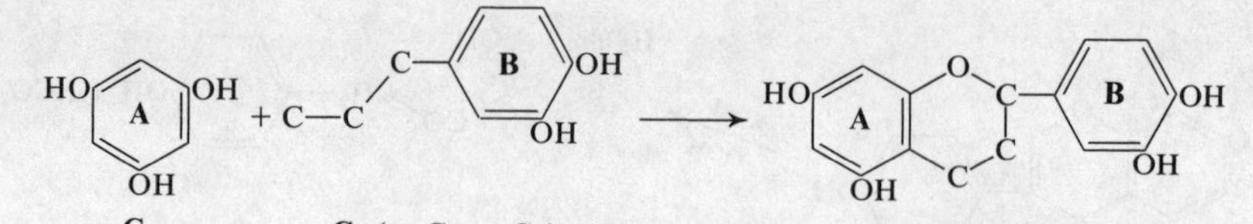

$$C_6 \qquad\qquad C_9\,(=C_3+C_6) \qquad\qquad C_{15}$$

Not very much is yet known about the large number of individual steps through which the biosynthesis proceeds, but it is well established that rings **A** and **B** are formed by different routes. Ring **A** is produced by the acetate pathway. This was proposed by Birch *et al.* (1953), and was shown to be correct by feeding experiments with labelled acetate, *e.g.*, Grisebach (1957) fed $^{14}CH_3CO_2H$ (C) and $CH_3{}^{14}CO_2H$ (C) to red cabbage plants and obtained cyanidin chloride labelled as shown. This is in keeping with a head-to-tail condensation between acetyl-coenzyme A units. However, by

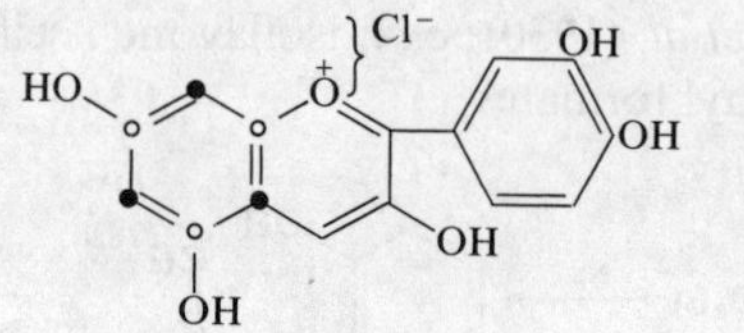

cyanidin chloride

analogy with the biosynthesis of fatty acids, it has been assumed that malonyl-coenzyme A rather than acetyl-coenzyme A is the intermediate in flavonoid biosynthesis. Feeding experiments in the study of the biosynthesis of fatty acids showed that malonate was an excellent precursor (Lynen *et al.*, 1961). Experiments using labelled sodium hydrogen carbonate ($NaH\overset{*}{C}O_3$) showed that this was not incorporated with labelled acetate. Hence, a possible pathway for the biosynthesis of the C_6-polyketide is:

(i) $\quad CH_3CO-SCoA \xrightarrow{\;\overset{*}{C}O_2\;} HO_2\overset{*}{C}CH_2CO-SCoA$

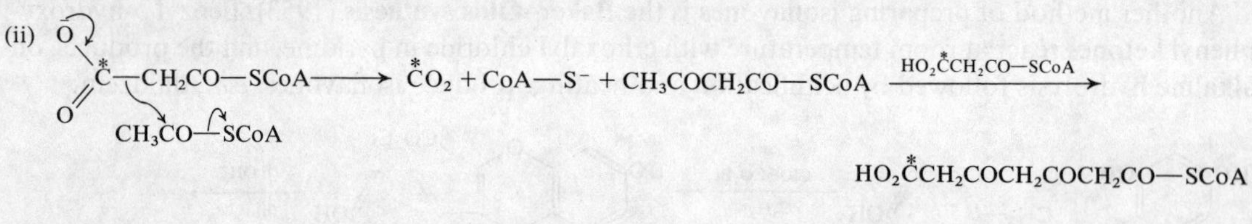

(ii)

$$\longrightarrow \overset{*}{C}O_2 + CoA-S^- + CH_3COCH_2CO-SCoA \xrightarrow{\;HO_2\overset{*}{C}CH_2CO-SCoA\;}$$

$$HO_2\overset{*}{C}CH_2COCH_2COCH_2CO-SCoA$$

Ring **B**, *i.e.*, the C_6-C_3 unit, arises from the shikimic acid pathway (**13** §18).

Shikimic acid → prephenic acid → phenylpyruvic acid → phenylalanine → cinnamic acid

This pathway is indicated by the fact that shikimic acid, phenylalanine and *p*-hydroxycinnamic acid are good precursors for quercetin. Underhill *et al.* (1957), using labelled compounds, showed the following distributions in the quercetin produced:

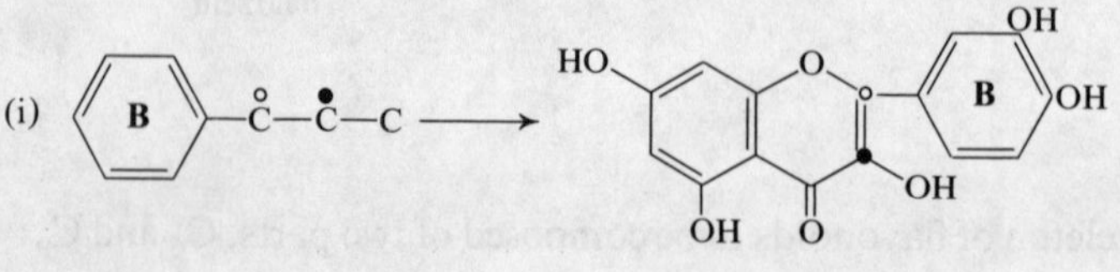

(i)

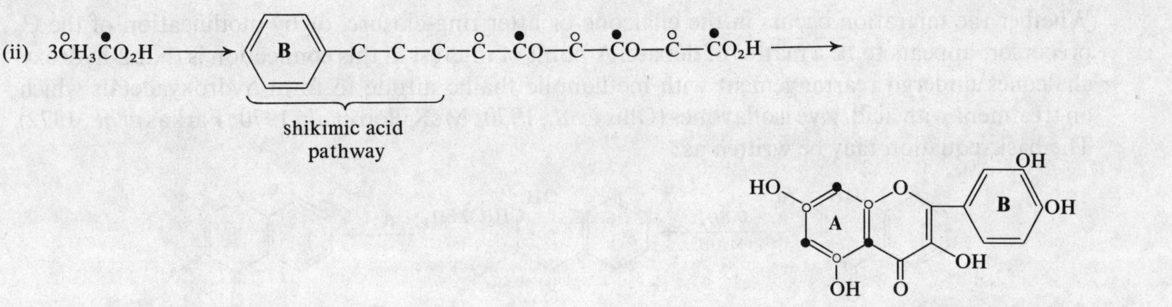

(ii) $3CH_3CO_2H$ ⟶ [B]—C—C—C—C—CO—C—CO—C—CO_2H ⟶

shikimic acid
pathway

quercetin

The general belief is that the two fragments, C_6 and C_9, join together to form a complex poly-ketide which then forms a chalcone.

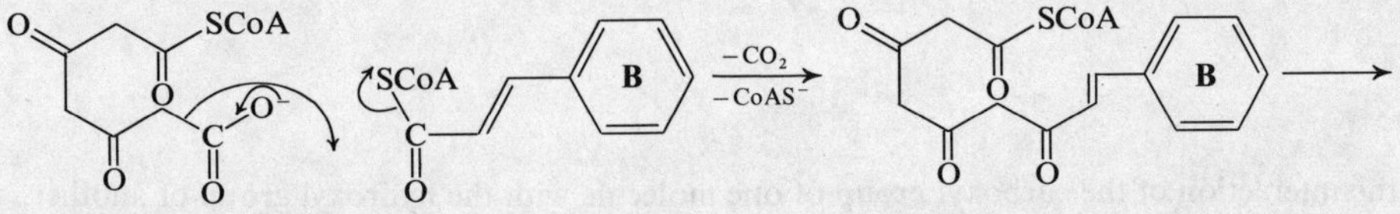

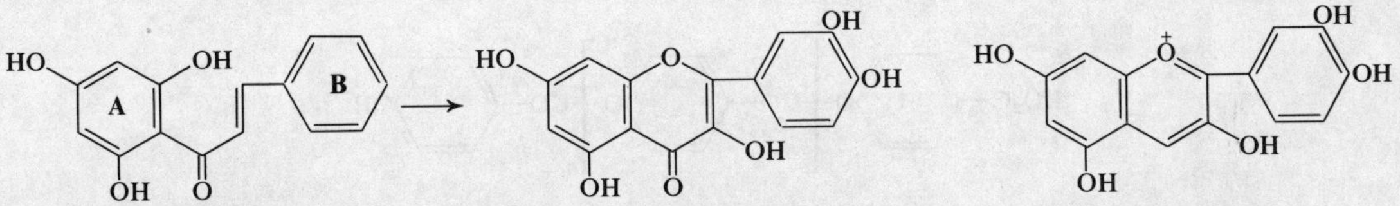

chalcone   quercetin   cyanidin

Feeding experiments with cinnamic acid labelled at the carboxyl group have shown that this carbon atom is retained at position 4 in quercetin.

As shown above, quercetin (a flavone) and cyanidin (an anthocyanidin) are produced from the chalcone by independent pathways. A possible sequence appears to be:

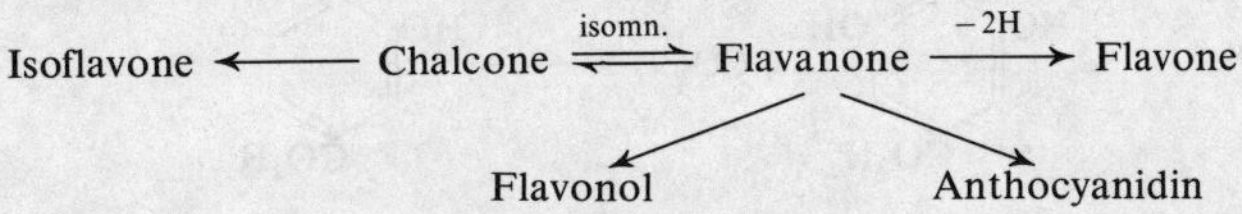

$$\text{Isoflavone} \longleftarrow \text{Chalcone} \underset{}{\overset{isomn.}{\rightleftharpoons}} \text{Flavanone} \xrightarrow{-2H} \text{Flavone}$$

$$\text{Flavonol} \qquad \text{Anthocyanidin}$$

Feeding experiments with labelled phenylalanine afford strong evidence that isoflavone is produced by migration of the aryl group (Grisebach, 1965).

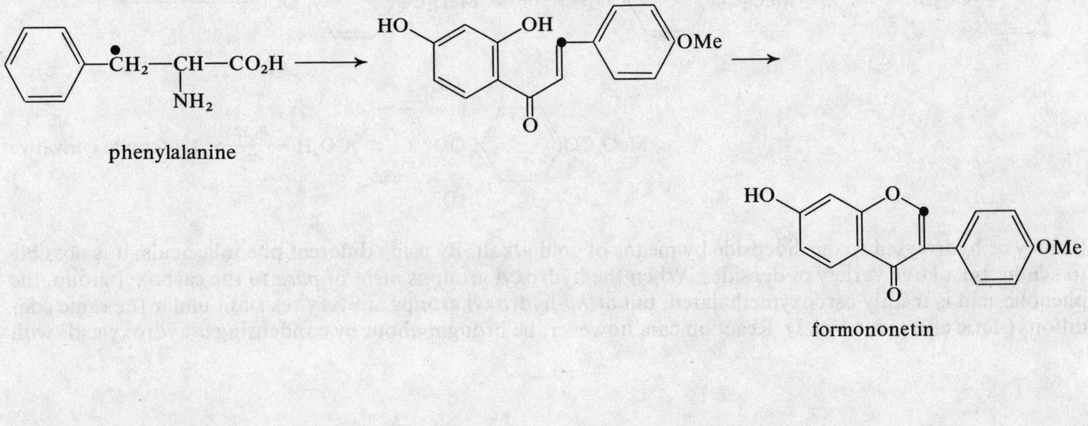

phenylalanine

formononetin

Whether the migration occurs in the chalcone or after ring-closure, or by modification of the C_9 precursor, appears to be a matter of debate. A point of interest in this connection is that 2-hydroxy-chalcones undergo rearrangement with methanolic thallic nitrate to form hydroxyacetals which, on treatment with acid, give isoflavones (Ollis *et al.*, 1970; McKillop *et al.*, 1970; Farkas *et al.*, 1972). The basic equation may be written as:

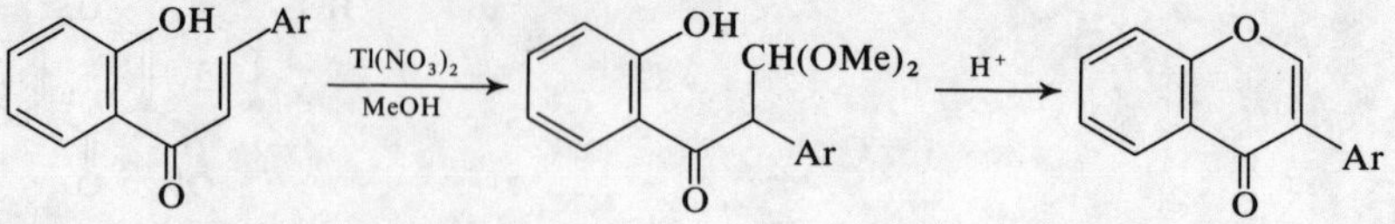

The final point that will be mentioned here is the order of hydroxylation (and methylation). Here again, the problem is still to be settled.

Depsides

§17. Depsides

Phenolic acids, by the interaction of the carboxyl group of one molecule with the hydroxyl group of another, give rise to **depsides**:

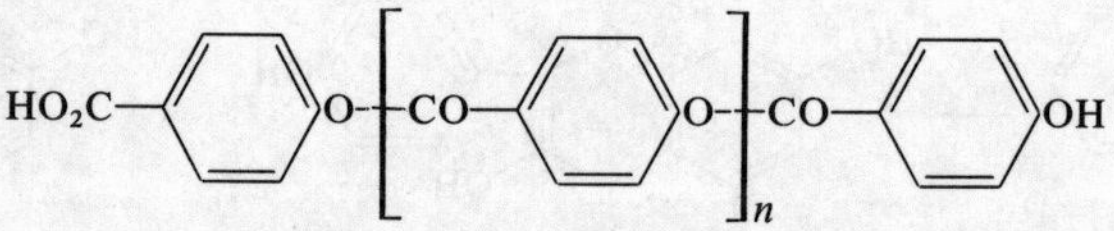

If *n* is zero, then the molecule is a didepside; if *n* is 1, then a tridepside; etc. The main sources of the depsides are the lichens.

In order to synthesise depsides in a known fashion, it is necessary to protect hydroxyl groups. Fischer (1919) carried this out by means of acetylation (acetic anhydride) or by introducing a carbomethoxy group (with methyl chloroformate); two hydroxyl groups in the *ortho*-position may be protected by means of carbonyl chloride, *e.g.*, gallic acid forms the following compound.

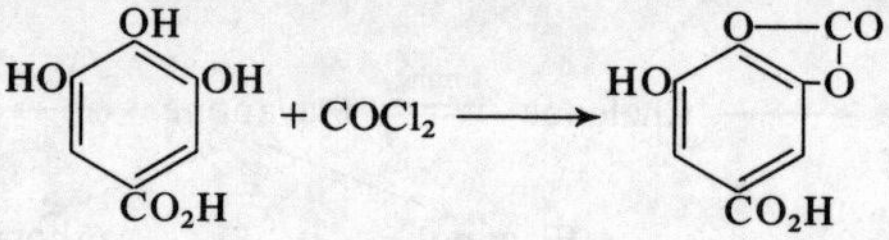

Let us consider the synthesis of a depside from a monohydroxybenzoic acid.

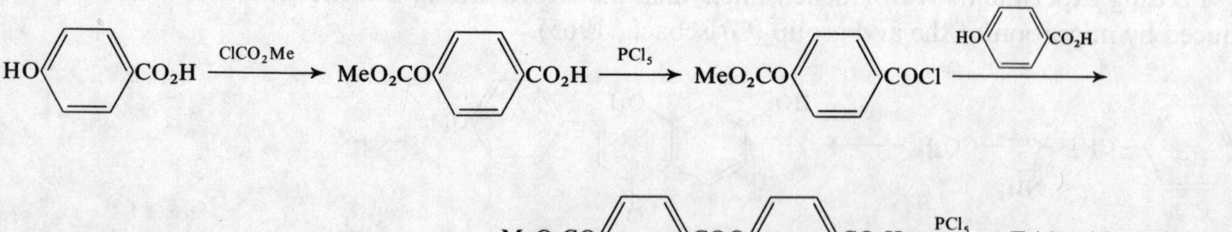

(I) may be hydrolysed to the didepside by means of cold alkali. By using different phenolic acids, it is possible to synthesise a large variety of depsides. When the hydroxyl group is *meta* or *para* to the carboxyl group, the phenolic acid is readily carboxymethylated, but *ortho*-hydroxyl groups are very resistant under the same conditions (steric effect; see Vol. I). Reaction can, however, be brought about by condensing *o*-hydroxyacids with methyl chloroformate in the presence of a base, *e.g.*, dimethylaniline. There is also the further difficulty that *ortho*-hydroxyl groups do not react with acid chlorides (steric effect). This has been overcome by condensing an acid chloride with an *o*-phenolic aldehyde, *e.g.*,

$$\text{MeO}_2\text{COC}_6\text{H}_4\text{COCl} + \text{HO}\!\!\underset{\text{OCO}_2\text{Me}}{\overset{\text{CHO}}{\bigcirc}} \longrightarrow \text{MeO}_2\text{COC}_6\text{H}_4\text{COO}\!\!\underset{\text{OCO}_2\text{Me}}{\overset{\text{CHO}}{\bigcirc}}$$

§18. Tannins

These are widely distributed in plants; many are glycosides. One of the best sources of tannin is nutgall. The tannins are colourless non-crystalline substances which form colloidal solutions in water; these solutions have an astringent taste. Tannins precipitate proteins from solution, and they form a bluish-black colour with ferric salts, a property which is used in the manufacture of ink. Tannins also precipitate many alkaloids from their solutions.

The name tannins is derived from their ability to *tan* leather, and is not based on a class of compounds with a common basic structure. There are two groups of tannins: the hydrolysable tannins, which are esters of gallic acid and also glycosides of these esters; and the condensed tannins, which are polymers derived from various flavonoids.

REFERENCES

BENTLEY, *The Natural Pigments*, Interscience (1960).

GEISSMAN (ed.), *The Chemistry of Flavonoid Compounds*, Pergamon (1962).

DEAN, *Naturally Occurring Oxygen Ring Compounds*, Butterworths (1963). Chs. 10–13. 'Flavones, Anthocyanins, etc.'

BERNFELD (ed.), *Biogenesis of Natural Compounds*, Pergamon (1967, 2nd edn.). Ch. 12. 'The Biosynthesis of Phenolic Plant Products.'

GOODWIN (ed.), *Chemistry and Biochemistry of Plant Pigments*, Academic Press (1965).

HARBORNE, *Comparative Biochemistry of the Flavonoids*, Academic Press (1967).

GEISSMAN and CROUT, *Organic Chemistry of Secondary Plant Metabolism*, Freeman, Cooper and Co. (1969). Ch. 7. 'Flavonoid Compounds.'

PORTER and BALDAS, *Mass Spectrometry of Heterocyclic Compounds*, Wiley-Interscience (1971).

CHADENSON *et al.*, 'Synthesis of 2,5-Dihydroxy-7-methoxyflavonone,' *Chem. Comm.*, 1972, 107.

16   Purines and nucleic acids

§1. Introduction

Purine is the parent substance of a group of cyclic diureides and was used by E. Fischer to name systematically the naturally occurring derivatives. Its structure consists of a pyrimidine ring fused to an imidazole ring. Purine can exist in four tautomeric forms in which the hydrogen atom is joined to the different nitrogen atoms: N-1, N-3, N-7, and N-9. In the first two the aromaticity of the pyrimidine ring is lost, the ring now being virtually equivalent to the far less stable (and more reactive) *ortho*-quinonoid structure. In practice, purine appears to behave completely as the tautomers of N-7 H and N-9 H. In the earlier literature, the formula of purine was written as follows (the method of numbering is also shown):

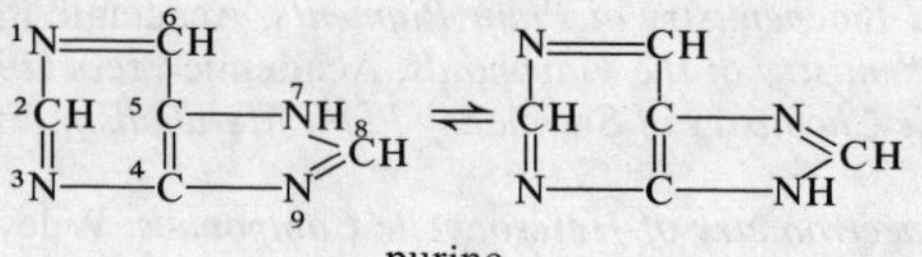

purine

These formulae are now written as **A** or **B** (*cf.* **12** §14). In this book, formula **A** is used (**B** is **A** turned upside down; there is no change in numbering, and so the reader can readily translate **A** into **B**).

A   B

§2. Uric acid

Guano (birds' excrement found on islands near the western coast of South America) contains up to about 25 per cent uric acid; about 90 per cent of snakes' excrement is ammonium urate. Small amounts of uric acid are also present in human urine; it was first discovered by Scheele (1776) in urinary calculi.

Liebig and Wöhler (1834) showed that the molecular formula of uric acid is $C_5H_4N_4O_3$. These authors also found, in 1838, that the oxidation of uric acid with nitric acid gives alloxan and urea in equimolecular proportions.

$$C_5H_4N_4O_3 + H_2O + [O] \xrightarrow{HNO_3} C_4H_2N_2O_4 + NH_2CONH_2$$

Structure of alloxan, $C_4H_2N_2O_4$

When hydrolysed with alkali, alloxan produces one molecule of urea and one molecule of mesoxalic acid.

$$C_4H_2N_2O_4 + 2H_2O \xrightarrow{KOH} NH_2CONH_2 + HO_2CCOCO_2H$$

Since alloxan contains no free amino or carboxyl groups, the products of hydrolysis suggest that alloxan is mesoxalylurea; this cyclic structure has been confirmed by the direct union of urea and mesoxalic acid to give alloxan (Liebig and Wöhler, 1838).

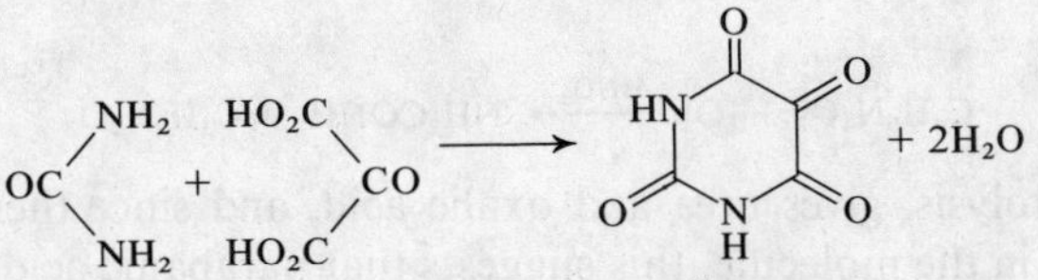

Alloxan, as its monohydrate, is conveniently prepared from barbituric acid as follows (see also **12** §13a):

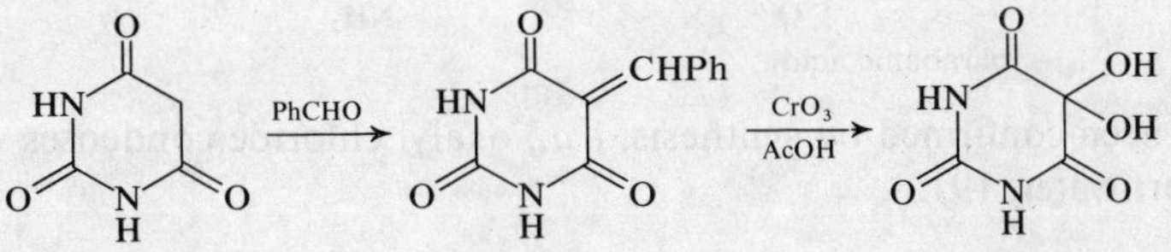

barbituric
acid

alloxan
monohydrate

Alloxan is a strongly acidic compound; it crystallises with four molecules of water of crystallisation. Three of these are readily lost on warming, but the fourth is lost only when the monohydrate is heated to 150°C. Because of this, it is believed that the fourth molecule of water is not water of crystallisation but water of constitution (*cf.* chloral hydrate, Vol. I).

Alloxan stains the skin purple (due to the formation of murexide). The 5-oxime of alloxan is violuric acid (**12** §13b), and when reduced with zinc and hydrochloric acid, alloxan forms dialuric acid (**12** §13b). When alloxan is reduced with hydrogen sulphide, the product is *alloxantin*. According to Tipson *et al.* (1951), however, if excess of hydrogen sulphide is used, the product is dialuric acid only. Alloxantin is produced by reducing alloxan (one molecule) with half a molecule of hydrogen sulphide, or by mixing aqueous solutions of alloxan and dialuric acid. When heated with ammonia in ethanolic solution, alloxantin forms *murexide*, which is the ammonium salt of *purpuric acid* (an unstable compound).

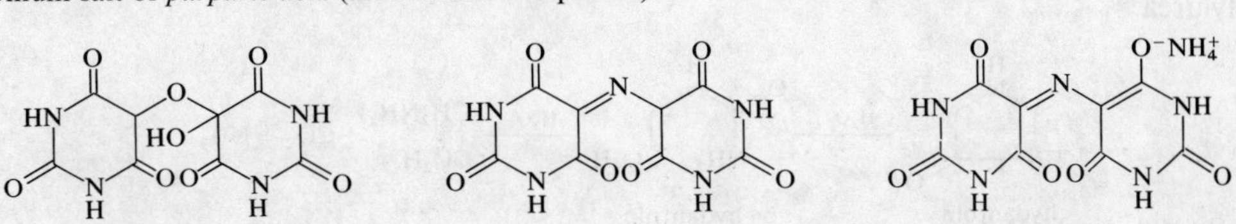

alloxantin   purpuric acid   murexide

Murexide is soluble in water, giving a purple solution which turns blue on the addition of alkali. Purpuric acid slowly hydrolyses in solution to form alloxan and uramil.

When uric acid is oxidised with an aqueous suspension of lead dioxide, the products are allantoin and carbon dioxide (Liebig and Wöhler, 1838). These products are obtained in quantitative yield if the oxidation is carried out with alkaline permanganate (Behrend, 1904).

$$C_5H_4N_4O_3 + H_2O + [O] \longrightarrow C_4H_6N_4O_3 + CO_2$$

Structure of allantoin, $C_4H_6N_4O_3$ (Baeyer, 1861–1864)

When hydrolysed with alkali, allantoin forms two molecules of urea and one molecule of glyoxylic acid.

$$C_4H_6N_4O_3 + 2H_2O \longrightarrow 2NH_2CONH_2 + OHCCO_2H$$

The formation of these hydrolytic products suggests that allantoin is the diureide of glyoxylic acid.
On oxidation with nitric acid, allantoin forms urea and *parabanic acid* in equimolecular proportions.

$$C_4H_6N_4O_3 + [O] \xrightarrow{\text{HNO}_3} NH_2CONH_2 + C_3H_2N_2O_3$$

Parabanic acid, on hydrolysis, gives urea and oxalic acid, and since there are no free amino or carboxyl groups present in the molecule, this suggests that parabanic acid is oxalylurea.

parabanic acid

This structure has been confirmed by synthesis, *e.g.*, oxalyl chloride condenses with urea to form parabanic acid (Bornwater, 1912).

Thus, from the above facts, it can be seen that allantoin contains the parabanic acid nucleus joined to a molecule of urea. The point of the attachment is deduced from the following experimental evidence. When reduced with concentrated hydriodic acid at 100°C, allantoin forms urea and *hydantoin*.

$$C_4H_6N_4O_3 + 2[H] \xrightarrow{\text{HI}} NH_2CONH_2 + C_3H_4N_2O_2$$

Hydantoin, on controlled hydrolysis, gives *hydantoic acid* (*ureidoacetic acid*) and this, on further hydrolysis, gives glycine, ammonia and carbon dioxide. These results suggest that hydantoin is glycollylurea.

hydantoin   hydantoic
                             acid

This structure for hydantoin has been confirmed by synthesis, *e.g.*, West (1918).

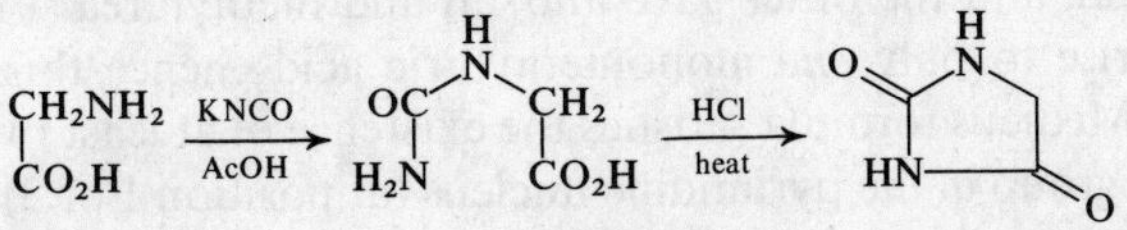

Hydantoin, m.p. 216°C, may also be prepared by the electrolytic reduction of parabanic acid, or by the action of bromoacetyl bromide on urea.

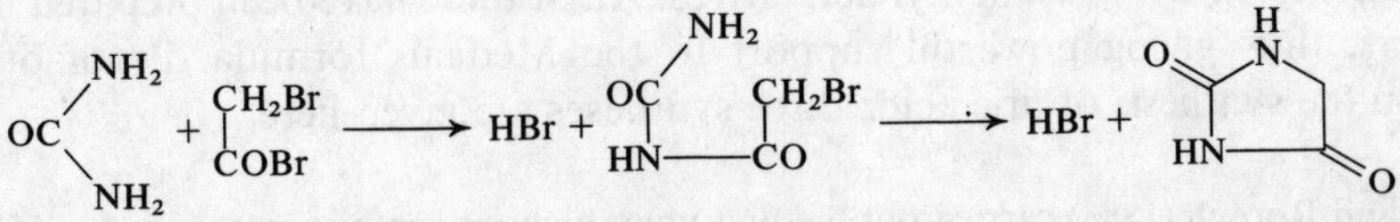

Thus the following structure for allantoin would account for all of the foregoing results:

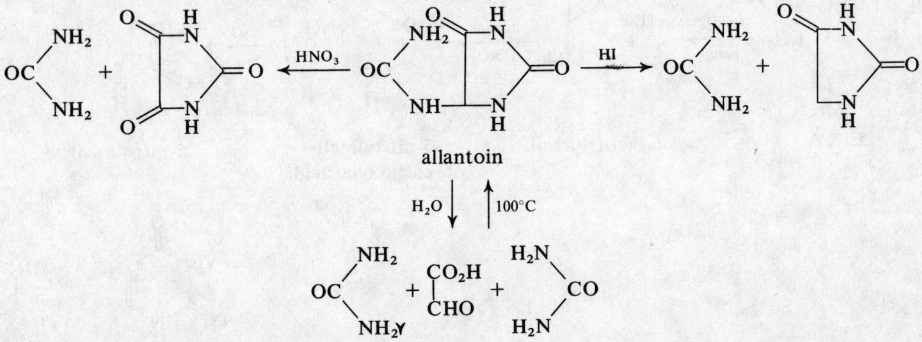

allantoin

This has been confirmed by synthesis by heating urea with glyoxylic acid at 100°C (Grimaux, 1876).

Examination of the structure of allantoin shows that it contains a chiral centre; hence two optically active forms are possible. Both forms have been obtained, and they have been found to racemise rapidly in solution; the racemisation probably occurs *via* enolisation (*cf.* 2 §8iii).

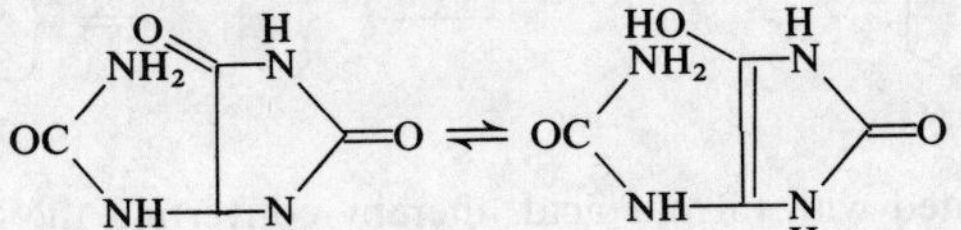

In the formation of allantoin from uric acid by oxidation, one carbon atom is lost from the latter as carbon dioxide. The problem, then, is to fit this carbon atom into the allantoin structure. At the same time, the structure thus given to uric acid must also include the alloxan skeleton in order to account for the formation of this compound. Two structures that were proposed which both agreed with the facts known at the time were by Medicus (1875) and by Fittig (1878).

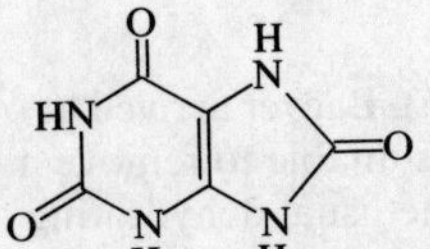

Medicus formula 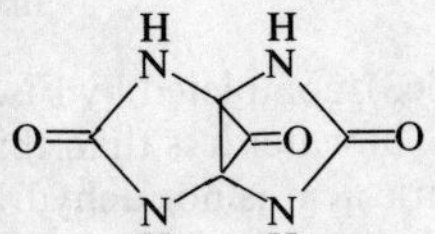   Fittig formula

Fischer (1884) prepared two isomeric monomethyluric acids; one gave methylalloxan and urea on oxidation with nitric acid, and the other gave alloxan and methylurea. Fittig's formula, which is symmetrical, can give rise to only *one* monomethyluric acid; hence this structure is untenable. On the other hand, the Medicus formula satisfies the existence of at least two isomeric monomethyl derivatives: one methyl group in the pyrimidine nucleus (at position 1 or 3) would produce methyl-alloxan and urea, and a methyl group in the imidazole nucleus (at position 7 or 9) would produce alloxan and methylurea (Fischer showed that the two monomethyluric acids were the 3- and 9-derivatives). Examination of the Medicus formula shows that it admits the possibility of four mono-methyl, six dimethyl and four trimethyl derivatives. All of these have been prepared by Fischer and his co-workers, thus giving powerful support to the Medicus formula. Proof of the Medicus formula lies in the synthesis of uric acid; three syntheses are given here.

(i) Behrend and Roosen (1888) carried out the first unambiguous synthesis (see also **12** §15).

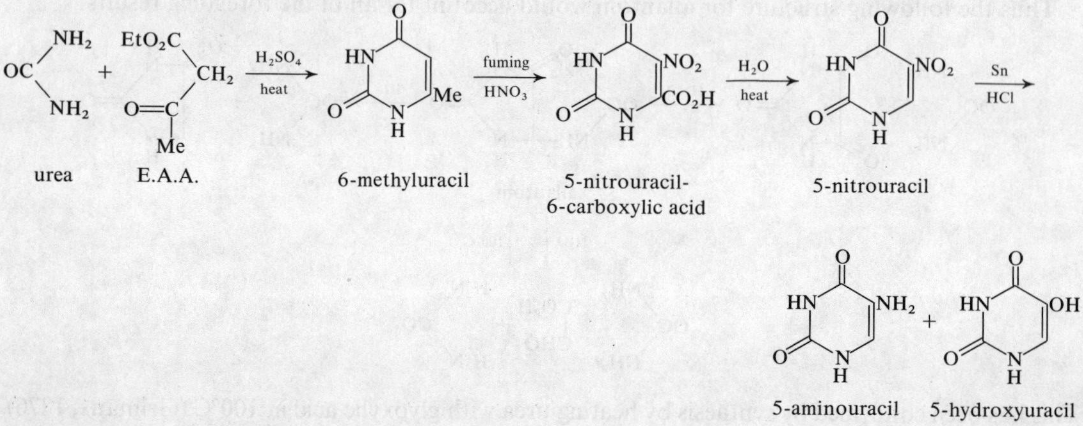

In this reduction, some of the aminouracil is converted into hydroxyuracil. The mechanism of this change is not certain, but a possibility is as follows:

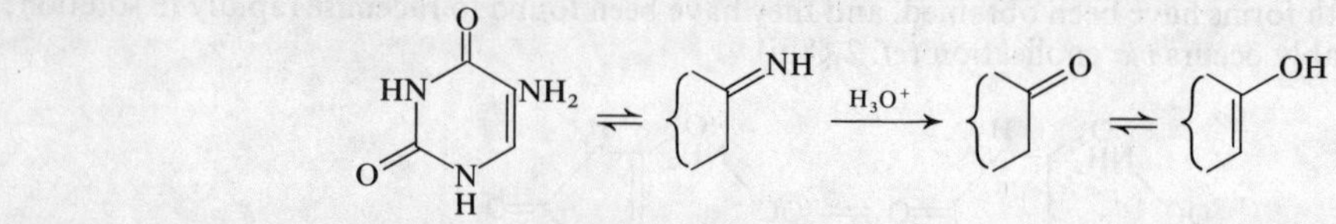

The reaction product was treated with nitrous acid, thereby converting the 5-aminouracil present into 5-hydroxyuracil; then the synthesis proceeded as follows:

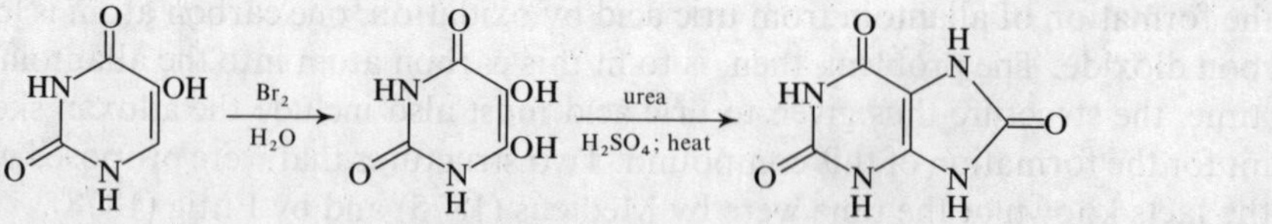

(ii) Baeyer's synthesis (1863), completed by Fischer (1895). Baeyer arrived at ψ-uric acid and knew that uric acid contained one molecule of water less than this, but was unable to remove it to form uric acid. His failure was due to the fact that ψ-uric acid is not dehydrated by the usual dehydrating agents; Fischer succeeded by fusion with anhydrous oxalic acid, and also obtained better results by boiling ψ-uric acid with 20 per cent hydrochloric acid.

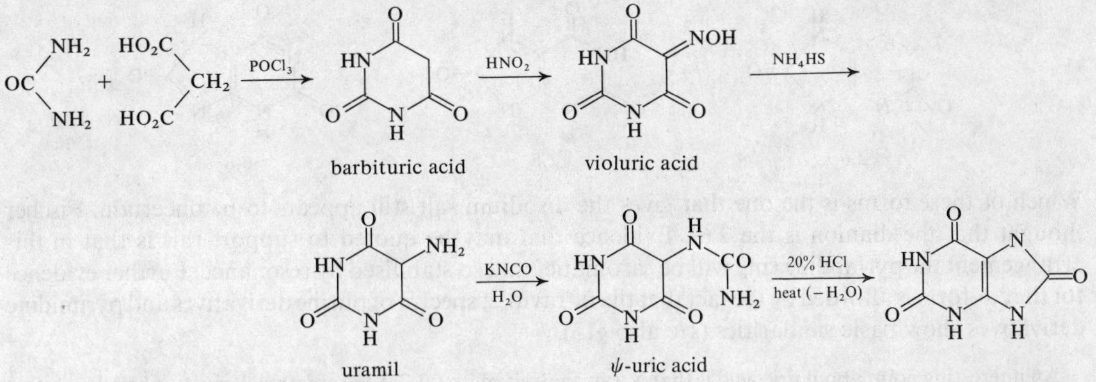

barbituric acid   violuric acid

uramil   ψ-uric acid

(iii) Traube's synthesis (1900) is the most important method, since it can be used to prepare any purine derivative; it is also the basis of various commercial methods for preparing the purines synthetically.

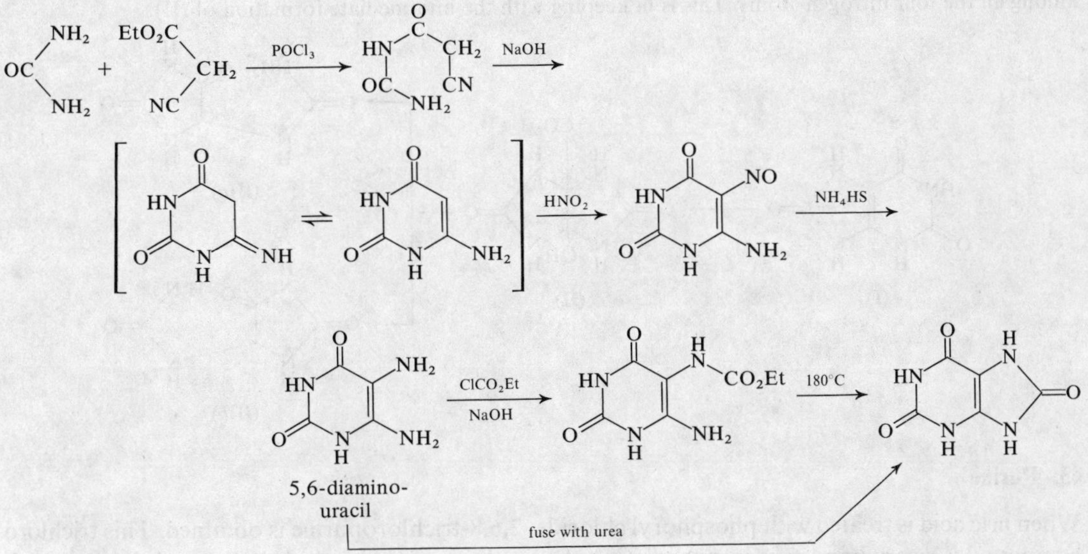

5,6-diamino-
uracil

fuse with urea

The reduction of the nitrosopyrimidine may also be carried out with sodium dithionite ($Na_2S_2O_4$).

Clusius *et al.* (1953), using urea labelled with ^{15}N, have shown that the two nitrogen atoms in the diamino-uracil are retained on fusion with urea.

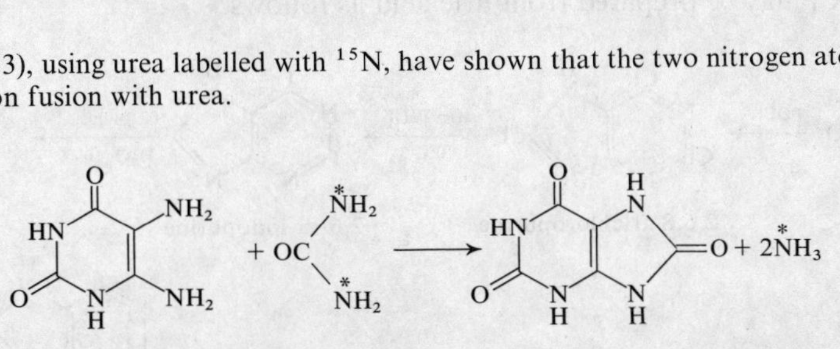

Uric acid is a white crystalline powder which is insoluble in the ordinary organic solvents. It behaves as a weak dibasic acid, forming two series of salts (*e.g.*, monosodium and disodium urate).

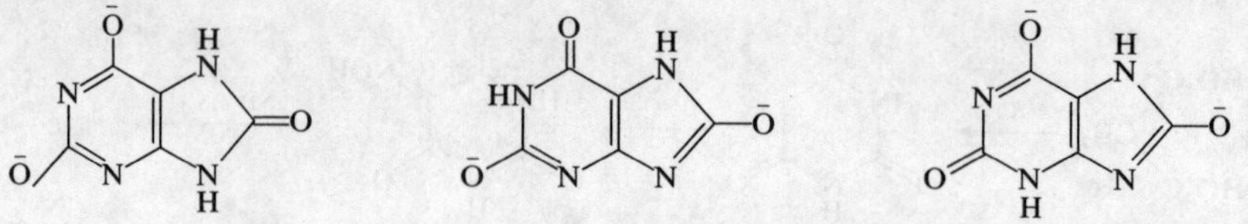

2,6   2,8   6,8

Which of these forms is the one that gives the disodium salt still appears to be uncertain. Fischer thought that the dianion is the 2,6-. Evidence that may be quoted to support this is that in this arrangement the pyrimidine ring will be 'aromatic' and so stabilised by resonance. Further evidence for the 2,6-form is afforded by the fact that the ultraviolet spectra of purine derivatives and pyrimidine derivatives show basic similarities (see also §13).

An interesting point about uric acid is that X-ray analysis of its 1,3,7,9-tetramethyl derivative has shown that there is hydrogen bonding between hydrogen (of the methyl group) and oxygen (Sutor, 1963).

It is also interesting to consider the path followed in the oxidation of uric acid to allantoin. Behrend (1904) suggested that the alkaline permanganate oxidation of uric acid (I) gives allantoin (IIIa and b) via the symmetrical intermediate (II). Cavalieri et al. (1948) have carried out this oxidation using uric acid labelled with ^{15}N at N-1 and N-3, and found that the allantoin produced had this isotopic nitrogen distributed uniformly among all the four nitrogen atoms. This is in keeping with the intermediate formation of (II).

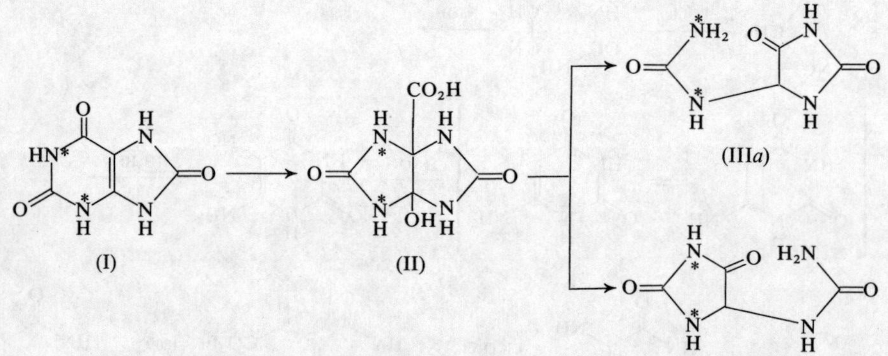

(I)   (II)   (IIIa)

(IIIb)

§3. Purine

When uric acid is treated with phosphoryl chloride, 2,6,8-trichloropurine is obtained. This trichloro compound is a very important intermediate in the synthesis of purine derivatives, and a point worth noting is that the reactivities of the chlorine atoms towards nucleophilic reagents are 6 > 2 > 8. **Purine**, m.p. 217°C, may be prepared from uric acid as follows:

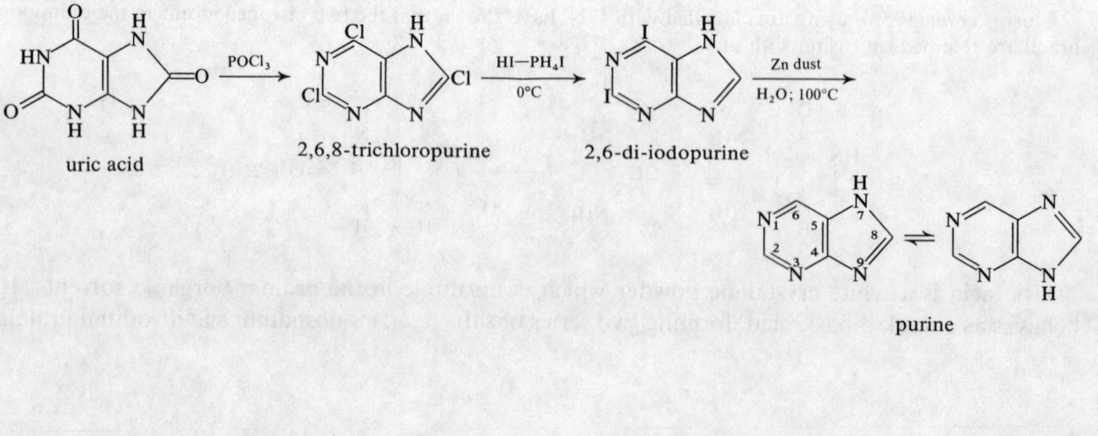

uric acid   2,6,8-trichloropurine   2,6-di-iodopurine

purine

Catalytic reduction of trichloropurine (H_2—Pd in aqueous sodium acetate) gives purine (Brodereck et al., 1962).

Purine behaves as a weak monoacid base (pK_a 8·96). Diazomethane or dimethyl sulphate and alkali methylate purine in the 9-position.

Purine has been found to occur naturally as its 9-D-ribofuranoside, *nebularine*.

The NMR spectrum of purine shows three singlets: τ 1·34 (6-H), 1·47 (2-H), and 1·72 (8-H). These values are in the aromatic region. The mass spectrum of purine shows fragments arising from the consecutive losses of hydrogen cyanide molecules. This often occurs in heterocyclic compounds containing two nitrogen atoms in one ring.

$$\xrightarrow[(-27)]{-HCN} [C_4H_3N_3]^{+} \xrightarrow[(-27)]{-HCN} [C_3H_2N_2]^{+}$$
$$M^{+}\ 120 \qquad\qquad m/e\ 93 \qquad\qquad m/e\ 66$$

PURINE DERIVATIVES

§4. Synthesis of purines

Before describing some individual purine derivatives, let us first consider some general methods of synthesising purines. Fischer (1897, 1898) prepared various purines starting from 2,6,8-trichloropurine. There are, however, two general synthetic methods in which the pyrimidine ring is synthesised first and then the imidazole ring 'built up' on this, or *vice versa*.

(i) *Traube's method.* This consists of synthesising a 4,5-diaminopyrimidine (see also later) and then condensing with formic acid to produce the imidazole ring; the formyl derivative is ring-closed by heating alone or by heating its sodium salt.

$$\text{(diaminopyrimidine)} + HCO_2H \longrightarrow \text{(formyl derivative)} \xrightarrow{heat} \text{(purine)}$$

This synthesis leads to the preparation of purines that are unsubstituted in position 8. This type of purine may also be prepared by heating a 5,6-diaminopyrimidine with dithioformic acid in the presence of sodium hydroxide solution, and then heating the product with a methanolic solution of sodium methoxide.

$$\text{(diaminopyrimidine)} \xrightarrow{HCS_2Na} \text{(thioformyl derivative)} \xrightarrow[CH_3OH]{CH_3ONa} \text{(purine)}$$

8-Hydroxypurines may be prepared by using ethyl chloroformate instead of formic acid. Alternatively, the diaminopyrimidine may be boiled with potassium isocyanate and the product, a ureido-pyrimidine, ring-closed by heating. Finally, diaminopyrimidines may be fused with urea to produce 8-hydroxypurines.

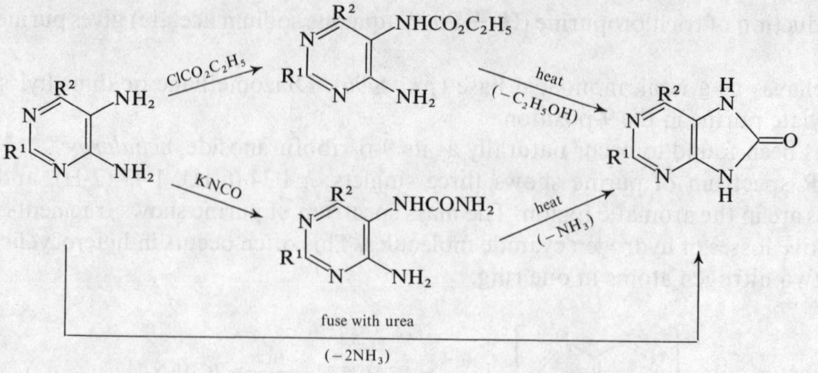

o-Aminohydroxypyrimidines may be used instead of *o*-diaminopyrimidines (*cf.* Baeyer's synthesis of ψ-uric acid, §2).

Bergmann *et al.* (1961) have prepared 8-substituted purines by condensing 5,6-diaminopyrimidines with amidine salts, *e.g.*,

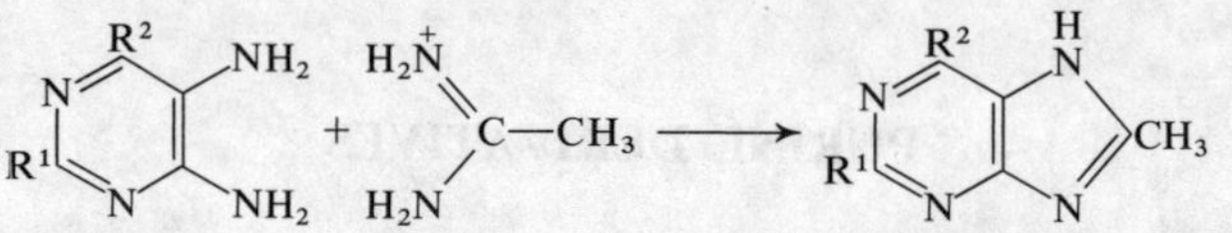

(ii) A less frequently used synthesis of purines starts with the imidazole derivative, *e.g.*, 7-methylxanthine from 4-amino-1-methylimidazole-5-carbonamide (Sarasin *et al.*, 1924):

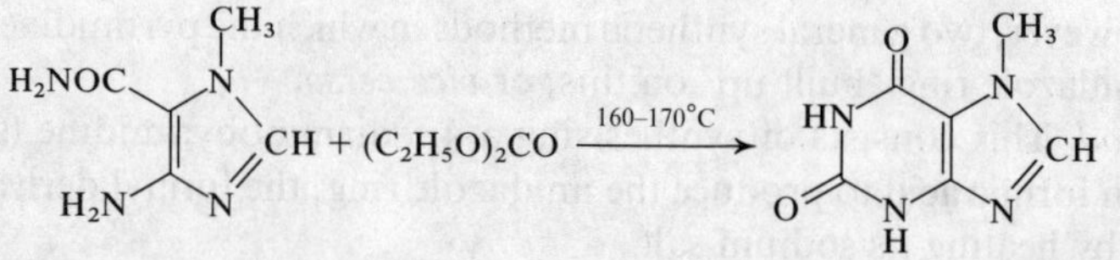

§5. Adenine (6-aminopurine), d. 365°C

This occurs in the pancreas of cattle and in tea extract. Its general reactions showed that adenine was a purine, and its structure was established by synthesis.

(i) Fischer (1897) (see also §6).

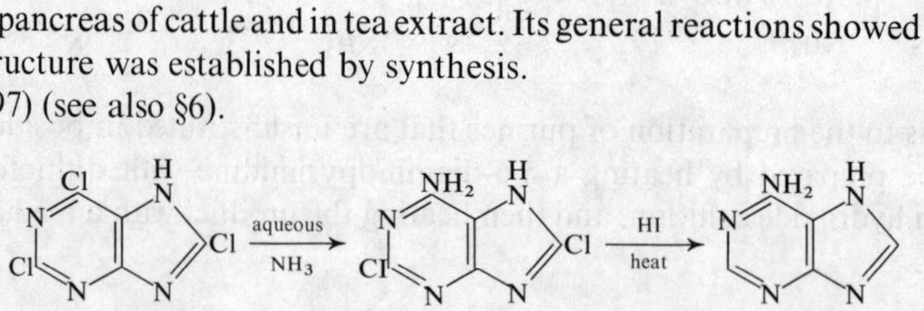

2,6,8-trichloro-
purine

adenine

(ii) Traube (1904).

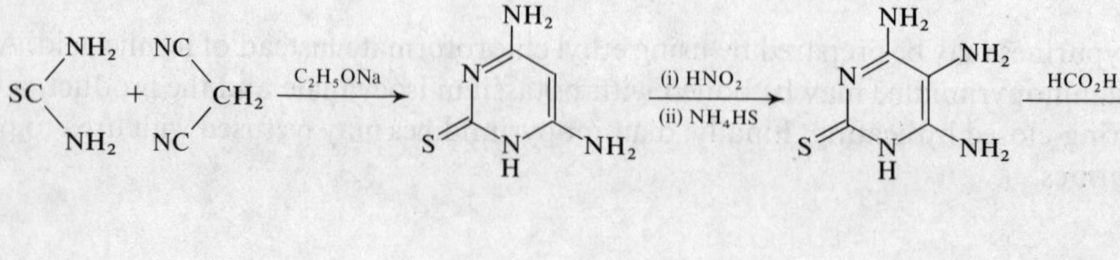

Bredereck *et al.* (1955) have modified this synthesis as follows:

(iii) Todd *et al.*, (1943).

formamidine   phenylazo-
       malononitrile

§6. Hypoxanthine (6-hydroxypurine), d. 150°C

This occurs in tea extract and in animal tissues. Its formation by the action of nitrous acid on adenine establishes its structure, and this has been confirmed by synthesis.

(i) Fischer (1897, 1898).

hypoxanthine

(ii) Traube (1904).

A new useful synthesis of hypoxanthines and adenines involves the condensation between 1,2,2-trimethylaminoacrylamide and ortho-esters (Richter *et al.*, 1960), *e.g.*, hypoxanthine:

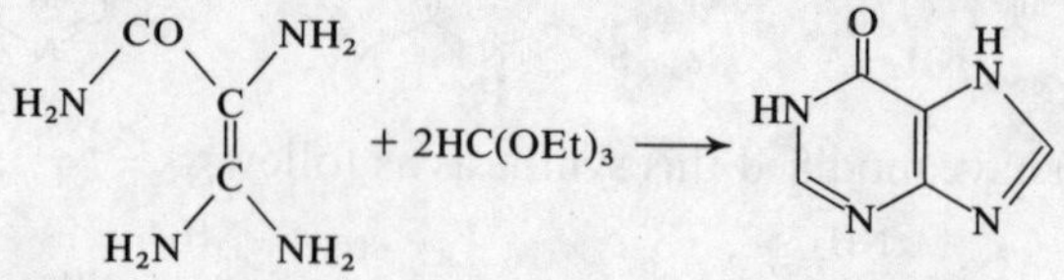

§7. Xanthine (2,6-dihydroxypurine), d. above 150°C

This occurs in tea extract and in animal tissues. When oxidised with potassium chlorate in hydrochloric acid solution, xanthine forms alloxan and urea; these products show the relationship of xanthine to uric acid, and its structure has been established by synthesis.

(i) Fischer (1898) (see also §10).

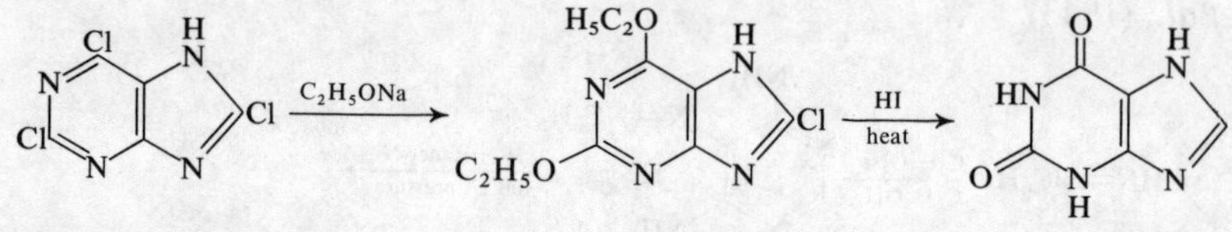

xanthine

(ii) Traube (1900).

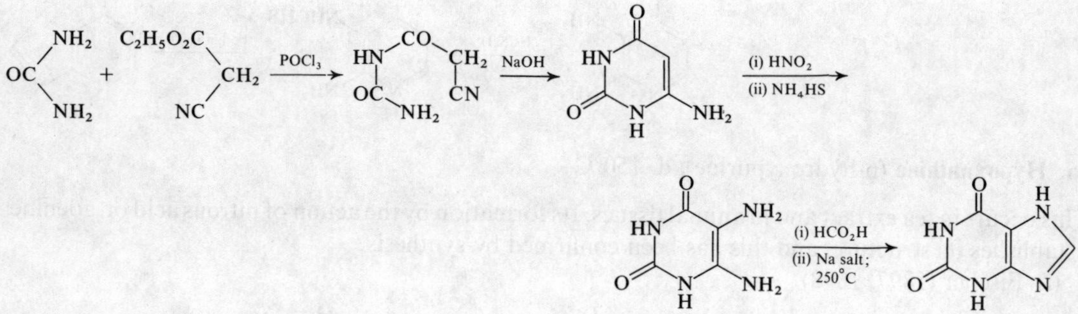

This synthesis has been modified by Bredereck *et al.* (1959):

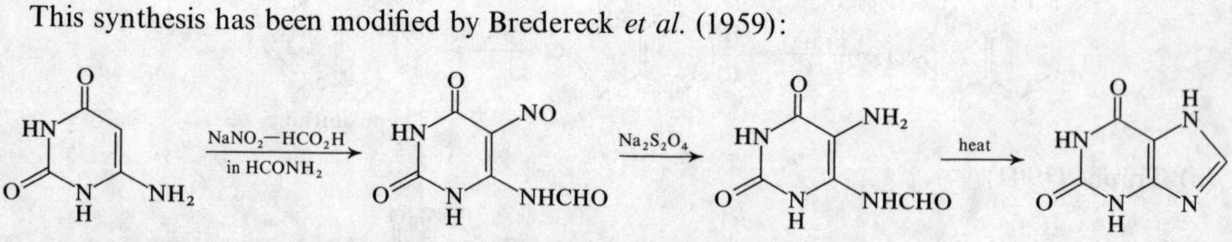

Xanthine is the parent substance of a number of compounds (see later).

§8. Guanine (2-amino-6-hydroxypurine), d. 360°C

This occurs in the pancreas of cattle, in guano and in certain fish scales. Its structure is shown by the fact that it gives xanthine on treatment with nitrous acid; this conversion is also effected by boiling guanine with 25 per cent hydrochloric acid (Fischer, 1910) (see also §13b).

(i) Fischer (1897).

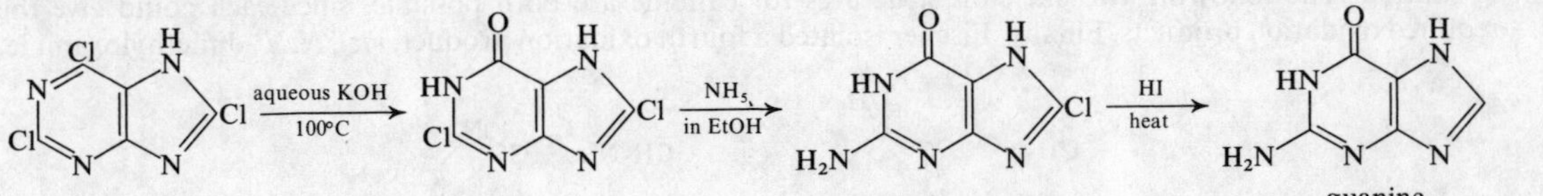

(ii) Traube (1900).

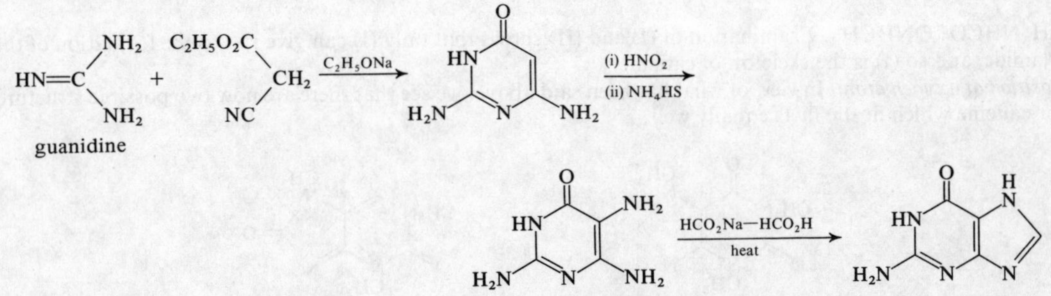

XANTHINE BASES

Three important methylated xanthines that occur naturally are caffeine, theobromine and theo-phylline. All three have been prepared from uric acid by Fischer and all have been synthesised by means of the Traube method.

§9. Caffeine (1,3,7-trimethylxanthine), m.p. 235–237°C

This occurs in tea, coffee, etc. Its molecular formula is $C_8H_{10}N_4O_2$, and its relationship to uric acid is shown by the fact that on oxidation with potassium chlorate in hydrochloric acid, caffeine gives dimethylalloxan and methylurea in equimolecular proportions. The structure of the former product is established by its conversion into N,N'-dimethylurea and mesoxalic acid on hydrolysis, and is confirmed by synthesis from these two compounds.

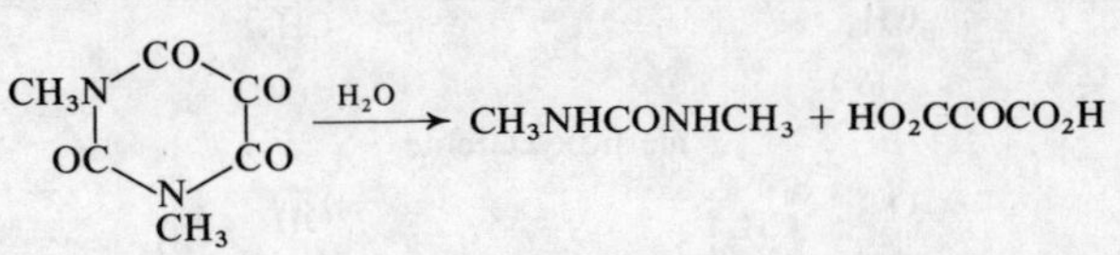

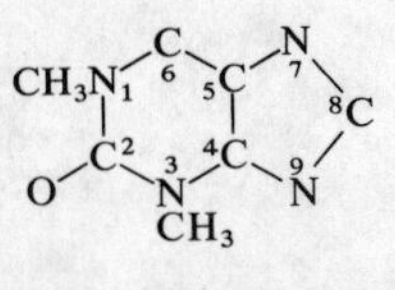

These results indicate that caffeine and uric acid have the same skeleton structure; at the same time the positions of two methyl groups and one oxygen atom in caffeine are also established. Thus the problem now is to ascertain the positions of the remaining methyl group and oxygen atom. The following skeleton structure for caffeine summarises the above information; the third methyl group is at either position 7 or 9, and the remaining oxygen atom at 6 or 8.

Position of the methyl group. As we have seen above, the oxidation of caffeine gives dimethylalloxan and methylurea. Fischer, however, also isolated another oxidation product which, on hydrolysis, gave N-methyl-glycine, carbon dioxide and ammonia. Thus this third oxidation product must be N-methylhydantoin:

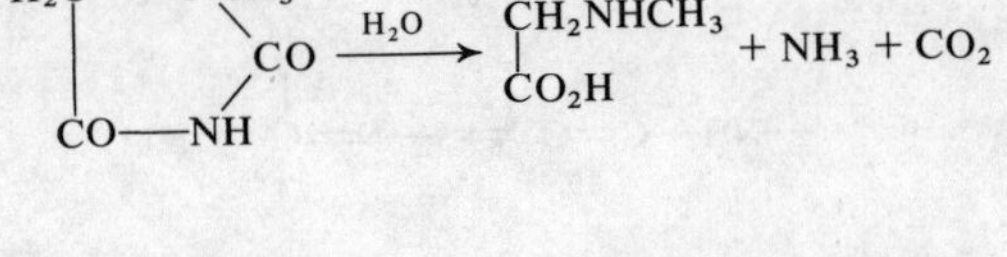

It therefore follows that caffeine contains two ring structures, that of dimethylalloxan and that of methyl-hydantoin. The following two skeleton structures for caffeine are both possible, since each could give the required oxidation products. Finally, Fischer isolated a fourth oxidation product, *viz.*, *N,N′*-dimethyloxamide,

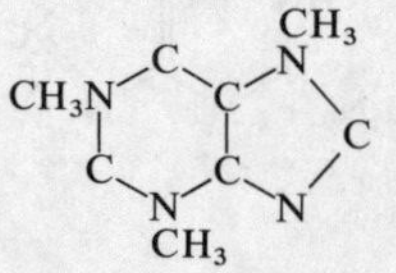

(I) 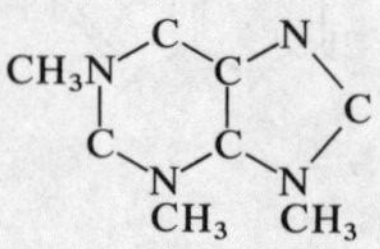   (II)

$CH_3NHCOCONHCH_3$. Examination of (I) and (II) shows that only (I) can give rise to the formation of this oxamide, and so (I) is the skeleton of caffeine.

Position of oxygen atom. In view of what has been said above, we see that there are now two possible structures for caffeine which fit the facts equally well:

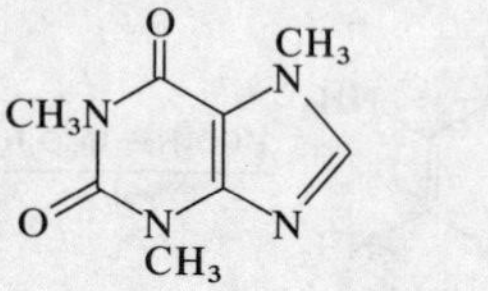

(III) 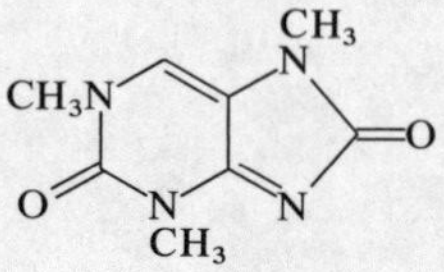   (IV)

By analogy with uric acid, (III) would appear the more likely one; this, however, is not proof. Fischer showed that (III) is caffeine as follows.

$$\text{Caffeine} \xrightarrow{\text{Cl}_2} \text{Chlorocaffeine} \xrightarrow[\text{NaOH}]{\text{CH}_3\text{OH}} \text{Methoxycaffeine} \xrightarrow[\text{boil}]{\text{dilute HCl}} \text{Oxycaffeine} + \text{CH}_3\text{Cl}$$

$$C_8H_{10}N_4O_2 \qquad\qquad C_8H_9ClN_4O_2 \qquad\qquad C_8H_9N_4O_2\text{—OCH}_3 \qquad\qquad C_8H_{10}N_4O_3$$

Fischer then showed that oxycaffeine was identical with a trimethyluric acid, since on methylation with methyl iodide in the presence of aqueous sodium hydroxide, oxycaffeine was converted into tetramethyluric acid. Thus methoxycaffeine is either (V) or (VI), and oxycaffeine (VII) or (VIII).

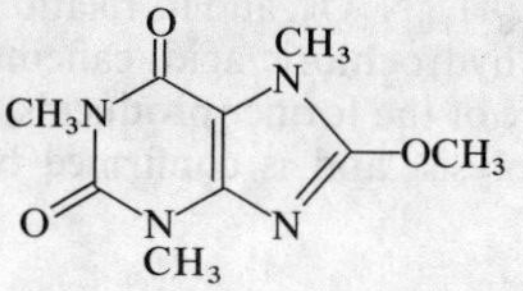

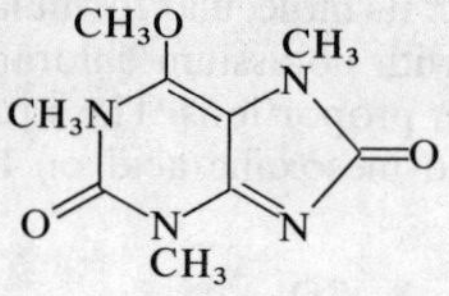

(V)   (VI)

methoxycaffeine

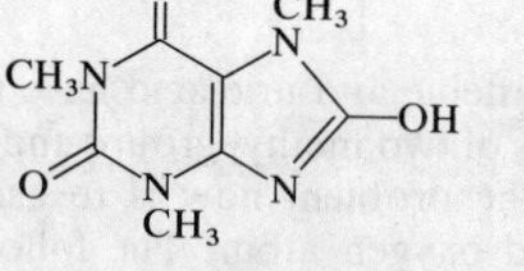

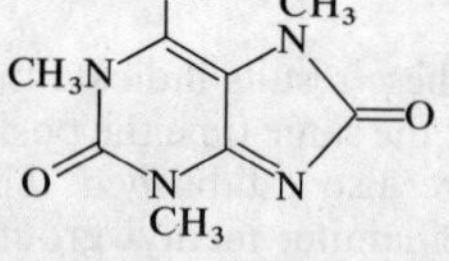

(VII)   (VIII)

oxycaffeine

When oxycaffeine, *as its silver salt*, is heated with methyl iodide, it is converted into a mixture of tetramethyluric acid (which contains four *N*-methyl groups) and methoxycaffeine (which contains three *N*-methyl groups and one methoxyl group). The simultaneous formation of these two products suggests that oxycaffeine is a tautomeric substance, *i.e.*, it contains the *amido-imidol triad system*:

$$-\text{NH—C}{=}\text{O} \rightleftharpoons -\text{N}{=}\text{C—OH}$$

Now this triad system can exist only in the imidazole nucleus in oxycaffeine, since neither nitrogen atom in the pyrimidine nucleus is attached to a hydrogen atom ((VII) can give rise to the above tautomeric system, whereas (VIII) cannot). Thus the methoxyl group in methoxycaffeine is in the imidazole nucleus, and consequently the chlorine atom in chlorocaffeine is also in this nucleus; hence caffeine is (IX) and chlorocaffeine is (X).

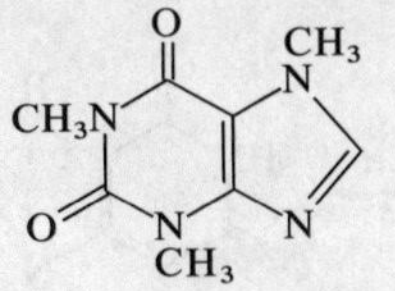

(IX)
caffeine

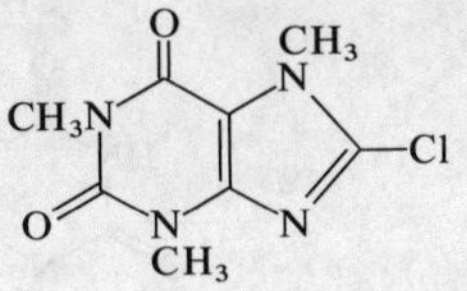

(X)
chlorocaffeine

This structure for caffeine has also been confirmed by various syntheses, *e.g.*,
(i) Fischer (1899) [see also §10].

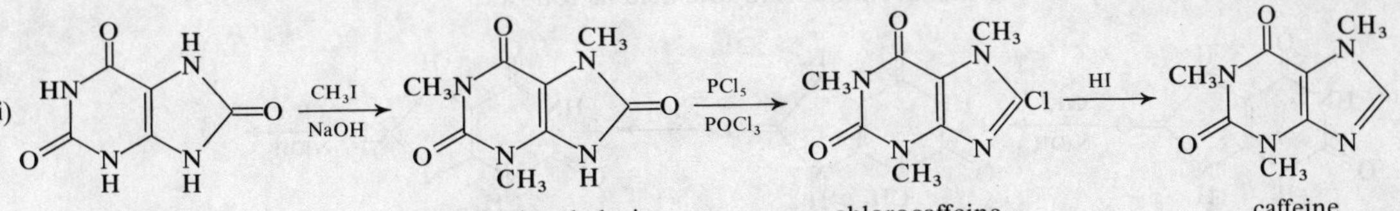

uric acid

1,3,7-trimethyluric
acid

chlorocaffeine

caffeine

(ii) A commercial synthesis based on Traube's method is:

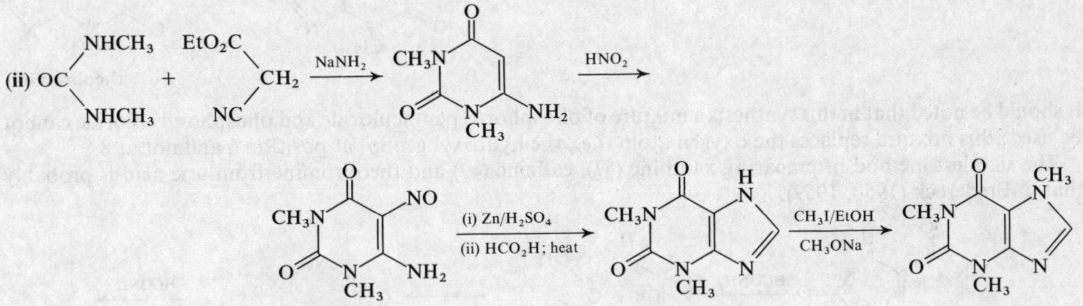

theophylline

caffeine

§10. Theobromine (3,7-dimethylxanthine), m.p. 337°C

This occurs in cocoa beans, tea, etc. The structure of theobromine has been deduced from the fact that, on oxidation with potassium chlorate in hydrochloric acid, it gives methylalloxan and methylurea, and also that it is converted into caffeine when its silver salt is heated with methyl iodide. Thus theobromine is either (I) or (II).

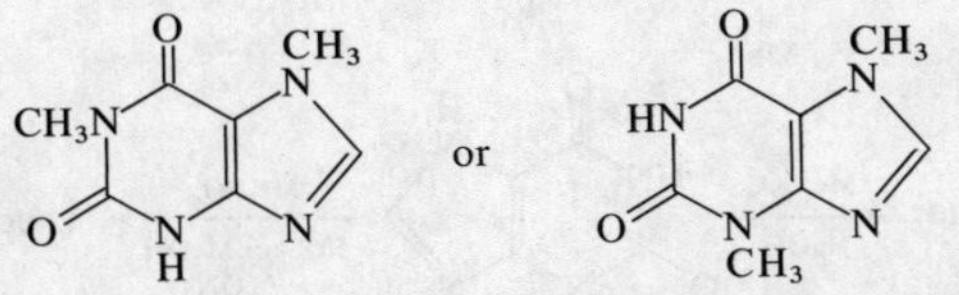

(I)

or

(II)

The position of the methyl group in the pyrimidine nucleus has been shown to be 3 (*i.e.*, structure (II)) by synthesis using Traube's method.

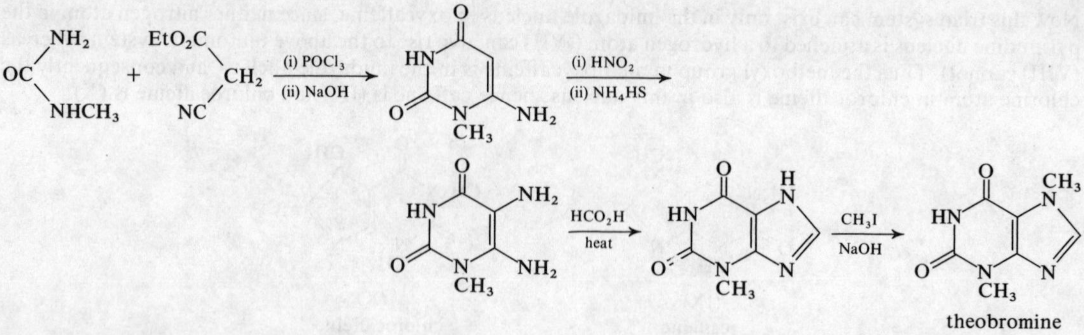

The product formed by the condensation between methylurea and ethyl cyanoacetate contained no free amino-group; hence the condensation must occur as shown (and not by the carbethoxyl group with the methylimino-group of the methylurea).

Fischer (1899) also prepared theobromine from uric acid as follows:

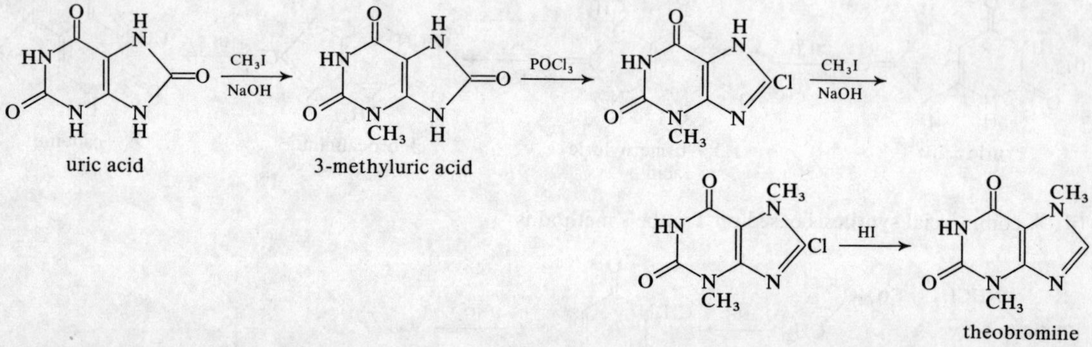

uric acid   3-methyluric acid

theobromine

It should be noted that in this synthesis a mixture of phosphorus pentachloride and phosphoryl chloride cannot be used; this mixture replaces the oxygen atom (*i.e.*, the hydroxyl group) at position 6 and not at 8.

The simplest method of preparing xanthine (§7), caffeine (§9) and theobromine from uric acid is probably that of Bredereck (1950, 1959):

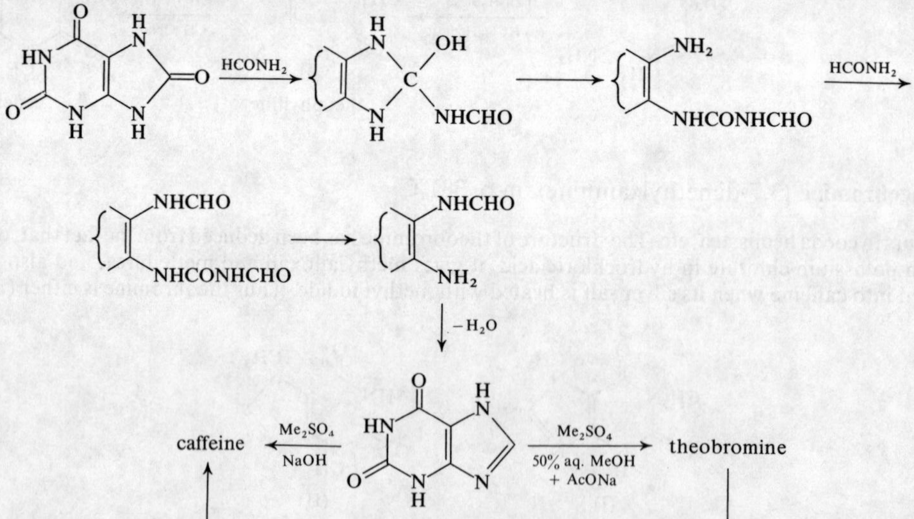

caffeine ← $\xrightarrow[\text{NaOH}]{\text{Me}_2\text{SO}_4}$ xanthine $\xrightarrow[\substack{50\% \text{ aq. MeOH} \\ + \text{AcONa}}]{\text{Me}_2\text{SO}_4}$ theobromine

$\text{Me}_2\text{SO}_4—\text{NaOH}$

§11. Theophylline (1,3-dimethylxanthine), m.p. 269–272°C

This occurs in tea. Its structure has been deduced from the fact that it is converted into caffeine on methylation, and that it forms dimethylalloxan and urea on oxidation. Thus theophylline is 1,3-dimethylxanthine, and this structure has been confirmed by synthesis.

(i) Fischer (1899).

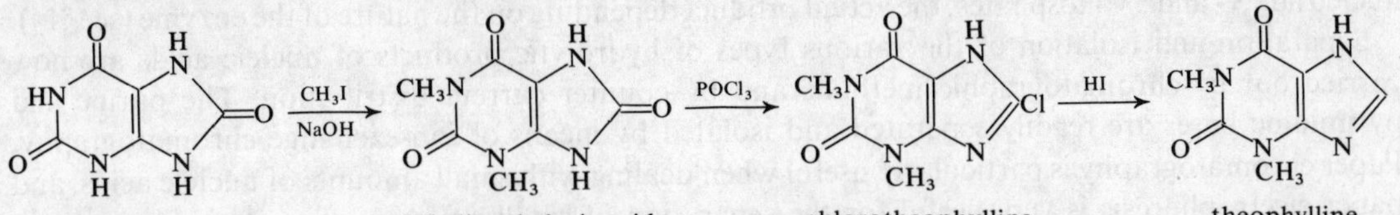

uric acid   1,3-dimethyluric acid   chlorotheophylline   theophylline

A simpler method is to heat 1,3-dimethyluric acid with formamide (*cf.* §10).

(ii) Theophylline has also been synthesised commercially by means of the Traube method (*cf.* caffeine, §9).

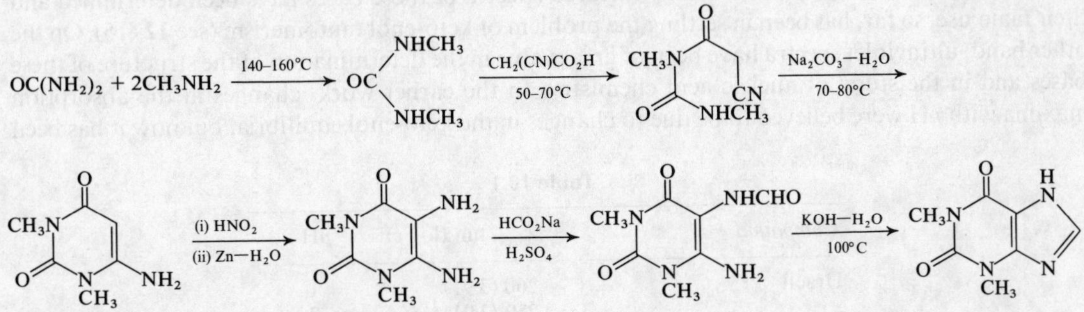

Nucleic acids

§12. Introduction

Nucleoproteins are one of the classes of conjugated proteins (13 §7B); the nucleic acid part is the prosthetic group, and the protein part consists of protamins and histones. These latter compounds are basic and form salt-like compounds, the nucleoproteins, with the nucleic acid. On careful hydrolysis, nucleoproteins are broken down into the nucleic acid and protein.

§13. Structure of the nucleic acids

Nucleic acids are colourless solids, all of which contain the following elements: carbon, hydrogen, oxygen, nitrogen and phosphorus. The following chart shows the nature of the products obtained by hydrolysis under different conditions.

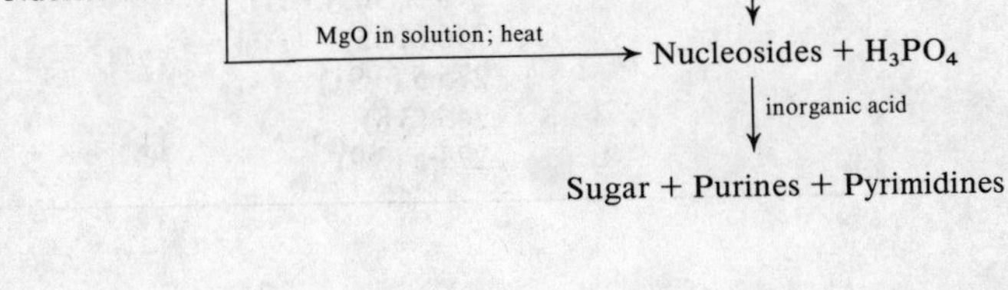

These earlier methods have been modified by later workers in this field of study. Complete hydrolysis of the purine nucleotides by dilute acid occurs relatively easily, but the pyrimidine nucleotides usually require heating under pressure. On the other hand, complete hydrolysis of nucleic acids may be carried out by heating with 12 N perchloric acid or with formic acid. Alkaline hydrolysis results in the formation of ribonucleoside 2'- and 3'-phosphates (see §13d). Enzymic hydrolysis produces nucleoside 3'- and 5'-phosphates, the actual product depending on the nature of the enzyme (see §14).

Separation and isolation of the various types of hydrolytic products of nucleic acids are now carried out by chromatographic methods and by counter current distribution. The purine and pyrimidine bases are readily separated and isolated by means of ion-exchange chromatography. Paper chromatography is particularly useful when dealing with small amounts of nucleic acids, and paper electrophoresis is very useful for the separation of small amounts of nucleotides. Column chromatography, counter current distribution, etc., have been used to separate and purify polynucleotides.

Spectra of pyrimidine and purine bases.   Infrared spectra of these bases have been determined and their main use, so far, has been in settling the problem of keto-enol tautomerism (see **12** §15). On the other hand, ultraviolet spectra have been of great value in the determination of the structure of these bases and in the study of nucleic acid chemistry. In the earlier work, changes in the absorption maxima with pH were believed to be due to changes in the keto-enol equilibria, but now it has been

Table 16.1

Compound	λ_{max}, nm (log ε)	pH
Uracil	260 (3·91)	1
	259 (3·91)	7
	284 (3·8)	13
Thymine	265 (3·88)	1
	264 (3·9)	7
	291 (3·74)	13
Cytosine	276 (4·0)	1
	267 (3·79)	7
	281·5 (3·85)	13
5-Methylcytosine	283·5 (3·99)	1
	273·5 (3·8)	7
	288 (3·84)	13
5-Hydroxymethylcytosine	279 (3·99)	1
	269·5	7·4
	283·5	13
Adenine	262·5 (4·12)	1
	260·5 (4·13)	7
	269 (4·09)	13
Guanine	248·5 (4·06)	
	275·5; sh. (3·87)	1
	246 (4·03)	
	275·5 (3·91)	7
	246 (3·8)	
	273·5 (3·9)	11

shown that these changes are due to ionisation into different species. Table 16.1 gives some absorption maxima at different pH values (water as solvent). Tinoco, Jr. *et al.* (1965) have correlated a number of the absorption bands (250–300 nm) in pyrimidine and purine bases; these are believed to be $\pi \to \pi^*$ transitions.

It can be seen from Table 16.1 that it is possible to identify various bases, and it has been found that the ultraviolet maxima of nucleosides generally lie fairly close to those of the bases that they contain. This is the case at the lower pH values, but at pH 13 there is a considerable difference, *e.g.*, uridine: λ_{max} 262 nm (4·0) at pH 1–7 and 263 nm (3·87) at pH 13; adenosine: 257 nm (4·18) at pH 2, 259 nm (4·19) at pH 7 and 259 nm (4·19) at pH 11.

The ultraviolet spectra of most nucleotides are very similar to those of their corresponding nucleosides, but the ultraviolet spectra of the nucleic acids generally show about 40 per cent lower absorbance than the equivalent solution of the component nucleotides. This result, known as *hypochromism*, is believed to be partly due to the hydrogen bonds between the base residues in the double helix system since, when this double helix is broken, *e.g.*, by heating above 80°C the absorbance increases by about 40 per cent. Another contributing factor to hypochromism is believed to be the change in the resonance effect in the bases when they are chemically bound in the polynucleotide (see also §14).

§13a. Sugars. Two sugars have been isolated from the hydrolysates of nucleic acids; both are pentoses: D(−)-ribose and 2-deoxy-D-(−)-ribose.

$$\underset{\text{ribose}}{\text{OHC(CHOH)}_3\text{CH}_2\text{OH}} \qquad \underset{\text{2-deoxyribose}}{\text{OHCCH}_2\text{(CHOH)}_2\text{CH}_2\text{OH}}$$

The nucleic acids are classified according to the nature of the sugar present: the *ribonucleic acids* (RNA), and the *deoxyribonucleic acids* (DNA). Ribonucleoproteins are found mainly in the cytoplasm of the cell, whereas deoxyribonucleoproteins are found mainly in the cell nucleus. D(−)-Ribose is the pentose of yeast, liver and pancreas RNAs; 2-deoxy-D(−)-ribose occurs in thymus DNA. Nucleic acids also occur in plant and animal viruses.

It has now been found that some RNAs contain minute amounts of 2′-*O*-methylribose.

§13b. Bases. There are two types of bases which occur in nucleic acids: purines and pyrimidines. The most common purine bases are **adenine** and **guanine**. Many other purines have been isolated,

adenine

guanine

uracil   thymine   cytosine   5-methylcytosine   5-hydroxymethylcytosine *e.g.*, 1-, 2-, and 3-methyladenine, 6-methylaminopurine, 3-methylguanine, etc. The most common pyrimidine bases are **uracil**, **thymine**, and **cytosine**. Other pyrimidines have been isolated, *e.g.*, 5-methylcytosine and 5-hydroxymethylcytosine.

Both types of nucleic acids (RNA and DNA) contain adenine and guanine. On the other hand, RNAs also contain uracil and cytosine, whereas DNAs contain thymine and cytosine. This distribution of pyrimidines, however, is not rigid, *e.g.*, uracil has been found in certain DNAs.

Angell (1961) has shown, from infrared studies, that in the *solid* state and in ribose and deoxyribose nucleosides derived from these bases, adenine exists in the amino form, cytosine and guanine exist in the keto-amino form and uracil in the diketo form. Furthermore, X-ray analysis of the various bases has shown that all are planar.

Combination of a base (either a purine or pyrimidine) with a sugar (ribose or deoxyribose) gives rise to a **nucleoside**, *e.g.*, adenosine (ribose + adenine), guanosine (ribose + guanine), cytidine (ribose + cytosine), uridine (ribose + uracil), thymidine (deoxyribose + thymine). The nucleoside derived from hypoxanthine and ribose is named inosine (see §13e).

Combination of a nucleoside with phosphoric acid produces a **nucleotide**, *i.e.*, nucleotides are nucleoside phosphates, *e.g.*, adenylic, guanylic, cytidylic, inosinic, and uridylic acids. It might be noted here that the term nucleotide is now used to embrace a large group of compounds composed of the phosphates of *N*-glycosides of heterocyclic bases, and the pyrophosphates and polyphosphates containing one or more nucleosides.

§13c. **Structure of nucleosides.** Hydrolysis of nucleotides with aqueous ammonia at 175°C under pressure gives nucleosides and phosphoric acid; thus in nucleosides the base is linked directly to the sugar. Furthermore, since nucleosides are non-reducing, the 'aldehyde group' of the sugar cannot be free, *i.e.*, nucleosides are *glycosides* (*cf.* **7** §24). The next problem is to decide which atom of the base is joined to C-1 of the sugar. Let us first consider the pyrimidines. Cytidine, on treatment with nitrous acid, is converted into uridine; it therefore follows that the sugar residue is linked in the *same* position in both of these nucleosides. The point of linkage cannot be 3 or 4, since cytidine has a *free* amino-group at position 4 and consequently there cannot be a hydrogen atom on N-3. Also, since uridine forms a 5-bromo derivative, C-5 must be free (Levene *et al.*, 1912). When uridine is treated with an excess of bromine, followed by the addition of phenylhydrazine, a uridine derivative is obtained which contains *two* phenylhydrazino groups. This compound was given structure (I) since work by Levene (1925) showed that this type of compound can be obtained only if uracil is substituted in position 1 and positions 5 and 6 are free. Thus the sugar is attached to N-1. In a similar way, it has been shown that the other pyrimidine nucleosides (ribosides and deoxyribosides) have the sugar residue linked at N-1. Todd *et al.* (1947) have synthesised uridine and cytidine, and thereby have confirmed the linkage at N-1. This linkage has also been confirmed by the X-ray analysis of cytidine (Furberg, 1950).

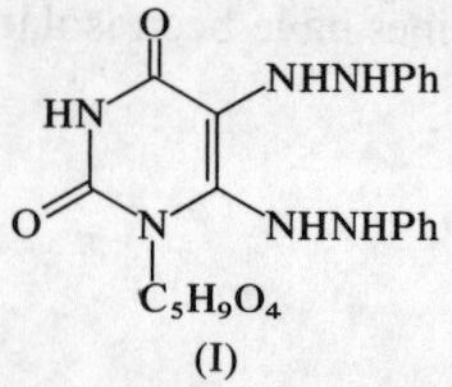

Now let us consider nucleosides containing purine bases. Adenosine has a free amino-group at position 6; therefore the sugar cannot be at C-6 or N-1 (*cf.* cytidine). Similarly, since guanosine has a free amino-group at position 2, the sugar cannot be at C-2 or N-3. Now Levene found that the two purine ribosides are equally readily hydrolysed by dilute acids and by the same enzyme. He therefore assumed that the sugar residue is linked at the same place in both nucleosides. On this basis, only positions 7, 8 and 9 are possible points of attachment. Position 8 was then excluded since this point would involve a carbon–carbon bond, a linkage which would be very stable, whereas nucleosides are very readily hydrolysed by dilute acids (see also below). Thus positions 7 or 9 are free. This is supported by the following evidence (Levene, 1923). When guanosine is treated with nitrous acid, xanthosine is produced and this, on methylation with diazomethane followed by hydrolysis, gives theophylline (1,3-dimethylxanthine). Thus positions 1 and 3 are free in guanosine, and so the sugar must be attached at positions 7 or 9. The evidence so far does not permit a decision to be made between these two positions since the system (in the imidazole nucleus) is tautomeric. It should be noted that had the sugar residue been attached to C-8, then a *trimethylxanthine* would have been obtained instead of theophylline (*cf.* above). The ultraviolet absorption spectrum of guanosine is very similar to that of 9-methylguanine and differs from that of 7-methylguanine; hence it appears likely that guanosine is the 9-guanine glycoside (Gulland *et al.*, 1936, 1938). Todd *et al.* (1947, 1948) have synthesised guanosine and adenosine in which the sugar is known to be in the 9-position, and showed that their synthetic compounds are identical with the natural products; *e.g.*, the synthesis of adenosine.

$$
\begin{array}{c}
\text{(4,5,6-triaminopyrimidine)} \;+\; OHC(CHOH)_3CH_2OH \;\xrightarrow[\text{Pd}]{H_2}\; [\text{pyrimidine-}NHC_5H_9O_4] \;\xrightarrow{ArN_2^+Cl^-}\; [\text{N}=\text{NAr derivative, }NHC_5H_9O_4] \;\xrightarrow[\text{(ii) }H_2-Ni]{\text{(i) }Ac_2O}
\end{array}
$$

$$
[\text{pyrimidine-}NHC_5H_6O(OAc)_3] \;\xrightarrow[\text{(ii) }CH_3ONa-C_2H_5OH]{\text{(i) }HCS_2Na}\; \text{adenosine } (C_5H_9O_4)
$$

A difficulty with the nitrous acid deamination is that it deaminates both aminopurines and aminopyrimidines *in nucleic acids*. Shapiro *et al.* (1970), however, have shown that cytosine but not adenine or guanine can be deaminated by means of sodium hydrogen sulphite under suitable conditions of *pH*.

It might be noted, in passing, that glycosides are compounds formed by the linking of a sugar (at C-1) with a COH group. Thus the nucleosides are, strictly speaking, not glycosides; they should be called ribosylpyrimidines and ribosylpurines.

The final problem to be elucidated in connection with the structure of nucleosides is the nature of the ring in the sugar residue and the type of linkage (α or β). Degradative experiments have shown that the sugar is present as the furanose form, *e.g.*, methylation of a pyrimidine riboside, followed by hydrolysis, gives a trimethylribose which, on oxidation, forms dimethyl*meso*tartaric acid. This product shows that the ribose ring is furanose; had the ring been pyranose, then the final product would have been trimethoxyglutaric acid (*cf.* **7** §§7a, 7b). This is confirmed by the fact that on oxidation with periodic acid one molecule of the reagent was consumed to form a dialdehyde with no loss of carbon (see below).

$$
>N_1\!-\!\overset{\overline{\quad\;\;O\;\;\quad}}{CHCHOHCHOHCHCH_2OH} \xrightarrow{(CH_3)_2SO_4} >N_1\!-\!\overset{\overline{\quad\;\;O\;\;\quad}}{CHCH(OCH_3)CH(OCH_3)CHCH_2OCH_3} \xrightarrow{acid}
$$

$$
\overset{\overline{\quad\;\;O\;\;\quad}}{CHOHCH(OCH_3)CH(OCH_3)CHCH_2OCH_3} \xrightarrow{[O]} HO_2CCH(OCH_3)CH(OCH_3)CO_2H
$$

Deoxyribose has also been shown to be of the furanose type, *e.g.*, Lythgoe *et al.* (1950) found that pyrimidine deoxyribosides consume a negligible amount of periodic acid; this agrees with the 2-deoxyribofuranose structure since, in this state, the molecule does not contain two adjacent hydroxyl groups (*cf.* **7** §7g).

$$
>N_1\!-\!\overset{\overline{\quad\;\;O\;\;\quad}}{CHCH_2CHOHCHCH_2OH}
$$

These results have been confirmed by other work (see below).

The configuration of the furanoside link has been shown to be β- by various means, e.g., Todd et al. (1947) oxidised adenosine with periodic acid, and showed that the product is identical with that from the oxidation of 9-β-D-mannopyranosidyladenine (a synthetic compound). This proves that

9-β-D-manno-   dialdehyde   adenosine
pyranosidyladenine

the sugar residue is at position 9, has the furanose structure and that the linkage is β-. Similar experiments with other ribonucleosides suggest that all these compounds have a β-configuration. Also, Todd et al. (1946–1948) have synthesised adenosine, guanosine, cytidine and uridine, and thereby

confirmed the β-configuration; e.g., adenosine has been synthesised as follows (Todd et al., 1948). Acetochloro-D-ribofuranose (II) is condensed with the silver salt of 2,8-dichloroadenine (III) and the product deacetylated with a methanolic solution of ammonia to give 2,8-dichloro-9-β-ribofuranosyladenine (IV). (IV), on catalytic reduction (palladium), is converted into adenosine. It should be noted that (II) is the α-form, and when this combines with the base, inversion occurs to give the β-linkage (see 7 §24). The best general method of preparing *purine* nucleosides uses chloromercuri derivatives of purines, e.g., guanosine (Davoll et al., 1951).

Pyrimidine nucleosides may be prepared by using dipyrimidinylmercury compounds, *e.g.*, Fox *et al.* (1956) condensed dithyminylmercury with tri-*O*-benzoyl-D-ribofuranosyl chloride, etc. (the exact structure of the mercury compound appears to be uncertain).

5-methyluridine

Pyrimidine nucleosides have also been synthesised by Shaw *et al.* (1959), *e.g.*, uridine by the condensation between a benzoylated ribofuranosylamine and β-ethoxy-*N*-ethoxycarbonylacryl-amide, followed by debenzoylation:

Deoxyribonucleosides have been more difficult to synthesise, but Shaw *et al.* (1959) have prepared thymidine as follows (RCl = Ph_3CCl; MsCl = methanesulphonyl chloride or mesyl chloride, $MeSO_2Cl$):

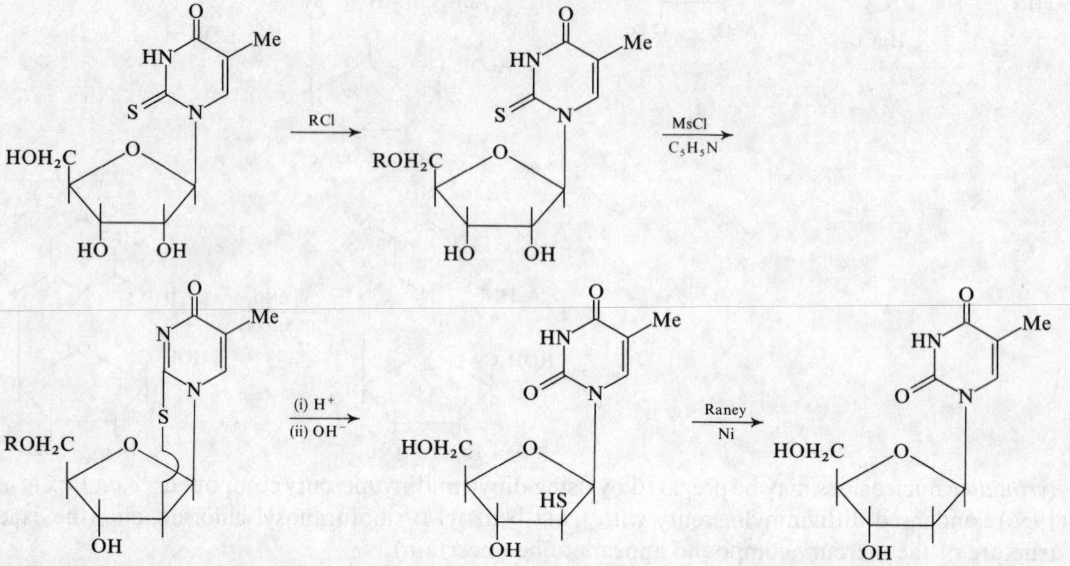

Furberg (1950) has shown by means of the X-ray analysis of cytidine that the sugar residue is attached to N-1 and is β-D-ribofuranoside. Since other ribonucleosides exhibit the same general pattern, it is inferred that all are furanosides with the β-configuration. Manson *et al.* (1951), from absorption spectra measurements, have shown that deoxyribonucleosides also exist in the β-configuration.

It will be noted from the foregoing account that the sugar residue is attached to a nitrogen atom in the base. Recently, however, Davis *et al.* (1957) and Cohn *et al.* (1959) have isolated a new nucleotide from, *e.g.*, yeast RNA. Its ultraviolet spectra at pH 7 and 12 closely resembled those of 5-hydroxymethyluracil, which was obtained from it by degradation. This attachment of the ribose residue to C-5 of uracil was also deduced from the NMR spectrum of the compound, and synthesis established it to be the 5β-D-ribofuranosyl derivative of uracil (Cohn, 1959).

Nucleosides are usually stable towards alkaline hydrolysis but are readily hydrolysed by acids. Deoxynucleosides undergo acid hydrolysis more readily than the ribonucleosides and, in general, the order of ease of hydrolysis is guanosine > adenosine > cytosine > uridine ~ thymidine. The reasons for this order are not certain. A possible mechanism for the hydrolysis of pyrimidine nucleosides is (note the concerted mechanism; see **7** §2):

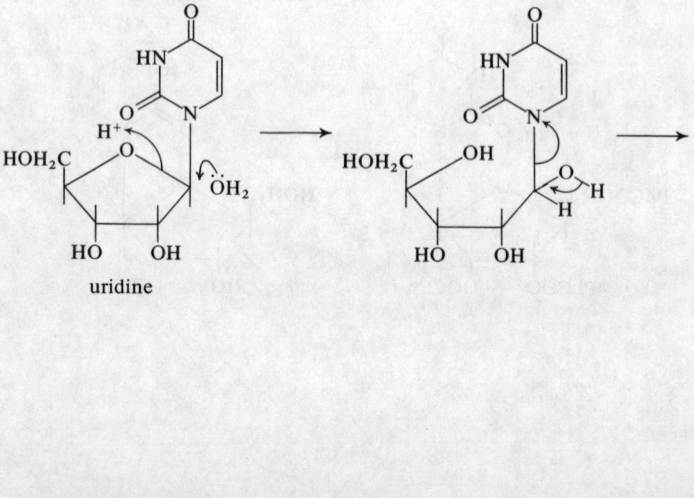

uridine

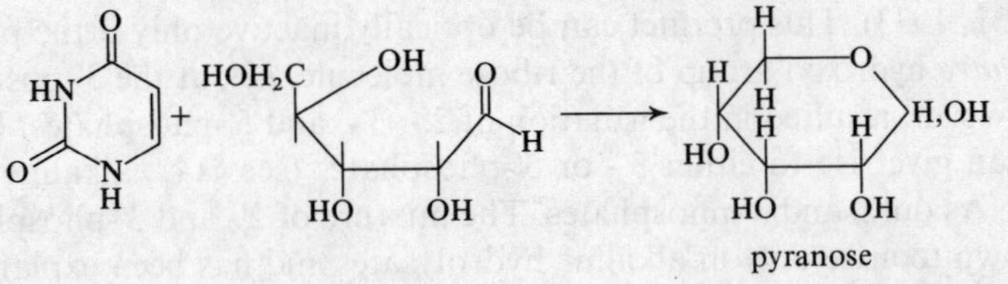

pyranose

It should be remembered that the furanose structure occurs only when the sugar is in the form of a glycoside; on hydrolysis, the furanose sugar first liberated immediately changes into the stable pyranose form (see **7** §7f).

The reason that the purine nucleosides are hydrolysed most rapidly may be explained by intramolecular catalysis involving the N-3 protonated species, *e.g.*, adenosine (see also **13** §17).

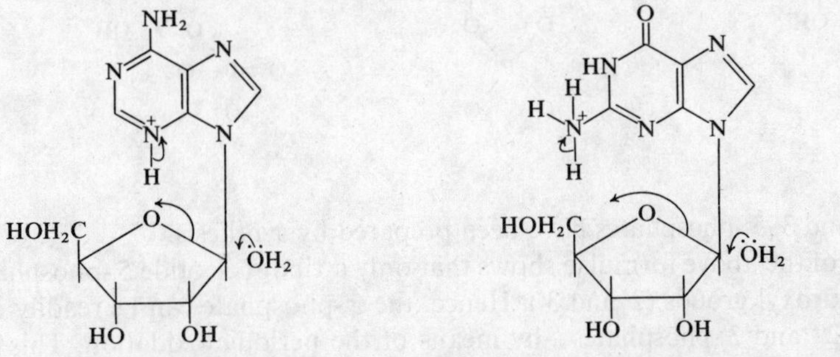

adenosine

guanosine

On the other hand, the fact that guanosine is hydrolysed more rapidly than adenosine may be due to intramolecular catalysis involving the 2-amino-group in the former. This amino-group is less basic than the 3-imino-group (in both purines) and so proton release is easier.

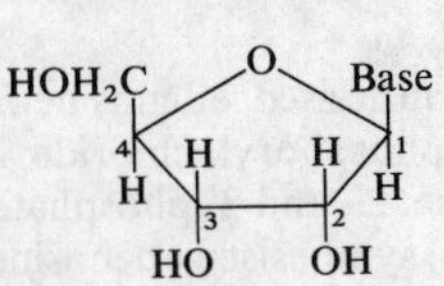

Comparatively little use of NMR spectroscopy has been made, so far, in nucleic acid chemistry. One investigation is that of Jardetzky *et al.* (1960), who examined a number of nucleosides and found that the NMR spectrum of D-ribose depends on whether the base present is a pyrimidine or a purine. Thus, if the base is uracil or cytosine, $J_{H_1H_2} = 2$–3 Hz, whereas if the base is adenine, guanine, or xanthine, $J_{H_1H_2} = 5$–7 Hz (*cf.* **1** §12e). Cushley *et al.* (1966) have investigated the anomeric configuration of pyrimidine nucleosides by NMR spectroscopy. They have shown that if the 5,6-double bond in the pyrimidine is removed (hydrogenation), it is possible to differentiate α-anomers from the β-anomers by means of the τ-values of the acetyl groups in the pentose.

§13d. Structure of nucleotides. When nucleotides are carefully hydrolysed, ribose monophosphate may be isolated from the products; thus the phosphoric acid is attached to the sugar residue in nucleotides. Examination of the nucleoside structures shows that the point of attachment may be 2′, 3′ or 5′ in the ribose molecule, and 3′ or 5′ in the deoxyribose molecule. On reduction with hydrogen in the presence of platinum, ribose phosphate is converted into an optically inactive phosphoribitol

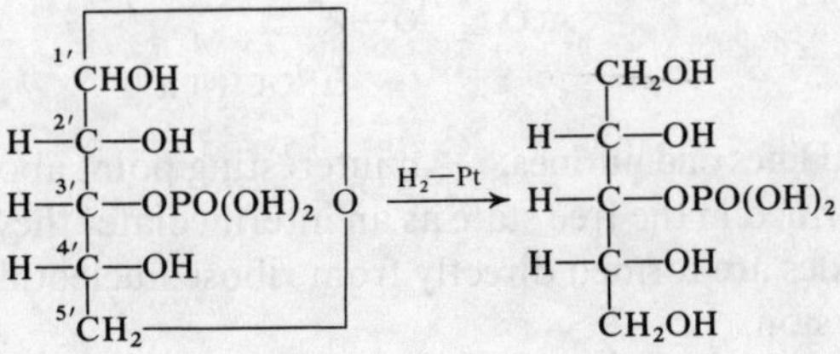

(Levene *et al.*, 1932, 1933). This product can be optically inactive only if the phosphate residue is attached to the *centre* hydroxyl group of the ribose molecule, *i.e.*, at the 3′-position.

Later work, however, resulted in the isolation of 2′-, 3′-, and 5′-phosphates. Enzymic hydrolysis of nucleic acids can give rise to either 3′- or 5′-phosphates (see §14); alkaline hydrolysis gives a mixture of 2′- (RNAs only) and 3′-phosphates. The mixture of 2′- and 3′-phosphates (from RNAs) has now been shown to arise only in alkaline hydrolysates and has been explained on the basis of the formation of an intermediate 2′,3′-cyclic phosphate (Todd *et al.*, 1953–1955). The mechanism proposed is (see also §14):

Cyclic 2′,3′- and 3′,5′-phosphates have been prepared by synthesis.

Inspection of the above formulae shows that only a ribonucleotide 5′-phosphate has an adjacent pair of *cis*-hydroxyl groups (2′ and 3′). Hence, the 5′-phosphate can be readily distinguished from its isomers—2′- and 3′-phosphates—by means of the periodic oxidation. This method, however, cannot differentiate between deoxyribonucleoside 3′- and 5′-phosphates since neither of these contains a 2′-hydroxyl group. The determination of the position of the phosphate residue (other than by the periodate oxidation) has been carried out by synthesis, X-ray analysis, etc.

Nucleoside di- and triphosphates are also known, *e.g.*, ADP and ATP (see **13**§15). These, however, do not occur in nucleic acids.

Nucleotides have been synthesised in various way, *e.g.*, Levene *et al.* (1937) synthesised adenosine-5′-phosphate from 2′,3′-*O*-isopropylideneadenosine. This was phosphorylated with phosphoryl chloride in pyridine, followed by careful hydrolysis with acid to remove the isopropylidene residue. 2′- and 3′-phosphates are more difficult to synthesise because of their ready interconversion. Todd *et al.* (1954) synthesised adenosine-2′-phosphate by phosphorylating 3′,5′-di-*O*-acetyladenosine in the 2′-position with dibenzylphosphochloridate [(PhCH$_2$O)$_2$POCl] and removing the benzyl groups (as toluene) by hydrogenation (Pd), and finally removing the acetyl groups by treatment with alkali. Under these conditions no phosphate migration is possible.

§13e. Biosynthesis of pyrimidines and purines.   An interesting point about the biosynthesis of these bases is that they are not formed in the free state as an intermediate; they are formed as nucleotides. Also, deoxyribose nucleotides are formed directly from ribose nucleotides, *i.e.*, the glycosidic bond is not broken in the conversion.

Pyrimidine biosynthesis. By means of labelled precursors (^{13}C and ^{15}N), the origin of the pyrimidine skeleton has been shown to be derived from carbon dioxide, ammonia, and aspartic acid.

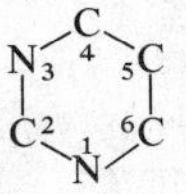

N-3 from NH_3.
C-2 from CO_2.
C(4)-C(5)-C(6)-N(1) from aspartic acid.

pyrimidine

Ammonia and carbon dioxide react to form carbamyl phosphate (I), which combines with aspartic acid to form, in turn, N-carbamylaspartic acid (II), dihydro-orotic acid (III), and orotic acid (IV). (IV) condenses with 5'-phosphoribosyl 1-pyrophosphate (PRPP) to give orotidine 5'-phosphate (V) which, on loss of carbon dioxide, produces uridine 5'-phosphate (uridylic acid; (VI)).

(i)

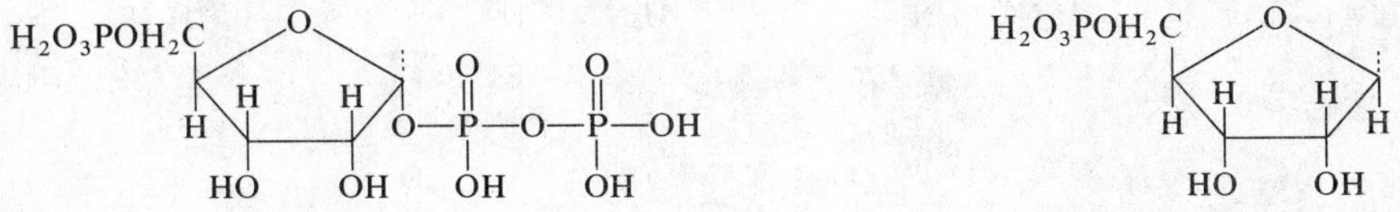

α-PRPP   β-RP

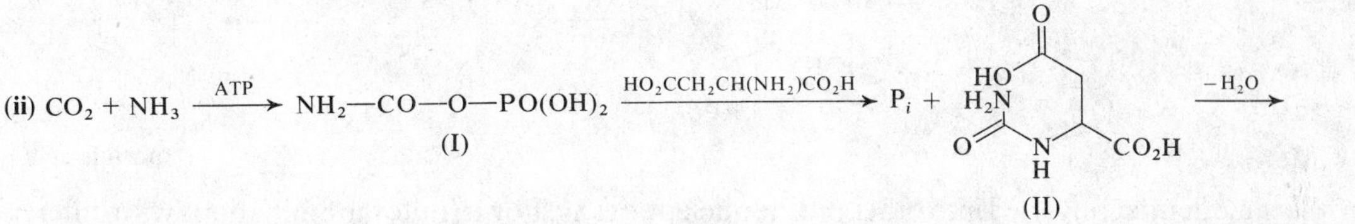

(ii) $CO_2 + NH_3 \xrightarrow{ATP} NH_2{-}CO{-}O{-}PO(OH)_2 \xrightarrow{HO_2CCH_2CH(NH_2)CO_2H} P_i +$ (II) $\xrightarrow{-H_2O}$

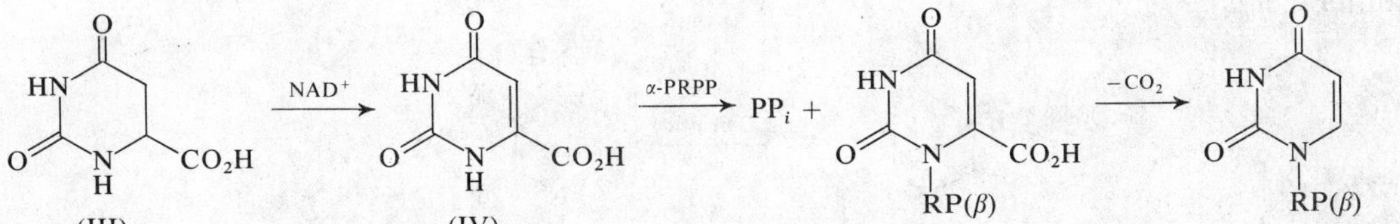

(I)

(III) $\xrightarrow{NAD^+}$ (IV) $\xrightarrow{\alpha\text{-}PRPP} PP_i +$ (V) $\xrightarrow{-CO_2}$ (VI)

(IV) orotic acid   RP(β)   RP(β)

(VI) uridylic acid

Uridylic acid (VI) appears to be the ribonucleotide from which all other pyrimidine nucleotides are biosynthesised. Thus, cytidylic acid (VII) is believed to be produced *via* uridine triphosphate.

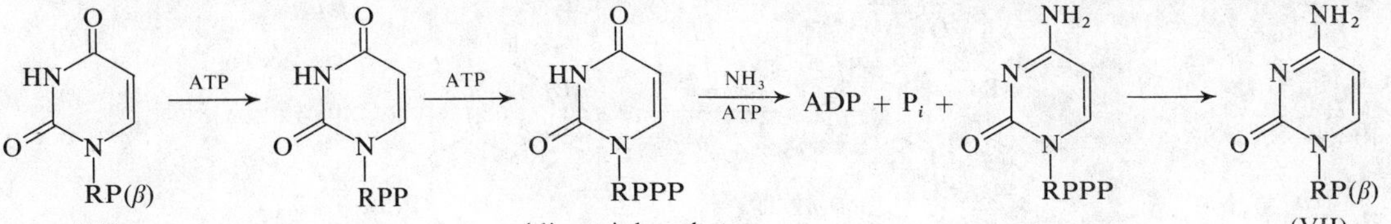

RP(β) $\xrightarrow{ATP}$ RPP $\xrightarrow{ATP}$ RPPP $\xrightarrow[ATP]{NH_3} ADP + P_i +$ RPPP $\longrightarrow$ RP(β)

(VI) uridylic acid   uridine triphosphate   (VII) cytidylic acid

Purine biosynthesis. By means of labelled precursors (^{13}C, ^{15}N), it has been found that the purine skeleton arises from the compounds shown.

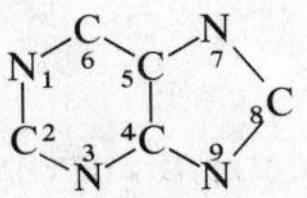

purine

N-1 from aspartic acid.
N-3 and N-9 from glutamine.
C-6 from carbon dioxide.

C-2 and C-8 from formic acid.
C-4, C-5, and N-7 from glycine.

The key purine ribonucleotide is inosinic acid (hypoxanthine is the purine base), *i.e.*, all other purine ribonucleotides are derived from this. The biosynthetic pathway of inosinic acid is believed to be (note the formation of the imidazole ring first).

Inosinic acid is converted into other purine nucleotides as shown (note the aminations with different amino-acids).

inosinic acid   adenylic acid

xanthylic acid   guanylic acid

The series of reactions leading to the formation of inosinic acid from common cell constituents is known as the *de novo* **synthesis of the pyrimidine and purine nucleotides**. This name is given to distinguish the pathways whereby an organism utilises *preformed* pyrimidines and purines (see §16).

§14. Ribonucleic acids

These are polymers of ribonucleotides, and hydrolysis by alkali or by certain enzymes results in a mixture of ribonucleotides. Hydrogen-ion titrations on purified RNAs showed that secondary phosphate ionisations are absent. This suggests that the individual ribonucleotides are linked together by phosphodiester bonds. As we have seen (§13d), the attachment of the phosphate is at the 3′-position in the ribose molecule. Hence possible internucleotide bonds are 2′-3′ and 3′-5′. The answer has been obtained by various means, the most important being the use of enzymes which are known to hydrolyse specific ester bonds in nucleotides. Thus, it has been shown that: (*a*) the enzyme *spleen phosphodiesterase* (specific for the C-5′—OP bond) converts RNAs into a mixture of ribonucleoside 3′-phosphates; (*b*) *snake venom phosphodiesterase* (specific for the C-3′—OP bond) hydrolyses RNAs to a mixture of ribonucleoside 5′-phosphates. Hence, RNAs have a linear structure of units linked by 3′—5′ bonds. There appears to be little, if any, branched chains.

As we have seen (§13b), the common bases in RNAs are adenine, guanine, uracil, and cytosine. Early work on the base composition of nucleic acids led to the conclusion that the four bases were present in equimolar proportions. Subsequent work, as a result of accurate methods of analysis (chromatography, etc.; §13), has shown that the molar proportions of the bases vary considerably according to the source of the nucleic acid: ribosomal (r) and transfer (t) RNAs (§17) and messenger (m) RNAs. The less common bases (§13b) are widespread in tRNAs. It has also been shown that the keto-bases (guanine and uracil) and the amino-bases (adenine and cytosine) are present in all RNAs in roughly equal amounts.

A great deal of work has been done to elucidate the sequence of the bases in RNAs and methods are, in principle, similar to those used in the determination of the primary structure of proteins

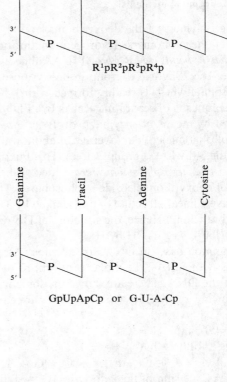

tetranucleotide

Fig. 16.1

(**13** §9). End groups have been determined by enzyme hydrolysis of the RNA with snake venom phosphodiesterase (see above). Among the nucleotides (mainly nucleoside 5'-phosphates) will be some nucleosides (R^1-end in Fig. 16.1) and some nucleoside 3',5'-diphosphates (R^4-end in Fig. 16.1). These can be identified and estimated by means of chromatographic methods. Hence, the end groups are determined and the length of the polynucleotide chain can be estimated.

The nucleotide sequence has been determined for some of the relatively short RNAs by the use of different enzymes, end-group analysis, and the application of the overlapping method (see **13** §9). A point of interest in this connection is that RNAs are synthesised in association with DNAs (§17). Hence it can be expected that there will be some correspondence in the base sequence between the DNA and its complementary RNA.

On the evidence discussed above, the primary structure of RNAs may be written as shown in Fig. 16.1. The abbreviated forms are also given; in these the letters refer to the nucleoside, *e.g.*, G = guanosine; U = uridine; etc.

Various methods have been used to determine the molecular weights of purified nucleic acids, *e.g.*, end-group assay (see above), ultracentrifugation, light scattering, etc. (see **13** §6). Values obtained for RNAs range from about 2×10^4 to 2×10^6.

The secondary structure of RNAs has also been investigated (*cf.* **13** §12a). The results (mainly from X-ray analysis) appear to indicate that RNAs exist as single strands which contain helical segments stabilised by hydrogen bonding. There are, however, some examples of RNAs which exist as double strands (double helical structure; see DNAs, §15).

§15. Deoxyribonucleic acids

These are polymers of the deoxyribonucleotides and hydrolysis by certain enzymes results in a mixture of the monomers. Hydrogen-ion titrations on purified DNAs showed the presence of *phosphodiester bonds* (see RNAs, §14). Alkaline hydrolysis of DNAs is very slow; this is due to the absence of the 2'-hydroxyl group in deoxyribose, thereby preventing the formation of the cyclic 2',3'-phosphate which is readily formed with RNAs. This difference towards alkaline hydrolysis is used as a means of separating RNAs from DNAs. The nature of the internucleotide bonds was established by means of enzymic hydrolysis. *Pancreatic deoxyribonuclease* converts DNAs into a mixture of oligonucleotides (average of about four nucleotide units) which contain a 5'-phosphate residue (the 3'-hydroxyl group is free). This mixture of oligonucleotides may then be subjected to the action of *spleen phosphodiesterase* (deoxyribonuclease II). This results in the formation of a mixture of deoxyribonucleoside 3'-phosphates. These experiments have led to the conclusion that DNAs have a linear structure of units linked by 3'—5' bonds. Also, as for the RNAs, there appears to be no branching. Hence, the structure of DNAs may be represented by Fig. 16.1 (replace ribose by deoxyribose, *i.e.*, 2'-OH by H).

The common bases in DNAs are adenine (A), guanine (G), thymine (T), and cytosine (C) [see §13b]. As with RNAs, the molar proportions of these bases vary considerably according to the source of the DNA. There are, however, some important differences between RNAs and DNAs. The following regularities (with very few exceptions) in the composition of DNAs have been observed:

(*a*) A = T; (*b*) G = C.

From this it follows that:

(*c*) A + G = T + C; (*d*) A + C = G + T.

With DNAs, the sum of the keto-bases (G + T) is *equal* to the sum of the amino-bases (A + C), and *not roughly equal* as in RNAs (§14). As we shall see later, the equivalence of A and T and of G and C are of paramount importance in connection with the secondary structure of DNAs.

The nucleotide sequence in DNAs has been investigated by controlled degradation with enzymes, acids, etc.

Khorana *et al.* (1970) have now synthesised a gene (see below).

The molecular weights of DNAs have been determined by various physical methods (see RNAs, §14); the values obtained range from about 10^6 to 10^9.

Now let us consider the secondary structure of DNAs. Wilkins *et al.* (1953), from their X-ray studies, showed that the DNA molecule has a helical form, and suggested the helix contains two intertwined strands. Watson and Crick (1953), however, proposed that the secondary structure was two DNA chains wound as right-handed helices round a common axis but heading in opposite directions (Fig. 16.2*a*). Furthermore, the two chains are wound in such a manner that pyrimidine and purine bases point towards each other, and it is hydrogen bonding between pairs of bases that holds the helices together. Also, the extremely important point made, based on steric considerations, is that pairing of bases can occur only between a pyrimidine and a purine, and that a given pyrimidine can pair only with its complementary purine. Such complementary pairs are A–T (Fig. 16.2*b*) and G–C (Fig. 16.2*c*). The A–T pair is held together by two hydrogen bonds and the G–C pair by three hydrogen bonds. The ring-planes of each pair of bases lie in the same plane and are perpendicular to the axis of the helix. The 'backbone' of each DNA strand consists of deoxyribose–phosphate units. This double helix accounts for the equivalence of A and T and of G and C (see above).

This Watson–Crick model of DNA has been confirmed, with slight corrections, by later work. X-ray studies have shown that the pairs are planar and that the hydrogen bonds are almost collinear, their lengths lying between 2·8 and 2·9 Å. Each turn of the helix contains 10 nucleotide pairs, and the diameter of the helix is about 20 Å. The spacing between adjacent pairs is 3·4 Å. It can be seen from this arrangement of the two helices that the two DNA chains must be complementary to each

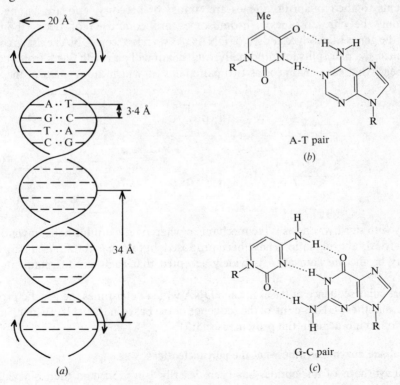

A-T pair
(*b*)

G-C pair
(*c*)

(*a*)

Fig. 16.2

other, *i.e.*, a chain with a given sequence of bases can pair only with another chain which has the complementary sequence of bases.

X-ray analysis has also shown that the crystalline shape of the double helix is dependent on the amount of water present. When the water content is about 40 per cent, X-ray analysis shows the presence of a regular three-dimensional crystalline structure (the A structure; repeat unit along the axis: 28 Å). On the other hand, at higher water content (70 per cent), the X-ray pattern shows that the double helices are parallel and packed side by side, but not in a regular manner (the B structure; repeat unit along the axis: 34 Å).

From 1959 onwards, it has been found that DNAs can exist as cyclic single strands, *i.e.*, as rings. Double helical DNAs have also been isolated in the form of a ring. These are examples of naturally occurring catenanes, the two rings of which are interlocked by a topological bond having a very large winding number (see also **4** §16).

DNAs, like proteins, undergo changes in helical content under certain conditions. These changes have been studied by the methods used in protein chemistry (see **13** §§12a, 12b). Thus, when DNAs are heated in dilute aqueous solution, they undergo helix-random coil transitions, *i.e.*, they undergo thermal denaturation (see **13** §§6, 12b). The double helix separates into two separate strands. If the solution is cooled rapidly the two strands remain separate, but if cooled slowly the original double helix is often formed (annealing, renaturation). Extremes of *p*H also bring about denaturation (irreversible). Single-stranded ring DNAs are extremely resistant to denaturation. DNAs in the form of catenanes, by suitable treatment, can undergo a single break in one of the strands. This broken strand can be made to unwind and to separate from the intact strand by careful denaturation. The single-stranded ring can be isolated.

Replication of DNAs. Heredity is the term applied to the transmission of the potential characteristics of parents to their offspring. Genes are 'units' of heredity, and are arranged in a linear sequence along the chromosomes. Chromosomes are composed of deoxyribonucleoproteins (**13** §7B), but the genes themselves consist of DNAs. As we have seen, DNAs exist as complementary pairs, and hence, if a pair splits longitudinally, each chain will pair with bases from the medium, the final result being that each chain forms two paired chains which are *replicas* of the *original* pairs.

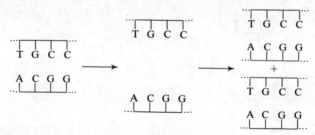

A difficulty with this hypothesis is the mechanism whereby the double helix unwinds to form two single strands. Several explanations have been proposed, but none is certain (see §16). Nevertheless, whatever may be the mechanism, it is widely accepted that each strand retains its structure on replication.

It is the particular sequence of bases in each DNA which determines the genetic properties of the chromosome, and these DNAs control the sequence of the bases in the RNAs which, in turn, control the sequence of amino-acids in the proteins (see §17).

§16. Chemical and enzymic syntheses of the polynucleotides

The chemical synthesis of nucleotides has been described in §13d, and their biosynthesis in §13e. Several methods have been used to prepare oligonucleotides of known sequence and also for the

polymerisation of these to give polynucleotides. One method widely used is that of Khorana *et al.*
(1961–1967). *p*-Methoxytrityl chloride (*p*-MeOC$_6$H$_4$CPh$_2$Cl; written as MPh$_3$CCl) is used as a
protecting reagent for the CH$_2$OH group (primary alcohol) and dicyclohexylcarbodi-imide (DCC)
as the condensing reagent (*cf.* **13** §10), *e.g.*, for deoxyribonucleotides; OH$^-$ removes the 3′—Ac
group; H$^+$ removes the MPh$_3$C group.

(III) may be converted into the 3′,5′-dinucleotide 5′-phosphate as follows (*via* the use of dibenzylphosphochloridate; see §13d).

By starting with (III), removing the acetyl group (by action of OH^- only), and condensing the product with (II) by means of DCC, a trinucleotide is formed; and so on.

It should be noted that in these syntheses involving bases containing an amino-group (A, G, C, etc.), this group is protected by, *e.g.*, benzoylation. In these cases, concentrated ammonium hydroxide removes the acetyl and the benzoyl group; acid is used to remove the MPh_3C group. Also, reagents besides DCC were used as condensing reagents, *e.g.*, aromatic sulphonyl chlorides.

Kornberg *et al.* (1961) have prepared *biosynthetic* DNA by the polymerisation of deoxyribonucleoside triphosphates (the four types in natural DNAs) by means of the enzyme *DNA-polymerase*. This enzymic synthesis, however, must be carried out in the presence of bivalent magnesium cations (Mg^{2+}) and a *primer* DNA (*i.e.*, some *natural* DNA which 'initiates' the polymerisation). The biosynthetic DNA closely resembles the natural DNA primer, and can itself behave as a primer for the enzymic synthesis of DNA from the deoxyribonucleoside triphosphates. It has also been shown that whatever are the relative proportions of the triphosphates in the mixture, the DNA produced is a replica of the primer DNA.

The most important difference between biosynthetic DNA and its natural primer is that the former possesses no biological activity. Further work showed that DNA polymerase acts on the strand of the double helix from the 3'-end to the 5'-end. Since the two strands run in opposite directions, the 3'-end of one is opposite the 5'-end of the other. Hence, continuous synthesis of the complementary DNA takes place only on *one* strand (the 3' to the 5' direction). Kornberg (1967) therefore proposed that synthesis occurs in a backwards direction on the other strand (5' to 3' direction). Thus, when some of the double helix has unwound, synthesis has begun from the 3'-end strand and from '3'-point' in the 5'-end strand. When the latter synthesis reaches its end (5'-), some more of the double helix has unwound and so synthesis starts again at a '3'-point', and so on. The net result is that continuous synthesis occurs on the 3'-end strand, but discontinuous short lengths are built up backwards on the 5'-end strand. In 1967 an enzyme was isolated that was capable of joining together short lengths of DNA. When Kornberg (1968) used this enzyme—*DNA ligase*—in the system described above, the DNA product was biologically active.

The enzymic synthesis of RNAs is believed to proceed by a method analogous to that of replication of DNAs. The appropriate ribonucleoside triphosphates are polymerised in the presence of RNA polymerase, and copy the pattern of the DNA molecule on which it is built.

§17. Biosynthesis of proteins

Only an introductory account is given here. The sequence of the amino-acids in the protein is determined by the sequence of the bases in DNA, and the relationship between these two sequences is called the **genetic code**. DNA molecules, which occur in the chromosomes found in the cell nucleus, usually exist as double helices. RNAs are usually single strands, but one RNA and one

DNA can also form a double helix (this is known as **hybridisation of RNA with DNA**). In this way, a given DNA determines the base sequence in its complementary RNA (see also §16). When the RNA strand is synthesised, the DNA–RNA 'double helix' splits. Three types of RNA are synthesised in this way, each performing one type of function in protein biosynthesis. One RNA acts as the **messenger** or **informational RNA**; this is mRNA. The second type of RNA is the **transfer** (soluble) **RNA**, tRNA (sRNA), and the third type of RNA is the **ribosomal RNA**, rRNA. The base composition of different mRNAs and different tRNAs vary; rRNAs show little variation. The variations are possible because RNA molecules are very much smaller than DNA molecules and so a number of RNAs can be synthesised on one DNA, each particular RNA being synthesised on a specified part of the DNA molecule.

The synthesis of proteins takes place mainly in the cytoplasm on the very small ribosome particles, and the 'information' of the sequence of the amino-acids is 'transferred' to the ribosomes by the mRNA. The four bases in mRNA: A (adenine), C (cytosine), G (guanine), and U (uracil), have been shown to act in the form of triplets, each triplet behaving as a code for the synthesis of a particular amino-acid. Since there are four bases, 64 triplet combinations are possible ($4 \times 4 \times 4$; each base can be used more than once in any combination). Also, because there are 20 common amino-acids, this implies that each amino-acid is associated with a number of particular triplets or **codons**. This has been demonstrated experimentally, *e.g.*, Phe (phenylalanine) is associated with the codons UUU and UUC; Ser (serine) with UCU, UCC, UCA, UCG, AGU, and AGC. Thus, a particular amino-acid is specified by a number of *codons whose first two letters (bases) are usually unchanged.*

From what has been said above, a particular polypeptide is coded by a specified length of mRNA. This length of mRNA is known as a **cistron**, and since proteins of different lengths are known, there are also different cistrons, *i.e.*, mRNAs of different lengths. Transfer RNA (tRNA) molecules are those which bring the amino-acids to the site where protein synthesis takes place. Each amino-acid has its own specific tRNA (or tRNAs), and combination between the two occurs at one end of the tRNA molecule *via* the carboxyl group of the amino-acid. Hence the amino-group in the bound amino-acid residue is free (tRNA—O—COCHRNH$_2$).

Ribosomes, which are composed of RNA and protein, consist of two subunits: a large one composed of a large RNA combined with different proteins, and a smaller RNA combined with different proteins. These subunits 'fit' together, and the first step in protein synthesis is the combination of an mRNA with a number of ribosomes to form a **polyribosome** (or **polysome**). The step involving the synthesis of mRNA is called **transcription** because the sequence of the nucleotides in the mRNA is complementary to that of its 'associated' DNA in the gene. The enzyme responsible for this synthesis is RNA polymerase (see also §§14, 15). In this way the **genetic code** is transcribed from the gene to its particular protein. A polyribosome now binds, presumably two tRNAs, each of which is attached to its specific amino-acid. The site of attachment of each tRNA to the mRNA is determined by a triplet of bases, the **anticodon** in the tRNA. This anticodon is complementary to the codon in the mRNA. Thus, each tRNA having a particular anticodon is always attached to a specific amino-acid. These two steps, the combination of each amino-acid with its specific tRNA, and the attachment of each 'charged' tRNA to a specific site on the mRNA, are called **translation**. This is because the genetic code specified in the mRNA as a nucleotide is now translated into the amino-acid sequence of its particular protein. The first charged tRNA, by means of enzymes, transfers its amino-acid to the amino-acid of the second charged tRNA, the liberated carboxyl group of the former combining with the free amino-group of the latter. Thus protein synthesis starts from the amino-terminal group. The 'free' tRNA (*i.e.*,, the first one) moves away and another charged tRNA moves in to the adjacent site (on the far side of the leaving tRNA), and the process of amino-acid transfer is repeated stepwise until synthesis of the protein, H_2N-1-2-3------n—CO_2H, is complete.

There are three codons—UAA, UAG, and UGA—which do not code for any of the amino-acids.

These are known as **nonsense** or **release** codons and their function is believed to be the termination of the protein synthesis. Figure 16.3 is a simple diagrammatic representation of the synthesis of a protein as described above (order is: (1) in; (2) transfer; (3) out).

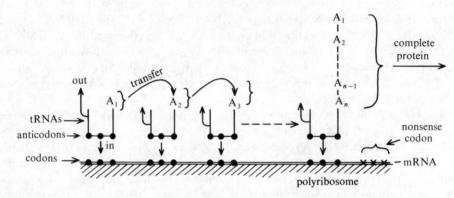

Fig. 16.3

REFERENCES

LEVENE and BASS, *Nucleic Acids*, Chemical Catalogue Co. (1931).

DAVIDSON, *The Biochemistry of the Nucleic Acids*, Methuen (1969, 6th edn.).

RODD (ed.), *Chemistry of Carbon Compounds*, Elsevier. Vol. IVC (1960). Ch. XX. 'Purines and Related Ring Systems.' Ch. XXI. 'Nucleosides, Nucleotides and Nucleic Acids.'

JORDAN, *The Chemistry of the Nucleic Acids*, Butterworths (1960).

FLORKIN and STOTZ (eds.), *Comprehensive Biochemistry*, Elsevier. Vol. 8 (1963), Part B. 'Nucleic Acids.'

CHARGAFF and DAVIDSON (eds.), *The Nucleic Acids*, Academic Press. Vols. I–III (1955–1960).

ULBRICHT, *Purines, Pyrimidines and Nucleotides*, Pergamon (1964).

CLARK and TINOCO, JR., 'Correlations in the Ultraviolet Spectra of the Purine and Pyrimidine Bases', *J. Am. chem. Soc.*, 1965, **87**, 11.

SANGSTER and STUART, 'Ultraviolet Spectra of Alkaloids', *Chem. Rev.*, 1965, **65**, 120.

MICHAELSON, *The Chemistry of Nucleosides and Nucleotides*, Academic Press (1963).

HARBERS, DOMAGK, and MULLER, *Introduction to Nucleic Acids*, Reinhold (1968).

INGRAM, *The Biosynthesis of Macromolecules*, Benjamin (1967, 2nd edn.).

EDWARDS and SHORTER, 'Macromolecular Structure and Properties of Deoxyribonucleic Acid', *Quart. Rev.*, 1965, **19**, 369.

COX, 'Macromolecular Structure and Properties of Ribonucleic Acid', *Quart. Rev.*, 1968, **22**, 499.

FASMAN and TIMASHEFF (eds.), *Fine Structure of Proteins and Nucleic Acids*, Dekker (1970).

DAVIDSON and COHN (eds.), *Progress in Nucleic Acid Research and Molecular Biology*, Academic Press. Vol. 1, 1963–.

BERNFELD (ed.), *Biogenesis of Natural Compounds*, Pergamon (1967, 2nd edn.). Chs. 2, 8. 'Biogenesis of Nucleotides and Nucleic Acids.' Ch. 7. 'The Biogenesis of Proteins.'

KHORANA, 'Nucleic Acid Synthesis', *Pure appl. Chem.*, 1969, **17**, 349.

17 Vitamins

§1. Introduction

In addition to oxygen, water, proteins, fats, carbohydrates and certain inorganic salts, a number of organic compounds are also necessary for the life, growth and health of animals (including man). These compounds are known as the 'accessory dietary factors' or **vitamins**, and are only necessary in very small amounts. Vitamins cannot be produced by the body and hence must be supplied. Vitamin D, however, may be supplied in food or may be produced in the skin by irradiation (ultraviolet) of sterols.

Many vitamins have now been isolated, and their structures elucidated. As each vitamin was isolated, it was named by a letter of the alphabet, but once its structure had been established (or almost established), the vitamin has generally been renamed (see text).

The vitamins have been arbitrarily classified into the 'fat-soluble group' (vitamins A, D, E and K), and the 'water-soluble group' (the remainder of the vitamins).

A number of vitamins have already been dealt with in various chapters dealing with natural products with which these particular vitamins are closely associated chemically, *viz.* vitamins A_1 and A_2 (**9** §7), vitamin C (**7** §11) and the vitamin D group (**11** §§11–11b). This chapter is devoted to a number of other vitamins (see the reading references for further information).

From the point of view of chemical structure, there is very little common to the various vitamins, but from the point of view of chemical reactions, many of the water-soluble vitamins have one feature in common, and that is their ability to take part in reversible oxidation–reduction processes. Thus they form a part of various co-enzymes (see **13** §§15, 17).

Vitamin B complex

§2. Introduction

Eijkman (1897) found that birds developed polyneuritis when fed with polished rice, and were cured when they were given rice polishings. Then Grijns (1901) found that rice polishings cured beriberi in man (beriberi in man corresponds to polyneuritis in birds; it is a form of paralysis). Grijns suggested that the cause of this paralysis was due to some 'deficiency' in the diet, and this was confirmed by Funk (1911, 1912), who prepared a concentrate of the active substance from rice polishings. Funk believed that this active substance was a definite chemical compound, and since he separated organic bases when he prepared his concentrate, he named his 'deficiency compound' a *vitamine*. It was then found that 'vitamine B' was a complex mixture, and when a number of 'vitamines' were obtained that contained no nitrogen, the name *vitamin* was retained for them. The name vitamin B is now reserved for the complex mixture of vitamins in this group.

§3. Vitamin B$_1$, thiamine (aneurin)

Thiamine is one member of the water-soluble vitamin B complex, and is in the thermolabile fraction; it is the absence of thiamine which is the cause of beriberi in man; thus this vitamin is the antineuritic factor (hence the name *aneurin*). Rice polishings and yeast have been the usual sources of thiamine; eggs are also a rich source. Thiamine occurs in all cells as its pyrophosphate ester (see also §4).

Thiamine is obtained crystalline in the form of its salts; the chloride hydrochloride has been shown to have the molecular formula $C_{12}H_{18}Cl_2N_4OS$ (Windaus *et al.*, 1932); this salt is isolated in the form of its hemihydrate, d. 248–250°C. When treated with a sodium sulphite solution saturated with sulphur dioxide at room temperature, thiamine is decomposed quantitatively into two compounds which, for convenience, we shall label (A) and (B) [R. R. Williams *et al.*, 1935].

$$C_{12}H_{18}Cl_2N_4OS + Na_2SO_3 \longrightarrow C_6H_9NOS + C_6H_9N_3O_3S + 2NaCl$$
$$(A) \qquad\qquad (B)$$

Compound (A), C_6H_9NOS.   This compound shows basic properties, and since it does not react with nitrous acid, it was inferred that the nitrogen atom is in the tertiary state. The functional nature of the oxygen atom was shown to be alcoholic, *e.g.*, when (A) is treated with hydrochloric acid, a hydroxyl group (one oxygen atom and one hydrogen atom) is replaced by a chlorine atom. Furthermore, since the ultraviolet spectrum of the chloro-derivative is almost the same as that of the parent (hydroxy) compound, this suggests that the hydroxyl group is in a side-chain. The sulphur did not give the reactions of a mercapto compound nor of a sulphide; in fact, the stability (*i.e.*, unreactivity) of this sulphur atom led to the suggestion that it was in a heterocyclic ring. This conclusion was confirmed by the fact that (A) has an ultraviolet spectrum characteristic of a thiazole (**12** §5).

R. R. Williams *et al.* (1935) found that oxidation of (A) with nitric acid gives the compound $C_5H_5NO_2S$, which can also be obtained by the direct oxidation of thiamine with nitric acid. This latter reaction had actually been carried out by Windaus *et al.* (1934), but these workers had not recognised the presence of the thiazole nucleus. Williams *et al.* showed that this oxidation product was a monocarboxylic acid, and found that it was identical with 4-methylthiazole-5-carboxylic acid (I), a compound already described in the literature (Wöhmann, 1890). From this it follows that (A) has a side-chain of two carbon atoms in place of the carboxyl group in (I) (one carbon atom is lost

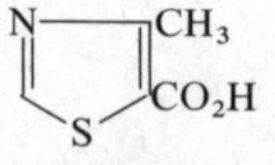

(I) 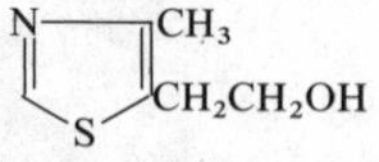   (II)

when (A) is oxidised to (I)). Since it is this side-chain which must contain the alcoholic group, the side-chain could be either —CH$_2$CH$_2$OH or —CHOHCH$_3$. Either of these could lose a carbon atom to form a carboxyl group directly attached to the thiazole nucleus. The second alternative, —CHOHCH$_3$, was excluded by the fact that (A) does not give the iodoform test, and that (A) is not optically active (the second alternative contains a chiral centre). Thus (A) was given structure (II) and this has been confirmed by synthesis (Clarke *et al.*, 1935).

(i)
$$\text{CH}_3\text{-CO-CH}^-\text{Na}^+\text{-CO}_2\text{C}_2\text{H}_5 + \text{BrCH}_2\text{CH}_2\text{OC}_2\text{H}_5 \longrightarrow \text{H}_3\text{C-CO-CH(CO}_2\text{C}_2\text{H}_5)\text{CH}_2\text{CH}_2\text{OC}_2\text{H}_5 \xrightarrow{\text{SO}_2\text{Cl}_2}$$

$$\text{CH}_3\text{-CO-CCl(CO}_2\text{C}_2\text{H}_5)\text{CH}_2\text{CH}_2\text{OC}_2\text{H}_5 \xrightarrow[\text{hydrolysis}]{\text{`ketonic'}} \text{CH}_3\text{-COCHClCH}_2\text{CH}_2\text{OC}_2\text{H}_5$$

(ii)

$$\underset{\text{thioformamide}}{\text{HC}(\text{NH}_2)\text{=S}} + \underset{\text{Cl}}{\text{O=CCH}_3,\ \text{CHCH}_2\text{CH}_2\text{OC}_2\text{H}_5} \xrightarrow[-\text{HCl}]{-\text{H}_2\text{O}} \text{[thiazole: }N\text{—CH}_3,\ \text{S, CH}_2\text{CH}_2\text{OC}_2\text{H}_5\text{]} \xrightarrow{\text{HCl}}$$

$$\text{[thiazole: }N\text{—CH}_3,\ S,\ \text{CH}_2\text{CH}_2\text{Cl}] \xrightarrow[\text{boil}]{\text{H}_2\text{O}} \text{[thiazole: }N\text{—CH}_3,\ S,\ \text{CH}_2\text{CH}_2\text{OH}]$$

(A)

The hydrochloride of this compound is identical with that of the product obtained from thiamine (by fission), and also gives (I) on oxidation with nitric acid.

Londergan *et al.* (1953) have synthesised (A) from 2-methylfuran as follows:

$$\text{[2-methylfuran]} \xrightarrow[\text{HCl}]{\text{H}_2/\text{Pd—C}} \text{CH}_2\text{—CH}_2,\ \text{CH}_2\text{OH, COCH}_3 \xrightarrow{-\text{H}_2\text{O}} \text{[furan-CH}_3\text{]} \xrightarrow{\text{Cl}_2} \text{[Cl, Cl, O, CH}_3\text{]} \xrightarrow[\text{in HCO}_2\text{H}]{\text{HCSNH}_2} \text{[thiazole: }N\text{—CH}_3,\ S,\ \text{CH}_2\text{CH}_2\text{OH]}$$

Compound (B), $C_6H_9N_3O_3S$. This was shown to be a sulphonic acid, *e.g.*, when heated with water under pressure at 200°C, (B) gives sulphuric acid; it also forms sodium sulphite when heated with concentrated sodium hydroxide solution. On treatment with nitrous acid, (B) evolves nitrogen; thus (B) contains one or more amino-groups. Analysis of the product showed that one amino-group is present in (B) [the product contained only one hydroxyl group]. Furthermore, since the evolution of nitrogen was slow, and the reaction of (B) with benzoyl chloride was also slow, this suggests that (B) contains an amidine structure (Williams *et al.*, 1935). Williams *et al.* (1935) then heated (B) with hydrochloric acid at 150°C under pressure, and obtained compound (C) and ammonia. The

$$\text{C}_6\text{H}_9\text{N}_3\text{O}_3\text{S} + \text{H}_2\text{O} \xrightarrow{\text{HCl}} \text{C}_6\text{H}_8\text{N}_2\text{O}_4\text{S} + \text{NH}_3$$
(C)

formation of ammonia indicates the replacement of an amino-group by a hydroxyl group. This type of reaction is characteristic of 2- and 4-aminopyrimidines; it was therefore inferred that (B) is a pyrimidine derivative (*cf.* **12** §14). This is supported by the fact that the ultraviolet absorption spectrum of compound (C) was similar to that of synthetic 4-hydroxypyrimidines; thus (B) is probably a 4-aminopyrimidine.

When (B) is reduced with sodium in liquid ammonia, a sulphonic acid group is eliminated with the formation of an aminodimethylpyrimidine (Williams, 1936). Comparison of the ultraviolet

$$\underset{\text{acetamidine}}{\text{CH}_3\text{C}(\text{NH}_2)\text{=NH}} + \underset{\substack{\text{formylpropionic} \\ \text{ester}}}{\text{C}_2\text{H}_5\text{O}_2\text{C-CCH}_3\text{=CH-OH}} \xrightarrow{\text{C}_2\text{H}_5\text{ONa}} \text{[pyrimidinone: O, HN, CH}_3,\ \text{CH}_3,\ N] \xrightarrow[\text{(ii) NH}_3\text{—C}_2\text{H}_5\text{OH}]{\text{(i) POCl}_3} \text{[pyrimidine: NH}_2,\ N,\ \text{CH}_3,\ \text{CH}_3,\ N]$$

absorption spectrum of this product with various synthetic compounds showed that it was 4-amino-2,5-dimethylpyrimidine, and this was confirmed by synthesis (Williams *et al.*, 1937).

Thus (B) is 4-amino-2,5-dimethylpyrimidine with one hydrogen atom (other than one of the amino-group) replaced by a sulphonic acid group. When thiamine is treated with sodium in liquid ammonia, one of the products is the diamino derivative (D), $C_6H_{10}N_4$ (Williams *et al.*, 1937). Compound (D) was identified as 4-amino-5-aminomethyl-2-methylpyrimidine by comparison with the ultraviolet spectra of methylated aminopyrimidines of known structure (Williams *et al.*, 1937). This is confirmed by the synthesis of Grewe (1936); Williams *et al.* had arrived at their conclusion independently of Grewe's work (see below for this synthesis). Thus, in compound (D), there is an amino-group instead of the sulphonic acid group in (B).

Williams therefore concluded that the sulphonic acid group (in (B)) is joined to the methyl group at position 5. This was confirmed (in 1937) by treating 5-ethoxymethyl-4-hydroxy-2-methylpyrimidine (see the synthesis described for thiamine) with sodium sulphite, whereby 4-hydroxy-2-methylpyrimidyl-5-methanesulphonic acid was obtained, and this was shown to be identical with compound (C).

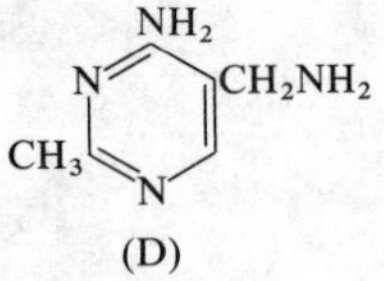

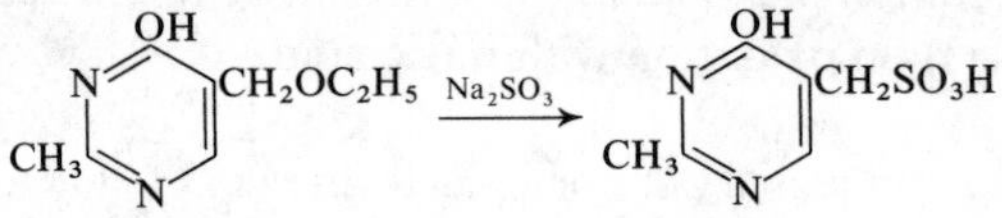

Thus (B) has the following structure:

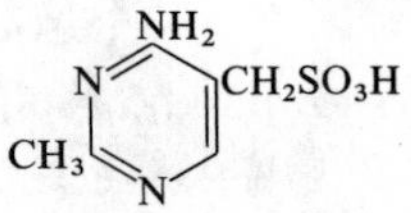

This structure is confirmed by synthesis (Grewe, 1936; Andersag *et al.*, 1937).

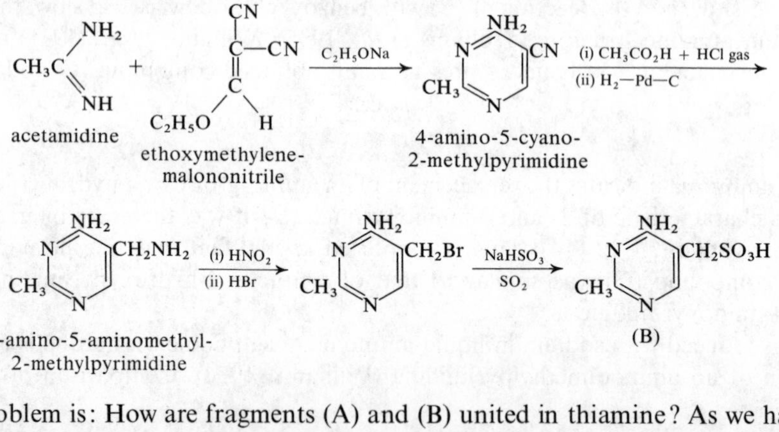

The final problem is: How are fragments (A) and (B) united in thiamine? As we have seen, the sulphonic acid group in (B) is introduced during the fission of thiamine with sodium sulphite; thus the point of attachment of fragment (B) is at the CH_2 group at position 5. To account for the formation of (D), fragment (B) must be linked to the nitrogen atom of fragment (A); in this position, the nitrogen atom of the thiazole ring is in a quaternary state, and so accounts for the chloride hydrochloride of thiamine. Had (B) been connected to (A) through a carbon atom of the latter, it would not be easy to account for the ready fission of this carbon–carbon bond by means of sodium and liquid ammonia, nor for the fact that thiamine does not form a *dihydrochloride*. Thus the chloride hydrochloride of thiamine is:

thiamine chloride hydrochloride

This structure has been confirmed by synthesis, *e.g.*, that of Williams *et al.* (1936, 1937). The route adopted was the separate syntheses of the pyrimidine and thiazole moieties and then linking these together.

This synthesis has been used commercially for the production of thiamine.

§4. Cocarboxylase

This is the coenzyme of *carboxylase*, and has been shown to be the pyrophosphate of thiamine (Lohmann *et al.*, 1937). Carboxylase, which requires the coenzyme for action (see **13** §15), breaks down pyruvic acid, formed in alcoholic fermentation, to acetaldehyde and carbon dioxide.

$$CH_3COCO_2H \xrightarrow{\text{carboxylase}} CH_3CHO + CO_2$$

Cocarboxylase is:

The mechanism of the cocarboxylase action appears to depend on the ionisation of the proton at C-2 in the thiazolium ring. The lability of this hydrogen atom has been demonstrated by its ready replacement by deuterium when thiazolium salts are dissolved in acidified deuterium oxide.

§5. Thiochrome

Isolated from yeast by Kuhn *et al.* (1935) it is a yellow basic solid and its solutions show a blue fluorescence. Thiochrome is also formed by the oxidation of thiamine with alkaline potassium ferricyanide (Todd *et al.*, 1935); it has also been synthesised by Todd *et al.* (1936).

thiochrome

§6. Vitamine B_2, riboflavin (lactoflavin), $C_{17}H_{20}N_4O_6$

Riboflavin is a water-soluble, thermostable vitamin which occurs in the vitamin B complex. It is necessary for growth and health, and occurs widely distributed in nature, *e.g.*, in yeast, green vegetables, milk, meat, etc. It occurs free or as the phosphate, or joined to specific proteins to form enzymes. Chemically, vitamin B_2 is closely related to the yellow water-soluble pigments known as *flavins* (isoalloxazines), and since it was first isolated from milk, vitamin B_2 is also known as *lactoflavin*.

Riboflavin is a bright yellow powder, d.p. $\sim 280°C$, showing a green fluorescence; it is soluble in water and in ethanol, but is insoluble in chloroform and other organic solvents. The aqueous solution, which is yellow and shows a yellowish-green fluorescence, has a λ_{max} 565 nm. This property has been used as a means of determining riboflavin quantitatively.

When exposed to light, riboflavin in sodium hydroxide solution forms mainly lumi-lactoflavin, $C_{13}H_{12}N_4O_2$ (this is soluble in chloroform). Lumi-lactoflavin, on boiling with barium hydroxide solution, is hydrolysed to one molecule of urea and one molecule of the barium salt of a β-keto-carboxylic acid (I), $C_{12}H_{12}N_2O_3$ (Kuhn *et al.*, 1933, 1934). The nature of this acid is shown by the fact that, on acidification of the barium salt, the free acid immediately eliminates carbon dioxide to form the compound (II), $C_{11}H_{12}N_2O$. This compound showed the properties of a lactam, and on vigorous hydrolysis by boiling with sodium hydroxide solution, it forms one molecule of glyoxylic acid and one molecule of the compound $C_9H_{14}N_2$ (III).

$$C_{17}H_{20}N_4O_6 \xrightarrow[\text{light}]{\text{NaOH}} C_{13}H_{12}N_4O_2 \xrightarrow{\text{Ba(OH)}_2} CO(NH_2)_2 + [C_{12}H_{12}N_2O_3] \xrightarrow[-CO_2]{\text{acid}} C_{11}H_{12}N_2O \xrightarrow{\text{NaOH}} OHCCO_2H + C_9H_{14}N_2$$

riboflavin   lumi-lactoflavin   (I)   (II)   (III)

The structure of (III) was elucidated as follows (Kuhn *et al.*, 1934). Preliminary tests showed that (III) was an aromatic diamino compound. Then it was found that it gave a blue precipitate with

(IV)

(III)

ferric chloride, and since this reaction is characteristic of monomethyl-*o*-phenylenediamine, it suggests that (III) contains the nucleus (IV). The molecular formula of (IV) is $C_7H_{10}N_2$, and since (III) is $C_9H_{14}N_2$, two carbon and four hydrogen atoms must be accounted for. This can be done by assuming the presence of an ethyl group or of two methyl groups in the benzene ring. Kuhn *et al.* carried out a series of synthetic experiments and showed that (III) has the structure given, *N*-methyl-4,5-diamino-*o*-xylene.

Kuhn then proposed (II) as the structure of the precursor of (III), since this would produce the required products of hydrolysis.

(II) could therefore have been produced from the β-ketocarboxylic acid (I).

Since (I) and a molecule of urea are obtained from lumi-lactoflavin, the latter could be 6,7,9-trimethylisoalloxazine (6,7,9-trimethylflavin).

lumi-lactoflavin

This structure for lumi-lactoflavin has been confirmed by synthesis (Kuhn *et al.*, 1934). *N*-Methyl-4,5-diamino-*o*-xylene is condensed with alloxan hydrate (**16** §4) in aqueous solution at 50–60°C.

Methylation (methyl sulphate) of this synthetic product gives a tetramethyl compound identical with the product obtained by the methylation of the natural lumi-lactoflavin.

Side-chain of riboflavin. Exposure of a *neutral* solution of lactoflavin to light produces *lumichrome*, $C_{12}H_{10}N_4O_2$ (Karrer *et al.*, 1934). Analytical work similar to that described for lumi-lactoflavin showed that the structure of lumichrome is 6,7-dimethylalloxazine (A).

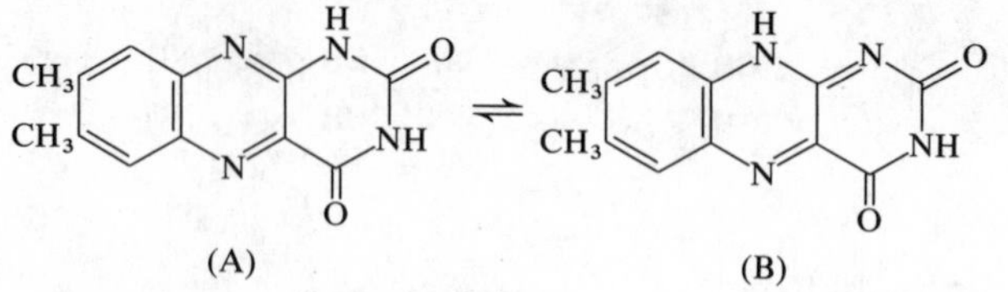

(A)   (B)

lumichrome

The isoalloxazine (structure (B)) is a tautomer of the alloxazine (structure (A)); (B) does not exist as such, but this structure is fixed when there is a substituent at position 9 (see also **12** §25). Stern *et al.* (1934) have shown that the ultraviolet spectra of compounds containing a 9-substituent are different from those in which the mobile 9-hydrogen atom is present. Also in the latter case, the alloxazine structure (A) predominates.

Thus lumichrome is lumi-lactoflavin with a hydrogen atom instead of a methyl group at position 9. This suggests that riboflavin contains a side-chain (of five carbon atoms) attached to N-9. The Zerewitinoff procedure shows that riboflavin contains five active hydrogen atoms; thus the molecule contains four hydroxyl groups (one active hydrogen atom is the hydrogen of the NH group at position 3). The presence of these four hydroxyl groups is supported by the fact that the silver salt of riboflavin (the silver atom replaces the hydrogen of the NH group) forms a tetra-acetate. Thus the side-chain is a tetrahydroxy derivative. Furthermore, since oxidation with lead tetra-acetate produces formaldehyde, the side-chain contains a terminal CH_2OH group, and since riboflavin forms a diisopropylidene derivative (*cf.* **7** §8), this indicates two 1,2-glycol systems are present (Kuhn *et al.*, 1933). All these facts can be explained if riboflavin has the structure shown. This side-chain contains three chiral centres, and so there are eight optically active forms possible. Which configuration is actually present was solved by synthesising a number of pentose derivatives, and it was finally shown by Karrer *et al.*

riboflavin

(1935) that the configuration is that of $D(-)$-ribose. The following syntheses are due to Karrer *et al.* (1935).

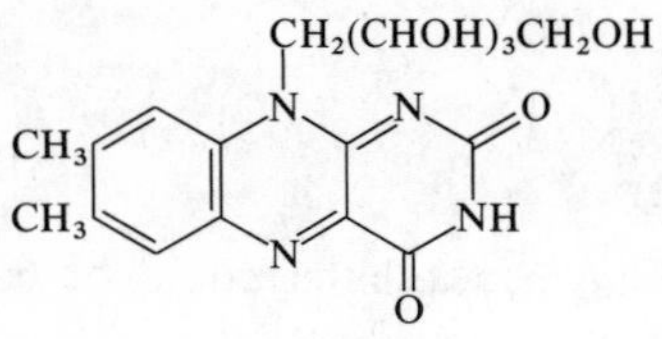

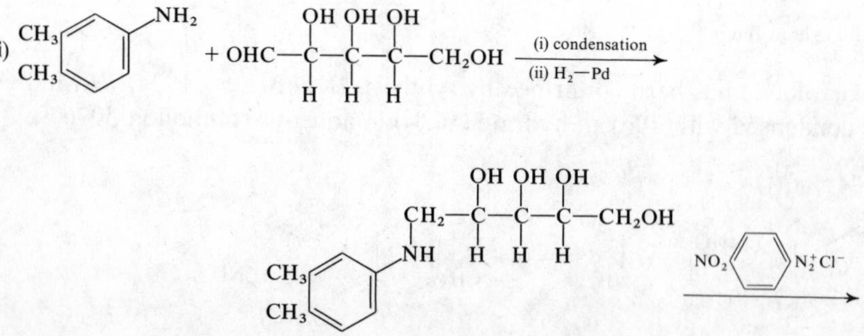

Thus riboflavin is 6,7-dimethyl-9-[D-1'-ribityl]-isoalloxazine. Of all the pentoses (and hexoses) used, only the compound from D-ribose shows growth-promoting properties.

Many other procedures for synthesising riboflavin have now been developed, but only that of Tishler *et al.* (1947) will be described. These workers found that the azo compound, prepared by Karrer in synthesis (i) above, combined directly with barbituric acid (used instead of alloxan) in acetic acid solution. The yield of riboflavin was good and the product was very pure.

§7. Pantothenic acid, $C_9H_{17}NO_5$

A chick antidermatitis factor, and also capable of promoting the growth of yeast and of bacteria, it has been isolated from many sources, *e.g.*, liver, kidney, yeast, etc. Pantothenic acid is a pale yellow viscous oil.

Pantothenic acid shows the reactions of a monocarboxylic acid, *e.g.*, it can be esterified to form monoesters (R. J. Williams *et al.*, 1939). The application of the method for determining active hydrogen atoms shows that pantothenic acid contains two hydroxyl groups, and since the acid condenses with benzaldehyde (to form a benzylidene derivative) and with acetone to form an iso-propylidene derivative), this suggests that the two hydroxy groups are in either the 1,2- or 1,3-position (cf. 7 §§8, 9). Since periodic acid has no action on pantothenic acid, the 1,2-glycol structure is eliminated; the compound is therefore a 1,3-glycol. When warmed with dilute hydrochloric acid, pantothenic acid is hydrolysed into compounds (I) and (II). Investigation of (I) showed that it was

$$C_9H_{17}NO_5 \xrightarrow{\text{HCl}} C_3H_7NO_2 + C_6H_{10}O_3$$
$$\text{(I)} \qquad\qquad \text{(II)}$$

β-alanine (actually present as the hydrochloride, $\bar{C}l\{H_3\overset{+}{N}CH_2CH_2CO_2H)$. On the other hand, when hydrolysed with alkali, pantothenic acid forms β-alanine (I) and the salt of an acid which, on acidification, spontaneously forms the lactone (II). Thus the free acid of (II) is probably a γ- or δ-hydroxycarboxylic acid; also, since the rate of lactonisation is fast, (II) is more likely a γ-lactone than a δ-lactone (cf. **7** §7c). As pointed out above, pantothenic acid contains two hydroxyl groups. One of these has now been accounted for, and so the problem is to find the position of the second one. This was shown to be α- by the fact that the sodium salt of the acid of the lactone (II) gives a canary-yellow colour with ferric chloride (a test characteristic of α-hydroxyacids), and also by the fact that (II), on warming with concentrated sulphuric acid, liberates carbon monoxide (a test also characteristic of α-hydroxyacids). Thus (II) is most probably the γ-lactone of an α-hydroxyacid (R. J. Williams et al., 1940).

(II) was shown to contain one active hydrogen atom, and the application of the Kuhn–Roth methyl side-chain determination (**9** §3) showed the presence of a *gem*-dimethyl group (Stiller et al., 1940); the presence of this group is confirmed by the formation of acetone when the lactone (II) is oxidised with barium permanganate. Thus a possible structure for (II) is α-hydroxy-β,β-dimethyl-γ-butyrolactone:

$$CH_2\text{---}C(CH_3)_2\text{---}CHOH\text{---}CO \equiv C_6H_{10}O_3$$
$$\underset{O}{\rule{0pt}{0pt}}$$
$$(II)$$

This has been confirmed as follows. Treatment of the lactone with methylmagnesium iodide, followed by hydrolysis, gives a trihydric alcohol which, on oxidation with lead tetra-acetate, gives acetone and an aldehyde. This aldehyde, on oxidation with silver oxide, gave a compound (III), which was shown to be β-hydroxy-α,α-dimethylpropionic acid, a known compound. The foregoing reactions may be formulated as follows:

$$CH_2C(CH_3)_2CHOHCO \xrightarrow[\text{(ii) H}_2\text{O}]{\text{(i) CH}_3\text{MgI}} HOCH_2C(CH_3)_2CHOHC(OH)(CH_3)_2 \xrightarrow{\text{(CH}_3\text{CO)}_4\text{Pb}}$$
$$\underset{O}{\rule{0pt}{0pt}}$$
$$(II)$$

$$CH_3COCH_3 + HOCH_2C(CH_3)_2CHO \xrightarrow{Ag_2O} HOCH_2C(CH_3)_2CO_2H$$
$$(III)$$

Examination of (II) shows that it contains one chiral centre. The lactone, **pantolactone** (the acid is known as **pantoic acid**), obtained from pantothenic acid is laevorotatory, and the structure assigned to it has been confirmed by synthesis (Stiller et al., 1940).

$$(CH_3)_2CHCHO + CH_2O \xrightarrow{K_2CO_3} (CH_3)_2C\underset{CHO}{\overset{CH_2OH}{<}} \xrightarrow[\text{(ii) KCN}]{\text{(i) NaHSO}_3} (CH_3)_2C\underset{CHOHCN}{\overset{CH_2OH}{<}} \xrightarrow[\text{boil}]{HCl}$$

isobutyraldehyde formalin

$(\pm)$-lactone

The ($\pm$)-lactone (as the sodium salt of the acid) was resolved with quinine hydrochloride, and the ($-$)-form was identical with the lactone obtained from pantothenic acid. Grussner et al. (1940) have correlated the chiral centre with $\text{D}(+)$-glyceraldehyde by use of Hudson's amide rule (**7** §6a).

In pantothenic acid, the nitrogen atom is not basic. Also, since hydrolysis of pantothenic acid produces a free amino-group (in β-alanine), this suggests that the group —CONH— is present, *i.e.*, pantothenic acid is an amide. Thus the hydrolysis may be formulated:

$$HOCH_2C(CH_3)_2CHOHCONHCH_2CH_2CO_2H \xrightarrow{HCl} [HOCH_2C(CH_3)_2CHOHCO_2H] + NH_2CH_2CH_2CO_2H \xrightarrow{lactonisn.}$$

pantothenic acid

$$CH_2C(CH_3)_2CHOHCO$$
$$\underline{\qquad\qquad O\qquad\qquad}$$

This interpretation of the results has been confirmed by the synthesis of pantothenic acid. Stiller *et al.* (1940) warmed pantolactone (synthesised as described above) with the ethyl ester of β-alanine, and removed the ester group by hydrolysis with a cold solution of barium hydroxide.

$$CH_2C(CH_3)_2CHOHCO + NH_2CH_2CH_2CO_2C_2H_5 \xrightarrow{warm} HOCH_2C(CH_3)_2CHOHCONHCH_2CH_2CO_2C_2H_5 \xrightarrow{Ba(OH)_2}$$
$$\underline{\qquad O\qquad}$$

$$HOCH_2C(CH_3)_2CHOHCONHCH_2CH_2CO_2H$$

A better yield of pantothenic acid is obtained by warming the dry lactone with the dry sodium salt of β-alanine (R. J. Williams *et al.*, 1940).

§8. Folic acid

This has been isolated from various sources, *e.g.*, yeast, spinach, etc., and is necessary for the growth of a number of micro-organisms and is effective in the treatment of certain types of anaemia. Folic acid is **pteroylglutamic acid**, but it also exists in forms which contain three or seven glutamic acid residues.

2-amino-4-
hydroxypteridine   *p*-aminobenzoic acid   glutamic acid

pteroic acid

pteroylglutamic acid
(folic acid)

(A) is the system which corresponds to purine numbering (**16** §1), and has been used in some of the earlier publication. (B), however, is now the recommended system, and is used here.

(A)   pteridine   (B)

The structure of folic acid was elucidated by Angier *et al.* (1946). The alkaline hydrolysis of the fermentation *Lactobacillus casei* factor, in the absence of oxygen, formed two molecules of D-glutamic acid and the DL-form of liver *L. casei* factor. On the other hand, the alkaline hydrolysis of the fermentation *L. casei* factor, in the presence of air, gave two substances, (I) and (II). (I) was shown to be a monocarboxylic acid, and the examination of its ultraviolet absorption spectrum led to the conclusion that it was a pteridine derivative. A further examination of (I) showed that it also contained one hydroxyl and one amino-group. Oxidation of (I) with chlorine water, followed by hydrolysis with hydrochloric acid, produced guanidine, $NH{=}C(NH_2)_2$, as one of the products.

The formation of this compound suggests that the amino-group is at position 2. Also, decarboxylation of (I) gave a compound which appeared to be identical with the known compound, 2-amino-4-hydroxypteridine, thereby suggesting that the hydroxyl group in (I) is in position 4. Finally, (I) was shown to be 2-amino-4-hydroxypteridine-6-carboxylic acid by synthesis.

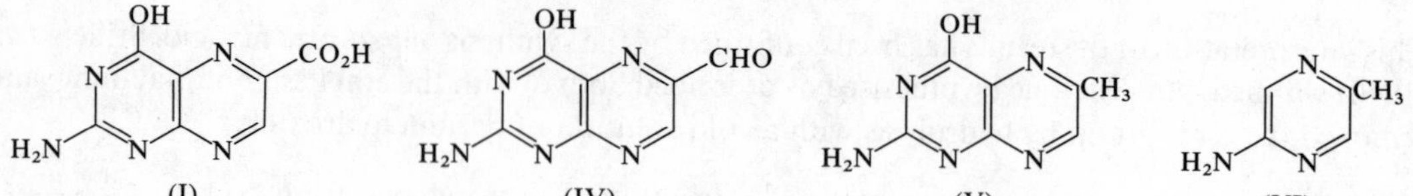

The reactions of (II) showed that it was a primary aromatic amine, and on hydrolysis it gave one molecule of *p*-aminobenzoic acid and three molecules of glutamic acid.

Hydrolysis of the fermentation *L. casei* factor with sulphurous acid gave an aromatic amine (III) and an aldehyde (IV). (III), on hydrolysis, gave one molecule of *p*-aminobenzoic acid and three molecules of glutamic acid, *i.e.*, (II) and (III) are identical. When the aldehyde (IV) was allowed to stand in dilute sodium hydroxide solution in the absence of air, (I) and another compound (V) were produced. (V), on vigorous hydrolysis, gave 2-amino-5-methylpyrazine (VI). From this it was concluded that (V) is 2-amino-4-hydroxy-6-methylpteridine, and (IV) is 2-amino-4-hydroxypteridine-6-aldehyde. Consideration of this evidence led to the suggestion that the liver *L. casei* factor has the structure given above; this has been confirmed by synthesis, *e.g.*, that of Angier *et al.* (1946).

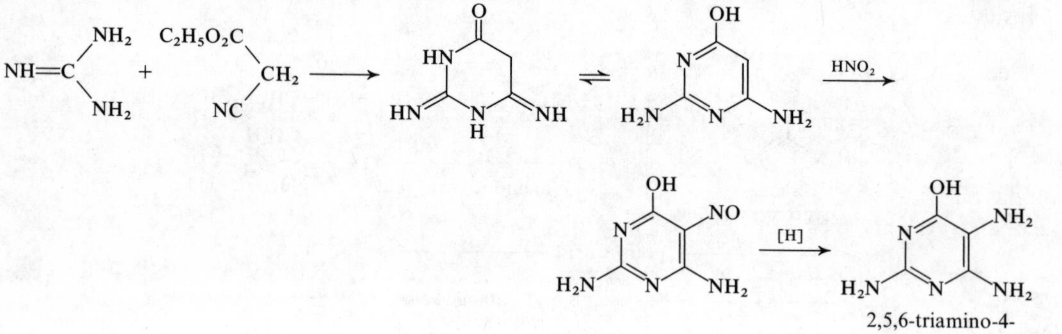

2,5,6-triamino-4-hydroxypyrimidine

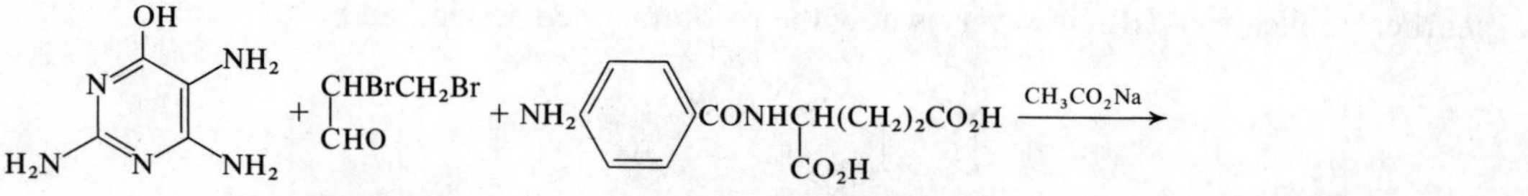

2,3-dibromo-propionaldehyde

p-aminobenzoyl-L(+)-glutamic acid

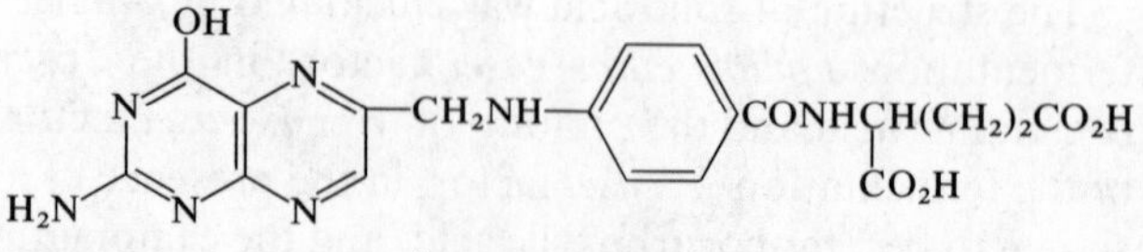

liver *L.casei* factor

From this it follows that the fermentation *L. casei* factor contains three glutamic acid residues, and synthesis showed that these are joined by peptide links (Stokstad *et al.*, 1948):

$$-CO-[-NHCH(CH_2)_2CO-]_2-NHCH(CH_2)_2CO_2H$$
$$\qquad\qquad\;\; CO_2H \qquad\qquad\qquad\qquad\quad CO_2H$$

Animal tissues contain an enzyme which hydrolyses the naturally occurring pteroylpolyglutamic acids to pteroylglutamic acid and free glutamic acid.

It might be noted, in passing, that the **pterins** are pigments of butterfly wings, wasps, etc.; they were first isolated from butterfly wings.

xanthopterin   leucopterin

§9. Biotins (vitamin H)

Bios, an extract of yeast, was shown to be necessary for the growth of yeast (Wildiers, 1901). It was then found that bios consisted of at least two substances (Fulmer *et al.*, 1922), and two years later, Miller showed that three substances were present in bios. The first of these was named Bios I, and was shown to be *myo*inositol (Eastcott, 1928; see also §13). The second constituent, named Bios IIA, was then shown to be β-alanine (Miller, 1936) or pantothenic acid (Rainbow *et al.*, 1939). The third substance, named Bios IIB, was found to be identical with *biotin*, a substance that had been isolated by Kögl *et al.* (1936) as the methyl ester from egg-yolk. Subsequently other factors present in bios have been isolated, *e.g.*, pyridoxine (see §10) and nicotinic acid (§11).

Biotin is a vitamin, being necessary for the growth of animals. In 1940, du Vigneaud *et al.* isolated from liver a substance which had the same biological properties as biotin. Kögl *et al.* (1943) named their extract from egg-yolk α-biotin, and that from liver β-biotin. Both compounds have the same molecular formula $C_{10}H_{16}N_2O_3S$. However, Krueger *et al.* (1948) compared the biological properties of α- and β-biotin and concluded that these two compounds are most probably identical. It thus appears very doubtful that the two biotins exist, and current practice is to use the term biotin for Kögl's β-biotin.

Biotin (Bios IIB or β-biotin), m.p. 230–232°C, behaved as a saturated compound (the usual tests showed the absence of an ethylenic double bond). Biotin formed a monomethyl ester $C_{11}H_{18}N_2O_3S$ which, on hydrolysis, gave an acid the titration curve of which corresponded to a monocarboxylic acid; thus the formula of biotin may be written $C_9H_{15}N_2OSCO_2H$. When heated with barium hydroxide solution at 140°C, biotin was hydrolysed to carbon dioxide and an acid, $C_9H_{18}N_2O_2S$. This acid was shown to contain two primary amino-groups. Since the acid formed a dibenzoyl derivative which was soluble in alkali, this led to the suggestion that biotin contained a cyclic ureide structure. This was confirmed by the fact that the acid, on treatment with carbonyl chloride, was reconverted into biotin (du Vigneaud *et al.*, 1941). Furthermore, since the diaminocarboxylic acid condensed with phenanthraquinone to form a quinoxaline derivative, it follows that the two amino-groups are in the 1,2-positions (*cf.* **12** §19), and thus the cyclic ureide is five-membered. Hence we may write the foregoing reactions as follows:

β-biotin   diamino-compound

When this diaminocarboxylic acid was oxidised with alkaline permanganate, adipic acid was produced (du Vigneaud *et al.*, 1941). This could arise from an aliphatic side-chain in biotin or from the opening of a six-membered ring. In the former case the carboxyl group will appear in adipic acid, but in the latter case neither of the carboxyl groups is present in biotin. When the carbomethoxyl group of the methyl ester of biotin was replaced by an amino-group by means of the Curtius reaction (ester → hydrazide → azide → urethan → NH_2; see Vol. I), and the product hydrolysed with barium hydroxide solution, a triamine was obtained which did not give adipic acid on oxidation with alkaline permanganate (du Vigneaud *et al.*, 1941, 1942). Thus the carboxyl group in adipic acid must be that which was originally present in biotin, and it was therefore inferred that biotin contains a $-(CH_2)_4CO_2H$ side-chain (n-valeric acid side-chain).

The ultraviolet spectrum of the quinoxaline derivative (formed from phenanthraquinone and the diaminocarboxylic acid) showed that it was a quinoxaline (I) and not a dihydroquinoxaline (II); thus the diaminocarboxylic could be (III) but not (IV).

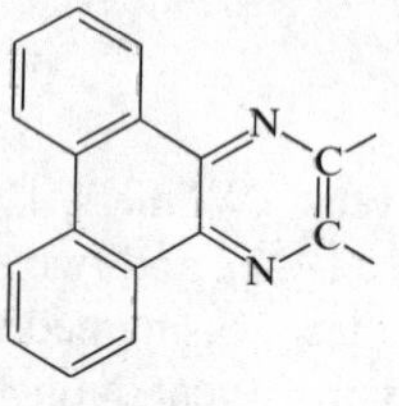

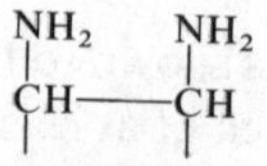

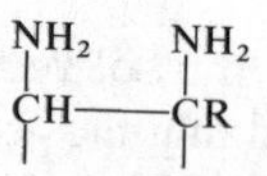

It therefore follows that the n-valeric acid side-chain cannot be attached to a carbon atom joined to an amino-group.

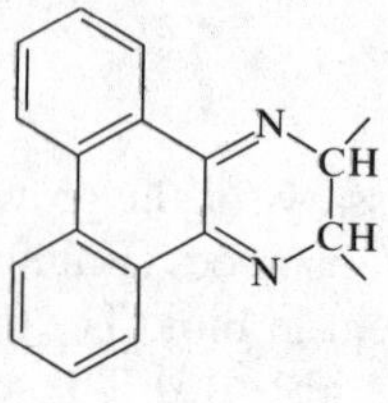

The nature of the sulphur atom in biotin was shown to be of the thioether type (*i.e.*, C—S—C) since:

(i) Oxidation of biotin with hydrogen peroxide produced a sulphone.

(ii) When the methyl ester of biotin was treated with methyl iodide, a sulphonium iodide was formed.

As we have seen, biotin does not contain a double bond; hence, from its molecular formula, it was deduced that biotin contained two rings (du Vigneaud *et al.*, 1941; Kögl *et al.*, 1941). This may be readily established by use of the double bond equivalent method (**1** §12e). D.B.E. = $10 + 1 - (16 - 2)/2 = 4$. As we have seen above, biotin is a saturated compound. It contains, however, a carbonyl group as ureide and another as carboxyl. Hence, since this accounts for *two double bonds*, *two rings* must also be present.

When heated with Raney nickel, biotin formed *dethiobiotin* by elimination of the sulphur atom (this is an example of the *Mozingo reaction*, 1943). Dethiobiotin, on hydrolysis with hydrochloric acid, gave a diaminocarboxylic acid which, on oxidation with periodic acid, gave pimelic acid (du Vigneaud *et al.*, 1942). These results can be explained by assuming that the sulphur atom is in a five-membered ring and the n-valeric acid side-chain is in the position shown.

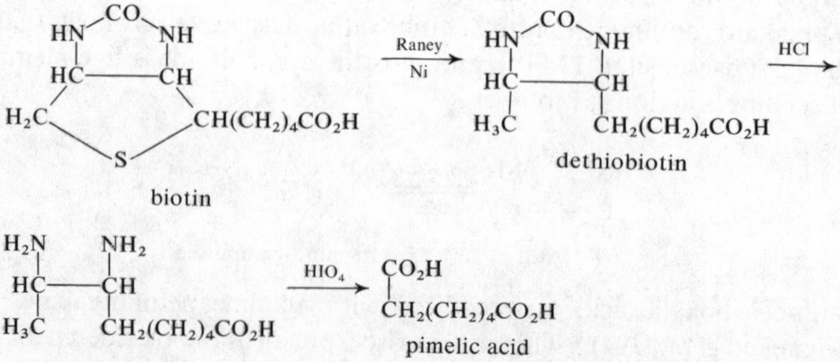

Further evidence for this structure was given by the fact that the exhaustive methylation of the diaminocarboxylic acid (produced from biotin) gave δ-(2-thienyl)valeric acid (du Vigneaud *et al.*, 1942); the structure of this compound was confirmed by synthesis.

thiophen + glutaric anhydride $\xrightarrow{\text{AlCl}_3}$ $\text{CO(CH}_2)_3\text{CO}_2\text{H}$ $\xrightarrow[\text{HCl}]{\text{Zn—Hg}}$

$(\text{CH}_2)_4\text{CO}_2\text{H}$ $\xleftarrow[\text{(ii) conc. HCl}]{\text{(i) Me}_2\text{SO}_4/\text{NaOH}}$ $\text{H}_2\text{N} \quad \text{NH}_2$ $(\text{CH}_2)_4\text{CO}_2\text{H}$

δ-(2-thienyl)-valeric acid

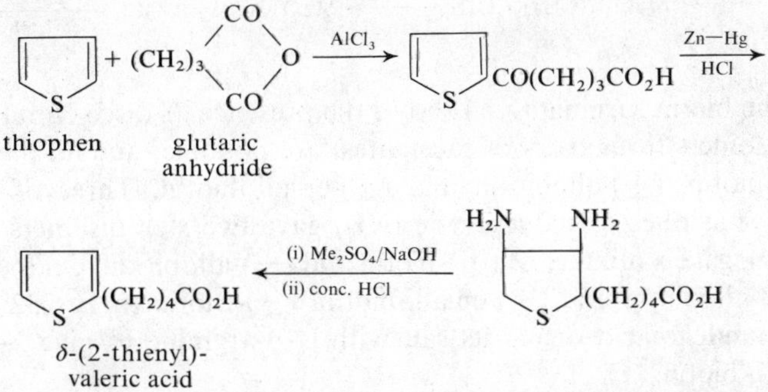

The above structure for biotin has been confirmed by synthesis (Harris *et al.*, 1943, 1944). The starting materials were the sodium salt of L-cysteine (V) and sodium chloroacetate, and it was found that racemisation occurred during cyclisation to (VIII) [see also later].

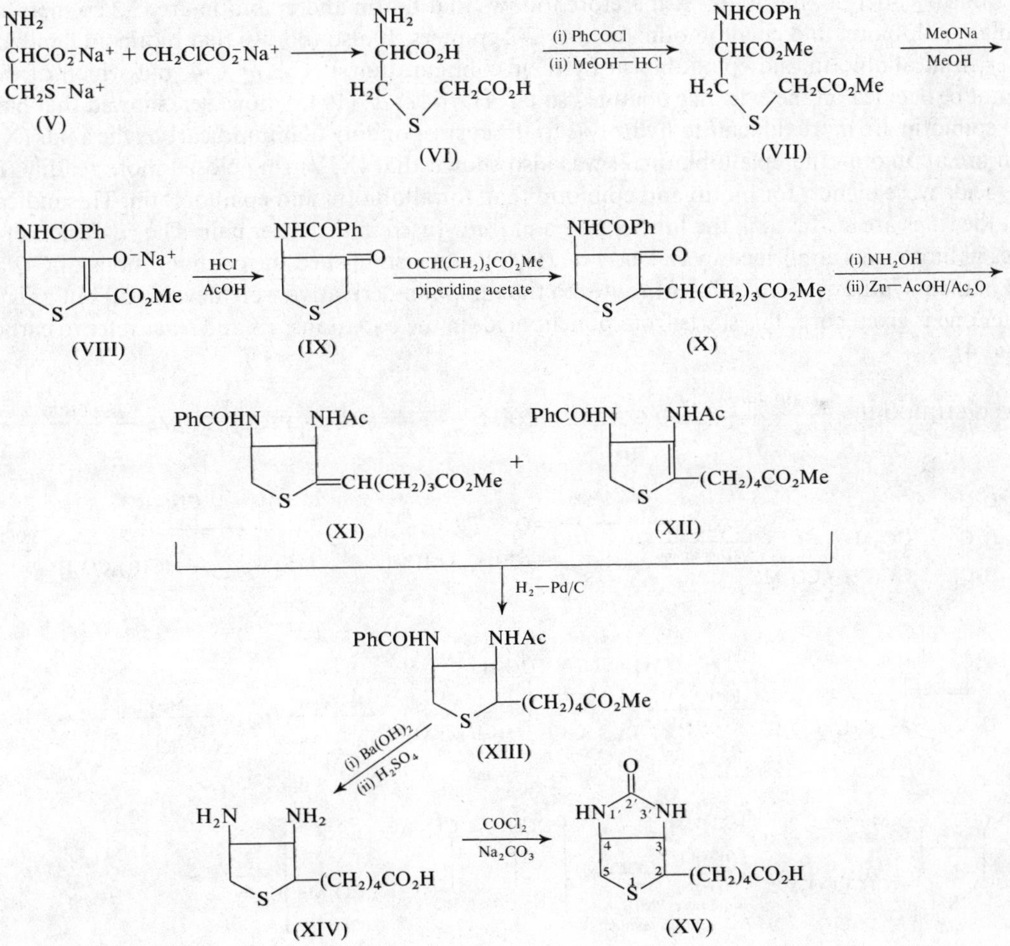

$$\begin{array}{l}\text{NH}_2 \\ \text{CHCO}_2^-\text{Na}^+ + \text{CH}_2\text{ClCO}_2^-\text{Na}^+ \\ \text{CH}_2\text{S}^-\text{Na}^+\end{array}$$

(V)

$\longrightarrow$ (VI) $\xrightarrow[\text{(ii) MeOH—HCl}]{\text{(i) PhCOCl}}$ (VII) $\xrightarrow[\text{MeOH}]{\text{MeONa}}$

(VI): NH$_2$, CHCO$_2$H, H$_2$C, CH$_2$CO$_2$H, S

(VII): NHCOPh, CHCO$_2$Me, H$_2$C, CH$_2$CO$_2$Me, S

(VIII) $\xrightarrow[\text{AcOH}]{\text{HCl}}$ (IX) $\xrightarrow[\text{piperidine acetate}]{\text{OCH(CH}_2)_3\text{CO}_2\text{Me}}$ (X) $\xrightarrow[\text{(ii) Zn—AcOH/Ac}_2\text{O}]{\text{(i) NH}_2\text{OH}}$

(VIII): NHCOPh, O$^-$Na$^+$, CO$_2$Me, S

(IX): NHCOPh, O, S

(X): NHCOPh, O, =CH(CH$_2$)$_3$CO$_2$Me, S

(XI): PhCOHN, NHAc, =CH(CH$_2$)$_3$CO$_2$Me, S   +   (XII): PhCOHN, NHAc, (CH$_2$)$_4$CO$_2$Me, S

$\xrightarrow{\text{H}_2\text{—Pd/C}}$

(XIII): PhCOHN, NHAc, S, (CH$_2$)$_4$CO$_2$Me

$\xrightarrow[\text{(ii) H}_2\text{SO}_4]{\text{(i) Ba(OH)}_2}$

(XIV): H$_2$N, NH$_2$, S, (CH$_2$)$_4$CO$_2$H

$\xrightarrow[\text{Na}_2\text{CO}_3]{\text{COCl}_2}$

(XV): HN—NH (1', 2', 3'), O, positions 4, 3, 5, S, 2, (CH$_2$)$_4$CO$_2$H

The carbomethoxyaldehyde used in stage (IX) → (X) was prepared from glutaric anhydride, the sequence of reactions involving a Rosenmund reduction.

Examination of the biotin formula (XV) shows the presence of three chiral centres (2, 3 and 4). Thus eight optical isomers (four pairs of racemates) are possible, and all have been synthesised: (±)-biotin, (±)-epibiotin, (±)-allobiotin and (±)-epiallobiotin. Three of the racemates were obtained in the above synthesis. Reduction of (XII) gave two stereoisomers of (XIII) and these, *via* the isomers of (X), gave a mixture of (±)-biotin and (±)-allobiotin. On the other hand (XI) led to a mixture of (±)-allobiotin and (±)-epiallobiotin. (±)-Biotin (m.p. 232°C) was resolved *via* its ester with (−)-mandelic acid or *via* its salt with (−)-arginine to give (+)-biotin which was identical with natural biotin.

The stereochemical relationships of the isomers have been established by chemical methods (Harris *et al.*, 1945). Desulphurisation of each (±)-form by Raney nickel gave the corresponding (±)-dethio compound. In these, the chirality of C-2 is destroyed, and it was found that (±)-biotin and (±)-epibiotin gave the same (±)-dethiobiotin, and (±)-allobiotin and (±)-epiallobiotin gave the same (±)-dethio-allobiotin. It therefore follows that biotin and epibiotin are C-2 epimers, and similarly allobiotin and epiallobiotin are also C-2 epimers. It also follows that biotin and epibiotin differ from allobiotin and epiallobiotin by their configuration at C-3 *or* C-4, but which of these cannot be decided on the evidence obtained so far. Harris *et al.* (1945), however, showed that biotin and epibiotin are more difficult to hydrolyse to the corresponding diaminodicarboxylic acids (XIV) than are allobiotin and epiallobiotin. It was also shown that (XIV) ring-closed more readily (*i.e.*, the yields were higher) for biotin and epibiotin than for allobiotin and epiallobiotin. This indicates that the rings are *cis*-fused in the former pair and *trans*-fused in the latter pair. The *cis*-fusion of the rings in biotin was confirmed by Baker *et al.* (1947), who established the configurations of C-3 and C-4 in their synthesis. Two different routes to the thiophan derivative were developed, but only the better one is given here; this starts from pimelic acid (in the equations, *cis* and *trans* refer to carbons 3 and 4):

In the work described so far, the stereochemistry of C-2 has been left unsolved. Harris *et al.* (1945) and Grob *et al.* (1952) deduced from their chemical work that biotin is the all-*cis*-isomer, *i.e.*, the ureido ring and the side-chain at C-2 are in the *cis*-position. This has been confirmed by Traub (1956) from his X-ray studies.

Of all the isomers, only (+)-biotin is biologically active.

§10. Pyridoxine (Adermin, vitamin B₆), $C_8H_{11}NO_3$, m.p. 160°C

This is obtained from rice bran and yeast; it cures dermatitis in rats. Pyridoxine behaves as a weak base, and the usual tests showed the absence of methoxyl and methylamino-groups. Application of the Zerewitinoff method showed the presence of three active hydrogen atoms. When treated with di-azomethane, pyridoxine formed a monomethyl ether which, on acetylation, gave a diacetyl derivative (Kuhn *et al.*, 1938). It therefore appears that the three oxygen atoms in pyridoxine are present as hydroxyl groups, and since one is readily methylated, this one is probably phenolic. This conclusion is supported by the fact that pyridoxine gives the ferric chloride colour reaction of phenols. Thus the other two hydroxyl groups are alcoholic.

Examination of the ultraviolet absorption spectrum of pyridoxine showed that it is similar to that of 3-hydroxypyridine. It was therefore inferred that pyridoxine is a pyridine derivative with the phenolic group in position 3. Since lead tetra-acetate has no action on the monomethyl ether of pyridoxine, this leads to the conclusion that the two alcoholic groups are not on adjacent carbon atoms in a side-chain (Kuhn *et al.*, 1939). When this methyl ether is *very carefully* oxidised with alkaline potassium permanganate, the product is a methoxypyridinetricarboxylic acid, $C_9H_7NO_7$. This acid gave a blood-red colour with ferrous sulphate, a reaction which is characteristic of pyridine-2-carboxylic acid; thus one of the three carboxyl groups is in the 2-position. When the methyl ether of pyridoxine was oxidised with alkaline permanganate under the usual conditions, the products were carbon dioxide and the anhydride of a dicarboxylic acid, $C_8H_5NO_4$; thus these two carboxyl groups are in the *ortho*-position. Furthermore, since this anhydride, on hydrolysis to its corresponding acid, did not give a red colour with ferrous sulphate, there is no carboxyl group in the 2-position. It therefore follows that, on decarboxylation, the tricarboxylic acid eliminates the 2-carboxyl group to form the anhydride; thus the tricarboxylic acid could have either of the following structures.

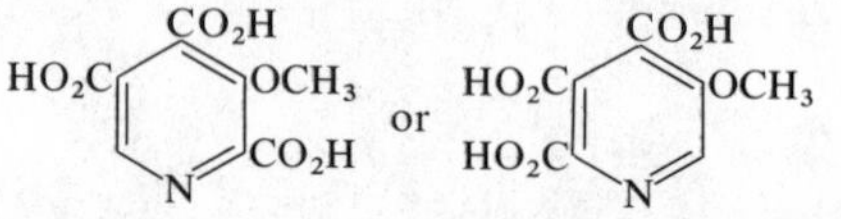

Now pyridoxine methyl ether contains three oxygen atoms (one as methoxyl and the other two alcoholic); it is therefore possible that two carboxyl groups in the tricarboxylic acid could arise from two CH_2OH groups, and the third from a methyl group, *i.e.*, pyridoxine could be either of the following:

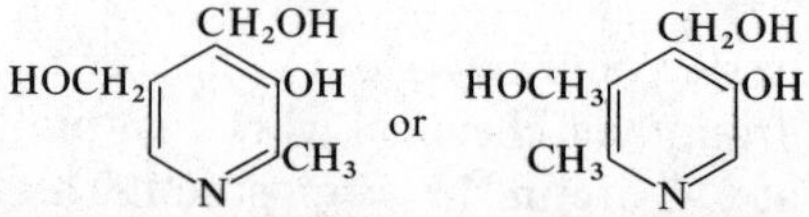

A decision between the two structures was made on the following evidence. When pyridoxine methyl ether was oxidised with barium permanganate, the product was a dicarboxylic acid, $C_9H_9NO_5$, which did not give a red colour with ferrous sulphate; thus there is no carboxyl group in the 2-position. Also, since the dicarboxylic acid formed an anhydride and gave a phthalein on fusion with resorcinol, the two carboxyl groups must be in the *ortho*-position. Furthermore, analysis of both the dicarboxylic acid and its anhydride showed the presence of a methyl group. Thus the structure of this dicarboxylic acid is either (I) or (II).

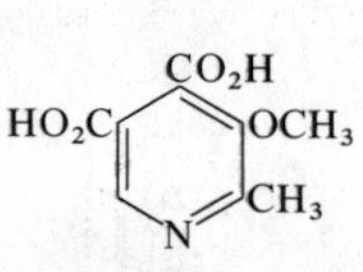

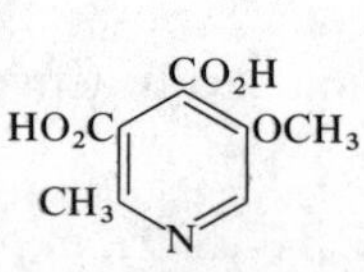

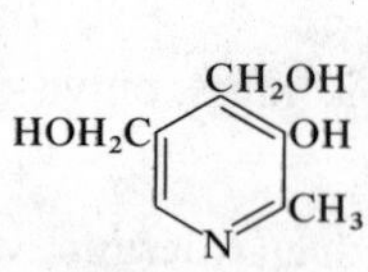

Kuhn *et al.* (1939) showed that the anhydride was that of (I) from its formation by the oxidation of 4-methoxy-3-methylisoquinoline (a synthetic compound of known structure).

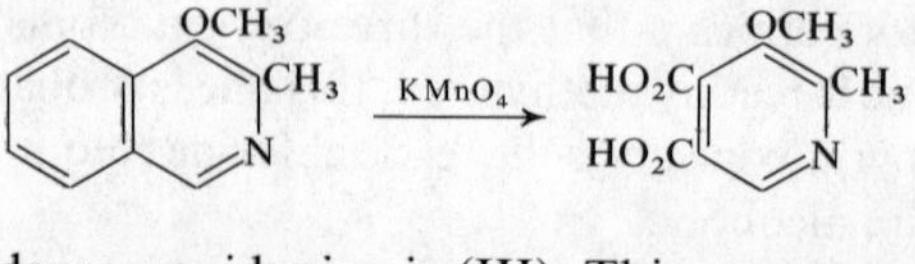

Hence, on the foregoing evidence, pyridoxine is (III). This structure has been confirmed by synthesis, *e.g.*, that of Harris and Folkers (1939):

CH$_2$OC$_2$H$_5$
CO
H$_2$C
CH$_3$CO
ethoxyacetyl-
acetone

+

CH$_2$CN
CO
H$_2$N
cyano-
acetamide

$\xrightarrow[\text{C}_2\text{H}_5\text{OH}]{\text{piperidine}}$

CH$_2$OC$_2$H$_5$
CN
CH$_3$ N   O
         H

$\xrightarrow[\text{(CH}_3\text{CO)}_2\text{O}]{\text{HNO}_3}$

CH$_2$OC$_2$H$_5$
O$_2$N   CN
CH$_3$ N   O
         H

$\xrightarrow{\text{PCl}_5}$

CH$_2$OC$_2$H$_5$
O$_2$N   CN
CH$_3$ N   Cl

$\xrightarrow{\text{H}_2-\text{Pt}}$

CH$_2$OC$_2$H$_5$
H$_2$N   CN
CH$_3$ N   Cl

$\xrightarrow{\text{H}_2 + \text{Pd}-\text{C}}$

CH$_2$OC$_2$H$_5$
H$_2$N   CH$_2$NH$_2$
CH$_3$ N

$\xrightarrow{\text{HNO}_2}$

CH$_2$OC$_2$H$_5$
HO   CH$_2$OH
CH$_3$ N

$\xrightarrow{\text{HBr}}$

CH$_2$Br
HO   CH$_2$Br
CH$_3$ N

$\xrightarrow[\text{AgCl}]{\text{H}_2\text{O}}$

CH$_2$OH
HO   CH$_2$OH
CH$_3$ N
pyridoxine

Another synthesis by Harris *et al.* (1962, 1967) started with 5-ethoxy-4-methyloxazole (IV), which was prepared by heating the ethyl ester of N-formyl-DL-alanine with phosphorus pentoxide in chloroform. This underwent the Diels–Alder reaction with diethyl maleate to give (V) which, after treatment with acid followed by reduction with lithium aluminium hydride, was converted into pyridoxine.

NH—CHCH$_3$
OHC   CO$_2$C$_2$H$_5$

$\xrightarrow{\text{P}_2\text{O}_5}$

N   CH$_3$
    OC$_2$H$_5$
O

+

CHCO$_2$C$_2$H$_5$
‖
CHCO$_2$C$_2$H$_5$

$\longrightarrow$

(IV)

CO$_2$C$_2$H$_5$
C$_2$H$_5$O   O   CO$_2$C$_2$H$_5$
CH$_3$ N

(V)

$\xrightarrow[\text{EtOH}]{\text{HCl}}$

CO$_2$C$_2$H$_5$
HO   CO$_2$C$_2$H$_5$
CH$_3$ N

$\xrightarrow{\text{LAH}}$

CH$_2$OH
HO   CH$_2$OH
CH$_3$ N

Although pyridoxine has vitamin activity, it was subsequently shown by Snell *et al.* (1942, 1944) that the related compounds, *pyridoxal* and *pyridoxamine*, are more active than pyridoxine. Furthermore, it was established that these compounds were produced by rats from ingested pyridoxine. Thus pyridoxine, pyridoxal and pyridoxamine are now collectively referred to as **vitamins B$_6$**. They

HNO$_2$

CH$_2$OH
HO   CH$_2$OH
CH$_3$ N
pyridoxine

$\xrightarrow[\substack{\text{or} \\ \text{KMnO}_4}]{\text{MnO}_2 \\ \text{(acid soln.)}}$

CHO
HO   CH$_2$OH
CH$_3$ N
pyridoxal

$\xrightarrow{\text{NH}_2\text{OH}}$

CH=NOH
HO   CH$_2$OH
CH$_3$ N

Ac$_2$O

HNO$_2$

H$_2$—Ni

CH$_2$OAc
HO   CH$_2$OAc
CH$_3$ N

$\xrightarrow[\text{MeOH}]{\text{NH}_3}$

CH$_2$NH$_2$
HO   CH$_2$OH
CH$_3$ N
pyridoxamine

are, in the form of their phosphates, interconvertible in the body, and the aldehyde and amine have been shown to be the main constituents of naturally occurring 'vitamin B_6'.

Pyridoxal is best isolated from the oxidation products by first converting it into the oxime and then regenerating the aldehyde by the action of nitrous acid.

The structures of pyridoxal and pyridoxamine have been established by synthesis, starting from pyridoxine (Harris *et al.*, 1944).

The structure of pyridoxal is not as straightforward as indicated in the synthesis. Hydroxyaldehydes (*e.g.*, β- and γ-) can exist as cyclic structures, *i.e.*, hemiacetals (*cf.* **7** §2), and so the following equilibrium may be present (*cf.* **11** §28b):

It is therefore possible that pyridoxal phosphate (*codecarboxylase*) could be

Pyridoxal phosphate has been synthesised in several ways, *e.g.*, by the action of phosphoryl chloride on pyridoxal (Gunsalus *et al.*, 1952), and its ultraviolet spectrum was different from that of pyridoxal. Thus the aldehyde structure is indicated.

§11. Nicotinic acid and nicotinamide

These two compounds have been shown to be the human pellagra-preventing (P.P.) factor. Nicotinamide is part of the coenzymes codehydrogenase I and II, which play a part in many biological oxidations.

Nicotinic acid (*Niacin*) was first prepared by the oxidation of nicotine (**14** §21). This is now used as a commercial method; another commercial method is the vapour-phase oxidation of 3-methylpyridine (β-picoline) in the presence of a vanadium and iron catalyst.

Still another commercial method is the oxidation of quinoline to quinolinic acid, which is then decarboxylated to nicotinic acid (see also **14** §21).

Nicotinamide, m.p. 131°C, is manufactured by various methods, *e.g.*, by the action of ammonia on nicotinyl chloride, or by heating nicotinic acid with urea in the presence of a molybdenum catalyst. Another commercial method is by the action of hydrogen peroxide on 3-cyanopyridine in alkaline solution.

§12. Vitamin B$_{12}$, Cyanocobalamin

This is the anti-pernicious anaemia factor, and has been isolated from liver extract. Folic acid (§8) also has anti-anaemic properties. Vitamin B$_{12}$ has been obtained as a red crystalline substance (Folkers *et al.*, 1948; Smith *et al.*, 1948, 1949), and the elements present have been shown to be C, H, O, N, P, Co; this vitamin is the first natural product found to contain cobalt.

The different values of the molecular weight obtained by the ebullioscopic method (1 490 ± 150) and from the X-ray data (1 360–1 575) were subsequently shown to be due mainly to the different states of hydration of the crystals. Elemental analysis also gave variable results, but the structure now accepted requires a formula of C$_{63}$H$_{88}$CoN$_{14}$O$_{14}$P (molecular weight, 1 355). The ultraviolet spectrum of vitamin B$_{12}$ (in aqueous solution) shows absorption maxima at 278, 361 and 550 nm, and these are unaffected by the *p*H of the solution. Magnetic susceptibility measurements indicated that the cobalt atom is in the tervalent state, and infrared measurements showed the presence of a cyano group and that this group is attached to the cobalt atom. The vitamin is

optically active and behaves as a polyacidic base; it forms a hexaperchlorate. The hydrolysis of vitamin B$_{12}$ with hydrochloric acid under different conditions produces ammonia, 1-aminopropan-2-ol (I), 5,6-dimethylbenzimidazole (II), 5,6-dimethylbenzimidazole-1-α-D-ribofuranoside (III) and

vitamin B$_{12}$

the 3′-phosphate of (III) [Folkers *et al.*, 1949, 1950; Todd *et al.*, 1950]. (IV) [a succinimide derivative] has also been isolated by the chromic acid oxidation of hydrolysed vitamin B_{12} (Folkers, 1955). The structure of (I) was elucidated by examination of the products formed by periodic acid oxidation, and it was also shown to be the D-isomer by synthesis. (II) was identified by its ultraviolet absorption spectrum, and its structure was confirmed by synthesis. (III) was found to be different from the known isomer, and comparison of the periodic acid oxidation products with model compounds led to the conclusion that (III) had the α-configuration (*cf.* **16** §13c). This was confirmed by synthesis (Folkers *et al.*, 1952; Todd *et al.*, 1953), and further confirmed by X-ray analysis of the vitamin itself (see also below). Other work has shown that six amido groups are present in the molecule. Also, alkaline hydrolysis of vitamin B_{12} gives a mixture consisting mainly of a penta- and a hexacarboxylic acid, in both of which the nucleotide fragment is absent. As the result of a detailed X-ray analysis of the hexacarboxylic acid, vitamin B_{12} has been assigned the structure shown.

The X-ray analysis of the vitamin was carried out by Hodgkin *et al.* (1957), and this conclusively showed that the position of the phosphate residue in (III) is 3′-, that the linkage of D-ribose is α-, and that the cyano group is attached to the cobalt atom. It was also possible, from the X-ray data, to work out the absolute stereochemistry of the vitamin molecule. The presence of six double bonds permits resonance among the four resonating structures (V)–(VIII). Of these, (V) is preferred.

(V)   (VI)   (VII)   (VIII)

A point of interest is that the arrangement of the four pyrrole nuclei is somewhat similar to that in the natural porphin derivatives such as haem and chlorophyll (**19** §§2, 7). The closed system of

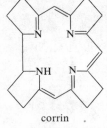
corrin

four pyrrole nuclei (joined through the three bridge carbons) has been named *corrin*, and compounds containing this nucleus are *corrinoid* compounds.

The simplest known corrinoid natural product is *cobyric acid*. This is vitamin B_{12} with a C_{17} side-chain of $-CH_2CH_2CO_2H$ and another CN group attached to the cobalt atom instead of the nucleotide fragment (in vitamin B_{12}). Cobyric acid has been used as the starting material for a partial synthesis of vitamin B_{12} (Friedrich *et al.*, 1960). Thus, the synthesis of cobyric acid is the immediate goal of all work aiming at a total synthesis of vitamin B_{12}. The cobyric acid molecule contains nine chiral centres in the corrin nucleus: carbon atoms 1, 2, 3, 7, 8, 13, 17,

18, and 19. To obtain the correct configurations at these centres has proved to be a most formidable problem. Cobyric acid has now been synthesised (1971), and so this constitutes a total synthesis of vitamin B_{12}.

§13. Other compounds of the vitamin B complex

Other compounds which have definitely been isolated from the vitamin B complex are:
  (i) *p*-**Aminobenzoic acid**; this is a growth factor for bacteria.
  (ii) *myo*-**Inositol** (m.p. 225–226°C). This is a growth factor in animals, and its configuration has been elucidated by Posternak (1942; see also **4** §11c).
  (iii) **Choline.** The absence of this compound leads to the formation of a fatty liver in animals.
  (iv) **Carnitine** is β-hydroxy-γ-butyrobetaine; it is a necessary requirement in the diet of certain insects. It is involved in the oxidation of fatty acids.

(v) **Lipoic acid** is the cyclic disulphide, 6,8-dithio-octanoic acid; it is a growth factor for some micro-organisms. It is involved in the oxidative decarboxylation of pyruvic acid.

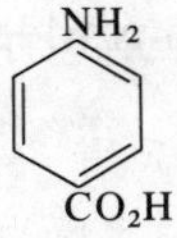

p-amino-benzoic acid

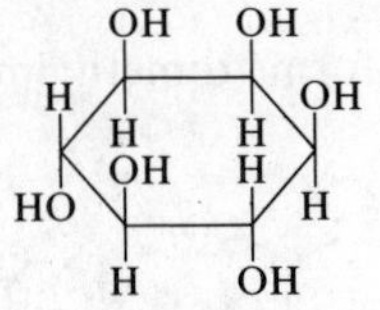

myo-inositol

choline

$(CH_3)_3\overset{+}{N}CH_2CH(OH)CH_2CO_2^-$

carnitine

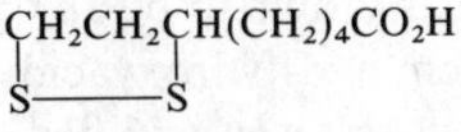

$\underset{S\text{———}S}{CH_2CH_2CH(CH_2)_4CO_2H}$

lipoic acid

Vitamin E group

§14. Introduction

The term 'vitamin E' refers to a group of closely related compounds which occur naturally and which are, to different degrees, anti-sterility factors. Eight compounds, collectively called *tocopherols*, have been characterised: α-, β-, γ-, δ-, ε-, ζ_1-, ζ_2-, and η-tocopherol. The most biologically active one is α-tocopherol, with the β- and γ-compounds exhibiting about half the activity of the α-compound. Only the first four will be discussed here. The main source of α- and β-tocopherol is wheat germ oil; the γ-compound is obtained from cotton seed oil. Wheat germ oil was first subjected to chromatographic analysis to remove sterols, etc., and then the α- and β-tocopherols were purified by conversion into their crystalline allophanates (see **12** §12) or 3,5-dinitrobenzoates. Hydrolysis of these derivatives gave the tocopherols as pale yellow oils.

§15. α-Tocopherol, $C_{29}H_{50}O_2$, λ_{max} 294 nm

When α-tocopherol is heated at 350°C, duroquinol is obtained (Fernholz, 1937). On the other hand, when heated with selenium, α-tocopherol forms duroquinone (McArthur *et al.*, 1937). Finally, when heated with hydriodic acid, ψ-cumenol is formed (John *et al.*, 1937).

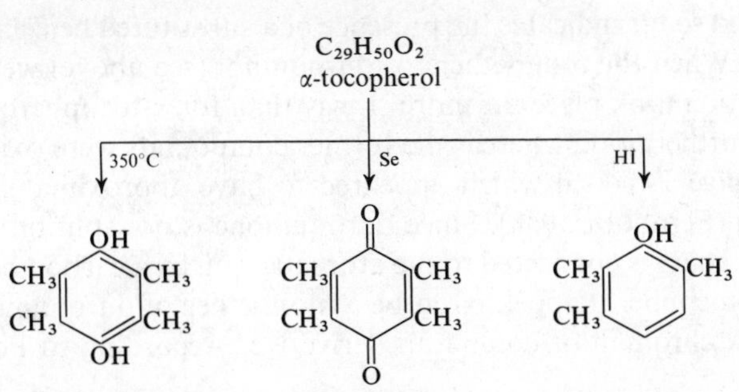

$C_{29}H_{50}O_2$
α-tocopherol

duroquinol

duroquinone

ψ-cumenol

The formation of these products led to the suggestion that α-tocopherol was the monoether of duroquinol; the possibility that it might be the diether was ruled out by the fact that α-tocopherol forms an allophanate, which indicates the presence of one free hydroxyl group. This was confirmed by the fact that the ultraviolet spectrum of α-tocopherol showed the presence of a hydroxyl group and that it was phenolic (John, 1937). However, this monoether structure was shown to be incorrect by the fact that the ultraviolet absorption spectra of various monoethers of duroquinol were different from that of α-tocopherol (Fernholz, 1938).

Oxidation of α-tocopherol with chromic acid forms dimethylmaleic anhydride and a compound $C_{21}H_{40}O_2$.

$$C_{29}H_{50}O_2 \xrightarrow{CrO_3} \begin{array}{c} H_3C-C-CO \\ \parallel \quad \quad O \\ H_3C-C-CO \end{array} + C_{21}H_{40}O_2$$

This latter compound was shown to be an optically active saturated lactone. This lactone was then shown to be derived from a γ-hydroxyacid in which the hydroxyl group is tertiary, e.g., the acid lactonised immediately its salt was acidified, and also could not be oxidised to a keto-acid. Thus the structure of this lactone may be written ($R^1 + R^2 = 17C$) as shown. Now α-tocopherol acetate, on oxidation with chromic acid, forms an acid, $C_{16}H_{32}O_2$ (I) and a ketone, $C_{18}H_{36}O$ (II). Both of these compounds must be produced by the oxidation of the lactone at different points in the chain. Fernholz therefore suggested that if in the lactone $R^1 = C_{16}H_{33}$ and $R^2 = CH_3$, then the products (I) and (II) can be accounted for; thus:

$$R^1-\overset{R^2}{\underset{\underset{O}{|}}{C}}CH_2CH_2CO$$

(i) $C_{16}H_{33}{-}\overset{CH_3}{\underset{\underset{O}{|}}{C}}CH_2CH_2CO \xrightarrow{CrO_3} C_{16}H_{32}O_2$ (I)

(ii) $C_{16}H_{33}{-}\overset{CH_3}{\underset{\underset{O}{|}}{C}}CH_2CH_2CO \xrightarrow{CrO_3} C_{16}H_{33}COCH_3$ (II)

Fernholz then showed that the acid (I) contained methyl groups (cf. 9 §3), and was led to propose a structure based on the isoprene unit, viz.

$$\overset{CH_3}{\underset{}{|}}\quad\overset{CH_3}{\underset{}{|}}\quad\overset{CH_3}{\underset{}{|}}$$
$$CH_3CH(CH_2)_3CH(CH_2)_3CH(CH_2)_2CO_2H$$

The evidence obtained so far indicates the presence of a substituted benzene ring and a long side-chain in α-tocopherol. When the monoethers of duroquinol (see above) were oxidised with silver nitrate solution, the action took place far more slowly than for α-tocopherol when oxidised under the same conditions. Furthermore, whereas the former compounds were oxidised to duroquinone, the latter compound gave a red oil which appeared to have approximately the same molecular weight as α-tocopherol (Fernholz, 1938). Since duroquinone is not split off during this oxidation, it suggests that the side-chain is connected to the aromatic ring by a carbon bond as well as an ether link (remember that α-tocopherol appeared to be a monoether of duroquinol; see above). Hence, α-tocopherol is either a chroman or coumaran derivative. According to Fernholz, the oxidation

chroman structure   coumaran structure

products are best explained on the chroman structure. This has been supported by ultraviolet absorption measurements of α-tocopherol (John *et al.*, 1938).

Karrer *et al.* (1938) have synthesised (±)-α-tocopherol by condensing trimethylquinol with phytyl bromide (**8** §31).

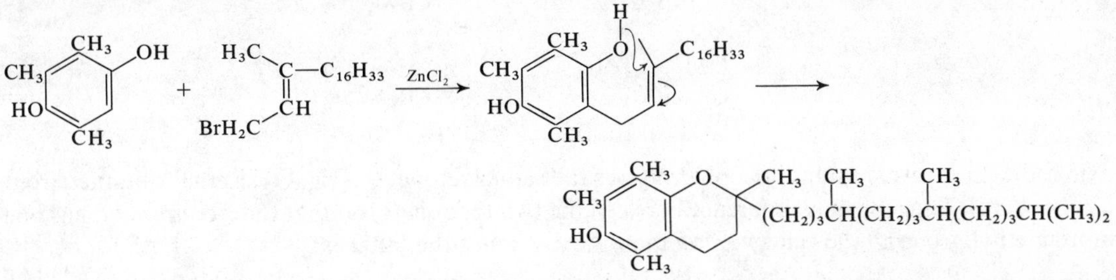

(±)-α-tocopherol

This synthesis, however, is not completely unambiguous, since phenols may condense with allyl compounds to form coumarans. Smith *et al.* (1939) have shown that γ,γ-disubstituted halides form only chromans, and since phytyl bromide is a halide of this type, this strengthens the course of the synthesis given above. Finally, Smith *et al.* (1942) have carried out an unambiguous synthesis of α-tocopherol as follows:

(i)

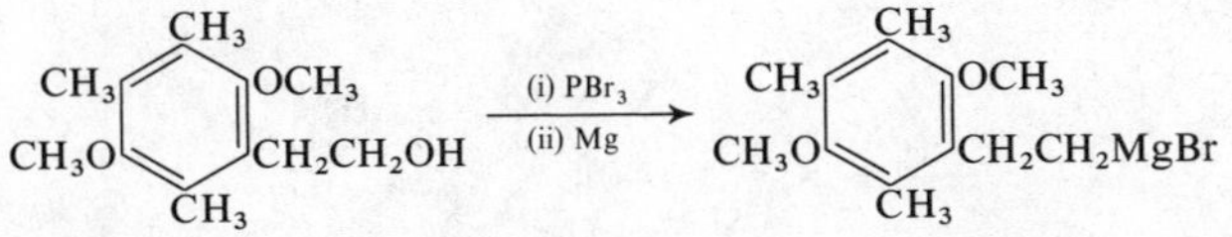

(III)

(ii)

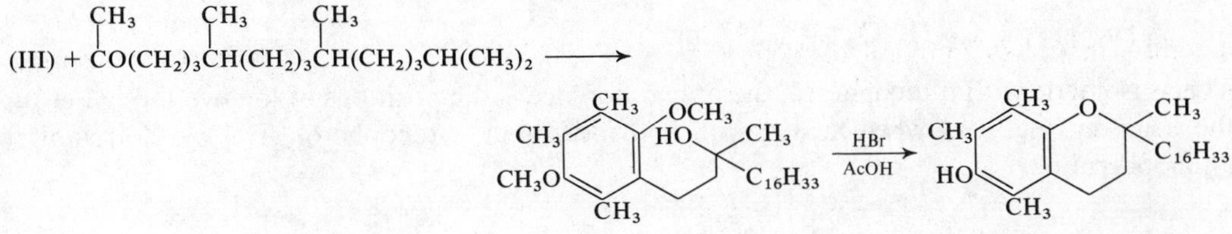

(±)-α-tocopherol

Smith *et al.* prepared the methyl ketone by ozonolysis of phytol, and also by oxidation of phytol with chromic acid.

A recent synthesis, carried out by heating 2,3,5-trimethylquinol with phytyl diphenyl phosphate (a 3,3-dialkylallyl diphenyl phosphate ester), gives an 89 per cent yield of α-tocopherol (Miller *et al.*, 1965).

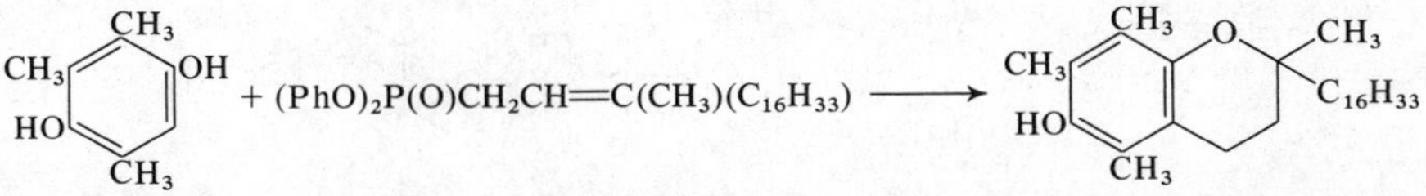

Inspection of the α-tocopherol molecule shows the presence of three chiral centres. The two in phytol have been established to be both D (see §20), and it is assumed that these are the same in natural (+)-α-tocopherol (*cf.* the above syntheses). The configuration of the third chiral centre (C-2) has not yet been elucidated.

§16. β-Tocopherol, $C_{28}H_{48}O_2$, λ_{max} 297 nm

This formula differs from that of α-tocopherol by CH_2. Thermal decomposition of β-tocopherol gives trimethylquinol (I) and heating with hydriodic acid p-xylenol (II) [John et al., 1937]. When

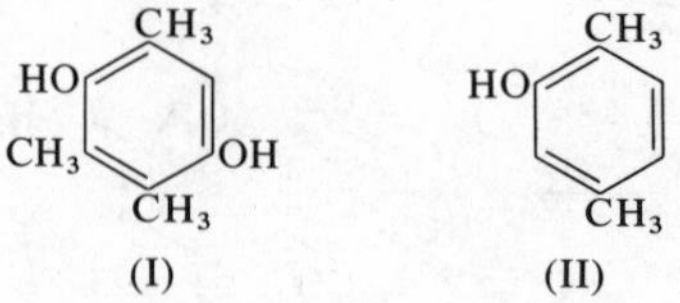

(I)   (II)

oxidised with chromic acid, β-tocopherol gives the same lactone ($C_{21}H_{40}O_2$) as that obtained from α-tocopherol. Thus the only difference between the two tocopherols is that the α-compound has one more methyl group in the benzene ring than the β-; hence the latter is:

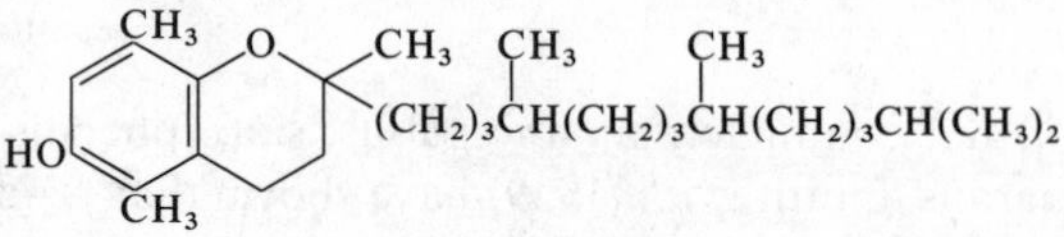

(±)-β-tocopherol

This has been confirmed by synthesis, starting from the monoacetate of p-xyloquinol and phytyl bromide (cf. §15).

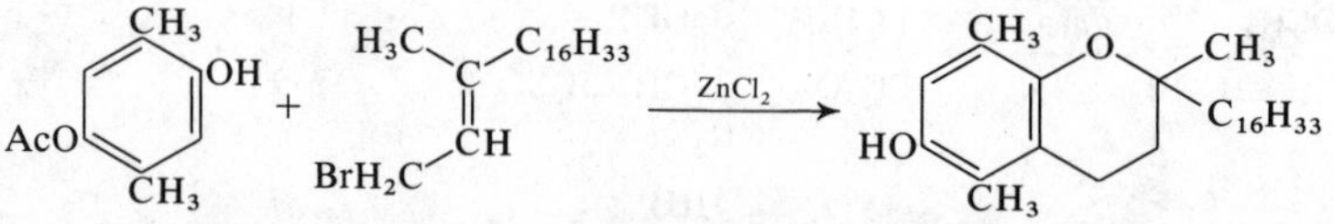

§17. γ-Tocopherol, $C_{28}H_{48}O_2$, λ_{max} 298 nm

This is isomeric with β-tocopherol; the only difference is the positions of the two methyl groups in the benzene ring, e.g., when heated with hydriodic acid, γ-tocopherol gives o-xyloquinol. Thus γ-tocopherol is:

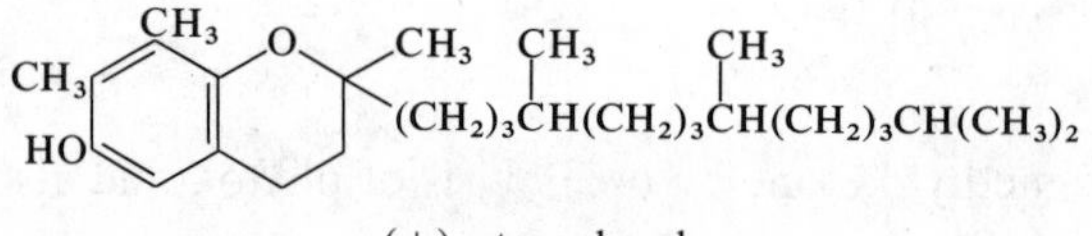

(±)-γ-tocopherol

This structure has been confirmed by synthesis, starting from the monoacetate of o-xyloquinol and phytyl bromide.

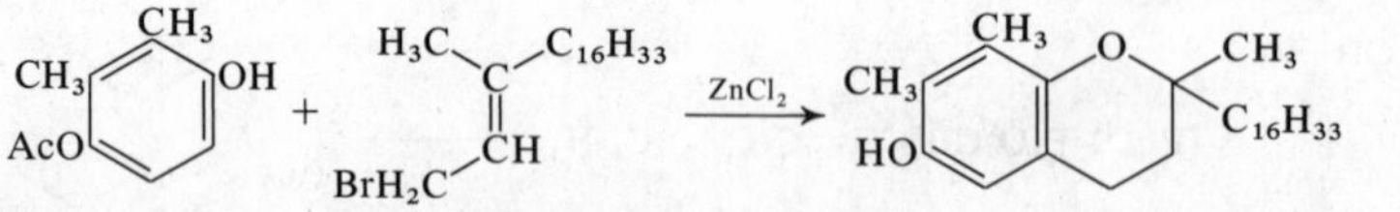

§18. δ-Tocopherol, $C_{27}H_{46}O_2$, λ_{max} 298 nm

This was isolated from soya bean oil by Stern et al. (1947); it is a yellow oil, and is almost inactive physiologically. The structure of δ-tocopherol is:

$$(\pm)\text{-}\delta\text{-tocopherol}$$

Vitamin K group

§19. Introduction

Dam *et al.* (1939) and Doisy *et al.* (1939) isolated vitamin K from alfalfa, and called it vitamin K_1 to distinguish it from a substance called K_2 which had been isolated from putrefied fish meal by Doisy *et al.* (1939). The best sources of vitamin K_1 are alfalfa, cabbage, spinach and carrot tops; vitamin K_2 occurs mainly in bacteria. Both are antihaemorrhagic vitamins; they are connected with the enzymes involved in blood clotting, a deficiency of them lengthening the time of blood clotting.

In addition to these two vitamins, there are several synthetic compounds, some of which were subsequently found to occur naturally (see §21).

Ultraviolet spectroscopy has been very useful in the elucidation of the structures of these vitamins. The ultraviolet spectra of vitamins K_1 and K_2 show absorption maxima at 243, 249, 260, 270 nm (all with $\varepsilon \sim 20\,000$), and 325 nm ($\varepsilon \sim 3\,000$). These bands are due to the presence of the same chromophore, *viz.*, a 2,3-disubstituted 1,4-naphthaquinone. The absorption maxima of 2,3-dimethyl-1,4-naphthaquinone are 243, 249, 260, 269 nm ($\varepsilon \sim 20\,000$), and 330 nm ($\varepsilon \sim 3\,000$).

§20. Vitamin K_1 (phylloquinone), $C_{31}H_{46}O_2$

This is a light yellow oil. The redox potential of vitamin K_1 is very similar to that of 1,4-quinones (Karrer *et al.*, 1939), and its ultraviolet spectrum is very similar to that of 2,3-disubstituted 1,4-naphthaquinones (McKee *et al.*, 1939). Thus vitamin K_1 appears to be a 1,4-naphthaquinone derivative, and this is in keeping with the fact that the vitamin is very sensitive to light and to alkalis. Now the catalytic hydrogenation of vitamin K_1 causes the addition of four molecules of hydrogen (McKee *et al.*, 1939); the product is a colourless compound. Since it is known that three molecules of hydrogen are added when 1,4-naphthaquinone is reduced under these conditions, the addition of a fourth molecule of hydrogen to the vitamin suggests the presence of an ethylenic double bond in a side-chain.

When subjected to reductive acetylation (*i.e.*, acetylated under reducing conditions), vitamin K_1 is converted into the diacetate of dihydrovitamin K_1 (Binkley *et al.*, 1939). This diacetate is difficult to hydrolyse; this is a property characteristic of 2,3-disubstituted 1,4-naphthaquinones. When oxidised with chromic acid, vitamin K_1 give phthalic acid, but when the oxidation is carried out under controlled conditions, the product is a compound with the molecular formula $C_{13}H_{10}O_4$. This latter compound was subsequently shown to be 2-methyl-1,4-naphthaquinone-3-acetic acid (Binkley *et al.*, 1939).

Thus the presence of the 1,4-naphthaquinone structure is confirmed, and at the same time these products show that one ring is unsubstituted and that the other (the quinonoid ring) has substituents in the 2- and 3-positions. This was also supported by the fact that the ultraviolet spectrum of vitamin K_1, when compared with the spectra of various substituted 1,4-naphthaquinones, showed very close similarity only with the 2,3-dialkyl derivatives (Ewing *et al.*, 1939).

When the diacetate of dihydrovitamin K_1 (see above) was subjected to ozonolysis, a compound $C_{18}H_{36}O$ was obtained, which was then shown to be identical with the ketone produced by the oxidation of phytol (McKee *et al.*, 1939; *cf.* Smith's synthesis of α-tocopherol, §15). Hence, on the evidence obtained above, vitamin K_1 is 2-methyl-3-phytyl-1,4-naphthaquinone.

vitamin K_1

This structure has been confirmed by synthesis: Almquist *et al.* (1939) obtained vitamin K_1 by condensing 2-methyl-1,4-naphthaquinone with phytol; Fieser *et al.* (1939) obtained a better yield by heating 2-methyl-1,4-naphthaquinol with phytol in dioxan solution in the presence of anhydrous oxalic acid, and then oxidising the product, dihydrovitamin K_1, with silver oxide in ether. The yield was about 25 per cent, losses occurring due to the formation of the by-product, 2,3-dihydro-2-methyl-2-phytyl-1,4-naphthaquinone (I).

Fieser's synthesis has been improved by Wendler *et al.* (1954), who have obtained vitamin K_1 in good yield by condensing the 1-acetyl derivative of 2-methyl-1,4-naphthaquinol (II) with phytol in the presence of boron trifluoride.

(I)   (II)

Sato *et al.* (1972) have synthesised vitamin K_1 using a π-allylic nickel (I) complex. Phytyl bromide ((III); R = $C_{15}H_{31}$), on treatment with nickel carbonyl in benzene solution under nitrogen, gave the π-allylic nickel (I) bromide (IV). The benzene was replaced by hexamethylphosphoramide as solvent, (V) was added and the product was chromatographed (silica gel) to give (VI). (VI) was hydrolysed with alkali to give (VII) which, on oxidation with ferric chloride, gave vitamin K_1 in high yield. The reaction of (IV) with (V) is an example of *selective* combination of two *unlike* organic halides (Corey *et al.*, 1967; *cf.* Wurtz reaction; see Vol. I). These complexes do not react readily with halides in hydrocarbon solvents, but react readily in polar solvents such as hexamethylphosphoramide or dimethylformamide (see also **8** §26d).

(i)   R ⟶ Br + Ni(CO)₄ $\xrightarrow[3h]{52°C}$

(III)   (IV)

(ii) (IV) + ⟶ $\xrightarrow[5h]{50°C}$ ⟶ $\xrightarrow{OH^-}$

(V)   (VI)

$\xrightarrow{FeCl_3}$

(VII)   vitamin K_1

Inspection of the structural formula of vitamin K_1 shows that two chiral centres are present (carbon atoms 7′ and 11′), and that geometrical isomerism is possible about the 2′,3′-double bond. In view of the fact that the vitamin has been synthesised from natural phytol (see above), it can be expected that the two chiral centres in the vitamin would have the same configurations as those in natural phytol (7 and 11), *i.e.*, 7′R and 11′R (see **8** §31). This was confirmed by comparing the optical rotation and the ORD curve of the C_{18}-ketone obtained by ozonolysis of vitamin K_1 with those of the C_{18}-ketone from natural phytol (Weedon *et al.*, 1959, 1966). The *trans*-configuration at the 2′,3′-double bond corresponds to that in natural phytol, and this was confirmed by means of NMR spectroscopy (Jackman *et al.*, 1965).

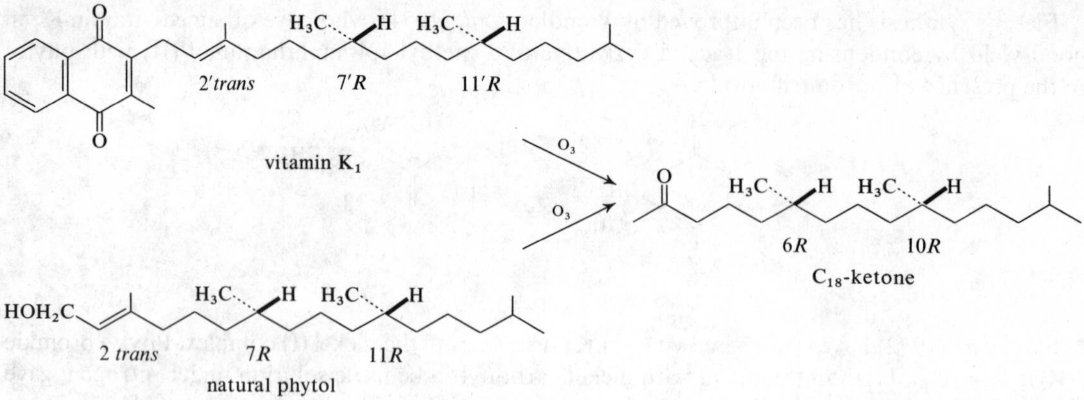

vitamin K₁

C_{18}-ketone

natural phytol

§21. Vitamin K₂, $C_{41}H_{56}O_2$

This is a yellow solid, m.p. 54°C; it is less potent than vitamin K₁. It was shown to contain a 1,4-naphthaquinone nucleus by the facts that it is sensitive to light and to alkalis, and that it has an ultraviolet spectrum similar to that of vitamin K₁ (McKee *et al.*, 1939). When catalytically reduced, vitamin K₂ adds on nine molecules of hydrogen, and since three of these are absorbed by the naphthaquinone nucleus (see §20), it therefore suggests that there is a side-chain present which contains six double bonds. Furthermore, since vitamin K₂ does not form an adduct with maleic anhydride, no conjugation is present (McKee *et al.*, 1939). That these six double bonds are ethylenic is shown by the fact that on reductive acetylation, vitamin K₂ forms the diacetate of dihydrovitamin K₂, which can add on six molecules of bromine.

The oxidation of vitamin K₂ with permanganate produces phthalic acid; therefore one ring is unsubstituted. On the other hand, when ozone is passed into a solution of vitamin K₂ in acetic acid, and the product then treated with zinc dust in ether, 1,4-diacetoxy-2-methylnaphthalene-3-acetaldehyde (I) is produced. At the same time there is obtained laevulaldehyde (II) in a yield of 93 per cent calculated on the basis that one molecule of vitamin K₂ can produce five molecules of the aldehyde.

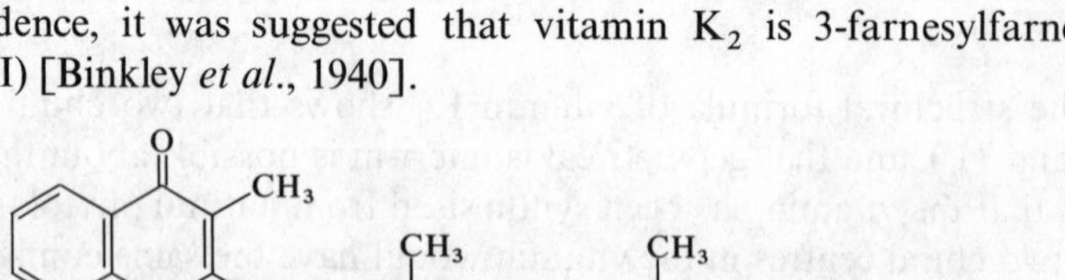

Acetone is also formed in this reaction, and is obtained in a yield of 56 per cent based on the assumption that one molecule of acetone is produced from one molecule of vitamin K₂ (McKee *et al.*, 1940). On this evidence, it was suggested that vitamin K₂ is 3-farnesylfarnesyl-2-methyl-1,4-naphthaquinone (III) [Binkley *et al.*, 1940].

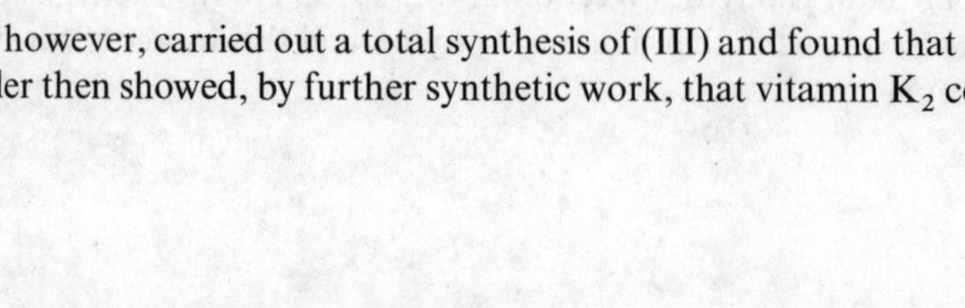

(III)

Isler *et al.* (1958), however, carried out a total synthesis of (III) and found that it was not identical with vitamin K₂. Isler then showed, by further synthetic work, that vitamin K₂ contains a C_{35}-side-chain and not the C_{30}-side-chain proposed (in (III)). Vitamin K_2 is actually 3-farnesylgeranyl-geranyl-2-methyl-1,4-naphthaquinone (the all-*trans* isomer). Isler also isolated from the mother

vitamin $K_{2(35)}$

liquors (in his synthesis of vitamin K_2) a small amount of a substance, m.p. 50°C, which was shown to be (III). In order to distinguish between (III) and vitamin K_2, the former is designated as vitamin $K_{2(30)}$ and the latter as vitamin $K_{2(35)}$. Other members of the vitamin K group have also been isolated, *e.g.*, vitamin $K_{2(45)}$.

These various vitamins K_2 have also been designated as follows, based on the common name of 'menaquinone', which is followed by a number indicating the number of isoprene units in the side-chain: menaquinone-6 (vitamin $K_{2(30)}$); menaquinone-7 (vitamin $K_{2(35)}$); menaquinone-9 (vitamin $K_{2(45)}$); etc. (10, 11, 12, 13).

Isler's synthesis of vitamin $K_{2(35)}$ was carried out by condensing 2-methyl-1,4-naphthaquinone (Menadione, (IV)) with all-*trans*-farnesylgeranyl-linalool (V).

(IV)

→ vitamin $K_{2(35)}$

The menaquinones do not contain any chiral centre, and synthetic work and NMR studies have shown that all the double bonds have the *trans*-configuration (*cf.* the synthesis of vitamin $K_{2(35)}$, above).

§22. Other compounds possessing antihaemorrhagic properties

It has been shown that simple 1,4-naphthaquinones have blood-clotting properties. 2-Methyl-1,4-naphthaquinone (Menadione) is more active than either vitamin K_1 or K_2 (Fernholz *et al.*, 1939); it is therefore used instead of the natural vitamins. It appears, however, to have toxic effects. *Phthiocol* (3-hydroxy-2-methyl-1,4-naphthaquinone) is also an active compound, and is water-soluble. It is also interesting to note that many quinones other than 1,4-naphthaquinones have also been found to be active, *e.g.*, some *p*-benzoquinones.

REFERENCES

Vitamins and Hormones, Academic Press (1943–).
The Vitamins, Academic Press (1967, 2nd edn.). Sebrell and Harris (eds.), Vols. I–V; György and Pearson (eds.), Vols. VI and VII.
RODD (ed.), *Chemistry of Carbon Compounds*, Elsevier. Vol. IV C (1960). Ch. XXII. 'Pteridines, Alloxazines, Flavins.'
FLORKIN and STOTZ (eds.), *Comprehensive Biochemistry*, Elsevier (1963). Vol. 11. Part A. 'Water-Soluble Vitamins.'
SMITH, *Vitamin B_{12}*, Methuen (1965, 3rd edn.).

BERNFELD (ed.), *Biogenesis of Natural Compounds*, Pergamon (1967, 2nd edn.). Ch. 11. 'The Biosynthesis of the Water-Soluble Vitamins.'

PENZER and RADDA, 'The Chemistry and Biological Function of Isoalloxazine. (Flavines)', *Quart. Rev.*, 1967, **21**, 43.

ROBINSON, *The Vitamin Co-factors of Enzyme Synthesis*, Pergamon Press (1966).

ESCHENMOSER, 'Roads to Corrins', *Quart. Rev.*, 1970, **24**, 366.

18 Chemotherapy

§1. Introduction

The term *chemotherapy* was introduced by Ehrlich (1909), and it now appears to be used in the sense of the treatment of diseases due to bacterial invasion by chemical compounds which destroy the micro-organisms without affecting, to any material extent, the tissues (of the host). Many compounds, *e.g.*, formaldehyde, phenol, iodine, etc., are also active in destroying bacteria. These compounds, however, are applied *externally*, and tend to destroy the tissues; thus they are not included under the heading of therapeutic agents, but are known as *disinfectants*.

The first compounds to be used by Ehrlich (1907) were organic dyes. From then onwards, organic compounds of diverse chemical structures have been used in chemotherapy. It has now been found that a given compound is specific in its toxicity towards a particular micro-organism. The relationship between chemical structure and chemotherapeutic action is extremely complicated, but some progress has been made in this field.

Compounds which exert various physiological effects of therapeutic value are collectively known as *drugs*. The ideal requirement of a drug is that, on administration (to the host), it should be localised at the site where it is required. In practice, however, no drug behaves in this way, but tends to distribute itself anywhere in the tissues of the host. Another difficulty is that cells, which were originally susceptible to a particular drug, may acquire a tolerance (resistance) to that drug. In some cases it has been found that the drug actually reverses its original action, *i.e.*, it stimulates the cell instead of inhibiting it.

There have been three approaches to the problem of finding a drug to combat a particular disease:

(i) The method of trial and error. This involves the trial of all kinds of compounds, natural and synthetic.

(ii) The method requiring a knowledge of the cell system, and then synthesising compounds which interfere with it.

(iii) The method in which one starts with a compound known to have some of the required activity (this information has been gained from the previous methods), and then to vary the structure of the molecule systematically. This method has, so far, proved to be the most fruitful.

§2. Sulphonamides

Sulphanilamide (*p*-aminobenzenesulphonamide) and its derivatives have great antibacterial powers; sulphanilamide itself is widely used in medicine against 'cocci infections'—streptococci, gonococci and pneumococci. Sulphanilamide has been largely replaced in medicine by various derivatives which are less toxic or which are preferable for particular infections. These derivatives have substituents on the nitrogen atom of the sulphonamido group. Research in the sulphonamide field was stimulated by the discovery of Domagk (1934) that *prontosil* (see below) had a curative effect when injected into mice infected with streptococci.

The system of numbering is as follows: substituents of the amide group of sulphanilamide are called N^1-substituents, and substituents of the amino-group are called N^4-substituents.

$$H_2\overset{4}{N}\text{—}\langle\text{C}_6\text{H}_4\rangle\text{—}SO_2\overset{1}{N}H_2$$

sulphanilamide

Sulphanilamide may be prepared from acetanilide:

$$CH_3CONH\langle\text{C}_6\text{H}_5\rangle \xrightarrow{ClSO_3H} CH_3CONH\langle\text{C}_6\text{H}_4\rangle SO_2Cl \xrightarrow{NH_3}$$

$$CH_3CONH\langle\text{C}_6\text{H}_4\rangle SO_2NH_2 \xrightarrow{NaOH} NH_2\langle\text{C}_6\text{H}_4\rangle SO_2NH_2$$

Sulphapyridine (N^1-2-pyridylsulphanilamide) was the first drug to effect cures of pneumonia; it is more potent than sulphanilamide. It may be prepared as follows:

$$CH_3CONH\langle\text{C}_6\text{H}_4\rangle SO_2Cl + H_2N\text{—}\langle\text{pyridyl}\rangle \longrightarrow$$

$$CH_3CONH\langle\text{C}_6\text{H}_4\rangle SO_2NH\text{—}\langle\text{pyridyl}\rangle \xrightarrow{NaOH} NH_2\langle\text{C}_6\text{H}_4\rangle SO_2\text{—}NH\text{—}\langle\text{pyridyl}\rangle$$

This compound was introduced under the trade name of *M and B* 693.

Sulphathiazole (N^1-2-thiazolylsulphanilamide) is more potent than *Sulphapyridine* and less toxic;

$$NH_2\langle\text{C}_6\text{H}_4\rangle SO_2\text{—}NH\text{—}\langle\text{thiazolyl}\rangle$$

sulphathiazole

$$NH_2\langle\text{C}_6\text{H}_4\rangle SO_2\text{—}NH\text{—}\langle\text{pyrimidyl}\rangle$$

sulphadiazine

it is used mainly in severe infections. It is prepared in the same way as *Sulphapyridine* except that 2-aminothiazole is used instead of 2-aminopyridine.

Sulphadiazine (N^1-2-pyrimidylsulphanilamide; *Sulphapyrimidine*) is less toxic than *Sulphathiazole*; it is the most widely used of the 'sulpha' drugs, its main use being for mild infections. It is prepared in the same way as the previous compound, except that 2-aminopyrimidine is used in this case.

Sulphamezathine (N^1-2-(4,6-dimethylpyrimidyl)sulphanilamide) is also used for general purposes.

Sulphaguanidine, since it is only slightly absorbed in the intestinal tract, can therefore be given in relatively large doses in the treatment of bacillary dysentery.

$$H_2N\langle\text{C}_6\text{H}_4\rangle SO_2\text{—}NH\text{—}C\begin{cases}NH\\NH_2\end{cases}$$

Prontosil (4-sulphonamido-2′,4′-diaminoazobenzene) was the first sulphonamide to be used in medicine. It is prepared by diazotising sulphanilamide and then coupling with *m*-phenylenediamine.

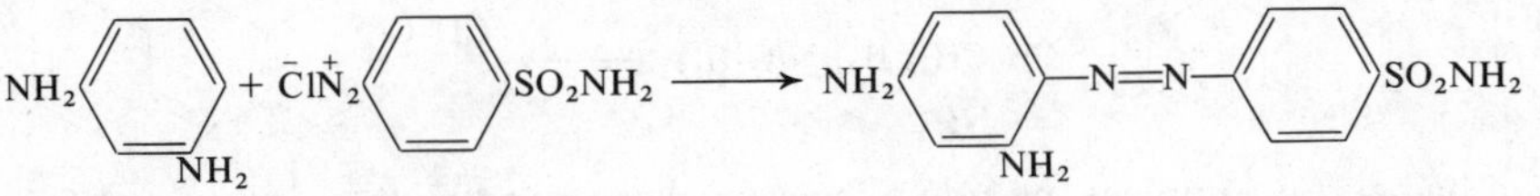

It was suggested that *Prontosil* broke down in the body to sulphanilamide; this led to the discovery that the latter compound is very active against bacteria.

Prontosil S is more soluble than *Prontosil*.

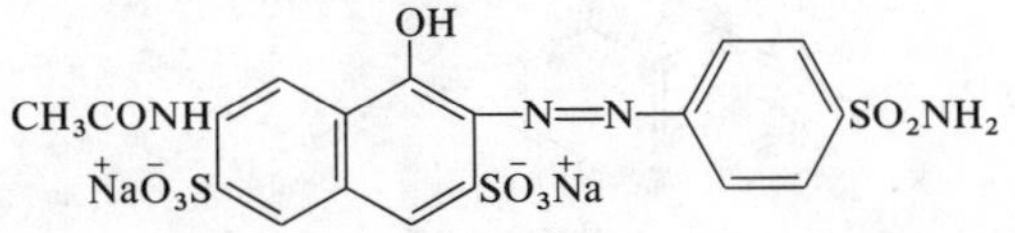

§3. Antimalarials

Quinine (**14** §25b) was originally the only drug known to be effective against malaria. Now there is a number of synthetic compounds used for this purpose, *e.g.*, *Plasmoquin, Mepacrine, Proguanil*.

Plasmoquin (*Pamaquin*) is 8-(4′-diethylamino-3′-methylbutylamino)-6-methoxyquinoline. One preparation that has been described for this compound is the condensation between 4-bromo-1-diethylaminopentane and 8-amino-6-methoxyquinoline, the latter being prepared from 4-amino-3-nitroanisole by means of the Skraup synthesis (see Vol. I).

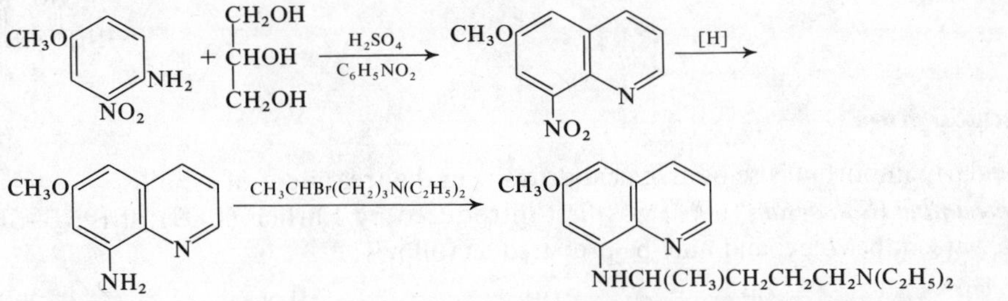

Mepacrine (*Atebrin, Quinacrine*) is 3-chloro-9-(4′-diethylamino-3′-methylbutylamino)-7-methoxy-acridine. It is better than quinine, and it has been prepared as follows:

(i) $[CH_3COCHCO_2C_2H_5]^-Na^+ + ClCH_2CH_2N(C_2H_5)_2 \longrightarrow CH_3COCHCH_2CH_2N(C_2H_5)_2 \xrightarrow[\text{hydrolysis}]{\text{ketonic}}$

with $CO_2C_2H_5$ group on the central carbon

$CH_3CO(CH_2)_3N(C_2H_5)_2 \xrightarrow[H_2-\text{Raney Ni}]{NH_3} CH_3CH(CH_2)_3N(C_2H_5)_2$ with NH_2

(ii)

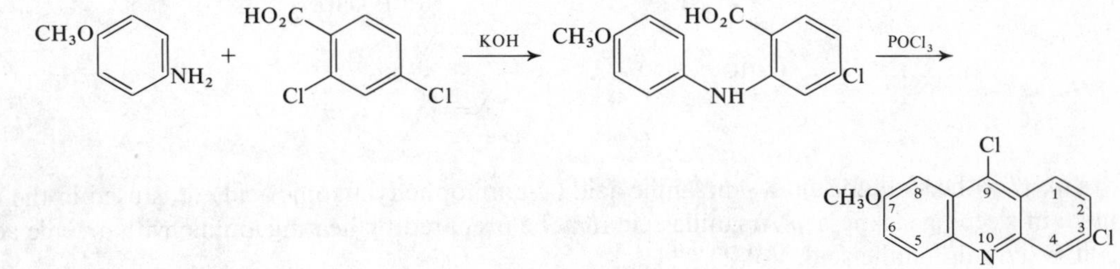

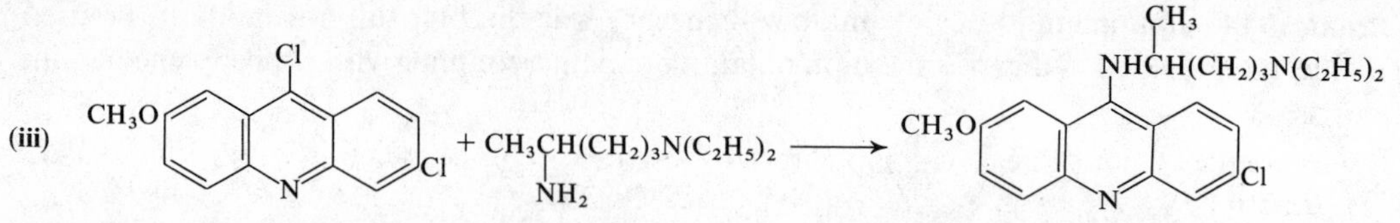

(iii)

Mepacrine has certain unpleasant side-effects (such as producing a yellow colour in the skin, nausea, etc.), and a drug superior to both quinine and *Mepacrine* is *Chloroquine* (*Aralen*).

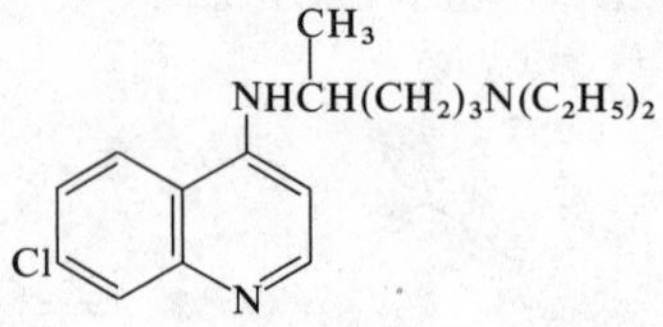

Chloroquine

Proguanil (*Paludrine*) is N^1-*p*-chlorophenyl-N^5-isopropyldiguanide, and is superior to *Mepacrine* and *Chloroquine*, and appears to be the best antimalarial known at the present time. It may be prepared by coupling *p*-chlorobenzenediazonium chloride with dicyanodiamide, and then treating the product with isopropylamine in the presence of copper sulphate:

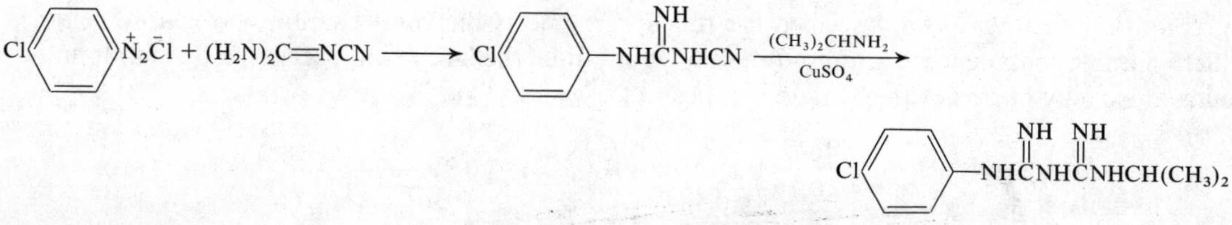

§4. Arsenical drugs

A particularly important use of arsenical drugs is in the treatment of syphilis.

Arsphenamine (*Salvarsan*, '606') was first introduced by Ehrlich (1909); it is 3,3'-diamino-4,4'-dihydroxyarsenobenzene, and may be prepared as follows:

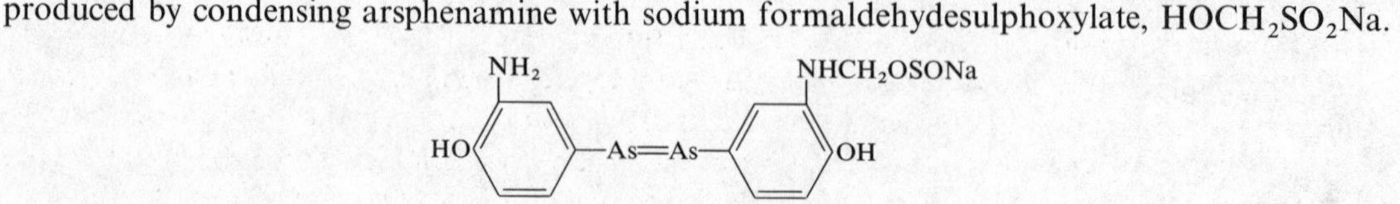

Arsphenamine is an unstable compound; it is stable as its dihydrochloride which, however, cannot be used as such but must be converted into the soluble sodium salt. Ehrlich (1912) overcame this difficulty by preparing **neoarsphenamine** (*Neosalvarsan*), a soluble compound, which may be produced by condensing arsphenamine with sodium formaldehydesulphoxylate, $HOCH_2SO_2Na$.

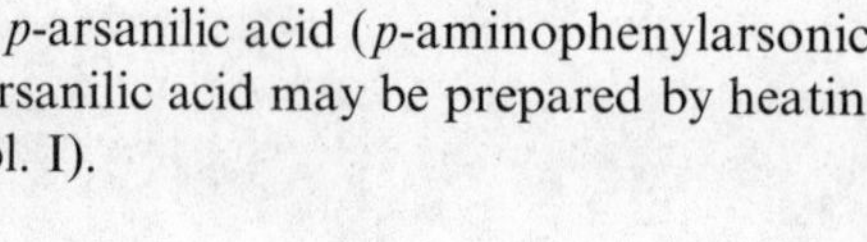

neoarsphenamine

Atoxyl is the sodium salt of *p*-arsanilic acid (*p*-aminophenylarsonic acid); it is used in the treatment of sleeping sickness. *p*-Arsanilic acid may be prepared by heating aniline with arsenic acid at 200°C (*cf.* sulphanilic acid, Vol. I).

$$NH_2 \langle \rangle + H_3AsO_4 \longrightarrow NH_2 \langle \rangle AsO_3H_2 + H_2O$$

Tryparsamide is the sodium salt of *N*-phenylglycineamide-*p*-arsonic acid; it is less toxic than *Atoxyl*, and may be prepared by refluxing the latter with chloroacetamide.

$$NH_2 \langle \rangle AsO_3H_2 + ClCH_2CONH_2 \longrightarrow NH_2COCH_2NH \langle \rangle AsO_3H_2 + HCl$$

§5. Antibiotics

Many micro-organisms produce within themselves chemical substances which, when excreted, interfere with the growth or metabolism of other micro-organisms. Such compounds are known as *antibiotics*, and need be present only in low concentration to bring about this antibiotic action. Antibiotics are thus chemotherapeutic agents.

In 1929, Fleming discovered a mould of the *Penicillium* species which inhibited the growth of certain bacteria. This observation was investigated later by a number of workers and culminated in the isolation of the active principle *penicillin*. At the same time, research along this line led to the isolation of many other antibiotics.

The antibiotics cover a wide range of compounds of different chemical structures. A rational classification is very difficult, and many schemes have been suggested, *e.g.*, classification on their chemical structures or according to the nature of their activity.

§6. The penicillins

Penicillin is the name given to the mixture of natural compounds having the molecular formula $C_9H_{11}N_2O_4SR$, and differing only in the nature of R. There are at least six natural penicillins.

Chemical name	Other names	R
Pent-2-enylpenicillin	Penicillin-I or F	$-CH_2CH=CHCH_2CH_3$
Benzylpenicillin	Penicillin-II or G	$-CH_2C_6H_5$
p-Hydroxybenzylpenicillin	Penicillin-III or X	$-CH_2C_6H_4OH(1,4)$
n-Heptylpenicillin	Penicillin-IV or K	$-(CH_2)_6CH_3$
n-Amylpenicillin	Dihydro-F-penicillin	$-(CH_2)_4CH_3$
Phenoxymethylpenicillin	Penicillin V	$-CH_2OC_6H_5$

Commercial preparations of penicillin contain one or more of the penicillins in varying proportions. It has been found that the addition to the culture medium of various compounds containing a benzyl group, *e.g.*, phenylacetic acid, phenylacetamide, etc., increases the total yield of penicillin, and also the proportion of benzylpenicillin. Similarly, the addition of compounds containing the *p*-hydroxybenzyl group to the culture medium increases the proportion of *p*-hydroxybenzylpenicillin. On the other hand, by adding various compounds to the culture medium, a number of 'unnatural' penicillins have been prepared (see §6b).

§6a. Structure of the penicillins. The penicillins are all strong monobasic acids, *e.g.*, they form salts. They are hydrolysed by hot dilute inorganic acids; one carbon atom is eliminated as carbon dioxide, and two products are obtained in equimolecular amounts, one being an amine, *penicillamine*, and the other an aldehyde, *penilloaldehyde*. All the penicillins give the same amine, but different aldehydes; it is the latter which contain the R group.

$$C_9H_{11}N_2O_4SR + 2H_2O \xrightarrow{HCl} CO_2 + C_5H_{11}NO_2S + C_3H_4NO_2R$$

D-Penicillamine, $C_5H_{11}NO_2S$. This compound gave colour reactions with sodium nitroprusside and ferric chloride which were characteristic of the thiol group (SH). Electrometric titration showed three pK_a values: 1·8, 7·9, and 10·5. These correspond to carboxyl, α-amino, and thiol groups, respectively. Since penicillamine combined with acetone to give an isopropylidene derivative which no longer contained a free amino or free thiol group and was reconverted into penicillamine on hydrolysis, this suggested that these two groups were attached to adjacent carbon atoms (*cf.* **7** §8). Oxidation of penicillamine with bromine water gave a sulphonic acid (this reaction is characteristic of a thiol). The Kuhn–Roth determination of methyl side-chains gave a very low value (~ 0.2 molecules). This suggested that the amine contained an isopropyl end-group and not a methyl end-group (see **9** §3). It was therefore proposed on the foregoing evidence that penicillamine was β,β-dimethylcysteine, and this was confirmed by synthesis, *e.g.*,

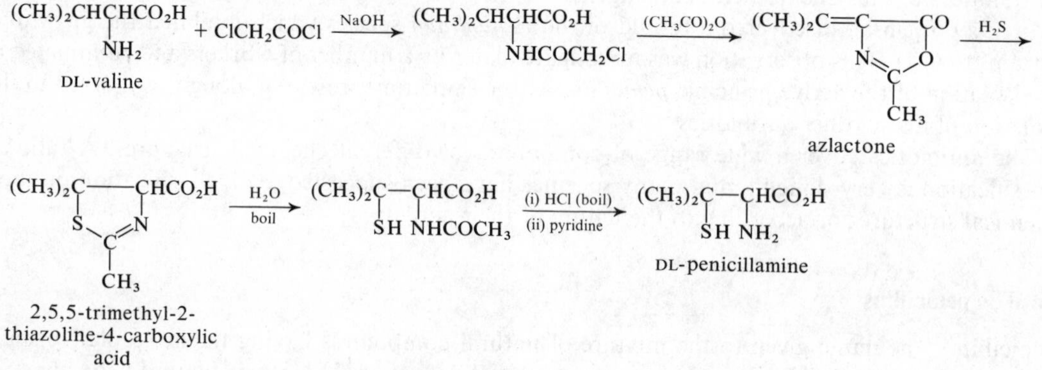

Some of the steps leading to the azlactone and from this to the thiazoline derivative are uncertain; a possible sequence is:

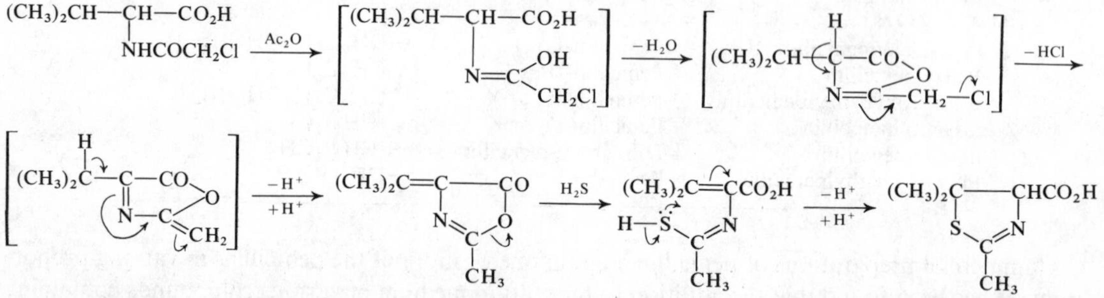

The racemic amine was resolved as follows: the amine was converted into the formyl derivative, which was then resolved by means of brucine. D-Penicillamine was obtained after removal of the formyl group by hydrolysis.

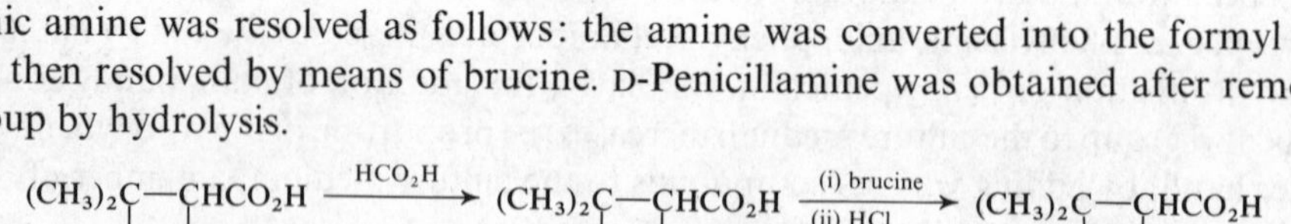

This was found to be identical with the natural penicillamine.

When treated with diazomethane, penicillin is converted into its methyl ester and this, on treatment with an aqueous solution of mercuric chloride, gives the methyl ester of penicillamine. Thus the carboxyl group in penicillamine is the carboxyl group in penicillin itself.

Penilloaldehyde. On vigorous hydrolysis, all the penilloaldehydes give a substituted acetic acid and aminoacetaldehyde. Thus the penilloaldehydes are acylated derivatives of aminoacetaldehyde.

$$RCONHCH_2CHO + H_2O \longrightarrow RCO_2H + NH_2CH_2CHO$$

This structure has been confirmed by synthesis:

$$RCOCl + NH_2CH_2CH(OC_2H_5)_2 \longrightarrow RCONHCH_2CH(OC_2H_5)_2 \xrightarrow{HCl} RCONHCH_2CHO$$

As pointed out above, the acid hydrolysis of penicillin gives penicillamine, penilloaldehyde and carbon dioxide. The formation of this molecule of carbon dioxide gave rise to the belief that it is formed by the ready decarboxylation of an unstable acid. Such an acid is a β-keto-acid, and so a possible explanation is that penilloaldehyde carboxylic acid (penaldic acid) is formed as an intermediate in the hydrolysis of penicillin (see also below):

$$\begin{array}{c} RCONHCHCHO \\ | \\ CO_2H \end{array} \longrightarrow CO_2 + RCONHCH_2CHO$$

penaldic acid

The problem now is: How are the two fragments, penicillamine and penilloaldehyde, combined in penicillin? The hydrolysis of penicillin with dilute alkali or with the enzyme penicillinase produces *penicilloic acid* (a dicarboxylic acid), which readily eliminates a molecule of carbon dioxide to form *penilloic acid*. This suggests that a carboxyl group is in the β-position with respect to an electron-attracting group (*cf.* above). Penilloic acid, on hydrolysis with aqueous mercuric chloride, gives penicillamine and penilloaldehyde. This hydrolysis is characteristic of compounds containing a thiazolidine ring (*cf.* **12** §5b). Thus penilloic acid could be (I) since this structure would give the required products.

Hence, if (I) is penilloic acid, then penicilloic acid would be (II).

Structure (II) is supported by the fact that the treatment of penicillin with methanol gives methyl penicilloate which, on hydrolysis with aqueous mercuric chloride, gives methyl penaldate (see also above) and penicillamine.

On the basis of the foregoing evidence, two structures are possible for penicillin, *viz.* (III) and (IV). It was not possible to decide between them on chemical evidence alone, since penicillin readily undergoes molecular rearrangements, *e.g.*, on treatment with dilute acid, penicillin rearranges to penillic acid. It was therefore desirable to examine the molecule by physical methods (thereby leaving the molecule intact).

(III)
oxazolone structure

(IV)
β-lactam structure

(i) The infrared spectra of many penicillins were examined and a correlation between various bands and functional groups was carried out by examining the spectra of synthetic model compounds which contained different parts of structures (III) and (IV) that had been proposed on chemical evidence. This may be illustrated with the methyl ester and sodium salt of benzylpenicillin, which showed the following maxima (characteristic of all the penicillins in these regions).

$$\text{Methyl ester:} \quad 3\,333,\ 1\,770,\ 1\,748,\ 1\,684,\ 1\,506\ cm^{-1}$$
$$\text{Sodium salt:} \quad 3\,333,\ 1\,770,\ 1\,613,\ 1\,681,\ 1\,515\ cm^{-1}$$

The band at $3\,333\ cm^{-1}$ in both compounds was assigned to the NH group (str.), and the $1\,748\ cm^{-1}$ band of the ester and the $1\,613\ cm^{-1}$ band of the salt were assigned to the carbonyl group (str.) in the carboxyl group (as ester or salt). Then model oxazolones were studied; these showed two characteristic bands, one at $1\,825\ cm^{-1}$ for the carbonyl group, and one at $1\,675\ cm^{-1}$ for the C=N group. The absence of the first but possible presence of the second in the benzylpenicillin derivatives would not permit a decision to be reached between (III) and (IV). When a large number of thiazolidines were examined in the double bond region down to $1\,470\ cm^{-1}$, only the carbonyl band was found to be present ($\sim 1\,748$ and $1\,613\ cm^{-1}$). A large number of amides

oxazolones

(Z = CO_2Me, CO_2^-, etc.)
thiazolidines

R^1CONH_2
R^1CONHR^2
$R^1CONR_2^2$
amides

were now examined. All three types had a band close to $1\,670\ cm^{-1}$, which can be attributed to the carbonyl group, but with the primary amides there was also a band near $1\,613\ cm^{-1}$, and with the secondary amides the band was close to $1\,515\ cm^{-1}$. These results suggest that penicillins have the secondary amide structure (*i.e.*, (IV)), since the secondary amide band at $1\,670\ cm^{-1} \equiv 1\,684$ and $1\,681\ cm^{-1}$, and the band at $1\,515\ cm^{-1} \equiv 1\,506$ and $1\,515\ cm^{-1}$. Thus, four of the five bands have been accounted for. Finally, a number of simple β-lactams and fused thiazolidine-β-lactams were examined. The former did not show a band near $1\,770\ cm^{-1}$, but all the latter were found to have a band at $1\,770\ cm^{-1}$. This accounts for the fifth band, and so it follows that (IV) is the structure of the penicillins.

(ii) The X-ray analysis of the sodium, potassium and rubidium salts of benzylpenicillin showed the presence of a β-lactam ring; thus (IV) is the structure of penicillin.

Using this structure, we can now formulate the chemical reactions described above.

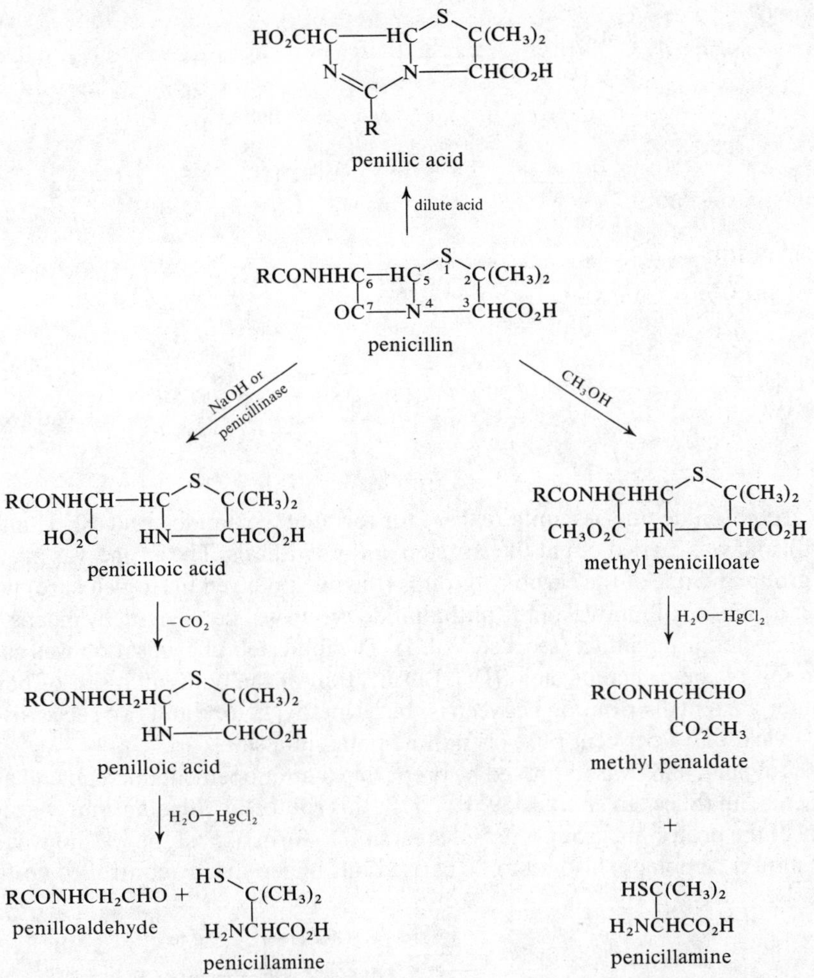

$$HO_2CHC\!-\!\!-\!HC\overset{S}{\diagdown}C(CH_3)_2$$
$$\underset{\underset{R}{C}}{N}\qquad\underset{}{N}\!-\!CHCO_2H$$

penillic acid

↑ dilute acid

$$RCONHHC\underset{6}{}\!-\!\!HC\underset{5}{\overset{S}{\diagup}}\underset{2}{}C(CH_3)_2$$
$$OC\underset{7}{}\!-\!N\underset{4}{}\!-\!\underset{3}{}CHCO_2H$$

penicillin

↙ NaOH or penicillinase   ↘ CH₃OH

$$RCONHCH\!-\!HC\overset{S}{\diagdown}C(CH_3)_2$$
$$HO_2C\quad HN\!-\!\!-\!CHCO_2H$$

penicilloic acid

$$RCONHCHHC\overset{S}{\diagdown}C(CH_3)_2$$
$$CH_3O_2C\quad HN\!-\!\!-\!CHCO_2H$$

methyl penicilloate

↓ −CO₂

$$RCONHCH_2HC\overset{S}{\diagdown}C(CH_3)_2$$
$$HN\!-\!\!-\!CHCO_2H$$

penilloic acid

$$RCONHCHCHO$$
$$CO_2CH_3$$

methyl penaldate

↓ H₂O—HgCl₂

$$RCONHCH_2CHO +$$ penilloaldehyde

$$\overset{HS}{\diagdown}C(CH_3)_2$$
$$H_2NCHCO_2H$$
penicillamine

+

$$HSC(CH_3)_2$$
$$H_2NCHCO_2H$$
penicillamine

The first successful synthesis of penicillins was carried out by Sheehan *et al.* (1957, 1959), who synthesised penicillin (V) (phenoxymethylpenicillin) as follows. t-Butyl phthalimidomalonalde-hydate was prepared *via* a Gabriel synthesis (**13** §2) followed by a Claisen condensation (formylation of an active methylene group). The aldehydate was condensed with D-penicillamine, etc.

(i) 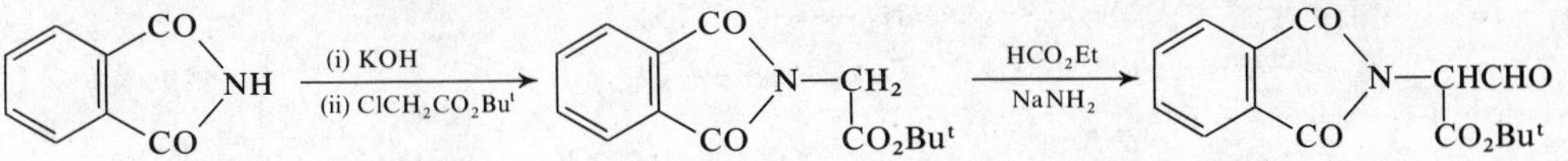 [phthalimide] —(i) KOH / (ii) ClCH₂CO₂Buᵗ→ [N—CH₂CO₂Buᵗ] —HCO₂Et / NaNH₂→ [N—CHCHO / CO₂Buᵗ]

Every step in reactions (i) and (ii) was carried out at room temperature (or below).

Sheehan's early attempts (1955, 1956) to cyclise penicilloic acids (II) to penicillins (IV) failed because of the preferential ring-closure to form azlactones (oxazolones; see (III), above). Sheehan then protected the amino-group by, *e.g.*, a phthalimido or a benzenesulphonyl group. In this case, oxazolone formation was prevented and ring-closure resulted in the formation of 'unnatural' penicillins (see §6b). These unnatural (synthetic) penicillins showed some antibacterial activity.

Sheehan's later approach (1957, 1959) was the ring-closure of 'natural' penicilloic acids. Because of the sensitivity of the β-lactam ring to acids in particular, ring-closure was effected by means of

(ii)

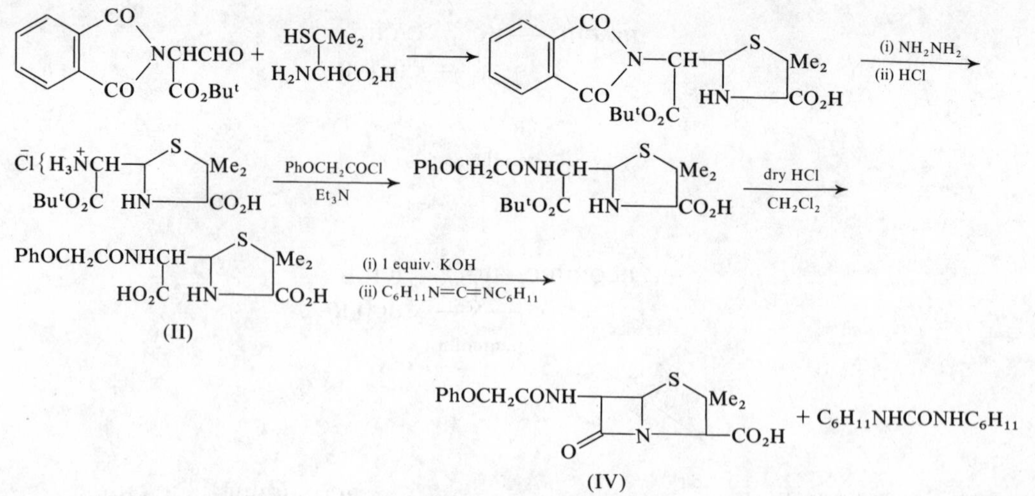

dicyclohexylcarbodi-imide; this is a mild reagent for forming the amide bond (Sheehan *et al.*, 1955; see also **13** §10), and was carried out at the last step of the synthesis. The amine was protected by the phthalimido group and one of the carboxyl groups (the one involved in ring-closure) was protected by t-butyl ester formation. Removal of the phthalimido group was carried out by means of hydrazine since this left the ester group intact (see also Vol. I). The final step of cyclisation was carried out on the potassium salt of the penicilloic acid (IV). Purification of the potassium salt of penicillin V by means of counter-current distribution between isobutyl methyl ketone and two successive phosphate buffers, gave a yield of 5·4 per cent pure crystalline potassium salt.

The synthesis of penicillins was improved by preparing 6-aminopenicillanic acid and acylating this directly to a penicillin (Sheehan *et al.*, 1959, 1962). In this route, the β-lactam ring was formed *prior* to the removal of the protecting groups; no side reaction to form oxazolone was now possible. Also, the final step should be noted; this had to be carried out under strictly controlled conditions.

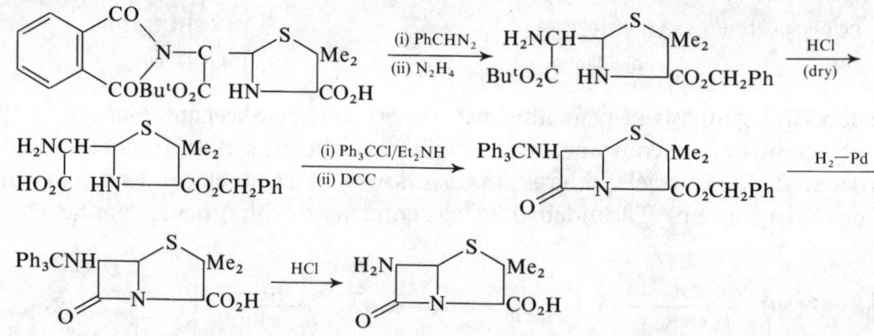

6-aminopenicillanic acid

The formation of the aldehydate results in the introduction of one chiral centre and so the product is the ($\pm$)-form. Condensation of this with D-penicillamine produces a new chiral centre in (V) [$\overset{*}{\text{C}}$; see also Schiff bases, Vol. I].

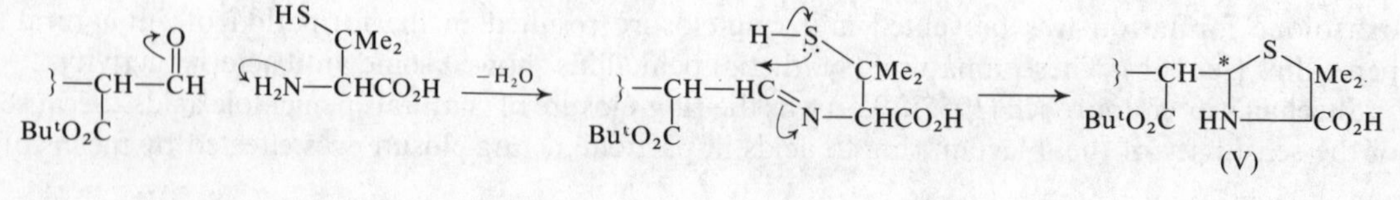

(V) therefore contains three chiral centres, but since D-penicillamine was used as one of the starting materials, all possible optical isomers are derived from D-penicilloates. However, in the formation of (V), ring-closure has occurred to give the thiazolidine ring. Hence, (V) can theoretically exist as two geometrical isomers, (VI) and (VII), and each of these can theoretically give rise to four optical

cis

(VI)   (VII)

isomers (two diastereoisomers). Because of steric effects, it can be anticipated that the $CHZCO_2Bu^t$ group would take up preferentially the *trans* position with respect to the carboxyl group already in the ring, *i.e.*, (VII) is the anticipated product (exclusive or predominant). Of the four possible diastereoisomers only two in fact appeared to have been formed, α and γ, corresponding to structure (VII). The minor one was the required α-isomer; this was the form which had the same stereochemistry as that of the corresponding product obtained by degradation of natural penicillins. The two isomers were separated by fractional crystallisation (α more soluble than γ). Since the γ-isomer underwent epimerisation (in pyridine solution in an atmosphere of hydrogen) to give an equilibrium mixture containing about 25 per cent of the α-isomer, it was therefore possible to increase the amount of the required α-isomer for completion of the synthesis. Presumably, epimerisation is possible at both chiral centres, the $CHZCO_2Bu^t$ and the ring CO_2H group (*via* enolisation of CH with the adjacent carboxyl group; see also **11** §5). The $CHZCO_2Bu^t$ group cannot change its geometrical configuration with respect to the ring, and if the ring carboxyl group underwent epimerisation, this would bring it into the *cis*-configuration (VI). Hence, it can be anticipated that only the $\overset{*}{C}$ of $\overset{*}{C}HZCO_2Bu^t$ is epimerised.

As mentioned above, both (VI) and (VII) can *each* give rise to two diastereoisomers, *i.e.*, four diastereoisomers of the D-penicilloates are possible. All have been prepared and are designated as D-α-, D-β-, D-γ-, and D-δ-isomers. As was also mentioned above, the natural compounds are the D-α-isomer, the configuration of which has been established by the X-ray analysis of the penicillins.

natural penicillins

§6b. 'Synthetic' penicillins. It has been found that most strains of staphylococci are highly sensitive to penicillin, but after a time become resistant. This result has been shown to be due to the fact that these resistant strains produce the enzyme penicillinase which converts penicillin into the inactive penicilloic acid (see §6a).

Of all the natural penicillins, benzylpenicillin (penicillin G) is still the best. It has been recently found that different types of penicillin are produced by *Penicillium chrysogenum* when the cultural conditions are changed. Batchelor *et al.* (1959) isolated pure 6-aminopenicillanic acid from fermentation liquors to which *no* precursors had been added. This acid had already been synthesised by Sheehan (see §6a).

It has also been shown that (1) is the site of action of the enzyme penicillin amidase (Rolinson *et al.*, 1960; Claridge *et al.*, 1960) and, as mentioned above, (2) is the site of action of penicillinase.

Many 'synthetic' penicillins have now been prepared (by the method described in §6). α-Amino-benzylpenicillin (Rolinson *et al.*, 1961) has been synthesised and shows considerable activity against many organisms against which benzylpenicillin is not very effective. 6-Aminopenicillanic acid itself has also been used as the starting point of many new penicillins by acylation of the acid (Doyle *et al.*, 1963).

§6c. Cephalosporin C.

Cephalosporin N is an antibiotic produced by a species of *Cephalosporium*, and was shown to be a penicillin in which the R group (not written as the dipolar ion) is: $HO_2CCH(NH_2)CH_2CH_2CH_2$— (Abraham *et al.*, 1954). Then Abraham *et al.* (1956) isolated another antibiotic from crude cephalosporin N and named it cephalosporin C. It was shown to have antibacterial activity and was much more stable to acid than cephalosporin N and, unlike the penicillins, was resistant to hydrolysis by the enzyme penicillase.

The structure of cephalosporin C was elucidated by Abraham *et al.* (1961). Its molecular formula was found to be $C_{16}H_{21}N_3O_8S$ (λ_{max} 260 nm (sodium salt); $[\alpha]_D +103°$). It gave a positive ninhydrin reaction, thereby indicating the presence of an α-amino-acid (**13** §4). Furthermore, cephalosporin C behaved as an aminodicarboxylic acid on electrometric titration; three ionisable groups were found with pK_a values <2·6, 3·1, and 9·8, respectively. The infrared spectrum showed a band at 1 783 cm^{-1}; this corresponds to the band at 1 770 cm^{-1} in penicillins due to the carbonyl group in the β-lactam ring in the fused thiazolidine-β-lactam system (§6).

Hydrolysis of cephalosporin C with acid gave one molecule of carbon dioxide, one molecule of D-α-aminoadipic acid (I), and two molecules of ammonia. When cephalosporin C was heated with Raney nickel (hydrogenolysis) followed by hydrolysis, the products were (I) and L-alanine (II), and some DL-valine. On the other hand, controlled hydrolysis gave a dipeptide (III) together with (I) and α,β-diaminopropionic acid.

$$HO_2CCH(NH_2)(CH_2)_3CO_2H \qquad CH_3CH(NH_2)CO_2H \qquad HO_2CCH(NH_2)(CH_2)_3CONHCH(CO_2H)CH_2NH_2$$

(I)   (II)   (III)

(IV)   (V)

When the hydrolysis of cephalosporin C was carried out in neutral aqueous solution at 37°C, D-2-(4-amino-4-carboxybutyl)thiazole-4-carboxylic acid (IV) was obtained. Electrometric titration of (IV) indicated the presence of a basic group (pK_a 9·9) and two acidic groups ($pK_a \sim$ 2·6 and 4·0, respectively). The ultraviolet spectrum of (IV) [λ_{max} 237 nm (H_2O) and 233 (N HCl)] was similar to that of 2-(1-amino-2-methylpropyl)thiazole-4-carboxylic acid (2-H_2NCH_2CHMe-CH_2—). This, and other evidence, led to the suggestion of structure (IV). The isolation of these products and consideration of the infrared data led to the suggestion of (V) as the partial structure of cephalosporin C.

Hydrolysis of cephalosporin C with sulphuric acid gave one molecule of acetic acid. The infrared spectrum of cephalosporin C (see above) also showed bands at 1 773 and 1 031 cm^{-1}. The former suggested that the acetic acid was derived from an acetoxyl group. Hence, the latter band could be attributed to the O—C (str.) in the grouping CH_3CO—O—C; *i.e.*, an acetoxyl group was present in the fragment $C_7H_8O_4$. This left the rest of the fragment containing five carbon atoms (see (V)). Now, hydrogenolysis of cephalosporin C with Raney nickel gave, among the products, DL-valine and α-oxoisovaleric acid. On the other hand, penicillin N under the same conditions gave D-valine (from the penicillamine fragment by removal of the sulphur atom; see §6). Furthermore, cephalosporin C, unlike the penicillins, did not give penicillamine on hydrolysis. Thus, the structures of the fragment attached to the β-lactam ring in cephalosporin C and the penicillins are quite different. This was confirmed by the fact that the NMR spectrum of cephalosporin C did not show a signal at τ 7·9, which is to be expected from a *gem*-dimethyl group. There was, however, a sharp peak at τ 7·4 which corresponded to one methyl group; this τ-value can be assigned to the methyl in an acetoxyl group (see Table 1.9). Another signal at τ 4·3 was assigned to a CH—CH group (since this signal was also observed in benzylpenicillin).

Hydrolysis of cephalosporin C with 1·25N HCl at 100°C gave two lactones which contained sulphur. Examination of their physical and chemical properties led to the conclusion that these lactones

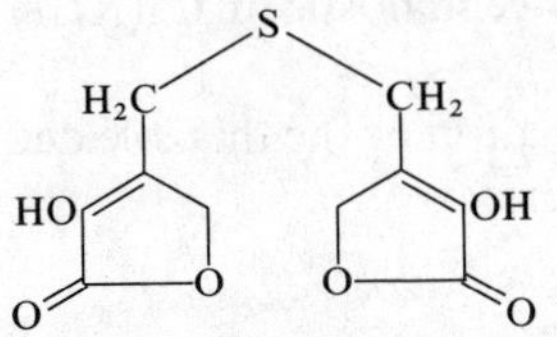

(VI) 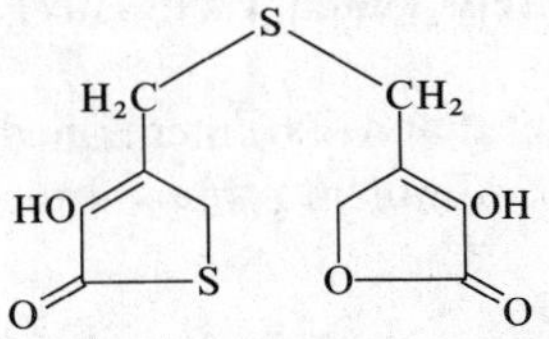   (VII)

had structures (VI) and (VII); the former is an α-tetronic acid and the latter is the corresponding thiolactone. Both compounds, on treatment with Raney nickel, gave β-methyl-α-tetronic acid (VIII). The formation of (VI) and (VII) were attributed to the five-carbon fragments from two molecules of cephalosporin C. When dissolved in 0·1N HCl at room temperature, cephalosporin C lost an *O*-acetyl group and gave a lactone, cephalosporin C_c (λ_{max} 257 nm). This lactone on treatment with

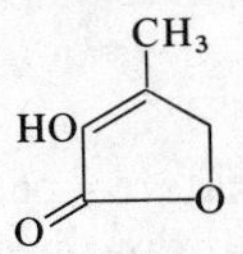

(VIII) 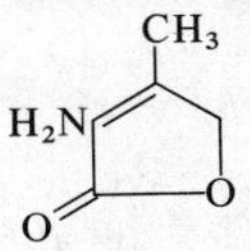   (IX) 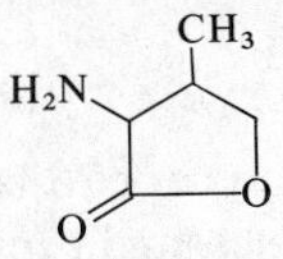   (X)

Raney nickel gave a α-amino-β-methylbutenolide (IX) and this, on hydrogenation (Pt—PtO), gave γ-hydroxyvaline lactone (X). It was then concluded that the formation of (VI), (VII), and (IX) could be explained on the basis that cephalosporin C contained the grouping (XI). The position of the double bond was deduced to be that given in (XI) since this was consistent with the isolation of the

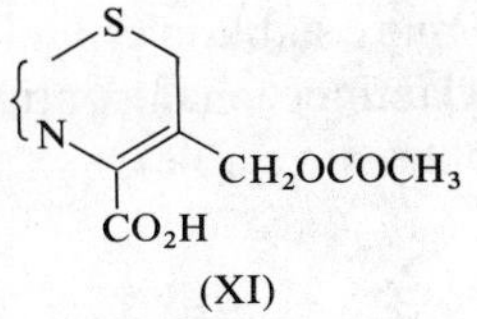

(XI)

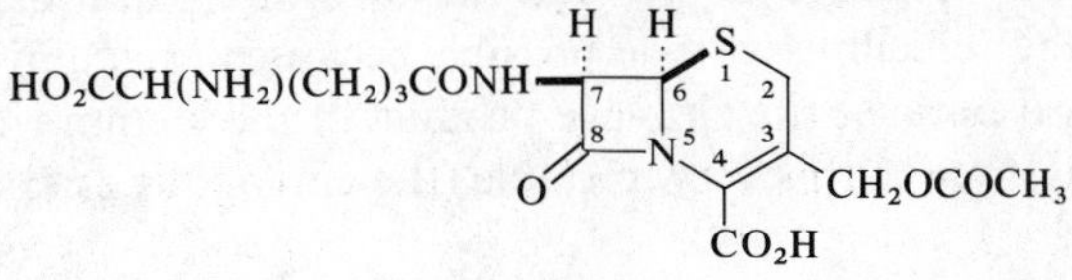

(XII)
cephalosporin C

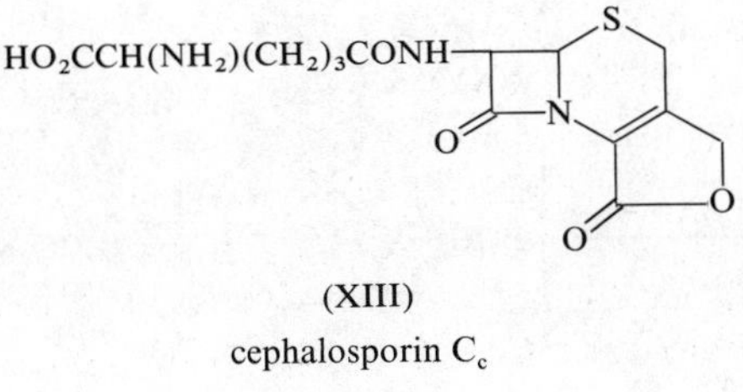

(XIII)
cephalosporin C_c

2,4-dinitrophenylhydrazone of hydroxyacetone after cephalosporin C had been subjected to ozonolysis and the resulting product treated with Raney nickel.

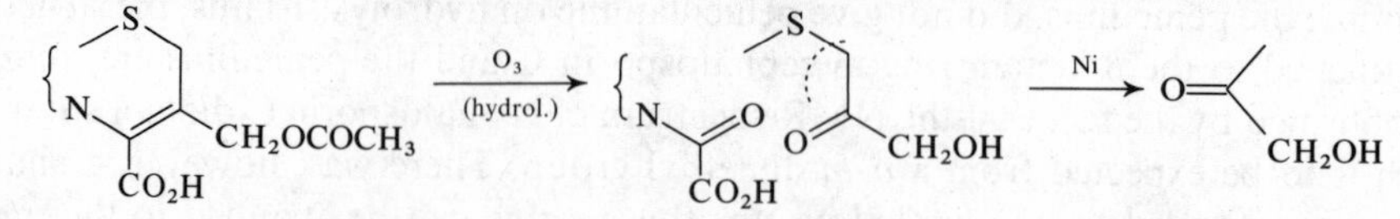

(XI)

From these results of the chemical work, Abraham *et al.* proposed structure (XII) for cephalosporin C and structure (XIII) for cephalosporin C$_c$ (deacetylcephalosporin C lactone). These structures have been confirmed by means of the X-ray analysis of cephalosporin C and its absolute configuration has also been elucidated (Hodgkin *et al.*, 1961); and of cephalosporin C$_c$ (XIII) [Diamond *et al.*, 1963].

One other point that will be mentioned here is the formation of the thiazole derivative (IV) from cephalosporin C. Abraham proposed the following scheme:

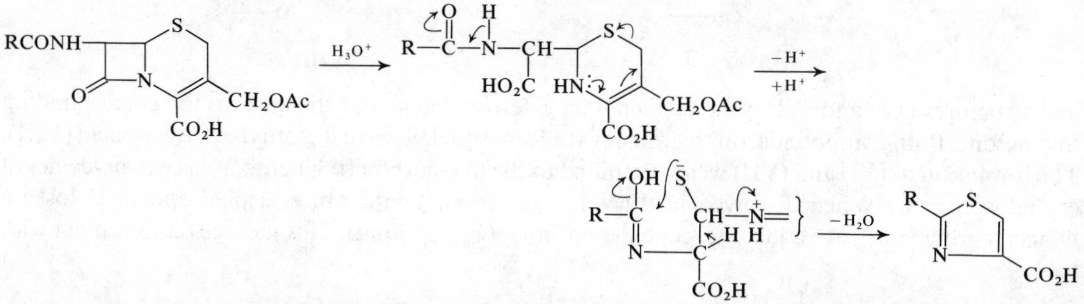

(V)

So far, only two types of β-lactam antibiotics have been found in nature—penicillins, which are β-lactamthiazolidines, and cephalosporins, which are β-lactamdihydrothiazines. Also, the stereochemistry is the same in both types of compounds.

A total synthesis of cephalosporin C has been carried out by Woodward *et al.* (1966). Their approach was the synthesis of the β-lactam ring with substituents introduced in the proper stereochemical configurations by means of stereospecific reactions. The dihydrothiazine ring was then added with retention of configurations of the chiral centres in the β-lactam ring. Because of this, there was no need for any resolution step in the synthesis. The start from the β-lactam ring, unlike that for the penicillins (§6) was possible because the lactam ring is much more stable in cephalosporin C and also because the cleavage product of the lactam ring of a 7-acylaminocephalosporanic acid ((XXVIII); see §6d) is very unstable (the analogous esters of penicilloates are stable).

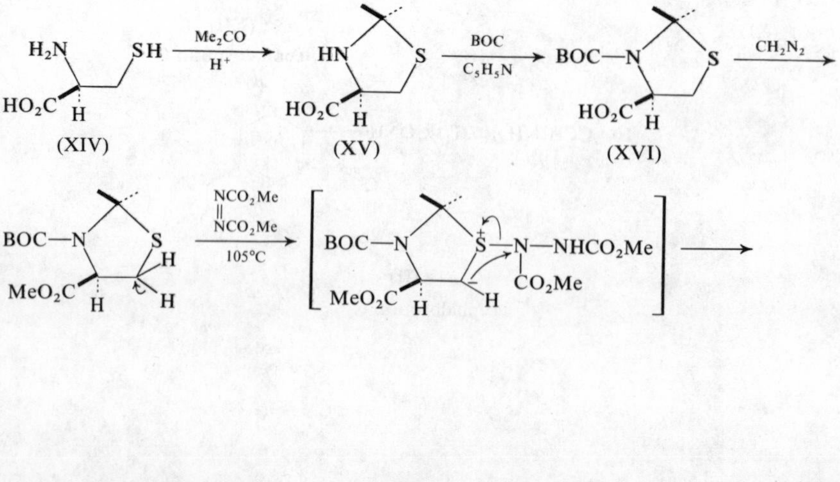

(XIV)   (XV)   (XVI)

(XVII) → [(i) Pb(OAc)₄/C₆H₆ (ii) AcONa/MeOH] → (XVIII) → [(i) Pr₂ⁱNH; MsCl (ii) NaN₃] →

BOC—N / S thiazolidine ring, MeO₂C, H, NNHCO₂Me, CO₂Me
(XVII)

BOC—N / S, MeO₂C, H, OH
(XVIII)

BOC—N / S, MeO₂C, H N₃, H
(XIX)

→ [Al—Hg / MeOH] →

BOC—N / S, MeO₂C, H NH₂, H
(XX)

→ [Buᵗ₃Al / PhCH₃] →

BOC—N / S β-lactam, H, H, O, NH
(XXI)

→ [with aldehyde reagent (CO₂TCE); octane; 80°C] →

BOC—N / S, H, H, O, N, CO₂TCE (with CHO...H O enol)
(XXII)

→ [TFA] →

H₂N, H H / S, O, N, CHO, CO₂TCE
(XXIII)

→ [(i) HO₂CCH(NHCO₂TCE)(CH₂)₃CO₂H/DCC (ii) TCE/DCC/C₅H₅N] →

NHCO₂TCE, CHCO₂TCE, (CH₂)₃CONH—, H H / S, O, N, CHO, CO₂TCE

→ [(i) B₂H₆/THF (ii) Ac₂O/C₅H₅N] →

NHCO₂TCE, CHCO₂TCE, (CH₂)₃CONH—, H H / S, O, N, CH₂OAc, CO₂TCE
(XXIV)

→ [C₅H₅N] →

NHCO₂TCE, CHCO₂TCE, (CH₂)₃CONH—, H H / S, O, N, CH₂OAc, CO₂TCE
(XXV)

→ [Zn/AcOH] →

HO₂CCH(NH₂)(CH₂)₃CONH—, H H / S, O, N, CH₂OAc, CO₂H
(XII)
cephalosporin C

L(+)-Cysteine (XIV) was converted into the L(−)-thiazolidine derivative (XV) followed by treatment with t-butoxycarbonyl chloride (BOC; see also **13** §10) to give L(−)-(XVI). The purpose of these two steps was to enhance the reactivity of the methylene group in (XIV) to produce (XVII) by reaction with dimethyl azodicarboxylate. *trans*-(XVII) is produced because of the steric effect of the adjacent carbomethoxyl group, and its oxidation gave the *trans*-hydroxy-ester (XVIII). The steps suggested in this conversion were:

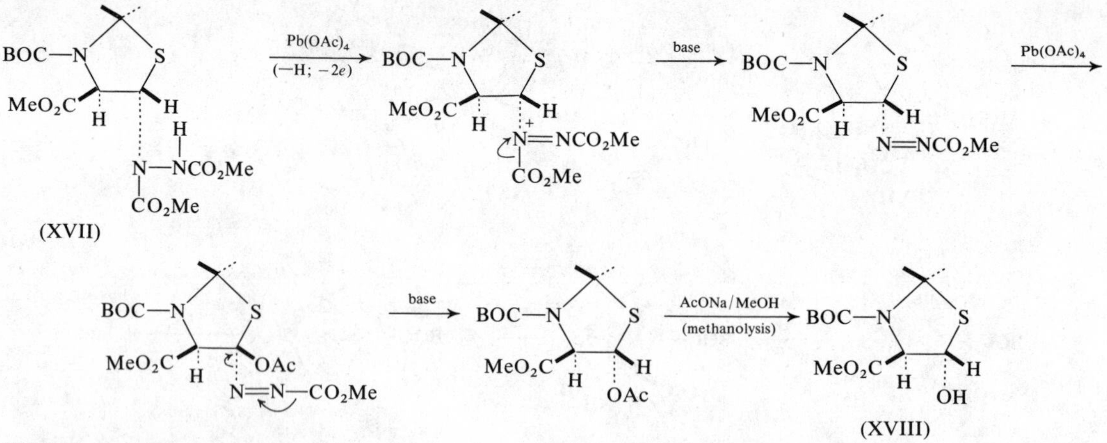

(XVII) (XVIII)

(XVIII), on treatment with di-isopropylamine in the presence of methanesulphonyl chloride, gave a product which, with sodium azide, gave *cis*-(XIX) with inversion (*via* the methanesulphonate). (XIX) was reduced to *cis*-(XX). The structures and orientations of (XVIII) and (XX) were established by X-ray analysis. Treatment of (XX) with tri-isobutylaluminium in toluene gave the β-lactam (XXI). A novel dialdehyde was synthesised in which the carboxyl group was protected as its β,β,β-trichloroethyl ester; this was a new protecting group that could be removed by reduction. The dialdehyde was prepared as follows (TCE $= CCl_3CH_2-$):

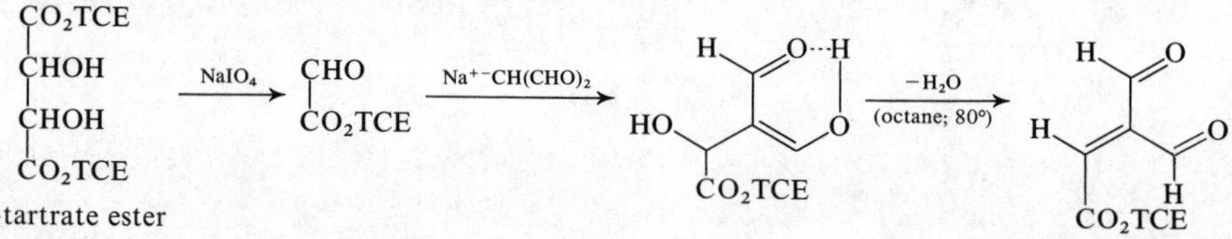

D-tartrate ester

This dialdehyde was condensed with (XXI) in octane at 80°C to give (XXII) which, in trifluoroacetic acid, underwent cyclisation to yield the aminoaldehyde (XXIII). This was converted into cephalosporin C by acetylation with *N*-β,β,β-trichloroethyloxycarbonyl-D-α-aminoadipic acid, etc. (XXIV), on standing in pyridine for three days at room temperature, isomerised to (XXV). (XXV) is more stable than (XXIV) because in the former there is now extended conjugation (α,β-unsaturated ester).

§6d. 7-Aminocephalosporanic acid. When subjected to mild acid hydrolysis, the α-aminoadipoyl side-chain in cephalosporin C (XII) is removed to give 7-aminocephalosporanic acid (XXVI) in

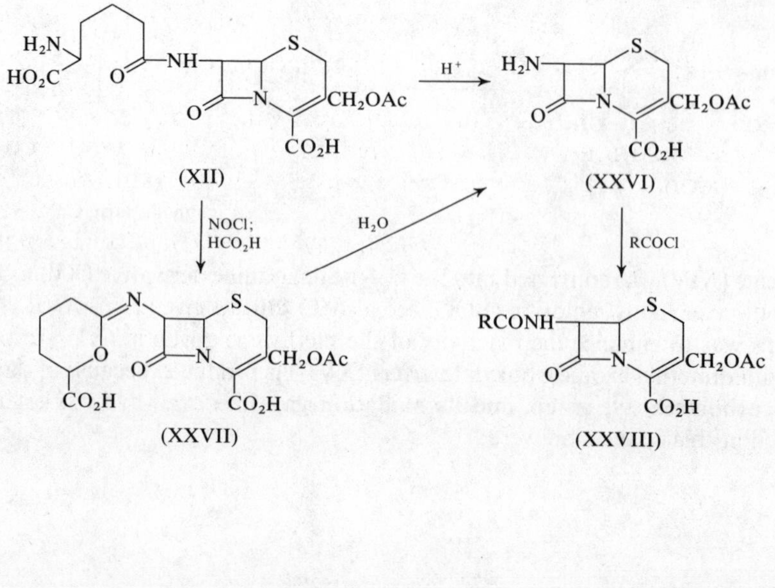

(XII) (XXVI) (XXVII) (XXVIII)

very poor yield. On the other hand, treatment of cephalosporin C with nitrosyl chloride in formic acid results in the formation of an intermediate iminolactone (XXVII), which is hydrolysed in aqueous solution to (XXVI) [yield: 40 per cent], together with α-hydroxyadipic acid.

Acylation of (XXVI) with acid chlorides gives various cephalosporins (XXVIII), many of which have general clinical use. The side-chain (RCO) may still be the α-aminoadipoyl group (as in cephalosporin C), and the acetate group (OAc) may be OH, SEt, etc.

§7. Streptomycin

Streptomycin was isolated by Waksman *et al.* (1944) from cultures of *Streptomyces griseus.* This antibiotic is very effective in the treatment of tuberculosis, meningitis and pneumonia. Streptomycin is a solid with a laevorotation, and its structure has been shown to be composed of the three units streptose (I), *N*-methyl-L-glucosamine (II) and streptidine (III) [but see later].

(II)   (III)

The following is a very brief account of the evidence that led to this structure for streptomycin. The molecular formula was shown to be $C_{21}H_{39}N_7O_{12}$. Three nitrogen atoms are strongly basic (the molecule forms a trihydrochloride), and on mild acid hydrolysis, streptomycin gives one molecule of streptidine, $C_8H_{18}N_6O_4$, and one molecule of streptobiosamine, $C_{13}H_{23}NO_9$ (Folkers *et al.*, 1945).

Streptidine (unit (III)), on oxidation with potassium permanganate, gave two molecules of guanidine (Peck *et al.*, 1946); thus two guanido groups are present in streptidine. Streptidine, on alkaline hydrolysis, gave *streptamine* and ammonia (Brink *et al.*, 1945). Streptamine was shown to be a diaminotetrahydroxycyclohexane, and the examination of the oxidation products of dibenzoylstreptamine with periodic acid led to the suggestion that streptidine is 1,3-diguanido-2,4,5,6-tetrahydroxycyclohexane (Carter *et al.*, 1946). Streptidine has been synthesised from streptamine (Wolfrom *et al.*, 1948). Since streptidine is not optically active, the configuration of the molecule must be *meso*, with the two guanido groups *cis* (see unit (III)).

streptamine

N-**Methyl-L-glucosamine** (unit (II)). When streptomycin is treated with methanolic hydrogen chloride (methanolysis), and then subjected to acid hydrolysis followed by acetylation, the pentaacetate of *N*-methyl-L-glucosamine is obtained; the parent compound is obtained by hydrolysis. The structure of *N*-methyl-L-glucosamine was confirmed by synthesis from L-arabinose (Kuehl *et al.*, 1946, 1947).

maltol

Streptose (unit (I)). The streptose fragment has not been isolated from streptomycin by degradation. It appears to be too unstable, but its structure was elucidated by various degradative experiments, *e.g.*, the alkaline hydrolysis of streptomycin gives *maltol* (Schneck *et al.*, 1945), and this is produced by the conversion of a *furanose ring* into γ-pyrone. Dyer *et al.* (1965) have now synthesised streptose and confirmed the structure assigned (I), and also showed that it had the L-lyxo configuration.

Streptobiosamine (units (I) and (II)). Analytical work showed that this compound was a disaccharide, and from it was isolated N-methyl-L-glucosamine (see above). The formation of maltol and other analytical work led to the structure (I) + (II) for streptobiosamine, and then the points of attachment between streptobiosamine and streptidine were found, and so led to the structure given above for streptomycin (Kuehl *et al.*, 1947, 1948). Inspection of this structure shows that streptose (which is the L-isomer) is linked to streptidine (III) by a β-L-glycosidic linkage and that N-methyl-L-glucosamine (II) is linked to streptose by an α-L-glycosidic linkage (*cf.* **7** §7h). These linkages have long been accepted; they were proposed by Wolfrom *et al.* (1953) on the basis of the application of Hudson's isorotation rules (**7** §6). Rinehart *et al.* (1965), however, from their NMR spectral studies, have concluded that the linkage between (I) and (III) is α-L, and have assigned the following structure to streptomycin (also note the 1C conformation of (II)):

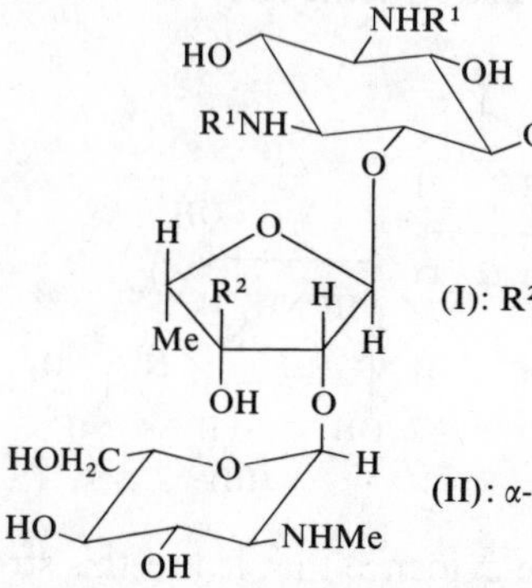

(III): $R^1 = -\overset{\overset{\displaystyle NH}{\|}}{C}NH_2$

(I): $R^2 = CHO$; α-linkage

(II): α-linkage

§7a. Tetracycline antibiotics. Aureomycin was isolated from cultures of *Streptomyces aureofaciens*, and is used in the treatment of typhoid fever, etc. Terramycin was isolated from cultures of *Streptomcyes rimosus*, and is very effective in the treatment of trachoma. The structures of these antibiotics are:

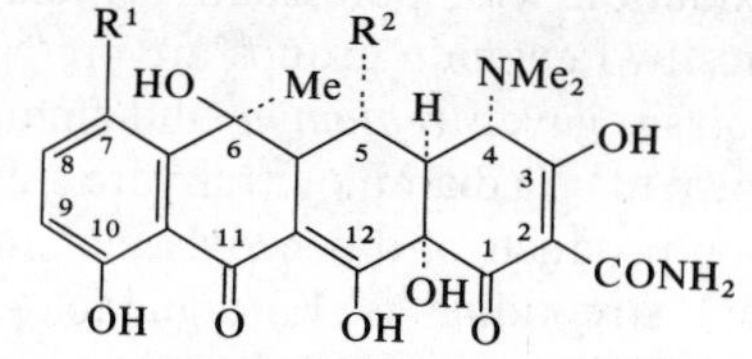

Aureomycin: $R^1 = Cl$; $R^2 = H$
Terramycin: $R^1 = H$; $R^2 = OH$

These compounds are classified as *tetracyclines*, tetracycline itself being obtained by replacement of the chlorine atom ($R^1 = Cl$) in aureomycin by hydrogen ($R^1 = H$). This conversion is readily carried out by the catalytic hydrogenation of aureomycin. The stereochemistry of aureomycin had been partly established from the chemical work, but it was completely determined by the X-ray analysis of its hydrochloride (Pepinsky *et al.*, 1959), and Shemyakin *et al.* (1962) have established the absolute configuration of the tetracyclines by means of optical rotatory dispersion studies.

The structure of terramycin was the first of this group to be elucidated (Woodward *et al.*, 1953). The molecular formula was shown to be $C_{22}H_{24}N_2O_9$ and the compound was found to contain eight active hydrogen atoms. Also present were a dimethylamino and a carbonamido group, and a C-methyl group. Diazomethane formed a dimethyl ether; this showed the presence of two acidic hydroxyl groups; the other two hydroxyl groups were shown to be alcoholic. On the evidence so far, the structure of terramycin may be written as:

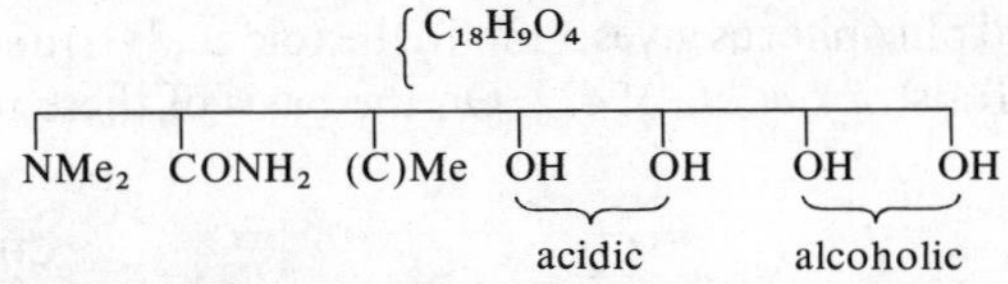
$C_{18}H_9O_4$
NMe_2 $CONH_2$ (C)Me OH OH OH OH
acidic
alcoholic

Alkaline, acidic, and reductive degradations were now carried out and some of the products isolated and characterised are shown in the chart.

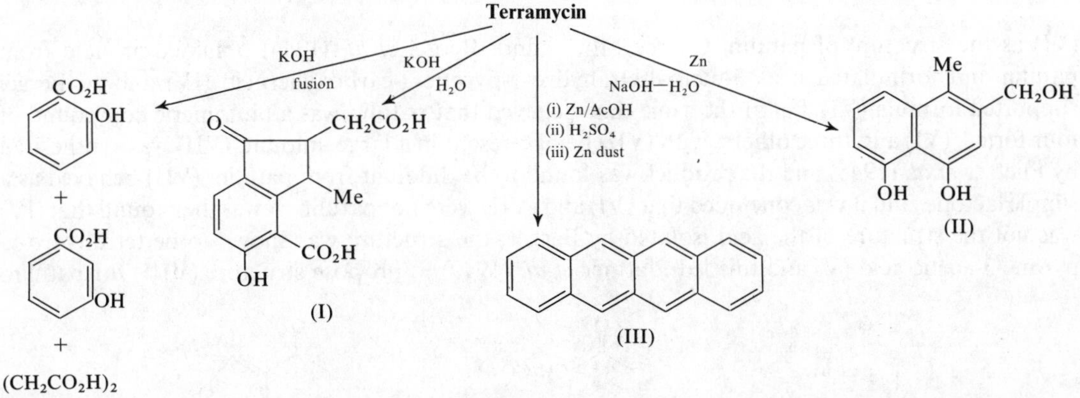
Terramycin
KOH fusion
KOH H_2O
Zn NaOH—H_2O
(i) Zn/AcOH
(ii) H_2SO_4
(iii) Zn dust
CO_2H
OH
+
CO_2H
OH
+
$(CH_2CO_2H)_2$
CH_2CO_2H
Me
CO_2H
OH
(I)
(III)
Me
CH_2OH
OH OH
(II)

(I) is terracinoic acid (formed by a naphthacene rearrangement); (II) is terranaphthol; and (III) is naphthacene. On the basis of the isolation of the hydroxybenzoic acids, compounds (I) and (II), the compound with structure (IV) was synthesised as a model for ultraviolet spectroscopic examination. The spectrum of (IV) resembled that of terramycin itself and this led to the proposal of (V) as

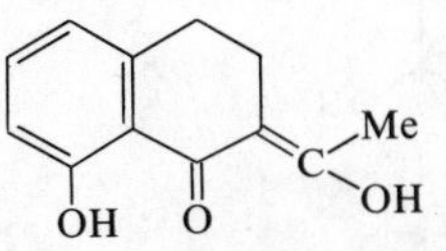
Me
OH
OH O

(IV)

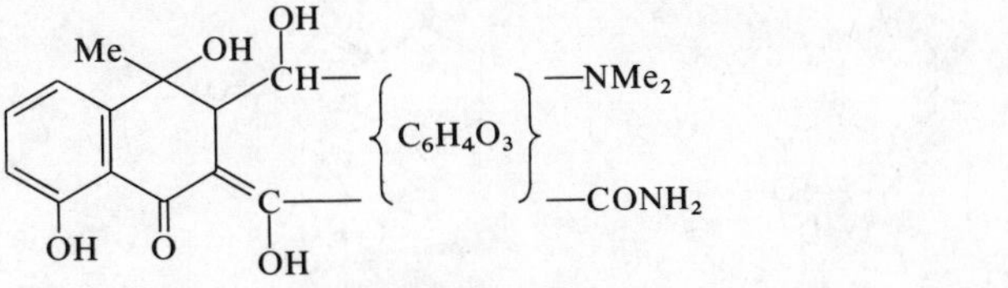
OH
Me OH
CH—
$C_6H_4O_3$
—NMe_2
—$CONH_2$
OH O
OH

(V)

the partial structure of the antibiotic. The isolation of (III) and further work led to the structure given above for terramycin (5-oxytetracycline).

Once the structure of terramycin had been elucidated, structure determination of the tetracyclines was facilitated by the use of spectroscopic methods. Total syntheses have also been carried out.

§8. Patulin

This has been obtained from various moulds. It is an optically inactive solid, and it inhibits Staphylococci and coliforms. It has, however, never become important as an antibiotic because it has bad side-effects, *e.g.*, it slows down the healing process, although limiting the infection. Nevertheless, it is discussed here because the elucidation of its structure is a very good example of the use of ultraviolet and infrared spectroscopy.

The molecular formula of patulin is $C_7H_6O_4$; it is a neutral substance and forms a monoacetate. Hydrolysis of patulin with acid produces one molecule of formic acid and a small yield (10 per cent) of tetrahydro-γ-pyrone-2-carboxylic acid (I). Catalytic reduction followed by further reduction with hydrogen iodide and red phosphorus gives 3-methylhexoic acid (II) and the lactone of 4-hydroxy-3-methylhexoic acid (III) [Raistrick *et al.*, 1943]. On the basis of these results, Raistrick proposed

(I)   (II)   (III)

(VI) as the structure of patulin. On the other hand, Bergel *et al.* (1944) obtained an acid from patulin and formulated it as 3-methyltetrahydro-γ-pyrone-2-carboxylic acid (IV) and so Bergel supported formula (VI), but at the same time believed that patulin was a tautomeric compound of four forms, (VI) and three others, with (VII) being present in a large amount. (VII) was synthesised by Puetzer *et al.* (1945) and the product was found to be different from patulin. (VII) behaved as a simple lactone, and it was concluded that (VI) and (VII) were not patulin. It was then found that (IV) was not the structure of the acid isolated by Bergel; the structure was shown to be tetrahydro-γ-pyrone-3-acetic acid (V) and this led Plattner *et al.* (1949) to propose structure (VIII) for patulin.

(IV)   (V)   (VI)

(VII)   (VIII)   (IX)   (X)

Woodward *et al.* (1950) examined the ultraviolet and infrared spectra of patulin, as well as its chemical properties. The ultraviolet spectrum showed a maximum at 276 nm (ε 16 600), which suggests the presence of a keto group conjugated with *more* than one double bond (the chromophore $C=C-C=O$ absorbs around 220 nm and may be raised to $\sim$250 nm by substituents on the α- and β-carbon atoms). Partly on the basis of this fact, Woodward rejected structure (VIII) and proposed (IX). Furthermore, Woodward synthesised (VIII) and showed it was different from patulin ((VIII) is now known as *allopatulin*). Patulin is readily acetylated and readily converted into an ether. It therefore appears that patulin contains a hydroxyl group. This was supported by the fact that the infrared spectrum showed a band at 3 660 cm^{-1}, a region typical of a free hydroxyl group. Furthermore, when patulin was acetylated, this band disappeared, but most of the other bands were still present, in particular, the bands at 1 792 (v.s.), 1 685 (s), and 1 636 cm^{-1} (s). Now, the band corresponding to a keto group is always very strong (usually being the most intense band in the infrared spectrum), and so the maximum at 1 792 cm^{-1} was assigned to a keto group. This frequency is higher than the usual range for acyclic (1 725–1 700 cm^{-1}) and 5- and 6-ring ketones (1 750–1 700 cm^{-1}), and α, β-unsaturated ketones (1 690–1 660 cm^{-1}). This information, taken in conjunction with the ultraviolet spectrum, thus suggests the presence of a γ-lactone (1 800–1 760 cm^{-1}). Woodward synthesised (X) [as a model compound] and found that its infrared spectrum was essentially identical with that of patulin in the 1 600–1 800 cm^{-1} region, and then finally synthesised patulin itself as follows:

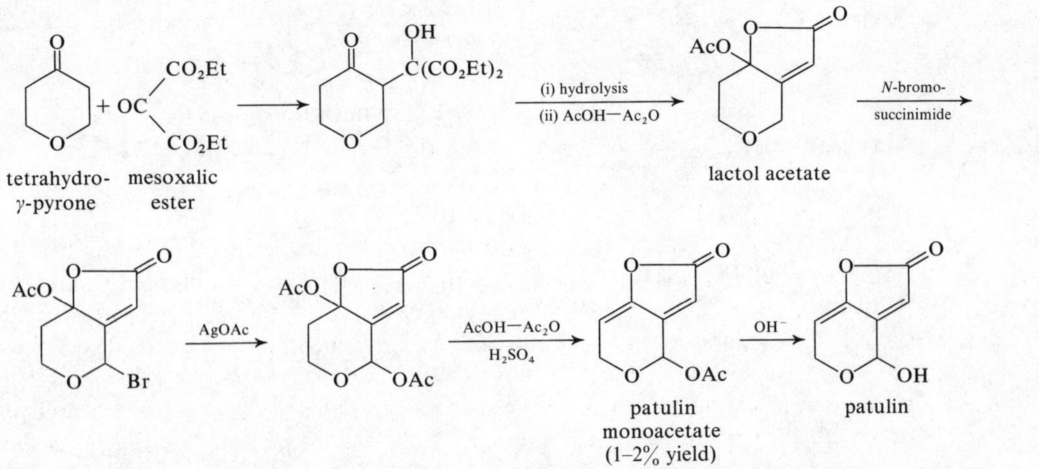

tetrahydro- mesoxalic
γ-pyrone ester

lactol acetate

patulin
monoacetate
(1–2% yield)

patulin

The monoacetate (obtained above) was shown to be identical with that obtained from patulin.

§9. Chloramphenicol (Chloromycetin)

Chloramphenicol is a laevorotatory compound that is produced by *Streptomyces venezuelae* (Carter *et al.*, 1948); it is very effective in the treatment of typhoid fever, etc.

The molecular formula of chloramphenicol is $C_{11}H_{13}Cl_2N_2O_5$, and its absorption spectrum is similar to that of nitrobenzene. The presence of a nitro-group was confirmed by the reduction of chloramphenicol with tin and hydrochloric acid, followed by diazotisation and then coupling to give an orange-red precipitate with 2-naphthol (Rebstock *et al.*, 1949). When catalytically reduced (palladium), chloramphenicol gives a product which has an absorption spectrum similar to that of *p*-toluidine, and the solution contains ionic chlorine. The hydrolysis of chloramphenicol with acid or alkali produces dichloroacetic acid and an optically active base, $C_9H_{12}N_2O_4$. This base was shown to contain a primary amino-group, and when treated with methyl dichloroacetate, the base reformed chloramphenicol (Rebstock *et al.*, 1949).

Chloramphenicol is converted into a diacetyl derivative on treatment with acetic anhydride in pyridine; the base obtained from chloramphenicol forms a triacetyl derivative on similar treatment. Thus chloramphenicol probably contains two hydroxyl groups. When the base is treated with periodic acid, two molecules of the latter are consumed with the formation of one molecule each of ammonia, formaldehyde and *p*-nitrobenzaldehyde. These products may be accounted for if the base is assumed to be 2-amino-1-*p*-nitrophenylpropane-1,3-diol (Rebstock *et al.*, 1949).

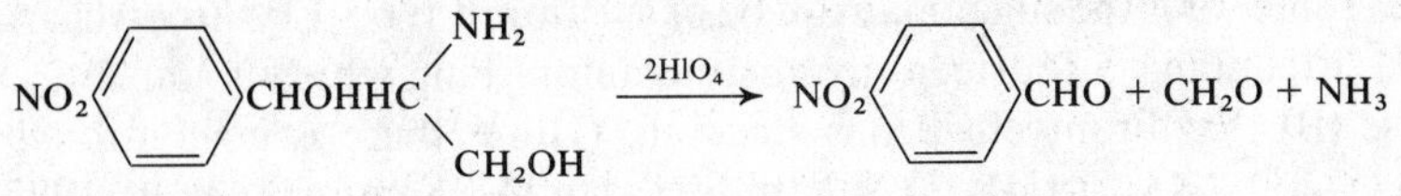

Thus chloramphenicol will be

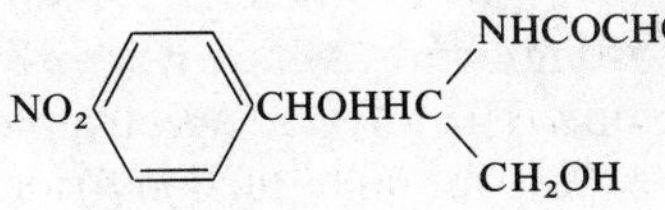

This structure has been confirmed by synthesis, *e.g.*, that of Long *et al.* (1949).

NO_2⟨benzene⟩$COCH_3$ $\xrightarrow{Br_2}$ NO_2⟨benzene⟩$COCH_2Br$ $\xrightarrow[\text{(ii) HCl—}C_2H_5OH]{\text{(i) }(CH_2)_6N_4}$ NO_2⟨benzene⟩$COCH_2NH_2$ $\xrightarrow{(CH_3CO)_2O}$

NO_2⟨benzene⟩$COCH_2NHCOCH_3$ $\xrightarrow[Na_2CO_3\text{aq.}]{CH_2O}$ NO_2⟨benzene⟩$COHC\begin{smallmatrix}NHCOCH_3\\ \\CH_2OH\end{smallmatrix}$ $\xrightarrow{[(CH_3)_2CHO]_3Al}$

(I)

NO_2⟨benzene⟩$CHOHHC\begin{smallmatrix}NHCOCH_3\\ \\CH_2OH\end{smallmatrix}$ $\xrightarrow{HCl}$ NO_2⟨benzene⟩$CHOHHC\begin{smallmatrix}NH_2\\ \\CH_2OH\end{smallmatrix}$ $\xrightarrow[\text{(ii) }CHCl_2CO_2CH_3]{\text{(i) resolved}}$

(II)   (III)

NO_2⟨benzene⟩$CHOHHC\begin{smallmatrix}NHCOCHCl_2\\ \\CH_2OH\end{smallmatrix}$

(−)-chloramphenicol

Reduction of (I) with aluminium isopropoxide gave predominantly the *threo*-compound (II) together with a small amount of the *erythro*-isomer. The *threo*-racemate was separated from the *erythro*-racemate by fractional crystallisation. (II), on hydrolysis, gave *threo*-(III), which was resolved by means of (+)-camphorsulphonic acid. D-*threo*-(III) was converted into (−)-chloramphenicol with methyl dichloroacetate.

This structure has also been confirmed by crystallographic studies (Dunitz, 1952).

Chloramphenicol and the base contain two chiral centres; thus there are two possible pairs of enantiomers. Comparison of the properties of the base with those of norephedrine and nor-ψ-ephedrine (**14** §7) showed that the configuration of the base was similar to that of nor-ψ-ephedrine (Rebstock *et al.*, 1949). Thus chloramphenicol is D-(−)-*threo*-2-dichloroacetamino-1-*p*-nitrophenylpropane-1,3-diol. It is interesting to note that chloramphenicol is the first natural compound found to contain a nitro-group; the presence of the $CHCl_2$ group is also most unusual.

§10. The macrolide group of antibiotics

These are macrocyclic lactones and are also known as the **erythromycin group** because the most useful macrolide is erythromycin. The lactone ring is joined by glycosidic links to one or more amino-sugars; in some cases the sugar may not be of the amino-type. **Erythromycin A**, $C_{37}H_{67}NO_{13}$, has structure (I). It contains a fourteen-membered lactone ring which is joined to desosamine (A) and to cladinose (B). Erythromycin B has structure (I) but there is no hydroxyl group at C-12.

Methymycin, $C_{25}H_{43}NO_7$, is (II); the sugar is desosamine. Kinumaki *et al.* (1972) isolated a new antibiotic, m.p. 68–70°C, from cultures producing methymycin (II). The mass spectrum of this new compound showed its molecular formula to be $C_{25}H_{43}NO_6$ (M^+ 453·3048). The ultraviolet spectrum (ethanol) showed the following bands, which were assigned as indicated: λ_{max} 225–226 and 285 nm; an α,β-unsaturated ketone. The infrared spectrum data and their assignments were: ν_{max} 3 420 cm^{-1} (OH); 1 730 cm^{-1} (lactone and carbonyl); 1 695 cm^{-1} (conjugated ketone);

and 1 635 cm^{-1} (conjugated double bond). These spectroscopic data suggested a structural similarity to methymycin (II). The NMR spectrum of the new antibiotic showed the presence of six

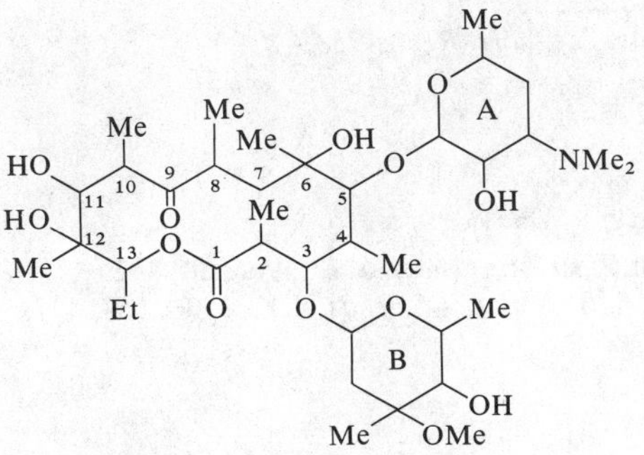

(I)
erythromycin A

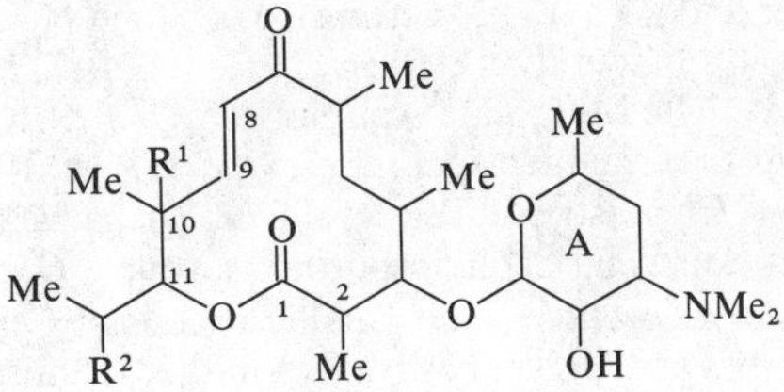

(II): $R^1 = OH$; $R^2 = H$
(III): $R^1 = H$; $R^2 = H$

C-methyl groups and one NMe$_2$ group. There were also the following signals: τ 3·6 (d, J 16 Hz; 8-H) and τ 3·18 (dd, J 16, 4·5 Hz; 9-H). The assignments were made as shown, and because of the shift to lower field (than the usual τ-values for olefinic protons, τ 4·8), the authors suggested these values indicated the presence of the grouping —CO—CH=CH—CH<. There was also a broad triplet at τ 5·02, and this was assigned to the methine proton at C-11 (III).

§11. Polypeptide antibiotics

Many antibiotics formed by micro-organisms of the genus *Bacillus* and the genus *Streptomyces* are polypeptides containing six to twelve amino-acid residues. Their structures have been elucidated mainly by the methods used in protein chemistry (Ch. 13). All contain rings and D-amino-acids are often present (see also antanamide, **13** §11), *e.g.*, **bacitracin A** (note the presence of the thiazoline ring).

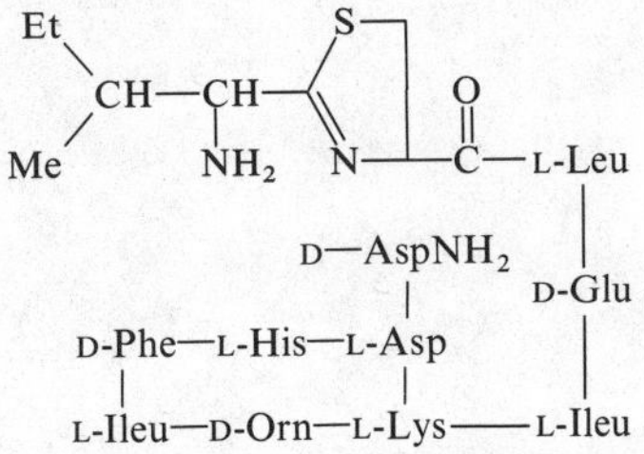

bacitracin A

§12. Polyacetylene antibiotics

Many of this group are known, some are highly toxic and apparently none has been used clinically. Their structures are unbranched carbon chains which, in addition to acetylenic bonds, may contain ethylenic bonds and functional groups, *e.g.*, hydroxyl, carboxyl, carbonamido; *e.g.*, mycomycin (**5** §6) and **agrocybin**.

$$HOCH_2—C{\equiv}C—C{\equiv}C—C{\equiv}C—CONH_2$$
agrocybin

REFERENCES

EVANS, *The Chemistry of the Antibiotics used in Medicine*, Pergamon (1965).

COOK, 'The Chemistry of the Penicillins', *Quart. Rev.*, 1948, **2**, 203.

BRINK and HARMAN, 'Chemistry of Some Newer Antibiotics', *Quart. Rev.*, 1958, **12**, 93.

GROVE, 'Griseofulvin', *Quart. Rev.*, 1963, **17**, 1.

BERRY, 'The Macrolide Antibiotics', *Quart. Rev.*, 1963, **17**, 343.

RUSSELL, 'Cyclodepsipeptides', *Quart. Rev.*, 1966, **20**, 559.

CLIVE, 'Chemistry of Tetracyclines', *Quart. Rev.*, 1968, **22**, 435.

ABRAHAM, 'The Cephalosporin C Group', *Quart. Rev.*, 1967, **21**, 231.

WOODWARD et al., 'The Total Synthesis of Cephalosporin C', *J. Am. chem. Soc.*, 1966, **88**, 852.

WOODWARD, 'Recent Advances in the Chemistry of Natural Products', *Science N.Y.*, 1966, **153**, 487.

19 Haemoglobin, chlorophyll and phthalocyanines

§1. Introduction

Two of the most important compounds of the natural porphyrins are haemoglobin and chlorophyll. The bile pigments, which are formed mainly in the liver, are degradation products of haemoglobin. Haemoglobin and chlorophyll act as catalysts (biological) in many biological processes.

A point that might be noted here is the method of spelling (and writing) the names of various compounds described in this chapter. For many years, hæmoglobin, hæm, etc., were written as shown, but the tendency now is to write them as haemoglobin, haem, etc. There is also a tendency to spell them as hemoglobin, heme, etc. (the latter is common American practice; *cf.* Steroids, Ch. 11).

Haemoglobin

§2. Degradation products of the haemoglobin

Haemoglobin occurs in all vertebrates (with certain exceptions) and in many invertebrates; it has also been found in certain strains of yeasts, moulds, etc. It is a chromoprotein (**13** §7B), the protein part being *globin* (94 per cent), and the prosthetic group being *haem* (6 per cent). The composition of haemoglobin varies slightly, depending on the species from which it is isolated; the variation occurs only in the globin part of the molecule.

The way in which the globin part is bound to haem has been the subject of much discussion. Globin consists of four polypeptide chains, and in human haemoglobin the chains are of two types which have different terminal acid groups: α-chain, valyl-leucyl end-group; β-chain, valyl-histidyl-leucyl end-group. Normal adult haemoglobin contains two α-chains (141 amino-acids each) and two β-chains (146 amino-acids each) [Pauling *et al.*, 1957]. Braunitzer *et al.* (1961) have now worked out the amino-acid sequence in these chains.

Haem is an iron-protoporphyrin complex (see §2a). When the iron atom is in the ferrous state, the complex is called *ferrous protoporphyrin, ferroprotoporphyrin, protohaem,* or *haem,* and the molecule is electrically neutral. When the iron atom is in the ferric state, the complex is called *ferric protoporphyrin, ferriprotoporphyrin,* or *haemin,* and the molecule carries a unit positive charge (and is consequently associated with an anion). In the animal body, haemoglobin readily combines with oxygen to form *oxyhaemoglobin* and this, when treated with glacial acid, forms *haematin*, $[C_{34}H_{32}N_4O_4Fe(III)]^+OH^-$. The chloride of haematin is *haemin chloride*, $[C_{34}H_{32}N_4O_4Fe(III)]^+Cl^-$. Haemin may be prepared by warming blood with acetic acid and sodium chloride (Teichmann, 1853). The iron atom can be removed from haemin and from haem, but it is easier to do this with the latter. Hence, in general, haemin is reduced to haem, $(C_{34}H_{32}N_4O_4Fe)$, by, *e.g.*, sodium hyposulphite, followed by treatment with acid (hydrochloric or sulphuric acid; see also below).

In haem the four ligands (the four pyrrole groups) form a square-planar complex (*via* the nitrogen atoms). The two remaining positions of co-ordination are perpendicular to this plane (*i.e.*, the plane of the porphyrin ring). Now, haemoglobin contains four molecules of haem for each molecule of globin (which consists of two α- and two β-chains; see above). Each iron atom (ferrous) has formed a square-planar complex with the protoporphyrin molecule and a fifth position is occupied by an imidazole ring (of the histidine amino-acid residue). It appears that the iron atom is bound to histidine-87 in the α-chain and to histidine-92 in the β-chain. Furthermore, it has been shown that each haem molecule is embedded in one of the four chains of the globin molecule.

If the sixth valency of the ferrous ion is unoccupied, the arrangement is a square pyramid. This is considered to be the case with haemoglobin, but it is possible that the sixth position is occupied by a water molecule, resulting in an octahedral complex. In either case, when haemoglobin combines with one molecule of oxygen to form oxyhaemoglobin (see above), it is this sixth position which co-ordinates with the oxygen molecule (the iron atom is still in the ferrous state); the water molecule, if present in haemoglobin, is readily displaced.

The mechanism of the incorporation of a metal ion into porphyrin molecules is uncertain. Hambright *et al.* (1972) have proposed a mechanism in which the first stage involves deformation of the porphyrin, and in the second stage the metal is introduced by attack on this deformed species.

Since haemin forms a diester with methanol, the molecule therefore contains two carboxyl groups. Also, since haemin absorbs two molecule of hydrogen when catalytically reduced (palladium), two ethylenic double bonds are thus probably present in the molecule. When subjected to vigorous reduction with hydriodic acid and phosphonium iodide or hydriodic acid and acetic acid, haemin is degraded into the four pyrrole derivatives opsopyrrole (I), haemopyrrole (II), cryptopyrrole (III),

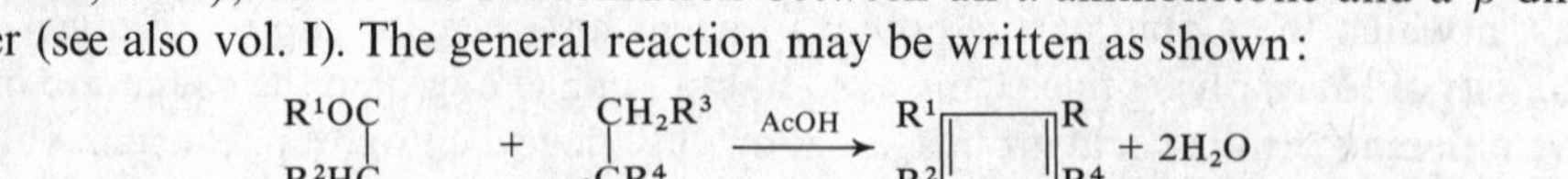

opsopyrrole   haemopyrrole   cryptopyrrole   phyllopyrrole
(I)   (II)   (III)   (IV)

and phyllopyrrole (IV). All four compounds have been synthesised by means of the Knorr pyrrole synthesis (1884, 1886); this is the condensation between an α-aminoketone and a β-diketone or β-keto-ester (see also vol. I). The general reaction may be written as shown:

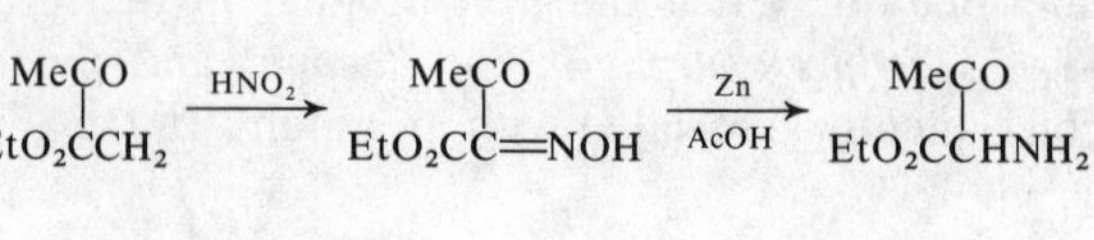

Detailed studies of this reaction have shown that the yields depend on the nature of the R groups. When R^3 is an alkyl group, the yields are poor (or the reaction fails). When R^2 and R^3 are acyl or carbalkoxyl groups, the yields are usually very good. The α-aminoketone is generally prepared *in situ*, *e.g.*,

Various modifications of the Knorr pyrrole synthesis are used now, *e.g.*, t-butyl or benzyl oximino-acetoacetic esters are used instead of the corresponding ethyl ester; removal of the ester group is facilitated (*cf.* **13** §10). Also, reduction is carried out with sodium dithionite instead of zinc and acetic acid.

As an example of this synthesis, let us consider the preparation of opsopyrrole (I) and crypto-pyrrole (III). Opsopyrrole may be synthesised by condensing aminoacetone with ethyl 2,4-diketo-pentanoate, and then subjecting the product to the Wolff–Kishner reduction, *i.e.*, first converting the product into the hydrazone and then heating the latter with sodium ethoxide at 160°C. By this means a keto-group is converted into a methylene group (see also Vol. I). By using an excess of sodium ethoxide, decarboxylation is also effected at the same time.

$$CH_3CO,\ H_2C{-}NH_2 \ +\ CH_2COCH_3,\ COCO_2C_2H_5 \ \longrightarrow \ [CH_3,\ COCH_3,\ CO_2C_2H_5\text{-pyrrole}] \ \xrightarrow{N_2H_4} \ [CH_3,\ C({=}NNH_2)CH_3,\ CO_2C_2H_5\text{-pyrrole}] \ \xrightarrow[160°C]{C_2H_5ONa}$$

$$[CH_3,\ CH_2CH_3,\ CO_2C_2H_5\text{-pyrrole}] \ \xrightarrow[160°C]{C_2H_5ONa} \ [CH_3,\ CH_2CH_3\text{-pyrrole}]$$

opsopyrrole

Cryptopyrrole may be prepared in a similar manner, starting from ethyl α-aminoacetoacetate and acetylacetone (penta-2,4-dione).

$$CH_3CO,\ C_2H_5O_2CHC{-}NH_2 \ +\ CH_2COCH_3,\ COCH_3 \ \longrightarrow \ [CH_3,\ COCH_3,\ C_2H_5O_2C,\ CH_3\text{-pyrrole}] \ \xrightarrow[\text{(ii) }C_2H_5ONa\text{ at }160°C]{\text{(i) }N_2H_4} \ [CH_3,\ CH_2CH_3,\ CH_3\text{-pyrrole}]$$

cryptopyrrole

When reduced with tin and hydrochloric acid, haemin is again degraded into four pyrrole deriva-tives, but in this case the products are all carboxylic acids in which each of the four pyrroles (I)–(IV) contains a carboxyl group attached to the ethyl group:

opsopyrrole-carboxylic acid	haemopyrrole-carboxylic acid	cryptopyrrole-carboxylic acid	phyllopyrrole-carboxylic acid
$CH_3,\ CH_2CH_2CO_2H$	$CH_3,\ CH_2CH_2CO_2H,\ CH_3$	$CH_3,\ CH_2CH_2CO_2H,\ CH_3$	$CH_3,\ CH_2CH_2CO_2H,\ CH_3,\ CH_3$
(V)	(VI)	(VII)	(VIII)

The propionic acid residue can be introduced into the β-position of pyrrole in several ways, *e.g.*, (note the use of the Gattermann aldehyde synthesis and the Knoevenagel reaction):

$$[CH_3,\ C_2H_5O_2C,\ CH_3\text{-pyrrole}] \ \xrightarrow[AlCl_3]{HCN/HCl} \ [CH_3,\ CHO,\ C_2H_5O_2C,\ CH_3\text{-pyrrole}] \ \xrightarrow[C_5H_5N]{CH_2(CO_2H)_2} \ [CH_3,\ CH{=}CHCO_2H,\ C_2H_5O_2C,\ CH_3\text{-pyrrole}] \ \xrightarrow[\text{or }H_2/Ni]{Na/Hg}$$

$$[CH_3,\ CH_2CH_2CO_2H,\ C_2H_5O_2C,\ CH_3\text{-pyrrole}]$$

When oxidised with chromic acid, haemin gives two molecules of *haematinic acid* (IX). On the other hand, *mesoporphyrin* (see below) gives, on oxidation, two molecules of ethylmethylmaleimide (X).

haematinic acid
(X)

ethylmethylmaleimide
(IX)

The treatment of haemin with iron dust and formic acid results in the removal of the iron atom and the formation of *protoporphyrin*, $C_{34}H_{34}N_4O_4$. The iron atom is also removed from haemin by the action of hydrobromic acid in acetic acid, but in this case the product is *haematoporphyrin*, $C_{34}H_{38}N_4O_6$. If, however, haemin is treated with hydriodic acid in acetic acid, the iron atom is again removed and *mesoporphyrin*, $C_{34}H_{38}N_4O_4$, is obtained.

Finally, when porphyrins containing two carboxyl groups are decarboxylated, the products obtained (after reduction, if necessary) are known as *aetioporphyrins*, *e.g.*, when protoporphyrin is decarboxylated, and the product then reduced, the final product is *aetioporphyrin*, $C_{32}H_{38}N_4$, which is also a degradation product of chlorophyll. Thus haemin and chlorophyll are closely related chemically.

Table 19.1 summarises the reactions that have been discussed.

Table 19.1

Compound	Reaction	Products
Haemoglobin	Atmospheric oxidation	Oxyhaemoglobin
Oxyhaemoglobin	CH_3CO_2H	Haematin
Oxyhaemaglobin	$CH_3CO_2H + NaCl$	Haemin
Haemin	$Na_2S_2O_4$	Haem
Haemin	$HI + PH_4I$	Opsopyrrole, Haemopyrrole, Cryptopyrrole and Phyllopyrrole
Haemin	Sn—HCl	Opsopyrrole-, Haemopyrrole-, Cryptopyrrole- and Phyllopyrrolecarboxylic acids
Haemin	CrO_3—H_2SO_4	Haematinic acid
Mesoporphyrin	CrO_3—H_2SO_4	Ethylmethylmaleimide
Haemin	Fe—HCO_2H	Protoporphyrin
Haemin	HBr—CH_3CO_2H	Haematoporphyrin
Haemin	HI—CH_3CO_2H	Mesoporphyrin
Porphyrin	Decarboxylation (and then reduction, if necessary)	Aetioporphyrins

From the foregoing evidence (the molecular formula and the degradation products of haemin), it is reasonable to infer that haemin contains four substituted pyrrole nuclei linked together. The isolation of the pyrroles (I)–(IV) suggests that each of the four pyrrole nuclei contains a methyl group in the β-position. The isolation of the oxidation products (IX) and (X) [oxidation at the α-position], and of the reduction products (I)–(VIII) [appearance of a methyl group at the α-position], suggests that the pyrrole nuclei are linked at the α-positions *via* one carbon atom. The isolation of two molecules of (IX) suggests the presence of two propionic acid residues each in the β-position of two pyrrole nuclei (this would also account for the two carboxyl groups present in haemin). The appearance of ethyl groups in (I)–(IV) on the reduction of haemin could be explained by the presence of two vinyl groups in the β-position of two pyrrole nuclei (haemin contains two ethylenic double bonds). A possible structure for haemin is thus a ring structure containing four pyrrole nuclei linked at the α-positions *via* one carbon atom, with four β-positions occupied by methyl groups, two β'-positions by vinyl groups and the remaining two β'-positions by propionic acid residues. Küster (1912) was the first to propose that the four pyrrole nuclei formed a cyclic structure, and this has been proved correct by synthetic work; the porphyrins so obtained had the same absorption spectra as the natural porphyrins. At the same time, this synthetic work established the nature and the positions of the substituent groups.

These methods, reductive and oxidative degradations, were used by the earlier workers, but the latter is now the preferred method. The difficulty with reductive degradation was that it gave rise to many products, the separation of which was difficult. More recently, however, the pyrroles have been isolated and identified by means of GLC (**1** §15g). A difficulty with oxidative degradation is that only a few imides are obtained because others, which would have been formed from pyrrole nuclei containing β-substituents such as formyl, vinyl, etc., are further oxidised. This problem has been overcome by first converting these sensitive β-substituents into more stable groups, *e.g.*, vinyl into ethyl. After oxidation, the imides are separated by GLC. A semi-micro oxidative degradation has also been developed. Oxidation is carried out with potassium permanganate–potassium hydrogen carbonate solution and the resulting pyrrolecarboxylic acids are separated and identified by paper chromatography (the R_F values have been obtained from synthetic specimens).

§2a. Porphyrins. The various compounds described in §2 are all derivatives of the parent substance known as **porphin** (I), and this may be written as (II) (Fischer). (I) is now usually written as (I*a*) and the alternative method of numbering (IUPAC rules, 1960) is also given. The carbon atoms forming the methine bridges are labelled α, β, γ, and δ in (I) or numbered 5, 10, 15, and 20 in (I*a*) [see also §7]. The hydrogen atoms attached to these methine carbon atoms are referred to as *meso* hydrogens. The pyrrole rings have been labelled A, B, C, and D in (I*a*), but in the earlier literature they have also been labelled (I), (II), (III), and (IV), respectively (as in (I)).

Examination of structure (I) or (I*a*) shows the presence of an inner eighteen-membered ring containing a complete arrangement of conjugated double bonds. Thus many resonating structures

porphin
(I)

(II)

(I*a*)

(I*b*)

contribute to this molecule, and consequently its stability will be great; this is observed in practice, *e.g.*, the molecule has a very large heat of combustion. Also, the resonance gives rise to the colour in porphin derivatives (see Ch. 31, Vol. I); porphin itself does not occur naturally.

The geometry of porphin has been investigated by various workers, and the more recent results are in conflict with the earlier ones. The resonance energy of porphin would be a maximum if the molecule had structure (I) or (I*a*) and was flat. Earlier work, based on analogy with the X-ray data of the phthalocyanines (§9), led to the conclusion that the porphin molecule is planar, and this was also in agreement with magnetic measurements. Crute (1959) examined nickel aetioporphyrin II (see Table 19.2) by X-ray analysis and the results indicated a flat molecule. On the other hand, Fleischer (1963) has shown, from X-ray analysis, that nickel aetioporphyrin I (see Table 19.2) is not planar; the alternate pyrrole rings are bent up and down from the mean plane. Fleischer *et al.* (1965) have also examined porphin by X-ray analysis, and found that the molecule is nearly planar, the observed small deviations from planarity not being large enough to be significant. These authors have also proposed an alternative electronic structure (I*b*) for porphin. All 3,4-bonds in the pyrrole nuclei are represented as double bonds. The inner ring π-cloud has 16 atoms, each atom in the ring contributing one electron to the π-system of this ring. Since porphin with no protons or metal ions bonded to the nitrogens is a dianion, two more electrons are therefore added to the π-system of the 16-membered ring. Thus the total number of electrons is 18, and this is consistent with the $(4n + 2)$ electrons required by Hückel's rule for a stable aromatic system. The inner ring is now similar to the cyclo-octatetraene dianion (which has 10 electrons; see also Ch. 20, Vol. I). Addition of two protons or a di-positive metal ion to the centre of the dianion ring produces a neutral species.

The authors suggest that a better description of the molecule may be a combination of the two electronic structure, (I*a*) and (I*b*).

The NMR spectrum ($CDCl_3$) of coproporphyrin I methyl ester (all P groups are methyl esters; see Table 19.2) has been examined (Becker *et al.*, 1959). Two singlets were observed at τ 0·04 and 13·89. The low-field singlet was assigned to the four 'outer' *meso* hydrogens, the large shift to lower field of olefinic protons being due to the presence of a large ring current. On the other hand, the very high-field signal was attributed to the imino hydrogens (NH) which are *inside* the ring (see the ring current effect, **1** §12e). The existence of a ring current is evidence for aromaticity (see also Vol. I, and below).

Substituted porphins are known as **porphyrins**. Let us first consider the aetioporphyrins, $C_{32}H_{38}N_4$. These are tetra-ethyltetramethylporphins, and on the assumption that two identical groups do not occur in the same pyrrole nucleus, there will be four possible isomers (H. Fischer). All four have been synthesised by Fischer, and they are known as aetioporphyrins I, II, III and IV, respectively. The degradation of haemin gives aetioporphyrin III. Some common porphyrins are listed in Table 19.2; all the aetioporphyrins have been given, since these illustrate the distributions of the substituents. When there are three different substituent groups and each pyrrole nucleus has two different types, then fifteen isomers are possible. Some porphyrins occur free in nature, *e.g.*, protoporphyrin IX and coproporphyrins I and III occur in blood. Inspection of the Table shows that protoporphyrin IX, coproporphyrin III and uroporphyrin III have the same 'pattern' as aetioporphyrin III. All the porphyrins which possess some biological function belong to this pattern.

Spectral properties of porphyrins. Infrared studies of porphyrins have shown that most of the functional groups absorb in the expected regions and so may be detected, *e.g.*, OH, CO_2H, CO_2R, etc. The band for the NH group (str.) occurs around 3 300 cm^{-1}, and since it is almost unaffected in a dilute solution in carbon tetrachloride, this is strong evidence that there is intramolecular hydrogen bonding. Also, this band is consistent with there being hydrogen atoms attached to opposite nitrogen atoms and each being bonded to an adjacent nitrogen atom (*cf.* formula (I)).

The visible spectra of porphyrins have been studied in great detail. The neutral metal-free

Table 19.2

Porphyrin	Substituent (Fischer numbering)							
	1	2	3	4	5	6	7	8
Aetioporphyrin I	M	E	M	E	M	E	M	E
Aetioporphyrin II	M	E	E	M	M	E	M	E
Aetioporphyrin III	M	E	M	E	M	E	E	M
Aetioporphyrin IV	E	M	M	E	M	E	E	M
Coproporphyrin I	M	P	M	P	M	P	M	P
Coproporphyrin III	M	P	M	P	M	P	P	M
Uroporphyrin I	A	P	A	P	A	P	A	P
Uroporphyrin III	A	P	A	P	A	P	P	A
Protoporphyrin IX	M	V	M	V	M	P	P	M
Deuteroporphyrin IX	M	H	M	H	M	P	P	M
Haematoporphyrin IX	M	hE	M	hE	M	P	P	M
Mesoporphyrin IX	M	E	M	E	M	P	P	M
Pyrroporphyrin IX	M	E	M	E	M	H	P	M
Rhodoporphyrin XV	M	E	M	E	M	C	P	M

Substituent symbols; $A = -CH_2CO_2H$; $C = -CO_2H$; $E = -C_2H_5$; $H = -H$;
$hE = -CHOHCH_3$; $M = CH_3$; $P = -CH_2CH_2CO_2H$; $V = -CH=CH_2$.

porphyrins usually have four absorption bands between 500 and 650 nm. These bands have been numbered I, II, III and IV, the wavelengths of the maxima decreasing from I to IV. Figure 19.1 illustrates (diagrammatically) these spectra, and the intensity of any given band depends on the

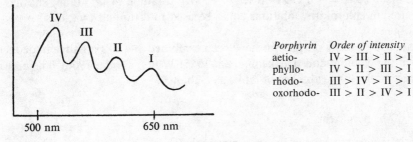

Porphyrin	Order of intensity
aetio-	IV > III > II > I
phyllo-	IV > II > III > I
rhodo-	III > IV > II > I
oxorhodo-	III > II > IV > I

Fig. 19.1

porphyrin under investigation. In practice four types have been observed; these are given in Fig. 19.1. As pointed out above, the aetio 'pattern' is the most important one; three examples are listed in Table 19.3.

Table 19.3

Porphyrin	Band λ_{max} nm (ε)			
	I	II	III	IV
Deuteroporphyrin	618 (4 330)	565 (6 800)	525 (8 750)	495 (15 950)
Mesoporphyrin	620 (5 410)	567 (6 590)	528 (9 820)	496 (14 240)
Protoporphyrin	630 (5 580)	575 (6 780)	537 (11 580)	503 (14 640)

In addition to the four bands (I–IV), there is a band in the region of 400 nm. This is known as the *Soret band* and is characteristic of all conjugated tetrapyrroles. It is absent when this conjugation is broken; *e.g.*, bile pigments do not show this band. The Soret band has about twenty times the intensity of the strongest visible band and can be used to characterise porphyrins.

The spectra of porphyrin mono-cations usually consist of a Soret band and three visible bands (I–III), and those of porphyrin di-cations usually consist of a Soret band and two visible bands (I and II). Metalloporphyrins generally exhibit two maxima in the visible region. These are known as the α- (nearer the red) and β-bands, and there is also the Soret band (γ-band) near 400 nm.

Substituent groups in which a 'saturated' carbon atom is directly joined to the pyrrole nucleus have very little effect on the spectrum, *e.g.*, groups such as Me, Et, CH_2CO_2H, $CH_2CH_2CO_2H$. In cases such as these the 'resonance path' of the porphin molecule is very little changed. When, however, the substituent group can give rise to different resonance paths (by extended conjugation), then both the wavelengths and intensities of the bands are changed. Such groups are $-CH{=}CH_2$, CO_2H, CHO (*cf.* Table 19.3).

Examination of the visible spectra of a large number of porphyrins of known structure has resulted in correlations being made between the nature of the side-chain and the position and intensity of its visible bands. These correlations are very important as a means of identifying porphyrins, and are also of great help in elucidating structures of unknown porphyrins. The ultraviolet and visible absorption maxima of haemin itself are: 390, 505, 540, 578 and 659 nm.

Abraham *et al.* (1961, 1966) have studied the NMR spectra of porphyrins in trifluoroacetic acid and showed that the τ-values of the protons in various groups lie between ranges which clearly distinguish them from one another: *meso*-hydrogen, τ $-1{\cdot}22$ to $-0{\cdot}98$; methyl hydrogens, τ $6{\cdot}24$–$6{\cdot}16$; ethyl hydrogens: CH_2, τ $5{\cdot}71$–$5{\cdot}69$; CH_3, $8{\cdot}18$–$8{\cdot}15$; etc. Furthermore, it was shown that the τ-values of *meso*-hydrogens were affected by the nature of the adjacent β-substituents, *e.g.*, in porphin itself, τ of meso-hydrogen $= -1{\cdot}22$; for a *meso*-hydrogen flanked on both sides by β-propionate residues, $\tau = -1{\cdot}19$. Further work by Abraham *et al.* (1966) showed that NMR spectra measured in chloroform solutions could be used to distinguish various porphyrin isomers from one another.

The mass spectra of many porphyrins have been examined and it is possible to deduce structural information of these compounds (Jackson *et al.*, 1965; Whitten *et al.*, 1966). The molecular ion is usually the base peak (in the absence of labile side-chains).

§3. Synthesis of the porphyrins

The first step in the synthesis of porphyrins is usually the synthesis of dipyrrylmethenes. This was the method adopted by the earlier workers, but pure porphyrins were obtained in poor yield. Later syntheses start with dipyrrylmethanes; the yield of porphyrin is high (see §7b).

(i) Dipyrrylmethenes may be prepared by the bromination of a 2-*methylpyrrole in which position 5 is vacant* (H. Fischer, 1915); *e.g.*,

(ii) When pyrroles, in which the 5-position is vacant, are coupled by means of formic acid in the presence of hydrobromic acid, dipyrrylmethenes are produced (H. Fischer *et al.*, 1922); *e.g.*, (reaction scheme: two pyrrole units (EtO₂C, Me, Me) + HCO₂H →(HBr) dipyrrylmethene product with Br⁻)

(iii) Unsymmetrical dipyrrylmethenes, *i.e.*, those containing two different substituted pyrroles, may be prepared as follows (Piloty *et al.*, 1912, 1914; H. Fischer *et al.*, 1926), *e.g.* (see also §2):

(*a*) (pyrrole) + HCN + HCl →(AlCl₃) (pyrrole-CHO)

(*b*) (reaction scheme showing condensation of aldehyde pyrrole with methyl pyrrole, HBr, intermediate structures, −H⁺, (i) +H⁺ (ii) −H₂O giving dipyrrylmethene product with Br⁻)

(iv) Another method of preparing unsymmetrical dipyrrylmethenes is (H. Fischer *et al.*, 1928):

(*a*) (pyrrole) + MeOCH₂Cl → (pyrrole-CH₂OMe) + HCl

(*b*) (pyrrole-CH₂OMe) + (pyrrole) →(HCl) (dipyrrylmethene product with Cl⁻)

(v) Dipyrrylmethanes have been prepared as shown in method (i) [see also §7b].

Many methods were introduced by H. Fischer to convert dipyrrylmethenes into porphyrins, but the most useful were: (i) Condensation between the hydrobromides of two 5-bromo-5′-methyl-dipyrrylmethenes; (ii) condensation between the hydrobromides of a 5,5′-dibromo- and a 5,5′-dimethyldipyrrylmethene. The condensations were carried out by heating with succinic acid at 220°C (see also §4).

The particular value of these two methods was that only one product was obtained. Many of the other methods resulted in a mixture of isomers. These were difficult to separate, but Marks *et al.* (1960) have separated such mixtures by counter-current distribution between dilute hydrochloric acid and ether.

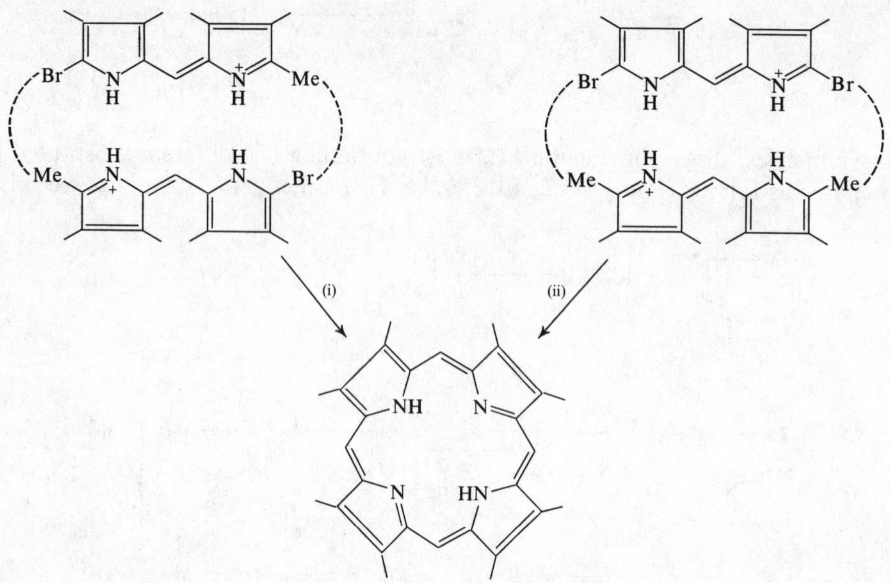

H. Fischer *et al.* (1926) prepared aetioporphyrin I as shown (M = Me, E = Et):

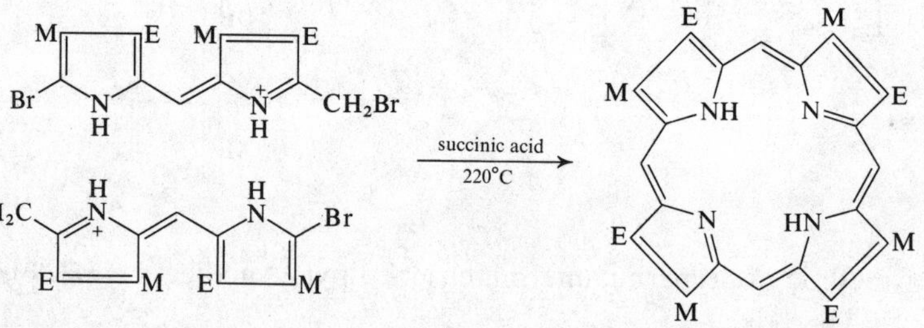

aetioporphyrin I

Porphin itself was synthesised by H. Fischer *et al.* (1935) by heating pyrrole-2-aldehyde with formic acid and ethanol. A later synthesis was carried out by heating pyrrole with formaldehyde in a mixture of methanol and pyridine (Rothemund, 1936, 1939; Calvin *et al.*, 1943).

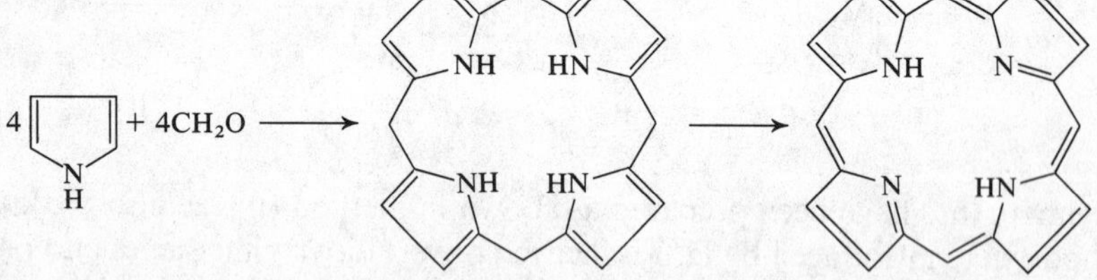

porphin

Dipyrrylmethanes, as pointed out above, have recently been used to synthesise porphyrins (see §§7a, 7b).

§4. Synthesis of haemin (H. Fischer *et al.*, 1929)

The approach to this synthesis has already been discussed, *viz.*, synthesis of pyrroles containing methyl groups and propionic acid residues in the correct positions (§2), followed by their combination to dipyrrylmethenes (§3), and then formation of the porphyrin (§3). However, at the time, there was no existing method for synthesising porphyrins with unsaturated side-chains. Fischer solved

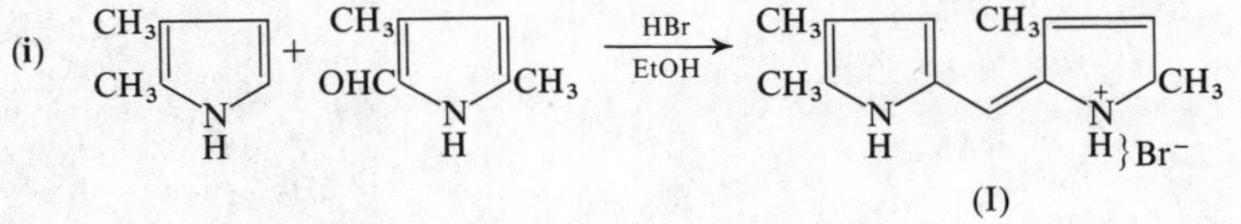

(i)

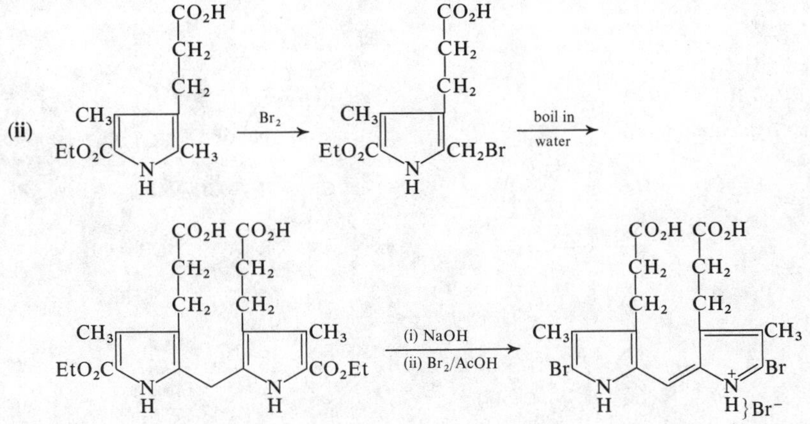

(I)

(ii)

(iii) (I) + (II)

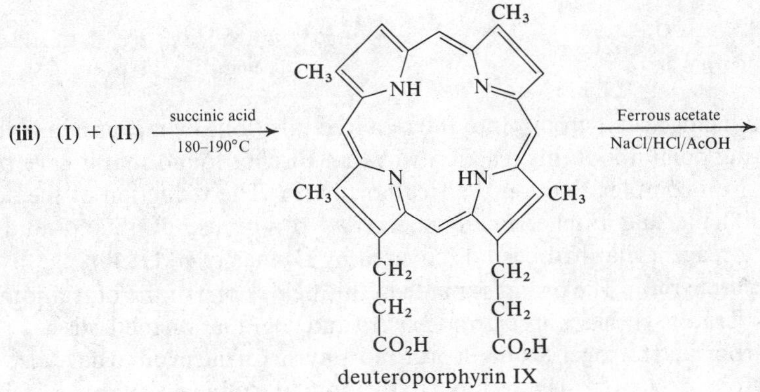

deuteroporphyrin IX

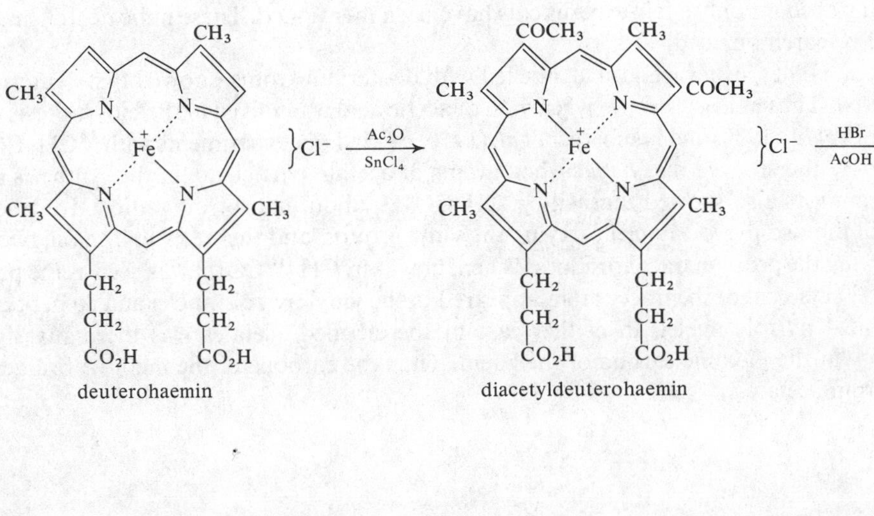

deuterohaemin

diacetyldeuterohaemin

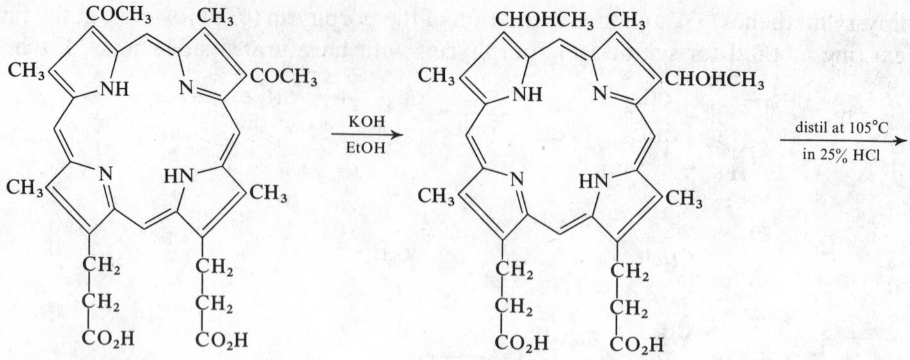

diacetyldeuteroporphyrin

haematoporphyrin IX

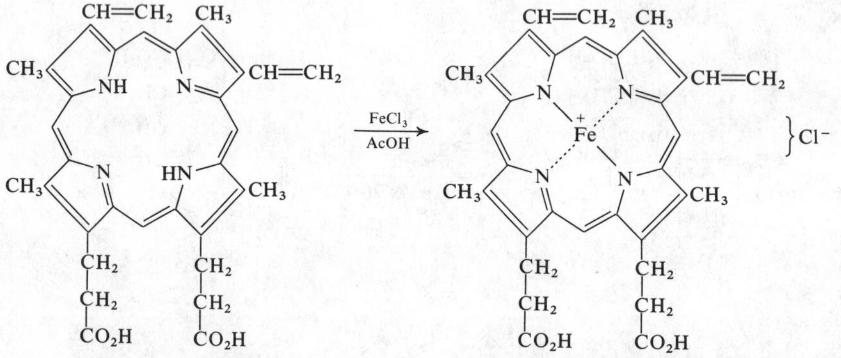

KOH
EtOH

distil at 105°C
in 25% HCl

protoporphyrin IX

haemin

FeCl₃
AcOH

this problem by introducing acetyl groups into the required positions by means of a Friedel–Crafts reaction. An interesting point about this reaction was that Fischer found that it gave better yields when carried on the iron complex than on the free porphyrin. The reduction of the acetyl group proved to be very difficult, and Fischer finally succeeded by the use of ethanol and potassium hydroxide, a reducing reagent that had been discovered by Dumas *et al.* (1840).

§4a. **Biosynthesis of porphyrin.** The progress made in this field is one of the outstanding examples of the use of isotopes. Tracer syntheses *in vivo* and *in vitro* and degradation methods have established the origin of all the carbon and nitrogen atoms in protoporphyrin (of haem), and have also established the nature of the pyrrole precursors. The results are the outcome of a large volume of work, but in the following account only a few experiments have been mentioned. These indicate, to some extent, the lines of research pursued.

Bloch *et al.* (1945), using acetic acid labelled with deuterium atoms, showed that deuteriohaemin was produced. Thus at least the methyl carbon of acetic acid is involved in the biosynthesis of haem. Then Shemin *et al.* (1950) and Neuberger *et al.* (1950) carried out experiments with $^{14}CH_3CO_2H$ and $CH_3{}^{14}CO_2H$, and showed that *both* carbon atoms of acetate participate in the synthesis of haem. The latter authors also showed that with $^{14}CH_3CO_2H$, about half of the radioactive tracer atom appeared in the two pyrrole nuclei carrying the vinyl groups, and the other half in the two pyrrole nuclei carrying the propionic acid residues. When, however, $CH_3{}^{14}CO_2H$ was used as the precursor, then about 20 per cent of the tracer atom appeared in the vinyl pyrrole nuclei and 80 per cent in the propionic acid pyrrole nuclei. In neither case of the labelled acetates was there any significant radioactivity in the methine carbon of the haem. Thus the carbons of the methine bridges do not originate from acetate.

Shemin *et al*. (1945, 1946) carried out experiments with [^{15}N] glycine, and showed that all the and showed that the carboxyl group of glycine is *not* incorporated into protoporphyrin. On the other hand, Altman *et al*. (1948), using $^{14}CH_2NH_2CO_2H$, showed that the α-carbon atom of glycine *is* used in the protoporphyrin synthesis. This was confirmed by Shemin *et al*. (1950) who used $^{14}CH_2{}^{15}NH_2CO_2H$ and showed that for each nitrogen used for haem synthesis, two α-carbon atoms of glycine were also incorporated into the molecule. Similar results were obtained by Neuberger *et al*. (1950) who also showed that the α-carbon atom of glycine is used in the formation of the methine bridge. Thus all the carbon atoms of protoporphyrin, except eight derived from the α-carbon of glycine, originate from acetate.

We may now summarise the foregoing results for the biosynthesis of protoporphyrin IX (and haems in general).

(i) All four nitrogen atoms are derived from the nitrogen of glycine.

(ii) The four methine carbon atoms are derived from the α-carbon atoms of glycine (see also below).

(iii) Four carbon atoms, one in each pyrrole ring (α-position), are derived from the α-carbon atoms of glycine (see also below).

(iv) The carbon atom of the carboxyl group in glycine is *not* incorporated into protoporphyrin IX.

(v) The remaining 26 carbon atoms in protoporphyrin IX are derived from either the methyl group or the carboxyl group of acetic acid.

A detailed study of the degradation products of the labelled protoporphyrins showed that it was very probable that the two sides of the pyrrole nuclei were synthesised from identical intermediates. It also seemed very reasonable that a *common* pyrrole of the type (I) was formed first. Also, consideration of the distribution of the radioactivity of the carbon atoms of the propionic acid residue and the (pyrrole) nuclear carbon to which it was attached led to the suggestion that succinic acid was a precursor. The tracer distribution of the labelled succinic acid could arise by acetate entering the *Krebs cycle* (**13** §18). Shemin *et al*. (1952) tested this succinic acid hypothesis by using $HO_2{}^{14}CCH_2CH_2{}^{14}CO_2H$ and $HO_2C^{14}CH_2{}^{14}CH_2CO_2H$, and showed that haem contained the labelled carbon.

In 1952, Westall isolated **porphobilinogen** from the urine of humans suffering from acute porphyria. Based on this, Shemin *et al*. (1953) now proposed that δ-aminolaevulic acid (II) can replace 'active' succinate and glycine in porphyrin synthesis. It should be noted that (i) the α-carbon atom of the pyrrole nucleus *not* attached to the aminomethyl side-chain is the only one in the ring which is derived from the α-carbon atom of glycine; (ii) the methine carbon atom is also derived from the α-carbon atom of glycine (see also above).

(II) + (II) ⟶ porphobilinogen - - - → protoporphyrin

This pyrrole synthesis is supported by various experiments, *e.g*., Shemin *et al*. (1954) used [$\delta^{14}C$]δ-aminolaevulic acid as precursor, and showed that half of the radioactivity is equally distributed among the four pyrrole nuclei and the other half is in the methine-bridge carbons. This distribution is in agreement with the equation given. Furthermore, Falk *et al.* (1953) have shown that prophobilinogen is the common precursor in porphyrin synthesis.

The enzyme ALA synthetase, which catalyses the reaction between succinyl-coenzyme A and glycine to give δ-aminolaevulic acid (ALA), was first isolated by Neuberger *et al.* (1958) and later by Kikuchi *et al.* (1958) and by Burnham (1962) in a purer form. Hence, the conversion of succinic acid (as succinyl-coenzyme A) and glycine into porphobilinogen may be formulated as shown.

$$
\begin{array}{c}
CO_2H \\
| \\
CH_2 \\
| \\
CH_2 \\
| \\
CO-SCoA
\end{array}
+
\begin{array}{c}
CH_2NH_2 \\
| \\
CO_2H
\end{array}
\xrightarrow[\text{synthetase}]{ALA}
\begin{array}{c}
CO_2H \\
| \\
CH_2 \\
| \\
CH_2 \\
| \\
CO \\
| \\
CHNH_2 \\
| \\
CO_2H
\end{array}
\xrightarrow{-CO_2}
\begin{array}{c}
CO_2H \\
| \\
CH_2 \\
| \\
CH_2 \\
| \\
CO \\
| \\
CH_2NH_2
\end{array}
\xrightarrow{\text{2 molecules}}
\text{porphobilinogen}
$$

α-amino-β-oxo-adipic acid   ALA (II)   porphobilinogen

Battersby *et al.* (1972) have synthesised porphobilinogen labelled with ^{13}C at the carbon atom of the aminomethyl side-chain ($-^{13}CH_2NH_2$) and used this as a precursor in the biosynthesis of protoporphyrin IX. Examination of the signals in the ^{13}C-NMR spectrum of the porphyrin (as methyl ester) showed that all four *meso*-carbon atoms (α, β, γ, and δ) were equally labelled with ^{13}C.

The final steps in the pathway are not certain, but there is a large amount of evidence to show that the sequence is probably as follows. Porphobilinogen is converted mainly into uroporphyrinogen III (this is uroporphyrin with methylene bridges instead of methine; see Table 19.2; §2a), and to a much smaller extent into uroporphyrinogen I. Uroporphyrinogen III then undergoes stepwise decarboxylation of the acetic acid residues to methyl groups to give coproporphyrinogen III which, on oxidative decarboxylation of the propionic acid residues in rings A and B (see formula (I*a*); §2a) to vinyl groups, thereby forms protoporphyrinogen IX. This is now oxidised to protoporphyrin IX (*i.e.*,

uroporphyrinogen III   coproporphyrinogen III

protoporphyrinogen   protoporphyrin IX   haem → haemoglobin

methine bridges are produced), and a ferrous ion is then incorporated to form haem which finally links up with globin to form haemoglobin. In the chart the symbols A, M, P, and V have the meanings given in Table 19.2, §2a.

§5. Bile pigments

Several pigments occur in bile, *e.g.*, bilirubin, mesobilirubin, etc.; the most important one is **bilirubin**, $C_{33}H_{36}N_4O_6$. On vigorous oxidation, bilirubin gives haematinic acid; and on vigorous reduction, it gives cryptopyrrole and cryptopyrrolecarboxylic acid. When catalytically reduced, bilirubin gives mesobilirubin, $C_{33}H_{40}N_4O_6$, which, on reduction with hydriodic acid in acetic acid, forms, among other products, bilirubic acid, $C_{17}H_{24}N_2O_3$, and neobilirubic acid, $C_{16}H_{22}N_2O_3$. Finally, the reduction of bilirubic acid gives crypto-pyrrolecarboxylic acid as the main product, and the reduction of neobilirubic acid gives haemopyrrolecarb-oxylic acid. From this evidence it is reasonable to conclude that bilirubin contains the four pyrrole nuclei that occur in haemoglobin.

Bilirubin is an orange solid, and its ultraviolet spectrum shows one maximum at 450–455 nm. This spectrum is totally different from those of the porphyrins (see §2a), and so it may be inferred that bilirubin has an open-chain structure. On the basis of its relation to haem (the same four pyrrole nuclei) and further degradative and synthetic work, bilirubin has been assigned the structure shown (M, P and V have the meanings given in Table 19.2, §2a).

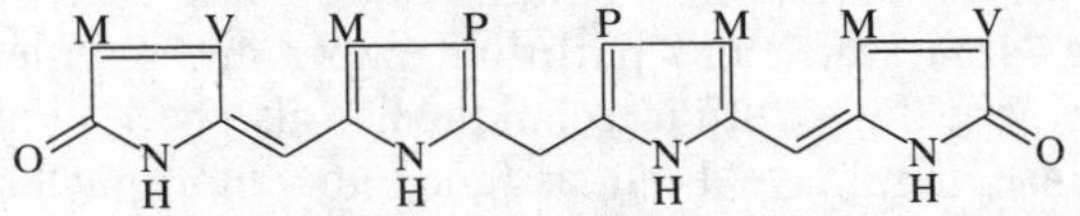

bilirubin

Until recently, the two end α-positions were considered to carry hydroxyl groups. It has now been shown that α-hydroxypyrroles are unstable and rapidly tautomerise to the stable keto form (Plieninger *et al.*, 1956). Plieninger *et al.* (1962) have also studied the NMR spectra of 3,4-dialkyl α-hydroxypyrroles and showed these compounds exist as pyrrolin-2-ones. These results are supported by the ultraviolet spectroscopic examination of the titration curves of a number of bile pigments (Gray *et al.*, 1961).

Chlorophyll

§6. Introduction

Chlorophyll is the green colouring matter of leaves and green stems, and its presence is essential for photosynthesis. Photosynthesis is the process in which light energy is used by plants to synthesise carbohydrates, proteins and fats. In green plants it is the chlorophyll which absorbs the light energy (see also 7 §23a).

The name *chlorophyll* was given to the green pigment in leaves by Pelletier and Caventou (1818). There the matter rested until 1864, when Stokes showed, from spectroscopic evidence, that chloro-phyll was a mixture. This paper apparently did not attract much attention, and it was not until Willstätter entered the field that any progress in the chemistry of chlorophyll was made.

When an ethereal solution of chlorophyll is shaken with methanolic potassium hydroxide solution, various colour changes occur. With chlorophyll-*a* the green colour immediately changes to yellow; with chlorophyll-*b*, from green to carmine red; and with a mixture of the two chlorophylls, from green to yellowish brown. Then, after a few moments, the green colour reappears in the lower layer; the ether is colourless. This set of colour reactions is known as the *phase test*, and chlorophyll prepara-tions that fail to give it are said to be *allomerised*. It is now known that the phase test involves the cyclopentanone ring in chlorophyll (see formula (XI); §7); the alkali forms traces of some intermediate which undergoes slow oxidation by oxygen (atmospheric).

When dried leaves are powdered and then digested with ethanol, a 'crystalline' chlorophyll is obtained after concentration of the solvent. If, however, ether or aqueous acetone is used instead of ethanol, then the product is 'amorphous' chlorophyll (Willstätter *et al.*, 1908). The extraction of chlorophyll is also accompanied by the extraction of two other pigments, carotene and xanthophyll (see Ch. 9). Willstätter *et al.* (1920) then showed that 'crystalline' chlorophyll was produced during the extraction of chlorophyll by means of ethanol, a molecule of phytyl alcohol being replaced by ethanol under the influence of an enzyme, chlorophyllase (which is present in leaves).

Willstätter *et al.* (1911) originally gave chlorophyll the molecular formula $C_{55}H_{72}MgN_4O_6$, but in 1912 Willstätter *et al.* showed that chlorophyll, obtained from a wide variety of sources, was a mixture of two compounds, chlorophyll-*a* and chlorophyll-*b*. The separation was effected by shaking a light petrol solution of chlorophyll with aqueous methanol; chlorophyll-*a* remains in the light petrol, and chlorophyll-*b* passes into the aqueous methanol. Chlorophyll-*a* is a bluish-black giving a green solution in organic solvents; chlorophyll-*b* is a dark green solid, also giving a green solution in organic solvents. The two components occur in proportions of approximately 3 of *a* to 1 of *b* in natural chlorophyll. The chlorophylls (and chlorophyll degradation products) are now separated by chromatography. Column chromatography (alumina, sugar, starch, etc.) may be used on a large scale, and partition, paper and thin-layer chromatography are used for small-scale work, but the partition technique has also been used on a preparative scale.

The molecular formulae that have been assigned to chlorophyll-*a* and chlorophyll-*b* are $C_{55}H_{72}N_4O_4Mg$ and $C_{55}H_{70}N_4O_6Mg$, respectively (Willstätter, 1913); the two compounds have different absorption spectra: chlorophyll-*a*, 380, 418, 428, 510, 580 and 700 nm; chlorophyll-*b*, 428, 464 and 675 nm. These characteristic absorption maxima have been used to estimate the amounts of each chlorophyll in a mixture. Infrared spectroscopy has been used to detect functional groups (*cf.* §2a), and Oster *et al.* (1964), from their examination of the infrared spectra of the chlorophylls, have shown that these spectra provide a means of detecting trace amounts of chlorophyll-*b* in samples of chlorophyll-*a* and, at the same time, offer a means of estimating the proportions of the two components.

The hydrolysis of both chlorophylls with cold dilute potassium hydroxide solution gives one molecule of phytol, $C_{20}H_{40}O$ (see **8** §31), one molecule of methanol, and one molecule of chlorophyllide-*a* (chlorophyllin-*a*) [I] or chlorophyllide-*b* (chlorophyllin-*b*) [II]. Thus the chlorophylls are diesters. When either chlorophyll is heated with an ethanolic solution of hydrated oxalic acid, the magnesium atom is replaced by two hydrogen atoms to produce phytyl phaeophorbide-*a* (III) or *b* ((IV)); these phytyl phaeophorbides are also known as phaeophytins *a* and *b*, and 'crystalline' chlorophyll is ethyl chlorophyllide). The foregoing reactions may be formulated as shown.

$$\underset{\text{chlorophyll-}a}{C_{32}H_{30}N_4OMg\diagup\overset{\displaystyle CO_2CH_3}{\underset{\displaystyle CO_2C_{20}H_{39}}{}}}$$

$$\xrightarrow[]{KOH}\quad C_{32}H_{30}N_4OMg\diagup\overset{\displaystyle CO_2H}{\underset{\displaystyle CO_2H}{}}\quad + C_{20}H_{40}O + CH_3OH$$

(I)
chlorophyllide-*a*

$$\xrightarrow[C_2H_5OH]{(CO_2H)_2}\quad C_{32}H_{32}N_4O\diagup\overset{\displaystyle CO_2CH_3}{\underset{\displaystyle CO_2C_{20}H_{39}}{}}$$

(III)
phytyl phaeophorbide-*a*

$$\text{C}_{32}\text{H}_{28}\text{N}_4\text{O}_2\text{Mg} \xrightarrow{\text{KOH}} \text{C}_{32}\text{H}_{28}\text{N}_4\text{O}_2\text{Mg}\begin{smallmatrix}\text{CO}_2\text{H}\\ \\\text{CO}_2\text{H}\end{smallmatrix} + \text{C}_{20}\text{H}_{40}\text{O} + \text{CH}_3\text{OH}$$

(II)
chlorophyllide-*b*

chlorophyll-*b*
$$\text{C}_{32}\text{H}_{28}\text{N}_4\text{O}_2\text{Mg}\begin{smallmatrix}\text{CO}_2\text{CH}_3\\ \\\text{CO}_2\text{C}_{20}\text{H}_{39}\end{smallmatrix}$$

$$\xrightarrow[\text{C}_2\text{H}_5\text{OH}]{(\text{CO}_2\text{H})_2} \text{C}_{32}\text{H}_{30}\text{N}_4\text{O}_2\begin{smallmatrix}\text{CO}_2\text{CH}_3\\ \\\text{CO}_2\text{C}_{20}\text{H}_{39}\end{smallmatrix}$$

(IV)
phytyl phaeophorbide-*b*

§6a. Nomenclature of the chlorophyll degradation products.

Porphyrins are substituted porphins (see §2a). Phyllins, phyllides and chlorophylls contain magnesium, whereas phorbins, phorbides and phytins are magnesium-free compounds, the magnesium atom having been removed and replaced by two hydrogen atoms. 7,8-Dihydroporphin is the nucleus of the *chlorin* series of compounds (tricarboxylic derivatives) which are derived from chlorophyll-*a*; *rhodins* are the corresponding compounds derived from chlorophyll-*b*. The introduction of the extra ring—two methylene groups across the 6,γ-positions (see §7)—gives rise to the *phorbins*. The prefix phaeo designates those compounds which have the same substituents that occur in chlorophyll. Chlorin itself is dihydroporphin, and the natural *red* porphyrin pigments are derivatives of porphin, whereas the *green* chlorophylls and their derivatives are derivatives of chlorin. In some cases a subscript is used to indicate the number of oxygen atoms in the molecule, *e.g.*, phaeoporphyrin-a_5 contains five oxygen atoms.

§7. Structure of chlorophyll-*a*

When phytyl phaeophorbide-*a* is hydrolysed with boiling methanolic potassium hydroxide (30 seconds), the product is chlorin-*e*. This is a tricarboxylic acid (*e.g.*, it forms a trimethyl ester), and its molecular formula may thus be written as $\text{C}_{31}\text{H}_{33}\text{N}_4(\text{CO}_2\text{H})_3$. Chlorin-*e*, on oxidation with chromic acid or with Caro's acid, gives haematinic acid (I) and ethylmethylmaleimide (II) [Willstätter *et al.*, 1910]. When chlorin-*e* is reduced with hydriodic acid in acetic acid, haemopyrrole (III) and phyllo-

pyrrole (IV) are produced (Willstätter *et al.*, 1911). When phylloporphyrin (see below) is reduced under the same conditions, the products are now (III), (IV) and cryptopyrrole (V). From these results it is reasonable to infer that chlorophyll-*a* contains four pyrrole nuclei, each probably having a methyl group in the β-position (see (II)–(V)). It is also reasonable to suppose that at least one pyrrole nucleus contains a propionic acid residue in the β'-position (see (I)). It also appears likely that a vinyl group is present in the molecule (this would account for the presence of an ethyl group on reduction; at the same time, the presence of an ethyl group, as such, is not excluded). Furthermore, the isolation of (I) and (II) on oxidation (giving oxidation at the α-position), and of (III) and

(VI)

(IV) on reduction (the appearance of a methyl group at the α-position), can be interpreted as meaning that the four pyrrole nuclei are joined to each other at their α-positions *via* one carbon atom (*cf.* §2). Thus a possible skeleton structure for chlorin-*e* could be a cyclic one, (VI); the positions of the various substituent groups cannot be assigned on the evidence obtained so far, *e.g.*, a methyl group at 1 and a propionic acid residue at 2 would produce the same oxidation product (I) had the positions of the two groups been interchanged in (VI). It is also necessary to fit a second carboxyl group into this structure (VI), since chlorophyll-*a* forms chlorophyllide-*a* on hydrolysis (the latter compound contains two carboxyl groups). Furthermore, since chlorophyllide-*a*, on further hydrolysis, forms chlorin-*e*, a tricarboxylic acid, some group must be present which can give rise to this third carboxyl group. Such a group could be a lactone; it must be *cyclic* since no carbon atoms are lost after the hydrolysis.

By the further degradation of chlorin-*e*, *e.g.*, heating in a sealed tube with ethanolic potassium hydroxide, various porphyrins are obtained. Three of these are pyrroporphyrin, rhodoporphyrin and phylloporphyrin.

Pyrroporphyrin $C_{30}H_{33}N_4(CO_2H)$ has an absorption spectrum closely resembling that of meso-porphyrin (see §2b); this agrees with the tentative skeleton structure (VI) proposed for chlorin-*e*. Pyrroporphyrin, on bromination followed by oxidation with chromic acid, gives bromocitraconimide (VII) as one of the products (Treibs *et al.*, 1928). It therefore follows that at least one of the pyrrole nuclei in pyrroporphyrin has a free β-position available for bromination. Synthetic work then showed that pyrroporphyrin has structure (VIII) [H. Fischer *et al.*, 1929, 1930, 1933]; thus the positions of the four methyl groups and the position of the propionic acid group are now established.

(VII)

(VIII)
pyrroporphyrin IX

Rhodoporphyrin $C_{30}H_{32}N_4(CO_2H)_2$, on heating with sodium ethoxide, readily loses *one* carboxyl group to form pyrroporphyrin (VIII). From a detailed study of the haemin series, it was observed that a carboxyl group in a *side-chain* of a pyrrole nucleus was difficult to remove. Hence it is probable that the carboxyl group lost from rhodoporphyrin is attached *directly* to a pyrrole nucleus. The only position for this carboxyl group is at 6 (see structure (VIII)); elimination of the carboxyl group from rhodoporphyrin would then give one pyrrole nucleus with a free β-position (6), *i.e.*, pyrroporphyrin. Furthermore, comparison of the absorption spectra of rhodoporphyrin with compounds of known structure showed that the two carboxyl groups are in positions 6 and 7 (the latter is the propionic acid residue), and this was confirmed by the synthesis of rhodoporphyrin.

Phylloporphyrin $C_{31}H_{35}N_4(CO_2H)$ contains one CH_2 group more than pyrroporphyrin, and may be converted into the latter by heating with sodium ethoxide. It therefore follows that the alkyl groups in both compounds occupy similar positions. Synthetic work then showed that phylloporphyrin contains a methyl group attached to the γ-methine carbon atom (H. Fischer *et al.*, 1930, 1933).

Consideration of the information obtained from the structures of the porphyrins described above shows that the skeleton structure (IX) is present in chlorin-*e*. Now chlorin-*e* contains three carboxyl groups and one more carbon atom than the structure shown in (IX). The formation of a methyl group (at the γ carbon atom) could be explained by assuming a carboxyl group is attached as shown in structure (X).

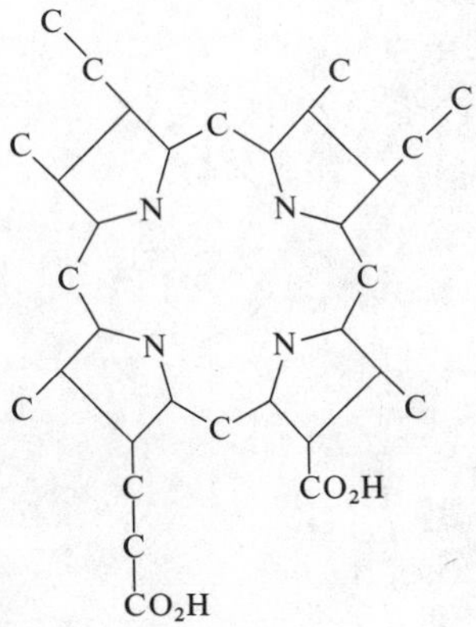

(IX)

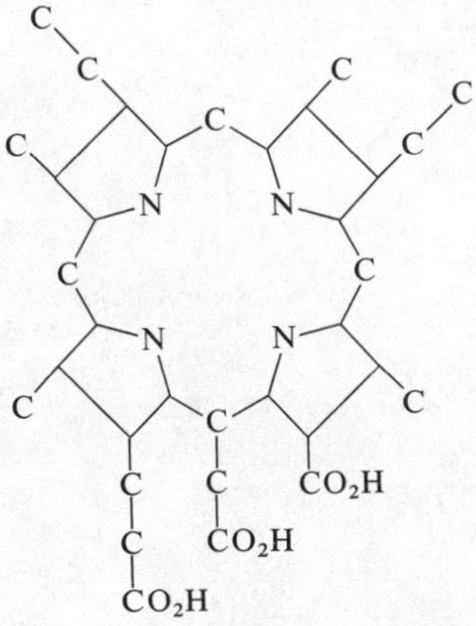

(X)

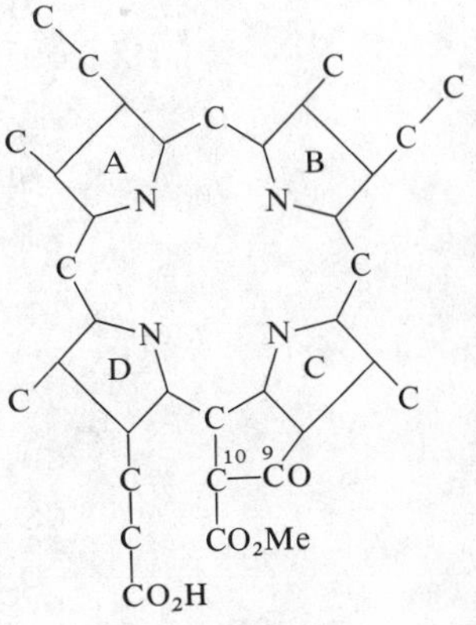

(XI)

When phytyl phaeophorbide-*a* ((III), §6) is hydrolysed with acid, the phytyl group is removed to form phaeophorbide-*a*.

$$C_{32}H_{32}N_4O\begin{matrix}CO_2CH_3\\ CO_2C_{20}H_{39}\end{matrix} \xrightarrow{\text{acid}} C_{32}H_{32}N_4O\begin{matrix}CO_2CH_3\\ CO_2H\end{matrix} + C_{20}H_{40}O$$

phytyl phaeophorbide-*a*   phaeophorbide-*a*

When phaeophorbide-*a* is treated with hydriodic acid in acetic acid and followed by atmospheric oxidation, the product is phaeophorphyrin-a_5. This, on further treatment with hydriodic acid in acetic acid, forms phylloerythrin, $C_{33}H_{34}N_4O_3$, by loss of the carbomethoxyl group; phylloerythrin has the same absorption spectrum as that of the porphyrins, and so the porphin structure is still present. Now both phaeophorbide-*a* and phylloerythrin contain a keto group (as is shown by the formation of an oxime, etc.), and so when the carbomethoxyl group is hydrolysed, the elimination of carbon dioxide can be expected if the keto group is in the β-position with respect to the carboxyl group (produced on hydrolysis). Furthermore, the hydrolysis of phaeophorbide-*a* with methanolic potassium hydroxide gives chlorin-*e*. In this reaction, apart from the hydrolysis of the carbomethoxyl group, the keto group is lost and a carboxyl group is introduced *without the loss of any carbon atoms.* This may be explained by assuming that this carboxyl group (the third one in chlorin-*e*) is produced by the fission of a *cyclic ketone*, and not from a lactone as suggested previously (see above). Thus a possible skeleton structure for phaeophorbide-*a* is (XI); if the ketone ring is opened, then the formation of (X) can be expected. Also, the hydrolysis of (XI) would produce a β-keto-acid, which can be expected to lose carbon dioxide readily to form phylloerythrin.

Phaeophorbide-*a* can be reduced catalytically to its dihydro-derivative in which the keto group remains intact. This suggests the presence of a readily reducible double bond. Oxidation experiments on phaeophorbide-*a* and dihydrophaeophorbide-*a* showed the presence of one vinyl group in the former. Furthermore, the existence of a vinyl group in the ester of chlorin-*e* was shown by the reaction with diazoacetic ester to give a cyclopropane derivative, which was isolated by the oxidation of the addition product (H. Fischer *et al.*, 1935; *cf.* **12** §2a). Thus one of the ethyl groups (see pyrroporphyrin (VIII)) must have been a vinyl group before reduction. Further degradative and synthetic work by H. Fischer *et al.* (1934–1936) showed that phaeophorbide-*a* is (XII) and that phytyl phaeophorbide-*a* is (XIII).

The replacement of the two imino hydrogen atoms in (XIII) by a magnesium atom would therefore give chlorophyll-*a*; this is (XIV). Chlorophyll-*b* has been assigned structure (XV).

(XII): R = H; phaeophorbide-*a*
(XIII): R = $C_{20}H_{39}$; phytyl phaeophorbide-*a*

(XIV): R = Me; chlorophyll-*a*
(XV): R = CHO; chlorophyll-*b*

§7a. Synthesis of chlorophyll.   The following is a brief account of the total synthesis of chlorophyll-*a* by Woodward *et al.* (1960). Their approach to the synthesis was guided by some of the known reactions of chlorophyll, *e.g.*, an unusual property of chlorophyll is that, although a chlorin (7,8-dihydroporphyrin), it is difficult to oxidise to the porphyrin. Since the two groups (methyl and the propionic acid residue) are in the same positions in haemin (§4), it was argued that the substituent on the γ-carbon atom (see §7, structure (VI)) must create large steric effects when all three groups lie in one plane. In the chlorin, the groups at 7 and 8 are now *trans* and so the steric effects are minimised. On the basis of this argument and also for other reasons, porphyrin (I) was chosen as the key intermediate of the synthesis and its conversion to the chlorin left to a later stage. This chlorin, chlorin-*e* trimethyl ester (XVII), had previously been converted into chlorophyll-*a*; hence the Woodward synthesis is a total synthesis.

(I)   (II)

This was dissected into the four pyrrole derivatives shown in (II) which were then synthesised. The synthesis then proceeded as follows:

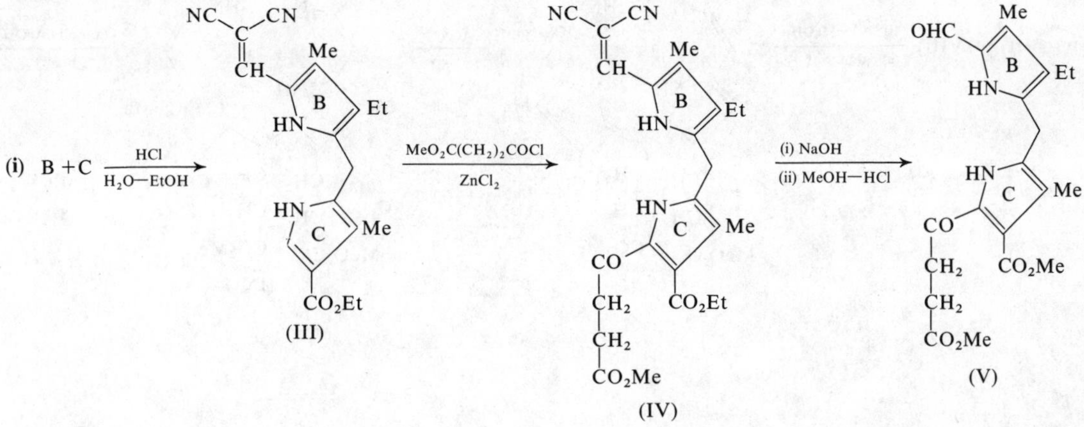

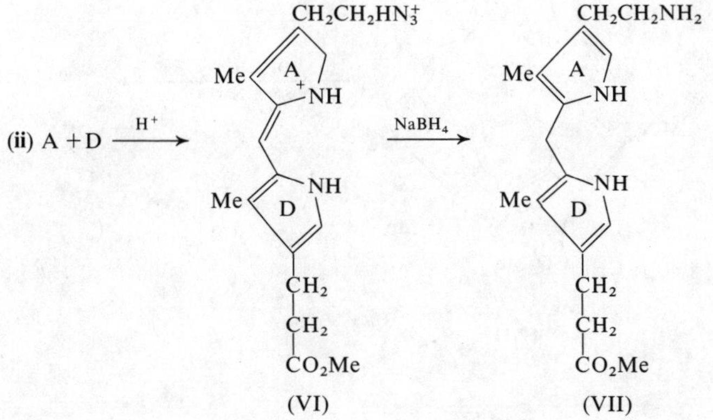

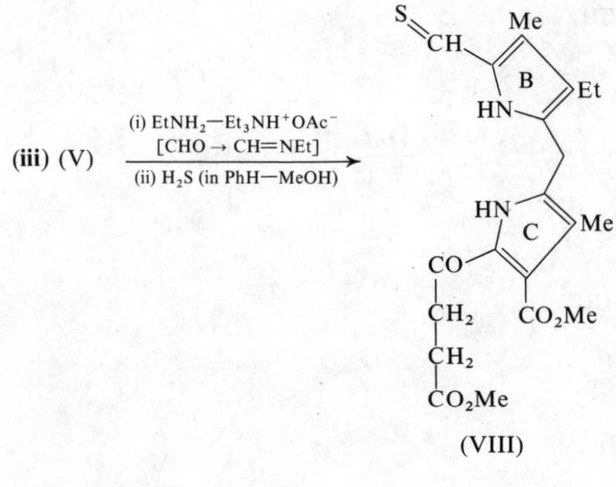

(i) $B + C$ $\xrightarrow[\text{H}_2\text{O}-\text{EtOH}]{\text{HCl}}$ (III) $\xrightarrow[\text{ZnCl}_2]{\text{MeO}_2\text{C(CH}_2)_2\text{COCl}}$ (IV) $\xrightarrow[\text{(ii) MeOH}-\text{HCl}]{\text{(i) NaOH}}$ (V)

(III)

(IV)

(V)

(ii) $A + D$ $\xrightarrow{\text{H}^+}$ (VI) $\xrightarrow{\text{NaBH}_4}$ (VII)

(VI)

(VII)

(iii) (V) $\xrightarrow[\text{(ii) H}_2\text{S (in PhH}-\text{MeOH)}]{\text{(i) EtNH}_2-\text{Et}_3\text{NH}^+\text{OAc}^- \quad [\text{CHO} \rightarrow \text{CH}=\text{NEt}]}$ (VIII)

(VIII)

(iv) (VII) + (VIII) $\xrightarrow[\text{(ii) oxidn. with } I_2]{\text{(i) HCl—MeOH}}$

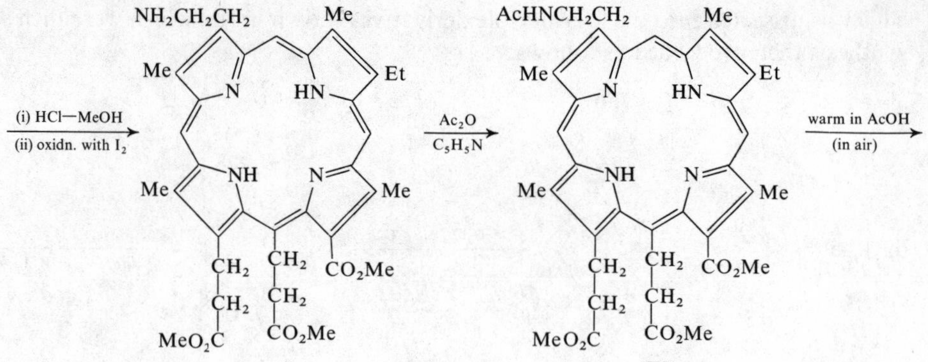

(I)

$\xrightarrow[\text{C}_5\text{H}_5\text{N}]{\text{Ac}_2\text{O}}$

(IX)

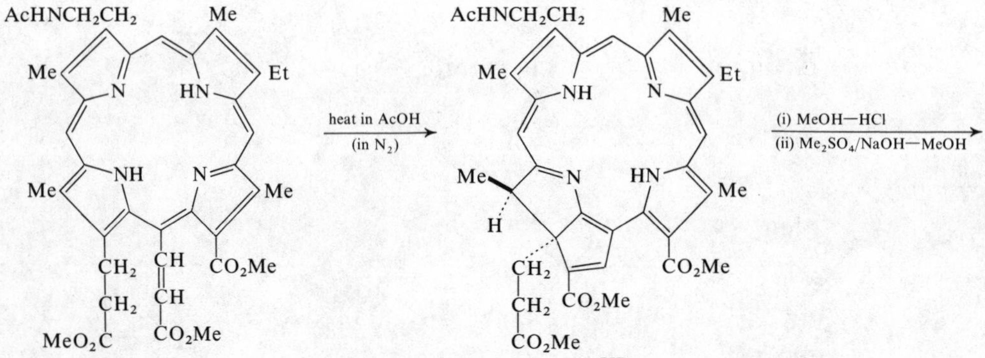

$\xrightarrow[\text{(in air)}]{\text{warm in AcOH}}$

(X)

$\xrightarrow[\text{(in N}_2)]{\text{heat in AcOH}}$

(XI)

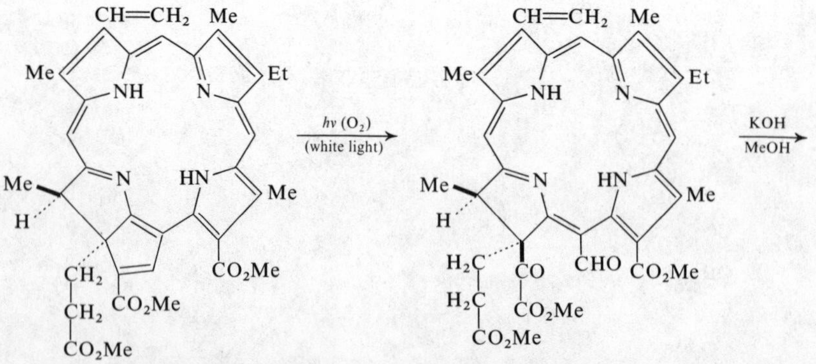

$\xrightarrow[\text{(ii) Me}_2\text{SO}_4/\text{NaOH—MeOH}]{\text{(i) MeOH—HCl}}$

(XII)

$\xrightarrow[\text{(white light)}]{h\nu \text{ (O}_2)}$

(XIII)

$\xrightarrow[\text{MeOH}]{\text{KOH}}$

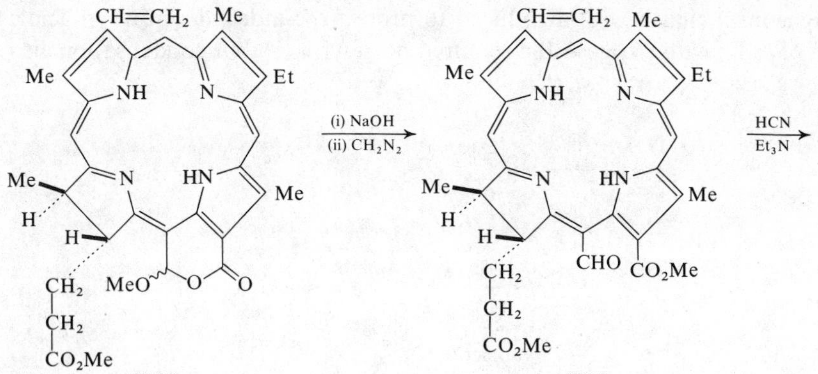

(XIV)

(i) NaOH
(ii) CH₂N₂

(XV)

HCN
Et₃N

(XVI)

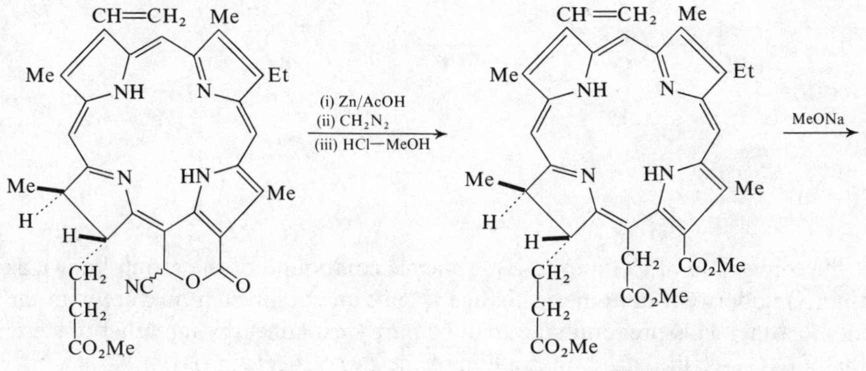

(i) Zn/AcOH
(ii) CH₂N₂
(iii) HCl—MeOH

(XVII)
chlorin-*e* trimethyl ester

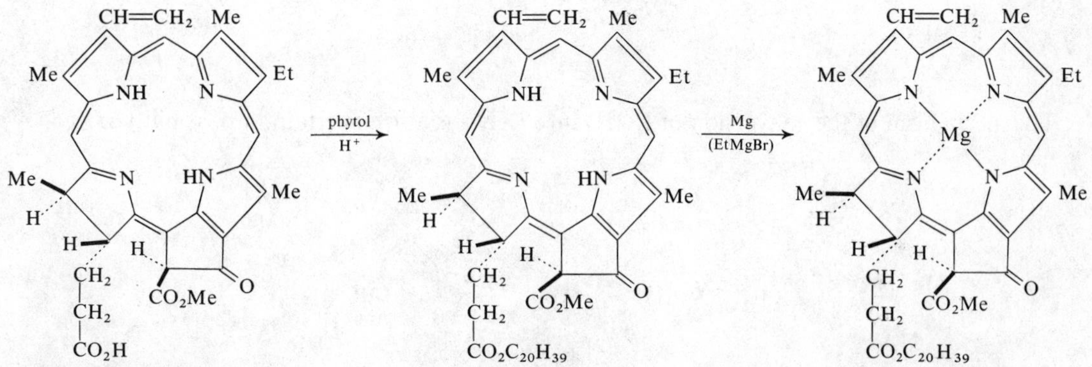

MeONa

(XVIII)
phaeophorbide-*a*

phytol
H⁺

(XIX)
phaeophytin-*a*

Mg
(EtMgBr)

chlorophyll-*a*

The malondinitrile fragment in ring B was introduced to protect the aldehyde group in acidic media. The condensation of (VII) with (V) gave the required porphyrin (I), but condensation also occurred in the opposite way.

Woodward therefore devised a method to give only (I). The formyl group in (V) was converted into the 5-thioformyl group (VIII). This reacted rapidly with the amino-group in (VII) to form a Schiff base which, on treatment with methanolic hydrogen chloride, gave (I).

The mechanism of the conversion of (X) into ((XI); a purple compound of the group known as *purpurins*) is uncertain. (X) underwent tautomeric change to give an equilibrium mixture with the cyclic form (XI) predominating. This predominance can be partly explained by the relief of steric strain in the formation of (XI) [see the earlier discussion of the steric effects in (I)].

The mechanism of the conversion of (XIII) into (XIV) is also uncertain; a possibility is:

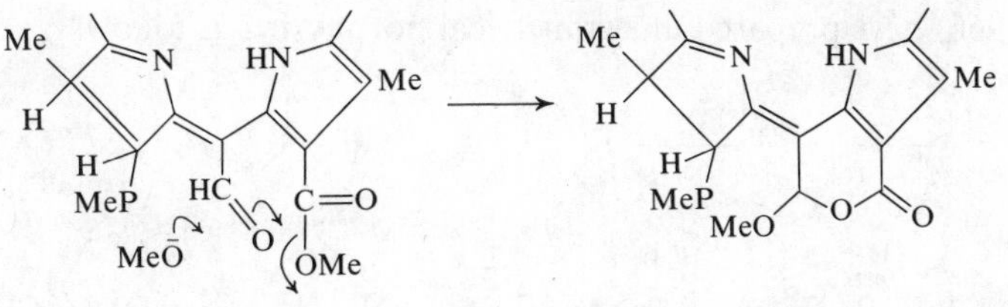

(XIV)

Biosynthesis of chlorophyll. The steps outlined in §4a for the biosynthesis of protoporphyrin IX are also believed to constitute the pathway for chlorophyll biosynthesis. This porphyrin then incorporates magnesium to form magnesium protoporphyrin IX which, by a series of steps (some completely hypothetical so far), is converted into chlorophylls a and b.

§7b. Recent syntheses of porphyrins. In more recent methods, one approach to porphyrin synthesis has been *via* tetrapyrrolic intermediates. These compounds are usually split by acids, but were stabilised in this work by the presence of an internuclear oxo group (Kenner *et al.*, 1965); *e.g.* (MeP = $-CH_2CH_2CO_2Me$; Bzl = $PhCH_2-$):

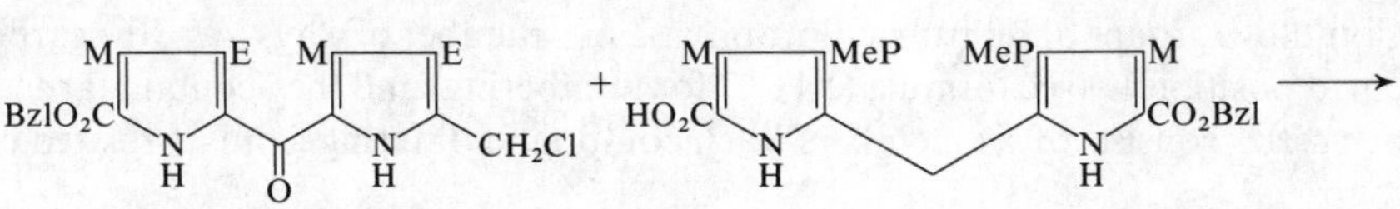

(I)   (II)

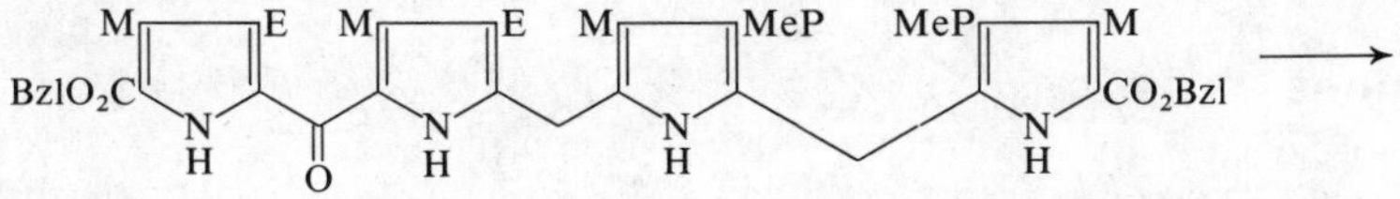

(III)

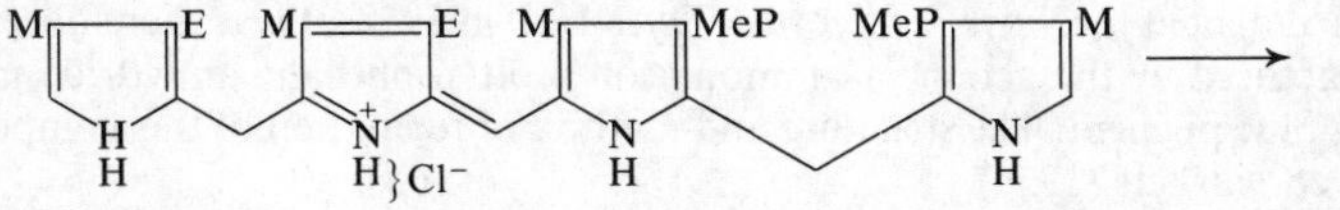

(IV)

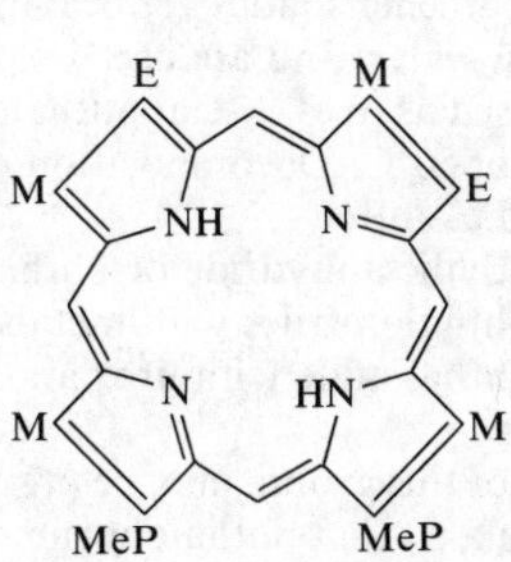

(V)
mesoporphyrin IX dimethyl ester

The pyridinium derivative of (I) was condensed with the lithium salt of (II) to give (III). Reduction of (III) gave (IV) which, on cyclisation, gave mesoporphyrin IX dimethyl ester (V).

Johnson *et al.* (1966) have prepared unsymmetrical porphyrins as follows:

(VI)

(VI) was ring-closed to the corresponding porphyrin by heating in *o*-dichlorobenzene.

§7c.   A number of new chlorophylls have been isolated recently, *e.g.*, chlorophyll-*d* (vinyl group at position 2 in chlorophyll-*a* is replaced by CHO); bacteriochlorophyll-*a* (this is chlorophyll-*a* with an acetyl group instead of the vinyl group (at 2) and with the 3,4-double bond in ring B reduced in *trans* configuration). There are also the *Chlorobium* chlorophylls. These have been classified into two groups, the '650' and '660' series, these numbers being the respective 'red' absorption maxima in ether solution. Both groups differ from chlorophyll-*a* in a number of ways, *e.g.*, the carbomethoxy group is absent at position 10 (see formula (XI), §7 for numbering) and they contain farnesol instead of phytol. Each series consists of six members, each compound differing from its related compound by a CH_2 group.

Phthalocyanines

§8. Preparation of the phthalocyanines

Phthalocyanines are a very important class of organic dyes and pigments; they are coloured blue to green. They were discovered by accident at the works of Scottish Dyes Ltd. in 1928. It was there observed that some lots of phthalimide, manufactured by the action of ammonia on molten phthalic anhydride in an iron vessel, were contaminated with a blue pigment. The structure and method of formation of this compound were established by Linstead and his co-workers (1934).

The phthalocyanines form metallic complexes with many metals, and the colour depends on the nature of the metal (copper, magnesium, lead, etc.); greener shades are obtained by direct chlorination or bromination. The metal phthalocyanines are insoluble in water, and are used as pigments. They are made water-soluble by sulphonation, and these soluble salts are used as dyes. Metal phthalocyanines have great thermal stability and sublime (usually without melting) at about 550°C. Decomposition occurs at higher temperatures.

Metal phthalocyanines may be prepared as follows:

(i) By passing ammonia into molten phthalic anhydride or phthalimide in the presence of a metal salt.

(ii) By heating *o*-cyanobenzamides or phthalonitriles with metals or metallic salts.

(iii) By heating phthalic anhydride or phthalimide with urea and a metallic salt, preferably in the presence of a catalyst such as boric acid.

Phthalocyanine (I) the parent substance of this group, may be prepared by heating phthalonitrile with a little triethanolamine. It can be seen from formula (I) that phthalocyanine contains four isoindole nuclei joined in a ring by means of nitrogen atoms. If we ignore the benzene nuclei, then we have four pyrrole nuclei linked by nitrogen atoms, a structure similar to the porphyrins, in which the pyrrole nuclei are linked by methine groups ((II) is porphin; *cf.* §2a). Both types of compounds are coloured, and both contain two imino hydrogen atoms which can be replaced to form metal complexes. Because of these similarities the phthalocyanines are often known as the tetra-azaporphyrins. The first commercial phthalocyanine pigment was **Monastral Fast Blue BS**; this is copper phthalocyanine (III).

(I)

phthalocyanine

(II)

porphin

(III)

Monastral Fast Blue BS

§9. Structure of the phthalocyanines

Analysis showed that the phthalocyanines had an empirical formula $C_{32}H_{16}N_8M$, where M is a bivalent metal, *e.g.*, copper, magnesium, etc. The molecular weight determination of magnesium phthalocyanine by the ebullioscopic method with naphthalene as solvent showed that the empirical formula was also the molecular formula (Linstead *et al.*, 1934). This has been confirmed by means of X-ray measurements (Robertson, Linstead *et al.*, 1935).

Linstead showed that the phthalocyanines can be obtained by reaction between a metal and phthalonitrile (I), *o*-cyanobenzamide (II), phthalamide (III), but *not* with, for example, terephthalonitrile (IV), homophthalonitrile (V), or *o*-xylylene dicyanide (VI). It is therefore reasonable to infer that in the formation of phthalocyanines, the two nitrile groups involved must be in the *ortho*-position. Thus there are probably four $C_8H_4N_2$

(I)

(II)

(III)

(IV)

(V)

(VI)

(VII)

(VIII)

units, each having an isoindole structure (VII) or a phthalazine structure (VIII). (VIII) was shown to be untenable since no phthalocyanine could be prepared from compounds containing this skeleton.

The oxidation of phthalocyanines with hot nitric acid, cold acid permanganate or ceric sulphate produces phthalimide and ammonium salts, the amount of phthalimide being that which would correspond to the presence of four isoindole units. The problem then is: How are these units joined together? The treatment of magnesium phthalocyanine with sulphuric acid replaces the magnesium atom by two hydrogen atoms.

$$(C_8H_4N_2)_4Mg \xrightarrow{\text{H}_2\text{SO}_4} (C_8H_4N_2)_4H_2$$

This suggests that in metal phthalocyanines, the metal has replaced two *imino* hydrogen atoms. A reasonable structure for phthalocyanine is one in which the four isoindole units are joined through nitrogen atoms to form a cyclic structure (IX). On the other hand, an open-chain structure could also be produced by joining four isoindole units through nitrogen atoms (X); in this case the molecular formula would be $(C_8H_4N_2)_4H_4$. It seems unlikely that (X) could be rejected on these grounds alone, since in a large molecule of this type it is difficult to estimate the hydrogen with certainty ((IX) contains approximately 3·5 per cent hydrogen, and (X)

(IX)   (X)

3·9 per cent). (X), however, is unlikely, since phthalocyanine is a very stable substance; the presence of an imino group at the end of the molecule could be expected to render the compound unstable to, *e.g.*, acid reagents. Furthermore, the oxidation of phthalocyanine with ceric sulphate in dilute sulphuric acid proceeds according to the following equation (over 90 per cent of the phthalimide has been isolated).

$$(C_8H_4N_2)_4H_2 + 7H_2O + [O] \longrightarrow 4C_8H_5NO_2 + 4NH_3$$

This agrees with (IX), but had the structure been (X) then the molecule would have required *two* atoms of oxygen.

$$(C_8H_4N_2)_4H_4 + 6H_2O + 2[O] \longrightarrow 4C_8H_5NO_2 + 4NH_3$$

Thus (IX) represents best the known properties of phthalocyanine. The two imino hydrogen atoms are replaceable by a bivalent metal, and the remaining two nitrogen atoms form co-ordinate links (see formula (III), §8).

The most common metals in phthalocyanines are in the bivalent state, *e.g.*, Cu^{2+}, Fe^{2+}, Ni^{2+}, etc. It is also possible for the central metal atom to have a valency of three or four, and in this case one or two anions are also attached to the metal, *e.g.*, bromoaluminium and dichlorostannic phthalocyanines (*cf.* haem and haemin, §2). Phthalocyanines containing two alkali metal ions, *e.g.*, Na, K (each metal atom joined to an adjacent pair of pyrrole N atoms) have been prepared, but these are readily hydrolysed by dilute acids to the metal-free phthalocyanine. Finally, the metal may have a zero valency. Thus, copper phthalocyanines are known in which the copper is copper (O), copper (I), or copper (II).

In metal phthalocyanines resonance is possible, and so all four nitrogen atoms linked to the metal atom would be equivalent (18π-electrons; $4n + 2$; see (I) and (II)). Phthalocyanines (with and without a central metal atom) have been examined by means of X-ray analysis (Robertson, 1936), and the results shows that these compounds are large *flat* molecules with a centre of symmetry. The bond lengths of the C—N bonds indicate resonance, as do those of the benzene ring (all the lengths are equal). Robertson also showed that for nickel phthalocyanine, if the radius of the nickel atom be assumed, then the positions of the other atoms in the molecule are exactly those obtained by chemical evidence.

Phthalocyanines are known to exist in at least three polymorphic forms: α, β and γ. The β-form is the most stable one, and is the one produced by sublimation of the phthalocyanine. Kendall (1953) has distinguished between the three forms by means of their infrared spectra, and Kahn *et al.* (1965) have shown the difference in the polymorphic structures between α- and β-cobalt phthalocyanines by means of their ESR spectra.

Phthalocyanines can act as catalysts, *e.g.*, they catalyse the combination of hydrogen and oxygen to form water, the decomposition of hydrogen peroxide, the isomerisation of dimethyl maleate to dimethyl fumarate, etc.

REFERENCES

FISCHER and ORTH, *Die Chemie des Pyrrols*, Leipsig. Vol. II (Part I, 1937; Part II, 1940).
BENTLEY, *The Natural Pigments*, Interscience (1960).
FLORKIN and STOTZ (eds.), *Comprehensive Biochemistry*, Elsevier. Vol. 9 (1963). Part A. 'Pyrrole Pigments.'
PERUTZ, 'The Anatomy of Haemoglobin', *Chem. in Britain*, 1965, 9.
WEBB and FLEISCHER, 'The Structure of Porphine', *J. Am. chem. Soc.*, 1965, **87**, 667.

The Chemistry of Natural Products (IUPAC Symposium), Butterworths (1961). Woodward, 'The Total Synthesis of Chlorophyll', p. 383.

JOHNSON *et al.*, 'The Synthesis of Porphins and Related Macrocycles', *Quart. Rev.*, 1966, **20**, 211.

MARKS, *Heme and Chlorophyll*, Van Nostrand (1969).

CHERRY, 'Semiconduction and Photoconduction of Biological Pigments', *Quart. Rev.*, 1968, **22**, 160.

SMITH, 'Recent Developments in the Chemistry of Pyrrolic Compounds', *Quart. Rev.*, 1971, **25**, 31.

BERNFELD (ed.), *Biogenesis of Natural Compounds*, Pergamon (1967, 2nd edn.). Ch. 5. 'The Biogenesis of Haem, Chlorophylls, and Bile Pigments.'

GOODWIN (ed.), *Chemistry and Biochemistry of Plant Pigments*, Academic Press (1965).

MOSER and THOMAS, 'Phthalocyanine Compounds', *J. Chem. Educ.*, 1964, **41**, 245.

HOFFMAN, 'Semiconductivity of the Phthalocyanines', *Quart. Rev.*, 1964, **18**, 113.

Index

Salts of acids are listed under the parent acid, acetates of sugars under the parent sugar, and essential oils under Oil. Many ethyl esters are listed as acid esters. Deuterio-compounds are listed under Deuterium compounds. Name reactions which have been used in the text are listed in this index. Page numbers printed in bold type are the more important references, and substituted derivatives have often been listed under the parent compound by numbers in italics; more important substituted derivatives have been listed separately.